Acid Solutions

Prepare the following reagents by cautiously adding required amount of concentrated acid, with mixing, to designated volume of proper type of distilled water. Dilute to 1000 mL and mix thoroughly.

See Table A for preparation of HCl, H_2SO_4, and HNO_3 solutions.

Alkaline Solutions

a. Stock sodium hydroxide, NaOH, $15N$ (for preparing $6N$, $1N$, and $0.1N$ solutions): Cautiously dissolve 625 g solid NaOH in 800 mL distilled water to form 1 L of solution. Remove sodium carbonate precipitate by keeping solution at the boiling point for a few hours in a hot water bath or by letting particles settle for at least 48 h in an alkali-resistant container (wax-lined or polyethylene) protected from atmospheric CO_2 with a soda lime tube. Use the supernate for preparing dilute solutions listed in Table B.

Alternatively prepare dilute solutions by dissolving the weight of solid NaOH in distilled

water and diluting to 1000 mL.

Store NaOH solutions in polyethylene (rigid, heavy-type) bottles with polyethylene screw caps, paraffin-coated bottles with rubber or neoprene stoppers, or borosilicate-glass bottles with rubber or neoprene stoppers. Check solutions periodically. Protect them by attaching a tube of CO_2-absorbing granular material such as soda lime or a commercially available CO_2-removing agent.* Use at least 70 cm of rubber tubing to minimize vapor diffusion from bottle. Replace absorption tube before it becomes exhausted. Withdraw solution by a siphon to avoid opening bottle.

b. Ammonium hydroxide solutions: NH_4OH: Prepare $5N$, $3N$, and $0.2N$ NH_4OH solutions by diluting 333 mL, 200 mL, and 13 mL, respectively, of the concentrated reagent (sp gr 0.90, 29.0%, $15N$) to 1000 mL with distilled water.

Indicator Solutions

a. Phenolphthalein indicator solution: Use either the aqueous (1) or alcoholic (2) solution.

1) Dissolve 5 g phenolphthalein disodium salt in distilled water and dilute to 1 L.

2) Dissolve 5 g phenolphthalein in 500 mL 95% ethyl or isopropyl alcohol and add 500 mL distilled water.

If necessary, add $0.02N$ NaOH dropwise until a faint pink color appears in solution 1) or 2).

b. Methyl orange indicator solution: Dissolve 500 mg methyl orange powder in distilled water and dilute to 1 L.

TABLE B: PREPARATION OF UNIFORM SODIUM HYDROXIDE SOLUTIONS

Normality of NaOH Solution	Required Weight of NaOH to Prepare 1,000 mL of Solution g	Required Volume of $15N$ NaOH to Prepare 1,000 mL of Solution mL
6	240	400
1	40	67
0.1	4	6.7

SELECTED PHYSICAL
AND CHEMICAL
STANDARD METHODS
FOR STUDENTS

SELECTED PHYSICAL AND CHEMICAL STANDARD METHODS FOR STUDENTS

Prepared and published jointly by:

American Public Health Association
American Water Works Association
Water Pollution Control Federation

Joint Editorial Board

Lenore S. Clesceri, WPCF, Chairman
Arnold E. Greenberg, APHA
R. Rhodes Trussell, AWWA

Mary Ann H. Franson
Managing Editor

Publication Office:

American Public Health Association
1015 Fifteenth Street NW
Washington, DC 20005

PREFACE

This new edition of selected methods from *Standard Methods for the Examination of Water and Wastewater*, 17th edition, is intended for the use of both teachers and students of water and wastewater analysis. The selection of methods was made by surveying a representative group of those currently teaching in the field. The editors of *Standard Methods* hope that this volume will serve as a valuable introduction to the complete text.

PREFACE TO THE SEVENTEENTH EDITION

The Sixteenth and Earlier Editions

The first edition of *Standard Methods* was published in 1905. Each subsequent edition presented significant improvements of methodology and enlarged its scope to include techniques suitable for examination of many types of samples encountered in the assessment and control of water quality and water pollution.

A brief history of *Standard Methods* is of interest because of its contemporary relevance. A movement for "securing the adoption of more uniform and efficient methods of water analysis" led in the 1880's to the organization of a special committee of the Chemical Section of American Association for the Advancement of Science. A report of this committee, published in 1889, was entitled: A Method, in Part, for the Sanitary Examination of Water, and for the Statement of Results, Offered for General Adoption.[*] Five topics were covered: (1) "free" and "albuminoid" ammonia; (2) oxygen-consuming capacity; (3) total nitrogen as nitrates and nitrites; (4) nitrogen as nitrites; and (5) statement of results.

In 1895, members of the American Public Health Association, recognizing the need for standard methods in the bacteriological examination of water, sponsored a convention of bacteriologists to discuss the problem. As a result, an APHA committee was appointed "to draw up procedures for the study of bacteria in a uniform manner and with special references to the differentiation of species." Submitted in 1897,[†] the procedures found wide acceptance.

In 1899, APHA appointed a Committee on Standard Methods of Water Analysis, charged with the extension of standard procedures to all methods involved in the analysis of water. The committee report, published in 1905, constituted the first edition of *Standard Methods* (then entitled *Standard Methods of Water Analysis*). Physical, chemical, microscopic, and bacteriological methods of water examination were included. In its letter of transmittal, the Committee stated:

> The methods of analysis presented in this report as "Standard Methods" are believed to represent the best current practice of American water analysts, and to be generally applicable in connection with the ordinary problems of water purification, sewage disposal and sanitary investigations. Analysts

---

[*] *J. Anal. Chem.* 3:398 (1889).
[†] *Proc. Amer. Pub. Health Assoc.* 23:56 (1897).

working on widely different problems manifestly cannot use methods which are identical, and special problems obviously require the methods best adapted to them; but, while recognizing these facts, it yet remains true that sound progress in analytical work will advance in proportion to the general adoption of methods which are reliable, uniform and adequate.

It is said by some that standard methods within the field of applied science tend to stifle investigations and that they retard true progress. If such standards are used in the proper spirit, this ought not to be so. The Committee strongly desires that every effort shall be continued to improve the techniques of water analysis and especially to compare current methods with those herein recommended, where different, so that the results obtained may be still more accurate and reliable than they are at present.

Revised and enlarged editions were published by APHA under the title *Standard Methods of Water Analysis* in 1912 (Second Edition), 1917 (Third), 1920 (Fourth), and 1923 (Fifth). In 1925, the American Water Works Association joined APHA in publishing the Sixth Edition, which had the broader title, *Standard Methods of the Examination of Water and Sewage.* Joint publication was continued in the Seventh Edition, dated 1933.

In 1935, the Water Pollution Control Federation (then the Federation of Sewage Works Associations) issued a committee report, "Standard Methods of Sewage Analysis." ‡ With minor modifications, these methods were incorporated into the Eighth Edition (1936) of *Standard Methods,* which was thus the first to provide methods for the examination of "sewages, effluents, industrial wastes, grossly polluted waters, sludges, and muds." The Ninth Edition, appearing in 1946, likewise contained these methods, and in the following year the Federation became a full-fledged publishing partner. Since 1947, the work of the *Standard Methods* committees of the three associations—APHA, AWWA, and WPCF—has been coordinated by a Joint Editorial Board, on which all three are represented.

The Tenth Edition (1955) included methods specific for examination of industrial wastewaters; this was reflected by a new title: *Standard Methods for the Examination of Water, Sewage and Industrial Wastes.* To describe more accurately and concisely the contents of the Eleventh Edition (1960), the title was shortened to *Standard Methods for the Examination of Water and Wastewater.* It remained unchanged in the Twelfth Edition (1965), the Thirteenth Edition (1971), the Fourteenth Edition (1976), and the Fifteenth Edition (1981).

In the Fourteenth Edition, the separation of test methods for water from those for wastewater was discontinued. All methods for a given component or characteristic appeared under a single heading. With minor differences, the organization of the Fourteenth Edition was retained for the Fifteenth and Sixteenth (1985) Editions. Two major policy decisions of the Joint Editorial Board were implemented for the Sixteenth Edition. First, the International System of Units (SI) was adopted except where prevailing field systems or practices require English units. Second, the use of trade names or proprietary materials was eliminated insofar as possible, to avoid potential claims regarding restraint of trade or commercial favoritism.

---

‡ *Sewage Works J.* 7:444 (1935).

The Seventeenth Edition

The organization of the Seventeenth Edition reflects a commitment to develop and retain a permanent numbering system. New numbers have been assigned to all sections, and numbers unused in the present edition have been reserved for future use. All part numbers have been expanded to multiples of 1000 instead of 100. The parts have retained their identity from the previous edition, with the exception of Part 6000, which now contains methods for the measurement of specific organic compounds. The more general procedures for organics are found in Part 5000.

The Seventeenth Edition has undergone a major revision in the introductory Part 1000. Sections dealing with statistical analysis, data quality, and methods development have been greatly expanded. The section on reagent water has been updated to include the current classification scheme for various types of reagent water. Part 1000 contains important information on the proper execution of procedures and should be studied by every user of this manual. At the beginning of each of the subsequent parts of the manual are sections discussing quality assurance and other matters of general application within the specific subject area, to minimize repetition in the succeeding text. Successful analysis rests on close adherence to the introductory recommendations and cautions. Before undertaking an analysis, read and understand the complete discussion of each procedure, including methods selection, sampling and sample storage, and interferences.

Part 2000 (physical and aggregate properties) contains a new section on dissolved gas supersaturation. It also includes analyses for certain aggregate properties (acidity, alkalinity, and hardness) that had appeared in other parts of previous editions and the tests for sludge digester gas from Part 500 of previous editions. The sections on salinity and calcium carbonate saturation have been revised to reflect the current state of the art in these measurements.

Part 3000 (metals) now includes a brief section on quality assurance and the section on sample preparation has been revised. Instrumental methods (atomic absorption spectrometric and inductively coupled plasma) that are useful for determining numerous metals are next presented; the atomic absorption methods have been revised and a new method using continuous hydride generation has been added. To the sections concerned with analysis for specific metals have been added brief sections referring the reader to instrumental methods for the determination of antimony, arsenic, bismuth, cesium, iridium, molybdenum, osmium, palladium, platinum, rhenium, rhodium, ruthenium, thallium, thorium, tin, and titanium. The section for lithium has been revised to reflect methods providing lower detection limits. New methods for selenium speciation and aluminum have been added.

Part 4000 (inorganic nonmetals) also contains a brief new quality assurance section. Analysis methods, including the ion chromatography method for measurement of a number of anions and the methods for specific anions, remain largely unchanged and have been reaffirmed by consensus ballot. New low-level amperometric titration and iodometric techniques have been added for the determination of residual chlorine, and the leuco crystal violet method has been deleted. More accurate methods have been added for chlorine dioxide and ozone. Several methods for nitrate have been deleted and a new titanium chloride method for nitrate has been added.

Part 5000 (aggregate organics) now contains only methods determining overall concentrations of groups of organic compounds. Methods for determining specific compounds (methane, pesticides and herbicides, halogenated methanes and ethanes, taste- and odor-causing compounds, and organic contaminants by gas chromatographic/mass spectrometric analysis) have been either moved to Part 6000 or superseded by new methods in that Part. Methods for DOX (formerly TOX) have been revised significantly. New methods have been added for humic substances and trihalomethane formation potential.

Part 6000 (individual organics) is new. It contains introductory information on sample collection and preservation for organics as well as operation principles and interferences for instrumental analytical methods. A method for constituent concentration by gas extraction (closed-loop stripping), included in Part 500 of the Sixteenth Edition as a method for taste- and odor-causing organics, has been revised. Each group of organic compounds is introduced by information on its presence in the environment and on selection of analytical method. Most methods in Part 6000 are completely edited and revised EPA-approved procedures that originally appeared in the supplement to the Sixteenth Edition. Several methods for the identification of specific compounds that appeared in Part 500 of the Sixteenth Edition also are included.

Part 7000 (radioactivity) contains no changes in methods. The introductory sections have been re-edited to give additional prominence to quality control.

Part 8000 (toxicity testing) also retains the methods of the previous edition. The introductory section has been revised and a short section on mutagenesis has been added. The section on zooplankton of the Sixteenth Edition no longer appears as a unit; the methods for ciliated protozoa, *Daphnia,* and *Acartia* have been placed elsewhere in the Part to reflect taxonomic relationships.

Part 9000 (microbiological examination) generally has been revised and updated. A new method for direct counts has been added and the tests for pathogenic protozoa have been separated from those for pathogenic bacteria. In testing for coliform bacteria the production of acid in a lactose-containing presumptive broth medium has been restored as a positive reaction. The rewritten section on streptococci stresses procedures for enterococci.

Part 10000 (biological examination) contains substantial revisions of methods for plankton, macrophyton, and fish. The major change in the section on plankton is the inclusion of a high-performance liquid chromatographic method for chlorophyll. Other methods have undergone general updating and revision.

Making Reagents

Following the instructions for making reagents may result in preparation of quantities larger than actually needed. In some cases these materials are toxic. To promote economy and minimize waste, the analyst should review needs and scale down solution volumes where appropriate. This conservative attitude also should extend to purchasing policies so that unused chemicals do not accumulate or need to be discarded as their shelf lives expire.

Selection and Approval of Methods

For each new edition both the technical criteria for selection of methods and the formal procedures for their approval and inclusion are reviewed critically. In regard to the approval procedures, it is considered particularly important to assure that the methods presented have been reviewed and are supported by the largest number of qualified people, so that they may represent a true consensus of expert opinion.

For the Fourteenth Edition a Joint Task Group was established for each test. This scheme has continued for each subsequent edition. Appointment of an individual to a Joint Task Group generally was based on the expressed interest or recognized expertise of the individual. The effort in every case was to assemble a group having maximum available expertise in the test methods of concern.

Each Joint Task Group was charged with reviewing the pertinent methods in the Sixteenth Edition along with other methods from the literature, recommending the methods to be included in the Seventeenth Edition, and presenting those methods in the form of a proposed section manuscript. Subsequently, each section manuscript (except for Part 1000) was ratified by vote of those members of the Standard Methods Committee who asked to review sections in that part. Every negative vote and every comment submitted in the balloting was reviewed by the Joint Editorial Board. Relevant suggestions were referred appropriately for resolution. When negative votes on the first ballot could not be resolved by the Joint Task Group or the Joint Editorial Board, the section was reballoted among all who voted affirmatively or negatively on the original ballot. Only a few issues could not be resolved in this manner and the Joint Editorial Board made the final decision.

The general and quality assurance information presented in Part 1000 was treated somewhat differently. Again, Joint Task Groups were formed, given a charge, and allowed to produce a consensus draft. This draft was reviewed by the Joint Editorial Board Liaison and subsequently by the Joint Editorial Board. The draft sections were sent to the Standard Methods Committee and comments resulting from this review were used to develop the final draft.

The methods presented here, as in previous editions, are believed to be the best available and generally accepted procedures for the analysis of water, wastewaters, and related materials. They represent the recommendations of specialists, ratified by a large number of analysts and others of more general expertise, and as such are truly consensus standards, offering a valid and recognized basis for control and evaluation.

The technical criteria for selection of methods were applied by the Joint Task Groups and by the individuals reviewing their recommendations, with the Joint Editorial Board providing only general guidelines. In addition to the classical concepts of precision, bias, and minimum detectable concentration, selection of a method also must recognize such considerations as the time required to obtain a result, needs for specialized equipment and for special training of the analyst, and other factors related to the cost of the analysis and the feasibility of its widespread use.

Status of Methods

All methods in the Seventeenth Edition are dated to assist users in determining those methods that have been changed significantly between editions. The year the section was approved by the Standard Methods Committee is indicated in a footnote at the beginning of each section. Sections or methods that appeared in the Sixteenth Edition that are unchanged, or changed only editorially in the Seventeenth Edition, show the publication date of the Sixteenth Edition, 1985. Sections or methods that were changed significantly, or that were reaffirmed by general balloting of the Standard Methods Committee, are dated 1988. If only one individual method within a section was revised, then that individual method is dated 1988, and the remaining methods retain the 1985 date.

Methods in the Seventeenth Edition are divided into fundamental classes: PRO-POSED, SPECIALIZED, STANDARD, and GENERAL. Irrespective of assigned class, all methods must be approved by the Standard Methods Committee. The four classes are described below:

1. PROPOSED—A PROPOSED method must undergo development and validation that meets the requirements set forth in Section 1040A of *Standard Methods.*

2. SPECIALIZED—A procedure qualifies as a SPECIALIZED method in one of two ways: a) The procedure must undergo development and validation and collaborative testing that meet the requirements set forth in Sections 1040B and C of *Standard Methods,* respectively; or b) The procedure is the "METHOD OF CHOICE" of the members of the Standard Methods Committee actively conducting the analysis and it has appeared in TWO PREVIOUS EDITIONS of *Standard Methods.*

3. STANDARD—A procedure qualifies as a STANDARD method in one of two ways: a) The procedure must undergo development and validation and collaborative testing that meet the requirements set forth in Sections 1040B and C of *Standard Methods,* respectively, and it is "WIDELY USED" by the members of the Standard Methods Committee; or b) The procedure is "WIDELY USED" by the members of the Standard Methods Committee and it has appeared in TWO PREVIOUS EDITIONS of *Standard Methods.*

4. GENERAL—A procedure qualifies as a GENERAL method if it has appeared in TWO PREVIOUS EDITIONS of *Standard Methods.*

Assignment of a classification to a method is done by the Joint Editorial Board. When making method classifications, the Joint Editorial Board evaluates the results of the survey on method use by the Standard Methods Committee that is conducted at the time of general balloting of the method. In addition, the Joint Editorial Board considers recommendations offered by Joint Task Groups and the Part Coordinator.

Methods categorized as "PROPOSED," "SPECIALIZED," and "GENERAL" are so designated in their titles; methods with no designation are "STANDARD."

Technical progress makes advisable the establishment of a program to keep *Standard Methods* abreast of advances in research and general practice. The Joint Editorial Board has developed the following procedure for effecting interim changes in methods between editions:

1. Any method given proposed status in the current edition may be elevated by action of the Joint Editorial Board, on the basis of adequate published data supporting such a change as submitted to the Board by the appropriate Joint Task Group. Notification of such a change in status shall be accomplished by publication in the official journals of the three associations sponsoring *Standard Methods.*

2. No method may be abandoned or reduced to a lower status during the interval between editions.

3. A new method may be adopted as proposed, specialized, or standard by the Joint Editorial Board between editions, such action being based on the usual consensus procedure. Such new methods may be published in supplements to editions of *Standard Methods.*

Even more important to maintaining the current status of these standards is the intention of the sponsors and the Joint Editorial Board that subsequent editions will appear regularly at reasonably short intervals.

Reader comments and questions concerning this manual should be addressed to: Standard Methods Manager, American Water Works Association, 6666 West Quincy Avenue, Denver, CO 80235.

Acknowledgments

For the major portion of the work in preparing and revising the methods in the Sixteenth Edition, the Joint Editorial Board gives full credit to the Standard Methods Committees of the American Water Works Association and of the Water Pollution Control Federation, and to the Subcommittee on Standard Methods for the Examination of Water and Wastewater and the Committee on Laboratory Standards and Practices of the American Public Health Association. Members of these committees chair and serve as members of the Joint Task Groups. They were assisted often by advisors, not formally members of the committees, and in many cases not members of the sponsoring societies. To the advisors, special gratitude is extended in recognition of their efforts. A list of the committee members and advisors follows these pages. Robert Booth, Senior Science Advisor, U.S. Environmental Protection Agency, served as a liaison from EPA to the Joint Editorial Board; thanks are due for his interest and help.

The Joint Editorial Board expresses its appreciation to William H. McBeath, M.D., Executive Director, American Public Health Association, to John B. Mannion, Executive Director, American Water Works Association, and to Quincalee Brown, Executive Director, Water Pollution Control Federation, for their cooperation and advice in the development of this publication. Steven J. Posavec, Standard Methods Manager and Joint Editorial Board Secretary, provided a variety of important services that are vital to the preparation of a volume of this type.

Jaclyn Alexander, Director of Publications, American Public Health Association, functioned as publisher, and Brigitte Coulton, also with APHA, served as production manager. Special recognition for her valuable services is due to Mary Ann H. Franson, Managing Editor, who discharged most efficiently the extensive and detailed responsibilities on which this publication depends.

Acknowledgement is made to past Executive Director Paul A. Schulte of the American Water Works Association for his extensive assistance to this and previous editions of *Standard Methods*. The late Robert A. Canham made invaluable contributions to the continuous growth and improvement of *Standard Methods* during his long tenure as Executive Director of the Water Pollution Control Federation; his wisdom and leadership will be remembered gratefully. The Joint Editorial Board acknowledges the significant service of Frederick W. Pontius, Regulatory Engineer, American Water Works Association, who formerly was Secretary to the Joint Editorial Board, and of Adrienne Ash of the American Public Health Association, who acted as publisher during the early phases of the preparation of this edition.

Joint Editorial Board
Arnold E. Greenberg, American Public Health Association
R. Rhodes Trussell, American Water Works Association
Lenore S. Clesceri, Water Pollution Control Federation, Chairman

---

At several places in this text, a manufacturer's name or trade name of a product, chemical, or chemical compound is referenced. The use of such a name is intended only to be a shorthand reference for the functional characteristics of the manufacturer's item. These references are not intended to be an endorsement of any item by the copublishers, and materials or reagents with equivalent characteristics may be used.

TABLE C
INTERNATIONAL
RELATIVE
ATOMIC WEIGHTS

TABLE C. INTERNATIONAL RELATIVE ATOMIC WEIGHTS, 1987
Scaled to the relative atomic mass, $A_r(^{12}C) = 12$

The atomic weights of many elements are not invariant but depend on the origin and treatment of the material. The footnotes to this table elaborate the types of variation to be expected for individual elements. The values of $A_r(E)$ given here apply to elements as they exist naturally on earth and to certain artificial elements. When used with due regard to the footnotes they are considered reliable in the last digit to ± the figure given in parentheses.

Name	Symbol	Atomic number	Atomic weight	Footnotes
Actinium*	Ac	89	227.0278	A
Aluminium	Al	13	26.981539(5)	
Americium*	Am	95	241.0568	A
Antimony	Sb	51	121.75(3)	
Argon	Ar	18	39.948(1)	g, r
Arsenic	As	33	74.92159(2)	
Astatine*	At	85	209.9871	A
Barium	Ba	56	137.327(7)	g
Berkelium*	Bk	97	247.0703	A
Beryllium	Be	4	9.012182(3)	
Bismuth	Bi	83	208.98037(3)	
Boron	B	5	10.811(5)	g, m, r
Bromine	Br	35	79.904(1)	
Cadmium	Cd	48	112.411(8)	g
Calcium	Ca	20	40.078(4)	g
Californium*	Cf	98	249.0748	A
Carbon	C	6	12.011(1)	r
Cerium	Ce	58	140.115(4)	g
Cesium	Cs	55	132.90543(5)	
Chlorine	Cl	17	35.4527(9)	
Chromium	Cr	24	51.9961(6)	
Cobalt	Co	27	58.93320(1)	
Copper	Cu	29	63.546(3)	r
Curium*	Cm	96	243.0614	A
Dyprosium	Dy	66	162.50(3)	g
Einsteinium*	Es	99	252.083	A
Erbium	Er	68	167.26(3)	g
Europium	Eu	63	151.965(9)	g
Fermium*	Fm	100	257.0951	A
Fluorine	F	9	18.9984032(9)	
Francium*	Fr	87	223.0197	A
Gadolinium	Gd	64	157.25(3)	g
Gallium	Ga	31	69.723(1)	
Germanium	Ge	32	72.61(2)	
Gold	Au	79	196.96654(3)	
Hafnium	Hf	72	178.49(2)	
Helium	He	2	4.002602(2)	g, r
Holmium	Ho	67	164.93032(3)	
Hydrogen	H	1	1.00794(7)	g, m, r
Indium	In	49	114.82(1)	
Iodine	I	53	126.90447(3)	
Iridium	Ir	77	192.22(3)	
Iron	Fe	26	55.847(3)	g, m
Krypton	Kr	36	83.80(1)	g
Lanthanum	La	57	138.9055(2)	g
Lawrencium*	Lr	103	262.11	A
Lead	Pb	82	207.2(1)	g, r
Lithium	Li	3	6.941(2)	g, m, r
Lutetium	Lu	71	174.967(1)	g
Magnesium	Mg	12	24.3050(6)	
Manganese	Mn	25	54.93805(1)	
Mendelevium*	Md	101	256.094	A
Mercury	Hg	80	200.59(3)	
Molybdenum	Mo	42	95.94(1)	g
Neodymium	Nd	60	144.24(3)	g
Neon	Ne	10	20.1797(6)	g, m

Element	Symbol	Z	Atomic Weight	Notes	Element	Symbol	Z	Atomic Weight	Notes
Neptunium*	Np	93	237.0482	A	Silver	Ag	47	107.8682(2)	g
Nickel	Ni	28	58.69(1)		Sodium	Na	11	22.989768(6)	
Niobium	Nb	41	92.90638(2)		Strontium	Sr	38	87.62(1)	g, r
Nitrogen	N	7	14.00674(7)	g, r	Sulfur	S	16	32.066(6)	r
Nobelium*	No	102	259.1009	A	Tantalum	Ta	73	180.9479(1)	
Osmium	Os	76	190.2(1)	g, r	Technetium*	Tc	43	96.9064	A
Oxygen	O	8	15.9994(3)	g	Tellurium	Te	52	127.60(3)	g
Palladium	Pd	46	106.42(1)	g	Terbium	Tb	65	158.92534(3)	
Phosphorus	P	15	30.973762(4)		Thallium	Tl	81	204.3833(2)	
Platinum	Pt	78	195.08(3)		Thorium*	Th	90	232.0381(1)	g, Z
Plutonium*	Pu	94	238.0496	A	Thulium	Tm	69	168.93421(3)	
Polonium*	Po	84	208.9824	A	Tin	Sn	50	118.710(7)	g
Potassium	K	19	39.0983(1)		Titanium	Ti	22	47.88(3)	
Praseodymium	Pr	59	140.90765(3)		Tungsten	W	74	183.85(3)	
Promethium*	Pm	61	144.9127	A	Unnilhexium	Unh	106	263.118	A
Protactinium*	Pa	91	231.0359		Unnilpentium	Unp	105	262.114	A
Radium*	Ra	88	223.0185	A	Unnilquadium	Unq	104	261.11	A
Radon*	Rn	86	210.9906	A	Unnilseptium	Uns	107	262.12	A
Rhenium	Re	75	186.207(1)		Uranium*	U	92	238.0289(1)	g, m, Z
Rhodium	Rh	45	102.90550(3)		Vanadium	V	23	50.9415(1)	
Rubidium	Rb	37	85.4678(3)	g	Xenon	Xe	54	131.29(2)	g, m
Ruthenium	Ru	44	101.07(2)	g	Ytterbium	Yb	70	173.04(3)	
Samarium	Sm	62	150.36(3)	g	Yttrium	Y	39	88.90585(2)	
Scandium	Sc	21	44.955910(9)		Zinc	Zn	30	65.39(2)	
Selenium	Se	34	78.96(3)		Zirconium	Zr	40	91.224(2)	g
Silicon	Si	14	28.0855(3)	r					

* Element has no stable nuclides.

g geological specimens are known in which the element has an isotopic composition outside the limits for normal material. The difference between the atomic weight of the element in such specimens and that given in the table may exceed considerably the implied uncertainty.

m modified isotopic compositions may be found in commercially available material because it has been subjected to an undisclosed or inadvertent isotopic separation.

r Substantial deviations in atomic weight of the element from that given in the table can occur. range in isotopic composition of normal terrestrial material prevents a more precise atomic weight being given; the tabulated $A_r(E)$ value should be applicable to any normal material.

A Radioactive element that lacks a characteristic terrestrial isotopic composition. The weight listed is that of the lowest-atomic-weight isotope.

Z An element, without stable nuclide(s), exhibiting a range of characteristic terrestrial compositions of long-lived radionuclide(s) such that a meaningful atomic weight can be given.

Source: INTERNATIONAL UNION OF PURE AND APPLIED CHEMISTRY. 1988. Atomic weights of the elements, 1987. Pure Appl. Chem. 60:841.

TABLE OF CONTENTS

FIGURES

TABLES

PART 1000

GENERAL

INTRODUCTION

1010   INTRODUCTION*

1010 A.   Scope and Application of Methods

The procedures described in these standards are intended for the examination of waters of a wide range of quality, including water suitable for domestic or industrial supplies, surface water, ground water, cooling or circulating water, boiler water, boiler feed water, treated and untreated municipal or industrial wastewater, and saline water. The unity of the fields of water supply, receiving water quality, and wastewater treatment and disposal is recognized by presenting methods of analysis for each constituent in a single section for all types of waters.

An effort has been made to present methods that apply generally. Where alternative methods are necessary for samples of different composition, the basis for selecting the most appropriate method is presented as clearly as possible. However, samples with extreme concentrations or otherwise unusual compositions may present difficulties that preclude the direct use of these methods. Hence, some modification of a procedure may be necessary in specific instances. Whenever a procedure is modified, the analyst should state plainly the nature of modification in the report of results.

Certain procedures are intended for use with sludges and sediments. Here again, the effort has been to present methods of the widest possible application, but when chemical sludges or slurries or other samples of highly unusual composition are encountered, the methods of this manual may require modification or may be inappropriate.

Most of the methods included here have been endorsed by regulatory agencies. Procedural modification without formal approval may be unacceptable to a regulatory body.

The analysis of bulk chemicals received for water treatment is not included herein. A committee of the American Water Works Association prepares and issues standards for water treatment chemicals.

Part 1000 contains information that is common to, or useful in, laboratories desiring to produce analytical results of known quality, that is, of known accuracy and with known uncertainty in that accuracy. To accomplish this, apply the quality assurance methods described herein to the standard methods described elsewhere in this publication. Other sections of Part 1000 address laboratory equipment, laboratory safety, sampling procedures, and method development and validation, all of which provide necessary information.

---

* Part 1000 was submitted to the Standard Methods Committee on a "Review and Comment" basis and is provided for information purposes only. It is not considered a part of the procedures described in these standards.

1010 B.   Statistics

1. Normal Distribution

If a measurement is repeated many times under essentially identical conditions, the results of each measurement, x, will be distributed randomly about a mean value (arithmetic average) because of uncontrollable or experimental error. If an infinite number of such measurements were to be accumulated, the individual values would be distributed in a curve similar to those shown in Figure 1010:1. The curve at left illustrates the Gaussian or normal distribution, which is described precisely by the mean, μ, and the standard deviation, σ. The mean, or average, of the distribution is simply the sum of all values divided by the number of values so summed, i.e., $\mu = (\Sigma_i x_i)/n$. Because no measurements are repeated an infinite number of times, an *estimate* of the mean is made, using the same summation procedure but with n equal to a finite number of repeated measurements (10, or 20, or. . .). This estimate of μ is denoted by $\overline{x}$. The standard deviation of the normal distribution is defined as $\sigma = [\Sigma(x-\mu)^2/n]^{1/2}$. Again, the analyst can only estimate the standard deviation because the number of observations made is finite; the estimate of σ is denoted by s

and is calculated as follows:

$$s = [\Sigma(x-\overline{x})^2/n-1]^{1/2}$$

The standard deviation fixes the width, or spread, of the normal distribution, and also includes a fixed fraction of the values making up the curve. For example, 68.27% of the measurements lie between $\mu \pm 1\sigma$, 95.45% between $\mu \pm 2\sigma$, and 99.70% between $\mu \pm 3\sigma$. It is sufficiently accurate to state that 95% of the values are within $\pm 2\sigma$ and 99% within $\pm 3\sigma$. When values are assigned to the $\pm \sigma$ multiples, they are confidence limits. For example, 10 $\pm$ 4 indicates that the confidence limits are 6 and 14, while values from 6 to 14 represent the confidence interval.

Another useful statistic is the standard error of the mean, σ_μ, which is the standard deviation divided by the square root of the number of values, or $\sigma/\sqrt{n}$. This is an estimate of the accuracy of the mean and implies that another sample from the same population would have a mean within some multiple of this. Multiples of this statistic include the same fraction of the values as stated above for σ. In practice, a relatively small number of average values is available, so the confidence intervals of the mean are

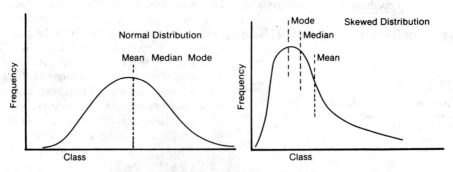

Figure 1010:1. Normal and skewed distributions.

expressed as $\bar{x} \pm ts/\sqrt{n}$ where t has the following values for 95% confidence intervals:

n	t
2	12.71
3	4.30
4	3.18
5	2.78
10	2.26
∞	1.96

The use of t compensates for the tendency of a small number of values to underestimate uncertainty. For $n > 15$, it is common to use $t = 2$ to estimate the 95% confidence interval.

Still another statistic is the relative standard deviation, also known as the coefficient of variation (CV), which commonly is expressed as a percentage. This statistic is calculated as $100\ \sigma/\mu$ and its estimate is $100\ s/\bar{x}$. This statistic normalizes the standard deviation and sometimes facilitates making direct comparisons among analyses that include a wide range of concentrations. For example, if analyses at low concentrations yield a result of 10 ± 1.5 mg/L and at high concentrations 100 ± 8 mg/L, the standard deviations do not appear comparable. However, the relative standard deviations are 100 (1.5/10) = 15% and 100 (8/100) = 8%, which indicate the smaller variability obtained by using this parameter.

2. Log-Normal Distribution

In many cases the results obtained from analysis of environmental samples will not be normally distributed, i.e., a graph of the data will be obviously skewed, as shown at right in Figure 1010:1, with the mode, median, and mean being distinctly different. To obtain a nearly normal distribution, convert the results to logarithms and then calculate $\bar{x}$ and s. The antilogarithms of these two values are estimates of the geometric mean and the geometric standard deviation, $\bar{x}_g$ and s_g.

3. Rejection of Data

Quite often in a series of measurements, one or more of the results will differ greatly from the other values. Theoretically, no result should be rejected, because it may indicate either a faulty technique that casts doubt on all results or the presence of a true variant in the distribution. In practice, reject the result of any analysis in which a known error has occurred. In environmental studies, extremely high and low concentrations of contaminants may indicate the existence of areas with problems or areas with no contamination, so they should not be rejected arbitrarily.

An objective test for outliers has been described.[1] If a set of data is ordered from low to high: $x_L, x_2 \ldots x_H$, and the average and standard deviation are calculated, then suspected high or low outliers can be tested by the following procedure. First, calculate the statistic T:

$$T = (x_H - \bar{x})/s \text{ for a high value, or}$$
$$T = (\bar{x} - x_L)/s \text{ for a low value.}$$

Second, compare the value of T with the value from Table 1010:I for either a 5% or 1% level of significance. If the calculated T is larger than the table value for the number of measurements, n, then the x_H or x_L is an outlier at that level of significance.

Further information on statistical techniques is available elsewhere.[2,3]

4. References

1. BARNETT, V. & T. LEWIS. 1984. Outliers in Statistical Data. John Wiley & Sons, New York, N.Y.
2. NATRELLA, M.G. 1966. Experimental Statistics. National Bur. Standards Handbook 91, Washington, D.C.
3. SNEDECOR, G.W. & W.G. COCHRAN. 1980. Statistical Methods. Iowa State University Press, Ames.

TABLE 1010:I. CRITICAL VALUES FOR 5% AND 1% TESTS OF DISCORDANCY FOR A SINGLE
OUTLIER IN A NORMAL SAMPLE

Number of Measurements n	Critical Value	
	5%	1%
3	1.15	1.15
4	1.46	1.49
5	1.67	1.75
6	1.82	1.94
7	1.94	2.10
8	2.03	2.22
9	2.11	2.32
10	2.18	2.41
12	2.29	2.55
14	2.37	2.66
15	2.41	2.71
16	2.44	2.75
18	2.50	2.82
20	2.56	2.88
30	2.74	3.10
40	2.87	3.24
50	2.96	3.34
60	3.03	3.41
100	3.21	3.60
120	3.27	3.66

Source: BARNETT, V. & T. LEWIS. 1984. Outliers in Statistical Data. John Wiley & Sons, New York, N.Y.

1010 C. Glossary

1. Definition of Terms

Accuracy—combination of bias and precision of an analytical procedure, which reflects the closeness of a measured value to a true value (see Figure 1030:1).

Bias—consistent deviation of measured values from the true value, caused by systematic errors in a procedure.

Calibration check standard—standard used to determine the state of calibration of an instrument between periodic recalibrations.

Confidence coefficient—the probability, %, that a measurement result will lie within the confidence interval or between the confidence limits.

Confidence interval—set of possible values within which the true value will lie with a specified level of probability.

Confidence limit—one of the boundary values defining the confidence interval.

Detection limits—Various limits in increasing order are:

Instrumental detection limit (IDL)—the constituent concentration that produces a signal greater than five times the signal/noise ratio of the instrument. This is similar, in many respects, to "critical level" and "criterion of detection." The latter limit is stated as 1.645 times the *s* of blank analyses.

Lower limit of detection (LLD)—the constituent concentration in reagent water that produces a signal 2(1.645)*s* above the mean of blank analyses. This sets both Type I and Type II errors at 5%. Other names for this limit are "detection limit" and "limit of detection" (LOD).

Method detection limit (MDL)—the constituent concentration that, when processed through the complete method, produces a signal with a 99% proability that it is different from the blank. For seven replicates of the sample, the mean must be 3.14s above the blank where s is the standard deviation of the seven replicates. The MDL will be larger than the LLD because of the few replications and the sample processing steps and may vary with constituent and matrix.

Limit of quantitation (LOQ)—the constituent concentration that produces a signal sufficiently greater than the blank that it can be detected within specified limits by good laboratories during routine operating conditions.[1] Typically it is the concentration that produces a signal 10s above the reagent water blank signal.

Duplicate—usually the smallest number of replicates (two) but specifically herein refers to duplicate samples, i.e., two samples taken at the same time from one location.

Internal standard—a pure compound added to a sample extract just before instrumental analysis to permit correction for inefficiencies.

Laboratory control standard—a standard, usually certified by an outside agency, used to measure the bias in a procedure. For certain constituents and matrices, use National Institute of Standards and Technology (NIST)* Standard Reference Materials when they are available.

---

* Formerly National Bureau of Standards (NBS).

Precision—measure of the degree of agreement among replicate analyses of a sample, usually expressed as the standard deviation.

Quality assessment—procedure for determining the quality of laboratory measurements by use of data from internal and external quality control measures.

Quality assurance—a definitive plan for laboratory operation that specifies the measures used to produce data of known precision and bias.

Quality control—set of measures within a sample analysis methodology to assure that the process is in control.

Random error—the deviation in any step in an analytical procedure that can be treated by standard statistical techniques.

Replicate—repeated operation occurring within an analytical procedure. Two or more analyses for the same constituent in an extract of a single sample constitute replicate extract analyses.

Surrogate standard—a pure compound added to a sample in the laboratory just before processing so that the overall efficiency of a method can be determined.

Type I error—also called alpha error, is the probability of deciding a constituent is present when it actually is absent.

Type II error—also called beta error, is the probability of not detecting a constituent when it actually is present.

2. Reference

1. U.S. ENVIRONMENTAL PROTECTION AGENCY. 1985. National Primary Drinking Water Regulations. 40 CFR Part 141; *Federal Register* 50: 46936.

1020   QUALITY ASSURANCE

1020 A.   Introduction

Quality assurance (QA) is a set of operating principles that, if strictly followed during sample collection and analysis, will produce data of known and defensible quality. That is, the accuracy of the analytical result can be stated with a high level of confidence. Included in quality assurance are quality control (Section 1020B) and quality assessment (Section 1020C).

1. Quality Assurance Planning

Establish a set of operating principles that will constitute a quality-assurance program. Prepare a QA plan[1] including the following: cover sheet with plan approval signatures, staff organization and responsibilities, sample control and documentation procedures, standard operating procedure for each analytical method (SOP), analyst training requirements, equipment preventive maintenance procedures, calibration procedures, corrective actions, internal quality control activities, performance audits, data assessment procedures for bias and precision, and data reduction, validation, and reporting.

The cover sheet with approval signatures indicates that the plan has been reviewed and judged suitable, and that the organization and responsibilities section outlines the chain-of-command and assigns specific functions to each person involved.

Sample control and documentation procedures permit tracing a sample and its derivatives through all steps from collection to analysis and display of results. Documentation always is important but is especially so when chain-of-custody requirements are imposed.

A standard operating procedure for the analytical method describes the method in such detail that an experienced analyst unfamiliar with the method can obtain acceptable results. Training requirements for analysts must be specified. The number of analyses required and the uncertainty of the results will vary with the type of analysis, sample characteristics, and the experience of the analyst.

Equipment preventive maintenance procedures are required. A strict preventive maintenance program will reduce instrument malfunctions, maintain calibration, and reduce downtime.

Calibration procedures, corrective actions, internal quality control activities, performance audits, and data assessments for bias and precision are discussed in Section 1020B and C.

Data reduction, validation, and reporting are the final features of a QA program. The reading obtained from an analytical instrument must be adjusted for such factors as instrument efficiency, extraction efficiency, sample size, and background value, before it becomes a useful result. The QA plan specifies the correction factors to be applied as well as the steps to be followed in validating the result. Report results in standard units of mass, volume, or concentration. Use a prescribed method for reporting results below the method detection limit. Accompany each result or set of results by a statement of uncertainty.

2. Reference

1. STANLEY, T.W. & S.S. VERNER. 1983. Interim Guidelines and Specifications for Preparing Quality Assurance Project Plans. EPA-600/4-83-004, U.S. Environmental Protection Agency, Washington, D.C.

1020 B. Quality Control

Quality control (QC) may be either internal or external. Internal QC is the subject of this section; external QC, also known as "quality assessment," is discussed in 1020C. All analysts use some QC as an intuitive effort to produce credible results. However, a good quality control program consists of at least seven elements: certification of operator competence, recovery of known additions, analysis of externally supplied standards, analysis of reagent blanks, calibration with standards, analysis of duplicates, and maintenance of control charts. Sections 1010 and 1030 contain the necessary calculations.

1. Certification of Operator Competence

Before an analyst is permitted to do reportable work, competence in making the analysis is to be demonstrated. Requirements vary, but for most inorganic and organic chemical analyses, demonstration of acceptable single-operator precision and bias is sufficient. Make a minimum of four replicate analyses of an independently prepared check sample having a concentration between 5 and 50 times the method detection limit (MDL) for the analysis in that laboratory. General limits for acceptable work are shown in Table 1020:I; certain methods may specify more stringent limits.

2. Recovery of Known Additions

Use the recovery of known additions as part of a regular analytical protocol. Use known additions to verify the absence of matrix effects. When a new matrix type is to be analyzed, verify the amount of interference. Where duplicates are not applicable, for example, when the constituent of interest is absent, make recovery of known additions for 10% of the samples. Where

duplicates also are being analyzed, the sum of the duplicates and known additions must equal at least 10% of the number of samples. Make the known addition between 5 and 50 times the MDL or between 1 and 10 times the ambient level, whichever is greater. Do not use a known addition above the demonstrated linear range of the method; use concentrated solutions so volume change in sample is negligible. See Table 1020:I for acceptable limits.

3. Analysis of Externally Supplied Standards

As a minimum, analyze externally supplied standards whenever analysis of known additions does not result in acceptable recovery or once each day, whichever is more frequent. Use laboratory control standards with a concentration between 5 and 50 times the MDL or near sample ambient levels, whichever is greater. Where possible, use certified reference materials as laboratory control standards. National Institute of Standards and Technology (NIST)* Standard Reference Materials are preferred, if available. If internal reference materials are used, prepare them independently from the standards used for calibration. See Table 1020:I for acceptable limits for high-level duplicates.

4. Analysis of Reagent Blanks

Analyze reagent blanks whenever new reagents are used and as often as required in specific methods. Analyze a minimum of 5% of the sample load as reagent blanks; this monitors purity of reagents and the overall procedural blank. Analyze a reagent blank after any sample with a con-

---

* Formerly National Bureau of Standards (NBS).

TABLE 1020:I. ACCEPTANCE LIMITS FOR DUPLICATE SAMPLES AND KNOWN ADDITIONS TO WATER
AND WASTEWATER

Analysis	Recovery of Known Additions* %	Precision of Low-Level Duplicates*† %	Precision of High-Level Duplicates*†‡ %
Metals	80–120	75–125	90–110
Volatile organics	70–130	60–140	80–120
Volatile gases	50–150	50–150	70–130
Base/neutrals	70–130	60–140	80–120
Acids	60–140	60–140	80–120
Anions	80–120	75–125	90–110
Nutrients	80–120	75–125	90–110
Other inorganics	80–120	75–125	90–110
Total organic carbon	80–120	75–125	90–110
Total organic halogens	80–120	75–125	85–115
Herbicides	40–160	60–140	80–120
Organochlorine pesticides	50–140	60–140	80–120
Captan	20–130	60–140	80–120
Endosulfans	25–140	60–140	80–120
Endrin aldehyde	25–140	60–140	80–120
Organophosphorus pesticides	50–200	60–140	80–120
Trichlorophon	20–200	60–140	80–120
Triazine pesticides	50–200	60–140	80–120
Carbamate pesticides	50–150	60–140	80–120

* Additions calculated as % of the known addition recovered, duplicates calculated as the difference as a percentage of the mean $[100(x_1 - x_2)/\bar{x}]$.
† Low-level refers to concentrations less than 20 times the MDL. High-level refers to concentrations greater than 20 times the MDL.
‡ Also acceptance limits for independent laboratory control standards and certification of operator competence.
Source: NATRELLA, M. G. 1966. Experimental Statistics. National Bur. Standards Handbook 91, Washington, D.C.

centration greater than that of the highest standard or that might result in carryover from one sample to the next.

5. Calibration with Standards

As a minimum, measure three different dilutions of the standard when an analysis is initiated. Subsequently, verify the standard curve daily by analyzing one or more standards within the linear range, as specified in the individual method. Reportable analytical results are those within the range of the standard dilutions used. Do not report values above the highest standard unless an initial demonstration of greater linear range has been made, no instrument parameters have been changed, and the value is less than 1.5 times the highest standard. The lowest reportable value is the MDL, provided that the lowest calibration standard is less than 10 times the MDL. If a blank is subtracted, report the result even if it is negative.

6. Analysis of Duplicates

When most samples have measurable levels of the constituent being determined, analysis of duplicate samples is effective for assessing precision. Analyze 5% or more of the samples in duplicate. Analyze duplicates and known additions in matrices representative of the samples analyzed in the laboratory. See Table 1020:I for acceptable limits for duplicate analyses.

7. Control Charts

Three types of control charts commonly are used in laboratories[1]: a means chart for standards—laboratory control standards (LCS) or calibration check standards (CCS); a means chart for background or reagent blank results; and a range chart for replicate analyses.

The charts are essential instruments for quality control. Each type of chart is described below.

a. Means chart: The means chart for standards is constructed from the average and standard deviation of a standard. It includes upper and lower warning levels (WL) and upper and lower control levels (CL). Common practice is to use $\pm 2s$ and $\pm 3s$ limits for the WL and CL, respectively, where s represents standard deviation. Derive these values from stated values for standard reference materials, if used for the laboratory control standard (LCS) or calibration check standard (CCS), or from replicate analyses of a CCS. The chart can be set up by using either the calculated values for mean and standard deviation or by using percentages. Percentage is necessary if the concentration varies. Construct a chart for each analytical instrument. Enter results on the chart each time the LCS or CCS is analyzed. Examples of control charts for means are given in Figure 1020:1.

b. Range chart: If the standard deviation of the method is known, use the factors from Table 1020:II to construct the central line and warning and control limits as in Figure 1020:2. Perfect agreement between duplicates results in no difference when the values are subtracted, so the base line on the chart is zero. The standard deviation is converted to the range so that the analyst need only subtract the two results to plot the value on the control chart. The mean range is computed as:

$$\overline{R} = D_2 s$$

the control limit as

$$CL = \overline{R} \pm 3s(R) = D_4 \overline{R}$$

and the warning limit as

$$WL = \overline{R} \pm 2s(R) = \overline{R} \pm 2/3\, D_4 \overline{R}$$

where:

D_2 = factor to convert s to the range (1.128 for duplicates, as given in Table 1020:II),

$s(R)$ = standard deviation of the range, and

D_4 = factor to convert mean range to $3s(R)$ (3.267 for duplicates, as given in Table 1020:II).

A range chart is rather simple when duplicate analyses of a standard are used (Figure 1020:2). For duplicate analyses of samples, the plot will appear different because of the variation in sample concentration. If a constant relative standard deviation in the concentration range of interest is assumed, the $\overline{R}$, $D_4 \overline{R}$, etc. may be computed as above for several concentrations, a smooth curve drawn through the points obtained, and so an acceptable range for duplicates for any mean concentration can be determined. Figure 1020:3 illustrates such a chart. A separate table, as suggested below the figure, will be needed to track precision over time.

More commonly, the range can be expressed as a function of the relative standard deviation (coefficient of variation). Normalize the range by dividing by the average. Determine the mean range for the pairs analyzed by

$$\overline{R} = (\Sigma\, R_i)/n$$

and the variance (square of the standard deviation) as

$$s_R{}^2 = (\Sigma R_i{}^2 - n\overline{R}{}^2)/(n-1)$$

Then draw lines on the chart at $\overline{R} + 2s_R$ and $\overline{R} + 3s_R$ and, for each duplicate analysis, calculate normalized range and enter

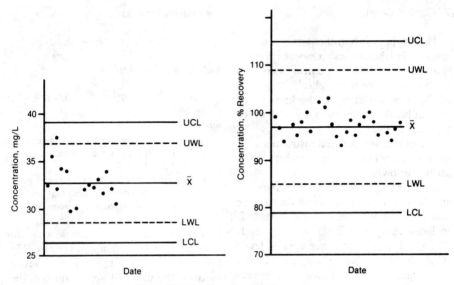

Figure 1020:1. Control charts for means.

TABLE 1020:II. FACTORS FOR COMPUTING LINES ON RANGE CONTROL CHARTS

Number of Observations n	Factor for Central Line (D_2)	Factor for Control Limits (D_4)
2	1.128	3.267
3	1.693	2.575
4	2.059	2.282
5	2.326	2.115
6	2.534	2.004

Source: ROSENSTEIN, M. & A. S. GOLDEN. 1964. Statistical Techniques for Quality Control of Environmental Radioassays. AQCS Rep. Stat-1. Public Health Serv., Winchester, Mass.

the result on the chart. Figure 1020:4 is an example of such a chart.

c. Chart analyses: If the warning limits (WL) are at the 95% level, 1 out of 20 points, on the average, would exceed that limit whereas only 1 out of 100 would exceed the control limits (CL). Take the following actions, based on these statistical parameters, which are illustrated in Figure 1020:5:

Control limit—If one measurement exceeds a CL, repeat the analysis immediately. If the repeat is within the CL, continue analyses; if it exceeds the CL, discontinue analyses and correct the problem.

Warning limit—If two out of three successive points exceed a WL, analyze another sample. If the next point is less than WL, continue analyses; if next point exceeds WL, discontinue analyses and correct the problem.

Standard deviation—If four out of five successive points exceed 1 *s*, or are in decreasing or increasing order, analyze another sample. If the next point is less than 1 *s*, or changes the order, continue analyses; otherwise, discontinue analyses and correct the problem.

Central line—If six successive samples are above the central line, analyze another

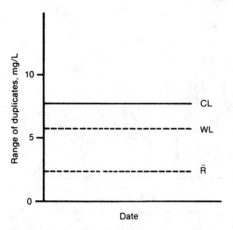

Figure 1020:2. Duplicate analyses of a standard.

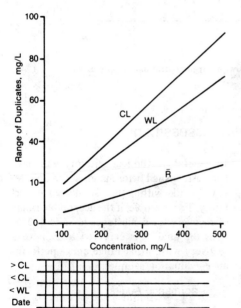

Figure 1020:3. Range chart for variable concentrations.

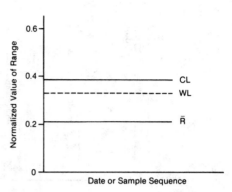

Figure 1020:4. Range chart for variable ranges.

sample. If the next point is below the central line, continue analyses; if the next point is on the same side, discontinue analyses and correct the problem.

The above considerations apply when the conditions are either above or below the central line, but not on *both* sides, e.g., four of five values must exceed either $+1\ s$ or $-1\ s$. After correcting the problem, reanalyze half the samples analyzed between the last in-control measurement and the out-of-control one.

Another important function of the control chart is assessment of improvements in method precision. In the means and range charts, if measurements never or rarely exceed the WL, recalculate the WL and CL using the 20 most recent data points. Trends in precision can be detected sooner if running averages of 20 are kept on a daily basis.

8. Reference

1. GOLDEN, A.S. 1984. Evaluation of internal control measurements in radioassay. *Health Phys.* 47:361.

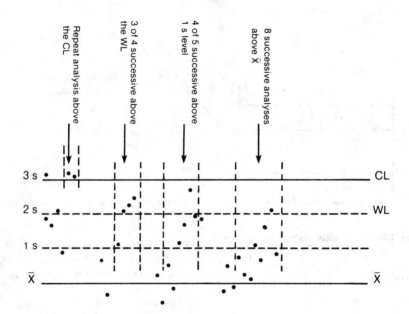

Figure 1020:5. Means control chart with out-of-control data (upper half).

1020 C. Quality Assessment

Quality assessment is the process of using external and internal quality control measures to determine the quality of the data produced by the laboratory. It includes such items as performance evaluation samples, laboratory intercomparison samples, and performance audits as well as the internal QC described in Section 1020B. They are applied to test the recovery, bias, precision, detection limit, and adherence to standard operating procedure requirements.

1. Performance Evaluation Samples

Use samples with known amounts of the constituent of interest supplied by an outside agency or blind additions prepared independently within the laboratory to determine recovery achieved by an analyst.

In general, method uncertainty will have been established beforehand; acceptable recovery falls within the established uncertainty. For example, if the acceptable range of recovery for a substance is 85 to 115%, then the analyst is expected to achieve a recovery within that range on all performance evaluation samples.

2. Performance Audits

Make only unscheduled performance audits using a check list made to document the manner in which a sample is treated from time of receipt to final reporting of the result. The goal is to detect any deviations from the standard operating procedure so that corrective action can be taken. A recommended format with a few initial items in the check list is shown in Table 1020:III.

TABLE 1020:III. AUDIT OF A SOIL ANALYSIS PROCEDURE

Procedure	Comment	Remarks
1. Sample entered into logbook	yes	lab number assigned
2. Sample weighed	yes	dry weight
3. Drying procedure followed	no	maintenance of oven not done
4a. Balance calibrated	yes	once per year
b. Cleaned and zero adjusted	yes	weekly
5. Sample ground	yes	to pass 50 mesh
6. Ball mill cleaned	yes	should be after each sample
.		
.		
.		

3. Laboratory Intercomparison Samples

Commercial and governmental programs supply samples containing various constituents in various matrices. A good quality assessment program requires participation in periodic laboratory intercomparison studies. Adjust frequency of participation to the quality of the results produced by the analysts being tested. For routine procedures, quarterly analyses are reasonable. Official agencies conducting such studies are listed below.

a. *Organic and inorganic compounds in water:* Samples are available from the Environmental Monitoring Systems Laboratory, U.S. EPA, 26 West St. Clair, Cincinnati, Ohio 45268. These samples can be used as performance evaluation samples or as standards for laboratory intercomparison studies.

b. *Radioisotopes in various media:* These samples are available from the Environmental Monitoring Systems Laboratory, U.S. EPA, P.O. Box 93478, Las Vegas, Nevada 89193-3478. These can be supplied for use as performance evaluation samples; the Laboratory also conducts laboratory intercomparison studies.[1] Environmental samples with background levels of radioisotopes are available from the Division of Laboratories and Research, International Atomic Energy Agency, P.O. Box 100, A-1400 Vienna, Austria.

4. Reference

1. JARVIS, A.N. & L. SIU. 1981. Environmental Radioactivity Laboratory Intercomparison Studies Program. EPA-600/4-81-004, U.S. Environmental Protection Agency, Las Vegas, Nev.

1030   DATA QUALITY

1030 A.   Introduction

1. Quality Indicators

The principal indicators of data quality are its bias (Section 1030B) and precision (Section 1030C), which, when combined, express its accuracy. The relationship among these terms is shown in Figure 1030:1. Of the four possible outcomes, only the condition of low bias and high precision is accurate.[1]

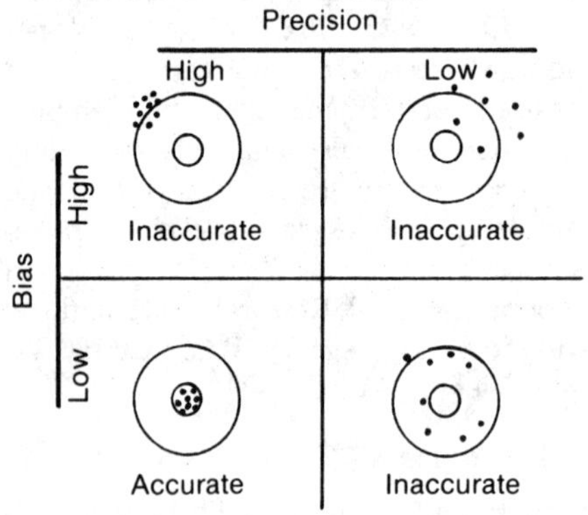

Figure 1030:1. Definition of accuracy.

Subsidiary data quality indicators are method detection limit (Section 1030E) and representativeness. Representativeness can relate both to the sample itself and to the sampled population. A method may be highly accurate, but if the results do not represent the sample or if the sample does not represent the population, the data are not useful. Representativeness of the sample is best assessed by analysis of a number of samples from the same location or from a well-mixed bulk lot. The representativeness of the method is best determined through collaborative studies using a variety of methods.

2. Reference

1. U.S. ENVIRONMENTAL PROTECTION AGENCY. 1980. Health Physics Society Committee Report HPSR-1: Upgrading Environmental Radiation Data. EPA-520/1-80-012, U.S. Environmental Protection Agency, Washington, D.C.

1030 B.   Bias

Bias is a measure of systematic error. It has two components: one due to the method, and the other to a laboratory's use of the method. The bias of a method is measured best by a laboratory intercomparison study in which the difference between the grand average and the known (or true) value is the method bias. The laboratory bias is the difference between the laboratory average recovery and the true value and is, therefore, a combination of the two biases. Assess the laboratory bias by measuring the recovery of known additions or by analyzing duplicate samples and retaining the sign of the differences when calculating the average difference. From this value, subtract the method bias from an intercomparison study to determine the bias due to the laboratory's practices as it interprets the method.

1030 C. Precision

1. Definition

Precision is a measure of the closeness with which multiple analyses of a given sample agree with each other. Assess precision by replicate analyses, by repeated analyses of a stable standard, or by analysis of known additions to samples. Precision is specified by the standard deviation of the results.[1] If overall precision of a study is desired, analyze duplicate samples. This latter precision includes the random errors involved in sampling as well as the errors in sample preparation and analysis.

When only a few replications are used, for example, duplicate sample analysis or duplicate extract analysis, the range of results, R, is nearly as efficient as the standard deviation because the two measures differ by a constant ($1.128s = R$ for duplicates, $1.693s = R$ for triplicates).

2. Computation

Table 1030:I lists the results of duplicate analyses and recovery values from repetitive analysis of a stable standard. Table 1030:II shows the precision calculation us-

TABLE 1030:I. PRECISION CALCULATIONS USING DUPLICATES

Duplicate Analyses			Standard Analyses
1st Result mg/L	2nd Result mg/L	Difference mg/L	Result mg/L
50	46	4	35.1
37	36	1	33.2
22	19	3	33.7
17	20	3	35.9
32	34	2	33.5
46	46	0	34.5
26	28	2	34.4
26	30	4	34.3
61	58	3	31.8
44	45	1	35.0
40	44	4	31.4
36	35	1	35.6
29	31	2	30.2
36	36	0	32.7
47	45	2	31.1
16	20	4	34.8
18	21	3	34.3
26	22	4	36.4
35	36	1	32.1
26	25	1	38.2
49	51	2	33.1
33	32	1	34.9
40	38	2	36.2
16	13	3	34.0
39	42	3	33.8
		$\Sigma = 56, n = 25$	$\Sigma = 850.2$

$\overline{R} = 56/25 = 2.24$

$s = 2.24/1.128 = 1.98$

$\overline{x} = 34.01$

$s = 1.83$

TABLE 1030:II. PRECISION CALCULATION FROM KNOWN ADDITIONS

(1) Value for Sample with Known Additions	(2) Sample	(3) Calculated Recovery (1)–(2)	(4) Known Additions	(5) Deviation from Expected (3)–(4)
1.91	0.68	1.23	1.30	−0.07
1.78	0.57	1.21	1.30	−0.09
1.53	0.23	1.30	1.30	0.00
1.74	0.15	1.59	1.30	0.29
2.10	0.53	1.57	1.30	0.27
1.82	0.61	1.21	1.30	−0.09
2.07	0.54	1.53	1.30	0.23
1.39	0.14	1.25	1.30	−0.05
1.16	0.20	0.96	1.30	−0.34
1.55	0.19	1.36	1.30	0.06
2.02	0.41	1.61	1.30	0.31
1.58	0.36	1.22	1.30	−0.08
13.01	11.97	1.04	1.30	−0.26
1.46	0.17	1.29	1.30	−0.01
1.63	0.31	1.32	1.30	0.02
11.95	10.98	0.97	1.30	−0.33
1.68	0.27	1.41	1.30	0.11
1.83	0.47	1.36	1.30	0.06
1.62	0.43	1.19	1.30	−0.11
5.04	3.96	1.08	1.30	−0.22
2.53	1.22	1.31	1.30	0.01
2.69	1.09	1.60	1.30	0.30
1.50	0.25	1.25	1.30	−0.05
1.77	0.51	1.26	1.30	−0.04
1.88	0.55	1.33	1.30	0.03

$s^2 = (\Sigma \text{ deviations}^2)/(n-1)$
$s = \sqrt{0.8035/24} = 0.183$

ing known additions. From duplicate analyses, the average difference, or average range, is calculated by summing all the differences (absolute values) and dividing by the number of observations: $\overline{R} = \Sigma d_i / n$. This is converted to standard deviation by dividing by 1.128. For multiple analyses of a stable standard, calculate the standard deviation as usual. The true value of the standard is irrelevant for this analysis.

In using known additions to determine precision, as in the example of Table 1030:II, subtract recovery from the known value (subtract Column 3 from Column 4) and calculate the standard deviation by the usual method as shown at the bottom of the table. If the standard deviation is a constant proportion of the amount present, then the coefficient of variation (relative standard deviation, $s/\overline{x}$) may be used instead of the standard deviation.

3. Reference

1. AMERICAN SOCIETY FOR TESTING AND MATERIALS. 1977. Standard Practice for Determination of Precision and Bias of Methods. Committee D-19 on Water, Designation D2777-77, American Soc. Testing & Materials, Philadelphia, Pa.

1030 D. Total Uncertainty

1. Definition and Computation

This statistic is some appropriate combination of the random and systematic uncertainties in a given measurement system. The random uncertainties are assessed by calculating precision; they are ascertained statistically. The systematic uncertainties are the biases and those random uncertainties that cannot be evaluated statistically. Because the latter can be estimated only from a thorough knowledge of all steps in the measurement process, using the judgment of an experienced analyst, there is considerable vagueness in the assessment. Because the biases can be assessed, it is customary to consider only them in evaluating total uncertainty. These biases can occur at several points in the system, for example, in weighing the sample, in the result produced by the analytical instrument, in changes in quality of reagents, or in incomplete extraction. If random uncertainties have been assessed by the standard deviation (s_x) and if biases are represented by b_i, these quantities may be combined in quadratic form to calculate uncertainty[1]:

$$U_x = (s_x^2 + 1/3 \ \Sigma b_i^2)^{1/2}$$

Generally, the instrumental and extraction biases (B) are the largest and the equation simplifies to:

$$U_x = (s_x^2 + B^2)^{1/2}$$

To express the uncertainty in the form of confidence levels, assume that the bias is known with little error and add it to higher confidence levels of the variance; for example, for 95% confidence level:

$$U_{x(95\%)} = (2s_x^2 + B^2)^{1/2}$$

If the concentration of the constituent is within a narrow range, use the concentration units for B and s_x; otherwise, use the coefficient of variation for s_x and the fractional form of B.

2. Reference

1. U.S. ENVIRONMENTAL PROTECTION AGENCY. 1980. Health Physics Society Committee Report HPSR-1: Upgrading Environmental Radiation Data. EPA-520/1-80-012, U.S. Environmental Protection Agency, Washington, D.C.

1030 E.   Method Detection Limit

1. Introduction

Detection limits are controversial, principally because of inadequate definition and confusion of terms. Frequently, the instrumental detection limit is used for the method detection limit and *vice versa*. Whatever term is used, most analysts agree that the smallest amount that can be detected above the noise in a procedure and within a stated confidence limit is the detection limit. The confidence limits are set so that the probabilities of both Type I and Type II errors are acceptably small.

Current practice identifies several detection limits (see 1010C), each of which has a defined purpose. These are the instrument detection limit (IDL), the lower limit of detection (LLD), the method detection limit (MDL), and the limit of quantitation (LOQ). Occasionally the instrument detection limit is used as a guide for determining the MDL. The relationship among these limits is approximately IDL:LLD:MDL:LOQ = 1:2:4:10.

2. Determining Detection Limits

An operating analytical instrument usually produces a signal (noise) even when no sample is present or when a blank is being analyzed. Because any QA program requires frequent analysis of blanks, the mean and standard deviation become well known; the blank signal becomes very precise, i.e., the Gaussian curve of the blank distribution becomes very narrow. The IDL is the constituent concentration that produces a signal greater than three standard deviations of the mean noise level or that can be determined by injecting a standard to produce a signal that is five times the signal-to-noise ratio. The IDL is useful for estimating the constituent concentration or amount in an extract needed to produce a signal to permit calculating an estimated method detection limit.

The LLD is the amount of constituent that produces a signal sufficiently large that 99% of the trials with that amount will produce a detectable signal. Determine the LLD by multiple injections of a standard at near zero concentration (concentration no greater that five times the IDL). Determine the standard deviation by the usual method. To reduce the probability of a Type I error (false detection) to 5%, multiply s by 1.645 from a cumulative normal probability table. Also, to reduce the probability of a Type II error (false nondetection) to 5%, double this amount to 3.290. As an example, if 20 determinations of a low-level standard yielded a standard deviation of 6 μg/L, the LLD is 3.29 $\times$ 6 = 20 μg/L.[1]

The MDL differs from the LLD in that samples containing the constituent of interest are processed through the complete analytical method. The method detection limit is greater than the LLD because of extraction efficiency and extract concentration factors. The MDL can be achieved by experienced analysts operating well-calibrated instruments on a nonroutine basis. For example, to determine the MDL, add a constituent to reagent water, or to the matrix of interest, to make a concentration near the estimated MDL.[2] Analyze seven portions of this solution and calculate the standard deviation (s). From a table of the one-sided t distribution select the value of t for 7 − 1 = 6 degrees of freedom and at the 99% level; this value is 3.14. The product 3.14 times s is the desired MDL.

Although the LOQ is useful within a

laboratory, the practical quantitation limit (PQL) has been proposed as the lowest level achievable among laboratories within specified limits during routine laboratory operations.[3] The PQL is significant because different laboratories will produce different MDLs even though using the same analytical procedures, instruments, and sample matrices. The PQL is about five times the MDL and represents a practical and routinely achievable detection limit with a relatively good certainty that any reported value is reliable.

3. Description of Limits

Figure 1030:2 illustrates the detection limits discussed above. For this figure it is assumed that the signals from an analytical instrument are distributed normally and can be represented by a normal (Gaussian) curve.[4] The curve labeled B is representative of the background or blank signal distribution. As shown, the distribution of the blank signals is nearly as broad as for the other distributions, that is $\sigma_B = \sigma_I = \sigma_L$. As blank analyses continue, this curve will become narrower because of increased degrees of freedom.

The curve labeled I represents the IDL. Its average value is located $k\sigma_B$ units distant from the blank curve, and k represents the value of t (from the one-sided t distribution) that corresponds to the confidence limit chosen to describe instrument performance. For a 95% limit and $n = 14$, $k = 1.782$ and for a 99% limit, $k = 2.68$. The overlap of the B and I curves indicates the probability of not detecting a constituent when it is present (Type II error).

The curve at the extreme right of Figure 1030:2 represents the LLD. Because only a finite number of determinations are used for calculating the IDL and LLD, the curves are broader than the blank but are similar, so it is reasonable to choose $\sigma_I = \sigma_L$. Therefore, the LLD is $k\sigma_I + k\sigma_L = 2k\sigma_L$ from the blank curve.

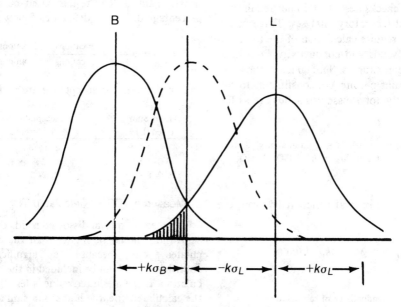

Figure 1030:2. Detection limit relationship.

4. References

1. AMERICAN SOCIETY FOR TESTING AND MA-
TERIALS. 1983. Standard Practice for Intralaboratory Quality Control Procedures and a
Discussion on Reporting Low-Level Data. Designation D4210-83, American Soc. Testing &
Materials, Philadelphia, Pa.
2. GLASER, J.A., D.L. FOERST, J.D. McKEE,
S.A. QUAVE & W.L. BUDDE. 1981. Trace analyses for wastewaters. *Environ. Sci. Technol.*
15:1426.
3. U.S. ENVIRONMENTAL PROTECTION AGENCY.
1985. National Primary Drinking Water Standards: Synthetic Organics, Inorganics, and Bac-
teriologicals. 40 CFR Part 141; *Federal Register*
50: No. 219, November 13, 1985.
4. OPPENHEIMER, J. & R. TRUSSELL. 1984. Detection limits in water quality analysis. *In* Proc.
Water Quality Technology Conference (Denver, Colorado, December 2-5, 1984). American
Water Works Assoc., Denver, Colo.

1030 F.   Checking Correctness of Analyses

The following procedures for checking correctness of analyses are applicable specifically to water samples for which relatively complete analyses are made.[1] These include pH, conductivity, total dissolved solids (TDS), and major anionic and cationic constituents that are indications of general water quality.

The checks described do not require additional laboratory analyses. Three of the checks require calculation of the total dissolved solids and conductivity from measured constituents. Sum concentrations (in milligrams per liter) of constituents to calculate the total dissolved solids are as follows:

$$\text{Total dissolved solids} = 0.6 \text{ (alkalinity)} + \text{Na} + \text{K} + \text{Ca} + \text{Mg} + \text{Cl} + \text{SO}_4 + \text{SiO}_3 + (\text{NO}_3\text{-N}) + \text{F}$$

Calculate electrical conductivity from the equation:

$$G = \lambda C - (k_1 \lambda + k_2) (C)^{3/2}$$

where:

G = conductivity of salt solution,
C = concentration of salt solution,
λ = equivalent conductance of salt solution at infinite dilution,
k_1, k_2 = constants for relaxation of ion cloud effect and electrophoretic effect relative to ion mobility.[1]

1. Anion-Cation Balance[2]

The anion and cation sums, when expressed as milliequivalents per liter, must balance because all potable waters are electrically neutral. The test is based on the percentage difference defined as follows:

$$\% \text{ difference} = 100 \frac{\Sigma \text{ cations} - \Sigma \text{ anions}}{\Sigma \text{ cations} + \Sigma \text{ anions}}$$

and the criteria for acceptance are as follows:

Anion Sum (meq/L)	Acceptable % Difference
0–3.0	±0.2 meq/L
3.0–10.0	± 2%
20.0–800	± 2–5%

2. Measured TDS = Calculated TDS[2]

The measured total dissolved solids concentration should be higher than the calculated one because a significant contributor may not be included in the calculation. If the measured value is less than the calculated one, the higher ion sum and measured value are suspect; the sample should be reanalyzed. If the measured solids concentration is more than 20% higher than the calculated one, the low ion sum is suspect and selected constituents should be reanalyzed. The acceptable ratio is as follows:

$$1.0 < \frac{\text{measured TDS}}{\text{calculated TDS}} < 1.2$$

3. Measured EC = Calculated EC

If the calculated conductivity is higher than the measured value, reanalyze the higher ion sum. If the calculated EC is less than the measured one, reanalyze the lower ion sum. The acceptable ratio is as follows:

$$0.9 < \frac{\text{calculated EC}}{\text{measured EC}} < 1.1$$

4. Measured EC and Ion Sums

Both the anion and cation sums should be $\frac{1}{100}$ of the measured EC value. If either of the two sums does not meet this criterion, that sum is suspect; reanalyze the sample. The acceptable criteria are as follows:

$$100 \times \text{anion (or cation) sum, meq/L} = (0.9\text{--}1.1)\ EC$$

5. Calculated TDS to EC Ratio

If the ratio of calculated TDS to conductivity falls below 0.55, the lower ion

sum is suspect; reanalyze it. If the ratio is above 0.7, the higher ion sum is suspect; reanalyze it. If reanalysis causes no change in the lower ion sum, an unmeasured constituent, such as ammonia or nitrite, may be present at a significant concentration. If poorly dissociated calcium and sulfate ions are present, the TDS may be as high as 0.8 times the EC. The acceptable criterion is as follows:

$$\text{calculated TDS/conductivity} = 0.55\text{--}0.7$$

6. Measured TDS to EC Ratio

The acceptable criteria for this ratio are from 0.55 to 0.7. If the ratio of TDS to EC is outside these limits, measured TDS or measured conductivity is suspect; reanalyze.

A more complete exposition[3] of the above quality-control checks has been published.

7. References

1. ROSSUM, J.R. 1975. Checking the accuracy of water analyses through the use of conductivity. *J. Amer. Water Works Assoc.* 67:204.
2. FRIEDMAN, L.C. & D.E. ERDMANN. 1982. Quality Assurance Practices for Analyses of Water and Fluvial Sediments. Tech. Water Resources Inc., Book 5, Chapter A6. U.S. Government Printing Off., Washington, D.C.
3. OPPENHEIMER, J. & A.D. EATON. 1986. Quality control and mineral analysis. *In* Proc. Water Quality Technology Conference (Houston, Texas, December 8-11, 1985). American Water Works Assoc., Denver, Colo.

1040   METHOD DEVELOPMENT AND EVALUATION

1040 A.   Introduction

Although standard methods are available from many nationally recognized sources, there may be occasions when they cannot be used or when no standard method exists for a particular constituent.

Therefore, method development may be required. Method development is the set of experimental procedures devised for measuring a known amount of a constituent in various matrices.

1040 B.   Method Validation

Whether an entirely new method is developed by accepted research procedures or an existing method is modified to meet special requirements, validation by a three-step process is required: determination of single-operator precision and bias, analysis of independently prepared unknown samples, and determination of method ruggedness.

1. Single-Operator Characteristics

This part of the validation procedure requires determining the method detection limit (MDL) as in Section 1030; the bias of the method, i.e., the systematic error of the method; and the precision obtainable by a single operator, i.e., the random error introduced in using the method. To make these determinations, analyze at least 7 but preferably 10 or more portions of a standard at each of several concentrations in each matrix that may be used. Use one concentration at, or slightly above, the MDL and one relatively high so that the range of concentrations for which the method is applicable can be specified.

The use of several concentrations to determine bias and precision will reveal the form of the relationship between these method characteristics and the concentration of the substance. This relationship may be constant, linear, or curvilinear and is a significant characteristic of the method that should be explained clearly. Calculation of precision and bias for a single concentration in a single matrix is shown in the following table of results from eight replicate analyses of a standard with a known concentration of 1.30 mg/L.

Result mg/L	Difference (−1.30)	Squared Difference
1.23	−0.07	0.0049
1.21	−0.09	0.0081
1.30	0.0	0.0
1.59	0.29	0.0841
1.57	0.27	0.0729
1.21	−0.09	0.0081
1.53	0.23	0.0529
1.25	−0.05	0.0025
Sum	0.49	0.2335

The bias is $0.49/8 = 0.06$ mg/L and the precision is the square root of $0.2335/(8-1) = \sqrt{0.03336}$, or 0.18 mg/L (note that this is similar to the calculation for standard deviation).

2. Analysis of Unknown Samples

This step in the method validation procedure requires analysis of independently prepared standards where the value is unknown to the analyst. Analyze each unknown in replicate by following the standard operating procedure for the method. The mean amount recovered should be within three standard deviations (s) of the mean value of the standard but preferably within 2 s.

Obtain the unknowns from other personnel in the analyst's laboratory using either purchased analytical-grade reagents or standards available from National Institute of Standards and Technology (NIST)*, EPA, or other suitable sources. If available for the particular constituent, performance evaluation samples from EPA-Cincinnati (Section 1020) are particularly useful.

---

* Formerly National Bureau of Standards (NBS).

3. Method Ruggedness

A test of the ruggedness, i.e., stability of the result produced when steps in the method are varied, is the final validation step. It is especially important to determine this characteristic of a method if it is to be proposed as a standard or reference method. A properly conducted ruggedness test will point out those procedural steps in which rigor is critical and those in which some leeway is permissible.

The Association of Official Analytical Chemists[1] has suggested a method for this test in which eight separate analyses can be used to determine the effect of varying seven different steps in an analytical procedure. To illustrate, suppose the effect of changing the following factors is to be determined:

Factor	Nominal	Variation
Mixing time	10 min	12 min
Portion size	5 g	10 g
Acid concentration	$1M$	$1.1M$
Heat to	100°C	95°C
Hold heat for	5 min	10 min
Stirring	yes	no
pH adjust	6.0	6.5

To make the determination, denote the nominal factors by capital letters A through G and the variations by the corresponding lower-case letters. Then set up a table of the factors as follows:

	Combinations							
Factor value	1	2	3	4	5	6	7	8
A or a	A	A	A	A	a	a	a	a
B or b	B	B	b	b	B	B	b	b
C or c	C	c	C	c	C	c	C	c
D or d	D	D	d	d	d	d	D	D
E or e	E	e	E	e	e	E	e	E
F or f	F	f	f	F	F	f	f	F
G or g	G	g	g	G	g	G	G	g
Result	s	t	u	v	w	x	y	z

Source: YOUDEN, W. J. & E. H. STEINER. 1975. Statistical Manual of AOAC. Assoc. Official Analytical Chemists, Washington, D.C.

If combination 1 is analyzed, the result will be s. If combination 2 is analyzed, the result will be t, and so on until all eight combinations have been analyzed. To determine the effect of varying a factor, find the four results where the factor was nominal (all caps) and the four where it was varied (all lower case) and compare the averages of the two groups. For example, to compare the effect of changing C to c, use results $(s + u + w + y)/4$ and $(t + v + x + z)/4$. Calculate all seven pairs to get seven differences, which can then be ranked to reveal those with a significant effect on the results. If there is no outstanding difference, calculate the average and standard deviation of the eight results s through z. The standard deviation is a realistic estimate of the precision of the method. This design tests main effects, not interactions.

4. Equivalency Testing

After a new method has been validated by the procedures listed above, it may be prudent to test the method for equivalency to standard methods, unless none exist. This requires analysis of a minimum of three concentrations by the alternate and by the standard method. If the range of concentration is very broad, test more concentrations. Once an initial set of analyses (five or more) has been made at each chosen concentration, apply the following statistical steps:[2]

1. Test the distribution of data for normality and transform the data if necessary (Section 1010B).

2. Select an appropriate sample size based on an estimate of the standard deviation.[3]
3. Test the variances of the two methods using the F-ratio statistic.
4. Test the average values of the two methods using a Student-t statistic.

An explanation of each of these steps with additional techniques and examples has been published.[4] Because the number of analyses can be very large, the calculations become complex and familiarity with basic statistics is necessary. A listing of standard, reference, and equivalent methods for water analysis is available.[5]

5. References

1. YOUDEN, W.J. & E.H. STEINER. 1975. Statistical Manual of AOAC. Assoc. Official Analytical Chemists, Washington, D.C.
2. WILLIAMS, L.R. 1985. Harmonization of Biological Testing Methodology: A Performance Based Approach in Aquatic Toxicology and Hazard Assessment. 8th Symp. ASTM STP 891, R.C. Bahner & D.J. Hansen, eds. American Soc. Testing & Materials, Philadelphia, Pa.
3. NATRELLA, M.G. 1963. Experimental Statistics. National Bureau of Standards Handbook 91, Washington, D.C.
4. U.S. ENVIRONMENTAL PROTECTION AGENCY. 1983. Guidelines for Establishing Method Equivalency to Standard Methods. Rep. 600/X-83-037, Environmental Monitoring Systems Lab., Las Vegas, Nev.
5. U.S. ENVIRONMENTAL PROTECTION AGENCY. 1987. Guidelines establishing test procedures for the analysis of pollutants under the Clean Water Act. Interim final rule. 40 CFR Part 136; *Federal Register* 52:171:33542.

1040 C.　Collaborative Testing

Once a new or modified method has been developed and validated it is appropriate to determine whether the method should be made a standard method. The procedure to convert a method to standard status is the collaborative test.[1] In this test, a num-

ber of laboratories use the standard operating procedure to analyze a select number of samples to determine the method's bias and precision as would occur in normal practice.

In planning for a collaborative test, consider the following factors: a precisely written standard operating procedure, the number of variables to be tested, the number of levels to be tested, and the number of replicates required. Because method precision is estimated by the standard deviation, which itself is the result of many sources of variation, the variables that affect it must be tested. These may include the laboratory, operator, apparatus, and concentration range.

1. Variables

Test at least the following variables:

Laboratory—Involve at least three different laboratories, although more are desirable to provide a better estimate of the standard deviation;

Apparatus—Because model and manufacturer differences can be sources of error, analyze at least two replicates of each concentration per laboratory;

Operators—To determine overall precision, involve at least six analysts with not more than two from each laboratory;

Levels—If the method development has indicated that the relative standard deviation is constant, test three levels covering the range of the method. If it is not constant, use more levels spread uniformly over the operating range.

If matrix effects are suspected, conduct the test in each medium for which the method was developed. If this is not feasible, use appropriate grades of reagent water as long as this is stipulated in the resulting statement of method characteristics.

2. Number of Replicates

Calculate the number of replicates after the number of variables to be tested has been determined by using the formula:

$$r > 1 + (30/P)$$

where:
r = number of replicates and
P = the product of several variables.

The minimum number of replicates is two. As an example, if three levels of a substance are to be analyzed by single operators in six laboratories on a single apparatus, then P is calculated as follows:

$$P = 3 \times 1 \times 6 \times 1 = 18$$

and the number of replicates is

$$r > 1 + (30/18) > 2.7 \text{ or } r = 3.$$

3. Illustrative Collaborative Test

Send each of five laboratories four concentrations of a compound (4.3, 11.6, 23.4, and 32.7 mg/L) with instructions to analyze in triplicate using the procedure provided. Tabulate results as shown in the table below (the results for only one concentration are shown). Because there are no obviously aberrant values (use the method in Section 1010B to reject outliers), use all the data.

Calculate the average and standard deviation for each laboratory; use all 15 results to calculate a grand average and standard deviation. The difference between the average of each laboratory and the grand average reveals any significant bias, such as that shown for Laboratories 1 and 3. The difference between the grand average and the known value is the method bias, e.g., $33.0 - 32.7 = 0.3$ mg/L or 0.9%. The relative standard deviation of the grand average (1.5 mg/L) is 4.5%, which is the method precision, and the s for each laboratory is the single-operator precision.

Laboratory	Result mg/L	Experimental $x \pm s$	Deviation From Known	Deviation From Grand Average
1	32.7 35.2 36.3	34.7 ± 1.8	2.0	1.7
2	32.6 33.7 33.6	33.3 ± 0.6	0.6	0.3
3	30.6 30.6 32.4	31.2 ± 1.0	−1.5	−1.8
4	32.6 32.5 33.9	33.0 ± 0.8	0.3	0
5	32.4 33.4 32.9	32.6 ± 0.8	−0.1	−0.4
$(\Sigma x)/n = 33$ $s = 1.5$			$\Sigma = 1.3$	$\Sigma = -0.2$

As noted in the table, the sum of the deviations from the known value for the laboratories was 1.3, so the average deviation (bias) was $1.3/5 = 0.26$, rounded to 0.3, which is the same as the difference between the grand average and the known value.

For all four unknowns in this test, the percentage results indicated increasing bias and decreasing precision as the concentration decreased. Therefore, to describe the method in a formal statement, the precision would be given by a straight line with the formula $y = mx + b$; where y is the relative standard deviation, m is the slope of the line, x is the concentration, and b is the relative standard deviation at concentration $= 0$. The values found from the collaborative test are shown in the following table.

Known Amount mg/L	Amount Found mg/L	CV (% Standard Deviation)	Bias %
4.3	4.8	12.5	11.5
11.6	12.2	10.2	5.6
23.4	23.8	5.4	1.9
32.7	33	4.5	0.9

These results indicate that the method is acceptable. However, concentrations of less than about 10 mg/L require greater care in analysis.

4. Reference

1. YOUDEN, W.J. & E.H. STEINER. 1975. Statistical Manual of the AOAC. Assoc. Official Analytical Chemists, Washington, D.C.

1050   EXPRESSION OF RESULTS

1050 A.   Units

This text uses the International System of Units (SI) and chemical and physical results are expressed in milligrams per liter (mg/L). Record only the significant figures. If concentrations generally are less than 1 mg/L, it may be more convenient to express results in micrograms per liter (μg/L). Use μg/L when concentrations are less than 0.1 mg/L.

Express concentrations greater than 10 000 mg/L in percent, 1% being equal to 10 000 mg/L when the specific gravity is 1.00. In solid samples and liquid wastes of high specific gravity, make a correction if the results are expressed as parts per million (ppm) or percent by weight:

$$\text{ppm by weight} = \frac{\text{mg/L}}{\text{sp gr}}$$

$$\% \text{ by weight} = \frac{\text{mg/L}}{10\ 000 \times \text{sp gr}}$$

TABLE 1050:I. CONVERSION FACTORS*
(Milligrams per Liter—Milliequivalents per Liter)

Ion (Cation)	me/L = mg/L×	mg/L = me/L×	Ion (Anion)	me/L = mg/L×	mg/L = me/L×
Al^{3+}	0.111 2	8.994	BO_2^-	0.023 36	42.81
B^{3+}	0.277 5	3.603	Br^-	0.012 52	79.90
Ba^{2+}	0.014 56	68.67	Cl^-	0.028 21	35.45
Ca^{2+}	0.049 90	20.04	CO_3^{2-}	0.033 33	30.00
Cr^{3+}	0.057 70	17.33	CrO_4^{2-}	0.017 24	58.00
			F^-	0.052 64	19.00
Cu^{2+}	0.031 47	31.77	HCO_3^-	0.016 39	61.02
Fe^{2+}	0.035 81	27.92	HPO_4^{2-}	0.020 84	47.99
Fe^{3+}	0.053 72	18.62	$H_2PO_4^-$	0.010 31	96.99
H^+	0.992 2	1.008	HS^-	0.030 24	33.07
K^+	0.025 58	39.10	HSO_3^-	0.012 34	81.07
			HSO_4^-	0.010 30	97.07
Li^+	0.144 1	6.941	I^-	0.007 880	126.9
Mg^{2+}	0.082 29	12.15	NO_2^-	0.021 74	46.01
Mn^{2+}	0.036 40	27.47	NO_3^-	0.016 13	62.00
Mn^{4+}	0.072 81	13.73	OH^-	0.058 80	17.01
Na^+	0.043 50	22.99	PO_4^{3-}	0.031 59	31.66
NH_4^+	0.055 44	18.04	S^{2-}	0.062 38	16.03
Pb^{2+}	0.009 653	103.6	SiO_3^{2-}	0.026 29	38.04
Sr^{2+}	0.022 83	43.81	SO_3^{2-}	0.024 98	40.03
Zn^{2+}	0.030 59	32.69	SO_4^{2-}	0.020 82	48.03

* Factors are based on ion charge and not on redox reactions that may be possible for certain of these ions. Cations and anions are listed separately in alphabetical order.

In such cases, if the result is given as milligrams per liter, state specific gravity.

The unit equivalents per million (epm), or the identical and less ambiguous term milligram-equivalents per liter, or milliequivalents per liter (me/L), can be valuable for making water treatment calculations and checking analyses by anion-cation balance.

Table 1050:I presents factors for converting concentrations of common ions from milligrams per liter to milliequivalents per liter, and vice versa. The term milliequivalent used in this table represents 0.001 of an equivalent weight. The equivalent weight, in turn, is defined as the weight of the ion (sum of the atomic weights of the atoms making up the ion) divided by the number of charges normally associated with the particular ion. The factors for converting results from milligrams per liter to milliequivalents per liter were computed by dividing the ion charge by weight of the ion. Conversely, factors for converting results from milliequivalents per liter to milligrams per liter were calculated by dividing the weight of the ion by the ion charge.

1050 B.   Significant Figures

1. Reporting Requirements

To avoid ambiguity in reporting results or in presenting directions for a procedure, it is the custom to use "significant figures." All digits in a reported result are expected to be known definitely, except for the last digit, which may be in doubt. Such a number is said to contain only significant figures. If more than a single doubtful digit is carried, the extra digit or digits are not significant. If an analytical result is reported as "75.6 mg/L," the analyst should be quite certain of the "75," but may be uncertain as to whether the ".6" should be .5 or .7, or even .4 or .8, because of unavoidable uncertainty in the analytical procedure. If the standard deviation were known from previous work to be ±2 mg/L, the analyst would have, or should have, rounded off the result to "76 mg/L" before reporting it. On the other hand, if the method were so good that a result of "75.61 mg/L" could have been conscientiously reported, then the analyst should not have rounded it off to 75.6.

Report only such figures as are justified by the accuracy of the work. Do not follow the all-too-common practice of requiring that quantities listed in a column have the same number of figures to the right of the decimal point.

2. Rounding Off

Round off by dropping digits that are not significant. If the digit 6, 7, 8, or 9 is dropped, increase preceding digit by one unit; if the digit 0, 1, 2, 3, or 4 is dropped, do not alter preceding digit. If the digit 5 is dropped, round off preceding digit to the nearest even number: thus 2.25 becomes 2.2 and 2.35 becomes 2.4.

3. Ambiguous Zeros

The digit 0 may record a measured value of zero or it may serve merely as a spacer to locate the decimal point. If the result of a sulfate determination is reported as 420 mg/L, the report recipient may be in doubt whether the zero is significant or not, because the zero cannot be deleted. If an analyst calculates a total residue of 1146 mg/L, but realizes that the 4 is somewhat doubtful and that therefore the 6 has no significance, the answer should be rounded off to 1150 mg/L and so reported but here, too, the report recipient will not know whether the zero is significant. Although the number could be expressed as a power of 10 (e.g., 11.5×10^2 or 1.15×10^3), this form is not used generally because it would not be consistent with the normal expression of results and might be confusing. In most other cases, there will be no doubt as to the sense in which the digit 0 is used. It is obvious that the zeros are significant in such numbers as 104 and 40.08. In a number written as 5.000, it is understood that all the zeros are significant, or else the number could have been rounded off to 5.00, 5.0, or 5, whichever was appropriate. Whenever the zero is ambiguous, it is advisable to accompany the result with an estimate of its uncertainty.

Sometimes, significant zeros are dropped without good cause. If a buret is read as "23.60 mL," it should be so recorded, and not as "23.6 mL." The first number indicates that the analyst took the trouble to estimate the second decimal place; "23.6 mL" would indicate a rather careless reading of the buret.

4. Standard Deviation

If a calculation yields as a result "1476 mg/L" with a standard deviation estimated as ±40 mg/L, report it as 1480 ± 40 mg/L. However, if the standard deviation is estimated as ±100 mg/L round off the answer still further and report as 1500 ±

100 mg/L. By this device, ambiguity is avoided and the report recipient can tell that the zeros are only spacers. Even if the problem of ambiguous zeros is not present, showing the standard deviation is helpful in that it provides an estimate of reliability.

5. Calculations

As a practical operating rule, round off the result of a calculation in which several numbers are multiplied or divided to as few significant figures as are present in the factor with the fewest significant figures. Suppose that the following calculations must be made to obtain the result of an analysis:

$$\frac{56 \times 0.003\ 462 \times 43.22}{1.684}$$

A ten-place calculator yields an answer of "4.975 740 998." Round off this number to "5.0" because one of the measurements that entered into the calculation, 56, has only two significant figures. It was unnecessary to measure the other three factors to four significant figures because the "56" is the "weakest link in the chain" and limits accuracy of the answer. If the other factors were measured to only three, instead of four, significant figures, the answer would not suffer and the labor might be less.

When numbers are added or subtracted, the number that has the fewest decimal places, not necessarily the fewest significant figures, puts the limit on the number of places that justifiably may be carried in the sum or difference. Thus the sum

$$
\begin{array}{r}
0.0072 \\
12.02 \\
4.0078 \\
25.9 \\
\underline{4886} \\
4927.9350
\end{array}
$$

must be rounded off to "4928," no decimals, because one of the addends, 4886, has no decimal places. Notice that another

addend, 25.9, has only three significant figures and yet it does not set a limit to the
number of significant figures in the answer.

The preceding discussion is necessarily
oversimplified. The reader is referred to for
more detailed mathematical texts discussion.

1060   COLLECTION AND PRESERVATION OF SAMPLES

1060 A.   Introduction

It is an old axiom that the result of any
analytical determination can be no better
than the sample on which it is performed.
It is not practical to specify detailed procedures for the collection of all samples
here because of varied purposes and analytical procedures. More detailed information appears in connection with specific
methods. This section presents general considerations, applicable primarily to chemical analyses.

The objective of sampling is to collect a
portion of material small enough in volume
to be transported conveniently and handled
in the laboratory while still accurately representing the material being sampled. This
objective implies that the relative proportions or concentrations of all pertinent
components will be the same in the samples
as in the material being sampled, and that
the sample will be handled in such a way
that no significant changes in composition
occur before the tests are made.

A sample may be presented to the laboratory for specific determinations with the
collector taking responsibility for its validity. Often, in water and wastewater work,
the laboratory conducts or prescribes the
sampling program, which is determined in
consultation with the user of the test results. Such consultation is essential to insure selecting samples and analytical
methods that provide a true basis for an-

swering the questions that prompted the
sampling.

1. General Precautions

Obtain a sample that meets the requirements of the sampling program and handle
it in such a way that it does not deteriorate
or become contaminated before it reaches
the laboratory. Before filling, rinse sample
bottle two or three times with the water
being collected, unless the bottle contains
a preservative or dechlorinating agent. Depending on determinations to be performed, fill container full (most organics
determinations) or leave space for aeration,
mixing, etc. (microbiological analyses). For
samples that will be shipped, preferably
leave an air space of about 1% of container
capacity to allow for thermal expansion.

Special precautions are necessary for
samples containing organic compounds
and trace metals. Because many constituents may be present at concentrations of
micrograms per liter, they may be totally
or partially lost if proper sampling and
preservation procedures are not followed.

Representative samples of some sources
can be obtained only by making composites
of samples collected over a period of time
or at many different sampling points. The
details of collection vary so much with local conditions that no specific recommendations would be universally applicable.

Sometimes it is more informative to analyze numerous separate samples instead of one composite so as not to obscure maxima and minima.

Sample carefully to insure that analytical results represent the actual sample composition. Important factors affecting results are the presence of suspended matter or turbidity, the method chosen for its removal, and the physical and chemical changes brought about by storage or aeration. Particular care is required when processing (grinding, blending, sieving, filtering) samples to be analyzed for trace constituents, especially metals and organic compounds. Some determinations, particularly of lead, can be invalidated by contamination from such processing. Treat each sample individually with regard to the substances to be determined, the amount and nature of turbidity present, and other conditions that may influence the results.

It is impractical to give directions covering all conditions, and the choice of technique for collecting a homogeneous sample must be left to the analyst's judgment. In general, separate any significant amount of suspended matter by decantation, centrifugation, or an appropriate filtration procedure. Often a slight turbidity can be tolerated if experience shows that it will cause no interference in gravimetric or volumetric tests and that its influence can be corrected in colorimetric tests, where it has potentially the greatest interfering effect. When relevant, state whether or not the sample has been filtered. To measure the total amount of a constituent, do not remove suspended solids but treat them appropriately.

Make a record of every sample collected and identify every bottle, preferably by attaching an appropriately inscribed tag or label. Record sufficient information to provide positive sample identification at a later date, including the name of the sample collector, the date, hour, and exact location, the water temperature, and any other data that may be needed for correlation, such as weather conditions, water level, stream flow, post-sampling handling, etc. Provide space on the label for the initials of those assuming sample custody and for the time and date of transfer. Fix sampling points by detailed description, by maps, or with the aid of stakes, buoys, or landmarks in a manner that will permit their identification by other persons without reliance on memory or personal guidance. Particularly when sample results are expected to be involved in litigation, use formal "chain-of-custody" procedures (see ¶ B.1 below), which trace sample history from collection to final reporting.

Cool hot samples collected under pressure while they are still under pressure.

Before collecting samples from distribution systems, flush lines sufficiently to insure that the sample is representative of the supply, taking into account the diameter and length of the pipe to be flushed and the velocity of flow.

Collect samples from wells only after the well has been pumped sufficiently to insure that the sample represents the groundwater source. Sometimes it will be necessary to pump at a specified rate to achieve a characteristic drawdown, if this determines the zones from which the well is supplied. Record pumping rate and drawdown.

When samples are collected from a river or stream, observed results may vary with depth, stream flow, and distance from shore and from one shore to the other. If equipment is available, take an "integrated" sample from top to bottom in the middle of the stream or from side to side at mid-depth, in such a way that the sample is integrated according to flow. If only a grab or catch sample can be collected, take it in the middle of the stream and at mid-depth.

Lakes and reservoirs are subject to considerable variations from normal causes such as seasonal stratification, rainfall, runoff, and wind. Choose location, depth, and frequency of sampling depending on local conditions and the purpose of the investigation. Avoid surface scum.

For certain constituents, sampling location is extremely important. Avoid areas of excessive turbulence because of potential loss of volatile constituents and of potential presence of toxic vapors. Avoid sampling at weirs because such locations tend to favor retrieval of lighter-than-water, immiscible compounds. Generally, collect samples beneath the surface in quiescent areas. If composite samples are required, take care that sample constituents are not lost during compositing because of improper handling of portions being pooled. For example, casual dumping together of portions rather than addition to the composite through a submerged siphon can cause unnecessary volatilization. When necessary refrigerate the composited portions to minimize volatilization[1].

Use only representative samples (or those conforming to a sampling program) for examination. The great variety of conditions under which collections must be made makes it impossible to prescribe a fixed procedure. In general, take into account the tests or analyses to be made and the purpose for which the results are needed.

2. Safety Considerations

Because sample constituents can be toxic, take adequate precautions during sampling and sample handling. Toxic substances can enter through the skin and, in the case of vapors, through the lungs. Inadvertent ingestion can occur via direct contact with foods or by adsorption of vapors onto foods. Precautions may be limited to wearing gloves or may include coveralls, aprons, or other protective apparel. Always wear eye protection. When toxic vapors might be present, sample only in well-ventilated areas or use a respirator or self-contained breathing apparatus. In a laboratory, open sample containers in a fume hood. Never have food near samples or sampling locations; always wash hands thoroughly before handling food.[1]

If flammable organic compounds may be present, take adequate precautions. Prohibit smoking near samples, sampling locations, and in the laboratory. Keep sparks, flames, and excessive heat sources away from samples and sampling locations. Avoid buildup of flammable vapors in a refrigerator storing samples because electrical arcing at contacts of the thermostat, the door-activated light switch, or other electrical components may trigger a fire or explosion. If flammable compounds are suspected or known to be present and samples are to be refrigerated, use only specially designed *explosion-proof* refrigerators.[1]

When in doubt as to the level of safety precautions needed, consult an appropriately trained industrial hygienist. Samples with radioactive contaminants require other safety considerations; consult a health physicist.

3. Types of Samples

a. Grab or catch samples: Strictly speaking, a sample collected at a particular time and place can represent only the composition of the source at that time and place. However, when a source is known to be fairly constant in composition over a considerable period of time or over substantial distances in all directions, then the sample may be said to represent a longer time period or a larger volume, or both, than the specific point at which it was collected. In such circumstances, some sources may be represented quite well by single grab samples. Examples are some water supplies, some surface waters, and rarely, some wastewater streams.

When a source is known to vary with time, grab samples collected at suitable intervals and analyzed separately can document the extent, frequency, and duration of these variations. Choose sampling intervals on the basis of the frequency with which changes may be expected, which may vary from as little as 5 min to as long as 1 h or more. Seasonal variations in natural systems may necessitate sampling over months. When the source composition varies in space rather than time, collect samples from appropriate locations.

Use great care in sampling wastewater sludges, sludge banks, and muds. No definite procedure can be given, but take every possible precaution to obtain a representative sample or one conforming to a sampling program.

b. Composite samples: In most cases, the term "composite sample" refers to a mixture of grab samples collected at the same sampling point at different times. Sometimes the term "time-composite" is used to distinguish this type of sample from others. Time-composite samples are most useful for observing average concentrations that will be used, for example, in calculating the loading or the efficiency of a wastewater treatment plant. As an alternative to the separate analysis of a large number of samples, followed by computation of average and total results, composite samples represent a substantial saving in laboratory effort and expense. For these purposes, a composite sample representing a 24-h period is considered standard for most determinations. Under certain circumstances, however, a composite sample representing one shift, or a shorter time period, or a complete cycle of a periodic operation, may be preferable. To evaluate the effects of special, variable, or irregular discharges and operations, collect composite samples representing the period during which such discharges occur.

For determining components or characteristics subject to significant and unavoidable changes on storage, do not use composite samples. Make such determinations on individual samples as soon as possible after collection and preferably at the sampling point. Analyses for all dissolved gases, residual chlorine, soluble sulfide, temperature, and pH are examples of this type of determination. Changes in such components as dissolved oxygen or carbon dioxide, pH, or temperature may produce secondary changes in certain inorganic constituents such as iron, manganese, alkalinity, or hardness. Use time-composite samples only for determining components that can be demonstrated to remain unchanged under the conditions of sample collection and preservation.

Take individual portions in a wide-mouth bottle having a diameter of at least 35 mm at the mouth and a capacity of at least 120 mL. Collect these portions every hour—in some cases every half hour or even every 5 min—and mix at the end of the sampling period or combine in a single bottle as collected. If preservatives are used, add them to the sample bottle initially so that all portions of the composite are preserved as soon as collected. Analysis of individual samples sometimes may be necessary.

It is desirable, and often essential, to combine individual samples in volumes proportional to flow. A final sample volume of 2 to 3 L is sufficient for sewage, effluents, and wastes.

Automatic sampling devices are available; however, do not use them unless the sample is preserved as described below. Clean sampling devices, including bottles, daily to eliminate biological growths and other deposits.

c. Integrated samples: For certain purposes, the information needed is provided best by analyzing mixtures of grab samples collected from different points simultaneously, or as nearly so as possible. Such mixtures sometimes are called integrated samples. An example of the need for such sampling occurs in a river or stream that varies in composition across its width and depth. To evaluate average composition or total loading, use a mixture of samples representing various points in the cross-section, in proportion to their relative flows. The need for integrated samples also may exist if combined treatment is proposed for several separate wastewater streams, the interaction of which may have a significant effect on treatability or even on composition. Mathematical prediction of the interactions may be inaccurate or impossible and testing a suitable integrated sample may provide more useful information.

Both natural and artificial lakes show variations of composition with both depth and horizontal location. However, under many conditions, neither total nor average results are especially significant; local variations are more important. In such cases, examine samples separately rather than integrate them.

Preparation of integrated samples usually requires special equipment to collect a sample from a known depth without contaminating it with overlying water. Knowledge of the volume, movement, and composition of the various parts of the water being sampled usually is required. Therefore, collecting integrated samples is a complicated and specialized process that cannot be described in detail.

4. Reference

1. WATER POLLUTION CONTROL FEDERATION. 1986. Removal of Hazardous Wastes in Wastewater Facilities—Halogenated Organics. Manual of Practice FD-11, Water Pollution Control Fed., Alexandria, Va.

1060 B.   Collection of Samples

1. Chain-of-Custody Procedures

It is essential to ensure sample integrity from collection to data reporting. This includes the ability to trace possession and handling of the sample from the time of collection through analysis and final disposition. This is referred to as chain of custody and is important in the event of litigation involving the results. Where litigation is not involved, chain-of-custody procedures are useful for routine control of sample flow.

A sample is considered to be under a person's custody if it is in the individual's physical possession, in the individual's sight, secured in a tamper-proof way by that individual, or is secured in an area restricted to authorized personnel. The following procedures summarize the major aspects of chain of custody. More detailed discussions are available.[1,2]

a. *Sample labels:* Use labels to prevent sample misidentification. Gummed paper labels or tags generally are adequate. Include at least the following information: sample number, name of collector, date and time of collection, and place of collection.

Affix labels to sample containers before or at the time of sampling. Fill label out with waterproof ink at time of collection.

b. *Sample seals:* Use sample seals to detect unauthorized tampering with samples up to the time of analysis. Use gummed paper seals that include, at least, the following information: sample number (identical with number on sample label), collector's name, and date and time of sampling. Plastic shrink seals also may be used.

Attach seal in such a way that it is necessary to break it to open the sample container. Affix seal to container before sample leaves custody of sampling personnel.

c. *Field log book:* Record all information pertinent to a field survey or sampling in a bound log book. As a minimum, include the following in the log book: purpose of sampling; location of sampling point; name and address of field contact; producer of material being sampled and address, if different from location; and type of sample. If sample is wastewater, identify process producing waste stream. Also provide suspected sample composition, including concentrations; number and volume of sample taken; description of sampling point and sampling method; date and time of collection; collector's sample identification number(s); sample distribution and how transported; references such as maps or photographs of the sampling site; field observations and measurements; and signatures of personnel responsible for observations. Because sampling situations vary widely no general rule can be given as to the information to be entered in the log book. It is desirable to record sufficient information so that one could reconstruct the sampling without reliance on the collector's memory. Protect the log book and keep it in a safe place.

d. Chain-of-custody record: Fill out a chain-of-custody record to accompany each sample or group of samples. The record includes the following information: sample number; signature of collector; date, time, and address of collection; sample type; signatures of persons involved in the chain of possession; and inclusive dates of possession.

e. Sample analysis request sheet: The sample analysis request sheet accompanies sample to the laboratory. The collector completes the field portion of such a form that includes most of the pertinent information noted in the log book. The laboratory portion of such a form is to be completed by laboratory personnel and includes: name of person receiving the sample, laboratory sample number, date of sample receipt, and determinations to be performed.

f. Sample delivery to laboratory: Deliver sample to laboratory as soon as practicable. Accompany sample with chain-of-custody record and a sample analysis request sheet. Deliver sample to sample custodian.

g. Receipt and logging of sample: In the laboratory, the sample custodian receives the sample and inspects its condition and seal, reconciles label information and seal against the chain-of-custody record, assigns a laboratory number, logs sample in the laboratory log book, and stores it in a secured storage room or cabinet until it is assigned to an analyst.

h. Assignment of sample for analysis: The laboratory supervisor usually assigns the sample for analysis. Once in the laboratory, the supervisor or analyst is responsible for the sample's care and custody.

2. Sampling Methods

a. Manual sampling: Manual sampling involves no equipment but may be unduly costly and time-consuming for routine or large-scale sampling programs.

b. Automatic sampling: Automatic samplers can eliminate human errors in manual sampling, can reduce labor costs, may provide the means for more frequent sampling,[3] and are used increasingly. Be sure that the automatic sampler does not contaminate the sample. For example, plastic components may be incompatible with certain organic compounds that are soluble in the plastic parts. If sample constituents are generally known, contact the manufacturer of an automatic sampler regarding potential incompatibility of plastic components. Manual sampling with a glass container and in accordance with appropriate safety procedures may be best.[3]

Program an automatic sampler in accordance with sampling needs. Carefully match pump speeds and tubing sizes to the type of sample to be taken.

3. Sample Containers

The type of sample container used is of utmost importance. Containers typically are made of plastic or glass, but one material may be preferred over the other. For example, silica and sodium may be leached from glass but not plastic, and trace levels of metals may sorb onto the walls of glass containers.[4] For samples containing organics, avoid plastic containers except those made of fluorinated polymers such as polytetrafluoroethylene (TFE).[3]

From samples containing volatile organics some compounds may dissolve into the walls of plastic containers or such compounds may even leach substances from the plastic. Container failure due to breakdown of the plastic is possible. Some organics are compatible with certain plastics (see manufacturer's literature). However, even if compatibility is assured, recognize that the walls of a plastic container can be porous to volatile organics. Glass containers generally are preferred with volatile organics.[3] Container caps, typically plastic, also can be a problem with organics. Use foil or TFE liners. Serum vials with TFE-lined rubber or plastic septa are useful.

4. Number of Samples

Given the random variations in both an analytical procedure and the occurrence of a constituent at a point of sampling, a single sample may be insufficient for a desired level of uncertainty. If an overall standard deviation is known, the required number of samples may be established by the following relationship:[4]

$$N \geq \left(\frac{ts}{U}\right)^2$$

where:
  N = number of samples,
  t = Student-t statistic for a given confidence level
  s = overall standard deviation, and
  U = acceptable level of uncertainty.

To assist in calculations, use curves such as those in Figure 1060:1. As an example, if s is 0.5 mg/L, U is ± 0.2 mg/L, and a 95% confidence level is desired, approximately 25 to 30 samples must be taken.

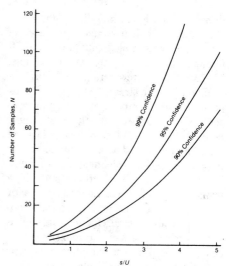

Figure 1060:1. Approximate number of samples required in estimating a mean concentration. Source: Methods for the Examination of Waters and Associated Materials: General Principles of Sampling and Accuracy of Results. 1980. Her Majesty's Stationery Off., London, England.

5. Quantity

Collect a 2-L sample for most physical and chemical analyses. For certain determinations, larger samples may be necessary. Table 1060:I shows the volumes ordinarily required for analyses.

Do not use the same sample for chemical (organic and inorganic), bacteriological, and microscopic examinations because methods of collecting and handling are different.

6. References

1. U.S. ENVIRONMENTAL PROTECTION AGENCY. 1986. Test Methods for Evaluating Solid Waste: Physical/Chemical Methods, 3rd ed. Publ. No. SW-846, Office of Solid Waste and Emergency Response, Washington, D.C.
2. U.S. ENVIRONMENTAL PROTECTION AGENCY. 1982. NEIC Policies and Procedures. EPA-330/9/78/001/-R (rev. 1982).
3. WATER POLLUTION CONTROL FEDERATION. 1986. Removal of Hazardous Wastes in Waste-

TABLE 1060:I. SUMMARY OF SPECIAL SAMPLING OR HANDLING REQUIREMENTS*

Determination	Container	Minimum Sample Size mL	Preservation	Maximum Storage Recommended/ Regulatory†
Acidity	P, G(B)	100	Refrigerate	24 h/14 d
Alkalinity	P, G	200	Refrigerate	24 h/14 d
BOD	P, G	1000	Refrigerate	6 h/48 h
Boron	P	100	None required	28 d/6 months
Bromide	P, G	—	None required	28 d/28 d
Carbon, organic, total	G	100	Analyze immediately; or refrigerate and add HCl to pH <2	7 d/28 d
Carbon dioxide	P, G	100	Analyze immediately	stat/N.S.
COD	P, G	100	Analyze as soon as possible, or add H₂SO₄ to pH <2; refrigerate	7 d/28 d
Chlorine, residual	P, G	500	Analyze immediately	0.5 h/stat
Chlorine dioxide	P, G	500	Analyze immediately	0.5 h/N.S.
Chlorophyll	P, G	500	30 d in dark	30 d/N.S.
Color	P, G	500	Refrigerate	48 h/48 h
Conductivity	P, G	500	Refrigerate	28 d/28 d
Cyanide:				
Total	P, G	500	Add NaOH to pH >12, refrigerate in dark	24 h/14 d; 24 h if sulfide present
Amenable to chlorination	P, G	500	Add 100 mg Na₂S₂O₃/L	stat/14 d; 24 h if sulfide present
Fluoride	P	300	None required	28 d/28 d
Hardness	P, G	100	Add HNO₃ to pH <2	6 months/6 months
Iodine	P, G	500	Analyze immediately	0.5 h/N.S.
Metals, general	P(A), G(A)	—	For dissolved metals filter immediately, add HNO₃ to pH <2	6 months/6 months
Chromium VI	P(A), G(A)	300	Refrigerate	24 h/24 h
Copper by colorimetry*				
Mercury	P(A), G(A)	500	Add HNO₃ to pH <2, 4°C, refrigerate	28 d/28 d
Nitrogen:				
Ammonia	P, G	500	Analyze as soon as possible or add H₂SO₄ to pH <2, refrigerate	7 d/28 d
Nitrate	P, G	100	Analyze as soon as possible or refrigerate	48 h/48 h (28d for chlorinated samples)
Nitrate + nitrite	P, G	200	Add H₂SO₄ to pH <2, refrigerate	none/28d
Nitrite	P, G	100	Analyze as soon as possible or refrigerate	none/48 h
Organic, Kjeldahl	P, G	500	Refrigerate; add H₂SO₄ to pH <2	7 d/28 d

TABLE 1060:I, CONT.*

Determination	Container	Minimum Sample Size mL	Preservation	Maximum Storage Recommended / Regulatory†
Odor	G	500	Analyze as soon as possible; refrigerate	6 h/N.S.
Oil and grease	G, wide-mouth calibrated	1000	Add H_2SO_4, to pH <2, refrigerate	28 d/28 d
Organic compounds:				
Pesticides	G(S), TFE-lined cap	—	Refrigerate; 1000 mg ascorbic acid/L if residual chlorine present	7 d/7 d until extraction; 40 d after extraction
Phenols	P, G	500	Refrigerate, add H_2SO_4, to pH <2	*/28 d
Purgeables by purge and trap	G, TFE-lined cap	50	Refrigerate; add HCl to pH < 2; 1000 mg ascorbic acid/L if residual chlorine present	7 d/14 d
Oxygen, dissolved:				
Electrode	G, BOD bottle	300	Analyze immediately	0.5 h/stat
Winkler			Titration may be delayed after acidification	8 h/8 h
Ozone	G	1000	Analyze immediately	0.5 h/N.S.
pH	P, G	—	Analyze immediately	2 h/stat
Phosphate	G(A)	100	For dissolved phosphate filter immediately; refrigerate	48 h/N.S.
Salinity	G, wax seal	240	Analyze immediately or use wax seal	6 months/N.S.
Silica	P	—	Refrigerate, do not freeze	28 d/28 d
Sludge digester gas	G, gas bottle	—	—	N.S.
Solids	P, G	—	Refrigerate	7 d/2–7 d; see cited reference
Sulfate	P, G	—	Refrigerate	28 d/28 d
Sulfide	P, G	100	Refrigerate; add 4 drops 2N zinc acetate/100 mL; add NaOH to pH > 9	28 d/7 d
Taste	G	500	Analyze as soon as possible; refrigerate	24 h/N.S.
Temperature	P, G	—	Analyze immediately	stat/stat
Turbidity	P, G	—	Analyze same day; store in dark up to 24 h, refrigerate	24 h/48 h

* See text for additional details. For determinations not listed, use glass or plastic containers; preferably refrigerate during storage and analyze as soon as possible. Refrigerate = storage at 4°C, in the dark. P = plastic (polyethylene or equivalent); G = glass; G(A) or P(A) = rinsed with 1 + 1 HNO_3; G(B) = glass, borosilicate; G(S) = glass, rinsed with organic solvents; N.S. = not stated in cited reference; stat = no storage allowed; analyze immediately.

† Environmental Protection Agency, Rules and Regulations. *Federal Register* 49; No. 209, October 26, 1984. See this citation for possible differences regarding container and preservation requirements.

water Facilities—Halogenated Organics. Manual of Practice FD-11, Water Pollution Control Fed., Alexandria, Va.

4. Methods for the Examination of Waters and Associated Materials: General Principles of Sampling and Accuracy of Results. 1980. Her Majesty's Stationery Off., London, England.

1060 C. Sample Preservation

Complete and unequivocal preservation of samples, whether domestic wastewater, industrial wastes, or natural waters, is a practical impossibility. Regardless of the sample nature, complete stability for every constituent never can be achieved. At best, preservation techniques only retard chemical and biological changes that inevitably continue after sample collection.

1. Sample Storage before Analysis

a. Nature of sample changes: Some determinations are more likely than others to be affected by sample storage before analysis. Certain cations are subject to loss by adsorption on, or ion exchange with, the walls of glass containers. These include aluminum, cadmium, chromium, copper, iron, lead, manganese, silver, and zinc, which are best collected in a separate clean bottle and acidified with nitric acid to a pH below 2.0 to minimize precipitation and adsorption on container walls.

Temperature changes quickly; pH may change significantly in a matter of minutes; dissolved gases (oxygen, carbon dioxide) may be lost. Determine temperature, pH, and dissolved gases in the field. With changes in the pH-alkalinity-carbon dioxide balance, calcium carbonate may precipitate and cause a decrease in the values for calcium and for total hardness.

Iron and manganese are readily soluble in their lower oxidation states but relatively insoluble in their higher oxidation states; therefore, these cations may precipitate or they may dissolve from a sediment, depending on the redox potential of the sample. Microbiological activity may be responsible for changes in the nitrate-nitrite-ammonia content, for decreases in phenol concentration and in BOD, or for reducing sulfate to sulfide. Residual chlorine is reduced to chloride. Sulfide, sulfite, ferrous iron, iodide, and cyanide may be lost through oxidation. Color, odor, and turbidity may increase, decrease, or change in quality. Sodium, silica, and boron may be leached from the glass container. Hexavalent chromium may be reduced to chromic ion.

Biological changes taking place in a sample may change the oxidation state of some constituents. Soluble constituents may be converted to organically bound materials in cell structures, or cell lysis may result in release of cellular material into solution. The well-known nitrogen and phosphorus cycles are examples of biological influences on sample composition.

Zero head-space is important in preservation of samples with volatile organics. Avoid loss of volatile materials by collecting sample in a completely filled container. Achieve this by overfilling bottle before capping or sealing. Serum vials with septum caps are particularly useful in that a sample portion for analysis can be taken through the cap by using a syringe.[1]

b. Time interval between collection and analysis: In general, the shorter the time that elapses between collection of a sample and its analysis, the more reliable will be the analytical results. For certain constituents and physical values, immediate analysis in the field is required. For composited samples it is common practice to use the time at the end of composite collection as the sample collection time.

It is impossible to state exactly how much elapsed time may be allowed between sample collection and analysis; this depends on the character of the sample, the analyses to be made, and the conditions of storage. Changes caused by growth of microorganisms are greatly retarded by keeping the sample in the dark and at a low temperature. When the interval between sample collection and analysis is long enough to produce changes in either the concentration or the physical state of the constituent to be measured, follow the preservation practices given in Table 1060:I. Record time elapsed between sampling and analysis, and which preservative, if any, was added.

2. Preservation Techniques

To minimize the potential for volatization or biodegradation between sampling and analysis, keep samples as cool as possible without freezing. Preferably pack samples in crushed or cubed ice or commercial ice substitutes before shipment. Avoid using dry ice because it will freeze samples and may cause glass containers to break. Dry ice also may effect a pH change in samples. Keep composite samples cool with ice or a refrigeration system set at 4°C during compositing. Analyze samples as quickly as possible on arrival at the laboratory. If immediate analysis is not possible, storage at 4°C is recommended for most samples.[1]

Use chemical preservatives only when they are shown not to interfere with the analysis being made. When they are used, add them to the sample bottle initially so that all sample portions are preserved as

soon as collected. No single method of preservation is entirely satisfactory; choose the preservative with due regard to the determinations to be made. Because a preservation method for one determination may interfere with another one, samples for multiple determinations may need to be split and preserved separately. All methods of preservation may be inadequate when applied to suspended matter. Because formaldehyde affects so many analyses, do not use it.

Methods of preservation are relatively limited and are intended generally to retard biological action, retard hydrolysis of chemical compounds and complexes, and reduce volatility of constituents.

Preservation methods are limited to pH control, chemical addition, the use of amber and opaque bottles, refrigeration, filtration, and freezing. Table 1060:I lists preservation methods by constituent.

The foregoing discussion is by no means exhaustive and comprehensive. Clearly it is impossible to prescribe absolute rules for preventing all possible changes. Additional advice will be found in the discussions under individual determinations, but to a large degree the dependability of an analytical determination rests on the experience and good judgment of the person collecting the sample.

3. Reference

1. WATER POLLUTION CONTROL FEDERATION. 1986. Removal of Hazardous Wastes in Wastewater Facilities—Halogenated Organics. Manual of Practice FD-11, Water Pollution Control Fed., Alexandria, Va.

4. Bibliography

KEITH, L.H., ed. 1988. Principles of Environmental Sampling. ACS Professional Reference Book, American Chemical Soc.

1070 LABORATORY APPARATUS, REAGENTS, AND TECHNIQUES

1070 A. Introduction

This section contains a discussion of requirements for laboratory apparatus, reagents, and techniques that are common to many of the analyses presented in this manual. Requirements that are more or less specific to the particular determination being performed are described under the methods to which they apply. In addition, observe the general considerations presented in this section. The requirements of radiological, bacteriological, biological, and bioassay methods tend to differ in many respects from those of chemical and physical tests. Special attention is directed to the descriptions of apparatus and procedures in the sections dealing with those methods.

1070 B. Apparatus

1. Containers

For general laboratory use, the most suitable material for containers is resistant borosilicate glass.* Special glassware is available with characteristics such as high resistance to alkali attack, low boron content, or exclusion of light. Choose stoppers, caps, and plugs to resist the attack of material contained in the vessel. Metal screw caps are a poor choice for samples that will cause them to corrode readily. Glass stoppers are unsatisfactory for strongly alkaline liquids because of their tendency to stick fast. Rubber stoppers are excellent for alkaline liquids but unacceptable for organic solvents, in which they swell or disintegrate, or trace metal solutions, which may be contaminated by them. Use polytetrafluoroethylene (TFE or PTFE)† for burets that contain strongly alkaline liquids. When appropriate, use other materials such as porcelain, nickel, iron, platinum, stainless steel, and high-silica glass.‡

Collect and store samples in bottles made of borosilicate glass, hard rubber, plastic, or other inert material as appropriate for specific analyses (Table 1060:I).

For relatively short storage periods, or for constituents that are not affected by storage in soft glass, such as calcium, magnesium, sulfate, chloride, and perhaps others, the 2.5-L acid-bottle "bell closure" is satisfactory. This closure holds a glass or polyethylene disk against the ground-glass surface or a polyethylene insert on the bottle lip and insures adequate protection. If part of the sample is to be analyzed later for silica, sodium, or other substances that would be affected by prolonged storage in soft glass, transfer it to a small plastic bottle, while leaving the remainder of the sample in the soft-glass bottle.

Carefully clean sample bottles before each use. Rinse glass bottles, except those to be used for chromium or manganese analyses, either with a cleaning mixture made by adding 1 L conc H_2SO_4 slowly, with stirring, to 35 mL saturated sodium dichromate solution, or with 2% $KMnO_4$ in 5% KOH solution followed by an oxalic acid solution. Commercial alternates also are available.§ Rinse with other concen-

---

*Pyrex, manufactured by Corning Glass Works; Kimax, Kimble Glass Co., Division of Owens-Illinois; or equivalent.

†Teflon or equivalent.

‡Vycor, manufactured by Corning Glass Works, or equivalent.

§Nochromix, Godax Laboratories, Inc., New York, N.Y., or equivalent.

trated acids to remove inorganic matter. Detergents are excellent cleansers for many purposes; use either detergents or conc HCl for cleaning hard-rubber and plastic bottles. After the bottles have been cleaned, rinse thoroughly with reagent-grade water.

For shipment, pack bottles in wooden, metal, plastic or heavy fiberboard cases, with a separate compartment for each bottle. Line boxes with insulating material to protect from breakage. Samples stored in plastic bottles need no protection against breakage by impact or through freezing.

2. Volumetric Glassware

Calibrate volumetric glassware or obtain a certificate of accuracy from a competent laboratory. Volumetric glassware is calibrated either "to contain" (TC) or "to deliver" (TD). Glassware designed "to deliver" will do so with accuracy only when the inner surface is so scrupulously clean that water wets it immediately and forms a uniform film upon emptying. Whenever possible, use borosilicate glassware. For accurate work use Class A volumetric glassware.

Carefully measure weights and volumes in preparing standard solutions and calibration curves. Observe similar precautions in measuring sample volumes. Use volumetric pipets or burets where the volume is designated to two decimal places (X.00 mL) in the text. Use volumetric flasks where specified and where the volume is given as 1000 mL rather than 1 L.

3. Nessler Tubes

Unless otherwise indicated use "tall"-form nessler tubes made of resistant glass and selected from uniformly drawn tubing. The glass should be clear and colorless and the tube bottoms should be plane-parallel. When the tubes are filled with liquid and viewed from the top with a light source beneath, there should be no dark spots nor any lenslike distortion of the transmitted light. The tops of the tubes should be flat, preferably fire-polished, and smooth enough to permit cover slips to be cemented on for sealing. Nessler tubes with standard-taper clear glass tops are available commercially. Graduation marks should completely encircle the tubes.

The 100-mL tubes should have a total length of approximately 375 mm. Their inside diameter should approximate 20 mm and the outside diameter 24 mm. The graduation mark should be as near as possible to 300 mm above the inside bottom. Tubes sold in sets should be of such uniformity that this distance does not vary more than 6 mm. (Sets are available commercially in which the maximum difference between tubes is not more than 2 mm.) A graduation mark at 50 mL is permissible.

The 50-mL tubes should have a total length of about 300 mm. Their inside diameter should approximate 17 mm and the outside diameter 21 mm. The graduation mark on the tube should be as near as possible to 225 mm above the inside bottom. Tubes sold in sets should be of such uniformity that this distance does not vary more than 6 mm. (Sets are available commercially in which the maximum difference between tubes is not more than 1.5 mm.) A graduation mark at 25 mL is permissible.

1070 C.   Reagents

1. Laboratory Water

See Section 1080.

2. Reagent Quality

Use only the best quality chemical reagents even though this instruction is not repeated in the description of a particular method. Order chemicals for which the American Chemical Society has published specifications in the "ACS grade." Order other chemicals as "analytical reagent grade" or "spectral grade organic solvents." Methods of checking purity of suspect reagents are found in books of reagent specifications listed in the Bibliography (¶ 4 below).

Unfortunately, many commercial dyes for which the ACS grade has not been established fail to meet exacting analytical requirements because of variations in the color response of different lots. In such cases, use dyes certified by the Biological Stain Commission.

Where neither an ACS grade nor a certified Biological Stain Commission dye is available, purify the solid dye through recrystallization.

The following standard substances, each bottle of which is accompanied by a certificate of analysis, are issued by the National Institute of Standards and Technology (NIST)*, Department of Commerce, Washington, D.C., for the purpose of standardizing analytical solutions:

Acidimetric:
    84j—Acid potassium phthalate
  350a—Benzoic acid
Oxidimetric:
    40h—Sodium oxalate
    83d—Arsenic trioxide
  136e—Potassium dichromate
Buffer:
  185f—Potassium hydrogen phthalate
  186Ic—Potassium dihydrogen phosphate
  186IIc—Disodium hydrogen phosphate
  187c—Borax
  188—Potassium hydrogen tartrate
  189a—Potassium tetroxalate
  191a—Sodium bicarbonate
  192a—Sodium carbonate

Many hundreds of other standards issued by NIST are described in Special Publication 260 (see Bibliography).

A successful dithizone test demands reagents of the highest purity. Chloroform and carbon tetrachloride are available in a grade declared to be suitable for dithizone

methods. Select reagents of this quality for the dithizone methods described in this manual.

Water-soluble sodium salts of the common indicators usually are recommended for indicator preparation because of their general availability and reasonable cost.

When alcohol or ethyl alcohol is specified for preparing such indicators as phenolphthalein, use 95% ethyl alcohol. When isopropyl alcohol is specified use a similar grade.

Certain organic reagents are somewhat unstable upon exposure to the atmosphere. If the stability of a chemical is limited or unknown, purchase small lots at frequent intervals.

Dry all anhydrous reagent chemicals required for preparation of standard calibration solutions and titrants in an oven at 105 to 110°C for at least 1 to 2 h and preferably overnight. After cooling to room temperature in an efficient desiccator, promptly weigh the proper amount for dissolution. Should a different drying temperature be necessary, this is specified for the particular chemical. For hydrated salts, substitute milder drying in an efficient desiccator for oven-drying.

3. Common Acid and Alkali Solutions

a. Concentration units used: Reagent concentrations are expressed in terms of normality, molarity, and additive volumes.

A *normal solution (N)* contains one gram equivalent weight of solute per liter of solution.

A *molar solution (M)* contains one gram molecular weight of solute per liter of solution.

In additive volumes ($a + b$), the first number, a, refers to the volume of concentrated reagent; the second number, b, refers to the volume of distilled water required for dilution. Thus, "1 + 9 HCl" denotes that 1 volume of concentrated HCl is to be diluted with 9 volumes of distilled water.

---

*Formerly National Bureau of Standards (NBS).

To make a solution of exact normality from a chemical that cannot be measured as a primary standard, prepare a relatively concentrated stock solution and then make an exact dilution to the desired strength. Alternatively, make a solution of slightly higher concentration than that desired, standardize, and make suitable adjustments in concentration by dilution; or, use the solution as first standardized and modify the calculation factor. This last procedure is useful especially for solutions that slowly change strength and must be restandardized frequently—for example, sodium thiosulfate solution. Adjustment to exact normality specified is desirable when a laboratory makes a large number of determinations with one standard solution.

Determinations are in accord with the instructions in this manual as long as normality of a standard solution does not result in a titration volume so small as to preclude accurate measurement or so large as to cause abnormal dilution of the reaction mixture, and as long as the solution is standardized properly and the calculations are made properly.

b. Preparation and dilution of solutions: If a solution of exact normality is to be prepared by dissolving a weighed amount of a primary standard or by diluting a stronger solution, bring it up to exact volume in a volumetric flask.

Accurately prepare stock and standard solutions prescribed for colorimetric determinations in volumetric flasks. Where concentration does not need to be exact, mix the concentrated solution or solid with measured amounts of water, using graduated cylinders for these measurements. There is usually a significant change of volume when strong solutions are mixed, resulting in a total volume less than the sum of volumes used. For approximate dilutions, volume changes are negligible when concentrations of $6N$ or less are diluted.

Mix thoroughly and completely when making dilutions. One of the most common sources of error in analyses using standard solutions diluted in volumetric flasks is failure to attain complete mixing.

c. Storage of solutions: Some standardized solutions alter slowly because of chemical or biological changes. The practical life, required frequency of standardization, or storage precautions are indicated for such standards. Others, such as dilute HCl, are nonreactive. Yet their strength, too, may change by evaporation that is not prevented by a glass stopper. Changes in temperatures cause a bottle to "breathe," and allow some evaporation.

Do not consider a standard valid for more than a year unless it is restandardized. It is valid for that length of time only if conditions minimize evaporation and it has been demonstrated previously that preservation techniques are adequate. If the bottle is opened often or it is much less than half full, significant evaporation occurs in a few months. Verify concentration of standard solutions that have been stored.

Use glass bottles of chemically resistant glass except where glass is incompatible (e.g., silica solutions). For standard solutions that do not react with rubber or neoprene, use stoppers of these materials, because they can, if properly fitted, prevent evaporation as long as the bottle is closed. Screw-cap bottles also are effective. If the cap has a gasket of reasonably resistant material, permissible usage will be about the same as for rubber stoppers.

d. Hydrochloric and sulfuric acid as alternatives: Dilute standardized H_2SO_4 and HCl are called for in various procedures. Often these solutions are interchangeable. Where one is mentioned, the other may be used if it is known to make no difference.

e. Preparation: Although instructions usually describe preparation of 1 L of solution, prepare smaller or larger volumes as needed. Instructions calling for the preparation of 100 mL usually involve either short-life reagents or those used in small amounts.

A safe general rule is to add more concentrated acid or alkali to water, with stirring, in a vessel that can withstand thermal shock, and then to dilute to final volume after cooling to room temperature.

f. Uniform reagent concentrations: An attempt has been made to establish a number of uniform common acid and base concentrations that will serve for adjustment of pH of samples before color development or final titration. The following acid concentrations are recommended for general laboratory use: the concentrated reagent of commerce, $6N$, $1N$, $0.1N$, and $0.02N$. See the inside front cover for directions for preparing these acid concentrations, as well as the required $15N$, $6N$, and $1N$ NaOH solutions, and $5N$, $3N$, and $0.2N$ NH$_4$OH solutions.

4. Bibliography

ROSIN, J. 1967. Reagent Chemicals and Standards, 5th ed. D. Van Nostrand Co., Princeton, N.J.

AMERICAN CHEMICAL SOCIETY. 1974. Reagent Chemicals—American Chemical Society Specifications, 5th ed. American Chemical Soc., Washington, D.C.

The United States Pharmacopoeia. 1975. 19th rev. U.S. Pharmacopeial Convention Inc., Rockville, Md.

NATIONAL BUREAU OF STANDARDS. 1988. Catalog of NBS Standard Reference Materials. Nat. Bur. Standards Spec. Publ. 260, 1988-89 ed.

1070 D. Techniques

Numerous works on both general and specific analytical techniques are available (see ¶ 5, Bibliography).

1. Ion Exchange

Ion-exchange resins are useful and flexible tools. Used in atmospheric- or high-pressure columns they effect analytical separations of both inorganic and organic ions. They commonly are in the form of sodium or hydrogen counter-ions (attached to the matrix) for cation exchangers and of chloride, formate, acetate, and hydroxide counter-ions for anion exchangers. The user may substitute other counter-ions by passing regenerating solutions through a resin column as recommended by the manufacturer. The form to be used in a specific case will depend not only on the relative affinity of the resin for counter-ions and sample ions, but also on the ions that can be tolerated if the concentrated sample ions are to be eluted for analysis. Sequential elution of organics usually is done with carefully selected buffer solutions.

In water analysis, ion exchangers can be applied to: (*a*) remove interfering ions, (*b*) determine total ion content, (*c*) indicate the approximate volume of sample for certain gravimetric determinations, (*d*) concentrate trace quantities of cations, and (*e*) separate anions from cations. This manual recommends the use of ion-exchange resins for the removal of interference in the sulfate determination and for the determination of total ion content. Inasmuch as the ion-exchange process can be applied in other determinations, a brief description of typical operations follows.

a. Selection of method: The batch method of ion exchange is satisfactory for sample volumes of less than 100 mL, although it does not result in complete ion removal or exchange. The column method can be used for any sample volume. In the batch method, the resin is agitated with the sample for a given time, after which the resin is removed by filtration. The column method is more efficient in that it provides continuous contact between the sample and the resin, thereby enabling the exchange reaction to go to completion. In this modification, the solution passes slowly through the resin bed and ions are removed quantitatively from the sample. Elution of the resin permits recovery of the exchanged substances.

b. Procedure: Use resins specifically manufactured for analytical applications. Prepare the ion exchanger by rinsing the resin with several volumes of ion-free water (good-quality distilled water) to remove any fines or coloring matter and other leachable material that might interfere with subsequent colorimetric procedures.

1) Batch method for cation removal—Pipet a sample portion containing 0.1 to 0.2 milliequivalents (me) of cations into a 250-mL erlenmeyer flask or beaker and add enough distilled water to bring final volume to 75 mL. Add 2.0 g strongly acidic cation-exchange resin and stir at moderate speed for 15 min. Filter through a plug of glass wool placed in the neck of a 10-cm borosilicate glass funnel. When filtration is complete, wash resin with two 10-mL portions of distilled water and make up to 100 mL total volume with distilled water.

To regenerate resin, transfer spent resin from the batch procedure to a flask containing 500 mL 3N HNO$_3$. When sufficient resin has accumulated, wash into a column (Figure 1070:1) and regenerate by passing 3N HNO$_3$ through the column at a rate of 0.1 to 0.2 mL acid/mL resin/min. Use about 20 mL 3N HNO$_3$/mL resin in the column. Finally, wash resin with sufficient distilled water until the effluent pH is 5 to 7, using the same rate of flow as in the regeneration step. Remove resin from column and store under distilled water in a wide-mouth container. Should the water become colored during storage, decant and replace with fresh distilled water. Before use, filter resin through a plug of glass wool placed in the neck of a funnel, wash with distilled water, and let drain. The resin is then ready for use.

2) Column method for cation re-

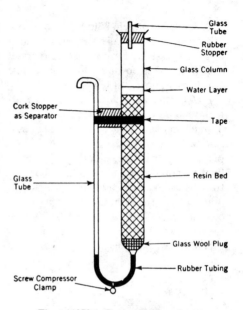

Figure 1070:1. Ion-exchange column.

moval—Prepare column as depicted in Figure 1070:1 (length of resin bed, 21.5 cm; diameter of column, 1.3 cm; representing approximately 21 mL, or 20 g resin). Other ion-exchange columns can be used equally well. One of the simplest consists of a buret containing a plug of glass wool immediately above the stopcock.

To make an effluent tube for a buret, *slowly* bend TFE tubing, 1/8 in. ID × 1/4 in. OD, into an elongated S-shape; bend to 45° angle to the straight portion, secure with rubber bands or adhesive tape, and set aside for at least 48 h to relieve stress. Repeat until desired conformation is achieved. Retain curved ends in place with plastic strips approximately 2 cm × 10 cm × 2 mm with suitably placed 3/16-in. drilled holes.

(Whatever type of column is adopted, never let liquid level in column fall below upper resin surface because trapped air causes uneven flow rates and poor efficiency of ion exchange. Adjust sample and column to the same temperature.)

Charge column by stirring resin in a

beaker with distilled water and then carefully wash the suspension through a funnel into the column already filled with distilled water. Backwash column if necessary by introducing distilled water at the bottom and passing it upward through the column until all air bubbles and channels are removed. Connect a separatory funnel to the column top or use an inverted volumetric flask to feed sample, regenerating, or rinsing solutions; make certain diameter of flask neck is large enough to permit automatic feed. More efficiently, use a small controllable peristaltic pump to apply solutions to column. Let sample flow through column at the rate of 0.2 mL solution/mL resin/min. After sample has passed through column, wash resin with distilled water until effluent pH is 5 to 7. Use a pH meter or pH test papers to determine when column has been washed free of acid. For convenience, when rinsing column or adsorbing cations from a sample of one or more liters, start this operation before the close of a workday and let exchange process proceed overnight. The column will not dry because of the curved outlet.

After distilled-water wash, elute adsorbed cations by passing 100 mL $3N$ HNO_3 through the column at a rate of 0.2 mL acid/mL resin /min. Because a volume of 100 mL $3N$ HNO_3 quantitatively removes 3 me of cations, use additional increments of 100 mL $3N$ HNO_3 for quantities of adsorbed cations in excess of 3 me. After elution, rinse column free of acid with enough distilled water to produce an effluent pH of 5 to 7. Wash at same flow rate for acid elution. The acid elution and washing regenerate the column for future use. The combined acid eluates contain the cations originally present in the sample.

2. Colorimetric Determinations

a. General: Many procedures depend on color determination with photometric instruments. To obtain the best possible results, understand the principles and limitations of these methods, especially because the choice of instrument and of technique is discretionary.

Photometric methods are not free from specific limitations. While an analyst will recognize that something has gone wrong on seeing an unusual color or turbidity when making a visual comparison, such a discrepancy easily may escape detection during a photometric reading, for the instrument always will yield a reading, whether meaningful or not. Check sensitivity and accuracy frequently by testing standard solutions to detect electrical, mechanical, or optical problems in the instrument and its accessories. Testing, maintaining, and repairing such instruments may call for specialized skills.

A photometer is not uniformly accurate over its entire scale. At very high absorbance the scale is crowded, so that a considerable change in relative concentration will cause only a slight change in position of the indicator dial or needle. At very low absorbance, slight differences between optical cells, the presence of condensed moisture, dust, bubbles, fingerprints, or a slight lack of reproducibility in positioning the cells can cause as great a change in readings as would a considerable change in concentration. The difficulties are minimized if readings are made to fall between 0.1 and 1.0 absorbance by diluting or concentrating the sample or varying the light path by selecting cells of appropriate size.

Some suggestions for suitable ranges and light paths are offered under individual methods in this manual, but much reliance necessarily must be placed on the knowledge and judgment of the analyst. Most photometers are capable of their best performance when readings fall in the range of approximately 1 to 0.1 absorbance with respect to a blank adjusted to read 0 absorbance. The closer the readings approach 0 or 3.0 absorbance, the less accurate they become. If it is impractical to use an optical cell with a sufficiently long light path—as in some commercial instruments—or to concentrate the sample or select a more sensitive color test, then it may be more accurate to compare very faint colors in nessler tubes than to attempt photometric readings close to 100% transmittance.

In general, the best wavelength or filter to select is that which produces the largest spread of readings between a standard and a blank. This usually corresponds to a visual color for the light beam that is complementary to that of the solution—for example, a green filter for a red solution, a violet filter for a yellow solution.

Absorptivities are useful in comparing method sensitivities and in estimating the concentration of absorbing solutions such as dithizone. The absorptivity may be computed from Beer's Law as follows:

$$a = \frac{A}{b\,c}$$

where:

a = absorptivity, L/(g · cm),
A = absorbance of a solution, dimensionless,
b = concentration, g/L, and
c = cell path length, cm.

Use of a photoelectric instrument makes unnecessary the preparation of a complete set of standards for each set of samples to be analyzed. However, prepare a reagent blank containing distilled water and all reagents and at least one standard in the upper end of the optimum concentration range, with every group of samples, to verify the constancy of the calibration curve. This precaution will reveal any unsuspected changes in the reagents, the instrument, or the technique. At regular intervals, or if at any time results fall under suspicion, prepare a complete set of standards—at least five or six spaced to cover the optimum concentration range—to check the calibration curve. Also valuable in this regard is the absorptivity informa-

tion given in this manual for a number of photometric methods.

Verify frequently the accuracy of the curves or permanent standards by comparing with standards prepared in the laboratory, using the same set of reagents, the same instrument, and the same procedures as those used for analyzing samples. Even if permanent calibration curves or artificial standards have been prepared accurately by the manufacturer, they may not be valid under conditions of use. Permanent standards may be subject to fading or color alteration. Their validity may depend also on certain arbitrary lighting conditions. Standards and calibration curves may be incorrect because of slight differences in reagents, instruments, or techniques between the manufacturer's and the analyst's laboratories.

Zero or null the instrument using a reagent blank or, if required, distilled water. Never zero with sample blank. Determine the absorbance of each standard; then plot absorbance against the concentrations of the standards to establish a working curve and the degree of agreement with Beer's Law. If readings are in terms of percentage transmittance, convert to absorbance before plotting or plot on semilogarithmic paper.

Should turbidity be present as an interference, several approaches are available to separate turbidity from a sample. The nature of the sample, the size of suspended particles, and the reasons for conducting the analysis will all combine to dictate the method for turbidity removal. Turbidity may be coagulated by adding zinc sulfate and an alkali, as is done in the direct nesslerization method for ammonia nitrogen. For samples of relatively coarse turbidity, centrifuging may suffice. In some instances, glass fiber filters, filter paper, or sintered-glass filters of fine porosity will serve the purpose. For very small particle sizes, membrane filters may provide the required retentiveness. Used with discretion, each of these methods will yield satisfactory results in a suitable situation. However, it must be emphasized that no single universally ideal method of turbidity removal is available. Moreover, be perpetually alert to adsorption losses possible with any flocculating or filtering procedure.

If the turbidity cannot be removed without compromising the sample, then use photometric compensation to correct for interference. Measure the sample without addition of reagents (the sample blank) against a reagent blank or a distilled water blank to determine instrument response. The response is due to sample absorbance or turbidity other than that caused by the element or compound being determined. Take into account volume changes from the omission of reagents. If the calibration curve is linear, the sample blank absorbance may be subtracted from the sample absorbance before the concentration is computed, or the concentration may be computed for the sample blank and subtracted from that of the sample. If a nonlinear calibration is used, compute the concentration of the sample blank and subtract it from the sample concentration. Subtracting the absorbance is not satisfactory in this case.

In the procedure, zero the instrument using a turbidity blank or, alternatively, determine the absorbance for this blank against a reagent blank or distilled water and then subtract it from the sample absorbance. Correct as before for volume difference caused by addition or omission of reagents in the calculation.

b. *Dithizone solutions:* Several colorimetric methods for metals (Cd, Pb, Hg, Ag, Zn) use dithizone (diphenylthiocarbazone) as an extractable, colored, metal-complexing agent. The methods presented later in this text have been based on three stock dithizone solutions, the preparation of which is described below. The dithizone concentration in the stock dithizone solutions is based on having a 100% pure dith-

izone reagent. Some commercial grades of dithizone are contaminated with the oxidation product diphenylthiocarbodiazone or with metals. Purify dithizone as directed below. For dithizone solutions not stronger than 0.001% (w/v), calculate the exact concentration by dividing the absorbance of the solution in a 1.00-cm cell at 606 nm by 40.6×10^3, the molar absorptivity.

Adjust dilutions of stock dithizone solutions to produce working dithizone solutions of the indicated strength based on the measured stock dithizone solution concentration.

1) *Stock dithizone solution I*, 100 mg dithizone/1000 mL $CHCl_3$: Dissolve 100 mg dithizone in 50 mL $CHCl_3$ in a 150-mL beaker and filter through a 7-cm-diam paper.* Receive filtrate in a 500-mL separatory funnel or in a 125-mL erlenmeyer flask under slight vacuum; use a filtering device designed to handle the $CHCl_3$ vapor. Wash beaker with two 5-mL portions $CHCl_3$, and filter. Wash the paper with three 5-mL portions $CHCl_3$, adding final portion dropwise to edge of paper. If filtrate is in flask, transfer with $CHCl_3$ to a 500-mL separatory funnel.

Add 100 mL 1 + 99 NH_4OH to separatory funnel and shake moderately for 1 min; excessive agitation produces slowly breaking emulsions. Let layers separate, swirling funnel gently to submerge $CHCl_3$ droplets held on surface of aqueous layer. Transfer $CHCl_3$ layer to 250-mL separatory funnel, retaining the orange-red aqueous layer in the 500-mL funnel. Repeat extraction, receiving $CHCl_3$ layer in another 250-mL separatory funnel and transferring aqueous layer, using 1 + 99 NH_4OH, to the 500-mL funnel holding the first extract. Repeat extraction, transferring the aqueous layer to 500-mL funnel. Discard $CHCl_3$ layer.

To combined extracts in the 500-mL separatory funnel add 1 + 1 HCl in 2-mL

---

*Whatman No. 42, or equivalent.

portions, mixing after each addition, until dithizone precipitates and solution is no longer orange-red. Extract precipitated dithizone with three 25-mL portions CHCl₃. Dilute combined extracts to 1000 mL with CHCl₃; 1.00 mL = 100 μg dithizone.

2) *Stock dithizone solution II,* 250 mg dithizone/250 mL CHCl₃: Dissolve 250 mg dithizone in 50 mL CHCl₃ in a 150-mL beaker and filter through a 7-cm-diam paper.† Receive filtrate in a 1000-mL separatory funnel or in a 125-mL erlenmeyer flask under slight vacuum; use a filtering device designed to handle CHCl₃ vapor. Wash beaker with two 5-mL portions CHCl₃ and filter. Wash paper with three 5-mL portions CHCl₃, adding the last portion dropwise to edge of paper. If filtrate is in flask, transfer with CHCl₃ to 1000-mL separatory funnel.

Add 200 mL 1 + 99 NH₄OH to separatory funnel and shake moderately for 1 min; excessive agitation produces slowly breaking emulsions. Let layers separate, swirling funnel gently to submerge CHCl₃ droplets held on surface of aqueous layer. Transfer CHCl₃ layer to 500-mL separatory funnel, retaining the orange-red aqueous layer in the 1000-mL funnel. Repeat extraction of CHCl₃ layer with 200 mL 1 + 99 NH₄OH, transferring CHCl₃ layer to another 500-mL separatory funnel. Transfer aqueous layer to 1000-mL funnel holding the first extract. Repeat extraction with third 200-mL portion 1 + 99 NH₄OH. Discard CHCl₃ layer, transfer aqueous layer to 1000-mL funnel. To the combined extracts add 1 + 1 HCl in 4-mL portions, mixing after each addition, until dithizone precipitates and solution is no longer orange-red. Extract precipitated dithizone with four 25-mL portions CHCl₃. Dilute combined extracts to 250 mL with CHCl₃; 1.00 mL = 1000 μg dithizone.

3) *Stock dithizone solution III,* 125 mg

dithizone/500 mL CCl₄: Dissolve 125 mg dithizone in 50 mL CHCl₃ and proceed as for dithizone solution II, but extract precipitated dithizone with 25-mL portions CCl₄. Dilute CCl₄ extracts to 500 mL; 1.00 mL = 250 μg dithizone. (CAUTION: *CCl₄ is toxic—avoid inhalation, ingestion, and contact with the skin.*)

3. Other Methods of Analysis

The use of an instrumental method of analysis not specifically described herein is permissible provided that the results so obtained are checked periodically, either against an included standard method or against a standard sample of undisputed composition. Identify any such instrumental method used in the laboratory report along with the analytical results.

a. Atomic absorption spectrometry: Atomic absorption spectrometry has been applied to the determination of metals in water without the need for prior concentration or extensive sample pretreatment. The use of organic solvents coupled with oxyacetylene, oxyhydrogen, or nitrous oxide-acetylene flames enables the determination of metals that form refractory oxides. These standards include atomic absorption methods—including certain flameless and electrothermal (heated graphite) techniques—for many metals.

b. Flame photometry: Flame photometry is used for the determination of sodium, potassium, lithium, and strontium.

c. Inductively coupled plasma (ICP) and related analytical systems: ICP is suggested for scanning samples for various metal ions, especially where the possible interferences in the colorimetric procedures are unknown. ICP has enabled the determination of multiple metals at the low microgram-per-liter level when a single 100-mL sample has been ashed with HNO₃. Polarographic techniques such as pulse polarography, differential pulse voltammetry, and differential pulse anodic stripping vol-

---

† Whatman No. 42, or equivalent.

tammetry also have gained acceptance for the determination of heavy metals, and their speciation, in water and wastewater.

A method closely allied to polarography is amperometric titration, which is suitable for determining residual chlorine, chlorine dioxide, and iodine, and in other iodometric methods.

d. Potentiometric titration: Many titrimetric methods can be performed potentiometrically, by using a millivoltmeter or pH meter with suitable electrodes.

e. Selective ion electrodes: Selective ion electrodes are available for rapid estimation of certain constituents in water. These electrodes function best in conjunction with an expanded-scale pH meter or a suitable millivoltmeter. For the most part, the electrodes operate on the ion-exchange principle. Selective ion electrodes now available are designed for measuring ammonia, cadmium, calcium, divalent copper, hardness, lead, potassium, silver, sodium, total monovalent and total divalent cations, and bromide, chloride, cyanide, fluoride, iodide, nitrate, perchlorate, and sulfide anions, among others.

These devices are subject to varying degrees of interference from other ions in the sample and many still must receive thorough study to warrant adoption as proposed and standard methods. Nonetheless, their value for monitoring activities is readily apparent. To remove all doubt of variations in reliability, check each electrode in the presence of interferences as well as the ion for which it is intended. This manual details several electrode methods.

Commercial dissolved oxygen (DO) probes vary considerably in their dependability and maintenance requirements. Despite these shortcomings, they have been applied to monitoring DO in a variety of waters and wastewaters. Most probes embody an electrolyte held in place by an oxygen-permeable membrane. The DO in solution diffuses through the membrane and electrolyte layer to react at the electrode, inducing a current proportional to the activity and hence, in solution of low or constant ionic strength, essentially proportional to concentration of DO. Satisfactory DO electrodes also are available without a membrane. In either case, keep the face of the DO sensor well agitated and provide temperature compensation to insure acceptable results.

f. Gas chromatography (GC) and gas chromatography/mass spectrometry (GC/MS): Many GC and GC/MS methods suitable for water and wastewater analysis are available. Appearing in this manual are such methods for determining chlorinated hydrocarbon pesticides, components in sludge digester gas, phenols, volatiles, PAHs, and taste- and odor-causing compounds, and generalized GC/MS analyses for volatiles and acid- and base-neutral extractables.

g. Continuous-flow analysis: Automated techniques are presented for chloride, fluoride, nitrogen (ammonia), nitrogen (nitrate), phosphate, silica, and sulfate.

h. Ion chromatography (IC): Ion chromatography is a technique for sequential determination of anions or cations using ion exchange and conductivity, amperometric, or colorimetric detectors. See Section 4110 for a generalized technique for anions.

i. Other methods of analysis: Instrumentation and new methods of analysis always are under development. The analyst will find it advantageous to keep abreast of current progress. Reviews of each branch of analytical chemistry are published regularly in *Analytical Chemistry* and the annual literature review in *Journal Water Pollution Control Federation.*

4. Interference Control

Many analytical procedures are subject to interferences from substances present in the sample. The more common and obvious interferences are known and information about them has been given in the details of individual procedures. It is inevitable that unknown or unexpected interferences may be encountered. Such occurrences are unavoidable because of the diverse nature of waters and particularly of wastewaters. Therefore, be alert to hitherto untested constituents, new treatment compounds (especially complexing agents), and new industrial wastes and their potential threat to the accuracy of chemical analyses.

Any sudden change in the apparent composition of water that has been rather constant, any abnormal color observed in a colorimetric test or during a titration, any unexpected turbidity, odor, or other laboratory finding is cause for suspicion. Such change may be due to normal variation in the relative concentrations of the usual constituents or it may be caused by the introduction of an unforeseen interfering substance.

A few substances—such as chlorine, chlorine dioxide, alum, iron salts, silicates, copper sulfate, ammonium sulfate, and polyphosphates—are so widely used that they deserve special mention as possible causes of interference. Of these, chlorine is probably the worst offender, in that it bleaches or alters the colors of many sensitive organic reagents that serve as titration indicators and as color developers for photometric methods. Among the methods that have proved effective in removing chlorine residuals are the addition of minimal amounts of sulfite, thiosulfate, or arsenite; exposure to sunlight or an artificial ultraviolet source, and prolonged storage.

Whenever interference is encountered or suspected and no specific recommendations are given for overcoming it, determine what technique, if any, will eliminate the interference without adversely affecting the analysis itself. If two or more choices of procedure are offered, often one procedure will be less affected than another by the presence of the interfering substance. If different procedures yield considerably differ-

ent results, it is likely that interference is present. Some interferences become less severe upon dilution or upon use of smaller samples; any tendency of the results to increase or decrease in a consistent manner with dilution indicates the likelihood of interference effects.

a. Types of interference: Interference may cause analytical results to be either too high or too low as a consequence of one of the following:

1) An interfering substance may react as though it were the substance sought and thus produce a high result; for example, bromide will respond to titration as though it were chloride.

2) An interfering substance may react with the substance sought and thus produce a low result.

3) An interfering substance may combine with the analytical reagent and prevent it from reacting with the substance sought; for example, chlorine will destroy many indicators and color-developing reagents.

Nearly every interference will fit one of these classes. For example, in a photometric method, turbidity may be considered as a "substance" that acts like the one being determined, that is, it reduces light transmission. Occasionally, two or more interfering substances, if present simultaneously, may interact in a nonadditive fashion, either canceling or enhancing one another's effects.

b. Counteracting interference: The best way to minimize interference is to remove the interfering substance or to render it innocuous by one of the following methods:

1) Physically remove either the substance sought or the interfering substance. For example, distill off fluoride and ammonia, leaving interferences behind. The interferences also may be absorbed on an ion-exchange resin.

2) Adjust the pH so that only the substance sought will react; for example, ad-

just the pH to 2 so that volatile acids will distill from a solution.

3) Oxidize (digest) or reduce the sample to convert the interfering substance to a harmless form. For example, reduce chlorine to chloride by adding thiosulfate; digest samples for analysis by atomic absorption spectrometry with one of a variety of digestion reagents to destroy organic matter.

4) Add a suitable agent to complex the interfering substance so that it is innocuous although still present. For example, complex iron with pyrophosphate to prevent it from interfering with the copper determination; complex copper with cyanide or sulfide to prevent interference with the titrimetric hardness determination.

5) A combination of the first four techniques may be used. For example, distill phenols from an acid solution to prevent amines from distilling; use thiosulfate in the dithizone method for zinc to prevent most of the interfering metals from passing into the CCl₄ layer.

6) Color and turbidity sometimes may be destroyed by wet or dry ashing or may be removed by using a flocculating agent. Some types of turbidity may be removed by filtration. These procedures, however, introduce the danger that the constituent that is the subject of the analysis also will be removed.

c. Compensation for interference: If none of these techniques is practical, several methods of compensation can be used:

1) If color or turbidity initially present interferes in a photometric determination, it may be possible to use photometric compensation. The technique is described in Section 1070D.2a.

2) Determine the concentration of interfering substances and add identical amounts to the calibration standards. This involves much labor.

3) If the interference does not continue to increase as the concentration of interfering substance increases, but tends to

level off, add a large excess of interfering substance to all samples and to all standards. This is called "swamping."

4) The presence in the chemical reagents of the substance sought may be accounted for by carrying out a blank determination.

5. Bibliography

General Analytical Techniques

FOULK, C.W., H.V. MOYER & W.M. MACNEVIN. 1952. Quantitative Chemical Analysis. McGraw-Hill Book Co., New York, N.Y.

WILLARD, H.H., N.H. FURMAN & C.E. BRICKER. 1956. Elements of Quantitative Analysis, 4th ed. D. Van Nostrand Co., Princeton, N.J.

HUGHES, J.C. 1959. Testing of Glass Volumetric Apparatus. Nat. Bur. Standards Circ. No. 602.

WILSON, C.L. & D.W. WILSON, eds. 1959, 1960, 1962. Comprehensive Analytical Chemistry, Vol. 1A, 1B, 1C. Elsevier Publishing Co., New York, N.Y.

MEITES, L., ed. 1963. Handbook of Analytical Chemistry. McGraw-Hill Book Co., New York, N.Y.

KOLTHOFF, I.M., E.J. MEEHAN, E.B. SANDELL & S. BRUCKENSTEIN. 1969. Quantitative Chemical Analysis, 4th ed. Macmillan Co., New York, N.Y.

WELCHER, F.J., ed. 1975. Standard Methods of Chemical Analysis, 6th ed. Vol. IIA, IIB, IIIA (reprint), Robert E. Krieger Publishing Co., Melbourne, Fla.

PECSOK, R. et al. 1976. Modern Methods of Chemical Analysis, 2nd ed. John Wiley & Sons, New York, N.Y.

VOGEL, A.I. 1978. Textbook of Quantitative Inorganic Analysis. Including Elementary Instrumental Analysis, 4th ed. Revised by J. Basset. Longman, New York, N.Y.

General Analytical Reviews and Bibliographies

WEIL, B.H. et al. 1948. Bibliography on Water and Sewage Analysis. State Engineering Experiment Sta., Georgia Inst. Technology, Atlanta.

Annual reviews of analytical chemistry. 1953-1987. *Anal. Chem.* 25:2; 26:2; 27:574; 28:559; 29:589; 30:553; 31:776; 32:3R; 33:3R; 34:3R; 35:3R; 36:3R; 37–59:1R.

WATER POLLUTION CONTROL FEDERATION RESEARCH COMMITTEE. 1960-1988. Annual literature review, nature and analysis of chemical species. *J. Water Pollut. Control Fed.* 32:443; 33:445; 34:419; 35:553; 36:535;

37:735; 38:869; 39:867; 40:897; 41:873;
42:863; 43:933; 44:903; 45:979; 46:1031;
47:1118; 48:998; 49:901; 50:1000; 51:1108;
52:1083; 53:620; 54:520; 55:555; 56:494;
57:438; 58:419; 59:306; 60:743.

Colorimetric Techniques

MELLON, M.G. 1947. Colorimetry and photometry in water analysis. *J. Amer. Water Works Assoc.* 39:341.

NATIONAL BUREAU OF STANDARDS. 1947. Terminology and Symbols for Use in Ultraviolet, Visible, and Infrared Absorptiometry. NBS Letter Circ. LC-857 (May 19).

GIBSON, K.S. & M. BALCOM. 1947. Transmission measurements with the Beckman quartz spectrophotometer. *J. Res. Nat. Bur. Standards* 38:601.

SNELL, F.D. & C.T. SNELL. 1948-1971. Colorimetric Methods of Analysis, 3rd ed. Vol. 1, 2, 2A, 3, 3A, 4, 4A, 4AA, 4AAA. Van Nostrand Reinhold, New York, N.Y.

MELLON, M.G., ed. 1950. Analytical Absorption Spectroscopy. John Wiley & Sons, New York, N.Y.

DISKANT, E.M. 1952. Photometric methods in water analysis. *J. Amer. Water Works Assoc.* 44:625.

SANDELL, E.B. 1978. Colorimetric Determination of Traces of Metals, 4th ed. John Wiley & Sons, New York, N.Y.

BOLTZ, D.F., ed. 1978. Colorimetric Determination of Nonmetals, 2nd ed. John Wiley & Sons, New York, N.Y.

Other Methods of Analysis

LEDERER, E. & M. LEDERER. 1957. Chromatography, 2nd ed. Elsevier Press, Houston, Tex.

LINGANE, J.J. 1958. Electroanalytical Chemistry, 2nd ed. Interscience Publishers, New York, N.Y.

SAMUELSON, O. 1963. Ion Exchangers in Analytical Chemistry. John Wiley & Sons, New York, N.Y.

HARLEY, J.H. & S.E. WIBERLEY. 1967. Instrumental Analysis, 2nd ed. John Wiley & Sons, New York, N.Y.

EWING, G.W. 1975. Instrumental Methods of Chemical Analysis, 4th ed. McGraw-Hill Book Co., New York, N.Y.

HEFTMANN, E., ed. 1975. Chromatography, 3rd ed. Reinhold Publishing Corp., New York, N.Y.

1080   REAGENT-GRADE WATER

1080 A.   Introduction

One of the most important aspects of analysis is the preparation of reagent-grade water to be used for dilution of reagents and for blank analysis. Reagent-grade water covers a range from Type I with no detectable concentration of the compound or element to be analyzed at the detection limit of the analytical method to Type III for washing and qualitative analysis (see Table 1080:I). Reagent-grade water should be free of substances that interfere with analytical methods. The quality of water required is related directly to the analysis being made. Requirements for water quality may differ for organic, inorganic, and microbiological constituents depending on the use(s) for which the water is intended.

Any method of preparation of reagent-grade water is acceptable provided that the requisite quality can be met. Improperly maintained systems may add contaminants. Reverse osmosis, distillation, and deionization in various combinations all can produce reagent-grade water when used in the proper arrangement. Ultrafiltration and/or ultraviolet treatment also may be used as part of the process. Section 1080 provides general guidelines for the preparation of reagent-grade water. Table 1080:II lists commonly available processes for water purification and major classes of contaminants removed by purification.

For details on preparing water for microbiological tests, see Section 9020B.3c.

TABLE 1080:I. REAGENT WATER SPECIFICATIONS*

Quality Parameter	Type I	Type II	Type III
Bacteria, CFU/mL	10	1000	NA
pH	NA	NA	5–8
Resistivity, megohm-cm at 25°C	>10	>1	0.1
Conductivity, μmho/cmat 25°C	<0.1	1	10
SiO_2, mg/L	<0.05	<0.1	<1
Total solids, mg/L	0.1	1	5
Total oxidizable organic carbon, mg/L	<0.05	<0.2	<1

* NA = not applicable.

TABLE 1080:II. WATER PURIFICATION PROCESSES

	Major Classes of Contaminants*					
Process	Dissolved Ionized Solids	Dissolved Ionized Gases	Dissolved Organics	Particulates	Bacteria	Pyrogens
Distillation	G–E†	P	G	E	E	E
Deionization	E	E	P	P	P	P
Reverse osmosis	G‡	P	G	E	E	E
Carbon adsorption	P	P§	G–E ‖	P	P	P
Filtration	P	P	P	E	E	P
Ultrafiltration	P	P	G#	E	E	G–E
Ultraviolet oxidation	P	P	G–E**	P	G††	P

Permission to use this table from C3-T2, "Preparation and Testing of Reagent Water in the Clinical Laboratory - Second Edition; Tentative Guideline," has been granted by the National Committee for Clinical Laboratory Standards. The complete current standard may be obtained from National Committee for Clinical Laboratory Standards, 771 E. Lancaster Ave., Villanova, Pa. 19085.

* E = Excellent (capable of complete or near total removal), G = Good (capable of removing large percentages), P = Poor (little or no removal).

† Resistivity of water purified by distillation is an order of magnitude less than water produced by deionization, due mainly to the presence of CO_2 and sometimes H_2S, NH_3, and other ionized gases if present in the feedwater.

‡ Resistivity of dissolved ionized solids depends on original feedwater resistivity.

§ Activated carbon removes chlorine by adsorption.

‖ When used in combination with other purification processes, special grades of activated carbon and other synthetic adsorbents exhibit excellent capabilities for removing organic contaminants. Their use, however, is targeted toward specific compounds and applications.

Ultrafilters have demonstrated usefulness in reducing specific feedwater organic contaminants based on the rated molecular weight cut-off of the membrane.

** 185 nm ultraviolet oxidation (batch process systems) is effective in removing trace organic contaminants when used as post-treatment. Feedwater makeup plays a critical role in the performance of these batch processors.

†† 254 nm UV sterilizers, while not physically removing bacteria, may have bactericidal or bacteriostatic capabilities limited by intensity, contact time, and flow rate.

1080 B.   Methods for Preparation of Reagent-Grade Water

1. Distillation

Prepare laboratory-grade distilled water by distilling water from a still of all-borosilicate glass, fused quartz, tin, or titanium. To remove ammonia distill from an acid solution. Remove CO_2 by boiling the water for 15 min and cooling rapidly to room temperature; exclude atmospheric CO_2 by using a tube containing soda lime or a commercially available CO_2-removing agent.*

Boiling the water may add other impurities by leaching impurities from the container. Pretreat feedwater and provide periodic maintenance to minimize scale formation within the still. Pretreatment may be required where the feedwater contains significant concentrations of calcium, magnesium, and bicarbonate ions; it may involve demineralization via reverse osmosis or ion exchange. Resistivity of distilled water (Type II) should be > 1.0 megohm-cm at 25°C and for Type I, 10 megohm-cm. Measurements are more accurately made with in-line cells.

2. Reverse Osmosis

Reverse osmosis is a process in which water is forced under pressure through a semipermeable membrane removing a portion of dissolved constituents and suspended impurities. Product water quality depends on feedwater quality.

Select the reverse osmosis membrane module appropriate to the characteristics of the feedwater. Obtain rejection data for contaminants in the feedwater at the operating pressure to be used in preparing reagent-grade water. Set overall water production to make the most economical use of water without compromising the final quality of the permeate. Selection of spiral-wound or hollow fiber configurations depends on fouling potential of the feedwater. Regardless of configuration used, pretreatment may be required to minimize membrane fouling with colloids or particulates and to minimize introduction of chlorine, iron, and other oxidizing compounds that may degrade reverse osmosis membranes. Periodic flushing of the membrane modules is necessary.

3. Ion Exchange

Prepare deionized water by passing feedwater through a mixed-bed ion exchanger, consisting of strong anion and strong cation resins mixed together. When the system does not run continuously, recirculate product water through ion-exchange bed. Resistivity for Type I water should be 10 megohm-cm (in-line) at 25°C.

Use separate anion and cation resin beds in applications where resin regeneration is economically attractive. In such instances, position the anion exchanger downstream of the cation exchanger to remove leachates from the cation resin. Proper bed sizing is critical to the performance of the resins. In particular, set the length-to-diameter ratio of the bed in accordance with the maximum process flow rate to ensure that optimal face velocities are not exceeded and that sufficient residence time is provided.

In applications where the feedwater has significant quantities of organic matter, remove organics to minimize potential fouling of the resins. Possible pretreatments

---

* Ascarite, Fisher Scientific Co., or equivalent.

include prefiltration, distillation, reverse osmosis, or adsorption.

4. Adsorption

Adsorption is generally used to remove chlorine and organic impurities. It is accomplished typically with granular activated carbon. Efficiency of organics removal depends on the nature of the organic contaminants, the physical characteristics of the activated carbon, and the operating conditions. In general, organics adsorption efficiency is inversely proportional to solubility and may be inadequate for the removal of low-molecular-weight, polar compounds. Performance differences among activated carbons are attributable to the use of different raw materials and activation procedures. Select the appropriate activated carbon with regard to these differences. Even with optimum activated carbon, proper performance will not be attained unless the column is sized to give required face velocity and residence time at the maximum process flow rate.

Use of activated carbon may adversely affect resistivity. This effect may be controlled by use of reverse osmosis, mixed resins, or special adsorbents. To achieve the lowest level of organic contamination, use mixtures of polishing resins with special carbons in conjunction with additional treatment steps, such as reverse osmosis, natural carbons, ultraviolet oxidation, or ultrafiltration.

1080 C.   Reagent Water Quality

1. Quality Guidelines

Several guidelines for reagent water quality, based on contaminant levels, are available (see Table 1080:I).[1-3] Methods and uses listed below are based on National Committee for Clinical Laboratory Standards (NCCLS) guidelines.

Use Type I water in test methods requiring minimum interference and bias and maximum precision. Type II water is intended to provide the user with water in which the presence of bacteria can be tolerated. It is used for the preparation of reagents, dyes, or staining. Type III water may be used for glassware washing, preliminary rinsing of glassware, and as feedwater for production of higher-grade waters.

Type I reagent water, having a minimum resistivity of 10 megohms-cm, 25°C (in line), typically is prepared by distillation, deionization, or reverse osmosis treatment of feedwater followed by polishing with a mixed-bed deionizer and passage through a 0.2-μm-pore membrane filter. Alternatively treat by reverse osmosis followed by carbon adsorption and deionization. Determine quality at the time of production. Mixed bed deionizers typically add small amounts of organic matter to water, especially if the beds are fresh. Resistivity of Type I water should be > 10 megohm-cm 25°C, measured in-line. Resistivity measurements will not detect organics or nonionized contaminants, nor will they provide an accurate assessment of ionic contaminants at the microgram-per-liter level. Thus, make separate measurements of contaminants such as TOC, SiO_2, and bacterial counts.

Type II water typically is produced by distillation or deionization. Resistivity should be > 1 megohm-cm at 25°C. Observe the same precautions on measurements of other contaminants.

Type III water should have a minimum resistivity of 0.1 megohm-cm.

Other contaminants in reagent water are listed in Table 1080:I.

The pH of Type I or Type II water cannot be measured accurately without contaminating the water. Measure other constituents as required for individual tests.

Type I water cannot be stored without significant degradation; produce it continuously and use it immediately after processing. Type II water may be stored, but keep storage to a minimum and provide quality consistent with the intended use. Store only in materials that protect the water from contamination, such as TFE and glass for organics analysis or plastics for metals. Store Type III water in materials that protect the water from contamination.

2. References

1. AMERICAN SOCIETY FOR TESTING AND MATERIALS. 1987. Annual Book of ASTM Standards, Part 31, Water: Atmospheric Analysis. American Soc. Testing & Materials, Philadelphia, Pa.
2. COMMISSION ON LABORATORY INSPECTION AND ACCREDITATION. 1985. Reagent Water Specifications. College of American Pathologists, Chicago, Ill.
3. NATIONAL COMMITTEE FOR CLINICAL LABORATORY STANDARDS. 1988. Preparation and Testing of Reagent Water in the Clinical Laboratory - Second Edition; Tentative Guideline. Publ. C3-T2, National Comm. for Clinical Laboratory Standards, Villanova, Pa.

1090   SAFETY

1090 A.   Introduction

1. General Discussion

Achievement of a safe and healthy work place is the responsibility of the institution, the laboratory manager, the supervisory personnel and, finally, of the laboratory personnel themselves. All laboratory employees must make every effort to protect themselves and their fellow workers. The laboratory manager should realize that accidents have causes, and therefore can be prevented by a good safety program.[1]

Once an employee has become thoroughly familiar and competent with the new, safe techniques, the manager can be assured that the employee will propose other safety ideas.

2. Organizing for Safety

Although responsibility for establishing and enforcing a laboratory safety program ultimately rests with the laboratory director, it is desirable, except in small laboratories, to delegate responsibility to a staff member designated as the safety officer.[2] The safety officer should be part of the management team to optimize safety training, inspections, indoctrination of new employees, and acquisition and updating of safety information. The safety officer should see that personal protective equipment is available and used appropriately. The officer should make periodic inspections of emergency equipment, such as fire extinguishers, alarm systems, eye wash, and safety showers; perform periodic inspections of the laboratory to uncover overlooked hazards; observe that personnel are following safety rules; and provide reminders for individuals to be aware of safe practices.

Radiation safety is a specialized part of an overall safety program. A technically qualified individual should be designated as the Radiation Safety Officer (RSO). The RSO ensures that radioactive sources and radiation equipment are used safely and in accordance with all pertinent state and federal regulations, and that proper licensing from the appropriate state and/or federal agency is maintained.

A safety committee should be established and it must have the support of the laboratory director. The committee's recommendations must be taken seriously and acted upon promptly. Safety committees involve persons with varying expertise in making decisions relating to safety practices. For example, chemists may have insight into the handling of hazardous chemicals in a bacteriology section. This assignment can be educationally valuable. It is desirable periodically to rotate members of the safety committee so that most personnel have an opportunity to become personally involved.

Keep good records of all accidents, inspections, training, etc. Preferably use a simple standard report form. The report should contain sufficient information to enable the safety officer, supervisor, and director to determine who was involved, what happened, when and where it happened, and what injuries, if any, resulted. The Occupational Safety and Health Act (OSHA) requires that those accidents causing major disability be recorded in a log, but it is useful to record all accidents to be able to evaluate the safety program. Recording time and nature of each accident may be of further importance if disability occurs and a Worker's Compensation claim is appropriate. Maintain a file of recommendations of the safety officer or safety committee, as well as actions taken by the staff as part of the safety program.

The OSHA "Hazard Communication Standard" or "Right-to-Know Regulation"[3] specifies a method of employee notification about hazards in the workplace. Exposed laboratory personnel must be under direct supervision and regular observation of a technically qualified individual, who must have knowledge of the hazards present, their health effects, and related emergency procedures. The supervisor must educate laboratory personnel in safe work practices. Personnel have a right to know what hazardous materials are present, the specific hazards created by those materials, and the required procedures to protect against these hazards.

Training in safety techniques requires deliberate effort by management. In larger laboratories, safety seminars are important. Use educational techniques including training films, demonstrations with devices such as fire extinguishers or respirators, charts listing hazardous chemicals and proper procedures for handling them, and manuals on safety. Periodically provide refresher training. Material Safety Data Sheets (MSDSs) are provided by chemical manufacturers and are an extremely important part of the whole approach of informing personnel of hazards in their workplace.[4] These MSDSs should be made available to personnel using hazardous materials.

3. References

1. INHORN, S. L., ed. 1978. Quality Assurance Practices for Health Laboratories. American Public Health Assoc., Washington, D.C.
2. STEERE, N. V., ed. 1971. Handbook of Laboratory Safety, 2nd ed. Chemical Rubber Co., Cleveland, Ohio.
3. Hazard Communication: Final Rule. 1983. Federal Register 48:53280; 1985. 29 CFR Part 1910.1200.
4. Chemical Safety Data Sheets. Manufacturing Chemists' Assoc., Inc. Washington, D.C.

1090 B.   Safety Equipment

1. Laboratory Equipment

a. Fire extinguishers: There are three general types of fire extinguishers:

1) Water-type extinguishers are useful for fires with ordinary combustibles, such as wood, paper, and rags.

2) Dry-chemical types are effective against most fires, but particularly those involving flammable liquids and metals and electrical fires.

3) Carbon dioxide types are useful for small fires involving flammable liquids and for limited use around electronic instrumentation and equipment.

Depending upon potential hazards, a laboratory may have more than one type in each room in an easily accessible location away from the area of greatest hazard.[1-5] Halon extinguishers are useful in special areas housing electronic or computer equipment that might be damaged by conventional extinguishers. Both Halon and carbon dioxide extinguishers create oxygen deficiencies. Use all extinguishers with care.

It is often recommended that multipurpose fire extinguishers (type ABC) be installed in the laboratory and that hoods containing organic materials be equipped with halon extinguishers. Be sure that extinguishers are properly serviced and recharged on a scheduled basis.

b. Fire blankets: Locate readily accessible fire blankets close to each laboratory.[6]

c. Safety showers: Safety showers are an integral part of the laboratory, and are to be used in accidents involving acids, caustic or other harmful liquids, clothing fires, and other emergencies. Locate showers conveniently, preferably near a doorway, keep the floor space under them uncluttered, and test regularly.[6]

d. Eye washes: Remove contact lenses if applicable. Flush eyes *immediately* and thoroughly (15 min) to prevent sight impairment or even blindness after a chemical splashes into the eye. Splashes to the face are rinsed off easily with a four-head eye wash. Some experts claim that the fountain-like stream of water from an eye wash tends to drive particulate matter (glass or metal shards, dirt, grit) into the eye rather than to wash it out. If this type of accident occurs, consult an eye expert after gentle flushing with water. Locate eye washes at or near sinks in a highly visible and central area away from electrical receptacles. Check eye washes routinely for correct function; if portable eye washes are used clean them weekly and change the water to reduce the possibility of contamination. The use of eye-wash bottles and some of their problems have been discussed elsewhere.[2]

e. Safety shields: The most generally used type of safety shield protects the worker from various forms of radiation, such as laser beams and ultraviolet emissions. Provide conventional chemical hoods with safety glass and movable doors. Consider shielding when working with glass vacuum or pressurized systems.

f. Safety containers: Safety containers are designed to minimize consequences of an accident or to prevent spread of harmful materials. Use safety containers to transport chemicals, especially concentrated acids and alkalies. For flammable solvents use safety cans approved by the Underwriters' Laboratories.

Glove boxes, laminar-flow hoods, or remotely operated confinements for radioactive material or dangerous pathogens are more complicated safety containers. Operate these under negative pressure, with primary filtration at the exit of gas or air vents leading to a major ventilation system. Periodically check filter for efficiency and change and test gloves to prevent accidental release of particulates by the pumping action created during use.

g. Storage facilities: In storing laboratory materials, it is necessary to know their properties as well as the consequences of accidents such as spilling, explosion, or fire.

As a general rule, do not store large containers of reagents in working areas, but use smaller containers holding only enough for the day's or week's work. Do not store chemicals that combine to form explosive, flammable, or dangerous compounds in a manner that would allow them to mix if an accident occurred. Store hazardous materials within a tray or catch bin area.

Store flammable solvents in properly vented cabinets approved by the National Fire Protection Association[5] or in a safety refrigerator. Use special containers for flammable solvents in quantities of more than 2 L or when the cumulative amount of flammable solvents in a room exceeds 8 L. (Flammable solvents are liquids with a flash point below 60°C and a vapor pressure exceeding 275 kPa atmospheric at 38°C.)

h. Laboratory fume hoods: Properly designed and operated fume hoods and biological safety cabinets are essential to a safe laboratory operation.[7] Use hoods to contain and vent operations with hazardous materials; do not use them primarily for storage.

Different air-flow and design classifications of fume hoods are available for different degrees of hazard. Know the air-moving capacity of the entire system; pay particular attention to the air stream exhausted to the community air. Check air flow of hoods on a scheduled basis with an anemometer. Indicate with a marking pen or tape the sash position required to obtain an air flow of 30 m/min.

i. Chemical spill kits: Provide work and storage areas with chemical spill kits obtained from commercial sources or assembled in the laboratory. Use kits of suitable size to accommodate the quantities of acids, alkalies, or solvents being used. Devise and post spill procedures before the need arises.

j. Safety wall chart: Post in central location for information on hazardous laboratory substances.

2. Personal Protective Equipment

Personal protective equipment and materials include such items as laboratory garments, gloves, shoes, hard hats, glasses, shields, and other safety items used by an individual. Their selection and use is governed by the particular tasks to be performed. Such equipment is important for protection but also serves as a constant reminder of the need for safety. If it is determined that such are needed, it is the manager's and supervisor's responsibility to insure that they are used.

a. Clothing: Personal clothing creates a barrier between the individual and the hazard. Employees using radioactive materials, suspected carcinogens, and pathogenic materials may be required to change from street to laboratory clothing when entering the work area and to change again on leaving. This not only prevents carrying hazardous materials outside the area but it also permits necessary handling and cleaning of the clothing. Disposable laboratory clothing should be fire-retardant.

b. Gloves frequently are important. Consult the material safety data sheet for a solvent or reagent to determine the type of glove to be used. Rubber gloves may be used when handling hazardous liquids, leaded gloves for handling radioactive materials, and surgical gloves for handling pathogenic material. Insulated gloves are essential for handling hot objects and extremely cold ones, but do not use asbestos gloves. White cotton gloves may be used to protect instruments.

c. Safety shoes are required in laboratories where heavy objects or equipment is to be moved. Hard hats may be required if there is overhead machinery in the laboratory.

d. Safety glasses: Even if the likelihood of accidents seems small, the consequences of an eye accident may be extremely serious. Require all laboratory personnel to wear safety glasses. Most laboratories prohibit use of contact lenses with safety glasses, but this is an area of controversy and should be evaluated in each laboratory. Safety glasses protect from splashes, flying objects, powders, or ultraviolet exposure. However, ordinary safety glasses do not provide total eye protection. If the work involves special hazard to the eyes, consider additional protection. For example, wear lenses with special filters for glassblowing, welding, laser work, or exposure to other forms of radiation. When working in a room with ultraviolet radiation, wear safety glasses with side shields or goggles with solid side pieces. For certain activities, provide protection for exposed skin. In working with acid or caustic materials wear a face shield to protect both the eyes and the face.

e. Respirators: Have respirators[8] available for emergency situations in which dangerous gases, fumes, or aerosols may be formed and the room must be entered before it is thoroughly ventilated. In laboratories using toxic gases, such as boron trifluoride, chlorine, dimethylamine, ethylene oxide, fluorine, and hydrogen bromide, provide respirators, preferably Self-Contained Breathing Apparatus (SCBA), or supplied air.

3. References

1. NATIONAL INSTITUTE FOR OCCUPATIONAL SAFETY AND HEALTH. 1974. The Industrial Environment—Its Evaluation and Control, 3rd ed. U.S. Dep. Health, Education & Welfare, National Inst. Occupational Safety & Health, Rockville, Md.
2. U.S. PUBLIC HEALTH SERVICE. 1975. Lab Safety at the Center for Disease Control. U.S. Dep. Health, Education & Welfare, Publ. No. CDC 76-8118, National Center Disease Control, Atlanta, Ga.
3. THE MATHESON COMPANY. 1971. Matheson Gas Data Book, 5th ed. Matheson Co., East Rutherford, N.J.
4. MEIDL, J. H. 1970. Flammable Hazardous Materials. Glenncoe Press, Beverly Hills, Calif.
5. McKINNON, G. P. 1976. Fire Protection Handbook, 14th ed. National Fire Protection Assoc., Boston, Mass.
6. STEERE, N.V., ed. 1971. Handbook of Laboratory Safety, 2nd ed. Chemical Rubber Co., Cleveland, Ohio.
7. AMERICAN CONFERENCE OF GOVERNMENTAL INDUSTRIAL HYGIENISTS. 1982. Industrial Ventilation, A Manual of Recommended Practices, 17th ed. American Conf. of Governmental Industrial Hygienists, Cincinnati, Ohio.
8. NATIONAL INSTITUTE FOR OCCUPATIONAL SAFETY AND HEALTH. 1976. Guide to Industrial Respiratory Protection. Publ. No. 76-189, U.S. Dep. Health, Education & Welfare, National Inst. Occupational Safety & Health, Cincinnati, Ohio.

1090 C.   Laboratory Hazards

Many laboratory hazards are fairly obvious, but identification of all likely hazards is important in developing an effective safety program. Develop a safety plan before any work is started. This is to provide all personnel working with or near hazardous materials information about them. Include Material Safety Data Sheets (MSDSs) in the safety plan and describe routine and emergency procedures; require that all personnel read and sign that they have read and understood the document.

To avoid ingestion of toxic or infectious material, prohibit eating, drinking, and smoking in all laboratory areas. Post adequate warning signs in the laboratory and insure that all containers have clear and readily recognizable labels. Avoid floor clutter so that escape routes and fire extinguishers are not blocked. Eliminate improper storage such as precarious shelving or heavy or glass objects overhead.

1. Chemical Hazards

Chemical injuries may be external or internal.[1-8] External injuries result from skin exposure to caustic or corrosive substances such as acids, bases, or reactive salts. Take care to prevent accidents, such as splashes and container spills. Coincidentally, pay attention to equipment corrosion that ultimately may lead to safety hazards from equipment failure. Internal injuries may result from toxic or corrosive effects of substances absorbed by the body.

a. Inorganic acids and bases: Many inorganic acids and bases have Occupational Safety and Health Personal Exposure Limits[9] and American Conference of Governmental Industrial Hygienists' Threshold Limit Values (TLV)[10] associated with them. These permissible exposure limits and threshold limit values indicate the maximum air concentration to which workers may be exposed. Fumes of these acids and bases are severe eye and respiratory system irritants. Liquid or solid acids and bases quickly can cause severe burns of the skin and eyes.[11] When acids are heated to increase the rate of digestion of organic materials, they pose a significantly greater hazard because fumes are produced and the hot acid reacts very quickly with the skin.

Store acids and bases separately in well-ventilated areas and away from volatile organic and oxidizable materials. Use containers (rubber or plastic buckets) to transport acids and bases. Work with strong acids and bases only in a properly functioning chemical fume hood. Slowly add acids and bases to water (with constant stirring) to avoid spattering. If skin contact is made, thoroughly flush the contaminated area with water and seek medical attention if irritation persists.[12] Do not rewear clothing until after it has been cleaned thoroughly. Leather items (e.g. belts and shoes) will retain acids even after rinsing with water and may cause severe burns if reworn. If eye contact is made, immediately flush both eyes for a full 15 min at the eye wash and seek medical attention.

Perchloric acid (see Sections 3030G and H and 4500-P.D) reacts violently or explosively on contact with organic material.[12] Do not use laboratory fume hoods used with perchloric acid for organic reagents, particularly volatile solvents. In addition to these hazards, perchloric acid produces severe burns when contact is made with the skin, eyes, or respiratory tract.[13] Preferably provide a dedicated perchloric acid hood. Follow manufacturer's instructions for proper cleaning because exhaust ducts become coated and must be washed down regularly.

The most common injuries suffered with sodium hydroxide are burns of the skin and eyes. Sodium hydroxide solutions as dilute as $2.5N$ can cause severe eye damage.[14] On dissolution, sodium hydroxide and other alkalies produce considerable heat (often sufficient to cause boiling).

b. Metals and inorganic compounds: In general, consider all laboratory chemicals hazardous and use only as prescribed. Handle chemicals in a fume hood, using eye protection and wearing a laboratory coat. In case of accidental skin contact, flush the affected area thoroughly with water. If irritation persists, medical examination is advisable. Toxicity, precautionary, and first-aid information is available from a variety of sources.[11-15]

Some hazards of specific metals and inorganic compounds are as follows: Some compounds of arsenic and nickel are highly toxic and may be carcinogenic.[14,15] Avoid inhalation, ingestion, and skin contact. Sodium azide is toxic and reacts with acid to produce still more toxic hydrazoic acid. When disposed of through a drain it may react with copper and lead plumbing to form metal azides that are extremely explosive. Azides may be destroyed by adding a concentrated solution of sodium nitrite, 1.5 g $NaNO_2$/g sodium azide.[16] The extreme toxicity of beryllium and its compounds is reflected by its low TLV of 2.0 $\mu g/m.^{3,11}$ Beryllium is a suspected carcinogen in humans.[9,15] Handle with extreme caution and only in a laboratory fume hood or glove box. Cyanides are used as reagents and may be present in samples. Hydrogen cyanide is a lethal gas. Do not acidify cyanide solutions except in a closed system or in a properly ventilated hood because hydrogen cyanide may be formed and liberated.

Mercury is unusual among the metals in that it is liquid at room temperature and has appreciable vapor pressure. One broken thermometer in a poorly ventilated room may cause the mercury TLV to be exceeded. Because of its high volatility and toxicity, handle mercury and its compounds very cautiously and provide a spill cleanup kit. Perchlorate salts are explosive when mixed with combustible material. They also are severe irritants to the skin, eyes, and respiratory system. Use care in handling and storing perchlorates. Sodium borohydride decomposes in water and liberates hydrogen, consequently creating an explosion hazard. Like many other inorganic chemicals, it is a strong skin and respiratory system irritant.

c. Organic solvents and reagents: Most solvents specified in this book have TLVs for workroom exposure[10] (see Table 1090:I). Many organic reagents, unlike most organic solvents, do not have TLVs (see Table 1090:II for those that do) but this does not mean that they are less hazardous. Some compounds are suspect carcinogens and should be treated with extreme caution. These compounds include both solvents and reagents such as benzene,[18] carbon tetrachloride,[11] chloroform,[11] 1,4-dioxane,[8,11,19] tetrachloroethylene,[20] and benzidine.[21] Lists of chemicals with special hazardous characteristics are available from the Occupational Safety and Health Administration and the National Institute for Occupational Safety and Health. The lists of "Regulated Carcinogens" and of "Chemicals Having Substantial Evidence of Carcinogenicity" are especially important. Determining labora-

TABLE 1090:I. THRESHOLD LIMIT VALUES*[10] FOR SOLVENTS SPECIFIED IN *Standard Methods*

Compound†	TLV ppm (v/v)
Acetic acid	10
Acetone	750
Acetonitrile (S)	40
Benzene (C)[17]	10
n-Butanol (S)	50
t-Butanol	100
Carbon disulfide (S)	10
Carbon tetrachloride (C)(S)	5
Chloroform (C)	10
Cyclohexanone (S)	25
Diethyl ether	400
1,4-Dioxane (C)(S)	25
Ethanol	1000
Ethyl acetate	400
Ethylene glycol	50
Hexane	50
Isoamyl alcohol	100
Isobutyl alcohol	50
Isopropyl alcohol	400
Isopropyl ether	250
Methanol (S)	200
2-Methoxyethanol (S)	5
Methylene chloride (C)	50
Pentane	600
Propanol (S)	200
Pyridine	5
Tetrachloroethylene	50
Toluene	100
Xylene	100

* These threshold limit values provide an indication of the maximum air concentrations to which workers may be exposed.

† (C) compound is a suspect carcinogen; (S) refers to potential contribution by skin absorption.

tory handling procedures on such authoritative lists decreases the chance for error.

Solvents used herein fall into several major categories: alcohols, chlorinated compounds, and hydrocarbons. Exposure to each of these classes of compounds can have a variety of health effects.[22-24] Alcohols, in general, are intoxicants, capable of causing irritation of the mucus membranes and drowsiness. While diols such as eth-

TABLE 1090:II. THRESHOLD LIMIT VALUES[10]
FOR REAGENTS SPECIFIED IN *Standard Methods*

Compound*	TLV
2-Aminoethanol	3 ppm (v/v)
Benzidine (C)(S)[17]	—
Benzyl chloride	1 ppm (v/v)
Chlorobenzene	75 ppm (v/v)
2-Chloro-6-(trichloromethyl) pyridine	10 mg/m^3
Diethanolamine	3 ppm (v/v)
Naphthalene	10 ppm (v/v)
Oxalic acid	1 mg/m^3
Phenol	5 ppm (v/v)

* (C) compound is a suspect carcinogen; (S) refers to potential contribution by skin absorption.

ylene glycol are poisonous, triols such as glycerol are not poisonous at all. Chlorinated hydrocarbons cause narcosis and damage to the central nervous system and liver. Hydrocarbons, like the other two groups, are skin irritants and may cause dermatitis after prolonged skin exposure. Because of the volatility of these compounds, hazardous vapor concentrations can occur (fire or explosion hazard). Proper ventilation is essential.[25]

Organic reagents used in this manual fall into four major categories: acids, halogenated compounds, dyes and indicators, and pesticides. Most organic acids have irritant properties.[22,24] They are predominantly solids from which aerosols may be produced. Dyes and indicators also present an aerosol problem. Handle pesticides with caution because they are poisons[22] and avoid contact with the skin. Wear gloves and protective clothing. The chlorinated compounds present much the same hazards as the chlorinated solvents (narcosis and damage to the central nervous system and liver). Proper labeling of the compound, including a date for disposal based on the manufacturer's recommendation, permits tracking chemical usage and disposal of outdated chemicals.

2. Biological Hazards

Water laboratory safety also includes microbiological hazards.[26-30] Pathogenic microorganisms may produce human disease by accidental ingestion, inoculation or injection or other means of cutaneous penetration. Good laboratory safety techniques will control these agents.[31] Primary dangers associated with microbiological hazards involve hand-mouth contact while handling contaminated laboratory materials and aerosols created by inoculating, pipetting, centrifuging, or blending of samples or cultures.[32]

Do not mix dilutions by blowing air through a pipet into a microbiological culture. When working with grossly polluted samples, such as sewage or high-density microbial cultures, use a pipetting device attached to the mouth end of the pipet to prevent accidental ingestion. *Never pipet by mouth.* Even for drinking water samples mouth pipetting is inadvisable. Because untreated waters may contain waterborne pathogens, discard all used pipets into a jar containing disinfectant solution for decontamination before glassware washing. Do not place discarded pipets on table tops, on laboratory carts, or in sinks without adequate decontamination. Quaternary ammonium compounds that include a compatible detergent, or solutions of sodium hypochlorite are satisfactory disinfectants for pipet discard jars. Use highest concentrations recommended for these commercial products provided that this concentration does not cause a loss of markings or fogging of pipets. Replace disinfectant solution in the discard container daily. Sterilize contaminated materials (cultures, samples, used glassware, serological discards, etc.) by autoclaving before throwing them away or processing for reuse. Shattering of culture-containing tubes during centrifugation also produces microbiological aerosols.[33,34] Use leakproof blenders and keep them tightly covered during operation. Inserting a hot loop into a flask of broth culture creates a serious hazard due to aerosolized microorganisms.[35] Using electric heater incineration for sterilizing inoculating loops or needles may be desirable, but avoid possible electrical shock that could occur by touching the loop to the inside of the heater core.[36]

Good personal hygienic practices are important in the control of contact exposures. Frequently disinfect hands and working surfaces. Provide drinking water outside the laboratory, preferably from a foot-operated drinking fountain. Suggest immunization of laboratory staff against tetanus and possibly typhoid or other appropriate infectious agents, depending on nature of the work. Eliminate flies and other insects to prevent contamination of sterile equipment, media, samples, and bacterial cultures and to prevent spread of infectious organisms to personnel via this vector. Install screens in all windows and outer doors if there is no air-conditioning, and spray periodically with pesticides along toe-stripping, sink and storage cabinet areas, and utility service channels. Because laboratories also may include a chemistry section that analyzes waters for pesticides, apply these carefully within the immediate areas of microbiological activity.

3. Radiation Hazards

All persons are exposed to ionizing radiation. The average annual radiation dose to the whole body from cosmic, terrestrial, and internal sources, medical and dental X-rays, etc., is about 185 mrems/year.[37] Prevent unnecessary continuous or intermittent occupational exposure, and prevent accidents that may result in dangerous radiation exposure. In laboratories, X-rays, ultraviolet light, and radioactive material represent hazards that must be minimized. Provide a Radiation Safety Manual,[38] Handbook of Laboratory Safety,[13] or similar manual to all persons working with radioactive materials or radiation-producing machines. This manual should discuss procedure for obtaining authorization to use, order, handle, and store radionuclides. It also should include procedures for safe handling of unsealed radioactive material and procedures to follow in case of radiation accidents, for decontamination, for personnel monitoring, for laboratory monitoring, and for disposal of radioactive materials.

a. Radioactive materials: Radionuclides are used in laboratories to develop and evaluate analytical methods, to prepare counting standards, and to calibrate detectors and counting instruments (see Part 7000). Sealed sources, such as the nickel 63 detector cell used in electron capture gas chromatograph units, are common. Instruct all persons dealing with radioactive materials about associated health hazards. Establish proper procedures and incorporate radiation safety measures to minimize exposure and accident.

b. Radiation-producing machines: Minimize hazards from devices, such as X-ray diffraction apparatus or electron microscope, by adhering strictly to manufacturer's operating manual and procedures outlined in the referenced safety manuals.

c. Ultraviolet radiation (UV): UV is used frequently. With properly constructed and operated instruments, it is not a significant hazard but can be harmful when used for controlling microorganisms in laboratory rooms or for sterilizing objects. Provide proper shielding, remembering that shiny metal surfaces reflect this energy; shut off UV lamps when not in use. Post warning signs and install indicator lights to serve as a constant reminder when UV lamps are *on.* Wear safety glasses or goggles with solid side pieces whenever there is a possibility of exposure to UV radiation.[39]

4. Physical Hazards

a. Electrical: Conform electrical wiring, connections, and apparatus to the latest

National Electrical Code. Fire, explosion, power outages, and electrical shocks are all serious hazards that may result from incorrect use of electrical devices. Ground all electrical equipment or use double insulation. Use ground fault circuit breakers to the maximum extent possible. Do not locate electrical receptacles inside fume hoods, do not use equipment with frayed cords or cracked insulation nor spark-producing electrical equipment near volatile flammable solvents. Use approved safety refrigerators. Disconnect electrical equipment from the power supply before service or repair is attempted and never bypass safety interlocks. Equipment repair by employees not thoroughly acquainted with electrical principles may present particularly dangerous situations.[40]

b. Mechanical: Shield or guard drive belts, pulleys, chain drivers, rotating shafts, and other types of mechanical power transmission apparatus.[9] Laboratory equipment requiring this guarding includes vacuum pumps, mixers, blenders, and grinders. Shield portable power tools used in laboratories.[9] Guard equipment such as centrifuges, which have high-speed revolving parts, against "fly-aways." Securely fasten equipment that has a tendency to vibrate (e.g., centrifuges and air compressors) to prevent the tendency to "walk" and locate away from bottles and other items that may fall from shelves or benches because of the vibration.[13]

c. Compressed gases: Gas cylinders may explode or "rocket" if improperly handled. Leaking cylinders may present an explosion hazard if the contents are flammable, they are an obvious health hazard if the contents are toxic, and they may lead to death by suffocation if the contents are inert gases. OSHA regulations govern use and storage of compressed gases.[9] Transfer gas cylinders only by carts, hand trucks, or dollies. Secure gas cylinders properly during storage, transport, and use and leave valve safety cover on cylinders during stor-

age and transport. Avoid the use of adapters or couplers with compressed gas. Permanently identify cylinder contents.

5. References

1. NATIONAL INSTITUTE FOR OCCUPATIONAL SAFETY AND HEALTH. 1976. Registry of Toxic Effects of Chemical Substances. U.S. Dep. Health, Education & Welfare, National Inst. Occupational Safety & Health, Rockville, Md.
2. AMERICAN CONFERENCE OF GOVERNMENTAL INDUSTRIAL HYGIENISTS. 1976. Documentation of the Threshold Limit Values for Substances in Workroom Air, 3rd ed. American Conf. of Governmental Industrial Hygienists, Cincinnati, Ohio.
3. WINDHOLZ, M. 1976. The Merck Index, 9th ed. Merck and Co., Rahway, N.J.
4. AMERICAN MUTUAL INSURANCE ALLIANCE. 1966. Handbook of Organic Solvents. Tech. Guide No. 6, American Mutual Insurance Alliance, Chicago, Ill.
5. BRAKER, W. & A. L. MOSSMAN. 1970. Effects of Exposure to Toxic Gases—First Aid and Medical Treatment. Matheson Gas Products, East Rutherford, N.J.
6. SAX, N. I. 1968. Dangerous Properties of Industrial Materials, 3rd ed. Van Nostrand Reinhold Co., New York, N.Y.
7. BROWNING, E. C. 1965. Toxicity and Metabolism of Industrial Solvents. Elsevier Scientific Publ. Co., New York, N.Y.
8. DEICHMANN, W. B. & H. W. GERARDE. 1969. Toxicology of Drugs and Chemicals. Academic Press, New York, N.Y.
9. Code of Federal Regulations. 1980. 29 Labor Part 1910. Washington, D.C.
10. AMERICAN CONFERENCE OF GOVERNMENTAL INDUSTRIAL HYGIENISTS. 1986–87. Threshold Limit Values. American Conf. Governmental Industrial Hygienists, Cincinnati, Ohio.
11. NATIONAL INSTITUTE FOR OCCUPATIONAL SAFETY AND HEALTH/OCCUPATIONAL SAFETY AND HEALTH ADMINISTRATION. 1981. Occupational Health Guidelines for Chemical Hazards. Publ. No. 81-123, U.S. Dep. Health & Human Services, U.S. Dep. Labor, Washington, D.C.
12. NATIONAL RESEARCH COUNCIL. 1981. Prudent Practices for Handling Hazardous Chem-

icals in Laboratories. National Academy Press, Washington, D.C.

13. STEERE, N.V. 1971. Handbook of Laboratory Safety, 2nd ed. Chemical Rubber Co., Cleveland, Ohio.

14. MUIR, G. C. 1977. Hazards in the Chemical Laboratory, 2nd ed. Chemical Soc., London, England.

15. CLAYTON, G. D. & F. E. CLAYTON. 1981. Patty's Industrial Hygiene and Toxicology, Vol. II A, 3rd ed. John Wiley & Sons, New York, N.Y.

16. AMERICAN PUBLIC HEALTH ASSOCIATION, AMERICAN WATER WORKS ASSOCIATION & WATER POLLUTION CONTROL FEDERATION. 1981. Standard Methods for the Examination of Water and Wastewater, 15th ed. American Public Health Assoc., Washington, D.C.

17. U.S. PUBLIC HEALTH SERVICE. 1975. Lab Safety at the Center for Disease Control. U.S. Dep. Health, Education & Welfare, Publ. No. CDC 76-8118. National Center Disease Control, Atlanta, Ga.

18. NATIONAL INSTITUTE FOR OCCUPATIONAL SAFETY AND HEALTH. 1974. Criteria for a Recommended Standard. Occupational Exposure to Benzene. Publ. No. 74-137, U.S. Dep. Health, Education & Welfare, U.S. Government Printing Off., Washington, D.C.

19. NATIONAL INSTITUTE FOR OCCUPATIONAL SAFETY AND HEALTH. 1977. Criteria for a Recommended Standard. Occupational Exposure to Dioxane. Publ. No. 77-226, U.S. Dep. Health, Education & Welfare, U.S. Government Printing Office, Washington, D.C.

20. NATIONAL INSTITUTE FOR OCCUPATIONAL SAFETY AND HEALTH. 1978. Current Intelligence Bulletin 20 Tetrachloroethylene (Perchloroethylene). Publ. No. 78-112, U.S. Dep. Health, Education & Welfare, U.S. Government Printing Off., Washington, D.C.

21. BOENIGER, M. 1980. Carcinogenicity and Metabolism of Azo Dyes, Especially Those from Benzidine. Publ. No. 80-119, U.S. Dep. Health & Human Services. U.S. Government Printing Off., Washington, D.C.

22. DOULL, J., C. D. KLASSEN & M. O. AMDUR, eds. 1980. Casarett and Doull's Toxicology, 2nd ed. Macmillan Co., New York, N.Y.

23. Toxic and Hazardous Industrial Chemicals Safety Manual for Handling and Disposal with Toxicity and Hazard Data. 1978. International Technical Information Inst., Tokyo, Japan.

24. PATTY, F. A. 1963. Patty's Industrial Hygiene and Toxicology, 2nd ed. John Wiley & Sons, New York, N.Y.

25. CLAYTON, G. D. & F. E. CLAYTON. 1978. Patty's Industrial Hygiene and Toxicology, 3rd ed. Vol. 1. John Wiley & Sons, New York, N.Y.

26. WEDEUN, A. G., E. HANEL, G. B. PHILLIPS & O.T. MILLER. 1956. Laboratory Design for Study of Infectious Disease. Amer. J. Pub. Health 46:1102.

27. DARLOW, H. M. 1969. Safety in the Microbiological Laboratory. In J. R. Norris & D. W. Ribbons, eds. Methods in Microbiology. Volume 1. Academic Press, New York, N.Y.

28. SCIENCE PRODUCTS DIVISION, MALLINCKRODT CHEMICAL WORKS. 1969. Laboratory Safety Handbook. Mallinckrodt Chemical Works, St. Louis, Mo.

29. SHAPTON, D. A. & R. J. BOARD. 1972. Safety in Microbiology. Soc. Applied Bacteriology, Tech. Ser. No. 6., Academic Press, New York, N.Y.

30. U.S. DEPARTMENT OF HEALTH AND HUMAN SERVICES, PUBLIC HEALTH SERVICE, CENTERS FOR DISEASE CONTROL & NATIONAL INSTITUTES OF HEALTH. 1984. Biosafety in Microbiological and Biomedical Laboratories. U.S. Government Printing Off., Washington, D.C.

31. OFFICE OF BIOSAFETY. 1974. Classification of Etiologic Agents on the Basis of Hazard, 4th ed. Center Disease Control, Atlanta, Ga.

32. PHILLIPS, G. B. 1961. Microbiological Safety in U.S. and Foreign Laboratories. Tech. Study 35, Biological Laboratories Project 4B11-05-015, U.S. Army Chemical Corps, Fort Detrick, Md.

33. REITMAN, M. & G. B. PHILLIPS. 1956. Biological hazards of common laboratory procedures. III. The centrifuge. Amer. J. Med. Technol. 22:100.

34. HALL, C. V. 1975. A biological safety centrifuge. Health Lab. Sci. 12:104.

35. PHILLIPS, G. B. & M. REITMAN. 1956. Biological hazards of common laboratory procedures. IV. The inoculating loop. Amer. J. Med. Technol. 22:16.

36. GORDON, R. C. & C. V. DAVENPORT. 1973.

Simple modification to improve usefulness of the bacti-cinerator. *Appl. Microbiol.* 26:423.

37. NATIONAL COUNCIL ON RADIATION PROTECTION AND MEASUREMENTS. 1987. Ionizing Radiation Exposure of the Population of the United States. Rep. No. 93, National Council Radiation Protection, Washington, D.C.

38. CALIFORNIA STATE DEPARTMENT OF HEALTH SERVICES. 1979. Radiation Safety Manual. Berkeley, Calif. (Similar manuals are available from most state health departments, universities, and national laboratories.)

39. WALLACE, L. A. 1981. Recent progress in developing and using personal monitors to measure human exposure to air pollutants. *Environ. International* 5:73.

40. INHORN, S.L., ed. 1978. Quality Assurance Practices for Health Laboratories. American Public Health Assoc., Washington, D.C.

6. Bibliography

NATIONAL COMMITTEE ON RADIATION PROTECTION. 1964. Safe Handling of Radioactive Materials. National Bur. Standards Handbook 92, U.S. Government Printing Off., Washington, D.C.

NATIONAL COUNCIL ON RADIATION PROTECTION AND MEASUREMENTS. 1976. Radiation Protection for Medical and Allied Health Personnel. Rep. No. 48, National Council Radiation Protection & Measurements, Washington, D.C.

WALTERS, D. B., ed. 1980. Safe Handling of Chemical Carcinogens, Mutagens, Teratogens and Highly Toxic Substances, Vols. 1 and 2. Ann Arbor Science, Ann Arbor, Mich.

FUSCALDO, A.A., B.J. ERLICK & B. HINDMAN. 1980. Laboratory Safety, Theory and Practice. Academic Press, New York, N.Y.

NATIONAL COUNCIL ON RADIATION PROTECTION AND MEASUREMENTS. 1987. Recommendations on Limits for Exposure to Ionizing Radiation. Rep. No. 91, National Council Radiation Protection & Measurements, Washington, D.C.

1090 D.   Hazard Management Practices

1. Monitoring

The establishment of policies, practices, procedures, and methods to prevent exposure of laboratory personnel to hazardous materials is only part of an effective safety program. Simultaneous establishment of a monitoring or feedback system is essential to insure that the protective features actually work.

a. Chemical monitors: Devices capable of direct measurement of concentration in a person's breathing zone have been described.[1] Use either active devices requiring a pump to pull air across the cell or passive monitors that rely on diffusion. These devices can measure inorganic as well as organic compounds with the appropriate sorbent. Particulates can be collected on a filter using an active device. A detailed discussion of the development and use of personal monitors for measuring exposure to chemical pollutants in the environment is available.[1]

b. Biohazard monitors: These are an essential part of microbiological monitoring. Include a pre-employment physical examination accompanied by hematological-serological and other tests related to exposure. Provide for subsequent annual examinations consisting of serological tests, biochemical function studies, and chest X-rays. Vaccination and other prophylactic measures are required. Archive serum specimens for future reference as necessary. Continual enforcement of basic laboratory safety rules completes the monitoring program.

c. Radiochemical monitors: These include wipes, portable survey instruments, and air samples. Multiple monitors usually are required. Measure external radiation exposure with personnel dosimeters, preferably the film dosimeter for measuring accumulated radiation over a period of time. Pocket ionization chambers, thermoluminescent dosimeters, and thimble chambers can be used to supplement the film dosimeter.

Whole body or gamma spectrometry radiation detectors determine the presence of radioactive substances in the body, but these instruments are expensive and require specialized training. Body waste also can be monitored for radionuclides.

In addition to personnel monitoring, carry out general area monitoring. Analyze all equipment and supplies that have been in contact with radioactive substances. Use dosimetric and wipe tests. Thin-windowed GM-counters are suitable for wipe samples and for monitoring skin and clothing. An alpha scintillation monitor is needed to detect alpha emitters. Steere[2] presents an excellent discussion of monitoring techniques for radioisotopes.

2. Disposal of Wastes

a. General considerations: Stringent requirements exist for the disposal of wastes involving potential criminal and civil liability on both organizations and individuals. Specifics vary by state and local area and are subject to change. Licenses and/or permits may be required; consult local and state authorities.

A plan for the safe disposal of chemical and biological substances used in the laboratory is important and should be discussed with the laboratory supervisor and, if appropriate, with the safety coordinator. Gaston[3] has discussed the care, handling, and disposal of dangerous chemicals. Install convenient collection systems, use properly labeled containers, provide fire-protected storage, and provide a special separate storage area for hazardous or highly toxic materials. Use metal safety cans for storing waste solvents and segregating incompatible materials. Consider using special containers for extremely

hazardous or highly toxic wastes and special packing procedures to avoid breakage or damage to the container in transportation. Store incompatible hazardous materials separately.[4]

b. Waste disposal methods include incineration, burial, evaporation, neutralization, chemical reaction, special treatments, and use of commercial disposal specialists. Safety information including the method of choice for waste disposal of specific inorganic and organic compounds is presented in a series of Material Safety Data Sheets (MSDSs).[5]

Sometimes it may be permissible to dispose of some hazardous chemicals down the drain at certain concentrations but only with written permission of the local wastewater authority on a chemical-by-chemical basis.

1) Chemical wastes—Used solvents can be distilled and recovered for reuse. Noncombustible solvents can be evaporated if vapors do not create an environmental problem. Small quantities of flammable solvents and chemicals can be burned on the ground, in shallow metal containers, or in incinerators, provided that this does not violate air regulations. Neutralize acidic and basic materials before final disposal. Many soluble, nontoxic materials can be diluted carefully into a sewer system if it is certain that they will not harm the plumbing system or environment. Whenever possible, convert hazardous materials by chemical reaction or other processes to innocuous compounds before disposal. If this is not feasible, engage a commercial disposal specialist to dispose of hazardous or highly toxic materials off the premises. Dispose of nonreturnable gas cylinders with the help of qualified personnel only.

2) Biological wastes—Sterilize all infectious or toxic substances, and all contaminated equipment or apparatus before washing, storage, or disposal.[6] Autoclaving is the sterilization method of choice. Generally, heat in an autoclave under a pres-

sure of 103 kPa to achieve a chamber temperature of at least 121°C for a minimum of 15 min. Measure time after the material being sterilized reaches 121°C. If materials are to be autoclaved in plastic bags, add water to the contents to insure wet heat. Dry heat and chemical treatment also have been used for sterilizing nonplastic items. After sterilization, the wastes can be handled safely by conventional disposal systems. Collect contaminated combustible wastes and animal carcasses in impermeable containers for disposal by incineration.

3) Radiochemical wastes—Generalized disposal criteria for radioactive wastes have been developed by the National Committee on Radiation Protection and Measurements.[7] These recommendations have been given official status by publication in the Federal Register.[8] Two general philosophies govern the disposal of radioactive wastes: (a) dilution and dispersion to reduce the concentration of radionuclide by carrier dilution or dilution in a receiving medium and (b) concentration and confinement, usually involving reduction in waste volume with subsequent storage for decay purposes.

Airborne wastes can be treated by either method. Ventilation includes discharge from hooded operations to the atmosphere. Typical radioactive gases include iodine, krypton, and xenon. Iodine can be removed by scrubbing or by reaction with silver nitrate. Noble gases can be removed by adsorption; standard techniques can be used for particulates. Dilution methods are suitable for liquids with low activity. Intermediate levels may be treated by various physical-chemical processes to separate the waste into a nonradioactive portion that can be disposed of by dilution and a high-activity portion to be stored. Solid wastes may consist of equipment, glassware, and other materials. When possible, decontaminate these materials and reuse. Decontamination usually results in a liquid waste.

Combustible materials that cannot be decontaminated often are burned with special precautions; permits for burning may be required. Use storage for decay or permanent storage for treating radioactive wastes when alternatives are not available.

4) Other special wastes—Federal regulations concerned with polychlorinated biphenyls (PCBs), dioxins, and asbestos require special attention for wastes containing these materials.

3. References

1. Proceedings of the Symposium on the Development and Usage of Personal Monitors for Exposure and Health Effect Studies, June 1979. Publ. EPA-600/9-79-032, U.S. Environmental Protection Agency, Washington, D.C.

2. STEERE, N.V., ed. 1971. Handbook of Laboratory Safety, 2nd ed. Chemical Rubber Co., Cleveland, Ohio.

3. GASTON, P. J. 1970. The Care, Handling, and Disposal of Dangerous Chemicals. Inst. of Science Technology, Northern Publishers (Aberdeen) Ltd., Aberdeen, Scotland.

4. U.S. ENVIRONMENTAL PROTECTION AGENCY. 1980. Hazardous waste compatibility chart. Publ. No. EPA-600/2-80-076, Cincinnati, Ohio.

5. Chemical Safety Data Sheets. Manufacturing Chemists' Assoc., Inc., Washington, D.C.

6. NATIONAL INSTITUTES OF HEALTH. 1974. Biohazard Safety Guide. GPO Stock No. 1740-00383, U.S. Dep. Health, Education & Welfare, Public Health Service, National Inst. Health, Washington, D.C.

7. U.S. ENVIRONMENTAL PROTECTION AGENCY. 1985. Environmental Standards for the Management and Disposal of Spent Nuclear Fuel, High-Level and Transuranic Wastes. 40 CFR Part 191.

8. U.S. ENVIRONMENTAL PROTECTION AGENCY. 1988. Environmental Standards for the Management, Storage and Land Disposal of Low-Level Radioactive Waste. Proposed Rule. 40 CFR Part 193.

4. Bibliography

GHASSEMI, M., S. QUINLIVAN, G. GRUBER & H. CASEY. 1976. Disposing of Small Batches of Hazardous Wastes. Publ. SW 562, Office of

Solid Waste, U.S. Environmental Protection Agency, Cincinnati, Ohio.

BORDNER, R. H., J.A. WINTER & P.V. SCARPINO, eds. 1978. Microbiological Methods for Monitoring the Environment, Water and Wastes. Publ. EPA-600/8-78-017, Environmental Monitoring and Support Lab., U.S. Environ-

mental Protection Agency, Cincinnati, Ohio.

NATIONAL ACADEMY OF SCIENCES, NATIONAL ACADEMY OF ENGINEERING & INSTITUTE OF MEDICINE. 1983. Prudent Practices for the Disposal of Chemicals from Laboratories. National Academy Press, Washington, D.C.

PART 2000

PHYSICAL

AND AGGREGATE

PROPERTIES

2010 INTRODUCTION

This part deals primarily with measurement of the physical properties of a sample, as distinguished from the concentrations of chemical or biological components. Many of the determinations included here, such as color, electrical conductivity, and turbidity, fit this category unequivocally. However, physical properties cannot be divorced entirely from chemical composition, and some of the techniques of this part measure aggregate properties resulting from the presence of a number of constituents. Others, for example, calcium carbonate saturation, are related to, or depend on, chemical tests. Also included here are tests for appearance, odor, and taste, which have been classified traditionally among physical properties, although the point could be argued. Finally, Section 2710, Tests on Sludges, includes certain biochemical tests. However, for convenience they are grouped with the other tests used for sludge.

With these minor exceptions, the contents of this part have been kept reasonably faithful to its name. Most of the methods included are either inherently or at least traditionally physical, as distinguished from the explicitly chemical, radiological, biological, or bacteriological methods of other parts.

2020 QUALITY CONTROL

Part 2000 contains a variety of analytical methods, many of which are not amenable to standard quality-control techniques. General information on quality control is provided in Part 1000 and specific quality-control techniques are outlined in the individual methods. The following general guidelines may be applied to many of the methods in this part:

Evaluate analyst performance for each method. Determine competence by analyses of samples containing known concentrations.

Calibrate instruments and ensure that instrument measurements do not drift.

Assess the precision of analytical procedures by analyzing at least 10% of samples in duplicate. Analyze a minimum of one duplicate with each set of samples.

Determine bias of an analytical procedure in each sample batch by analysis of blanks, known additions with a frequency of at least 5% of samples, and, if possible, an externally provided standard.

2110 APPEARANCE*

To record the general physical appearance of a sample, use any terms that briefly describe its visible characteristics. These terms may state the presence of color, turbidity, suspended solids, crustacea, larvae, worms, sediment, floating material, and similar particulate matter detectable by the unaided eye. Use numerical values when they are available, as for color, turbidity, and suspended solids.

---

*Approved by Standard Methods Committee, 1988.

2120 COLOR*

2120 A. Introduction

Color in water may result from the presence of natural metallic ions (iron and manganese), humus and peat materials, plankton, weeds, and industrial wastes. Color is removed to make a water suitable for general and industrial applications. Colored industrial wastewaters may require color removal before discharge into watercourses.

1. Definitions

The term "color" is used here to mean true color, that is, the color of water from which turbidity has been removed. The term "apparent color" includes not only color due to substances in solution, but also that due to suspended matter. Apparent color is determined on the original sample without filtration or centrifugation. In some highly colored industrial wastewaters color is contributed principally by colloidal or suspended material. In such cases both true color and apparent color should be determined.

2. Pretreatment for Turbidity Removal

To determine color by currently accepted methods, turbidity must be removed before analysis. The optimal method for removing turbidity without removing color has not been found yet. Filtration yields results that are reproducible from day to day and among laboratories. However, some filtration procedures also may remove

_____
*Approved by Standard Methods Committee, 1988.

some true color. Centrifugation avoids interaction of color with filter materials, but results vary with the sample nature and size and speed of the centrifuge. When sample dilution is necessary, whether it precedes or follows turbidity removal, it can alter the measured color if large color-bodies are present.

Acceptable pretreatment procedures are included with each method. State the pretreatment method when reporting results.

3. Selection of Method

The visual comparison method is applicable to nearly all samples of potable water. Pollution by certain industrial wastes may produce unusual colors that cannot be matched. In this case use an instrumental method. A modification of the tristimulus and the spectrophotometric methods allows calculation of a single color value representing uniform chromaticity differences even when the sample exhibits color significantly different from that of platinum cobalt standards. For comparison of color values among laboratories, calibrate the visual method by the instrumental procedures.

4. Bibliography

OPTICAL SOCIETY OF AMERICA. 1943. Committee Report. The concept of color. *J. Opt. Soc. Amer.* 33:544.
JONES, H. et al. 1952. The Science of Color. Thomas Y. Crowell Co., New York, N.Y.

2120 B. Visual Comparison Method

1. General Discussion

a. Principle: Color is determined by visual comparison of the sample with known concentrations of colored solutions. Comparison also may be made with special, properly calibrated glass color disks. The platinum-cobalt method of measuring color is the standard method, the unit of color being that produced by 1 mg platinum/L in the form of the chloroplatinate ion. The ratio of cobalt to platinum may be varied to match the hue in special cases; the proportion given below is usually satisfactory to match the color of natural waters.

b. Application: The platinum-cobalt method is useful for measuring color of potable water and of water in which color is due to naturally occurring materials. It is not applicable to most highly colored industrial wastewaters.

c. Interference: Even a slight turbidity causes the apparent color to be noticeably higher than the true color; therefore remove turbidity before approximating true color by differential reading with different color filters[1] or by differential scattering measurements.[2] Neither technique, however, has reached the status of a standard method. Remove turbidity by centrifugation or by the filtration procedure described under Method C. Centrifuge for 1 h unless it has been demonstrated that centrifugation under other conditions accomplishes satisfactory turbidity removal.

The color value of water is extremely pH-dependent and invariably increases as the pH of the water is raised. When reporting a color value, specify the pH at which color is determined. For research purposes or when color values are to be compared among laboratories, determine the color response of a given water over a wide range of pH values.[3]

d. Field method: Because the platinum-cobalt standard method is not convenient for field use, compare water color with that of glass disks held at the end of metallic tubes containing glass comparator tubes filled with sample and colorless distilled water. Match sample color with the color of the tube of clear water plus the calibrated colored glass when viewed by looking toward a white surface. Calibrate each disk to correspond with the colors on the plat-

inum-cobalt scale. The glass disks give results in substantial agreement with those obtained by the platinum-cobalt method and their use is recognized as a standard field procedure.

e. Nonstandard laboratory methods: Using glass disks or liquids other than water as standards for laboratory work is permissible only if these have been individually calibrated against platinum-cobalt standards. Waters of highly unusual color, such as those that may occur by mixture with certain industrial wastes, may have hues so far removed from those of the platinum-cobalt standards that comparison by the standard method is difficult or impossible. For such waters, use the methods in Sections 2120C and D. However, results so obtained are not directly comparable to those obtained with platinum-cobalt standards.

f. Sampling: Collect representative samples in clean glassware. Make the color determination within a reasonable period because biological or physical changes occurring in storage may affect color. With naturally colored waters these changes invariably lead to poor results.

2. Apparatus

a. Nessler tubes, matched, 50-mL, tall form.

b. pH meter, for determining sample pH (see Section 4500-H⁺).

3. Preparation of Standards

a. If a reliable supply of potassium chloroplatinate cannot be purchased, use chloroplatinic acid prepared from metallic platinum. Do not use commercial chloroplatinic acid because it is very hygroscopic and may vary in platinum content. Potassium chloroplatinate is not hygroscopic.

b. Dissolve 1.246 g potassium chloroplatinate, K_2PtCl_6 (equivalent to 500 mg metallic Pt) and 1.00 g crystallized cobaltous chloride, $CoCl_2 \cdot 6H_2O$ (equivalent to about 250 mg metallic Co) in distilled water with 100 mL conc HCl and dilute to 1000 mL with distilled water. This stock standard has a color of 500 units.

c. If K_2PtCl_6 is not available, dissolve 500 mg pure metallic Pt in aqua regia with the aid of heat; remove HNO_3 by repeated evaporation with fresh portions of conc HCl. Dissolve this product, together with 1.00 g crystallized $CoCl_2 \cdot 6H_2O$, as directed above.

d. Prepare standards having colors of 5, 10, 15, 20, 25, 30, 35, 40, 45, 50, 60, and 70 by diluting 0.5, 1.0, 1.5, 2.0, 2.5, 3.0, 3.5, 4.0, 4.5, 5.0, 6.0, and 7.0 mL stock color standard with distilled water to 50 mL in nessler tubes. Protect these standards against evaporation and contamination when not in use.

4. Procedure

a. *Estimation of intact sample:* Observe sample color by filling a matched nessler tube to the 50-mL mark with sample and comparing it with standards. Look vertically downward through tubes toward a white or specular surface placed at such an angle that light is reflected upward through the columns of liquid. If turbidity is present and has not been removed, report as "apparent color." If the color exceeds 70 units, dilute sample with distilled water in known proportions until the color is within the range of the standards.

b. Measure pH of each sample.

5. Calculation

a. Calculate color units by the following equation:

$$\text{Color units} = \frac{A \times 50}{B}$$

where:

A = estimated color of a diluted sample and
B = mL sample taken for dilution.

b. Report color results in whole numbers and record as follows:

Color Units	Record to Nearest
1–50	1
51–100	5
101–250	10
251–500	20

c. Report sample pH.

6. References

1. KNIGHT, A.G. 1951. The photometric estimation of color in turbid waters. *J. Inst. Water Eng.* 5:623.
2. JULLANDER, I. & K. BRUNE. 1950. Light absorption measurements on turbid solutions. *Acta Chem. Scand.* 4:870.
3. BLACK, A.P. & R.F. CHRISTMAN. 1963. Characteristics of colored surface waters. *J. Amer. Water Works Assoc.* 55:753.

7. Bibliography

HAZEN, A. 1892. A new color standard for natural waters. *Amer. Chem. J.* 14:300.
HAZEN, A. 1896. The measurement of the colors of natural waters. *J. Amer. Chem. Soc.* 18:264.
Measurement of Color and Turbidity in Water. 1902. U.S. Geol. Surv., Div. Hydrog. Circ. 8, Washington, D.C.
RUDOLFS, W. & W.D. HANLON. 1951. Color in industrial wastes. *Sewage Ind. Wastes* 23:1125.
PALIN, A.T. 1955. Photometric determination of the colour and turbidity of water. *Water Water Eng.* 59:341.
CHRISTMAN, R.F. & M. GHASSEMI. 1966. Chemical nature of organic color in water. *J. Amer. Water Works Assoc.* 58:723.
GHASSEMI, M. & R.F. CHRISTMAN. 1968. Properties of the yellow organic acids of natural waters. *Limnol. Oceanogr.* 13:583.

2120 C.   Spectrophotometric Method

1. General Discussion

a. Principle: The color of a filtered sample is expressed in terms that describe the sensation realized when viewing the sample. The hue (red, green, yellow, etc.) is designated by the term "dominant wavelength," the degree of brightness by "luminance," and the saturation (pale, pastel, etc.) by "purity." These values are best determined from the light transmission characteristics of the filtered sample by means of a spectrophotometer.

b. Application: This method is applicable to potable and surface waters and to wastewaters, both domestic and industrial.

c. Interference: Turbidity interferes. Remove by the filtration method described below.

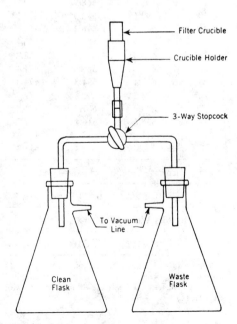

Figure 2120:1. Filtration system for color determinations.

2. Apparatus

a. Spectrophotometer, having 10-mm absorption cells, a narrow (10-nm or less) spectral band, and an effective operating range from 400 to 700 nm.

b. Filtration system, consisting of the following (see Figure 2120:1):

1) *Filtration flasks,* 250-mL, with side tubes.

2) *Walter crucible holder.*

3) *Micrometallic filter crucible,* average pore size 40 μm.

4) *Calcined filter aid.* *

5) *Vacuum system.*

3. Procedure

a. Preparation of sample: Bring two 50-mL samples to room temperature. Use one sample at the original pH; adjust pH of the other to 7.6 by using sulfuric acid (H_2SO_4) and sodium hydroxide (NaOH) of such concentrations that the resulting volume change does not exceed 3%. A standard pH is necessary because of the variation of color with pH. Remove excessive quantities of suspended materials by centrifuging. Treat each sample separately, as follows:

Thoroughly mix 0.1 g filter aid in a 10-mL portion of centrifuged sample and filter to form a precoat in the filter crucible. Direct filtrate to waste flask as indicated in Figure 2120:1. Mix 40 mg filter aid in a 35-mL portion of centrifuged sample. With vacuum still on, filter through the precoat and pass filtrate to waste flask until clear; then direct clear-filtrate flow to clean flask by means of the three-way stopcock and collect 25 mL for the transmittance determination.

b. Determination of light transmission characteristics: Thoroughly clean 1-cm absorption cells with detergent and rinse with

In the figure labels: Filter Crucible, Crucible Holder, 3-Way Stopcock, To Vacuum Line, Clean Flask, Waste Flask

*Celite No. 505, Manville Corp., or equivalent.

distilled water. Rinse twice with filtered sample, clean external surfaces with lens paper, and fill cell with filtered sample.

Determine transmittance values (in percent) at each visible wavelength value presented in Table 2120:I, using the 10 ordinates marked with an asterisk for fairly accurate work and all 30 ordinates for increased accuracy. Set instrument to read 100% transmittance on the distilled water blank and make all determinations with a narrow spectral band.

4. Calculation

a. Tabulate transmittance values corresponding to wavelengths shown in Columns X, Y, and Z in Table 2120:I. Total each transmittance column and multiply totals by the appropriate factors (for 10 or 30 ordinates) shown at the bottom of the table, to obtain tristimulus values X, Y, and Z. The tristimulus value Y is *percent luminance*.

b. Calculate the trichromatic coefficients x and y from the tristimulus values X, Y, and Z by the following equations:

$$x = \frac{X}{X + Y + Z}$$

$$y = \frac{Y}{X + Y + Z}$$

Locate point (x, y) on one of the chromaticity diagrams in Figure 2120:2 and determine the dominant wavelength (in nanometers) and the purity (in percent) directly from the diagram.

Determine hue from the dominant-wavelength value, according to the ranges in Table 2120:II.

TABLE 2120:I. SELECTED ORDINATES FOR SPECTROPHOTOMETRIC COLOR DETERMINATIONS†

Ordinate No.	X	Y	Z
		Wavelength *nm*	
1	424.4	465.9	414.1
2*	435.5*	489.5*	422.2*
3	443.9	500.4	426.3
4	452.1	508.7	429.4
5*	461.2*	515.2*	432.0*
6	474.0	520.6	434.3
7	531.2	525.4	436.5
8*	544.3*	529.8*	438.6*
9	552.4	533.9	440.6
10	558.7	537.7	442.5
11*	564.1*	541.4*	444.4*
12	568.9	544.9	446.3
13	573.2	548.4	448.2
14*	577.4*	551.8*	450.1*
15	581.3	555.1	452.1
16	585.0	558.5	454.0
17*	588.7*	561.9*	455.9*
18	592.4	565.3	457.9
19	596.0	568.9	459.9
20*	599.6*	572.5*	462.0*
21	603.3	576.4	464.1
22	607.0	580.4	466.3
23*	610.9*	584.8*	468.7*
24	615.0	589.6	471.4
25	619.4	594.8	474.3
26*	624.2*	600.8*	477.7*
27	629.8	607.7	481.8
28	636.6	616.1	487.2
29*	645.9*	627.3*	495.2*
30	663.0	647.4	511.2

Factors When 30 Ordinates Used		
0.032 69	0.033 33	0.039 38

Factors When 10 Ordinates Used		
0.098 06	0.100 00	0.118 14

† Insert in each column the transmittance value (%) corresponding to the wavelength shown. Where limited accuracy is sufficient, use only the ordinates marked with an asterisk.

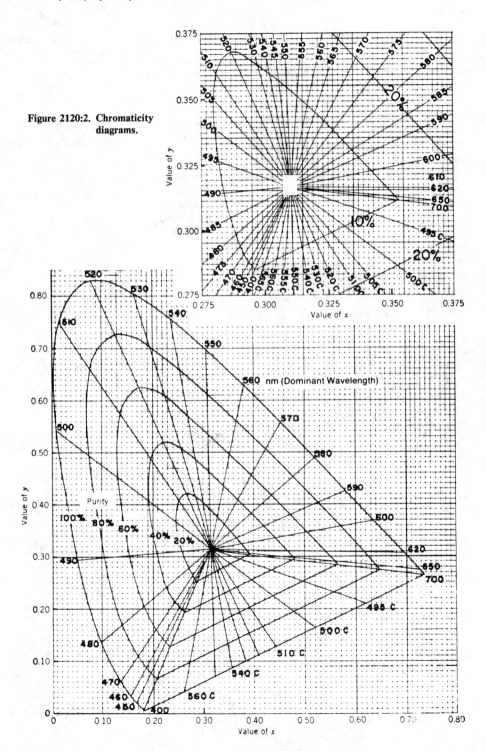

Figure 2120:2. Chromaticity diagrams.

5. Expression of Results

Express color characteristics (at pH 7.6 and at the original pH) in terms of *dominant wavelength* (nanometers, to the nearest unit), *hue* (e.g., blue, blue-green, etc.), *luminance* (percent, to the nearest tenth), and *purity* (percent, to the nearest unit). Report type of instrument (i.e., spectrophotometer), number of selected ordinates (10 or 30), and the spectral band width (nanometers) used.

6. Bibliography

HARDY, A.C. 1936. Handbook of Colorimetry. Technology Press, Boston, Mass.

TABLE 2120:II. COLOR HUES FOR DOMINANT WAVELENGTH RANGES

Wavelength Range nm	Hue
400–465	Violet
465–482	Blue
482–497	Blue-green
497–530	Green
530–575	Greenish yellow
575–580	Yellow
580–587	Yellowish orange
587–598	Orange
598–620	Orange-red
620–700	Red
400–530c*	Blue-purple
530c–700*	Red-purple

* See Figure 2120:2 for significance of "c".

2120 D. Tristimulus Filter Method

1. General Discussion

a. Principle: Three special tristimulus light filters, combined with a specific light source and photoelectric cell in a filter photometer, may be used to obtain color data suitable for routine control purposes.

The percentage of tristimulus light transmitted by the solution is determined for each of the three filters. The transmittance values then are converted to trichromatic coefficients and color characteristic values.

b. Application: This method is applicable to potable and surface waters and to wastewaters, both domestic and industrial. Except for most exacting work, this method gives results very similar to the more accurate Method C.

c. Interference: Turbidity must be removed.

2. Apparatus

*a. Filter photometer.**

b. Filter photometer light source: Tung-

sten lamp at a color temperature of 3000°C.†

c. Filter photometer photoelectric cells, 1 cm.‡

*d. Tristimulus filters.§

e. Filtration system: See Section 2120C.2b and Figure 2120:1.

3. Procedure

a. Preparation of sample: See Section 2120C.3a.

b. Determination of light transmission characteristics: Thoroughly clean (with detergent) and rinse 1-cm absorption cells with distilled water. Rinse each absorption cell twice with filtered sample, clean external surfaces with lens paper, and fill cell with filtered sample.

Place a distilled water blank in another cell and use it to set the instrument at 100%

---

*Fisher Electrophotometer or equivalent.

†General Electric lamp No. 1719 (at 6 V) or equivalent.
‡General Electric photovoltaic cell, Type PV-1, or equivalent.
§Corning CS-3-107 (No. 1), CS-4-98 (No. 2), and CS-5-70 (No. 3), or equivalent.

transmittance. Determine percentage of light transmission through sample for each of the three tristimulus light filters, with the filter photometer lamp intensity switch in a position equivalent to 4 V on the lamp.

4. Calculation

a. Determine luminance value directly as the percentage transmittance value obtained with the No. 2 tristimulus filter.

b. Calculate tristimulus values X, Y, and Z from the percentage transmittance (T_1, T_2, T_3) for filters No. 1, 2, 3, as follows:

$$X = T_3 \times 0.06 + T_1 \times 0.25$$
$$Y = T_2 \times 0.316$$
$$Z = T_3 \times 0.374$$

Calculate and determine trichromatic coefficients x and y, dominant wavelength, hue, and purity as in Section 2120C.4b above.

5. Expression of Results

Express results as prescribed in Section 2120C.5.

2120 E.   ADMI Tristimulus Filter Method (PROPOSED)

1. General Discussion

a. *Principle:* This method is an extension of Tristimulus Method 2120D. By this method a measure of the sample color, independent of hue, may be obtained. It is based on use of the Adams-Nickerson chromatic value formula[1] for calculating single number color difference values, i.e., uniform color differences. For example, if two colors, A and B, are judged visually to differ from colorless to the same degree, their ADMI color values will be the same. The modification was developed by members of the American Dye Manufacturers Institute (ADMI).[2]

b. *Application:* This method is applicable to colored waters and wastewaters having color characteristics significantly different from platinum-cobalt standards, as well as to waters and wastewaters similar in hue to the standards.

c. *Interference:* Turbidity must be removed.

2. Apparatus

a. *Filter photometer** equipped with CIE tristimulus filters (see 2120D.2d).

b. *Filter photometer light source:* Tungsten lamp at a color temperature of 3000°C (see 2120D.2b).

c. *Absorption cells and appropriate cell holders:* For color values less than 250 ADMI units, use cells with a 5.0-cm light path; for color values greater than 250, use cells with 1.0-cm light path.

d. *Filtration system:* See Section

---

*Fisher Electrocolorimeter, Model 181, or equivalent.

2120C.2b and Figure 2120:1; or a centrifuge capable of achieving 1000 × g. (See Section 2120B.)

3. Procedure

a. *Instrument calibration:* Establish curves for each photometer; calibration data for one instrument cannot be applied to another one. Prepare a separate calibration curve for each absorption cell path length.

1) Prepare standards as described in 2120B.3. For a 5-cm cell length prepare standards having color values of 25, 50, 100, 200, and 250 by diluting 5.0, 10.0, 20.0, 30.0, 40.0, and 50.0 mL stock color standard with distilled water to 100 mL in volumetric flasks. For the shorter path-length, prepare appropriate standards with higher color values.

2) Determine light transmittance (see ¶3c, below) for each standard with each filter.

3) Using the calculations described in ¶3d below, calculate the tristimulus values (X_s, Y_s, Z_s) for each standard, determine the Munsell values, and calculate the intermediate value (DE).

4) Using the DE values for each standard, calculate a calibration factor F_n for each standard from the following equation:

$$F_n = \frac{(APHA)_n (b)}{(DE)_n}$$

where:
$(APHA)_n$ = APHA color value for standard n,
$(DE)_n$ = intermediate value calculated for standard n, and
b = cell light path, cm.

Placing $(DE)_n$ on the X axis and F_n on the Y axis, plot a curve for the standard solutions. Use calibration curve to derive the F value from DE values obtained with samples.

b. *Sample preparation:* Prepare two 100-mL sample portions (one at the original pH, one at pH 7.6) as described in Section 2120C.3a, or by centrifugation. (NOTE: Centrifugation is acceptable only if turbidity removal equivalent to filtration is achieved.)

c. *Determination of light transmission characteristics:* Thoroughly clean absorption cells with detergent and rinse with distilled water. Rinse each absorption cell twice with filtered sample. Clean external surfaces with lens paper and fill cell with sample. Determine sample light transmittance with the three filters to obtain the transmittance values: T_1 from Filter 1, T_2 from Filter 2, and T_3 from Filter 3. Standardize the instrument with each filter at 100% transmittance with distilled water.

d. *Calculation of color values:* Tristimulus values for samples are X_s, Y_s, and Z_s; for standards X_r, Y_r, and Z_r; and for distilled water X_c, Y_c, and Z_c. Munsell values for samples are V_{xs}, V_{ys}, and V_{zs}; for standards V_{xr}, V_{yr}, and V_{zr}; and for distilled water V_{xc}, Y_{yc}, and V_{zc}.

For each standard or sample calculate the tristimulus values from the following equations:

$$X = (T_3 \times 0.1899) + (T_1 \times 0.791)$$
$$Y = T_2$$
$$Z = T_3 \times 1.1835$$

Tristimulus values for the distilled water blank used to standardize the instrument are always:

$$X_c = 98.09$$
$$Y_c = 100.0$$
$$Z_c = 118.35$$

Convert the six tristimulus values $(X_s, Y_s, Z_s, X_c, Y_c, Z_c)$ to the corresponding Munsell values using published tables 2, 3, 4† or by the equation given by Bridgeman.[3]

Calculate the intermediate value of DE from the equation:

---

†Instrumental Colour Systems, Ltd., 7 Bucklebury Place, Upper Woolhampton, Berkshire RG7 5UD, England.

$$DE = \{(0.23 \, \Delta V_y)^2 + [\Delta(V_x - V_y)]^2$$
$$+ [0.4 \, \Delta(V_y - V_z)]^2\}^{\frac{1}{2}}$$

where:

$$V_y = V_{ys} - V_{yc}$$
$$\Delta(V_x - V_y) = (V_{xs} - V_{ys}) - (V_{xc} - V_{yc})$$
$$\Delta(V_y - V_z) = (V_{ys} - V_{zs}) - (V_{yc} - V_{zc})$$

when the sample is compared to distilled water.

With the standard calibration curve, use the DE value to determine the calibration factor F.

Calculate the final ADMI color value as follows:

$$\text{ADMI value} = \frac{(F)(DE)}{b}$$

where:

b = absorption cell light path, cm.

Report ADMI color values at pH 7.6 and at the original pH.

4. Alternate Method

The ADMI color value also may be determined spectrophotometrically, using a spectrophotometer with a narrow (10-nm or less) spectral band and an effective operating range of 400 to 700 nm. This method is an extension of 2120C. Tristimulus values may be calculated from transmittance measurements, preferably by using the weighted ordinate method or by the selected ordinate method. The method has been described by Allen et al.,[2] who include work sheets and worked examples.

5. References

1. McLaren, K. 1970. The Adams-Nickerson colour-difference formula. *J. Soc. Dyers Colorists* 86:354.
2. Allen, W., W.B. Prescott, R.E. Derby, C.E. Garland, J.M. Peret & M. Saltzman. 1973. Determination of color of water and wastewater by means of ADMI color values. *Proc. 28th Ind. Waste Conf.*, Purdue Univ., Eng. Ext. Ser. No. 142:661.
3. Bridgeman, T. 1963. Inversion of the Munsell value equation. *J. Opt. Soc. Amer.* 53:499.

6. Bibliography

Judd, D.B. & G. Wyszecki. 1963. Color in Business, Science, and Industry, 2nd ed. John Wiley & Sons, New York, N.Y. (See Tables A, B, and C in Appendix.)
Wyszecki, G. & W.S. Stiles. 1967. Color Science. John Wiley & Sons, New York, N.Y. (See Tables 6.4, A, B, C, pp. 462-467.)

2130   TURBIDITY*

2130 A.   Introduction

1. Sources and Significance

Clarity of water is important in producing products destined for human consumption and in many manufacturing uses. Beverage producers, food processors, and treatment plants drawing on a surface water supply commonly rely on coagulation, settling, and filtration to insure an acceptable product. The clarity of a natural

*Approved by Standard Methods Committee, 1988.

body of water is a major determinant of the condition and productivity of that system.

Turbidity in water is caused by suspended matter, such as clay, silt, finely divided organic and inorganic matter, soluble colored organic compounds, and plankton and other microscopic organisms. Turbidity is an expression of the optical property that causes light to be scattered and absorbed rather than transmitted in straight lines through the sample. Correlation of turbidity with the weight concentration of suspended matter is difficult because the size, shape, and refractive index of the particulates also affect the light-scattering properties of the suspension. Optically black particles, such as those of activated carbon, may absorb light and effectively increase turbidity measurements.

2. Selection of Method

Historically, the standard method for determination of turbidity has been based on the Jackson candle turbidimeter[1]; however, the lowest turbidity value that can be measured directly on this instrument is 25 units. Because turbidities of treated water usually fall within the range of 0 to 1 unit, indirect secondary methods also were developed to estimate turbidity. Unfortunately, no instrument could duplicate the results obtained on the Jackson candle turbidimeter for all samples. Because of fundamental differences in optical systems, the results obtained with different types of secondary instruments frequently do not check closely with one another, even though the instruments are precalibrated against the candle turbidimeter.

Most commercial turbidimeters available for measuring low turbidities give comparatively good indications of the intensity of light scattered in one particular direction, predominantly at right angles to the incident light. These nephelometers are unaffected relatively by small changes in

design parameters and therefore are specified as the standard instrument for measurement of low turbidities. Nonstandard turbidimeters, such as forward-scattering devices, are more sensitive than nephelometers to the presence of larger particles and are useful for process monitoring.

A further cause of discrepancies in turbidity analysis is the use of suspensions of different types of particulate matter for the preparation of instrumental calibration curves. Like water samples, prepared suspensions have different optical properties depending on the particle size distributions, shapes, and refractive indices. A standard reference suspension having reproducible light-scattering properties is specified for nephelometer calibration.

Because there is no direct relationship between the intensity of light scattered at a 90° angle and Jackson candle turbidity, there is no valid basis for the practice of calibrating a nephelometer in terms of candle units. To avoid misinterpretation, report the results from nephelometric measurements as nephelometric turbidity units (NTU).

Its precision, sensitivity, and applicability over a wide turbidity range make the nephelometric method preferable to visual methods. The Jackson candle method has been eliminated from this edition of *Standard Methods.*

3. Storage of Sample

Determine turbidity on the day the sample is taken. If longer storage is unavoidable, store samples in the dark for up to 24 h. Do not store for long periods because irreversible changes in turbidity may occur. Vigorously shake all samples before examination.

4. References

1. AMERICAN PUBLIC HEALTH ASSOCIATION, AMERICAN WATER WORKS ASSOCIATION &

WATER POLLUTION CONTROL FEDERATION. 1985. Standard Methods for the Examination of Water and Wastewater, 16th ed. American Public Health Assoc., Washington, D.C.

2130 B. Nephelometric Method

1. General Discussion

a. Principle: This method is based on a comparison of the intensity of light scattered by the sample under defined conditions with the intensity of light scattered by a standard reference suspension under the same conditions. The higher the intensity of scattered light, the higher the turbidity. Formazin polymer is used as the reference turbidity standard suspension. It is easy to prepare and is more reproducible in its light-scattering properties than clay or turbid natural water. The turbidity of a specified concentration of formazin suspension is defined as 40 nephelometric units. This suspension has an approximate turbidity of 40 Jackson units when measured on the candle turbidimeter; therefore, nephelometric turbidity units based on the formazin preparation will approximate units derived from the candle turbidimeter but will not be identical to them.

b. Interference: Turbidity can be determined for any water sample that is free of debris and rapidly settling coarse sediments. Dirty glassware, the presence of air bubbles, and the effects of vibrations that disturb the surface visibility of the sample will give false results. "True color," that is, water color due to dissolved substances that absorb light, causes measured turbidities to be low. This effect usually is not significant in the case of treated water.

2. Apparatus

a. Turbidimeter consisting of a nephelometer with a light source for illuminating the sample and one or more photoelectric detectors with a readout device to indicate intensity of light scattered at 90° to the path of incident light. Use a turbidimeter designed so that little stray light reaches the detector in the absence of turbidity and free from significant drift after a short warmup period. The sensitivity of the instrument should permit detecting turbidity differences of 0.02 NTU or less in waters having turbidity of less than 1 NTU with a range from 0 to 40 NTU. Several ranges are necessary to obtain both adequate coverage and sufficient sensitivity for low turbidities.

Differences in turbidimeter design will cause differences in measured values for turbidity even though the same suspension is used for calibration. To minimize such differences, observe the following design criteria:

1) Light source—Tungsten-filament lamp operated at a color temperature between 2200 and 3000°K.

2) Distance traversed by incident light and scattered light within the sample tube—Total not to exceed 10 cm.

3) Angle of light acceptance by detector—Centered at 90° to the incident light path and not to exceed ± 30° from 90°. The detector, and filter system if used, shall have a spectral peak response between 400 and 600 nm.

b. Sample tubes, clear colorless glass. Keep tubes scrupulously clean, both inside and out, and discard when they become scratched or etched. Never handle them where the light strikes them. Use tubes with sufficient extra length, or with a protective case, so that they may be handled properly. Fill tubes with samples and standards that have been agitated thoroughly and allow sufficient time for bubbles to escape.

3. Reagents

a. Turbidity-free water: Turbidity-free water is difficult to obtain. The following method is satisfactory for measuring turbidity as low as 0.02 NTU.

Pass distilled water through a membrane filter having precision-sized holes of 0.2 μm;* the usual membrane filter used for bacteriological examinations is not satisfactory. Rinse collecting flask at least twice with filtered water and discard the next 200 mL.

Some commercial bottled demineralized waters are nearly particle-free. These may be used when their turbidity is lower than can be achieved in the laboratory. Dilute samples to a turbidity not less than 1 with distilled water.

b. Stock turbidity suspension:

1) Solution I—Dissolve 1.000 g hydrazine sulfate (CAUTION: *Carcinogen; avoid inhalation, ingestion, and skin contact.*), $(NH_2)_2 \cdot H_2SO_4$, in distilled water and dilute to 100 mL in a volumetric flask.

2) Solution II—Dissolve 10.00 g hexamethylenetetramine, $(CH_2)_6N_4$, in distilled water and dilute to 100 mL in a volumetric flask.

3) In a 100-mL volumetric flask, mix 5.0 mL Solution I and 5.0 mL Solution II. Let stand 24 h at 25 $\pm$ 3°C, dilute to mark, and mix. The turbidity of this suspension is 400 NTU.

4) Prepare solutions and suspensions monthly.

c. Standard turbidity suspension: Dilute 10.00 mL stock turbidity suspension to 100 mL with turbidity-free water. Prepare daily. The turbidity of this suspension is defined as 40 NTU.

d. Alternate standards: As an alternative to preparing and diluting formazin, use commercially available standards such as styrene divinylbenzene beads† if they are

*Nuclepore Corporation, 7035 Commerce Circle, Pleasanton, Calif., or equivalent.
†AMCO-AEPA-1 Standard, Advanced Polymer Systems, 3696 C Haven Ave., Redwood City, Calif.

demonstrated to be equivalent to freshly prepared formazin.

e. Dilute turbidity standards: Dilute portions of standard turbidity suspension with turbidity-free water as required. Prepare daily.

4. Procedure

a. Turbidimeter calibration: Follow the manufacturer's operating instructions. In the absence of a precalibrated scale, prepare calibration curves for each range of the instrument. Check accuracy of any supplied calibration scales on a precalibrated instrument by using appropriate standards. Run at least one standard in each instrument range to be used. Make certain that turbidimeter gives stable readings in all sensitivity ranges used. High turbidities determined by direct measurement are likely to differ appreciably from those determined by the dilution technique, ¶ 4c.

b. Measurement of turbidities less than 40 NTU: Thoroughly shake sample. Wait until air bubbles disappear and pour sample into turbidimeter tube. When possible, pour shaken sample into turbidimeter tube and immerse it in an ultrasonic bath for 1 to 2 s, causing complete bubble release. Read turbidity directly from instrument scale or from appropriate calibration curve.

c. Measurement of turbidities above 40 NTU: Dilute sample with one or more volumes of turbidity-free water until turbidity falls between 30 and 40 NTU. Compute turbidity of original sample from turbidity of diluted sample and the dilution factor. For example, if five volumes of turbidity-free water were added to one volume of sample and the diluted sample showed a turbidity of 30 NTU, then the turbidity of the original sample was 180 NTU.

d. Calibrate continuous turbidity monitors for low turbidities by determining turbidity of the water entering or leaving them, using a laboratory-model turbidimeter. When this is not possible, use an appropriate dilute turbidity standard, ¶ 3e. For turbidities above 40 NTU use undiluted stock solution.

5. Calculation

Nephelometric turbidity units (NTU)

$$= \frac{A \times (B + C)}{C}$$

where:

A = NTU found in diluted sample,
B = volume of dilution water, mL, and
C = sample volume taken for dilution, mL.

6. Interpretation of Results

a. Report turbidity readings as follows:

Turbidity Range NTU	Report to the Nearest NTU
0–1.0	0.05
1–10	0.1
10–40	1
40–100	5
100–400	10
400–1000	50
> 1000	100

b. For comparison of water treatment efficiencies estimate turbidity more closely than is specified above. Uncertainties and discrepancies in turbidity measurements make it unlikely that two or more laboratories will duplicate results on the same sample more closely than specified.

7. Bibliography

WHIPPLE, G.C. & D.D. JACKSON. 1900. A comparative study of the methods used for the measurement of turbidity of water. *Mass. Inst. Technol. Quart.* 13:274.

AMERICAN PUBLIC HEALTH ASSOCIATION. 1901. Report of Committee on Standard Methods of Water Analysis. *Pub. Health Papers & Rep.* 27:377.

WELLS, P.V. 1922. Turbidimetry of water. *J. Amer. Water Works Assoc.* 9:488.

BAYLIS, J.R. 1926. Turbidimeter for accurate measurement of low turbidities. *Ind. Eng. Chem.* 18:311.

WELLS, P.V. 1927. The present status of turbidity measurements. *Chem. Rev.* 3:331.

BAYLIS, J.R. 1933. Turbidity determinations. *Water Works Sewage* 80:125.

ROSE, H.E. & H.B. LLOYD. 1946. On the measurement of the size characteristics of powders by photo-extinction methods. *J. Soc. Chem. Ind.* (London) 65:52 (Feb.); 65:55 (Mar.).

ROSE, H.E. & C.C.J. FRENCH. 1948. On the extinction coefficient: Particle size relationship for fine mineral powders. *J. Soc. Chem. Ind.* (London) 67:283.

GILLETT, T.R., P.F. MEADS & A.L. HOLVEN. 1949. Measuring color and turbidity of white sugar solutions. *Anal. Chem.* 21:1228.

JULLANDER, I. 1949. A simple method for the measurement of turbidity. *Acta Chem. Scand.* 3:1309.

ROSE, H.E. 1950. Powder-size measurement by a combination of the methods of nephelometry and photo-extinction. *J. Soc. Chem. Ind.* (London) 69:266.

ROSE, H.E. 1950. The design and use of photoextinction sedimentometers. *Engineering* 169:350, 405.

BRICE, B.A., M. HALWER & R. SPEISER. 1950. Photoelectric light-scattering photometer for determining high molecular weights. *J. Opt. Soc. Amer.* 40:768.

KNIGHT, A.G. 1950. The measurement of turbidity in water. *J. Inst. Water Eng.* 4:449.

HANYA, T. 1950. Study of suspended matter in water. *Bull. Chem. Soc. Jap.* 23:216.

JULLANDER, I. 1950. Turbidimetric investigations on viscose. *Svensk Papperstidn.* 22:1.

ROSE, H.E. 1951. A reproducible standard for the calibration of turbidimeters. *J. Inst. Water Eng.* 5:310.

AITKEN, R.W. & D. MERCER. 1951. Comment on "The measurement of turbidity in water." *J. Inst. Water Eng.* 5:328.

ROSE, H.E. 1951. The analysis of water by the assessment of turbidity. *J. Inst. Water Eng.* 5:521.

KNIGHT, A.G. 1951. The measurement of turbidity in water: A reply. *J. Inst. Water Eng.* 5:633.

STAATS, F.C. 1952. Measurement of color, turbidity, hardness and silica in industrial waters. Preprint 156, American Soc. Testing & Materials, Philadelphia, Pa.

PALIN, A.T. 1955. Photometric determination of the colour and turbidity of water. *Water Water Eng.* 59:341.

SLOAN, C.K. 1955. Angular dependence light scattering studies of the aging of precipitates. *J. Phys. Chem.* 59:834.

CONLEY, W.R. & R.W. PITMAN. 1957. Microphotometer turbidity analysis. *J. Amer. Water Works Assoc.* 49:63.

PACKHAM, R.F. 1962. The preparation of turbidity standards. *Proc. Soc. Water Treat. Exam.* 11:64.

BAALSRUD, K. & A. HENRIKSEN. 1964. Measurement of suspended matter in stream water. *J. Amer. Water Works Assoc.* 56:1194.

HOATHER, R.C. 1964. Comparison of different methods for measurement of turbidity. *Proc. Soc. Water Treat. Exam.* 13:89.

EDEN, G.E. 1965. The measurement of turbidity in water. A progress report on the work of the analytical panel. *Proc. Soc. Water Treat. Exam.* 14:27.

BLACK, A.P. & S.A. HANNAH. 1965. Measurement of low turbidities. *J. Amer. Water Works Assoc.* 57:901.

HANNAH, S.A., J.M. COHEN & G.G. ROBECK. 1967. Control techniques for coagulation-filtration. *J. Amer. Water Works Assoc.* 59:1149.

REBHUN, M. & H.S. SPERBER. 1967. Optical properties of diluted clay suspensions. *J. Colloid Interface Sci.* 24:131.

DANIELS, S.L. 1969. The utility of optical parameters in evaluation of processes of flocculation and sedimentation. *Chem. Eng. Progr. Symp. Ser.* No. 97, 65:171.

LIVESEY, P.J. & F.W. BILLMEYER, JR. 1969. Particle-size determination by low-angle light scattering: new instrumentation and a rapid method of interpreting data. *J. Colloid Interface Sci.* 30:447.

OSTENDORF, R.G. & J.F. BYRD. 1969. Modern monitoring of a treated industrial effluent. *J. Water Pollut. Control Fed.* 41:89.

EICHNER, D.W. & C.C. HACH. 1971. How clear is clear water? *Water Sewage Works* 118:299.

HACH, C.C. 1972. Understanding turbidity measurement. *Ind. Water Eng.* 9(2):18.

SIMMS, R.J. 1972. Industrial turbidity measurement. *ISA (Instrum. Soc. Amer.) Trans.* 11(2):146.

TALLEY, D.G., J.A. JOHNSON & J.E. PILZER. 1972. Continuous turbidity monitoring. *J. Amer. Water Works Assoc.* 64:184.

2150   ODOR*

2150 A.   Introduction

1. Discussion

Odor, like taste, depends on contact of a stimulating substance with the appropriate human receptor cell. The stimuli are chemical in nature and the term "chemical senses" often is applied to odor and taste. Water is a neutral medium, always present on or at the membranes that perceive sensory response. In its pure form, water cannot produce odor or taste sensations. No satisfactory theory of olfaction ever has been devised, although many have been formulated. Man and animals can avoid many potentially toxic foods and waters because of adverse sensory response. Without this form of primitive sensory protection many species would not have survived. Today, these same senses often provide the first warning of potential hazards in the environment.

Odor is recognized[1] as a quality factor affecting acceptability of drinking water (and foods prepared with it), tainting of fish and other aquatic organisms, and esthetics of recreational waters. Most organic and some inorganic chemicals contribute taste or odor. These chemicals may origi-

---

*Approved by Standard Methods Committee, 1985.

nate from municipal and industrial waste discharges, from natural sources such as decomposition of vegetable matter, or from associated microbial activity.

Technological expansion in varieties and quantities of waste materials, demands for water disposal of former air pollutants, and continuous population growth with consequently increased reuse of available water supplies increase the potential for impairment of sensory water quality. Domestic consumers and process industries such as food, beverage, and pharmaceutical manufacturers require water essentially free of tastes and odors.

Some substances, such as certain inorganic salts, produce taste without odor and are evaluated by taste test. Many other sensations ascribed to the sense of taste actually are odors, even though the sensation is not noticed until the material is taken into the mouth. Despite rapid strides in relating sensory qualities to chemical analyses,[2] most odors are too complex and are detectable at concentrations too low to permit their definition by isolating and determining the odor-producing chemicals. The ultimate odor-testing device is the human nose. Odor tests are performed to provide qualitative descriptions and approximate quantitative measurements of odor intensity. The method for intensity measurement presented here is the *threshold odor test*, based on a method of limits.[2] *Suprathreshold* methods are not included. Section 6040B provides an analytical procedure for quantifying several organic odor-producing compounds including geosmin and methylisoborneol.

Sensory tests are useful as a check on the quality of raw and finished water and for control of odor through the treatment process. They can assess the effectiveness of different treatments and provide a means of tracing the source of contamination.

2. References

1. U.S. ENVIRONMENTAL PROTECTION AGENCY. 1973. Proposed Criteria for Water Quality. Vol. 1, Washington, D.C.
2. AMERICAN SOCIETY FOR TESTING AND MATERIALS COMMITTEE E-18. 1968. STP 433, Basic principles of sensory evaluation; STP 434, Manual on sensory testing methods; STP 440, Correlation of subjective-objective methods in the study of odors and taste. ASTM, Philadelphia, Pa.

3. Bibliography

MONCRIEFF, R.W. 1946. The Chemical Senses. John Wiley & Sons, New York, N.Y.

SECHENOV, I.M. 1956 and 1958. Problem of hygenic standards for waters simultaneously polluted with harmful substances [in Russian]. *Gig. Sanit.* Nos. 10 and 8.

Taste and Odor Control in Water Purification, 2nd ed. 1959. West Virginia Pulp & Paper Co. Industrial Chemical Sales Division, New York. [Contains 1,063 classified references.]

BAKER, R.A. 1961. Problems of tastes and odors. *J. Water Pollut. Control Fed.* 33:1099.

BAKER, R.A. 1963. Odor effects of aqueous mixtures of organic chemicals. *J. Water Pollut. Control Fed.* 35:728.

ROSEN, A.A., R.T. SKEEL & M.B. ETTINGER. 1963. Relationship of river water odor to specific organic contaminants. *J. Water Pollut. Control Fed.* 35:777.

WRIGHT, R.H. 1964. The Science of Smell. Basic Books, New York, N.Y.

AMERINE, M.A., R.M. PANGBORN & E.B. ROESSLER. 1965. Principles of Sensory Evaluation of Food. Academic Press, New York, N.Y.

ROSEN, A.A. 1970. Report of research committee on tastes and odors. *J. Amer. Water Works Assoc.* 62:59.

GELDARD, F.A. 1972. The Human Senses. John Wiley & Sons, New York, N.Y.

2150 B.   Threshold Odor Test

1. General Discussion

a. Principle: Determine the threshold odor by diluting a sample with odor-free water until the least definitely perceptible odor is achieved. There is no absolute threshold odor concentration, because of inherent variation in individual olfactory capability. A given person varies in sensitivity over time. Day-to-day and within-day differences occur. Furthermore, responses vary as a result of the characteristic, as well as concentration, of odorant. The number of persons selected to measure threshold odor will depend on the objective of the tests, economics, and available personnel. Larger-sized panels are needed for sensory testing when the results must represent the population as a whole or when great precision is desired. Under such circumstances, panels of not less than five persons, and preferably ten or more, are recommended.[1] Measurement of threshold levels by one person is often a necessity at water treatment plants. Interpretation of the single tester result requires knowledge of the relative acuity of that person. Some investigators have used specific odorants, such as *m*-cresol or *n*-butanol, to calibrate a tester's response.[2]

b. Application: This threshold method is applicable to samples ranging from nearly odorless natural waters to industrial wastes with threshold numbers in the thousands. There are no intrinsic difficulties with the highly odorous samples because they are reduced in concentration proportionately before being presented to the test observers.

c. Qualitative descriptions: A satisfactory system for characterizing odor has not been developed despite efforts over more than a century. Previous editions of this book contained a table of odor descriptions proposed as a guide in expressing odor quality. The reader may continue to encounter the obsolete standard abbreviations of that table. The 12th Edition presents an explanation of such terms.

d. Sampling and storage: Collect samples for odor testing in glass bottles with glass or TFE-lined closures. Complete tests as soon as possible after sample collection. If storage is necessary, collect at least 500 mL of sample in a bottle filled to the top; refrigerate, making sure that no extraneous odors can be drawn into the sample as it cools. Do not use plastic containers.

e. Dechlorination: Most tap waters and some wastewaters are chlorinated. Often it is desirable to determine the odor of the chlorinated sample as well as that of the same sample after dechlorination. Dechlorinate with arsenite or thiosulfate in exact stoichiometric quantity as described under Nitrogen (Ammonia), Section 4500-NH$_3$. CAUTION—*Do not use arsenic compounds as dechlorinating agents on samples to be tasted.*

f. Temperature: Threshold odor values vary with temperature. For most tap waters and raw water sources, a sample temperature of 60°C will permit detection of odors that might otherwise be missed; 60°C is the standard temperature for hot threshold tests. For some purposes—because the odor is too fleeting or there is excessive heat sensation—the hot odor test may not be applicable; where experience shows that a lower temperature is needed, use a standard test temperature of 40°C. For special purposes, other temperatures may be used. *Report temperature at which observations are made.*

2. Apparatus

To assure reliable threshold measurements, use odor-free glassware. Clean glassware shortly before use with nonodorous soap and acid cleaning solution and rinse with odor-free water. Reserve this glassware exclusively for threshold testing. Do not use rubber, cork, or plastic stoppers. Do not use narrow-mouth vessels.

a. Sample bottles, glass-stoppered or with TFE-lined closures.

b. Constant-temperature bath: A water bath or electric hot plate capable of temperature control of ± 1°C for odor tests at elevated temperatures. The bath must not contribute any odor to the odor flasks.

c. Odor flasks: Glass-stoppered, 500-mL (ST 32) erlenmeyer flasks, to hold sample dilutions during testing.

d. Pipets:

1) *Transfer and volumetric pipets or graduated cylinders:* 200-, 100-, 50-, and 25-mL.

2) *Measuring pipets:* 10-mL, graduated in tenths.

e. Thermometer: Zero to 110°C, chemical or metal-stem dial type.

3. Odor-Free Water

a. Sources: Prepare odor-free water by passing distilled, deionized, or tap water through activated carbon, insuring that the water contacts only glass or TFE. If it is impossible to make an all-glass and TFE apparatus, use the design indicated below. If product water is not odor-free, rebuild or purify the system. In all cases verify quality of product water daily.

b. Odor-free-water generator (Figures 2150:1 and 2150:2):*

1) *Borosilicate glass pipe,* 3-in. diam, 18-in. length.

2) *Asbestos inserts* (two) (CAUTION: *Carcinogen; handle with care.*), for 3-in. pipe.

3) *Flange sets* (two), for 3-in. pipe.

4) *Gaskets*† (two), 1/4-in. thickness, with 3-in. hole slotted to 3/8-in. depth to

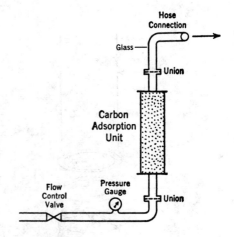

Figure 2150:1. Odor-free-water generator.

take screen. Drill three holes, 5/16-in. diam, to match flange.

5) *Stainless-steel screens* (two), 40-mesh, 3-3/4-in. diam.

6) *Brass plates* (two), 3/16-in. thickness × 6-1/4-in. diam. Tap hole in center for 3/4-in. nipple. Score a circular groove (1/16-in. depth × 1/16-in. width and 3-3/8-in. diam) into the plate to prevent leakage. Drill three holes, 5/16-in. diam, to coincide with the flange.

7) *Galvanized nipples* (two), 3/4-in. × 3-in. Thread nipple into brass plate and weld in place.

8) *Aluminum bolts and nuts* (six), 5/16-in. × 2-in., for holding assembly together.

9) *Activated carbon* of approximately 12 to 40 mesh grain size.‡

Attach end fittings of adsorption unit to the glass pipe. Draw bolts up evenly, holding brass plate to glass pipe to get a good seal on gasket. Fill unit with carbon. Tap cylinder gently but do not tamp carbon. Attach end fittings on adsorption unit and connect to water source as shown in Figure 2150:1.

Avoid organic contaminants in making pipe joints or other plumbing. Use TFE-

---

*For approximate metric dimensions in centimeters multiply dimensions in inches by 2.54.

†Neoprene, such as can be obtained from Netherland Rubber Co., Cincinnati, Ohio.

‡Nuchar WV-G, Westvaco, Covington, Va.; Filtrasorb 200, Calgon Corp., Pittsburgh, Pa.; or equivalent.

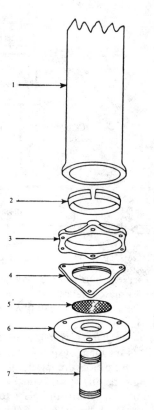

Figure 2150:2. End assembly of odor-free-water generator.

carbon indicates that a change of carbon is needed.

4. Procedure

a. Precautions: Carefully select by preliminary tests the persons to make taste or odor tests. Although extreme sensitivity is not required, exclude insensitive persons and concentrate on observers who have a sincere interest in the test. Avoid extraneous odor stimuli such as those caused by smoking and eating before the test or those contributed by scented soaps, perfumes, and shaving lotions. Insure that the tester is free from colds or allergies that affect odor response. Limit frequency of tests to a number below the fatigue level by frequent rests in an odor-free atmosphere. Keep room in which tests are conducted free from distractions, drafts, and odor.[2] If necessary, set aside a special odor-free room ventilated by air that is filtered through activated carbon and maintained at a constant comfortable temperature and humidity.[3]

For precise work use a panel of five or more testers. Do not allow persons making odor measurements to prepare samples or to know dilution concentrations being evaluated. Familiarize testers with the procedure before they participate in a panel test. Present most dilute sample first to avoid tiring the senses with the concentrated sample. Keep temperature of samples during testing within 1°C of the specified temperature.

Because many raw and waste waters are colored or have decided turbidity that may bias results, use opaque or darkly colored odor flasks, such as red actinic erlenmeyer flasks.

b. Characterization: As part of the threshold test or as a separate test, direct each observer to describe in his own words the characteristic sample odor. Compile the consensus that may appear among testers and that affords a clue to the origin of the odorous pollutant. The value of the

type tape or a paste made by mixing red lead powder and water. Clean all new fittings with kerosene and follow with a detergent wash. Rinse thoroughly with clean water.

c. Generator operation: Pass tap or distilled water through odor-free-water generator at a rate of 100 mL/min. When generator is started, flush to remove carbon fines and discard product.

Check quality of water obtained from the odor-free-water generator daily at 40 and 60°C before use. The life of the carbon will vary with the condition and amount of water filtered. Subtle odors of biological origin often are found if moist carbon filters stand idle between test periods. Detection of odor in the water coming through the characterization test increases as observers become more experienced with a particular category of odor, such as algae, chlorophenol, or mustiness.

c. *Threshold measurement:*§ The "threshold odor number," designated by the abbreviation T.O.N., is the greatest dilution of sample with odor-free water yielding a definitely perceptible odor. Bring total volume of sample and odor-free water to 200 mL in each test. Follow dilutions and record corresponding T.O.N. presented in Table 2150:I. These numbers have been computed thus:

$$\text{T.O.N.} = \frac{A + B}{A}$$

where:

A = mL sample and
B = mL odor-free water.

1) Place proper volume of odor-free water in the flask first, add sample to water (avoiding contact of pipet or sample with lip or neck of flask), mix by swirling, and proceed as follows:

Determine approximate range of the threshold number by adding 200 mL, 50 mL, 12 mL, and 2.8 mL sample to separate 500-mL glass-stoppered erlenmeyer flasks containing odor-free water to make a total volume of 200 mL. Use a separate flask containing only odor-free water as reference for comparison. Heat dilutions and reference to desired test temperature.

2) Shake flask containing odor-free water, remove stopper, and sniff vapors. Test sample containing least amount of odor-bearing water in the same way. If

---

§There are numerous methods of arranging and presenting samples for odor determinations. The methods offered here are practical and economical of time and personnel and generally are adequate. If extensive tests are planned and statistical analysis of data is required, become familiar with the triangle test and the methods that have been used extensively by flavor and allied industries.[4]

TABLE 2150:I. THRESHOLD ODOR NUMBERS CORRESPONDING TO VARIOUS DILUTIONS

Sample Volume Diluted to 200 mL *mL*	Threshold Odor No.	Sample Volume Diluted to 200 mL *mL*	Threshold Odor No.
200	1	12	17
140	1.4	8.3	24
100	2	5.7	35
70	3	4	50
50	4	2.8	70
35	6	2	100
25	8	1.4	140
17	12	1.0	200

odor can be detected in this dilution, prepare more dilute samples as described in ¶ 5) below. If odor cannot be detected in first dilution, repeat above procedure using sample containing next higher concentration of odor-bearing water, and continue this process until odor is detected clearly.

3) Based on results obtained in the preliminary test, prepare a set of dilutions using Table 2150:II as a guide. Prepare the five dilutions shown on the appropriate line and the three next most concentrated on the next line in Table 2150:II. For example, if odor was first noted in the flask containing 50 mL sample in the preliminary test, prepare flasks containing 50, 35, 25, 17, 12, 8.3, 5.7, and 4.0 mL sample, each diluted to 200 mL with odor-free water. This array is necessary to challenge the range of sensitivities of the entire panel of testers.

Insert two or more blanks in the series near the expected threshold, but avoid any repeated pattern. Do not let tester know which dilutions are odorous and which are blanks. Instruct tester to smell each flask in sequence, beginning with the least concentrated sample, until odor is detected with certainty.

4) Record observations by indicating

TABLE 2150:II. DILUTIONS FOR VARIOUS
ODOR INTENSITIES

Sample Volume in Which Odor Is First Noted mL	Volumes to Be Diluted to 200 mL mL
200	200, 140, 100, 70, 50
50	50, 35, 25, 17, 12
12	12, 8.3, 5.7, 4.0, 2.8
2.8	Intermediate dilution

whether odor is noted in each test flask. For example:

mL Sample Diluted to 200 mL	12	0	17	25	0	35	50
Response	−	−	−	+	−	+	+

5) If the sample being tested requires more dilution than is provided by Table 2150:II, prepare an intermediate dilution consisting of 20 mL sample diluted to 200 mL with odor-free water. Use this dilution for the threshold determination. Multiply T.O.N. obtained by 10 to correct for the intermediate dilution. In rare cases more than one tenfold intermediate dilution step may be required.

5. Calculation

The threshold odor number is the dilution ratio at which taste or odor is just detectable. In the example above, ¶ 4c4), the first detectable odor occurred when 25 mL sample was diluted to 200 mL. Thus the threshold is 200 divided by 25, or 8. Table 2150:I lists the threshold numbers corresponding to common dilutions.

The smallest T.O.N. that can be observed is 1, as in the case where the odor flask contains 200 mL undiluted sample. If no odor is detected at this concentration, report "No odor observed" instead of a threshold number. (In special applications, fractional threshold numbers have been calculated.[5])

Anomalous responses sometimes occur; a low concentration may be called positive and a higher concentration in the series may be called negative. In such a case, designate the threshold as that point after which no further anomalies occur. For instance:

	Increasing Concentration →
Response	− − + − + + + +
	↓
	Threshold

where:
   − signifies negative response and
   + signifies positive response.

Occasionally a flask contains residual odor or is contaminated inadvertently. For precise testing repeat entire threshold odor test to determine if the last flask marked "−" was actually a mislabelled blank of odor-free water or if the previous "+" was a contaminated sample.

Use appropriate statistical methods to calculate the most probable average threshold from large numbers of panel results. For most purposes, express the threshold of a group as the geometric mean of individual thresholds.

6. Interpretation of Results

A threshold number is not a precise value. In the case of the single observer it represents a judgment at the time of testing. Panel results are more meaningful because individual differences have less influence on the result. One or two observers can develop useful data if comparison with larger panels has been made to check their sensitivity. Do not make comparisons of data from time to time or place to place unless all test conditions have been standardized carefully and there is some basis for comparison of observed intensities.

7. References

1. AMERICAN SOCIETY FOR TESTING AND MATERIALS COMMITTEE E-18. 1968. STP 433, Basic principles of sensory evaluation; STP 434, Manual on sensory testing methods; STP 440, Correlation of subjective-objective methods in the study of odors and taste. ASTM, Philadelphia, Pa.
2. BAKER, R.A. 1962. Critical evaluation of olfactory measurement. *J. Water Pollut. Control Fed.* 34:582.
3. BAKER, R.A. 1963. Odor testing laboratory. *J. Water Pollut. Control Fed.* 35:1396.
4. Flavor Research and Food Acceptance. 1958. Reinhold Publishing Corp., New York, N.Y.
5. ROSEN, A.A., J.B. PETER & F.M. MIDDLETON. 1962. Odor thresholds of mixed organic chemicals. *J. Water Pollut. Control Fed.* 34:7.

8. Bibliography

HULBERT, R. & D. FEBEN. 1941. Studies on accuracy of threshold odor value. *J. Amer. Water Works Assoc.* 33:1945.

SPAULDING, C.H. 1942. Accuracy and application of threshold odor test. *J. Amer. Water Works Assoc.* 34:877.

THOMAS, H.A., JR. 1943. Calculation of threshold odor. *J. Amer. Water Works Assoc.* 35:751.

CARTWRIGHT, L.C., C.T. SNELL & P.H. KELLY. 1952. Organoleptic panel testing as a research tool. *Anal. Chem.* 24:503.

LAUGHLIN, H.F. 1954. Palatable level with the threshold odor test. *Taste Odor Control J.* 20:No. 8 (Aug.).

SHELLENBERGER, R.D. 1958. Procedures for determining threshold odor concentrations in aqueous solutions. *Taste Odor Control J.* 24: No. 5 (May).

LAUGHLIN, H.F. 1962. Influence of temperature in threshold odor evaluation. *Taste Odor Control J.* 28:No. 10 (Oct.).

The threshold odor test. 1963. *Taste Odor Control J.* 29:Nos. 6, 7, 8 (June, July, Aug.).

SUFFET, I.H. & S. SEGALL. 1971. Detecting taste and odor in drinking water. *J. Amer. Water Works Assoc.* 63:605.

STAHL, W.H., ed. 1973. Compilation of Odor and Taste Threshold Values Data. Amer. Soc. Testing & Materials Data Ser. DS 48, Philadelphia, Pa.

AMERICAN SOCIETY FOR TESTING AND MATERIALS. 1973. Annual Book of ASTM Standards. Part 23, D-1292-65, ASTM, Philadelphia, Pa.

* * *

2310 ACIDITY*

2310 A. Introduction

Acidity of a water is its quantitative capacity to react with a strong base to a designated pH. The measured value may vary significantly with the end-point pH used in the determination. Acidity is a measure of an aggregate property of water and can be interpreted in terms of specific substances only when the chemical composition of the sample is known. Strong mineral acids, weak acids such as carbonic and acetic, and hydrolyzing salts such as iron or aluminum sulfates may contribute to the measured acidity according to the method of determination.

Acids contribute to corrosiveness and influence chemical reaction rates, chemical speciation, and biological processes. The measurement also reflects a change in the quality of the source water.

*Approved by Standard Methods Committee, 1985.

2310 B. Titration Method

1. General Discussion

a. Principle: Hydrogen ions present in a sample as a result of dissociation or hydrolysis of solutes react with additions of standard alkali. Acidity thus depends on the end-point pH or indicator used. The construction of a titration curve by recording sample pH after successive small measured additions of titrant permits identification of inflection points and buffering capacity, if any, and allows the acidity to be determined with respect to any pH of interest.

In the titration of a single acidic species, as in the standardization of reagents, the most accurate end point is obtained from the inflection point of a titration curve. The inflection point is the pH at which curvature changes from convex to concave or vice versa.

Because accurate identification of inflection points may be difficult or impossible in buffered or complex mixtures, the titration in such cases is carried to an arbitrary end-point pH based on practical considerations. For routine control titrations or rapid preliminary estimates of acidity, the color change of an indicator may be used for the end point. Samples of industrial wastes, acid mine drainage, or other solutions that contain appreciable amounts of hydrolyzable metal ions such as iron, aluminum, or manganese are treated with hydrogen peroxide to ensure oxidation of any reduced forms of polyvalent cations, and boiled to hasten hydrolysis. Acidity results may be highly variable if this procedure is not followed exactly.

b. *End points:* Ideally the end point of the acidity titration should correspond to the stoichiometric equivalence point for neutralization of acids present. The pH at the equivalence point will depend on the sample, the choice among multiple inflection points, and the intended use of the data.

Dissolved carbon dioxide (CO_2) usually is the major acidic component of unpolluted surface waters; handle samples from such sources carefully to minimize the loss of dissolved gases. In a sample containing only carbon dioxide-bicarbonates-carbonates, titration to pH 8.3 at 25°C corresponds to stoichiometric neutralization of carbonic acid to bicarbonate. Because the color change of phenolphthalein indicator is close to pH 8.3, this value generally is accepted as a standard end point for titration of total acidity, including CO_2 and most weak acids. Metacresol purple also has an end point at pH 8.3 and gives a sharper color change.

For more complex mixtures or buffered solutions selection of an inflection point may be subjective. Consequently, use fixed end points of pH 3.7 and pH 8.3 for standard acidity determinations via a potentiometric titration in wastewaters and natural waters where the simple carbonate equilibria discussed above cannot be assumed. Bromphenol blue has a sharp color change at its end point of 3.7. The resulting titrations are identified, traditionally, as "methyl orange acidity" (pH 3.7) and "phenolphthalein" or total acidity (pH 8.3) regardless of the actual method of measurement.

c. *Interferences:* Dissolved gases contributing to acidity or alkalinity, such as CO_2, hydrogen sulfide, or ammonia, may be lost or gained during sampling, storage, or titration. Minimize such effects by titrating to the end point promptly after opening sample container, avoiding vigorous shaking or mixing, protecting sample from the atmosphere during titration, and letting sample become no warmer than it was at collection.

In the potentiometric titration, oily matter, suspended solids, precipitates, or other waste matter may coat the glass electrode and cause a sluggish response. Difficulty from this source is likely to be revealed in an erratic titration curve. Do *not* remove interferences from sample because they may contribute to its acidity. Briefly pause between titrant additions to let electrode come to equilibrium or clean the electrodes occasionally.

In samples containing oxidizable or hydrolyzable ions such as ferrous or ferric iron, aluminum, and manganese, the reaction rates at room temperature may be slow enough to cause drifting end points.

Do not use indicator titrations with colored or turbid samples that may obscure the color change at the end point. Residual free available chlorine in the sample may bleach the indicator. Eliminate this source of interference by adding 1 drop of $0.1M$ sodium thiosulfate ($Na_2S_2O_3$).

d. *Selection of procedure:* Determine sample acidity from the volume of standard alkali required to titrate a portion to a pH of 8.3 (phenolphthalein acidity) or pH 3.7 (methyl orange acidity of wastewaters and grossly polluted waters). Titrate at room temperature using a properly calibrated pH meter, electrically operated titrator, or color indicators.

Use the hot peroxide procedure (¶ 4a) to pretreat samples known or suspected to contain hydrolyzable metal ions or reduced forms of polyvalent cation, such as iron pickle liquors, acid mine drainage, and other industrial wastes.

Color indicators may be used for routine and control titrations in the absence of interfering color and turbidity and for preliminary titrations to select sample size and strength of titrant (¶ 4b).

e. Sample size: The range of acidities found in wastewaters is so large that a single sample size and normality of base used as titrant cannot be specified. Use a sufficiently large volume of titrant (20 mL or more from a 50-mL buret) to obtain relatively good volumetric precision while keeping sample volume sufficiently small to permit sharp end points. For samples having acidities less than about 1000 mg as calcium carbonate ($CaCO_3$)/L, select a volume with less than 50 mg $CaCO_3$ equivalent acidity and titrate with 0.02N sodium hydroxide (NaOH). For acidities greater than about 1000 mg as $CaCO_3$/L, use a portion containing acidity equivalent to less than 250 mg $CaCO_3$ and titrate with 0.1N NaOH. If necessary, make a preliminary titration to determine optimum sample size and/or normality of titrant.

f. Sampling and storage: Collect samples in polyethylene or borosilicate glass bottles and store at a low temperature. Fill bottles completely and cap tightly. Because waste samples may be subject to microbial action and to loss or gain of CO_2 or other gases when exposed to air, analyze samples without delay, preferably within 1 d. If biological activity is suspected analyze within 6 h. Avoid sample agitation and prolonged exposure to air.

2. Apparatus

a. Electrometric titrator: Use any commercial pH meter or electrically operated titrator that uses a glass electrode and can be read to 0.05 pH unit. Standardize and calibrate according to the manufacturer's instructions. Pay special attention to temperature compensation and electrode care. If automatic temperature compensation is not provided, titrate at 25 ± 5°C.

b. Titration vessel: The size and form will depend on the electrodes and the sample size. Keep the free space above the sample as small as practicable, but allow room for titrant and full immersion of the indicating portions of electrodes. For conventional-sized electrodes, use a 200-mL, tall-form Berzelius beaker without a spout. Fit beaker with a stopper having three holes, to accommodate the two electrodes and the buret. With a miniature combination glass-reference electrode use a 125-mL or 250-mL erlenmeyer flask with a two-hole stopper.

c. Magnetic stirrer.

d. Pipets, volumetric.

e. Flasks, volumetric, 1000-, 200-, 100-mL.

f. Burets, borosilicate glass, 50-, 25-, 10-mL.

g. Polyolefin bottle, 1-L.

3. Reagents

a. Carbon dioxide-free water: Prepare all stock and standard solutions and dilution water for the standardization procedure with distilled or deionized water that has been freshly boiled for 15 min and cooled to room temperature. The final pH of the water should be $\geq$ 6.0 and its conductivity should be <2 μmhos/cm.

b. Potassium hydrogen phthalate solution, approximately 0.05N: Crush 15 to 20 g primary standard $KHC_8H_4O_4$ to about 100 mesh and dry at 120°C for 2 h. Cool in a desiccator. Weigh 10.0 ± 0.5 g (to the nearest mg), transfer to a 1-L volumetric flask, and dilute to 1000 mL.

c. Standard sodium hydroxide titrant, 0.1N: Prepare solution approximately 0.1 N as indicated under Preparation of Desk Reagents (see inside front cover). Standardize by titrating 40.00 mL $KHC_8H_4O_4$ solution (3*b*), using a 25-mL buret. Titrate to the inflection point (¶ 1*a*), which should be close to pH 8.7. Calculate normality of NaOH:

$$\text{Normality} = \frac{A \times B}{204.2 \times C}$$

where:

 A = g KHC$_8$H$_4$O$_4$ weighed into 1-L flask,
 B = mL KHC$_8$H$_4$O$_4$ solution taken for titration, and
 C = mL NaOH solution used.

Use the measured normality in further calculations or adjust to $0.1000N$; 1 mL = 5.00 mg CaCO$_3$.

d. Standard sodium hydroxide titrant, 0.02N: Dilute 200 mL $0.1N$ NaOH to 1000 mL and store in a polyolefin bottle protected from atmospheric CO$_2$ by a soda lime tube or tight cap. Standardize against KHC$_8$H$_4$O$_4$ as directed in ¶ 3*c*, using 15.00 mL KHC$_8$H$_4$O$_4$ solution and a 50-mL buret. Calculate normality as above (¶ 3*c*); 1 mL = 1.00 mg CaCO$_3$.

e. Hydrogen peroxide, H$_2$O$_2$, 30%.

f. Bromphenol blue indicator solution, pH 3.7 indicator: Dissolve 100 mg bromphenol blue, sodium salt, in 100 mL water.

g. Metacresol purple indicator solution, pH 8.3 indicator: Dissolve 100 mg metacresol purple in 100 mL water.

h. Phenolphthalein indicator solution, alcoholic, pH 8.3 indicator.

i. Sodium thiosulfate, 0.1*M*: Dissolve 25 g Na$_2$S$_2$O$_3$·5H$_2$O and dilute to 1000 mL with distilled water.

4. Procedure

If sample is free from hydrolyzable metal ions and reduced forms of polyvalent cations, proceed with analysis according to *b*, *c*, or *d*. If sample is known or suspected to contain such substances, pretreat according to *a*.

a. Hot peroxide treatment: Pipet a suitable sample (see ¶ 1*e*) into titration flasks. Measure pH. If pH is above 4.0 add 5-mL increments of 0.02*N* sulfuric acid (H$_2$SO$_4$) (Section 2320B.3*c*) to reduce pH to 4 or less. Remove electrodes. Add 5 drops 30% H$_2$O$_2$ and boil for 2 to 5 min. Cool to room temperature and titrate with standard alkali to pH 8.3 according to the procedure of 4*d*.

b. Color change: Select sample size and normality of titrant according to criteria of ¶ 1*e*. Adjust sample to room temperature, if necessary, and with a pipet discharge sample into an erlenmeyer flask, while keeping pipet tip near flask bottom. If free residual chlorine is present add 0.05 mL (1 drop) 0.1*M* Na$_2$S$_2$O$_3$ solution, or destroy with ultraviolet radiation. Add 0.2 mL (5 drops) indicator solution and titrate over a white surface to a persistent color change characteristic of the equivalence point. Commercial indicator solutions or solids designated for the appropriate pH range (3.7 or 8.3) may be used. Check color at end point by adding the same concentration of indicator used with sample to a buffer solution at the designated pH.

c. Potentiometric titration curve:

1) Rinse electrodes and titration vessel with distilled water and drain. Select sample size and normality of titrant according to the criteria of ¶ 1*e*. Adjust sample to room temperature, if necessary, and with a pipet discharge sample while keeping pipet tip near the titration vessel bottom.

2) Measure sample pH. Add standard alkali in increments of 0.5 mL or less, such that a change of less than 0.2 pH units occurs per increment. After each addition, mix thoroughly but gently with a magnetic stirrer. Avoid splashing. Record pH when a constant reading is obtained. Continue adding titrant and measure pH until pH 9 is reached. Construct the titration curve by plotting observed pH values versus cumulative milliliters titrant added. A smooth curve showing one or more inflections should be obtained. A ragged or erratic curve may indicate that equilibrium was not reached between successive alkali additions. Determine acidity relative to a particular pH from the curve.

d. Potentiometric titration to pH 3.7 or 8.3: Prepare sample and titration assembly as specified in ¶ 4*c*1). Titrate to preselected end-point pH (¶ 1*d*) without recording intermediate pH values. As the end point is approached make smaller additions of alkali and be sure that pH equilibrium is reached before making the next addition.

5. Calculation

Acidity, as mg $CaCO_3/L$

$$= \frac{[(A \times B) - (C \times D)] \times 50\,000}{mL\ sample}$$

where:

A = mL NaOH titrant used,
B = normality of NaOH,
C = mL H_2SO_4 used (¶ 4*a*), and
D = normality of H_2SO_4.

Report pH of the end point used, as follows: "The acidity to pH _____ = _____ mg $CaCO_3/L$." If a negative value is obtained, determine the alkalinity according to Section 2320.

6. Precision and Bias

No general statement can be made about precision because of the great variation in sample characteristics. The precision of the titration is likely to be much greater than the uncertainties involved in sampling and sample handling before analysis.

Forty analysts in 17 laboratories analyzed synthetic water samples containing increments of bicarbonate equivalent to 20 mg $CaCO_3/L$. Titration according to the procedure of ¶ 4*d* gave a standard deviation of 1.8 mg $CaCO_3/L$, with negligible bias. Five laboratories analyzed two samples containing sulfuric, acetic, and formic acids and aluminum chloride by the procedures of ¶s 4*b* and 4*d*. The mean acidity of one sample (to pH 3.7) was 487 mg $CaCO_3/L$, with a standard deviation of 11 mg/L. The bromphenol blue titration of the same sample was 90 mg/L greater, with a standard deviation of 110 mg/L. The other sample had a potentiometric titration of 547 mg/L, with a standard deviation of 54 mg/L, while the corresponding indicator result was 85 mg/L greater, with a standard deviation of 56 mg/L. The major difference between the samples was the substitution of ferric ammonium citrate, in the second sample, for part of the aluminum chloride.

7. Bibliography

WINTER, J.A. & M.R. MIDGETT. 1969. FWPCA Method Study 1. Mineral and Physical Analyses. Federal Water Pollution Control Admin., Washington, D.C.

BROWN, E., M.W. SKOUGSTAD & M.J. FISHMAN. 1970. Methods for collection and analysis of water samples for dissolved minerals and gases. Chapter A1 *in* Book 5, Techniques of Water-Resources Investigations of United States Geological Survey. U.S. Geological Survey, Washington, D.C.

SNOEYINK, V.L. & D. JENKINS. 1980. Water Chemistry. John Wiley & Sons, New York, N.Y.

2320 ALKALINITY*

2320 A. Introduction

1. Discussion

Alkalinity of a water is its acid-neutralizing capacity. It is the sum of all the titratable bases. The measured value may vary significantly with the end-point pH used. Alkalinity is a measure of an aggregate property of water and can be interpreted in terms of specific substances only when the chemical composition of the sample is known.

Alkalinity is significant in many uses and treatments of natural waters and wastewaters. Because the alkalinity of many surface waters is primarily a function of carbonate, bicarbonate, and hydroxide content, it is taken as an indication of the concentration of these constitutents. The measured values also may include contributions from borates, phosphates, silicates, or other bases if these are present. Alkalinity in excess of alkaline earth metal concentrations is significant in determining the suitability of a water for irrigation. Alkalinity measurements are used in the interpretation and control of water and wastewater treatment processes. Raw domestic wastewater has an alkalinity less than, or only slightly greater than, that of the water supply. Properly operating anaerobic digesters typically have supernatant alkalinities in the range of 2000 to 4000 mg calcium carbonate ($CaCO_3$)/L.[1]

2. Reference

1. POHLAND, F.G. & D.E. BLOODGOOD. 1963. Laboratory studies on mesophilic and thermophilic anaerobic sludge digestion. *J. Water Pollut. Control Fed.* 35:11.

---

*Approved by Standard Methods Committee, 1985.

2320 B. Titration Method

1. General Discussion

a. Principle: Hydroxyl ions present in a sample as a result of dissociation or hydrolysis of solutes react with additions of standard acid. Alkalinity thus depends on the end-point pH used. For methods of determining inflection points from titration curves and the rationale for titrating to fixed pH end points, see Section 2310B.1a.

For samples of low alkalinity (less than 20 mg $CaCO_3$/L) use an extrapolation technique based on the near proportionality of concentration of hydrogen ions to excess of titrant beyond the equivalence point. The amount of standard acid required to reduce pH exactly 0.30 pH unit is measured carefully. Because this change in pH corresponds to an exact doubling of the hydrogen ion concentration, a simple extrapolation can be made to the equivalence point.[1,2]

b. *End points:* When alkalinity is due entirely to carbonate or bicarbonate content, the pH at the equivalence point of the titration is determined by the concentration of carbon dioxide (CO_2) at that stage. CO_2 concentration depends, in turn, on the total carbonate species originally present and any losses that may have occurred during titration. The following pH values are suggested as the equivalence points for the corresponding alkalinity concentrations as milligrams $CaCO_3$ per liter. "Phenolphthalein alkalinity" is the term traditionally used for the quantity measured by titration to pH 8.3 irrespective of the colored indicator, if any, used in the determination. The sharp end-point color changes produced by metacresol purple (pH 8.3) and bromcresol green (pH 4.5) make these indicators suitable for the alkalinity titration.

| | End Point pH | |
| | Total | Phenolphthalein |
	Alkalinity	Alkalinity
Alkalinity,		
mg $CaCO_3$/L:		
30	4.9	8.3
150	4.6	8.3
500	4.3	8.3
Silicates,		
phosphates known		
or suspected	4.5	8.3
Routine or		
automated		
analyses	4.5	8.3
Industrial waste or		
complex system	4.5	8.3

c. *Interferences:* Soaps, oily matter, suspended solids, or precipitates may coat the glass electrode and cause a sluggish re-

sponse. Allow additional time between titrant additions to let electrode come to equilibrium or clean the electrodes occasionally. Do not filter, dilute, concentrate, or alter sample.

d. *Selection of procedure:* Determine sample alkalinity from volume of standard acid required to titrate a portion to a designated pH taken from ¶ 1b. Titrate at room temperature with a properly calibrated pH meter or electrically operated titrator, or use color indicators.

Report alkalinity less than 20 mg $CaCO_3$/L only if it has been determined by the low-alkalinity method of ¶ 4d.

Construct a titration curve for standardization of reagents.

Color indicators may be used for routine and control titrations in the absence of interfering color and turbidity and for preliminary titrations to select sample size and strength of titrant (see below).

e. *Sample size:* See Section 2310B.1e for selection of size sample to be titrated and normality of titrant, substituting 0.02N or 0.1N sulfuric (H_2SO_4) or hydrochloric (HCl) acid for the standard alkali of that method. For the low-alkalinity method, titrate a 200-mL sample with 0.02N H_2SO_4 from a 10-mL buret.

f. *Sampling and storage:* See Section 2310B.1f.

2. Apparatus

See Section 2310B.2.

3. Reagents

a. *Sodium carbonate solution,* approximately 0.05N: Dry 3 to 5 g primary standard Na_2CO_3 at 250°C for 4 h and cool in a desiccator. Weigh 2.5 ± 0.2 g (to the nearest mg), transfer to a 1-L volumetric flask, fill flask to the mark with distilled water, and dissolve and mix reagent. Do not keep longer than 1 week.

b. Standard sulfuric acid or hydrochloric acid, 0.1*N:* Prepare acid solution of approximate normality as indicated under Preparation of Desk Reagents (see inside front cover). Standardize against 40.00 mL 0.05*N* Na$_2$CO$_3$ solution, with about 60 mL water, in a beaker by titrating potentiometrically to pH of about 5. Lift out electrodes, rinse into the same beaker, and boil gently for 3 to 5 min under a watch glass cover. Cool to room temperature, rinse cover glass into beaker, and finish titrating to the pH inflection point. Calculate normality:

$$\text{Normality, } N = \frac{A \times B}{53.00 \times C}$$

where:

A = g Na$_2$CO$_3$ weighed into 1-L flask,
B = mL Na$_2$CO$_3$ solution taken for titration, and
C = mL acid used.

Use measured normality in calculations or adjust to 0.1000*N*; 1 mL 0.1000*N* solution = 5.00 mg CaCO$_3$.

c. Standard sulfuric acid or hydrochloric acid, 0.02*N:* Dilute 200.00 mL 0.1000*N* standard acid to 1000 mL with distilled or deionized water. Standardize by potentiometric titration of 15.00 mL 0.05*N* Na$_2$CO$_3$ according to the procedure of ¶ 3*b*; 1 mL = 1.00 mg CaCO$_3$.

d. Bromcresol green indicator solution, pH 4.5 indicator: Dissolve 100 mg bromcresol green, sodium salt, in 100 mL distilled water.

e. Metacresol purple indicator solution, pH 8.3 indicator: Dissolve 100 mg metacresol purple in 100 mL water.

f. Phenolphthalein solution, alcoholic, pH 8.3 indicator.

g. Sodium thiosulfate, 0.1*N:* See Section 2310B.3*i*.

4. Procedure

a. Color change: See Section 2310B.4*b*.

b. Potentiometric titration curve: Follow the procedure for determining acidity (Section 2310B.4*c*), substituting the appropriate normality of standard acid solution for standard NaOH, and continue titration to pH 4.5 or lower. Do not filter, dilute, concentrate, or alter the sample.

c. Potentiometric titration to preselected pH: Determine the appropriate end-point pH according to ¶ 1*b*. Prepare sample and titration assembly (Section 2310B.4*c*). Titrate to the end-point pH without recording intermediate pH values and without undue delay. As the end point is approached make smaller additions of acid and be sure that pH equilibrium is reached before adding more titrant.

d. Potentiometric titration of low alkalinity: For alkalinities less than 20 mg/L titrate 100 to 200 mL according to the procedure of ¶ 4*c*, above, using a 10-mL microburet and 0.02*N* standard acid solution. Stop the titration at a pH in the range 4.3 to 4.7 and record volume and exact pH. Carefully add additional titrant to reduce the pH exactly 0.30 pH unit and again record volume.

5. Calculations

a. Potentiometric titration to end-point pH:

$$\text{Alkalinity, mg CaCO}_3/\text{L} = \frac{A \times N \times 50\,000}{\text{mL sample}}$$

where:

A = mL standard acid used and
N = normality of standard acid

or

$$\text{Alkalinity, mg CaCO}_3/\text{L} = \frac{A \times t \times 1000}{\text{mL sample}}$$

where:

t = titer of standard acid, mg CaCO$_3$/mL.

Report pH of end point used as follows: "The alkalinity to pH _____ = _____ mg CaCO$_3$/L" and indicate clearly if this pH corresponds to an inflection point of the titration curve.

b. Potentiometric titration of low alkalinity:

Total alkalinity, mg CaCO$_3$/L

$$= \frac{(2\ B\ -\ C) \times N \times 50\ 000}{\text{mL sample}}$$

where:

B = mL titrant to first recorded pH,
C = total mL titrant to reach pH 0.3 unit lower, and
N = normality of acid.

c. Calculation of alkalinity relationships: The results obtained from the phenolphthalein and total alkalinity determinations offer a means for stoichiometric classification of the three principal forms of alkalinity present in many waters. The classification ascribes the entire alkalinity to bicarbonate, carbonate, and hydroxide, and assumes the absence of other (weak) inorganic or organic acids, such as silicic, phosphoric, and boric acids. It further presupposes the incompatibility of hydroxide and bicarbonate alkalinities. Because the calculations are made on a stoichiometric basis, ion concentrations in the strictest sense are not represented in the results, which may differ significantly from actual concentrations especially at pH > 10. According to this scheme:

1) Carbonate (CO$_3^{2-}$) alkalinity is present when phenolphthalein alkalinity is not zero but is less than total alkalinity.

2) Hydroxide (OH$^-$) alkalinity is present if phenolphthalein alkalinity is more than half the total alkalinity.

3) Bicarbonate (HCO$_3^-$) alkalinity is present if phenolphthalein alkalinity is less than half the total alkalinity. These relationships may be calculated by the following scheme, where P is phenolphthalein alkalinity and T is total alkalinity (¶ 1*b*):

Select the smaller value of P or $(T-P)$. Then, carbonate alkalinity equals twice the smaller value. When the smaller value is P, the balance $(T-2P)$ is bicarbonate. When the smaller value is $(T-P)$, the balance $(2P-T)$ is hydroxide. All results are expressed as CaCO$_3$. The mathematical conversion of the results is shown in Table 2320:I. (A modification of Table 2320:I that is more accurate when $P \simeq \frac{1}{2}T$ has been proposed.[3])

Alkalinity relationships also may be computed nomographically (see Carbon Dioxide, Section 4500-CO$_2$). Accurately measure pH, calculate OH$^-$ concentration as milligrams CaCO$_3$ per liter, and calculate concentrations of CO$_3^{2-}$ and HCO$_3^-$ as milligrams CaCO$_3$ per liter from the OH$^-$ concentration, and the phenolphthalein and total alkalinities by the following equations:

$$CO_3^{2-} = 2P - 2[OH^-]$$

$$HCO_3^- = T - 2P + [OH^-]$$

Similarly, if difficulty is experienced with the phenolphthalein end point, or if a check on the phenolphthalein titration is desired, calculate phenolphthalein alkalinity as CaCO$_3$ from the results of the nomographic

TABLE 2320:I. ALKALINITY RELATIONSHIPS*

Result of Titration	Hydroxide Alkalinity as CaCO$_3$	Carbonate Alkalinity as CaCO$_3$	Bicarbonate Concentration as CaCO$_3$
$P = 0$	0	0	T
$P < \frac{1}{2}T$	0	$2P$	$T - 2P$
$P = \frac{1}{2}T$	0	$2P$	0
$P > \frac{1}{2}T$	$2P - T$	$2(T - P)$	0
$P = T$	T	0	0

*Key: P—phenolphthalein alkalinity; T—total alkalinity.

determinations of carbonate and hydroxide ion concentrations:

$$P = 1/2\,[CO_3^{2-}] + [OH^-]$$

6. Precision and Bias

No general statement can be made about precision because of the great variation in sample characteristics. The precision of the titration is likely to be much greater than the uncertainties involved in sampling and sample handling before the analysis.

In the range of 10 to 500 mg/L, when the alkalinity is due entirely to carbonates or bicarbonates, a standard deviation of 1 mg $CaCO_3$/L can be achieved. Forty analysts in 17 laboratories analyzed synthetic samples containing increments of bicarbonate equivalent to 120 mg $CaCO_3$/L. The titration procedure of ¶ 4b was used, with an end point pH of 4.5. The standard deviation was 5 mg/L and the average bias (lower than the true value) was 9 mg/L.[4]

Sodium carbonate solutions equivalent to 80 and 65 mg $CaCO_3$/L were analyzed by 12 laboratories according to the procedure of ¶ 4c.[5] The standard deviations were 8 and 5 mg/L, respectively, with negligible bias.[5] Four laboratories analyzed six samples having total alkalinities of about 1000 mg $CaCO_3$/L and containing various ratios of carbonate/bicarbonate by the procedures of both ¶ 4a and ¶ 4c. The pooled standard deviation was 40 mg/L, with negligible difference between the procedures.

7. References

1. LARSON, T.E. & L.M. HENLEY. 1955. Determination of low alkalinity or acidity in water. *Anal. Chem.* 27:851.
2. THOMAS, J.F.J. & J.J. LYNCH. 1960. Determination of carbonate alkalinity in natural waters. *J. Amer. Water Works Assoc.* 52:259.
3. JENKINS, S.R. & R.C. MOORE. 1977. A proposed modification to the classical method of calculating alkalinity in natural waters. *J. Amer. Water Works Assoc.* 69:56.
4. WINTER, J.A. & M.R. MIDGETT. 1969. FWPCA Method Study 1. Mineral and Physical Analyses. Federal Water Pollution Control Admin., Washington, D.C.
5. SMITH, R. 1980. Research Rep. No. 379, Council for Scientific and Industrial Research, South Africa.

8. Bibliography

AMERICAN SOCIETY FOR TESTING AND MATERIALS. 1982. Standard Methods for Acidity or Alkalinity of Water. Publ. D1067-70 (reapproved 1977), American Soc. Testing & Materials, Philadelphia, Pa.
SKOUGSTAD M.W., M.J. FISHMAN, L.C. FRIEDMAN, D.E. ERDMAN, & S.S. DUNCAN. 1979. Methods for determination of inorganic substances in water and fluvial sediments. *In* Techniques of Water-Resources Investigation of the United States Geological Survey. U.S. Geological Survey, Book 5, Chapter A1, Washington, D.C.

2330   CALCIUM CARBONATE SATURATION (PROPOSED)*

2330 A.   Introduction

1. General Discussion

Calcium carbonate ($CaCO_3$) saturation indices commonly are used to evaluate the scale-forming and scale-dissolving tendencies of water. Assessing these tendencies is useful in corrosion control programs and in preventing $CaCO_3$ scaling in piping and equipment such as industrial heat exchangers or domestic water heaters.

Waters oversaturated with respect to $CaCO_3$ tend to precipitate $CaCO_3$. Waters undersaturated with respect to $CaCO_3$ tend to dissolve $CaCO_3$. Saturated waters, i.e., waters in equilibrium with $CaCO_3$, have neither $CaCO_3$-precipitating nor $CaCO_3$-dissolving tendencies. Saturation represents the dividing line between "precipitation likely" and "precipitation not likely."

Several water quality characteristics must be measured to calculate the $CaCO_3$ saturation indices described here. Minimum requirements are total alkalinity (2320), total calcium (3500-Ca), pH (4500-H^+), and temperature (2550). The ionic strength also must be calculated or estimated from conductivity (2510) or total dissolved solids (2540C) measurements. Measure pH at the system's water temperature using a temperature-compensated pH meter. If pH is measured at a different temperature, for example in the laboratory, correct the measured pH.[1-3] In measuring

pH and alkalinity, minimize CO_2 exchange between sample and atmosphere. Ideally, seal the sample from the atmosphere during measurements[4]; at a minimum, avoid vigorous stirring of unsealed samples.

There are two general categories of $CaCO_3$ saturation indices: indices that determine whether a water has a *tendency* to precipitate $CaCO_3$ (i.e., is oversaturated) or to dissolve $CaCO_3$ (i.e., is undersaturated) and indices that estimate the *quantity* of $CaCO_3$ that can be precipitated from an oversaturated water and the amount that can be dissolved by an undersaturated water. Indices in the second category generally yield more information but are more difficult to determine.

2. Limitations

It is widely assumed that $CaCO_3$ will precipitate from oversaturated waters and that it cannot be deposited from undersaturated waters. Exceptions may occur. For example, $CaCO_3$ deposition from oversaturated waters is inhibited by the presence of phosphates (particularly polyphosphates), certain naturally occurring organics, and magnesium.[5-7] These materials can act as sequestering agents or as crystal poisons. Conversely, $CaCO_3$ deposits have been found in pipes conveying undersaturated water. This apparent contradiction is caused by high pH (relative to the bulk water pH) in the immediate vicinity of certain areas (cathodes) of corroding metal

---

*Approved by Standard Methods Committee, 1989.

surfaces. A locally oversaturated condition may occur even if the bulk water is undersaturated. A small, but significant, amount of $CaCO_3$ can be deposited.

The calculations referred to here, even the most sophisticated computerized calculations, do not adequately describe these exceptions. For this reason, do not consider saturation indices as absolutes. Rather, view them as guides to the behavior of $CaCO_3$ in aqueous systems and supplement them, where possible, with experimentally derived information.

Similarly, the effects predicted by the indices do not always conform to expectations. The relationship between the indices and corrosion rates is a case in point. Conceptually, piping is protected when $CaCO_3$ is precipitated on its surfaces. $CaCO_3$ is believed to inhibit corrosion by clogging reactive areas and by providing a matrix to retain corrosion products, thus further sealing the surfaces. Waters with positive indices traditionally have been assumed to be protective while waters with negative indices have been assumed to be not protective, or corrosive. The expected relationship is observed sometimes,[8,9] but not always.[10,11] Unexpected results may be due in part to limited capability to predict $CaCO_3$ behavior. Also, water characteristics not directly involved in the calculation of the indices (e.g., dissolved oxygen, buffering intensity, chloride, sulfate, and water velocity) may influence corrosion rates appreciably.[9,12–16] Thus, do not estimate corrosion rates on the basis of $CaCO_3$ indices alone.

3. References

1. MERRILL, D.T. & R.L. SANKS. 1978, 1979. Corrosion control by deposition of $CaCO_3$ films: A practical approach for plant operators. *J. Amer. Water Works Assoc.* 70:592; 70:634 & 71:12.

2. LOEWENTHAL, R.E. & G. V. R. MARAIS. 1976. Carbonate Chemistry of Aquatic Systems: Theory and Applications. Ann Arbor Science Publishers, Ann Arbor, Mich.

3. MERRILL, D.T. 1976. Chemical conditioning for water softening and corrosion control. *In* R.L. Sanks, ed. Water Treatment Plant Design. Ann Arbor Science Publishers, Ann Arbor, Mich.

4. SCHOCK, M.R., W. MUELLER & R.W. BUELOW. 1980. Laboratory techniques for measurement of pH for corrosion control studies and water not in equilibrium with the atmosphere. *J. Amer. Water Works Assoc.* 72:304.

5. PYTKOWICZ, R.M. 1965. Rates of inorganic carbon nucleation. *J. Geol.* 73:196.

6. FERGUSON, J.F. & P.L. MCCARTY. 1969. Precipitation of Phosphate from Fresh Waters and Waste Waters. Tech. Rep. No. 120, Stanford Univ., Stanford, Calif.

7. MERRILL, D.T. & R.M. JORDEN. 1975. Lime-induced reactions in municipal wastewaters. *J. Water Pollut. Control Fed.* 47:2783.

8. DE MARTINI, F. 1938. Corrosion and the Langelier calcium carbonate saturation index. *J. Amer. Water Works Assoc.* 30:85.

9. LARSON, T.E. 1975. Corrosion by Domestic Waters. Bull. 59, Illinois State Water Survey.

10. JAMES M. MONTGOMERY, CONSULTING ENGINEERS, INC. 1985. Water Treatment Principles and Design. John Wiley & Sons, New York, N.Y.

11. STUMM, W. 1960. Investigations of the corrosive behavior of waters. *J. San. Eng. Div., Proc. Amer. Soc. Civil Eng.* 86:27.

12. PISIGAN, R.A., JR. & J.E. SINGLEY. 1985. Evaluation of water corrosivity using the Langelier index and relative corrosion rate models. *Materials Perform.* 24:26.

13. LANE, R.W. 1982. Control of corrosion in distribution and building water systems. *In* Proceedings AWWA Water Quality Technology Conf., Nashville, Tenn., Dec. 5–8, 1982.

14. SONTHEIMER, H., W. KOLLE & V.L. SNOEYINK. 1982. The siderite model of the formation of corrosion-resistant scales. *J. Amer. Water Works Assoc.* 73:572.

15. SCHOCK, M.R. & C.H. NEFF. 1982. Chemical aspects of internal corrosion; theory, prediction, and monitoring. *In* Proceedings AWWA Water Quality Technology Conf., Nashville, Tenn., Dec. 5–8, 1982.

16. AMERICAN WATER WORKS ASSOCIATION. 1986. Corrosion Control for Plant Operators. ISBW-O-89867-350-X. Denver, Colo.

2330 B. Indices Indicating Tendency of a Water to Precipitate CaCO₃ or Dissolve CaCO₃

1. General Discussion

Indices that indicate $CaCO_3$ precipitation or dissolution tendencies define whether a water is oversaturated, saturated, or undersaturated with respect to $CaCO_3$. The most widely used indices are the Saturation Index (SI): the Relative Saturation (RS), also known as the Driving Force Index (DFI); and the Ryznar Index (RI). The SI is by far the most commonly used and will be described here. The RS and SI are related (see Equation 6, Section 2330D). The RI[1] has been used for many years, sometimes with good results. Because it is semi-empirical it may be less reliable than the SI.

2. Saturation Index by Calculation

SI is determined from Equation 1.

$$SI = pH - pH_s \qquad (1)$$

where:

pH = measured pH and
pH_s = pH of the water if it were in equilibrium with $CaCO_3$ at the existing calcium ion $[Ca^{2+}]$ and bicarbonate ion $[HCO_3^-]$ concentrations.

A positive SI connotes a water oversaturated with respect to $CaCO_3$. A negative SI signifies an undersaturated water. An SI of zero represents a water in equilibrium with $CaCO_3$.

a. *Analytical solution for pH_s:* Determine pH_s as follows[2]:

$$pH_s = pK_2 - pK_s + p[Ca^{2+}] \\ + p[HCO_3^-] + 5\ pf_m \qquad (2)$$

where:

K_2 = second dissociation constant for carbonic acid, at the water temperature,

K_s = solubility product constant for $CaCO_3$ at the water temperature,
$[Ca^{2+}]$ = calcium ion concentration, g-moles/L,
$[HCO_3^-]$ = bicarbonate ion concentration, g-moles/L, and
f_m = activity coefficient for monovalent species at the specified temperature.

In Equation 2, p preceding a variable designates $-\log_{10}$ of that variable.

Calculate values of pK_2, pK_s, and pf_m required to solve Equation 2 from the equations in Table 2330:I. To save computation time, values for pK_2 and pK_s have been precalculated for selected temperatures (see Table 2330:II).

Table 2330:II gives several values for pK_s. Different isomorphs of $CaCO_3$ can form in aqueous systems, including calcite, aragonite, and vaterite. Each has somewhat different solubility properties. These differences can be accommodated when computing pH_s simply by using the pK_s for the compound most likely to form. The form of $CaCO_3$ most commonly found in fresh water is calcite. Use the pK_s for calcite unless it is clear that a different form of $CaCO_3$ controls $CaCO_3$ solubility.

Estimate calcium ion concentration from total calcium measurements with Equation 3.

$$[Ca^{2+}] = Ca_t - Ca_{ip} \qquad (3)$$

where:

Ca_t = total calcium, g-moles/L, and
Ca_{ip} = calcium associated with ion pairs such as $CaHCO_3^+$, $CaSO_4^0$, and $CaOH^+$.

Calcium associated with ion pairs is not available to form $CaCO_3$.

Estimate $[HCO_3^-]$, the bicarbonate ion concentration, from Equation 4.

$[HCO_3^-] =$

$$\frac{Alk_t - Alk_o + 10^{(pf_m - pH)} - 10^{(pH + pf_m - pK_w)}}{1 + 0.5 \times 10^{(pH - pK_2)}}$$

(4)

where:

Alk_t = total alkalinity, as determined by acid titration to the carbonic acid end point, g-equivalents/L,

K_w = dissociation constant for water, at the water temperature, and

Alk_o = alkalinity contributed by NH_3^0, $H_3SiO_4^-$, HPO_4^{2-}, $B(OH)_4^-$, CH_3COO^- (acetate), HS^-, and ion pairs such as $CaHCO_3^+$ and $MgOH^+$.

These contributions usually are small compared to the contributions of components normally considered (HCO_3^-, CO_3^{2-}, OH^-, and H^+).

Calculations can be simplified. For example, in Equation 4, terms containing exponents (e.g., $10^{(pH + pf_m - pk_w)}$) usually can be neglected for waters that are approximately neutral (pH 6.0 to 8.5) with alkalinity greater than about 50 mg/L as $CaCO_3$. The terms Ca_{ip} in Equation 3 and Alk_o in Equation 4 are difficult to calculate without computers. Therefore they usually are neglected for hand calculations. The

TABLE 2330:I. ESTIMATING EQUILIBRIUM CONSTANTS AND ACTIVITY COEFFICIENTS

Equation	Temperature Range	References
When complete mineral analysis is available:		
$I = \frac{1}{2} \sum_{i=1}^{i} [X_i] Z_i^2$	—	3
When only conductivity is available:		
$I = 1.6 \times 10^{-5} C$	—	4
When only TDS is available:		
$I = TDS/40\ 000$	—	5
$pf_m = A \frac{\sqrt{I}}{1 + \sqrt{I}} - 0.3I$ \quad (valid to $I < 0.5$)	—	3
$A = 1.82 \times 10^6\ (ET)^{-1.5}$	—	3
$E = \frac{60\ 954}{T + 116} - 68.937$	—	6
$pK_2 = 107.8871 + 0.032\ 528\ 49T - 5151.79/T - 38.925\ 61$ $\log_{10}T + 563\ 713.9/T^2$	273–373	7
$pK_w = 4471/T + 0.017\ 06T - 6.0875$	280–338	8
$pK_{sc} = 171.9065 + 0.077\ 993T - 2839.319/T - 71.595 \log_{10}T$	273–363	7
$pK_{sa} = 171.9773 + 0.077\ 993T - 2903.293/T - 71.595 \log_{10}T$	273–363	7
$pK_{sv} = 172.1295 + 0.077\ 993T - 3074.688/T - 71.595 \log_{10}T$	273–363	7

*I = ionic strength

$[X_i]$ = concentration of component i, g-moles/L

Z_i = charge of species i

C = conductivity, μmhos/cm

TDS = total dissolved solids, mg/L

pY = $-\log_{10}$ of the value of any factor Y

f_m = activity coefficient for monovalent species

E = dielectric constant

T = temperature, °K (°C + 273.2)

K_2 = second dissociation constant for carbonic acid

K_w = dissociation constant for water

K_{sc} = solubility product constant for calcite

K_{sa} = solubility product constant for aragonite

K_{sv} = solubility product constant for vaterite

TABLE 2330:II. PRECALCULATED VALUES FOR pK AND A AT SELECTED TEMPERATURES

Temperature °C	pK_2	pK_s Calcite	pK_s Aragonite	pK_s Vaterite	pK_w	A
5	10.55	8.39	8.24	7.77	14.73	0.494
10	10.49	8.41	8.26	7.80	14.53	0.498
15	10.43	8.43	8.28	7.84	14.34	0.502
20	10.38	8.45	8.31	7.87	14.16	0.506
25*	10.33	8.48	8.34	7.91	13.99	0.511
30	10.29	8.51	8.37	7.96	13.83	0.515
35	10.25	8.54	8.41	8.00	13.68	0.520
40	10.22	8.58	8.45	8.05	13.53	0.526
45	10.20	8.62	8.49	8.10	13.39	0.531
50	10.17	8.66	8.54	8.16	13.26	0.537
60	10.14	8.76	8.64	8.28	13.02	0.549
70	10.13	8.87	8.75	8.40	—	0.562
80	10.13	8.99	8.88	8.55	—	0.576
90	10.14	9.12	9.02	8.70	—	0.591

NOTE: All values determined from the equations of Table 2330:I.
A is used to calculate pf_m (see Table 2330:I).
*pf_m estimated from TDS values at 25°C are as follows:

TDS	pf_m
100	0.024
200	0.033
400	0.044
800	0.060
1000	0.066

simplified version of Equation 2 under such conditions is:

$$pH_s = pK_2 - pK_s + p[Ca_i] + p[Alk_i] + 5 pf_m$$

1) Sample calculation—The calculation is best illustrated by working through an example. Assume that calcite controls $CaCO_3$ solubility and determine the SI for a water of the following composition:

Constituent	Concentration mg/L $\div$	$\frac{mg}{mole}$ =	g-moles/L
Calcium	152	40 000	3.80×10^{-3}
Magnesium	39	24 312	1.60×10^{-3}
Sodium	50	22 989	2.18×10^{-3}
Potassium	5	39 102	1.28×10^{-4}
Chloride	53	35 453	1.49×10^{-3}
Alkalinity (as $CaCO_3$)	130	50 000	2.60×10^{-3}*
Sulfate	430	96 060	4.48×10^{-3}
Silica (as SiO_2)	15	60 084	2.50×10^{-4}

*g-equivalents.
Water temperature = 20°C (293.2°K); pH = 9.00.

Before evaluating pf_m in Equation 2, determine the ionic strength (I) and another constant (A). Estimate ionic strength from the first equation of Table 2330:I, assuming all the alkalinity is due to bicarbonate ion. Use the alkalinity concentration (2.60×10^{-3}) and the bicarbonate charge (-1) to calculate the contribution of alkalinity to ionic strength. Assume silica is mostly H_4SiO_4. Because H_4SiO_4 has zero charge, silica does not contribute to ionic strength.

$$I = 0.5 \, [4(3.80 \times 10^{-3}) + 4(1.60 \times 10^{-3})$$
$$+ \, 2.18 \times 10^{-3} + 1.28 \times 10^{-4} + 1.49$$
$$\times \, 10^{-3} + 2.60 \times 10^{-3} + 4(4.48 \times 10^{-3})]$$
$$= 2.29 \times 10^{-2} \text{ g-moles/L}$$

In the absence of a complete water analysis, estimate ionic strength from conductivity or total dissolved solids measurements (see alternative equations, Table 2330:I).

Estimate A from the equation in Table 2330:I, after first determining the dielectric constant E from the formula in the same table. Alternatively, use precalculated values of A in Table 2330:II. In Table 2330:II, $A = 0.506$ at 20°C.

Next estimate pf_m from the equation in Table 2330:I:

$$pf_m = 0.506$$

$$\times \left[\frac{\sqrt{2.29 \times 10^{-2}}}{1 + \sqrt{2.29 \times 10^{-2}}} - 0.3 \, (2.29 \times 10^{-2}) \right]$$

$$= 0.063$$

Determine $[HCO_3^-]$ from Equation 4. Neglect Alk_o, but because the pH exceeds 8.5, calculate the other terms. From Table 2330:II, $pK_2 = 10.38$ and $pK_w = 14.16$.

$[HCO_3^-]$

$$= \frac{2.60 \times 10^{-3} + 10^{(0.063 - 9.0)} - 10^{(9.0 + 0.063 - 14.16)}}{1 + 0.5 \times 10^{(9.0 - 10.38)}}$$

$$= 2.54 \times 10^{-3} \text{ g-moles/L}$$

Therefore $p[HCO_3^-] = 2.60$.

Determine $[Ca^{2+}]$ from Equation 3. Neglect Ca_{ip}.

$$[Ca^{2+}] = Ca_t = 3.80 \times 10^{-3} \text{ g-moles/L}$$

Therefore $p[Ca^{2+}] = 2.42$.

From Table 2330:II, pK_s for calcite is 8.45.

Determine pH_s from Equation 2:

$$pH_s = 10.38 - 8.45 + 2.42$$
$$+ \, 2.60 + 5 \, (0.063) = 7.27$$

And finally, determine SI from Equation 1:

$$SI = 9.00 - 7.27 = 1.73$$

The positive SI indicates the water is oversaturated with respect to calcite.

2) Effect of neglecting Ca_{ip} and Alk_o— If Ca_{ip} is neglected, pH_s is underestimated and SI is overestimated by an amount equal to $p(1 - Y_{Ca_{ip}})$, where $Y_{Ca_{ip}}$ is the fraction of total calcium in ion pairs. For example, if $Y_{Ca_{ip}} = 0.30$ then the estimate for SI is 0.15 units too high. Similarly, if Alk_o is neglected, SI is overestimated by an amount equal to $p(1 - Y_{Alk_o})$, where Y_{Alk_o} is the fraction of total alkalinity contributed by species other than HCO_3^-, CO_3^{2-}, OH^-, and H^+. The effects of neglecting Ca_{ip} and Alk_o are additive.

Ca_{ip} and Alk_o may be neglected if the factors $Y_{Ca_{ip}}$ and Y_{Alk_o} are small and do not interfere with interpretation of the SI. The factors are small for waters of low and neutral pH, but they increase as pH values approach and exceed 9. At high pH values, however, the SI is typically much larger than its overestimate, so neglecting Ca_{ip} and Alk_o causes no problem. To return to the example above, when calculations were done with a computerized water chemistry code (SEQUIL) (see Table 2330:III) that considers Ca_{ip} and Alk_o, the SI was 1.48, i.e., 0.25 units lower than the result obtained by hand calculations. In this instance, neglecting Ca_{ip} and Alk_o did not interfere with interpreting the result. Both calculations showed the water to be strongly oversaturated.

The potential for misinterpretation is most acute in nearly-saturated waters of high sulfate concentration. Recirculating cooling water is an example. Calcium is sequestered by the robust $CaSO_4^0$ ion pair and the *SI* can be overestimated by as much as 0.3 to 0.5 units, even at neutral pH. Under these conditions, the *SI* may be thought to be zero (neither scale-forming or corrosive) when in fact it is negative.

Resolve this problem by determining pH_s using computerized water chemistry codes that consider ion pairs and the other forms of alkalinity. Section 2330D provides information about water chemistry codes. The most accurate calculations are obtained when a complete mineral analysis is provided.

An alternative but somewhat less rigorous procedure involves direct measurement of (Ca^{2+}), the calcium ion activity, with a calcium specific-ion electrode.[9] Use Equation 5 to determine $p[Ca^{2+}]$; then use $p[Ca^{2+}]$ in Equation 2.

$$p[Ca^{2+}] = p(Ca^{2+}) - 4pf_m$$

This approach eliminates the need to determine Ca_{ip}. However, no equivalent procedure is available to bypass the determination of Alk_o.

b. Graphical solutions for pH_s: Caldwell-Lawrence diagrams can be used to determine pH_s.[10-12] The diagrams are particularly useful for estimating chemical dosages needed to achieve desired water conditions. Consult the references for descriptions of how to use the diagrams; see Section 2330D for additional information about the diagrams.

3. Saturation Index by Experimental Determination

a. Saturometry: Saturometers were developed to measure the relative saturation of seawater with respect to $CaCO_3$. A water of known calcium and pH is equilibrated with $CaCO_3$ in a sealed flask containing a pH electrode. The water temperature is controlled with a constant-temperature bath. During equilibration the pH decreases if $CaCO_3$ precipitates and increases if $CaCO_3$ dissolves. When the pH stops changing, equilibrium is said to have been achieved. The initial pH and calcium values and the final pH value are used to calculate the relative saturation (RS).[13] Equation 6, Section 2330D, may then be used to determine SI.

A major advantage of this method is that the approach to equilibrium can be tracked by measuring pH, thus minimizing uncertainty about the achievement of equilibrium. The method is most sensitive in the range of minimum buffering intensity (pH 7.5 to 8.5). The calculations do not consider ion pairs or noncarbonate alkalinity, except borate. The technique has been used for *in situ* oceanographic measurements[14] as well as in the laboratory.

The saturometry calculations discussed above use K_s of the $CaCO_3$ phase assumed to control solubility. Uncertainties occur if the identity of the controlling solid is unknown. Resolve these uncertainties by measuring K_s of the controlling solid. It is equal to the $CaCO_3$ activity product, $[Ca^{2+}] \times [CO_3^{2-}]$, at equilibrium. Calculate the latter from the equilibrium pH and initial calcium, alkalinity, and pH measurements.[15]

b. Alkalinity difference technique:[16] SI also can be determined by equilibrating water of known pH, calcium, and alkalinity with $CaCO_3$ in a sealed, constant-temperature system. The $CaCO_3$ activity product before equilibration is determined from initial calcium, pH, and alkalinity (or total carbonate) values. The $CaCO_3$ solubility product constant (K_s) equals the $CaCO_3$ activity product after equilibration, which is determined by using the alkalinity change that occurred during equilibration. *RS* is found by dividing the initial activity product by K_s. Calculate *SI* by using Equation 6. The advantage of this method is that it makes no assumptions about the identity of the $CaCO_3$ phase. However it is more difficult to determine when equilibrium is achieved with this method than with the saturometry method.

Whatever the method used, use the temperatures that are the same as the temperature of the water source. Alternatively, correct test results to the temperature of the water source.[16]

4. References

1. RYZNAR, J.W. 1944. A new index for determining the amount of calcium carbonate formed by water. *J. Amer. Water Works Assoc.* 36:47.

2. SNOEYINK, V.L. & D. JENKINS. 1980. Water Chemistry. John Wiley & Sons, New York, N.Y.

3. STUMM, W. & J.J. MORGAN. 1981. Aquatic Chemistry, 2nd ed. John Wiley & Sons, New York, N.Y.

4. RUSSELL, L.L. 1976. Chemical Aspects of Groundwater Recharge with Wastewaters. Ph.D. thesis, Univ. California, Berkeley.

5. LANGELIER, W.F. 1936. The analytical control of anticorrosion water treatment. *J. Amer. Water Works Assoc.* 28:1500.

6. ROSSUM, J.R. & D.T. MERRILL. 1983. An evaluation of the calcium carbonate saturation indexes. *J. Amer. Water Works Assoc.* 75:95.

7. PLUMMER, L.N. & E. BUSENBERG. 1982. The solubilities of calcite, aragonite, and vaterite in CO_2-H_2O solutions between 0 and 90 degrees C, and an evaluation of the aqueous model for the system $CaCO_3$-CO_2-H_2O. *Geochim. Cosmochim. Acta* 46:1011.

8. ELECTRIC POWER RESEARCH INSTITUTE. 1982. Design and Operating Guidelines Manual for Cooling Water Treatment: Treatment of Recirculating Cooling Water. Section 4. Process Model Documentation and User's Manual. EPRI CS-2276, Electric Power Research Inst., Palo Alto, Calif.

9. GARRELS, R.M. & C.L. CHRIST. 1965. Solutions, Minerals, and Equilibria. Harper & Row, New York, N.Y.

10. MERRILL, D.T. & R.L. SANKS. 1978, 1979. Corrosion control by deposition of $CaCO_3$ films: A practical approach for plant operators. *J. Amer. Water Works Assoc.* 70:592; 70:634 & 71:12.

11. LOEWENTHAL, R.E. & G.v.R. MARAIS. 1976. Carbonate Chemistry of Aquatic Systems: Theory and Applications. Ann Arbor Science Publishers, Ann Arbor, Mich.

12. MERRILL, D.T. 1976. Chemical conditioning for water softening and corrosion control. *In* R.L. Sanks, ed., Water Treatment Plant Design. Ann Arbor Science Publishers, Ann Arbor, Mich.

13. BEN-YAAKOV, S. & I.R. KAPLAN. 1969. Determination of carbonate saturation of seawater with a carbonate saturometer. *Limnol. Oceanogr.* 14:874.

14. BEN-YAAKOV, S. & I.R. KAPLAN. 1971. Deep-sea in situ calcium carbonate saturometry. *J. Geophys. Res.* 76:72.

15. PLATH, D.C., K.S. JOHNSON & R.M. PYTKOWICZ. 1980. The solubility of calcite—probably containing magnesium—in seawater. *Mar. Chem.* 10:9.

16. BALZAR, W. 1980. Calcium carbonate saturometry by alkalinity difference. *Oceanol. Acta.* 3:237.

2330 C.   Indices Predicting the Quantity of $CaCO_3$ That Can Be Precipitated or Dissolved

The Calcium Carbonate Precipitation Potential (CCPP) predicts both tendency to precipitate or to dissolve $CaCO_3$ and quantity that may be precipitated or dissolved. The CCPP also is known by other names, e.g., Calcium Carbonate Precipitation Capacity (CCPC).

The CCPP is defined as the quantity of

$CaCO_3$ that theoretically can be precipitated from oversaturated waters or dissolved by undersaturated waters during equilibration.[1] The amount that actually precipitates or dissolves may be less, because equilibrium may not be achieved. The CCPP is negative for undersaturated waters, zero for saturated waters, and positive for oversaturated waters.

1. Calculating CCPP

The CCPP does not lend itself to hand calculations. Preferably calculate CCPP with computerized water chemistry models and Caldwell-Lawrence diagrams (see Section 2330D).

The most reliable calculations consider ion pairs and the contribution to alkalinity of other species besides HCO_3^-, CO_3^{2-}, OH^-, and H^+. Models that do not consider these factors overestimate the amount of $CaCO_3$ that can be precipitated and underestimate the amount of $CaCO_3$ that can be dissolved.

2. Experimental Determination of CCPP

Estimate CCPP by one of several experimental techniques.

a. Saturometry: See Section 2330B. The CCPP is determined as part of the RS calculation.

b. Alkalinity difference technique: See Section 2330B. The CCPP equals the difference between alkalinity (or calcium) values of the initial and equilibrated water, when they are expressed as $CaCO_3$.

c. Marble test: The marble test[1-5] is similar to the alkalinity difference technique. The CCPP equals the change in alkalinity (or calcium) values during equilibration, when they are expressed as $CaCO_3$.

d. Enslow test: The Enslow test[5] is a continuous version of the alkalinity difference or marble tests. Water is fed continuously to a leveling bulb or separatory funnel partly filled with $CaCO_3$. The effluent from this device is filtered through crushed mar-

ble so that the filtrate is assumed to be in equilibrium with $CaCO_3$. The CCPP equals the change in alkalinity (or calcium) values that occurs during passage through the apparatus.

e. Calcium carbonate deposition test:[6] The calcium carbonate deposition test (CCDT) is an electrochemical method that measures the electric current produced when dissolved oxygen is reduced on a rotating electrode. When an oversaturated water is placed in the apparatus, $CaCO_3$ deposits on the electrode. The deposits interfere with oxygen transfer and the current diminishes. The rate of $CaCO_3$ deposition is directly proportional to the rate at which the current declines. The CCDT and the CCPP are related, but they are not the same. The CCDT is a rate, and the CCPP is a quantity.

For realistic assessments of the CCPP (or CCDT) keep test temperature the same as the temperature of the water source. Alternatively, correct test results to the temperature of the water source.

3. References

1. MERRILL, D.T. & R.L. SANKS. 1978, 1979. Corrosion control by deposition of $CaCO_3$ films: A practical approach for plant operators. *J. Amer. Water Works Assoc.* 70:592; 70:634 & 71:12.

2. MERRILL, D.T. 1976. Chemical conditioning for water softening and corrosion control. *In* R.L. Sanks, ed. Water Treatment Plant Design. Ann Arbor Science Publishers, Ann Arbor, Mich.

3. DE MARTINI, F. 1938. Corrosion and the Langelier calcium carbonate saturation index. *J. Amer. Water Works Assoc.* 30:85.

4. HOOVER, C.P. 1938. Practical application of the Langelier method. *J. Amer. Water Works Assoc.* 30:1802.

5. DYE, J.F. & J.L. TUEPKER. 1971. Chemistry of the Lime-Soda Process. *In* American Water Works Association. Water Quality and Treatment. McGraw-Hill Book Co., New York, N.Y.

6. MCCLELLAND, N.I. & K.H. MANCY. 1979. CCDT bests Ryzner index as pipe $CaCO_3$ film predictor. *Water Sewage Works* 126:77.

2330 D. Diagrams and Computer Codes for CaCO$_3$ Indices

1. Description

Table 2330:III lists diagrams and computer codes that can be used to determine the SI and CCPP. It also provides a brief description of their characteristics.

Many computer codes do not calculate SI directly, but instead calculate the relative saturation (RS). When RS data are presented, calculate the SI from:[1]

$$SI = \log_{10} RS$$

where:

RS = ratio of CaCO$_3$ activity product to CaCO$_3$ solubility product constant.

The diagrams and a few of the codes define pH$_s$ as the pH the water would exhibit if it were in equilibrium with CaCO$_3$ at the existing calcium and total alkalinity concentrations.[2] This definition of pH$_s$ differs from the definition following Equation 1 because alkalinity is used instead of bicarbonate. Within the pH range 6 to 9, alkalinity-based pH$_s$ and bicarbonate-based pH$_s$ are virtually equal, because total alkalinity is due almost entirely to bicarbonate ion. Above pH 9 they differ and Equation 6 no longer applies if SI is calculated with alkalinity-based pH$_s$. However, if SI is determined from bicarbonate-based pH$_s$, Equation 6 continues to apply.

Furthermore, calculating SI with alkalinity-based pH$_s$ reverses the sign of the SI above pH values of approximately pK$_2$, i.e., a positive, not the usual negative, SI connotes an undersaturated water.[3] With bicarbonate-based pH$_s$ or RS, sign reversal does not occur, thereby eliminating the confusing sign change. For these reasons, bicarbonate-based pH$_s$ or RS is preferred.

Table 2330:III lists the definition of pH$_s$ used for each code.

Some models calculate only the amount of CaCO$_3$ that can be precipitated but not the amount of CaCO$_3$ that can be dissolved. Others calculate both.

The diagrams and codes can be used to determine many more parameters than the CaCO$_3$ saturation indices. A fee may be charged for computer software or graphs. The information in Table 2330:III describes parameters each code uses to calculate SI. Contact the sources listed below the table for current information.

2. References

1. SNOEYINK, V.L. & D. JENKINS. 1980. Water Chemistry. John Wiley & Sons, New York, N.Y.
2. LANGELIER, W.F. 1936. The analytical control of anticorrosion water treatment. *J. Amer. Water Works Assoc.* 28:1500.
3. LOEWENTHAL, R.E. & G.v.R. MARAIS. 1976. Carbonate Chemistry of Aquatic Systems: Theory and Applications. Ann Arbor Science Publishers, Ann Arbor, Mich.
4. MERRILL, D.T. & R.L. SANKS. 1978. Corrosion Control by Deposition of CaCO$_3$ Films: A Handbook of Practical Application and Instruction. American Water Works Assoc., Denver, Colo.
5. MERRILL, D.T. 1976. Chemical conditioning for water softening and corrosion control. *In* R.L. Sanks, ed., Water Treatment Plant Design. Ann Arbor Science Publishers, Ann Arbor, Mich.
6. ELECTRIC POWER RESEARCH INSTITUTE. 1982. Design and Operating Guidelines Manual for Cooling Water Treatment: Treatment of Recirculating Cooling Water. Section 4. Process Model Documentation and User's Manual. EPRI CS-2276, Electric Power Research Inst., Palo Alto, Calif.

TABLE 2330:III. GRAPHS AND COMPUTER SOFTWARE THAT CAN BE USED TO CALCULATE CaCO$_3$ SATURATION INDICES*

| Item† | CaCO$_3$ Indices | | Approximate Temperature Range °C | Approximate Limit of Ionic Strength | Ion Pairs Considered? | Alk$_o$ Considered?‡ | Minimum Equipment Required |
	Basis for Calculation of SI	CCPP					
1. Caldwell-Lawrence diagrams	pH$_{sa}$	P, D	2–25	0.030	No	No	Diagrams
2. ACAPP	RS	P, D	−10–110	6+	Yes	Yes	IBM-compatible PC, 512K bytes of RAM, MS DOS or PC DOS v.2.1 or higher
3. DRIVER	RS	P	7–65	2.5	Yes	Yes	Mainframe computer
4. INDEX C	pH$_{sa'}$ pH$_{sb}$	P, D	0–50	0.5	No	No	Hewlett-Packard 41C calculator, with three memory modules
5. LEQUIL	RS	No	5–90	0.5	Yes	Yes	IBM-compatible PC, 256K RAM, Lotus 1-2-3 or work-alike, PC DOS or MS DOS v.2.0 or higher
6. MINTEQA1	RS	P, D	0–100	0.5	Yes	Yes	IBM-compatible PC, 512K bytes of RAM, PC DOS v.3.0 or higher, 10 megabyte hard disk drive, math co-processor useful but not required
7. PHREEQE Standard	RS	P, D	0–100	0.5	Yes	Yes	IBM-compatible PC, known to work with 512K RAM, PC DOS or MS DOS v.2.11 or higher. Also available for mainframe computers.
For high-salinity waters	RS	P, D	0–80	7–8	Yes	Yes	IBM-compatible PC, 640K RAM recommended, with math coprocessor, MS DOS v.3.2 or higher
8. SEQUIL	RS	P, D	7–65	2.5	Yes	Yes	IBM-compatible PC, 512K bytes of RAM, MS DOS or PC DOS v.2.1 or higher.
9. SOLMINEQ.88	RS	P, D	0–350	6	Yes	Yes	IBM-compatible PC, 640K RAM, math coprocessor, PC

TABLE 2330:III, CONT.

Item[†]	CaCO₃ Indices		Approximate Temperature Range °C	Approximate Limit of Ionic Strength	Ion Pairs Considered?	Alk₀ Considered?[‡]	Minimum Equipment Required
	Basis for Calculation of SI	CCPP					
							DOS or MS DOS v.3.0 or higher. Also available for mainframe computer.
10. WTRCHEM	pH$_{sa}$	P, D	0–100	0.5	No	No	Any PC equipped with a BASIC interpreter, 5K RAM.
11. WATEQ4F	RS	No	0–100	0.5	Yes	Yes	IBM-compatible PC, known to work with 512K RAM, PC DOS or MS DOS v.2.11 or higher.

*SI   = saturation index
CCPP = CaCO₃ precipitation potential
pH$_{sa}$ = alkalinity-based pH$_s$
pH$_{sb}$ = bicarbonate-based pH$_s$
P   = calculates amount of CaCO₃ theoretically precipitated

D   = calculates amount of CaCO₃ theoretically dissolved
RS   = relative saturation
PC   = personal computer
RAM = random access memory

† 1. American Water Works Association, 6666 West Quincy Ave., Denver, Colo. 80235 provides 30.5- by 38.1-cm diagrams (order number 20204), and documentation[4] (order number 20203); Loewenthal and Marais[3] provide 10.2- by 11.4-cm diagrams, with documentation; Merrill[5] provides 10.2- by 16.5-cm diagrams, with documentation.
  2. Radian Corp., 8501 MoPac Blvd., P.O. Box 201088, Austin, Texas 78720-1088 Attn: J.G. Noblett (software and documentation).
  3. Power Computing Co., 1930 Hi Line Dr., Dallas, Texas, 74207 (software and documentation[6]).
  4. Brown and Caldwell, P.O. Box 8045, Walnut Creek, Calif. 94596-1220 Attn: D.T. Merrill (software and documentation).
  5. Illinois State Water Survey, Aquatic Chemistry Section, 2204 Griffith Dr., Champaign, Ill. 61820-7495 Attn: T.R. Holm (software and documentation).
  6. Center for Exposure Assessment Modeling, Environmental Research Laboratory, Office of Research and Development. U.S. Environmental Protection Agency, Athens, Ga. 30613 (software and documentation[7]).
  7. U.S. Geological Survey, National Center, MS 437, Reston, Va. 22902, Chief of WATSTORE Program (provides software for mainframe version of standard code); U.S. Geological Survey, Water Resources Division, MS 420, 345 Middlefield Rd., Menlo Park, Calif. 94025 Attn: K. Nordstrom (provides software for personal computer version of standard code); National Water Research Institute, Canada Centre for Inland Waters, 867 Lakeshore Rd., Burlington, Ont., Canada L7R 4A6 Attn: A.S. Crowe (provides software and documentation[8,9] for pesonal computer versions of both standard and high-salinity codes); U.S. Geological Survey, Books and Open File Report Section, Box 25425, Federal Center, Denver, Colo. (provides documentation[8,10] for mainframe and personal computer versions of standard code).
  8. Power Computing Company, 1930 Hi Line Dr., Dallas, Texas 74207 (software and documentation[11]).
  9. U.S. Geological Survey, Water Resources Division, MS 427, 345 Middlefield Rd., Menlo Park, Calif. 94025 Attn: Y.K. Kharaka (software and documentation[12]).
  10. For further information, contact D.T. Merrill, Brown and Caldwell, P.O. Box 8045, Walnut Creek, Calif. 94596-1220.
  11. U.S. Geological Survey, Water Resources Division, MS 420, 345 Middlefield Rd., Menlo Park, Calif. 94025 Attn: K. Nordstrom (software); U.S. Geological Survey, Books and Open File Report Section, Box 25425, Federal Center, Denver, Colo. (documentation[13]).
‡Codes differ in the species included in Alk₀.

7. BROWN, D.S. & J.D. ALLISON. 1987. MINTEQA1 Equilibrium Metal Speciation Model: A User's Manual. EPA-600/3-87-012.

8. PARKHURST, D.L., D.C. THORSTENSON & L.N. PLUMMER. 1980. PHREEQE—A Computer Program for Geochemical Calculations. USGS WRI 80-96 NTIS PB 81-167801.

9. CROWE, A.S. & F.J. LONGSTAFF. 1987. Extension of Geochemical Modeling Techniques to Brines: Coupling of the Pitzer Equations to PHREEQE. *In* Proceedings of Solving Groundwater Problems With Models, National Water Well Assoc., Denver, Colo. Feb. 10–12, 1987.

10. FLEMING, G.W. & L.N. PLUMMER. 1983. PHRQINPT—An Interactive Computer Program for Constructing Input Data Sets to the Geochemical Simulation Program PHREEQE. USGS WRI 83-4236.

11. ELECTRIC POWER RESEARCH INSTITUTE. SEQUIL—An Inorganic Aqueous Chemical Equilibrium Code for Personal Computers; Volume 1, User's Manual/Workbook, Version 1.0, GS-6234-CCML. Electric Power Research Inst., Palo Alto, Calif.

12. KHARAKA, Y.K., W.D. GUNTER, P. K. AGGARWAL, E.H. PERKINS & J.D. DEBRAAL. 1988. Solmineq.88—A Computer Program for Geochemical Modeling of Water–Rock Interactions. USGS WRIR 88-4227, Menlo Park, Calif.

13. BALL, J.W., D.K. NORDSTROM & D.W. ZACHMANN. 1987. WATEQ4F—A Personal Computer Fortran Translation of the Geochemical Model WATEQ2 With Revised Data Base. USGS OFR 87-50.

2340 HARDNESS*

2340 A.   Introduction

1. Definition

Originally, water hardness was understood to be a measure of the capacity of water to precipitate soap. Soap is precipitated chiefly by the calcium and magnesium ions present. Other polyvalent cations also may precipitate soap, but they often are in complex forms, frequently with organic constituents, and their role in water hardness may be minimal and difficult to define. In conformity with current practice, total hardness is defined as the sum of the calcium and magnesium concentrations, both expressed as calcium carbonate, in milligrams per liter.

When hardness numerically is greater than the sum of carbonate and bicarbonate alkalinity, that amount of hardness equivalent to the total alkalinity is called "carbonate hardness"; the amount of hardness in excess of this is called "noncarbonate hardness." When the hardness numerically is equal to or less than the sum of carbonate and bicarbonate alkalinity, all hardness is carbonate hardness and noncarbonate hardness is absent. The hardness may range from zero to hundreds of milligrams per liter, depending on the source and treatment to which the water has been subjected.

2. Selection of Method

Two methods are presented. Method B, hardness by calculation, is applicable to all waters and yields the higher accuracy. If a mineral analysis is performed, hardness by

---

*Approved by Standard Methods Committee, 1985.

calculation can be reported. Method C, the EDTA titration method, measures the calcium and magnesium ions and may be applied with appropriate modification to any kind of water. The procedure described affords a means of rapid analysis.

3. Reporting Results

When reporting hardness, state the method used, for example, "hardness (calc.)" or "hardness (EDTA)."

2340 B.   Hardness by Calculation

1. Discussion

The preferred method for determining hardness is to compute it from the results of separate determinations of calcium and magnesium.

2. Calculation

Hardness, mg equivalent $CaCO_3/L$
$$= 2.497 \text{ [Ca, mg/L]} + 4.118 \text{ [Mg, mg/L]}$$

2340 C.   EDTA Titrimetric Method

1. General Discussion

a. Principle: Ethylenediaminetetraacetic acid and its sodium salts (abbreviated EDTA) form a chelated soluble complex when added to a solution of certain metal cations. If a small amount of a dye such as Eriochrome Black T or Calmagite is added to an aqueous solution containing calcium and magnesium ions at a pH of 10.0 ± 0.1, the solution becomes wine red. If EDTA is added as a titrant, the calcium and magnesium will be complexed, and when all of the magnesium and calcium has been complexed the solution turns from wine red to blue, marking the end point of the titration. Magnesium ion must be present to yield a satisfactory end point. To insure this, a small amount of complexometrically neutral magnesium salt of EDTA is added to the buffer; this automatically introduces sufficient magnesium and obviates the need for a blank correction.

The sharpness of the end point increases with increasing pH. However, the pH cannot be increased indefinitely because of the danger of precipitating calcium carbonate, $CaCO_3$, or magnesium hydroxide, $Mg(OH)_2$, and because the dye changes color at high pH values. The specified pH of 10.0 ± 0.1 is a satisfactory compromise. A limit of 5 min is set for the duration of the titration to minimize the tendency toward $CaCO_3$ precipitation.

b. Interference: Some metal ions interfere by causing fading or indistinct end points or by stoichiometric consumption of EDTA. Reduce this interference by adding certain inhibitors before titration. Mg-CDTA [see 2b3)], selectively complexes heavy metals, releases magnesium into the sample, and may be used as a substitute for toxic or malodorous inhibitors. It is useful only when the magnesium substituted for heavy metals does not contribute significantly to the total hardness. With heavy metal or polyphosphate concentrations below those indicated in Table 2340:I, use Inhibitor I or II. When higher concen-

TABLE 2340:I. MAXIMUM CONCENTRATIONS
OF INTERFERENCES PERMISSIBLE WITH
VARIOUS INHIBITORS*

Interfering Substance	Max. Interference Concentration mg/L	
	Inhibitor I	Inhibitor II
Aluminum	20	20
Barium	†	†
Cadmium	†	20
Cobalt	over 20	0.3
Copper	over 30	20
Iron	over 30	5
Lead	†	20
Manganese (Mn^{2+})	†	1
Nickel	over 20	0.3
Strontium	†	†
Zinc	†	200
Polyphosphate		10

* Based on 25-mL sample diluted to 50 mL.
† Titrates as hardness.

trations of heavy metals are present, determine calcium and magnesium by a non-EDTA method (see Sections 3500-Ca and 3500-Mg) and obtain hardness by calculation. The figures in Table 2340:I are intended as a rough guide only and are based on using a 25-mL sample diluted to 50 mL.

Suspended or colloidal organic matter also may interfere with the end point. Eliminate this interference by evaporating the sample to dryness on a steam bath and heating in a muffle furnace at 550°C until the organic matter is completely oxidized. Dissolve the residue in 20 mL $1N$ hydrochloric acid (HCl), neutralize to pH 7 with $1N$ sodium hydroxide (NaOH), and make up to 50 mL with distilled water; cool to room temperature and continue according to the general procedure.

c. *Titration precautions:* Conduct titrations at or near normal room temperature. The color change becomes impractically slow as the sample approaches freezing temperature. Indicator decomposition becomes a problem in hot water.

The specified pH may produce an environment conducive to $CaCO_3$ precipitation. Although the titrant slowly redissolves such precipitates, a drifting end point often yields low results. Completion of the titration within 5 min minimizes the tendency for $CaCO_3$ to precipitate. The following three methods also reduce precipitation loss:

1) Dilute sample with distilled water to reduce $CaCO_3$ concentration. This simple expedient has been incorporated in the procedure. If precipitation occurs at this dilution of $1 + 1$ use modification 2) or 3). Using too small a sample contributes a systematic error due to the buret-reading error.

2) If the approximate hardness is known or is determined by a preliminary titration, add 90% or more of titrant to sample *before* adjusting pH with buffer.

3) Acidify sample and stir for 2 min to expel CO_2 *before* pH adjustment. Determine alkalinity to indicate amount of acid to be added.

2. Reagents

a. *Buffer solution:*

1) Dissolve 16.9 g ammonium chloride (NH_4Cl) in 143 mL conc ammonium hydroxide (NH_4OH). Add 1.25 g magnesium salt of EDTA (available commercially) and dilute to 250 mL with distilled water.

2) If the magnesium salt of EDTA is unavailable, dissolve 1.179 g disodium salt of ethylenediaminetetraacetic acid dihydrate (analytical reagent grade) and 780 mg magnesium sulfate ($MgSO_4 \cdot 7H_2O$) or 644 mg magnesium chloride ($MgCl_2 \cdot 6H_2O$) in 50 mL distilled water. Add this solution to 16.9 g NH_4Cl and 143 mL conc NH_4OH with mixing and dilute to 250 mL with distilled water. To attain the highest accuracy, adjust to exact equivalence through

appropriate addition of a small amount of EDTA or $MgSO_4$ or $MgCl_2$.

Store Solution 1) or 2) in a plastic or borosilicate glass container for no longer than 1 month. Stopper tightly to prevent loss of ammonia (NH_3) or pickup of carbon dioxide (CO_2). Dispense buffer solution by means of a bulb-operated pipet. Discard buffer when 1 or 2 mL added to the sample fails to produce a pH of 10.0 ± 0.1 at the titration end point.

3) Satisfactory alternate "odorless buffers" also are available commercially. They contain the magnesium salt of EDTA and have the advantage of being relatively odorless and more stable than the NH_4Cl-NH_4OH buffer. They usually do not provide as good an end point as NH_4Cl-NH_4OH because of slower reactions and they may be unsuitable when this method is automated. Prepare one of these buffers by mixing 55 mL conc HCl with 400 mL distilled water and then, slowly and with stirring, adding 300 mL 2-aminoethanol (free of aluminum and heavier metals). Add 5.0 g magnesium salt of EDTA and dilute to 1 L with distilled water.

b. Complexing agents: For most waters no complexing agent is needed. Occasionally water containing interfering ions requires adding an appropriate complexing agent to give a clear, sharp change in color at the end point. The following are satisfactory:

1) *Inhibitor I:* Adjust acid samples to pH 6 or higher with buffer or 0.1N NaOH. Add 250 mg sodium cyanide (NaCN) in powder form. Add sufficient buffer to adjust to pH 10.0 ± 0.1 (CAUTION: *NaCN is extremely poisonous. Take extra precautions in its use.* Flush solutions containing this inhibitor down the drain with large quantities of water after insuring that no acid is present to liberate volatile poisonous hydrogen cyanide.)

2) *Inhibitor II:* Dissolve 5.0 g sodium sulfide nonahydrate ($Na_2S \cdot 9H_2O$) or 3.7 g $Na_2S \cdot 5H_2O$ in 100 mL distilled water. Ex-

clude air with a tightly fitting rubber stopper. This inhibitor deteriorates through air oxidation. It produces a sulfide precipitate that obscures the end point when appreciable concentrations of heavy metals are present. Use 1 mL in ¶ 3*b* below.

3) *MgCDTA:* Magnesium salt of 1, 2-cyclohexanediaminetetraacetic acid. Add 250 mg per 100 mL sample and dissolve completely before adding buffer solution. Use this complexing agent to avoid using toxic or odorous inhibitors when interfering substances are present in concentrations that affect the end point but will not contribute significantly to the hardness value.

Commercial preparations incorporating a buffer and a complexing agent are available. Such mixtures must maintain pH 10.0 ± 0.1 during titration and give a clear, sharp end point when the sample is titrated.

c. Indicators: Many types of indicator solutions have been advocated and may be used if the analyst demonstrates that they yield accurate values. The prime difficulty with indicator solutions is deterioration with aging, giving indistinct end points. For example, alkaline solutions of Eriochrome Black T are sensitive to oxidants and aqueous or alcoholic solutions are unstable. In general, use the least amount of indicator providing a sharp end point. It is the analyst's responsibility to determine individually the optimal indicator concentration.

1) *Eriochrome Black T:* Sodium salt of 1-(1-hydroxy-2-naphthylazo)-5-nitro-2-naphthol-4-sulfonic acid; No. 203 in the Color Index. Dissolve 0.5 g dye in 100 g 2,2′,2″-nitrilotriethanol (also called triethanolamine) or 2-methoxymethanol (also called ethylene glycol monomethyl ether). Add 2 drops per 50 mL solution to be titrated. Adjust volume if necessary.

2) *Calmagite:* 1-(1-hydroxy-4-methyl-2-phenylazo)-2-naphthol-4-sulfonic acid. This is stable in aqueous solution and produces the same color change as Eriochrome

Black T, with a sharper end point. Dissolve 0.10 g Calmagite in 100 mL distilled water. Use 1 mL per 50 mL solution to be titrated. Adjust volume if necessary.

3) Indicators 1 and 2 can be used in dry powder form if care is taken to avoid excess indicator. Prepared dry mixtures of these indicators and an inert salt are available commercially.

If the end point color change of these indicators is not clear and sharp, it usually means that an appropriate complexing agent is required. If NaCN inhibitor does not sharpen the end point, the indicator probably is at fault.

d. Standard EDTA titrant, 0.01*M*: Weigh 3.723 g analytical reagent-grade disodium ethylenediaminetetraacetate dihydrate, also called (ethylenedinitrilo) tetraacetic acid disodium salt (EDTA), dissolve in distilled water, and dilute to 1000 mL. Standardize against standard calcium solution (¶ 2e) as described in ¶ 3b below.

Because the titrant extracts hardness-producing cations from soft-glass containers, store in polyethylene (preferable) or borosilicate glass bottles. Compensate for gradual deterioration by periodic restandardization and by using a suitable correction factor.

e. Standard calcium solution: Weigh 1.000 g anhydrous $CaCO_3$ powder (primary standard or special reagent low in heavy metals, alkalis, and magnesium) into a 500-mL erlenmeyer flask. Place a funnel in the flask neck and add, a little at a time, 1 + 1 HCl until all $CaCO_3$ has dissolved. Add 200 mL distilled water and boil for a few minutes to expel CO_2. Cool, add a few drops of methyl red indicator, and adjust to the intermediate orange color by adding 3*N* NH_4OH or 1 + 1 HCl, as required. Transfer quantitatively and dilute to 1000 mL with distilled water; 1 mL = 1.00 mg $CaCO_3$.

f. Sodium hydroxide, NaOH, 0.1*N*.

3. Procedure

a. Pretreatment of polluted water and wastewater samples: Use nitric acid-sulfuric acid or nitric acid-perchloric acid digestion (Section 3030).

b. Titration of sample: Select a sample volume that requires less than 15 mL EDTA titrant and complete titration within 5 min, measured from time of buffer addition.

Dilute 25.0 mL sample to about 50 mL with distilled water in a porcelain casserole or other suitable vessel. Add 1 to 2 mL buffer solution. Usually 1 mL will be sufficient to give a pH of 10.0 to 10.1. The absence of a sharp end-point color change in the titration usually means that an inhibitor must be added at this point (¶ 2b et seq.) or that the indicator has deteriorated.

Add 1 to 2 drops indicator solution or an appropriate amount of dry-powder indicator formulation [¶ 2c3)]. Add standard EDTA titrant slowly, with continuous stirring, until the last reddish tinge disappears. Add the last few drops at 3- to 5-s intervals. At the end point the solution normally is blue. Daylight or a daylight fluorescent lamp is recommended highly because ordinary incandescent lights tend to produce a reddish tinge in the blue at the end point.

If sufficient sample is available and interference is absent, improve accuracy by increasing sample size, as described in ¶ 3c below.

c. Low-hardness sample: For ion-exchanger effluent or other softened water and for natural waters of low hardness (less than 5 mg/L), take a larger sample, 100 to 1000 mL, for titration and add proportionately larger amounts of buffer, inhibitor, and indicator. Add standard EDTA titrant slowly from a microburet and run a blank, using redistilled, distilled, or deionized water of the same volume as the sample, to which identical amounts of buffer, inhibitor, and indicator have been added.

Subtract volume of EDTA used for blank from volume of EDTA used for sample.

4. Calculation

Hardness (EDTA) as mg $CaCO_3$/L
$$= \frac{A \times B \times 1000}{mL \text{ sample}}$$

where:

    A = mL titration for sample and
    B = mg $CaCO_3$ equivalent to 1.00 mL
    EDTA titrant.

5. Precision and Bias

A synthetic sample containing 610 mg/L total hardness as $CaCO_3$ contributed by 108 mg Ca/L and 82 mg Mg/L, and the following supplementary substances: 3.1 mg K/L, 19.9 mg Na/L, 241 mg Cl^-/L, 0.25 mg NO_2^--N/L, 1.1 mg NO_3^--N/L, 259 mg SO_4^{2-}/L, and 42.5 mg total alkalinity/L (contributed by $NaHCO_3$) in distilled water was analyzed in 56 laboratories by the EDTA titrimetric method with a relative standard deviation of 2.9% and a relative error of 0.8%.

6. Bibliography

CONNORS, J.J. 1950. Advances in chemical and colorimetric methods. *J. Amer. Water Works Assoc.* 42:33.

DIEHL, H., C.A. GOETZ & C.C. HACH. 1950. The versenate titration for total hardness. *J. Amer. Water Works Assoc.* 42:40.

BETZ, J.D. & C.A. NOLL. 1950. Total hardness determination by direct colorimetric titration. *J. Amer. Water Works Assoc.* 42:49.

GOETZ, C.A., T.C. LOOMIS & H. DIEHL. 1950. Total hardness in water: The stability of standard disodium dihydrogen ethylenediaminetetraacetate solutions. *Anal. Chem.* 22:798.

DISKANT, E.M. 1952. Stable indicator solutions for complexometric determination of total hardness in water. *Anal. Chem.* 24:1856.

BARNARD, A.J., JR., W.C. BROAD & H. FLASCHKA. 1956 & 1957. The EDTA titration. *Chemist Analyst* 45:86 & 46:46.

GOETZ, C.A. & R.C. SMITH. 1959. Evaluation of various methods and reagents for total hardness and calcium hardness in water. *Iowa State J. Sci.* 34:81 (Aug. 15).

SCHWARZENBACH, G. & H. FLASCHKA. 1969. Complexometric Titrations, 2nd ed. Barnes & Noble, Inc., New York, N.Y.

2510   CONDUCTIVITY*

2510 A.   Introduction

Conductivity is a numerical expression of the ability of an aqueous solution to carry an electric current. This ability depends on the presence of ions, their total concentration, mobility, valence, and relative concentrations, and on the temperature of measurement. Solutions of most inorganic acids, bases, and salts are relatively good conductors. Conversely, molecules of organic compounds that do not dissociate in aqueous solution conduct a current very poorly, if at all.

The physical measurement made in a laboratory determination of conductivity is usually of resistance, measured in ohms or megohms. The resistance of a conductor is inversely proportional to its cross-sectional area and directly proportional to its length

---

* Approved by Standard Methods Committee, 1988.

The magnitude of the resistance measured in an aqueous solution therefore depends on the characteristics of the conductivity cell used, and is not meaningful without knowledge of these characteristics. Specific resistance is the resistance of a cube 1 cm on an edge. In aqueous solutions such a measurement is rare because of the difficulties of electrode fabrication. Practical electrodes measure a given fraction of the specific resistance, the fraction being the cell constant, C:

$$C = \frac{\text{Measured resistance, } R_m}{\text{Specific resistance, } R_s}$$

The reciprocal of resistance is conductance. It measures the ability to conduct a current and is expressed in reciprocal ohms or mhos. A more convenient unit in water analysis is micromhos. When the cell constant is known and applied, the measured conductance is converted to the specific conductance or conductivity, K_s, the reciprocal of the specific resistance:

$$K_s = \frac{1}{R_s} = \frac{C}{R_m}$$

The term "conductivity" is preferred and customarily is reported in micromhos per centimeter (μmhos/cm). In the International System of Units (SI) the reciprocal of the ohm is the siemens (S) and conductivity is reported as millisiemens per meter (mS/m); 1 mS/m = 10 μmhos/cm. To report results in SI units divide μmhos/cm by 10.

Freshly distilled water has a conductivity of 0.5 to 2 μmhos/cm, increasing after a few weeks of storage to 2 to 4 μmhos/ cm. This increase is caused mainly by absorption of atmospheric carbon dioxide, and, to a lesser extent, ammonia.

The conductivity of potable waters in the ᵗed States ranges generally from 50 to ᵗ μmhos/cm. The conductivity of do- vastewaters may be near that of the

local water supply, although some industrial wastes have conductivities above 10 000 μmhos/cm. Conductivity instruments are used in pipelines, channels, flowing streams, and lakes and can be incorporated in multiple-parameter monitoring stations using recorders.

Laboratory measurement of conductivity is relatively accurate but less accurate means of determining conductivity find numerous applications such as signalling exhaustion of ion-exchange resins and rapid determination of large changes in inorganic content of waters and wastewaters. Monitoring devices can give continuous, unattended records of conductivity if they are properly installed and maintained. Most problems in obtaining good records with monitoring equipment are related to electrode fouling and to inadequate sample circulation.

Laboratory conductivity measurements are used to:

a. Establish degree of mineralization to assess the effect of the total concentration of ions on chemical equilibria, physiological effect on plants or animals, corrosion rates, etc.

b. Assess degree of mineralization of distilled and deionized water.

c. Evaluate variations in dissolved mineral concentration of raw water or wastewater. Minor seasonal variations found in reservoir waters contrast sharply with the daily fluctuations in some polluted river waters. Wastewater containing significant trade wastes also may show a considerable daily variation.

d. Estimate sample size to be used for common chemical determinations and to check results of a chemical analysis.

e. Determine amount of ionic reagent needed in certain precipitation and neutralization reactions, the end point being denoted by a change in slope of the curve resulting from plotting conductivity against buret readings.

f. Estimate total dissolved solids in a

sample by multiplying conductivity (in micromhos per centimeter) by an empirical factor. This factor may vary from 0.55 to 0.9, depending on the soluble components of the water and on the temperature of measurement. Relatively high factors may be required for saline or boiler waters, whereas lower factors may apply where considerable hydroxide or free acid is present. Even though sample evaporation results in the change of bicarbonate to carbonate the empirical factor is derived for a comparatively constant water supply by dividing dissolved solids by conductivity. Approximate the milliequivalents per liter of either cations or anions in some waters by multiplying conductivity (in micromhos per centimeter) by 0.01.

Electrolytic conductivity (unlike metallic conductivity) increases with temperature at a rate of approximately 1.9%/°C. Significant errors can result from inaccurate temperature measurement. Potassium chloride (KCl) solutions have a lower temperature coefficient of conductivity than typical potable water. Sodium chloride (NaCl), on the other hand, has a temperature coefficient that closely approximates that found in most waters from wells and surface sources. Note that each ion has a different temperature coefficient; thus, for precise work, determine conductivity at 25.0°C. The significance of the temperature correction, one part in 500 for 25 ± 0.1°C, depends on available equipment and precision desired.

2510 B. Laboratory Method

1. General Discussion

See Section 2510A.

2. Apparatus

a. Self-contained conductivity instruments: Use an instrument consisting of a source of alternating current, a Wheatstone bridge, a null indicator, and a conductivity cell or other instrument measuring the ratio of alternating current through the cell to voltage across it. The latter has the advantage of a linear reading of conductivity. Choose an instrument capable of measuring conductivity with an error not exceeding 1% or 1 μmho/cm, whichever is greater.

b. Thermometer, capable of being read to the nearest 0.1°C and covering the range 23 to 27°C. An electrical thermometer having a small thermistor sensing element is convenient because of its rapid response.

c. Conductivity cell:

1) Platinum-electrode type—Conductivity cells containing platinized electrodes are available in either pipet or immersion form. Cell choice depends on expected range of conductivity and resistance range of the instrument. Experimentally check range for complete instrument assembly by comparing instrumental results with the true conductivities of the KCl solutions listed in Table 2510:I. Clean new cells with chromic-sulfuric acid cleaning mixture and platinize the electrodes before use. Subsequently, clean and replatinize them whenever the readings become erratic, when a sharp end point cannot be obtained, or when inspection shows that any platinum black has flaked off. To platinize, prepare a solution of 1 g chloroplatinic acid, $H_2PtCl_6 \cdot 6H_2O$, and 12 mg lead acetate in 100 mL distilled water. A stronger solution reduces the time required to platinize electrodes and may be used when time is a factor, e.g., when the cell constant is 1.0/cm or more. Immerse the electrodes in this solution and connect both to the neg-

TABLE 2510:I. CONDUCTIVITY OF POTASSIUM
CHLORIDE SOLUTIONS AT 25°C.*

Concentration M	Equivalent Conductivity mho/cm/equiv.	Conductivity μmhos/cm
0	149.85	
0.0001	149.43	14.94†
0.0005	147.81	73.90
0.001	146.95	147.0
0.005	143.55	717.8
0.01	141.27	1 413
0.02	138.34	2 767
0.05	133.37	6 668
0.1	128.96	12 900
0.2	124.08	24 820
0.5	117.27	58 640
1	111.87	111 900

* Data drawn from Robinson & Stokes.[1]
† Computed from equation given in Lind et al.[2]

ative terminal of a 1.5-V dry cell battery. Connect positive side of battery to a piece of platinum wire and dip the wire into the solution. Use a current such that only a small quantity of gas is evolved. Continue electrolysis until both cell electrodes are coated with platinum black. Save platinizing solution for subsequent use. Rinse electrodes thoroughly and when not in use keep immersed in distilled water.

2) Nonplatinum-electrode type—Use conductivity cells containing electrodes constructed from durable common metals (stainless steel among others) for continuous monitoring and field studies. Calibrate such cells by comparing sample conductivity with results obtained with a laboratory instrument. Use properly designed and mated cell and instrument to minimize errors in cell constant.

3. Reagents

a. Conductivity water: Pass distilled water through a mixed-bed deionizer and discard first liter. Conductivity should be less than 1 μmho/cm.

b. Standard potassium chloride solution,

KCl, 0.0100M: Dissolve 745.6 mg anhydrous KCl in conductivity water and dilute to 1000 mL at 25°C. This is the standard reference solution, which at 25°C has a conductivity of 1413 μmhos/cm. It is satisfactory for most samples when the cell has a constant between 1 and 2. For other cell constants, use stronger or weaker KCl solutions listed in Table 2510:I. Store in a glass-stoppered borosilicate glass bottle.

4. Procedure

a. Determination of cell constant: Rinse conductivity cell with at least three portions of 0.01M KCl solution. Adjust temperature of a fourth portion to 25.0 ± 0.1°C. Measure resistance of this portion and note temperature. Compute cell constant, C:

$$C = (0.001\ 413)\,(R_{KCl})\,[1 + 0.0191\,(t - 25)]$$

where:

R_{KCl} = measured resistance, ohms, and
t = observed temperature, °C.

b. Conductivity measurement: Rinse cell with one or more portions of sample. Adjust temperature of a final portion to 25.0 ± 0.1°C. Measure sample resistance or conductivity and note temperature.

5. Calculation

The temperature coefficient of most waters is only approximately the same as that of standard KCl solution; the more the temperature of measurement deviates from 25.0°C, the greater the uncertainty in applying the temperature correction. Report all conductivities at 25.0°C.

a. When sample resistance is measured, conductivity at 25°C is:

$$K = \frac{(1\ 000\ 000)\,(C)}{R_m[1 + 0.0191\,(t - 25)]}$$

where:

K = conductivity, μmhos/cm,

C = cell constant, cm^{-1},
R_m = measured resistance of sample, ohms, and
t = temperature of measurement.

b. When sample conductivity is measured, conductivity at 25°C is:

$$K = \frac{(K_m)(1\ 000\ 000)(C)}{1 + 0.0191\ (t - 25)}$$

where:

K_m = measured conductivity, mhos at t°C, and other units are defined as above.

NOTE: If conductivity readout is in micromhos per centimeter, delete the factor 1 000 000 in the numerator.

c. For instruments giving values in SI units,

1 mS/m = 10 μmhos/cm, or conversely,
1 μmho/cm = 0.1 mS/m.

6. Precision and Bias

Three synthetic samples were tested with the following results:

Conductivity μmhos/cm	No. of Results	Relative Standard Deviation %	Relative Error %
147.0	117	8.6	9.4
303.0	120	7.8	1.9
228.0	120	8.4	3.0

7. References

1. ROBINSON, R.A. & R.H. STOKES. 1959. Electrolyte Solutions, 2nd ed. Academic Press, New York, p. 466.
2. LIND, J.E., J.J. ZWOLENIK & R.M. FUOSS. 1959. Calibration of conductance cells at 25°C with aqueous solutions of potassium chloride. J. Amer. Chem. Soc. 81:1557.

8. Bibliography

JONES, G. & B.C. BRADSHAW. 1933. The measurement of the conductance of electrolytes. V. A redetermination of the conductance of standard potassium chloride solutions in absolute units. J. Amer. Chem. Soc. 55:1780.

*   *   *

2540   SOLIDS*

2540 A.   Introduction

The terms "solids," "suspended," and "dissolved," as used herein, replace the terms "residue," "nonfiltrable," and "filtrable" of editions previous to the 16th. Solids refer to matter suspended or dissolved in water or wastewater. Solids may affect water or effluent quality adversely in a number of ways. Waters with high dissolved solids generally are of inferior palatability and may induce an unfavorable physiological reaction in the transient consumer. For these reasons, a limit of 500 mg dissolved solids/L is desirable for drinking waters. Highly mineralized waters also are unsuitable for many industrial applications. Waters high in suspended solids may be esthetically unsatisfactory for such purposes as bathing. Solids analyses are important in the control of biological and physical wastewater treatment processes and for assessing compliance with regulatory agency wastewater effluent limitations.

1. Definitions

"Total solids" is the term applied to the material residue left in the vessel after evap-

*Approved by Standard Methods Committee, 1985.

oration of a sample and its subsequent drying in an oven at a defined temperature. Total solids includes "total suspended solids," the portion of total solids retained by a filter, and "total dissolved solids," the portion that passes through the filter.

The type of filter holder, the pore size, porosity, area, and thickness of the filter and the physical nature, particle size, and amount of material deposited on the filter are the principal factors affecting separation of suspended from dissolved solids.

"Fixed solids" is the term applied to the residue of total, suspended, or dissolved solids after ignition for a specified time at a specified temperature. The weight loss on ignition is called "volatile solids." Determinations of fixed and volatile solids do not distinguish precisely between inorganic and organic matter because the loss on ignition is not confined to organic matter. It includes losses due to decomposition or volatilization of some mineral salts. Better characterization of organic matter can be made by such tests as total organic carbon (Section 5310), BOD (Section 5210), and COD (Section 5220).

"Settleable solids" is the term applied to the material settling out of suspension within a defined period. It may include floating material, depending on the technique (2540F.3b).

2. Sources of Error and Variability

The temperature at which the residue is dried has an important bearing on results, because weight losses due to volatilization of organic matter, mechanically occluded water, water of crystallization, and gases from heat-induced chemical decomposition, as well as weight gains due to oxidation, depend on temperature and time of heating.

Residues dried at 103 to 105°C may retain not only water of crystallization but also some mechanically occluded water. Loss of CO_2 will result in conversion of bicarbonate to carbonate. Loss of organic matter by volatilization usually will be very slight. Because removal of occluded water is marginal at this temperature, attainment of constant weight may be very slow.

Residues dried at 180 ± 2°C will lose almost all mechanically occluded water. Some water of crystallization may remain, especially if sulfates are present. Organic matter may be lost by volatilization, but not completely destroyed. Loss of CO_2 results from conversion of bicarbonates to carbonates and carbonates may be decomposed partially to oxides or basic salts. Some chloride and nitrate salts may be lost. In general, evaporating and drying water samples at 180°C yields values for dissolved solids closer to those obtained through summation of individually determined mineral species than the dissolved solids values secured through drying at the lower temperature.

Results for residues high in oil or grease may be questionable because of the difficulty of drying to constant weight in a reasonable time.

Analyses performed for some special purposes may demand deviation from the stated procedures to include an unusual constituent with the measured solids. Whenever such variations of technique are introduced, record and present them with the results.

3. Sample Handling and Preservation

Use resistant-glass or plastic bottles, provided that the material in suspension does not adhere to container walls. Begin analysis as soon as possible because of the impracticality of preserving the sample. Refrigerate sample at 4°C up to analysis to minimize microbiological decomposition of solids.

4. Selection of Method

Methods B through F are suitable for the determination of solids in potable, surface, and saline waters, as well as domestic and industrial wastewaters in the range up to 20 000 mg/L.

Method G is suitable for the determination of solids in sediments, as well as solid and semisolid materials produced during water and wastewater treatment.

5. Bibliography

THERIAULT, E.J. & H.H. WAGENHALS. 1923. Studies of representative sewage plants. *Pub. Health Bull.* No. 132.

U.S. ENVIRONMENTAL PROTECTION AGENCY. 1979. Methods for Chemical Analysis of Water and Wastes. Publ. 600/4-79-020, Environmental Monitoring and Support Lab., U.S. Environmental Protection Agency, Cincinnati, Ohio.

2540 B. Total Solids Dried at 103–105°C

1. General Discussion

a. Principle: A well-mixed sample is evaporated in a weighed dish and dried to constant weight in an oven at 103 to 105°C. The increase in weight over that of the empty dish represents the total solids. The results may not represent the weight of actual dissolved and suspended solids in wastewater samples (see above).

b. Interferences: Highly mineralized water with a significant concentration of calcium, magnesium, chloride, and/or sulfate may be hygroscopic and require prolonged drying, proper desiccation, and rapid weighing. Exclude large, floating particles or submerged agglomerates of nonhomogeneous materials from the sample if it is determined that their inclusion is not desired in the final result. Disperse visible floating oil and grease with a blender before withdrawing a sample portion for analysis. Because excessive residue in the dish may form a water-trapping crust, limit sample to no more than 200 mg residue.

2. Apparatus

a. Evaporating dishes: Dishes of 100-mL capacity made of one of the following materials:

1) Porcelain, 90-mm diam.
2) Platinum—Generally satisfactory for all purposes.

3) High-silica glass.*

b. Muffle furnace for operation at 550 ± 50°C.

c. Steam bath.

d. Desiccator, provided with a desiccant containing a color indicator of moisture concentration.

e. Drying oven, for operation at 103 to 105°C.

f. Analytical balance, capable of weighing to 0.1 mg.

3. Procedure

a. Preparation of evaporating dish: If volatile solids are to be measured ignite clean evaporating dish at 550 ± 50°C for 1 h in a muffle furnace. If only total solids are to be measured, heat clean dish to 103 to 105°C for 1 h. Store dish in desiccator until needed. Weigh immediately before use.

b. Sample analysis: Choose a sample volume that will yield a residue between 2.5 mg and 200 mg. Transfer a measured volume of well-mixed sample to preweighed dish and evaporate to dryness on a steam bath or in a drying oven. If necessary, add successive sample portions to the same dish after evaporation. When evaporating in a drying oven, lower temperature to approximately 2°C below boiling to prevent splattering. Dry evaporated sample for at least

---

*Vycor, product of Corning Glass Works, Corning, N.Y., or equivalent.

1 h in an oven at 103 to 105°C, cool dish in desiccator to balance temperature, and weigh. Repeat cycle of drying, cooling, desiccating, and weighing until a constant weight is obtained, or until weight loss is less than 4% of previous weight or 0.5 mg, whichever is less.

4. Calculation

$$\text{mg total solids} / L = \frac{(A - B) \times 1000}{\text{sample volume, mL}}$$

where:

A = weight of dried residue + dish, mg, and
B = weight of dish, mg.

5. Precision

Single-laboratory duplicate analyses of 41 samples of water and wastewater were made with a standard deviation of differences of 6.0 mg/L.

6. Bibliography

SYMONS, G.E. & B. MOREY. 1941. The effect of drying time on the determination of solids in sewage and sewage sludges. *Sewage Works J.* 13:936.

2540 C.   Total Dissolved Solids Dried at 180°C

1. General Discussion

a. Principle: A well-mixed sample is filtered through a standard glass fiber filter, and the filtrate is evaporated to dryness in a weighed dish and dried to constant weight at 180°C. The increase in dish weight represents the total dissolved solids.

The results may not agree with the theoretical value for solids calculated from chemical analysis of sample (see above). Approximate methods for correlating chemical analysis with dissolved solids are available.[1] The filtrate from the total suspended solids determination (Section 2540D) may be used for determination of total dissolved solids.

b. Interferences: Highly mineralized waters with a considerable calcium, magnesium, chloride, and/or sulfate content may be hygroscopic and require prolonged drying, proper desiccation, and rapid weighing. Samples high in bicarbonate require careful and possibly prolonged drying at 180°C to insure complete conversion of bicarbonate to carbonate. Because excessive residue in the dish may form a water-trapping crust, limit sample to no more than 200 mg residue.

2. Apparatus

Apparatus listed in 2540B.2*a-d* is required, and in addition:

*a. Glass-fiber filter disks** without organic binder.

b. Filtration apparatus: One of the following, suitable for filter disk selected:

1) *Membrane filter funnel.*

2) *Gooch crucible,* 25-mL to 40-mL capacity, with Gooch crucible adapter.

3) *Filtration apparatus* with reservoir and coarse (40- to 60-μm) fritted disk as filter support.

c. Suction flask, of sufficient capacity for sample size selected.

d. Drying oven, for operation at 180 ± 2°C.

3. Procedure

a. Preparation of glass-fiber filter disk: Insert disk with wrinkled side up into filtration apparatus. Apply vacuum and wash disk with three successive 20-mL volumes of distilled water. Continue suction to remove all traces of water. Discard washings.

---

*Whatman grade 934AH; Gelman type A/E; Millipore type AP40; E-D Scientific Specialties grade 161; or equivalent. Available in diameters of 2.2 cm to 4.7 cm.

b. Preparation of evaporating dish: If vo atile solids are to be measured, ignite cleaned evaporating dish at 550 ± 50°C for 1 h in a muffle furnace. If only total dissolved solids are to be measured, heat clean dish to 180 ± 2°C for 1 h in an oven. Store in desiccator until needed. Weigh immediately before use.

c. Selection of filter and sample sizes: Choose sample volume to yield between 2.5 and 200 mg dried residue. If more than 10 min are required to complete filtration, increase filter size or decrease sample volume but do not produce less than 2.5 mg residue.

d. Sample analysis: Filter measured volume of well-mixed sample through glass-fiber filter, wash with three successive 10-mL volumes of distilled water, allowing complete drainage between washings, and continue suction for about 3 min after filtration is complete. Transfer filtrate to a weighed evaporating dish and evaporate to dryness on a steam bath. If filtrate volume exceeds dish capacity add successive portions to the same dish after evaporation. Dry for at least 1 h in an oven at 180 ± 2°C, cool in a desiccator to balance temperature, and weigh. Repeat drying cycle of drying, cooling, desiccating, and weighing until a constant weight is obtained or until weight loss is less than 4% of previous weight or 0.5 mg, whichever is less.

4. Calculation

$$\text{mg total dissolved solids/L} = \frac{(A - B) \times 1000}{\text{sample volume, mL}}$$

where:

A = weight of dried residue + dish, mg, and
B = weight of dish, mg.

5. Precision

Single-laboratory analyses of 77 samples of a known of 293 mg/L were made with a standard deviation of differences of 21.20 mg/L.

6. Reference

1. SOKOLOFF, V.P. 1933. Water of crystallization in total solids of water analysis. *Ind. Eng. Chem.*, Anal. Ed. 5:336.

7. Bibliography

HOWARD, C.S. 1933. Determination of total dissolved solids in water analysis. *Ind. Eng. Chem.*, Anal. Ed. 5:4.

U.S. GEOLOGICAL SURVEY. 1974. Methods for Collection and Analysis of Water Samples for Dissolved Minerals and Gases. Techniques of Water-Resources Investigations, Book 5, Chap. A1. U.S. Geological Surv., Washington, D.C.

2540 D. Total Suspended Solids Dried at 103–105°C

1. General Discussion

a. Principle: A well-mixed sample is filtered through a weighed standard glass-fiber filter and the residue retained on the filter is dried to a constant weight at 103 to 105°C. The increase in weight of the filter represents the total suspended solids. If the suspended material clogs the filter and prolongs filtration, the difference between the total solids and the total dissolved solids may provide an estimate of the total suspended solids.

b. Interferences: Exclude large floating particles or submerged agglomerates of nonhomogeneous materials from the sample if it is determined that their inclusion is not desired in the final result. Because excessive residue on the filter may form a water-entrapping crust, limit the sample size to that yielding no more than 200 mg residue. For samples high in dissolved solids thoroughly wash the filter to ensure removal of the dissolved material. Prolonged filtration times resulting from filter clogging may produce high results owing to excessive solids capture on the clogged filter.

2. Apparatus

Apparatus listed in Sections 2540B.2 and 2540C.2 is required, except for evaporating dishes, steam bath, and 180°C drying oven. In addition:

*Planchet,** aluminum or stainless steel, 65-mm diam.

3. Procedure

a. Preparation of glass-fiber filter disk: Insert disk with wrinkled side up in filtration apparatus. Apply vacuum and wash disk with three successive 20-mL portions of distilled water. Continue suction to remove all traces of water, and discard washings. Remove filter from filtration apparatus and transfer to an aluminum or stainless steel planchet as a support. Alternatively remove crucible and filter combination if a Gooch crucible is used. Dry in an oven at 103 to 105°C for 1 h. If volatile solids are to be measured, ignite at 550 ± 50°C for 15 min in a muffle furnace. Cool in desiccator to balance temperature and weigh. Repeat cycle of drying or igniting, cooling, desiccating, and weighing until a constant weight is obtained or until weight loss is less than 0.5 mg between successive weighings. Store in desiccator until needed. Weigh immediately before use.

b. Selection of filter and sample sizes: See Section 2540C.3c. For nonhomogeneous samples such as raw wastewater, use a large filter to permit filtering a representative sample.

c. Sample analysis: Assemble filtering apparatus and filter and begin suction. Wet filter with a small volume of distilled water to seat it. Filter a measured volume of well-mixed sample through the glass fiber filter.

Wash with three successive 10-mL volumes of distilled water, allowing complete drainage between washings and continue suction for about 3 min after filtration is complete. Carefully remove filter from filtration apparatus and transfer to an aluminum or stainless steel planchet as a support. Alternatively, remove the crucible and filter combination from the crucible adapter if a Gooch crucible is used. Dry for at least 1 h at 103 to 105°C in an oven, cool in a desiccator to balance temperature, and weigh. Repeat the cycle of drying, cooling, desiccating, and weighing until a constant weight is obtained or until the weight loss is less than 4% of the previous weight or 0.5 mg, whichever is less.

4. Calculation

$$\text{mg total suspended solids/L} = \frac{(A - B) \times 1000}{\text{sample volume, mL}}$$

where:

A = weight of filter + dried residue, mg, and
B = weight of filter, mg.

5. Precision

The standard deviation was 5.2 mg/L (coefficient of variation 33%) at 15 mg/L, 24 mg/L (10%) at 242 mg/L, and 13 mg/L (0.76%) at 1707 mg/L in studies by two analysts of four sets of 10 determinations each.

Single-laboratory duplicate analyses of 50 samples of water and wastewater were made with a standard deviation of differences of 2.8 mg/L.

6. Bibliography

DEGEN, J. & F.E. NUSSBERGER. 1956. Notes on the determination of suspended solids. *Sewage Ind. Wastes* 28:237.

CHANIN, G., E.H. CHOW, R.B. ALEXANDER & J. POWERS. 1958. Use of glass fiber filter me-

---

*Available from New England Nuclear, Boston, Mass., or equivalent.

dium in the suspended solids determination. *Sewage Ind. Wastes* 30:1062.

NUSBAUM, I. 1958. New method for determination of suspended solids. *Sewage Ind. Wastes* 30:1066.

SMITH, A.L. & A.E. GREENBERG. 1963. Evaluation of methods for determining suspended solids in wastewater. *J. Water Pollut. Control Fed.* 35:940.

WYCKOFF, B.M. 1964. Rapid solids determination using glass fiber filters. *Water Sewage Works* 111:277.

NATIONAL COUNCIL OF THE PAPER INDUSTRY FOR AIR AND STREAM IMPROVEMENT. 1975. A Preliminary Review of Analytical Methods for the Determination of Suspended Solids in Paper Industry Effluents for Compliance with EPA-NPDES Permit Terms. Spec. Rep. No. 75-01. National Council of the Paper Industry for Air & Stream Improvement, New York, N.Y.

NATIONAL COUNCIL OF THE PAPER INDUSTRY FOR AIR AND STREAM IMPROVEMENT. 1977. A Study of the Effect of Alternate Procedures on Effluent Suspended Solids Measurement. Stream Improvement Tech. Bull. No. 291, National Council of the Paper Industry for Air & Stream Improvement, New York, N.Y.

TREES, C.C. 1978. Analytical analysis of the effect of dissolved solids on suspended solids determination. *J. Water Pollut. Control Fed.* 50:2370.

2540 E.   Fixed and Volatile Solids Ignited at 550°C

1. General Discussion

a. Principle: The residue from Method B, C, or D is ignited to constant weight at 550 ± 50°C. The remaining solids represent the fixed total, dissolved, or suspended solids while the weight lost on ignition is the volatile solids. The determination is useful in control of wastewater treatment plant operation because it offers a rough approximation of the amount of organic matter present in the solid fraction of wastewater, activated sludge, and industrial wastes.

b. Interferences: Negative errors in the volatile solids may be produced by loss of volatile matter during drying. Determination of low concentrations of volatile solids in the presence of high fixed solids concentrations may be subject to considerable error. In such cases, measure for suspect volatile components by another test, for example, total organic carbon (Section 5310).

2. Apparatus

See Sections 2540B.2, 2540C.2, and 2540D.2.

3. Procedure

Ignite residue produced by Method B, C, or D to constant weight in a muffle furnace at a temperature of 550 ± 50°C.

Have furnace up to temperature before inserting sample. Usually, 15 to 20 min ignition are required. Let dish or filter disk cool partially in air until most of the heat has been dissipated. Transfer to a desiccator for final cooling in a dry atmosphere. Do not overload desiccator. Weigh dish or disk as soon as it has cooled to balance temperature. Repeat cycle of igniting, cooling, desiccating, and weighing until a constant weight is obtained or until weight loss is less than 4% of previous weight.

4. Calculation

$$\text{mg volatile solids/L} = \frac{(A - B) \times 1000}{\text{sample volume, mL}}$$

$$\text{mg fixed solids/L} = \frac{(B - C) \times 1000}{\text{sample volume, mL}}$$

where:

A = weight of residue + dish before ignition, mg,

B = weight of residue + dish or filter after ignition, mg, and

C = weight of dish or filter, mg.

5. Precision

The standard deviation was 11 mg/L at 170 mg/L volatile total solids in studies by three laboratories on four samples and 10 replicates. Bias data on actual samples cannot be obtained.

2540 F. Settleable Solids

1. General Discussion

Settleable solids in surface and saline waters as well as domestic and industrial wastes may be determined and reported on either a volume (mL/L) or a weight (mg/L) basis.

2. Apparatus

The volumetric test requires only an Imhoff cone. The gravimetric test requires all the apparatus listed in Section 2540D.2 and a glass vessel with a minimum diameter of 9 cm.

3. Procedure

a. Volumetric: Fill an Imhoff cone to the 1-L mark with a well-mixed sample. Settle for 45 min, gently stir sides of cone with a rod or by spinning, settle 15 min longer, and record volume of settleable solids in the cone as milliliters per liter. If the settled matter contains pockets of liquid between large settled particles, estimate volume of these and subtract from volume of settled solids. The practical lower limit of measurement depends on sample composition and generally is in the range of 0.1 to 1.0 mL/L. Where a separation of settleable and floating materials occurs, do not estimate the floating material as settleable matter.

b. Gravimetric:

1) Determine total suspended solids of well-mixed sample (Section 2540D).

2) Pour a well-mixed sample into a glass vessel of not less than 9 cm diam using not less than 1 L and sufficient to give a depth of 20 cm. Alternatively use a glass vessel of greater diameter and a larger volume of sample. Let stand quiescent for 1 h and, without disturbing the settled or floating material, siphon 250 mL from center of container at a point halfway between the surface of the settled material and the liquid surface. Determine total suspended solids (milligrams per liter) of this supernatant liquor (Section 2540D). These are the nonsettleable solids.

4. Calculation

mg settleable solids/L

$$= \text{mg total suspended solids/L}$$
$$- \text{mg nonsettleable solids/L}$$

5. Precision and Bias

Precision and bias data are not now available.

6. Bibliography

FISCHER, A.J. & G.E. SYMONS. 1944. The determination of settleable sewage solids by weight. *Water Sewage Works* 91:37.

2540 G. Total, Fixed, and Volatile Solids in Solid and Semisolid Samples

1. General Discussion

a. Applicability: This method is applicable to the determination of total solids and its fixed and volatile fractions in such solid and semisolid samples as river and lake sediments, sludges separated from water and wastewater treatment processes, and sludge cakes from vacuum filtration, centrifugation, or other sludge dewatering processes.

b. Interferences: The determination of both total and volatile solids in these materials is subject to negative error due to loss of ammonium carbonate and volatile organic matter during drying. Although this is true also for wastewater, the effect tends to be more pronounced with sediments, and especially with sludges and sludge cakes. The mass of organic matter recovered from sludge and sediment requires a longer ignition time than that specified for wastewaters, effluents, or polluted waters. Carefully observe specified ignition time and temperature to control losses of volatile inorganic salts. Make all weighings quickly because wet samples tend to lose weight by evaporation. After drying or ignition, residues often are very hygroscopic and rapidly absorb moisture from the air.

2. Apparatus

All the apparatus listed in Section 2540B.2 is required except that a balance capable of weighing to 10 mg may be used.

3. Procedure

a. Total solids:

1) Preparation of evaporating dish—If volatile solids are to be measured, ignite a clean evaporating dish at 550 ± 50°C for 1 h in a muffle furnace. If only total solids are to be measured, heat dish at 103 to 105°C for 1 h in an oven. Cool in desiccator, weigh, and store in desiccator until ready for use.

2) Sample analysis

a) Fluid samples—If the sample contains enough moisture to flow more or less readily, stir to homogenize, place 25 to 50 g in a prepared evaporating dish, and weigh. Evaporate to dryness on a water bath, dry at 103 to 105°C for 1 h, cool to balance temperature in an individual desiccator containing fresh desiccant, and weigh.

b) Solid samples—If the sample consists of discrete pieces of solid material (dewatered sludge, for example), take cores from each piece with a No. 7 cork borer or pulverize the entire sample coarsely on a clean

surface by hand, using rubber gloves. Place 25 to 50 g in a prepared evaporating dish and weigh. Place in an oven at 103 to 105°C overnight. Cool to balance temperature in an individual desiccator containing fresh desiccant and weigh.

b. Fixed and volatile solids: Transfer to a cool muffle furnace, heat furnace to 550 ± 50°C, and ignite for 1 h. (If the residue from 2) above contains large amounts of organic matter, first ignite the residue over a gas burner and under an exhaust hood in the presence of adequate air to lessen losses due to reducing conditions and to avoid odors in the laboratory.) Cool in desiccator to balance temperature and weigh.

4. Calculation

$$\% \text{ total solids} = \frac{(A - B) \times 100}{C - B}$$

$$\% \text{ volatile solids} = \frac{(A - D) \times 100}{A - B}$$

$$\% \text{ fixed solids} = \frac{(D - B) \times 100}{A - B}$$

where:

A = weight of dried residue + dish, mg,
B = weight of dish,
C = weight of wet sample + dish, mg, and
D = weight of residue + dish after ignition, mg.

5. Precision and Bias

Precision and bias data are not now available.

6. Bibliography

GOODMAN, B.L. 1964. Processing thickened sludge with chemical conditioners. Pages 78 et seq. *in* Sludge Concentration, Filtration and Incineration. Univ. Michigan Continued Education Ser. No. 113, Ann Arbor.

GRATTEAU, J.C. & R.I. DICK. 1968. Activated sludge suspended solids determinations. *Water Sewage Works* 115:468.

2550   TEMPERATURE*

2550 A.   Introduction

Temperature readings are used in the calculation of various forms of alkalinity, in studies of saturation and stability with respect to calcium carbonate, in the calculation of salinity, and in general laboratory operations. In limnological studies, water temperatures as a function of depth

---

* Approved by Standard Methods Committee, 1988.

often are required. Elevated temperatures resulting from discharges of heated water may have significant ecological impact. Identification of source of water supply, such as deep wells, often is possible by temperature measurements alone. Industrial plants often require data on water temperature for process use or heat-transmission calculations.

2550 B.   Laboratory and Field Methods

1. Laboratory and Other Non-Depth Temperature Measurements

Normally, temperature measurements may be made with any good mercury-filled Celsius thermometer. As a minimum, the thermometer should have a scale marked for every 0.1°C, with markings etched on the capillary glass. The thermometer should have a minimal thermal capacity to permit rapid equilibration. Periodically check the thermometer against a precision thermometer certified by the National Institute of Standards and Technology (NIST, formerly National Bureau of Standards)* that is used with its certificate and correction chart. For field operations use a thermometer having a metal case to prevent breakage.

2. Depth Temperature Measurements

Depth temperature required for limnological studies may be measured with a reversing thermometer, thermophone, or thermistor. The thermistor is most convenient and accurate; however, higher cost

---

* Some commercial thermometers may be as much as 3°C in error.

may preclude its use. Calibrate any temperature measurement devices with a NIST-certified thermometer before field use. Make readings with the thermometer or device immersed in water long enough to permit complete equilibration. Report results to the nearest 0.1 or 1.0°C, depending on need.

The thermometer commonly used for depth measurements is of the reversing type. It often is mounted on the sample collection apparatus so that a water sample may be obtained simultaneously. Correct readings of reversing thermometers for changes due to differences between temperature at reversal and temperature at time of reading. Calculate as follows:

$$\Delta T = \left[\frac{(T^{1} - t)(T^{1} + V_{0})}{K} \right]$$

$$\times \left[1 + \frac{(T^{1} - t)(T^{1} + V_{0})}{K} \right] + L$$

where:

ΔT = correction to be added algebraically to uncorrected reading,

T^{1} = uncorrected reading at reversal,

t = temperature at which thermometer is read,

V_0 = volume of small bulb end of capillary up to 0°C graduation,

K = constant depending on relative thermal expansion of mercury and glass (usual value of $K = 6100$), and

L = calibration correction of thermometer depending on T^1.

If series observations are made it is convenient to prepare graphs for a thermometer to obtain ΔT from any values of T^1 and t.

3. Bibliography

WARREN, H.F. & G.C. WHIPPLE. 1895. The thermophone—A new instrument for determining temperatures. *Mass. Inst. Technol. Quart.* 8:125.

SVERDRUP, H.V., M.W. JOHNSON & R.H. FLEMING. 1942. The Oceans. Prentice- Hall, Inc., Englewood Cliffs, N.J.

AMERICAN SOCIETY FOR TESTING AND MATERIALS. 1949. Standard Specifications for ASTM Thermometers. No. E1-58, ASTM, Philadelphia, Pa.

REE, W.R. 1953. Thermistors for depth thermometry. *J. Amer. Water Works Assoc.* 45:259.

2710   TESTS ON SLUDGES*

2710 A.   Introduction

This section presents a series of tests uniquely applicable to sludges or slurries.

---

*Approved by Standard Methods Committee, 1985.

The test data are useful in designing facilities for solids separation and concentration and for assessing operational behavior, especially of the activated sludge process.

2710 B.   Oxygen-Consumption Rate

1. General Discussion

This test is used to determine the oxygen consumption rate of a sample of a biological suspension such as activated sludge. It is useful in laboratory and pilot-plant studies as well as in the operation of full-scale treatment plants. When used as a routine plant operation test, it often will indicate changes in operating conditions at an early stage. However, because test conditions are not necessarily identical to conditions at the sampling site, the observed measurement may not be identical with actual oxygen consumption rate.

2. Apparatus

a. Oxygen-consumption rate device: Either:

1) *Probe with an oxygen-sensitive electrode* (polarographic or galvanic), or

2) *Manometric or respirometric device* with appropriate readout and sample capacity of at least 300 mL. The device should have an oxygen supply capacity greater than the oxygen consumption rate of the biological suspension, or at least 150 mg/L·h.

b. Stopwatch or other suitable timing device.

c. Thermometer to read to $\pm$ 0.5°C.

3. Procedure

a. *Calibration of oxygen-consumption rate device:* Either:

1) Calibrate the oxygen probe and meter according to the method given in Section 4500-O.G, or

2) Calibrate the manometric or respirometric device according to manufacturer's instructions.

b. *Volatile suspended solids determination:* See Section 2540.

c. *Preparation of sample:* Adjust temperature of a suitable sample portion to that of the basin from which it was collected or to required evaluation temperature, and maintain constant during analysis. Record temperature. Increase DO concentration of sample by shaking it in a partially filled bottle or by bubbling air or oxygen through it.

d. *Measurement of oxygen consumption rate:*

1) Fill sample container to overflowing with an appropriate volume of a representative sample of the biological suspension to be tested.

2) If an oxygen-sensing probe is used, immediately insert it into a BOD bottle containing a magnetic stirring bar and the biological suspension. Displace enough suspension with probe to fill flared top of bottle and isolate its contents from the atmosphere. Activate probe stirring mechanism and magnetic stirrer. (NOTE: Adequate mixing is essential. For suspensions with high concentrations of suspended solids, i.e., > 5000 mg/L, more vigorous mixing than that provided by the probe stirring mechanism and magnetic stirrer may be required.) If a manometric or respirometric device is used, follow manufacturer's instructions for startup.

3) After meter reading has stabilized, record initial DO and manometric or respirometric reading, and start timing device. Record appropriate DO, manometric, or respirometric data at time intervals of less than 1 min, depending on rate of consumption. Record data over a 15-min period or until DO becomes limiting, whichever occurs first. The oxygen probe may not be accurate below 1 mg DO/L. If a manometric or respirometric device is used, refer to manufacturer's instructions for lower limiting DO value. Low DO (≤ 2 mg/L at the start of the test) may limit oxygen uptake by the biological suspension and will be indicated by a decreasing rate of oxygen consumption as the test progresses. Reject such data as being unrepresentative of suspension oxygen consumption rate and repeat test beginning with higher initial DO levels.

The results of this determination are quite sensitive to temperature variations and poor precision is obtained unless replicate determinations are made at the same temperature. When oxygen consumption is used as a plant control test, run periodic (at least monthly) replicate determinations to establish the precision of the technique. This determination also is sensitive to the time lag between sample collection and test initiation.

4. Calculations

If an oxygen probe is used, plot observed readings (DO, milligrams per liter) versus time (minutes) on arithmetic graph paper and determine the slope of the line of best fit. The slope is the oxygen consumption rate in milligrams per liter per minute.

If a manometric or respirometric device is used, refer to manufacturer's instructions for calculating the oxygen consumption rate.

Calculate specific oxygen consumption rate in milligrams per gram per hour as follows:

Specific oxygen consumption rate, $(\text{mg}/\text{g})/\text{h}$

$$= \frac{\text{oxygen consumption rate,} \atop (\text{mg/L})/\text{min}}{\text{volatile suspended solids, g/L}} \times \frac{60 \text{ min}}{\text{h}}$$

5. Precision and Bias

Bias is not applicable. The precision for this test has not been determined.

6. Bibliography

UMBREIT, W.W., R.H. BURRIS & J.F. STAUFFER. 1964. Manometric Techniques. Burgess Publishing Co., Minneapolis, Minn.

2710 C.   Settled Sludge Volume

1. General Discussion

The settled sludge volume of a biological suspension is useful in routine monitoring of biological processes. For activated sludge plant control, a 30-min settled sludge volume or the ratio of the 15-min to the 30-min settled sludge volume has been used to determine the returned-sludge flow rate and when to waste sludge. The 30-min settled sludge volume also is used to determine sludge volume index[1] (Section 2710D).

2. Apparatus

a. Settling column: Use 1-L graduated cylinder equipped with a stirring mechanism consisting of one or more thin rods extending the length of the column and positioned within two rod diameters of the cylinder wall. Provide a stirrer able to rotate the stirring rods at no greater than 4 rpm (peripheral tip speed of approximately 1.3 cm/s). See Figure 2710:1.

b. Stopwatch.

c. Thermometer.

3. Procedure

Place 1.0 L of sample in settling column and distribute the solids by covering the top and inverting the cylinder three times. Insert stirring rods, activate stirring mechanism, and let suspension settle. Continue stirring throughout test. Maintain suspension temperature during test at that in the basin from which the sample was taken.

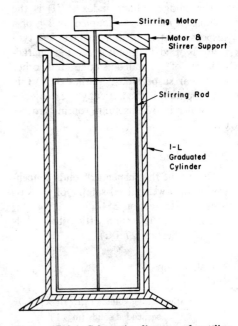

Figure 2710:1. Schematic diagram of settling vessel for settled sludge volume test.

Determine volume occupied by suspension at measured time intervals, e.g., 5, 10, 15, 20, 30, 45, and 60 min.

Report settled sludge volume of the suspension in milliliters for an indicated time interval.

Variations in suspension temperature, sampling and agitation methods, diameter of settling column, and time between sampling and start of the determination significantly affect results.

4. Precision and Bias

Bias is not applicable. The precision for this test has not been determined.

5. Reference

1. DICK, R.I. & P.A. VESILIND. 1969. The SVI—What is It? *J. Water Pollut, Control Fed.* 41:1285.

2710 D.   Sludge Volume Index

1. General Discussion

The sludge volume index (SVI) is the volume in milliliters occupied by 1 g of a suspension after 30 min settling. SVI typically is used to monitor settling characteristics of activated sludge and other biological suspensions.[1] Although SVI is not supported theoretically,[2] experience has shown it to be useful in routine process control.

2. Procedure

Determine the suspended solids concentration of a well-mixed sample of the suspension (See Section 2540D).

Determine the 30 min settled sludge volume (See Section 2710C).

3. Calculations

$$SVI = \frac{\text{settled sludge volume (mL/L)} \times 1000}{\text{suspended solids (mg/L)}}$$

4. Precision and Bias

Precision is determined by the precision achieved in the suspended solids measurement, the settling characteristics of the suspension, and variables associated with the measurement of the settled sludge volume. Bias is not applicable.

5. References

1. DICK, R.I. & P.A. VESILIND. 1969. The SVI—What is it? *J. Water Pollut. Control Fed.* 41:1285.
2. FINCH, J. & H. IVES. 1950. Settleability indexes for activated sludge. *Sewage Ind. Wastes* 22:833.

6. Bibliography

DONALDSON, W. 1932. Some notes on the operation of sewage treatment works. *Sewage Works J.* 4:48.
MOHLMAN, F.W. 1934. The sludge index. *Sewage Works J.* 6:119.
RUDOLFS, W. & I.O. LACY. 1934. Settling and compacting of activated sludge. *Sewage Works J.* 6:647.

2710 E.   Zone Settling Rate

1. General Discussion

At high concentrations of suspended solids, suspensions settle in the zone-settling regime. This type of settling takes place under quiescent conditions and is characterized by a distinct interface between the supernatant liquor and the sludge zone. The height of this distinct sludge interface is measured with time. Zone settling data for suspensions that undergo zone settling, e.g., activated sludge and metal hydroxide suspensions, can be used in the design, operation, and evaluation of settling basins.[1-3]

2. Apparatus

a. Settling vessel: Use a transparent cylinder at least 1 m high and 10 cm in diameter. To reduce the discrepancy between laboratory and full-scale thickener results, use larger diameters and taller cylinders.[1,3] Attach a calibrated millimeter tape to outside of cylinder. Equip cylinder with a stirring mechanism, e.g., one or more thin rods positioned within two rod diameters of the internal wall of settling vessel. Stir suspension near vessel wall over the entire depth of suspension at a peripheral speed no greater than 1 cm/s. Greater speeds may interfere with the thickening process and yield inaccurate results.[4] Provide the settling vessel with a port in the bottom plate for filling and draining. See Figure 2710:2.

  b. Stopwatch.
  c. Thermometer.

3. Procedure

Maintain suspension in a reservoir in a uniformly mixed condition. Adjust temperature of suspension to that of the basin from which it was collected or to required evaluation temperature. Record temperature. Remove a well-mixed sample from reservoir and measure suspended solids concentration (Section 2540D).

Activate stirring mechanism. Fill settling vessel to a fixed height by pumping suspension from reservoir or by gravity flow. Fill at a rate sufficient to maintain a uniform suspended solids concentration throughout settling vessel at end of filling. The suspension should agglomerate, i.e., form a coarse structure with visible fluid channels, within a few minutes. If suspension does not agglomerate, test is invalid and should be repeated.

Record height of solids-liquid interface at intervals of about 1 min. Collect data for sufficient time to assure that suspension is exhibiting a constant zone-settling velocity and that any initial reflocculation period, characterized by an accelerating interfacial settling velocity, has been passed.

Zone settling rate is a function of suspended solids concentration and suspen-

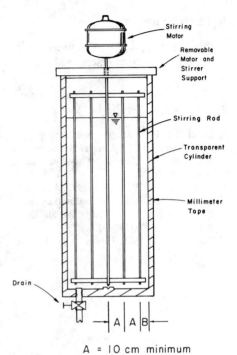

A = 10 cm minimum
B = 2 cm minimum

Figure 2710:2. Schematic diagram of settling vessel for zone settling rate test.

sion height as well as laboratory artifacts.[3] With the filling method described above and a sufficiently large cylinder, these artifacts should be minimized. However, even with careful testing suspensions often may behave erratically. Unpredictable behavior increases for sludges with high solids concentrations and poor settling characteristics, and in small cylinders.

4. Calculations

Plot interface height in centimeters vs. time in minutes.[1,3] Draw straight line through data points, ignoring initial shoulder or reflocculation period and compression shoulder. Calculate interfacial settling rate as slope of line in centimeters per minute.

5. Precision and Bias

Bias is not applicable. The precision for this test has not been determined.

6. References

1. DICK, R.I. 1972. Sludge treatment. *In* W.J. Weber, ed., Physicochemical Processes for Water Quality Control. Wiley-Interscience, New York, N.Y.
2. DICK, R.I. & K.W. YOUNG. 1972. Analysis of thickening performance of final settling tanks. *Proc. 27th Ind. Waste Conf.*, Purdue Univ., Eng. Ext. Ser. No. 141, 33.
3. VESILIND, P.A. 1975. Treatment and Disposal of Wastewater Sludges. Ann Arbor Science Publishing Co., Ann Arbor, Mich.
4. VESILIND, P.A. 1968. Discussion of Evaluation of activated sludge thickening theories. *J. San. Eng. Div., Proc. Amer. Soc. Civil Eng.* 94: SA1, 185.

7. Bibliography

DICK, R.I. & R.B. EWING. 1967. Evaluation of activated sludge thickening theories. *J. San. Eng. Div., Proc. Amer. Soc. Civil Eng.* 93:SA4, 9.
DICK, R.I. 1969. Fundamental aspects of sedimentation I & II. *Water Wastes Eng.* 3:47, 45, & 6:2.
DICK, R.I. 1970. Role of activated sludge final settling tanks. *J. San. Eng. Div., Proc. Amer. Soc. Civil Eng.* 96:SA2, 423.

2710 F.   Specific Gravity

1. General Discussion

The specific gravity of a sludge is the ratio of the masses of equal volumes of a sludge and distilled water. It is determined by comparing the mass of a known volume of a homogeneous sludge sample at a specific temperature to the mass of the same volume of distilled water at 4°C.

2. Apparatus

Container: A marked flask or bottle to hold a known sludge volume during weighing.

3. Procedure

Follow either *a* or *b*.

a. Record sample temperature, T. Weigh empty container and record weight, W. Fill empty container to mark with sample, weigh, and record weight, S. Fill empty container to mark with water, weigh, and record weight, R. Measure all masses to the nearest 10 mg.

b. If sample does not flow readily, add as much of it to container as possible without exerting pressure, record volume, weigh, and record mass, P. Fill container to mark with distilled water, taking care that air bubbles are not trapped in the sludge or container. Weigh and record mass, Q. Measure all masses to nearest 10 mg.

4. Calculation

Use *a* or *b*, matching choice of procedure above.

a. Calculate specific gravity, SG, from the formula

$$SG_{T/4°C} = \frac{\text{weight of sample}}{\begin{array}{c}\text{weight of equal volume}\\ \text{of water at 4°C}\end{array}}$$

$$= \frac{S - W}{R - W} \times F$$

The values of the temperature correction factor F are given in Table 2710:I.

b. Calculate specific gravity, SG, from the formula

$$SG_{T/4°C} = \frac{\text{weight of sample}}{\begin{array}{c}\text{weight of equal volume}\\\text{of water at 4°C}\end{array}}$$

$$= \frac{(P - W)}{(R - W) - (Q - P)} \times F$$

For values of F, see Table 2710:I.

TABLE 2710:I. TEMPERATURE CORRECTION FACTOR

Temperature °C	Temperature Correction Factor
15	0.9991
20	0.9982
25	0.9975
30	0.9957
35	0.9941
40	0.9922
45	0.9903

2720   SLUDGE DIGESTER GAS*

2720 A.   Introduction

1. Selection of Method

Gas produced during the anaerobic decomposition of wastes contains methane (CH_4) and carbon dioxide (CO_2) as the major components with minor quantities of hydrogen (H_2), hydrogen sulfide (H_2S), nitrogen (N_2), and oxygen (O_2). It is saturated with water vapor. Common practice is to analyze the gases produced to estimate their fuel value and to check on the treatment process. The relative proportions of CO_2, CH_4, and N_2 are normally of most concern and the easiest to determine because of the relatively high percentages of these gases.

Two procedures are described for gas analysis, the volumetric method (B), and the gas chromatographic method (C). The volumetric analysis is suitable for the determination of CO_2, H_2, CH_4, and O_2. Nitrogen is estimated indirectly by difference. Although the method is time-consuming, the equipment is relatively simple. Because no calibration is needed before use, the procedure is particularly appropriate when analyses are conducted infrequently.

The principal advantage of gas chromatography is speed. Commercial equipment is designed specifically for ambient-temperature gas analysis and permits the routine separation and measurement of

*Approved by Standard Methods Committee, 1988.

CO_2, N_2, O_2, and CH_4 in less than 5 min. The requirement for a recorder, pressure-regulated bottles of carrier gas, and certified standard gas mixtures for calibration raise costs to the point where infrequent analyses by this method may be uneconomical. The advantages of this system are freedom from the cumulative errors found in sequential volumetric measurements, adaptability to other gas component analyses, adaptability to intermittent on-line sampling and analysis, and the use of samples of 1 mL or less.[1]

2. Sample Collection

When the source of gas is some distance from the apparatus used for analysis, collect samples in sealed containers and bring to the instrument. Displacement collectors are the most suitable containers. Long glass tubes with three-way glass stopcocks at each end, as indicated in Figure 2720:1, are particularly useful. These also are available with centrally located ports provided with septa for syringe transfer of samples. Connect one end of collector to gas source and vent three-way stopcock to the atmosphere. Clear line of air by passing 10 to 15 volumes of gas through vent and open stopcock to admit sample. If large quantities of gas are available, sweep air away by passing 10 to 15 volumes of gas through tube. If the gas supply is limited, fill tube with a liquid that is displaced by gas. Use either mercury or

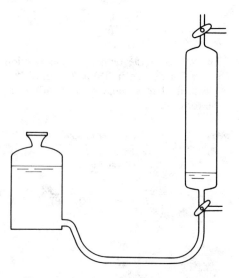

Figure 2720:1. Gas collection apparatus.

an acidified salt solution. The latter solution is easier and less expensive to use, but it dissolves gases to some extent. Therefore, fill collection tube completely with the gas and seal off from any contact with displacement fluid during temporary storage. When transferring gas to the gas-analyzing apparatus, do not transfer any fluid.

3. Reference

1. GRUNE, W.N. & C.F. CHUEH. 1962-63. Sludge gas analysis using gas chromatograph. *Water Sewage Works* 109:468; 110:43, 77, 102, 127, 171, 220, and 254.

2720 B.   Volumetric Method

1. General Discussion

a. Principle: This method may be used for the analysis either of digester gas or of methane in water (see Section 6211, Methane). A measured volume of gas is passed first through a solution of potassium hydroxide (KOH) to remove CO_2, next through a solution of alkaline pyrogallol to remove O_2, and then over heated cupric oxide, which removes H_2 by oxidation to water. After each of the above steps, the volume of gas remaining is measured; the decrease that results is a measure of the relative percentage of volume of each component in the mixture. Finally, CH_4 is determined by conversion to CO_2 and H_2O in a slow-combustion pipet or a catalytic oxidation assembly. The volume of CO_2 formed during combustion is measured to determine the fraction of methane originally present. Nitrogen is estimated by assuming that it represents the only gas remaining and equals the difference between 100% and the sum of the measured percentages of the other components.

When only CO_2 is measured, report only CO_2. No valid assumptions may be made about the remaining gases present without making a complete analysis.

Follow the equipment manufacturers' recommendations with respect to oxidation procedures.

CAUTION: *Do not attempt any slow-combustion procedure on digester gas because of the high probability of exceeding the explosive 5% by volume concentration of CH_4.*

2. Apparatus

Orsat-type gas-analysis apparatus, consisting of at least: (1) a water-jacketed gas buret with leveling bulb; (2) a CO_2-absorption pipet; (3) an O_2-absorption pipet; (4) a cupric oxide-hydrogen oxidation assembly; (5) a shielded catalytic CH_4-oxidation assembly or slow-combustion pipet assembly; and (6) a leveling bulb. With the slow-combustion pipet use a controlled source of current to heat the platinum filament electrically. Mercury is recommended as the displacement fluid; aqueous Na_2SO_4-H_2SO_4 solution also has been used successfully for sample collection. Use any

commercially available gas analyzer having these units.

3. Reagents

a. Potassium hydroxide solution: Dissolve 500 g KOH in distilled water and dilute to 1 L.

b. Alkaline pyrogallol reagent: Dissolve 30 g pyrogallol (also called pyrogallic acid) in distilled water and make up to 100 mL. Add 500 mL KOH solution.

c. Oxygen gas: Use approximately 100 mL for each gas sample analyzed.

d. Displacement liquid: Use either
1) *Mercury* or
2) *Sodium sulfate-sulfuric acid solution:* Dissolve 200 g Na_2SO_4 in 800 mL distilled water; add 30 mL conc H_2SO_4.

4. Procedure

a. Sample introduction: Transfer 5 to 10 mL gas sample into gas buret through a capillary-tube connection to the collector. Expel this sample to the atmosphere to purge the system. Transfer up to 100 mL gas sample to buret. Bring sample in buret to atmospheric or reference pressure by adjusting leveling bulb. Measure volume accurately and record as V_1.

b. Carbon dioxide absorption: Remove CO_2 from sample by passing it through the CO_2-absorption pipet charged with the KOH solution. Pass gas back and forth until sample volume remains constant. Before opening stopcocks between buret and any absorption pipet, make sure that the gas in the buret is under a slight positive pressure to prevent reagent in the pipet from contaminating stopcock or manifold. After absorption of CO_2, transfer sample to buret and measure volume. Record as V_2.

c. Oxygen absorption: Remove O_2 by passing sample through O_2-absorption pipet charged with alkaline pyrogallol reagent until sample volume remains constant. Measure volume and record as V_3. For digester gas samples, continue as directed in ¶ 4*d*. For CH_4 in water, store gas in CO_2 pipet and proceed to ¶ 4*e* below.

d. Hydrogen oxidation: Remove H_2 by passing sample through CuO assembly maintained at a temperature in the range 290 to 300°C. When a constant volume has been obtained, transfer sample back to buret, cool, and measure volume. Record as V_4.

Waste to the atmosphere all but 20 to 25 mL of remaining gas. Measure volume and record as V_5. Store temporarily in CO_2-absorption pipet.

e. Methane oxidation: Purge inlet connections to buret with O_2 by drawing 5 to 10 mL into buret and expelling to the atmosphere. Oxidize CH_4 either by the catalytic oxidation process for digester gas and gas phase of water samples or by the slow-combustion process for gas phase of water samples.

1) Catalytic oxidation process—For catalytic oxidation of digester gas and gas phase of water samples, transfer 65 to 70 mL O_2 to buret and record this volume as V_6. Pass O_2 into CO_2-absorption pipet so that it will mix with sample stored there. Return this mixture to buret and measure volume. Record as V_7. This volume should closely approximate V_5 plus V_6. Pass O_2-sample mixture through catalytic oxidation assembly, which should be heated in accordance with the manufacturer's directions. Keep rate of gas passage less than 30 mL/min. After first pass, transfer mixture back and forth through the assembly between buret and reservoir at a rate not faster than 60 mL/min until a constant volume is obtained. Record as V_8.

2) Slow-combustion process—For slow combustion of the gas phase of water samples, transfer 35 to 40 mL O_2 to buret and record volume as V_6. Transfer O_2 to slow-combustion pipet and then transfer sample from CO_2-absorption pipet to buret. Heat platinum coil in combustion pipet to yellow heat while controlling temperature by adjusting current. Reduce pressure of O_2 in pipet to somewhat less than atmospheric pressure by means of the leveling bulb attached to the pipet. Pass sample into slow-combustion pipet at rate of approximately 10 mL/min. After the first pass, transfer sample and O_2 mixture back and forth between pipet and buret several times at a faster rate, allowing mercury in pipet to rise to a point just below heated coil. Collect sample in combustion pipet, turn off coil, and cool pipet and sample to room temperature with a jet of compressed air. Transfer sample to buret and measure volume. Record as V_8.

f. Measurement of carbon dioxide produced: Determine amount of CO_2 formed in the reaction by passing sample through CO_2-absorption pipet until volume remains constant. Record volume as V_9.

Check accuracy of determination by absorbing residual O_2 from sample. After this absorption, record final volume as V_{10}.

5. Calculation

a. CH_4 and H_2 usually are the only combustible gases present in sludge digester gas. When this is the case, determine percentage by volume of each gas as follows:

$$\% \ CO_2 = \frac{(V_1 - V_2) \times 100}{V_1}$$

$$\% \ O_2 = \frac{(V_2 - V_3) \times 100}{V_1}$$

$$\% \ H_2 = \frac{(V_3 - V_4) \times 100}{V_1}$$

$$\% \ CH_4 = \frac{V_4 \times (V_8 - V_9) \times 100}{V_1 \times V_5}$$

$$\% \; N_2 = 100 - (\%CO_2 + \%O_2 \\ + \%H_2 + \%CH_4)$$

b. Alternatively, calculate CH_4 by either of the two following equations:

$$\% \; CH_4 = \frac{V_4 \times (V_6 + V_{10} - V_9) \times 100}{2 \times V_1 \times V_5}$$

$$\% \; CH_4 = \frac{V_4 \times (V_7 - V_8) \times 100}{2 \times V_1 \times V_5}$$

Results from the calculations for CH_4 by the three equations should be in reasonable agreement. If not, repeat analysis after checking apparatus for sources of error, such as leaking stopcocks or connections. Other combustible gases, such as ethane, butane, or pentane, will cause a lack of agreement among the calculations; however, the possibility that digester gas contains a significant amount of any of these is remote.

6. Precision and Bias

A gas buret measures gas volume with a precision of 0.05 mL and a probable accuracy of 0.1 mL. With the large fractions of CO_2 and CH_4 normally present in digester gas, the overall error for their determination can be made less than $\pm 1\%$. The error in the determination of O_2 and H_2, however, can be considerable because of the small concentrations normally present. For a concentration as low as 1%, an error as large as $\pm 20\%$ can be expected. When N_2 is present in a similar low-volume percentage, the error in its determination would be even greater, because errors in each of the other determinations would be reflected in the calculation for N_2.

7. Bibliography

YANT, W.F. & L.B. BERGER. 1936. Sampling of Mine Gases and the Use of the Bureau of Mines Portable Orsat Apparatus in Their Analysis. Miner's Circ. No. 34, U.S. Bur. Mines, Washington, D.C.

MULLEN, P.W. 1955. Modern Gas Analysis. Interscience Publishers, New York, N.Y.

2720 C.   Gas Chromatographic Method

1. General Discussion

a. Principle: See Section 6630B for a discussion of gas chromatography.

b. Equipment selection: Many columns have been proposed for gas mixture analyses. Any that is capable of the desired separation is acceptable, provided that all of the exact conditions of analysis are reported with the calibration standards. The following directions are necessarily general. Follow the manufacturer's recommendations for the specific instrumentation.

2. Apparatus

a. Gas chromatograph: Use any instrument equipped with a thermal conductivity detector. With some column packings, ovens and temperature controls are necessary. Preferably use a unit with a gas sample valve.

b. Recorder: Use a 10-mV full-span strip chart recorder with the gas chromatograph. When minor components such as H_2 and H_2S are to be detected, a 1-mV full-span recorder is preferable.

c. Column packing:* Some commercially available column packings useful for separating sludge gas components are listed below along with the routine separations possible at room temperature:[1,2]

1) Silica gel at room temperature: H_2, air $(O_2 + N_2)$, CH_4, $(CO_2$-slow);

2) Molecular Sieve 13X: H_2, O_2, N_2, CH_4;

3) HMPA (hexamethylphosphoramide) 30% on Chromosorb P: CO_2 from $(O_2$, N_2, H_2, $CH_4)$;

4) DEHS (di-2-ethylhexylsefacate) 30% on Chromosorb P: CO_2 from $(O_2$, N_2, H_2, $CH_4)$.

Combinations of Columns 1 and 2, 3 and 2, or 4 and 2 when properly sized and used in the sequence: 1st column, detector, 2nd column, detector, readily will separate H_2, O_2, N_2, CH_4, and CO_2. Commercial equipment specifically designed for such operations is available.[2]

d. Sample introduction apparatus: An instrument equipped with gas-sampling valves is designed to permit automatic injection of a specific sample volume into the chromatograph. If such an instrument is not available, introduce samples with a 2-mL syringe fitted with a 27-gauge hypodermic needle. Reduce escape of gas by greasing plunger lightly with mineral oil or preferably by using a special gas-tight syringe.

3. Reagents

a. Carrier gases: Use helium for separating digester gases. If H_2 is to be determined, use argon as a carrier gas to increase the sensitivity greatly.

b. Calibration gases: Use samples of CH_4, CO_2, and N_2 of known purity, or mixtures of known composition, for calibration. Also use samples of O_2, H_2, and H_2S of

---

*Gas chromatographic methods are extremely sensitive to the materials used. Use of trade names in *Standard Methods* does not preclude the use of other existing or as-yet-undeveloped products that give *demonstrably* equivalent results.

known purity if these gases are to be measured.

4. Procedure

a. Preparation of gas chromatograph: Adjust carrier gas flow rate to 60 to 80 mL/min. Turn on oven heaters, if used, and detector current and adjust to desired values. The instrument is ready for use when the recorder yields a stable base line. Silica gel and molecular sieve columns gradually lose activity because of adsorbed moisture or materials permanently adsorbed at room temperature. If insufficient separations occur, reactivate by heating or repacking.

b. Calibration: For accurate results, prepare a calibration curve for each gas to be measured because different gas components do not give equivalent detector responses on either a weight or a molar basis. Calibrate with synthetic mixtures or with pure gases.

1) Synthetic mixtures—Use purchased gas mixtures of known composition or prepare in the laboratory. Inject a standard volume of each mixture into the gas chromatograph and note response for each gas. Compute detector response, either as area under a peak or as height of peak, after correcting for attenuation. Read peak heights accurately and correlate with concentration of component in sample. Reproduce operating parameters exactly from one analysis to the next. If sufficient reproducibility cannot be obtained by this procedure, use peak areas for calibration. Prepare calibration curve by plotting either peak area or peak height against volume percent for each component.

2) Pure gases—Introduce pure gases into chromatograph individually with a syringe. Inject sample volumes of 0.25, 0.5, 1.0 mL, etc., and plot detector response, corrected for attenuation, against gas volume.

When the analysis system yields a linear detector response with increasing gas component concentration from zero to the range of interest, run standard mixtures along with samples. If the same sample size is used, calculate gas concentration by direct proportions.

c. *Sample analysis:* If samples are to be injected with a syringe, equip sample collection container with a port closed by a rubber or silicone septum. To take a sample for analysis, expel air from barrel of syringe by depressing plunger and force needle through the septum. Withdraw plunger to take gas volume desired, pull needle from collection container, and inject sample rapidly into chromatograph.

When samples are to be injected through a gas-sampling valve, connect sample collection container to inlet tube. Permit gas to flow from collection tube through the valve to purge dead air space and fill sample tube. About 15 mL normally are sufficient to clear the lines and to provide a sample of 1 to 2 mL. Transfer sample from loop into carrier gas stream by following manufacturer's instructions. Bring samples to atmospheric pressure before injection.

When calibration curves have been prepared with synthetic mixtures, use the same sample volume as that used during calibration. When calibration curves are prepared by the procedure using varying volumes of pure gases, inject any convenient gas sample volume up to about 2 mL.

5. Calculation

a. When calibration curves have been prepared with synthetic mixtures and the volume of the sample analyzed is the same as that used in calibration, read volume percent of each component directly from calibration curve after detector response for that component is computed.

b. When calibration curves are prepared with varying volumes of pure gases, calculate the percentage of each gas in the mixture as follows:

$$\text{Volume } \% = \frac{A}{B} \times 100$$

where:

A = partial volume of component (read from calibration curve) and
B = volume sample injected.

c. Where standard mixtures are run with samples and instrument response is linear from zero to the concentration range of interest:

$$\text{Volume } \% = \text{Volume } \% \text{ (std)} \times \frac{C}{D}$$

where:

C = recorder value of sample and
D = recorder value of standard.

6. Precision and Bias

Precision and bias depend on the instrument used and the techniques of operation. With proper care, a precision of 2% generally can be achieved. With digester gas the sum of the percent CH_4, CO_2, and N_2 should approximate 100%. If it does not, suspect errors in collection, handling, storage, and injection of gas, or in instrumental operation or calibration.

7. Reference

1. ANDREWS, J.F. 1968. Chromatographic analysis of gaseous products and reactants for biological processes. *Water Sewage Works* 115:54.
2. Column Systems for the Fisher Gas Partitioner. Tech. Bull. TB-154, Fisher Scientific Co., Atlanta, Ga. Catalog 77, Fisher Scientific Co.

3010 INTRODUCTION

3010 A. General Discussion

1. Significance

The effects of metals in water and wastewater range from beneficial through troublesome to dangerously toxic. Some metals are essential, others may adversely affect water consumers, wastewater treatment systems, and receiving waters. Some metals may be either beneficial or toxic, depending on concentration.

2. Types of Methods

Metals may be determined satisfactorily by atomic absorption, inductively coupled plasma, or, with somewhat less precision and sensitivity, colorimetric methods. The absorption methods include flame and electrothermal techniques. Flame methods generally are applicable at moderate concentration levels in clean and complex-matrix systems. Electrothermal methods generally can increase sensitivity if matrix effects are not severe. Matrix modifiers may compensate for some matrix effects. Inductively coupled plasma (ICP) techniques are applicable over a broad linear range and are especially sensitive for refractory elements. In general, detection limits for ICP methods are higher than those for electrothermal methods. Colorimetric methods are applicable when interferences are known to be within the capacity of the particular method. Preliminary treatment of samples often is required. Appropriate pretreatment methods are described for each type of analysis.

3. Definition of Terms

a. Dissolved metals: Those constituents (metals) of an unacidified sample that pass through a 0.45-μm membrane filter.

b. Suspended metals: Those constituents (metals) of an unacidified sample that are retained by a 0.45-μm membrane filter.

c. Total metals: The concentration of metals determined on an unfiltered sample after vigorous digestion, or the sum of the concentrations of metals in both dissolved and suspended fractions.

d. Acid-extractable metals: The concentration of metals in solution after treatment of an unfiltered sample with hot dilute mineral acid.

To determine dissolved and suspended metals separately, filter immediately after sample collection. Do not preserve with acid until after filtration.

3010 B. Sampling and Sample Preservation

Before collecting a sample, decide what fraction is to be analyzed (dissolved, suspended, total, or acid-extractable). This decision will determine in part whether the sample is acidified with or without filtration and the type of digestion required.

Serious errors may be introduced during sampling and storage because of contamination from sampling device, failure to remove residues of previous samples from sample container, and loss of metals by adsorption on and/or precipitation in sample container caused by failure to acidify the sample properly.

1. Sample Containers

The best sample containers are made of quartz or TFE. Because these containers are expensive, the preferred sample container is made of polypropylene or linear polyethylene with a polyethylene cap. Borosilicate glass containers also may be used, but avoid soft glass containers for samples containing metals in the microgram-per-liter range. Store samples for determination of silver in light-absorbing containers. Use only containers and filters that have been acid rinsed.

2. Preservation

Preserve samples immediately after sampling by acidifying with concentrated nitric acid (HNO_3) to pH < 2. Filter samples for dissolved metals before preserving (see Section 3030). Usually 1.5 mL conc HNO_3/L sample (or 3 mL $1 + 1$ HNO_3/L sample) is sufficient for short-term preservation. For samples with high buffer capacity, increase amount of acid (5 mL may be required for some alkaline or highly buffered samples). Use commercially available high-purity acid* or prepare high-purity acid by sub-boiling distillation of acid.

---

*Ultrex, J.T. Baker, or equivalent.

After acidifying sample, preferably store it in a refrigerator at approximately 4°C to prevent change in volume due to evaporation. Under these conditions, samples with metal concentrations of several milligrams per liter are stable for up to 6 months (except mercury, for which the limit is 5 weeks). For microgram-per-liter metal levels, analyze samples as soon as possible after sample collection.

Alternatively, preserve samples for mercury analysis by adding 2 mL/L 20% (w/v) $K_2Cr_2O_7$ solution (prepared in $1 + 1$ HNO_3). Store in a refrigerator not contaminated with mercury. (CAUTION: Mercury concentrations may increase in samples stored in plastic bottles in mercury-contaminated laboratories.)

3. Bibliography

STRUEMPLER, A.W. 1973. Adsorption characteristics of silver, lead, calcium, zinc and nickel on borosilicate glass, polyethylene and polypropylene container surfaces. *Anal. Chem.* 45:2251.

FELDMAN, C. 1974. Preservation of dilute mercury solutions. *Anal. Chem.* 46:99.

KING, W.G., J.M. RODRIGUEZ & C.M. WAI. 1974. Losses of trace concentrations of cadmium from aqueous solution during storage in glass containers. *Anal. Chem.* 46:771.

BATLEY, G.E. & D. GARDNER. 1977. Sampling and storage of natural waters for trace metal analysis. *Water Res.* 11:745.

SUBRAMANIAN, K.S., C.L. CHAKRABARTI, J.E. SUETIAS & I.S. MAINES. 1978. Preservation of some trace metals in samples of natural waters. *Anal. Chem.* 50:444.

BERMAN, S. & P. YEATS. 1985. Sampling of seawater for trace metals. *Crit. Rev. Anal. Chem.* 16:1.

WENDLANDT, E. 1986. Sample containers and analytical accessories made of modern plastics for trace analysis. *Gewaess. Wass. Abwass.* 86:79.

3010 C. General Precautions

1. Sources of Contamination

Avoid introducing contaminating metals from containers, distilled water, or membrane filters. Some plastic caps or cap liners may introduce metal contamination; for example, zinc has been found in black bakelite-type screw caps as well as in many rubber and plastic products, and cadmium has been found in plastic pipet tips. Lead is a ubiquitous contaminant in urban air and dust.

2. Contaminant Removal

Thoroughly clean sample containers with a metal-free nonionic detergent solution, rinse with tap water, soak in acid, and then rinse with metal-free water. For quartz, TFE, or glass materials, use $1 + 1$ HNO_3, $1 + 1$ HCl, or aqua regia (3 parts conc HCl + 1 part conc HNO_3) for soaking. For plastic material, use $1 + 1$ HNO_3 or $1 + 1$ HCl. Reliable soaking conditions are 24 h at 70°C. Chromic acid or chromium-free substitutes* may be used to re-

*Nochromix, Godax Laboratories, or equivalent.

move organic deposits from containers, but rinse containers thoroughly with water to remove traces of chromium. Do not use chromic acid for plastic containers or if chromium is to be determined. Always use metal-free water in analysis and reagent preparation (see 3111B.2c). In these methods, the word "water" means metal-free water.

3. Airborne Contaminants

For analysis of microgram-per-liter concentrations of metals, airborne contaminants in the form of volatile compounds, dust, soot, and aerosols present in laboratory air may become significant. To avoid contamination use "clean laboratory" facilities such as commercially available laminar-flow clean-air benches or custom-designed work stations and analyze blanks that reflect the complete procedure.

4. Bibliography

MITCHELL, J.W. 1973. Ultrapurity in trace analysis. *Anal. Chem.* 45:492A.
GARDNER, M., D. HUNT & G. TOPPING. 1986. Analytical quality control (AQC) for monitoring trace metals in the coastal and marine environment. *Water Sci. Technol.* 18:35.

3020 QUALITY CONTROL*

Detailed recommendations and general information concerning both quality assurance and quality control (QC) are provided in Part 1000 and in individual methods. Refer to individual methods for method-

*Approved by Standard Methods Committee, 1989.

specific QC requirements. Also read Part 1000 for definitions of terms.

Always remember the overall purpose of the measurements: Use replicates to establish precision and known-additions recovery to determine bias. Use standards, control charts, blanks, calibrations, and other necessary measures. Provide adequate documentation. Quality-control measures and substantiation for operational-control determinations may differ from those for determinations made for regulatory purposes. Levels of trace metals may be orders of magnitude less than potential sources of contamination.

Before using a method, determine its detection limit (see Section 1030E). Instrumental methods generally are more sensitive than colorimetric ones. Verify that the method being used provides sufficient sensitivity for the purpose of the measurement.

Keep adequate records so that those unfamiliar with an analysis can reconstruct final results directly from raw data and have available a complete set of standard operating procedures.

To analyze a new or unfamiliar matrix, use the method of known additions to demonstrate freedom from interferences before calibrating. Verify the absence of interferences by analyzing such samples undiluted and in a 1:10 dilution; results should be comparable. Analyze a full procedural blank with each set of samples by carrying a reagent water blank through every step, including any digestion steps. Many metals are present in measurable quantities in acids and glassware and can affect results. If blank measurements result in concentrations above the method detection limit, repeat sample preparation with cleaner reagents or glassware. Verify that all glassware and materials are specially cleaned for metals analysis.

As a minimum for each analytical run have a calibration curve composed of a blank and two or more standards (depending on instrumentation), an external reference standard, a replicate, and a known addition to verify the absence of matrix interferences. Make replicate measurements on subsamples from a single sample bottle to establish method precision (as distinguished from the precision of samples). Precision and known-addition recovery should be within historical limits. Maintain control charts for more rigorous control of precision and bias.

Analyze a midpoint check standard and calibration blank at the beginning, end, and periodically (normally after each set of nine unknowns) with each group of samples to verify that the instrument calibration has not drifted. Initially, as a guideline use the following criteria: A determined value of the check standard outside 95 to 105% of the expected concentration suggests a potential problem. When a value is outside 90 to 110% of the expected concentration, the calibration usually is considered to be out of control; take corrective action. Use of calculated control limits (see Section 1020) will provide better indications of performance and is recommended for laboratories performing an analysis frequently (i.e., weekly). This may provide tighter limits.

To determine whether matrix effects exist, make known additions to samples before any digestion. Recoveries between 85 and 115% indicate that matrix effects are not significant.

Verify calibration standards and known addition solutions against an outside source. Agreement should be ± 5%.

Certain regulatory programs may require additional mandatory quality-control measures, i.e., use of a check standard at the maximum contaminant level (MCL).

3030   PRELIMINARY TREATMENT OF SAMPLES*

3030 A.   Introduction

Samples containing particulates or organic material generally require pretreatment before analysis. "Total metals" includes all metals, inorganically and organically bound, both dissolved and particulate. Colorless, transparent samples (primarily drinking water) containing a turbidity of < 1 NTU, no odor, and single phase may be analyzed directly by atomic absorption spectroscopy or inductively coupled plasma spectroscopy for total metals without digestion. For further verification or if changes in existing matrices are encountered, compare digested and undigested samples to ensure comparable results. On collection, acidify such samples to pH < 2 with conc nitric acid (HNO_3) and analyze directly. Digest all other samples before determining total metals. To analyze for dissolved metals, filter sample, acidify filtrate, and analyze directly. To determine suspended metals, filter sample, digest filter and the material on it, and analyze. To determine acid-extractable metals, extract metals as indicated below and analyze extract.

---

*Approved by Standard Methods Committee, 1989.

This section describes general pretreatment for samples in which metals are to be determined according to Sections 3110 through 3500-Zn with several exceptions. The special digestion techniques for mercury are given in Sections 3112B.4*b* and *c*, and those for arsenic and selenium in Sections 3114 and 3500-Se.

Take care not to introduce metals into samples during preliminary treatment. During pretreatment avoid contact with rubber, metal-based paints, cigarette smoke, paper tissues, and all metal products including those made of stainless steel, galvanized metal, and brass. Conventional fume hoods can contribute significantly to sample contamination, particularly during acid digestion in open containers. Plastic pipet tips often are contaminated with copper, iron, zinc, and cadmium; before use soak in $2N$ HCl or HNO_3 for several days and rinse with deionized water. Check reagent-grade acids used for preservation, extraction, and digestion for purity. If excessive metal concentrations are found, purify the acids by distillation or use ultrapure acids. Carry blanks through all digestion and filtration steps and apply the necessary corrections to the results.

3030 B.   Preliminary Filtration

If dissolved or suspended metals are to be determined, filter sample at time of collection using a preconditioned plastic filtering device with either vacuum or pressure, containing a filter support of plastic or TFE, through a prewashed ungridded 0.4- to 0.45-μm-pore-diam membrane filter (polycarbonate or cellulose acetate). Before use filter a blank consisting of reagent water to insure freedom from contamination. Precondition filter and filter device by rinsing with 50 mL deionized water. If the filter blank contains significant metals concentrations, soak membrane filters in approximately $0.5N$ HCl or 1 + 1 HNO$_3$ (recommended for electrothermal analysis) and rinse with water before use.

NOTE: Different filters display different sorption and filtration characteristics; for trace analysis, test filter to verify complete recovery of metals.

If filter is to be digested for suspended metals, record sample volume filtered and include a filter in determination of blank. Before filtering, centrifuge highly turbid samples in acid-washed TFE or high-density plastic tubes to reduce loading on filters. Stirred, pressure filter units foul less readily than vacuum filters; filter at a pressure of 70 to 130 kPa. After filtration acidify filtrate to pH 2 with conc HNO$_3$ and analyze directly. If a precipitate forms on acidification, digest acidified filtrate before analysis using Method E. Retain filter and digest it for direct determination of suspended metals.

CAUTION: *Do not use perchloric acid to digest membrane filters.*

3030 C. Preliminary Treatment for Acid-Extractable Metals

Extractable metals are lightly adsorbed on particulate material. Because some sample digestion may be unavoidable use rigidly controlled conditions to obtain meaningful and reproducible results. Maintain constant sample volume, acid volume, and contact time. Express results as extractable metals and specify extraction conditions.

At collection, acidify entire sample with 5 mL conc HNO$_3$/L sample. To prepare sample, mix well, transfer 100 mL to a beaker or flask, and add 5 mL 1 + 1 high-purity HCl. Heat 15 min on a steam bath. Filter through a membrane filter, adjust filtrate volume to 100 mL with water, and analyze.

3030 D. Preliminary Digestion for Metals

To reduce interference by organic matter and to convert metal associated with particulates to a form (usually the free metal) that can be determined by atomic absorption spectrometry or inductively-coupled plasma spectroscopy, use one of the digestion techniques presented below. Use the least rigorous digestion method required to provide complete and consistent recovery compatible with the analytical method and the metal being analyzed.

Nitric acid will digest most samples adequately (Section 3030E). Nitrate is an acceptable matrix for both flame and electrothermal atomic absorption. Some samples may require addition of perchloric, hydrochloric, or sulfuric acid for complete digestion. These acids may interfere in the analysis of some metals and all provide a poorer matrix for electrothermal analysis. Confirm metal recovery for each digestion and analytical procedure used. Use Table 3030:I as a guide in determining which acids (in addition to HNO_3) to use for complete digestion. As a general rule, HNO_3 alone is adequate for clean samples or easily oxidized materials; HNO_3-H_2SO_4 or HNO_3-HCl digestion is adequate for readily oxidizable organic matter; HNO_3-$HClO_4$ or HNO_3-$HClO_4$-HF digestion is necessary for difficult-to-oxidize organic matter or minerals. Dry ashing is helpful if large amounts of organic matter are present.

For determining Ag concentrations greater than 0.03 mg/L, dilute sample to contain less than 1 mg/L Ag and digest using method 3030F.3*b*.

Report digestion technique used.

Acid digestion techniques (Section 3030E–I) generally yield comparable precision and bias for most sample types that are totally digested by the technique. Because acids used in digestion will add metals to the samples and blanks, minimize the volume of acids used.

Suggested sample volumes are indicated below. If the recommended volume exceeds digestion vessel capacity, add sample as evaporation proceeds.

When samples are concentrated during digestion (e.g., > 100 mL sample used) determine metal recovery for each matrix digested, to verify method validity. Using larger samples will require additional acid, which also would increase the concentration of impurities.

Estimated Metal Concentration mg/L	Sample Volume* mL
<1	1000
1–10	100
10–100	10
100–1000	1

*For flame atomic absorption spectrometry. For graphite furnace, smaller volumes are appropriate.

Dry ashing (Section 3030J) yields highly variable precision and bias, depending on sample type and metal being analyzed. Dry ash only samples that have been shown to yield acceptable precision and bias.

Report results as follows:

$$\text{Metal concentration, mg/L} = A \times \frac{B}{C}$$

where:

A = concentration of metal in digested solution, mg/L,

B = final volume of digested solution, mL, and

C = sample size, mL.

Prepare solid samples or liquid sludges with high solids contents on a weight basis. Mix sample and transfer a suitable amount (typically 1 g of a sludge with 15% total solids) to a preweighed digestion vessel. Reweigh and calculate weight of sample. Proceed with one of the digestion techniques

TABLE 3030:I. ACIDS USED IN CONJUNCTION WITH HNO_3 FOR SAMPLE PREPARATION

Acid	Recommended for	May Be Helpful for	Not Recommended for
HCl	—	Sb, Ru, Sn	Ag, Th, Pb
H_2SO_4	Ti	—	Ag, Pb, Ba
$HClO_4$	—	Organic materials	—
HF	—	Siliceous materials	—

presented below. Report results on wet- or dry-weight basis as follows:

Metal concentration, mg/kg (wet-weight basis)

$$= \frac{A \times B}{\text{g sample}}$$

Metal concentration, mg/kg (dry-weight basis)

$$= \frac{A \times B}{\text{g sample}} \times \frac{100}{D}$$

where:

A = concentration of metal in digested solution, mg/L,
B = final volume of digested solution, mL, and
D = total solids, % (see Section 2540G).

Always prepare acid blanks for each type of digestion performed. Experience indicates that a blank made with the same acids and subjected to the same digestion procedure as the sample can correct for impurities present in acids, in reagent water, or on glassware.

3030 E.   Nitric Acid Digestion

1. Apparatus

a. Hot plate.
b. Conical (erlenmeyer) flasks, 125-mL, or *Griffin beakers,* 150 mL, acid-washed and rinsed with water.

2. Reagents

Nitric acid, HNO_3, conc.

3. Procedure

Mix sample and transfer a suitable volume (50 to 100 mL) to a 125-mL conical flask or beaker. Add 5 mL conc HNO_3 and a few boiling chips, glass beads, or Hengar granules. Bring to a slow boil and evaporate on a hot plate to the lowest volume possible

(about 10 to 20 mL) before precipitation occurs. Continue heating and adding conc HNO_3 as necessary until digestion is complete as shown by a light-colored, clear solution. Do not let sample dry during digestion.

Wash down flask or beaker walls with water and then filter if necessary (see Section 3030B). Transfer filtrate to a 100-mL volumetric flask with two 5-mL portions of water, adding these rinsings to the volumetric flask. Cool, dilute to mark, and mix thoroughly. Take portions of this solution for required metal determinations. Alternatively, take a larger sample volume through the procedure for concentration (see 3030D).

3030 F.   Nitric Acid-Hydrochloric Acid Digestion

1. Apparatus

See 3030E.1

2. Reagents

a. Nitric acid, HNO_3, conc.
b. Hydrochloric acid, 1 + 1.

3. Procedure

a. Total HNO_3/HCl: Transfer a measured volume of well-mixed, acid-preserved sample appropriate for the expected metals concentrations to a flask or beaker (see 3030E.1b). Add 3 mL conc HNO_3. Place flask or beaker on a hot plate and cautiously evaporate to less than 5 mL, making certain that sample does not boil and that no area of the bottom of the container is allowed to go dry. Cool and add 5 mL conc HNO_3. Cover container with a watch glass and return to hot plate. Increase temperature of hot plate so that a gentle reflux action occurs. Continue heating, adding additional acid as necessary, until digestion is complete (generally indicated when the digestate is light in color or does not change in appearance with continued refluxing). Evaporate to less than 5 mL and cool. Add 10 mL 1 + 1 HCl and 15 mL water per 100 mL anticipated final volume. Heat for an additional 15 min to dissolve any precipitate or residue. Cool, wash down beaker walls and watch glass with water, and filter to remove insoluble material that could clog the nebulizer. Alternatively centrifuge or let settle overnight. Adjust to a predetermined volume based on the expected metals concentrations.

b. Recoverable HNO_3/HCl: For this less rigorous digestion procedure, transfer a measured volume of well-mixed, acid-preserved sample to a flask or beaker. Add 2 mL 1 + 1 HNO_3 and 10 mL 1 + 1 HCl and heat on a steam bath or hot plate until volume has been reduced to near 25 mL, making certain sample does not boil. Cool and filter to remove insoluble material or alternatively centrifuge or let settle overnight. Adjust volume to 100 mL and mix.

3030 G. Nitric Acid-Sulfuric Acid Digestion

1. Apparatus

See 3030E.1.

2. Reagents

a. *Methyl orange indicator solution.*
b. *Nitric acid,* HNO_3, conc.
c. *Sulfuric acid,* H_2SO_4, conc.

3. Procedure

Mix sample and pipet a suitable volume into a suitable flask or beaker (see 3030E.1b). If sample is not already acidified, acidify to methyl orange end point with conc H_2SO_4 and add 5 mL conc HNO_3 and a few boiling chips, glass beads, or Hengar granules. Bring to slow boil on hot plate and evaporate to 15 to 20 mL. Add 5 mL conc HNO_3 and 10 mL conc H_2SO_4. Evaporate on a hot plate until dense white fumes of SO_3 just appear. If solution does not clear, add 10 mL conc HNO_3 and repeat evaporation to fumes of SO_3. Heat to remove all HNO_3 before continuing treatment. All HNO_3 will be removed when the solution is clear and no brownish fumes are evident. Do not let sample dry during digestion.

Cool and dilute to about 50 mL with water. Heat to almost boiling to dissolve slowly soluble salts. Filter if necessary, then complete procedure as directed in Section 3030E.3 beginning with, "Transfer filtrate ..."

3030 H.   Nitric Acid-Perchloric Acid Digestion

1. Apparatus

See 3030E.1. The following are also needed:
  a. *Safety shield.*
  b. *Safety goggles.*

2. Reagents

  a. *Nitric acid,* HNO₃, conc.
  b. *Perchloric acid,* HClO₄.
  c. *Methyl orange indicator aqueous solution.*
  d. *Ammonium acetate solution:* Dissolve 500 g NH₄C₂H₃O₂ in 600 mL water.

3. Procedure

CAUTION: *Heated mixtures of HClO₄ and organic matter may explode violently. Avoid this hazard by taking the following precautions: (a) do not add HClO₄ to a hot solution containing organic matter; (b) always pretreat samples containing organic matter with HNO₃ before adding HClO₄; (c) avoid repeated fuming with HClO₄ in ordinary hoods (For routine operations, use a water pump attached to a glass fume eradicator.* Stainless steel fume hoods with adequate water washdown facilities are available commercially and are acceptable for use with HClO₄.); and (d) never let samples being digested with HClO₄ evaporate to dryness.*

Mix sample and transfer a suitable volume into a suitable flask or beaker (see 3030E.1*b*). If sample is not already acidified, acidify to methyl orange end point with conc HNO₃, add an additional 5 mL conc HNO₃ and a few boiling chips or glass beads, and evaporate on a hot plate to 15 to 20 mL. Add 10 mL each of conc HNO₃ and HClO₄, cooling flask or beaker between additions. Evaporate gently on a hot plate until dense white fumes of HClO₄ just appear. If solution is not clear, cover container with a watch glass and keep solution just boiling until it clears. If necessary, add 10 mL conc HNO₃ to complete digestion. Cool, dilute to about 50 mL with water, and boil to expel any chlorine or oxides of nitrogen. Filter, then complete procedure as directed in 3030E.3 beginning with, "Transfer filtrate . . ."

If lead is to be determined in the presence of high amounts of sulfate (e.g., determination of Pb in power plant fly ash samples), dissolve PbSO₄ precipitate as follows: Add 50 mL ammonium acetate solution to flask or beaker in which digestion was carried out and heat to incipient boiling. Rotate container occasionally to wet all interior surfaces and dissolve any deposited residue. Reconnect filter and slowly draw solution through it. Transfer filtrate to a 100-mL volumetric flask, cool, dilute to mark, mix thoroughly, and set aside for determination of lead.

---

*Such as those obtainable from GFS Chemical Co., Columbus, Ohio.

3030 I. Nitric Acid-Perchloric Acid-Hydrofluoric Acid Digestion

1. Apparatus

a. Hot plate.
b. TFE beakers, 250-mL, acid-washed and rinsed with water.

2. Reagents

a. Nitric acid, HNO_3, conc and 1 + 1.
b. Perchloric acid, $HClO_4$.
c. Hydrofluoric acid, HF, 48 to 51%.

3. Procedure

CAUTION: *See precautions for using $HClO_4$ in 3030H; handle HF with extreme care and provide adequate ventilation, especially for the heated solution. Avoid all contact with exposed skin. Provide medical attention for HF burns.*

Mix sample and transfer a suitable volume into a 250-mL TFE beaker. Add a few boiling chips and bring to a slow boil. Evaporate on a hot plate to 15 to 20 mL. Add 12 mL conc HNO_3 and evaporate to near dryness. Repeat HNO_3 addition and evaporation. Let solution cool, add 20 mL $HClO_4$ and 1 mL HF, and boil until solution is clear and white fumes of $HClO_4$ have appeared. Cool, add about 50 mL water, filter, and proceed as directed in 3030E.3 beginning with, "Transfer filtrate . . ."

3030 J. Dry Ashing

1. Apparatus

See Sections 2540B.2 and 2540C.2.

2. Procedure

Mix sample and transfer a suitable volume into a platinum or high-silica glass* evaporating dish. Evaporate to dryness on a steam bath. Transfer dish to a muffle furnace and heat sample to a white ash. If volatile elements are to be determined, keep temperature at 400 to 450°C. If sodium only is to be determined, ash sample at a temperature up to 600°C. Dissolve ash in a minimum quantity of conc HNO_3 and warm water. Filter diluted sample and adjust to a known volume, preferably so that the final HNO_3 concentration is about 1%.

Take portions of this solution for metals determination.

---

*Vycor, a product of Corning Glass Works, Corning, N.Y., or equivalent.

3110   METALS BY ATOMIC ABSORPTION SPECTROMETRY*

Because requirements for determining metals by atomic absorption spectrometry vary with metal and/or concentration to be determined, the method is presented as follows:

Section 3111, Metals by Flame Atomic Absorption Spectrometry, encompasses:

• Determination of antimony, bismuth, cadmium, calcium, cesium, chromium, cobalt, copper, gold, iridium, iron, lead, lithium, magnesium, manganese, nickel, palladium, platinum, potassium, rhodium, ruthenium, silver, sodium, strontium, thallium, tin, and zinc by direct aspiration into an air-acetylene flame (3111B),

• Determination of low concentrations of cadmium, chromium, cobalt, copper, iron, lead, manganese, nickel, silver, and zinc by chelation with ammonium pyrrolidine dithiocarbamate (APDC), extraction into methyl isobutyl ketone (MIBK), and

aspiration into an air-acetylene flame (3111C),

• Determination of aluminum, barium, beryllium, molybdenum, osmium, rhenium, silicon, thorium, titanium, and vanadium by direct aspiration into a nitrous oxide-acetylene flame (3111D), and

• Determination of low concentrations of aluminum and beryllium by chelation with 8-hydroxyquinoline, extraction into MIBK, and aspiration into a nitrous oxide-acetylene flame (3111E).

Section 3112 covers determination of mercury by the cold vapor technique.

Section 3113 concerns determination of micro quantities of aluminum, antimony, arsenic, barium, beryllium, cadmium, chromium, cobalt, copper, iron, lead, manganese, molybdenum, nickel, selenium, silver, and tin by electrothermal atomic absorption spectrometry.

Section 3114 covers determination of arsenic and selenium by conversion to their hydrides and aspiration into an argon-hydrogen or nitrogen-hydrogen flame.

---

* Approved by Standard Methods Committee, 1988.

3111 METALS BY FLAME ATOMIC ABSORPTION SPECTROMETRY*

3111 A. Introduction

1. Principle

Atomic absorption spectrometry resembles emission flame photometry in that a sample is aspirated into a flame and atomized. The major difference is that in flame photometry the amount of light emitted is measured, whereas in atomic absorption spectrometry a light beam is directed through the flame, into a monochromator, and onto a detector that measures the amount of light absorbed by the atomized element in the flame. For some metals, atomic absorption exhibits superior sensitivity over flame emission. Because each metal has its own characteristic absorption wavelength, a source lamp composed of that element is used; this makes the method relatively free from spectral or radiation interferences. The amount of energy at the characteristic wavelength absorbed in the flame is proportional to the concentration of the element in the sample over a limited concentration range. Most atomic absorption instruments also are equipped for operation in an emission mode.

2. Selection of Method

See Section 3110.

---

*Approved by Standard Methods Committee, 1989.

3. Interferences

a. Chemical interference: Many metals can be determined by direct aspiration of sample into an air-acetylene flame. The most troublesome type of interference is termed "chemical" and results from the lack of absorption by atoms bound in molecular combination in the flame. This can occur when the flame is not hot enough to dissociate the molecules or when the dissociated atom is oxidized immediately to a compound that will not dissociate further at the flame temperature. Such interferences may be reduced or eliminated by adding specific elements or compounds to the sample solution. For example, the interference of phosphate in the magnesium determination can be overcome by adding lanthanum. Similarly, introduction of calcium eliminates silica interference in the determination of manganese. However, silicon and metals such as aluminum, barium, beryllium, and vanadium require the higher-temperature, nitrous oxide-acetylene flame to dissociate their molecules. The nitrous oxide-acetylene flame also can be useful in minimizing certain types of chemical interferences encountered in the air-acetylene flame. For example, the interference caused by high concentrations of phosphate in the determination of calcium in the air-acetylene flame does not occur in the nitrous oxide-acetylene flame. MIBK extractions with APDC (see

3111C) are particularly useful where a salt matrix interferes, for example, in seawater. This procedure also concentrates the sample so that the detection limits are extended.

Brines and seawater can be analyzed by direct aspiration but sample dilution is recommended. Aspiration of solutions containing high concentrations of dissolved solids often results in solids buildup on the burner head. This requires frequent shutdown of the flame and cleaning of the burner head. Preferably use background correction when analyzing waters that contain in excess of 1% solids, especially when the primary resonance line of the element of interest is below 240 nm. Make more frequent recovery checks when analyzing brines and seawaters to insure accurate results in these concentrated and complex matrices.

Barium and other metals ionize in the flame, thereby reducing the ground state (potentially absorbing) population. The addition of an excess of a cation (sodium, potassium, or lithium) having a similar or lower ionization potential will overcome this problem. The wavelength of maximum absorption for arsenic is 193.7 nm and for selenium 196.0 nm—wavelengths at which the air-acetylene flame absorbs intensely. The sensitivity for arsenic and selenium can be improved by conversion to their gaseous hydrides and analyzing them in either a nitrogen-hydrogen or an argon-hydrogen flame with a quartz tube (see Section 3114).

b. Background correction: Molecular absorption and light scattering caused by solid particles in the flame can cause erroneously high absorption values resulting in positive errors. When such phenomena occur, use background correction to obtain accurate values. Use any one of three types of background correction: continuum-source, Zeeman, or Smith-Hieftje correction.

1) Continuum-source background correction—A continuum-source background corrector utilizes either a hydrogen-filled hollow cathode lamp with a metal cathode or a deuterium arc lamp. When both the line source hollow-cathode lamp and the continuum source are placed in the same optical path and are time-shared, the broadband background from the elemental signal is subtracted electronically, and the resultant signal will be background-compensated.

Both the hydrogen-filled hollow-cathode lamp and deuterium arc lamp have lower intensities than either the line source hollow-cathode lamp or electrodeless discharge lamps. To obtain a valid correction, match the intensities of the continuum source with the line source hollow-cathode or electrodeless discharge lamp. The matching may result in lowering the intensity of the line source or increasing the slit width; these measures have the disadvantage of raising the detection limit and possibly causing nonlinearity of the calibration curve. Background correction using a continuum source corrector is susceptible to interference from other absorbing lines in the spectral bandwidth. Miscorrection occurs from significant atomic absorption of the continuum source radiation by elements other than that being determined. When a line source hollow-cathode lamp is used without background correction, the presence of an absorbing line from another element in the spectral bandwidth will not cause an interference unless it overlaps the line of interest.

Continuum-source background correction will not remove direct absorption spectral overlap, where an element other than that being determined is capable of absorbing the line radiation of the element under study.

2) Zeeman background correction— This correction is based on the principle that a magnetic field splits the spectral line into two linearly polarized light beams parallel and perpendicular to the magnetic field. One is called the pi (π) component

and the other the sigma (σ) component. These two light beams have exactly the same wavelength and differ only in the plane of polarization. The π line will be absorbed by both the atoms of the element of interest and by the background caused by broadband absorption and light scattering of the sample matrix. The σ line will be absorbed only by the background.

Zeeman background correction provides accurate background correction at much higher absorption levels than is possible with continuum source background correction systems. It also virtually eliminates the possibility of error from structured background. Because no additional light sources are required, the alignment and intensity limitations encountered using continuum sources are eliminated.

Disadvantages of the Zeeman method include reduced sensitivity for some elements, reduced linear range, and a "rollover" effect whereby the absorbance of some elements begins to decrease at high concentrations, resulting in a two-sided calibration curve.

3) Smith-Hieftje background correction—This correction is based on the principle that absorbance measured for a specific element is reduced as the current to the hollow cathode lamp is increased while absorption of nonspecific absorbing substances remains identical at all current levels. When this method is applied, the absorbance at a high-current mode is subtracted from the absorbance at a low-current mode. Under these conditions, any absorbance due to nonspecific background is subtracted out and corrected for.

Smith-Hieftje background correction provides a number of advantages over continuum-source correction. Accurate correction at higher absorbance levels is possible and error from structured background is virtually eliminated. In some cases, spectral interferences also can be eliminated. The usefulness of Smith-Hieftje background correction with electrodeless discharge lamps has not yet been established.

4. Sensitivity, Detection Limits, and Optimum Concentration Ranges

The sensitivity of flame atomic absorption spectrometry is defined as the metal concentration that produces an absorption of 1% (an absorbance of approximately 0.0044). The instrument detection limit is defined here as the concentration that produces absorption equivalent to twice the magnitude of the background fluctuation. Sensitivity and detection limits vary with the instrument, the element determined, the complexity of the matrix, and the technique selected. The optimum concentration range usually starts from the concentration of several times the sensitivity and extends to the concentration at which the calibration curve starts to flatten. To achieve best results, use concentrations of samples and standards within the optimum concentration range of the spectrometer. See Table 3111:I for indication of concentration ranges measurable with conventional atomization. In many instances the concentration range shown in Table 3111:I may be extended downward either by scale expansion or by integrating the absorption signal over a long time. The range may be extended upward by dilution, using a less sensitive wavelength, rotating the burner head, or utilizing a microprocessor to linearize the calibration curve at high concentrations.

5. Preparation of Standards

Prepare standard solutions of known metal concentrations in water with a matrix similar to the sample. Use standards that bracket expected sample concentration and are within the method's working range. Very dilute standards should be prepared daily from stock solutions in concentrations greater than 500 mg/L. Stock standard solutions can be obtained from several

TABLE 3111:I. ATOMIC ABSORPTION CONCENTRATION RANGES WITH DIRECT ASPIRATION ATOMIC ABSORPTION

Element	Wavelength nm	Flame Gases*	Instrument Detection Limit mg/L	Sensitivity mg/L	Optimum Concentration Range mg/L
Ag	328.1	A–Ac	0.01	0.06	0.1–4
Al	309.3	N–Ac	0.1	1	5–100
Au	242.8	A–Ac	0.01	0.25	0.5–20
Ba	553.6	N–Ac	0.03	0.4	1–20
Be	234.9	N–Ac	0.005	0.03	0.05–2
Bi	223.1	A–Ac	0.06	0.4	1–50
Ca	422.7	A–Ac	0.003	0.08	0.2–20
Cd	228.8	A–Ac	0.002	0.025	0.05–2
Co	240.7	A–Ac	0.03	0.2	0.5–10
Cr	357.9	A–Ac	0.02	0.1	0.2–10
Cs	852.1	A–Ac	0.02	0.3	0.5–15
Cu	324.7	A–Ac	0.01	0.1	0.2–10
Fe	248.3	A–Ac	0.02	0.12	0.3–10
Ir	264.0	A–Ac	0.6	8	—
K	766.5	A–Ac	0.005	0.04	0.1–2
Li	670.8	A–Ac	0.002	0.04	0.1–2
Mg	285.2	A–Ac	0.0005	0.007	0.02–2
Mn	279.5	A–Ac	0.01	0.05	0.1–10
Mo	313.3	N–Ac	0.1	0.5	1–20
Na	589.0	A–Ac	0.002	0.015	0.03–1
Ni	232.0	A–Ac	0.02	0.15	0.3–10
Os	290.9	N–Ac	0.08	1	—
Pb†	283.3	A–Ac	0.05	0.5	1–20
Pt	265.9	A–Ac	0.1	2	5–75
Rh	343.5	A–Ac	0.5	0.3	—
Ru	349.9	A–Ac	0.07	0.5	—
Sb	217.6	A–Ac	0.07	0.5	1–40
Si	251.6	N–Ac	0.3	2	5–150
Sn	224.6	A–Ac	0.8	4	10–200
Sr	460.7	A–Ac	0.03	0.15	0.3–5
Ti	365.3	N–Ac	0.3	2	5–100
V	318.4	N–Ac	0.2	1.5	2–100
Zn	213.9	A–Ac	0.005	0.02	0.05–2

* A–Ac = air-acetylene; N–Ac = nitrous oxide-acetylene..

† The more sensitive 217.0 nm wavelength is recommended for instruments with background correction capabilities.

Copyright © ASTM. Reprinted with permission.

commercial sources. They also can be prepared from National Institute of Standards and Technology (NIST, formerly National Bureau of Standards) reference materials or by procedures outlined in the following sections.

For samples containing high and variable concentrations of matrix materials, make the major ions in the sample and the dilute standard similar. If the sample matrix is complex and components cannot be matched accurately with standards, use the method of standard additions, 3113B.4*d*2), to correct for matrix effects. If digestion is used, carry standards through the same digestion procedure used for samples.

6. Apparatus

a. Atomic absorption spectrometer, consisting of a light source emitting the line spectrum of an element (hollow-cathode lamp or electrodeless discharge lamp), a device for vaporizing the sample (usually a flame), a means of isolating an absorption line (monochromator or filter and adjustable slit), and a photoelectric detector with its associated electronic amplifying and measuring equipment.

b. Burner: The most common type of burner is a premix, which introduces the spray into a condensing chamber for removal of large droplets. The burner may be fitted with a conventional head containing a single slot; a three-slot Boling head, which may be preferred for direct aspiration with an air-acetylene flame; or a special head for use with nitrous oxide and acetylene.

c. Readout: Most instruments are equipped with either a digital or null meter readout mechanism. Most modern instruments are equipped with microprocessors capable of integrating absorption signals over time and linearizing the calibration curve at high concentrations.

d. Lamps: Use either a hollow-cathode lamp or an electrodeless discharge lamp (EDL). Use one lamp for each element being measured. Multi-element hollow-cathode lamps generally provide lower sensitivity than single-element lamps. EDLs take a longer time to warm up and stabilize.

e. Pressure-reducing valves: Maintain supplies of fuel and oxidant at pressures somewhat higher than the controlled operating pressure of the instrument by using suitable reducing valves. Use a separate reducing valve for each gas.

f. Vent: Place a vent about 15 to 30 cm above the burner to remove fumes and vapors from the flame. This precaution protects laboratory personnel from toxic vapors, protects the instrument from corrosive vapors, and prevents flame stability from being affected by room drafts. A damper or variable-speed blower is desirable for modulating air flow and preventing flame disturbance. Select blower size to provide the air flow recommended by the instrument manufacturer. In laboratory locations with heavy particulate air pollution, use clean laboratory facilities (Section 3010C).

7. Quality Assurance/Quality Control

Some data typical of the precision and bias obtainable with the methods discussed are presented in Tables 3111:II and III.

Analyze a blank between sample or standard readings to verify baseline stability. Rezero when necessary.

To one sample out of every ten (or one sample from each group of samples if less than ten are being analyzed) add a known amount of the metal of interest and reanalyze to confirm recovery. The amount of metal added should be approximately equal to the amount found. If little metal is present add an amount close to the middle of the linear range of the test. Recovery of added metal should be between 85 and 115%.

Analyze an additional standard solution after every ten samples or with each batch of samples, whichever is less, to confirm that the test is in control. Recommended concentrations of standards to be run, limits of acceptability, and reported single-operator precision data are listed in Table 3111:III.

8. References

1. AMERICAN SOCIETY FOR TESTING AND MATERIALS. 1986. Annual Book of ASTM Standards, Volume 11.01, Water and Environmental Technology. American Soc. Testing & Materials, Philadelphia, Pa.

2. U.S. DEPARTMENT HEALTH, EDUCATION AND

TABLE 3111:II. INTERLABORATORY PRECISION AND BIAS DATA FOR ATOMIC ABSORPTION METHODS—DIRECT ASPIRATION AND EXTRACTED METALS

Metal	Conc. mg/L	SD mg/L	Relative SD %	Relative Error %	No. of Participants
Direct determination:					
Aluminum[1]	4.50	0.19	4.2	8.4	5
Barium[2]	1.00	0.089	8.9	2.7	11
Beryllium[1]	0.46	0.0213	4.6	23.0	11
Cadmium[3]	0.05	0.0108	21.6	8.2	26
Cadmium[1]	1.60	0.11	6.9	5.1	16
Calcium[1]	5.00	0.21	4.2	0.4	8
Chromium[1]	3.00	0.301	10.0	3.7	9
Cobalt[1]	4.00	0.243	6.1	0.5	14
Copper[3]	1.00	0.112	11.2	3.4	53
Copper[1]	4.00	0.331	8.3	2.8	15
Iron[1]	4.40	0.260	5.8	2.3	16
Iron[3]	0.30	0.0495	16.5	0.6	43
Lead[1]	6.00	0.28	4.7	0.2	14
Magnesium[3]	0.20	0.021	10.5	6.3	42
Magnesium[1]	1.10	0.116	10.5	10.0	8
Manganese[1]	4.05	0.317	7.8	1.3	16
Manganese[3]	0.05	0.0068	13.5	6.0	14
Nickel[1]	3.93	0.383	9.8	2.0	14
Silver[3]	0.05	0.0088	17.5	10.6	7
Silver[1]	2.00	0.07	3.5	1.0	10
Sodium[1]	2.70	0.122	4.5	4.1	12
Strontium[1]	1.00	0.05	5.0	0.2	12
Zinc[3]	0.50	0.041	8.2	0.4	48
Extracted determination:					
Aluminum[2]	300	32	10.7	0.7	15
Beryllium[2]	5	1.7	34.0	20.0	9
Cadmium[3]	50	21.9	43.8	13.3	12
Cobalt[1]	300	28.5	9.5	1.0	6
Copper[1]	100	71.7	71.7	12.0	8
Iron[1]	250	19.0	7.6	3.6	4
Manganese[1]	21.5	2.4	11.2	7.4	8
Molybdenum[1]	9.5	1.1	11.6	1.3	5
Nickel[1]	56.8	15.2	26.8	13.6	14
Lead[3]	50	11.8	23.5	19.0	8
Silver[1]	5.2	1.4	26.9	3.0	7

Source: AMERICAN SOCIETY FOR TESTING AND MATERIALS. 1986. Annual Book of ASTM Standards. Volume 11.01, Water and Environmental Technology. American Soc. Testing & Materials, Philadelphia, Pa. Copyright ASTM. Reprinted with permission.

WELFARE. 1970. Water Metals No. 6, Study No. 37. U.S. Public Health Serv. Publ. No. 2029, Cincinnati, Ohio.

3. U.S. DEPARTMENT HEALTH, EDUCATION AND WELFARE. 1968. Water Metals No. 4, Study No. 30. U.S. Public Health Serv. Publ. No. 999-UTH-8, Cincinnati, Ohio.

4. U.S. ENVIRONMENTAL PROTECTION AGENCY. 1983. Methods for Chemical Analysis of Water and Wastes. Cincinnati, Ohio.

TABLE 3111:III. SINGLE-OPERATOR PRECISION AND RECOMMENDED CONTROL RANGES FOR ATOMIC ABSORPTION METHODS—DIRECT ASPIRATION AND EXTRACTED METALS

Metal	Conc. mg/L	SD mg/L	Relative SD %	No. of Participants	QC Std. mg/L	Acceptable Range mg/L
Direct determination:						
Aluminum[1]	4.50	0.23	5.1	15	5.00	4.3–5.7
Beryllium[1]	0.46	0.012	2.6	10	0.50	0.46–0.54
Calcium[1]	5.00	0.05	1.0	8	5.00	4.8–5.2
Chromium[1]	7.00	0.69	9.9	9	5.00	3.3–6.7
Cobalt[1]	4.00	0.21	5.3	14	4.00	3.4–4.6
Copper[1]	4.00	0.115	2.9	15	4.00	3.7–4.3
Iron[1]	5.00	0.19	3.8	16	5.00	4.4–5.6
Magnesium[1]	1.00	0.009	0.9	8	1.00	0.97–1.03
Nickel[4]	5.00	0.04	0.8	—	5.00	4.9–5.1
Silver[1]	2.00	0.25	12.5	10	2.00	1.2–2.8
Sodium[4]	8.2	0.1	1.2	—	5.00	4.8–5.2
Strontium[1]	1.00	0.04	4.0	12	1.00	0.87–1.13
Potassium[4]	1.6	0.2	12.5	—	1.6	1.0–2.2
Molybdenum[4]	7.5	0.07	0.9	—	10.0	9.7–10.3
Tin[4]	20.0	0.5	2.5	—	20.0	18.5–21.5
Titanium[4]	50.0	0.4	0.8	—	50.0	48.8–51.2
Vanadium	50.0	0.2	0.4	—	50.0	49.4–50.6
Extracted determination:						
Aluminum[1]	300	12	4.0	15	300	264–336
Cobalt[1]	300	20	6.7	6	300	220–380
Copper[1]	100	21	21	8	100	22–178
Iron[1]	250	12	4.8	4	250	180–320
Manganese[1]	21.5	202	10.2	8	25	17–23
Molybdenum[1]	9.5	1.0	10.5	5	10	5.5–14.5
Nickel[1]	56.8	9.2	16.2	14	50	22–78
Silver[1]	5.2	1.2	23.1	7	5.0	0.5–9.5

Source: AMERICAN SOCIETY FOR TESTING AND MATERIALS. 1986. Annual Book of ASTM Standards. Volume 11.01, Water and Environmental Technology. American Soc. Testing & Materials, Philadelphia, Pa. Copyright ASTM. Reprinted with permission.

9. Bibliography

KAHN, H.L. 1968. Principles and Practice of Atomic Absorption. Advan. Chem. Ser. No. 73, Div. Water, Air & Waste Chemistry, American Chemical Soc., Washington, D.C.

RAMIRIZ-MUNOZ, J. 1968. Atomic Absorption Spectroscopy and Analysis by Atomic Absorption Flame Photometry. American Elsevier Publishing Co., New York, N.Y.

SLAVIN, W. 1968. Atomic Absorption Spectroscopy. John Wiley & Sons, New York, N.Y.

PAUS, P.E. 1971. The application of atomic absorption spectroscopy to the analysis of natural waters. Atomic Absorption Newsletter 10:69.

EDIGER, R.D. 1973. A review of water analysis by atomic absorption. Atomic Absorption Newsletter 12:151.

PAUS, P.E. 1973. Determination of some heavy metals in seawater by atomic absorption spectroscopy. Fresenius Zeitschr. Anal. Chem. 264:118.

BURRELL, D.C. 1975. Atomic Spectrometric Analysis of Heavy-Metal Pollutants in Water. Ann Arbor Science Publishers, Inc., Ann Arbor, Mich.

3111 B.   Direct Air-Acetylene Flame Method

1. General Discussion

This method is applicable to the determination of antimony, bismuth, cadmium, calcium, cesium, chromium, cobalt, copper, gold, iridium, iron, lead, lithium, magnesium, manganese, nickel, palladium, platinum, potassium, rhodium, ruthenium, silver, sodium, strontium, thallium, tin, and zinc.

2. Apparatus

Atomic absorption spectrometer and associated equipment: See Section 3111A.6. Use burner head recommended by the manufacturer.

3. Reagents

a. Air, cleaned and dried through a suitable filter to remove oil, water, and other foreign substances. The source may be a compressor or commercially bottled gas.

b. Acetylene, standard commercial grade. Acetone, which always is present in acetylene cylinders, can be prevented from entering and damaging the burner head by replacing a cylinder when its pressure has fallen to 689 kPa (100 psi) acetylene.

c. Metal-free water: Use metal-free water for preparing all reagents and calibration standards and as dilution water. Prepare metal-free water by deionizing tap water and/or by using one of the following processes, depending on the metal concentration in the sample: single distillation, redistillation, or sub-boiling. Always check deionized or distilled water to determine whether the element of interest is present in trace amounts. (CAUTION: *If the source water contains Hg or other volatile metals, single- or redistilled water may not be suitable for trace analysis because these metals distill over with the distilled water. In such* cases, use sub-boiling to prepare metal-free water).

d. Calcium solution: Dissolve 630 mg calcium carbonate, $CaCO_3$, in 50 mL of 1 + 5 HCl. If necessary, boil gently to obtain complete solution. Cool and dilute to 1000 mL with water.

e. Hydrochloric acid, HCl, 1%, 10%, 20%, 1 + 5, 1 + 1, and conc.

f. Lanthanum solution: Dissolve 58.65 g lanthanum oxide, La_2O_3, in 250 mL conc HCl. Add acid slowly until the material is dissolved and dilute to 1000 mL with water.

g. Hydrogen peroxide, 30%.

h. Nitric acid, HNO_3, 2%, 1 + 1, and conc.

i. Aqua regia: Add 3 volumes conc HCl to 1 volume conc HNO_3.

j. Standard metal solutions: Prepare a series of standard metal solutions in the optimum concentration range by appropriate dilution of the following stock metal solutions with water containing 1.5 mL conc HNO_3/L. Thoroughly dry reagents before use. In general, use reagents of the highest purity. For hydrates, use fresh reagents.

1) *Antimony:* Dissolve 0.2669 g $K(SbO)C_4H_4O_6$ in water, add 10 mL 1 + 1 HCl and dilute to 1000 mL with water; 1.00 mL = 100 μg Sb.

2) *Bismuth:* Dissolve 0.100 g bismuth metal in a minimum volume of 1 + 1 HNO_3. Dilute to 1000 mL with 2% (v/v) HNO_3; 1.00 mL = 100 μg Bi.

3) *Cadmium:* Dissolve 0.100 g cadmium metal in 4 mL conc HNO_3. Add 8.0 mL conc HNO_3 and dilute to 1000 mL with water; 1.00 mL = 100 μg Cd.

4) *Calcium:* Suspend 0.2497 g $CaCO_3$ (dried at 180° for 1 h before weighing) in

water and dissolve cautiously with a minimum amount of 1 + 1 HNO_3. Add 10.0 mL conc HNO_3 and dilute to 1000 mL with water; 1.00 mL = 100 μg Ca.

5) *Cesium:* Dissolve 0.1267 g cesium chloride, CsCl, in 1000 mL water; 1.00 mL = 100 μg Cs.

6) *Chromium:* Dissolve 0.1923 g CrO_3 in water. When solution is complete, acidify with 10 mL conc HNO_3 and dilute to 1000 mL with water; 1.00 mL = 100 μg Cr.

7) *Cobalt:* Dissolve 0.1000 g cobalt metal in a minimum amount of 1 + 1 HNO_3. Add 10.0 mL 1 + 1 HCl and dilute to 1000 mL with water; 1.00 mL = 100 μg Co.

8) *Copper:* Dissolve 0.100 g copper metal in 2 mL conc HNO_3, add 10.0 mL conc HNO_3 and dilute to 1000 mL with water; 1.00 mL = 100 μg Cu.

9) *Gold:* Dissolve 0.100 g gold metal in a minimum volume of aqua regia. Evaporate to dryness, dissolve residue in 5 mL conc HCl, cool, and dilute to 1000 mL with water; 1.00 mL = 100 μg Au.

10) *Iridium:* Dissolve 0.1147 g ammonium chloroiridate, $(NH_4)_2IrCl_6$, in a minimum volume of 1% (v/v) HCl and dilute to 100 mL with 1% (v/v) HCl; 1.00 mL = 500 μg Ir.

11) *Iron:* Dissolve 0.100 g iron wire in a mixture of 10 mL 1 + 1 HCl and 3 mL conc HNO_3. Add 5 mL conc HNO_3 and dilute to 1000 mL with water; 1.00 mL = 100 μg Fe.

12) *Lead:* Dissolve 0.1598 g lead nitrate, $Pb(NO_3)_2$, in a minimum amount of 1 + 1 HNO_3, add 10 mL conc HNO_3, and dilute to 1000 mL with water; 1.00 mL = 100 μg Pb.

13) *Lithium:* Dissolve 0.5323 g lithium carbonate, Li_2CO_3, in a minimum volume of 1 + 1 HNO_3. Add 10.0 mL conc HNO_3 and dilute to 1000 mL with water; 1.00 mL = 100 μg Li.

14) *Magnesium:* Dissolve 0.1658 g MgO in a minimum amount of 1 + 1 HNO_3. Add 10.0 mL conc HNO_3 and dilute to 1000 mL with water; 1.00 mL = 100 μg Mg.

15) *Manganese:* Dissolve 0.1000 g manganese metal in 10 mL conc HCl mixed with 1 mL conc HNO_3. Dilute to 1000 mL with water; 1.00 mL = 100 μg Mn.

16) *Nickel:* Dissolve 0.1000 g nickel metal in 10 mL hot conc HNO_3, cool, and dilute to 1000 mL with water; 1.00 mL = 100 μg Ni.

17) *Palladium:* Dissolve 0.100 g palladium wire in a minimum volume of aqua regia and evaporate just to dryness. Add 5 mL conc HCl and 25 mL water and warm until dissolution is complete. Dilute to 1000 mL with water; 1.00 mL = 100 μg Pd.

18) *Platinum:* Dissolve 0.100 g platinum metal in a minimum volume of aqua regia and evaporate just to dryness. Add 5 mL conc HCl and 0.1 g NaCl and again evaporate just to dryness. Dissolve residue in 20 mL of 1 + 1 HCl and dilute to 1000 mL with water; 1.00 mL = 100 μg Pt.

19) *Potassium:* Dissolve 0.1907 g potassium chloride, KCl, (dried at 110°C) in water and make up to 1000 mL; 1.00 mL = 100 μg K.

20) *Rhodium:* Dissolve 0.386 g ammonium hexachlororhodate, $(NH_4)_3RhCl_6 \cdot 1.5H_2O$, in a minimum volume of 10% (v/v) HCl and dilute to 1000 mL with 10% (v/v) HCl; 1.00 mL = 100 μg Rh.

21) *Ruthenium:* Dissolve 0.205 g ruthenium chloride, $RuCl_3$, in a minimum volume of 20% (v/v) HCl and dilute to 1000 mL with 20% (v/v) HCl; 1.00 mL = 100 μg Ru.

22) *Silver:* Dissolve 0.1575 g silver nitrate, $AgNO_3$, in 100 mL water, add 10 mL conc HNO_3, and make up to 1000 mL; 1.00 mL = 100 μg Ag.

23) *Sodium:* Dissolve 0.2542 g sodium chloride, NaCl, dried at 140°C, in water, add 10 mL conc HNO_3 and make up to 1000 mL; 1.00 mL = 100 μg Na.

24) *Strontium:* Suspend 0.1685 g $SrCO_3$ in water and dissolve cautiously with a

minimum amount of $1 + 1$ HNO_3. Add 10.0 mL conc HNO_3 and dilute to 1000 mL with water: 1 mL = 100 μg Sr.

25) *Thallium:* Dissolve 0.1303 g thallium nitrate, $TlNO_3$, in water. Add 10 mL conc HNO_3 and dilute to 1000 mL with water; 1.00 mL = 100 μg Tl.

26) *Tin:* Dissolve 1.000 g tin metal in 100 mL conc HCl and dilute to 1000 mL with water; 1.00 mL = 1.00 mg Sn.

27) *Zinc:* Dissolve 0.100 g zinc metal in 20 mL $1 + 1$ HCl and dilute to 1000 mL with water; 1.00 mL = 100 μg Zn.

4. Procedure

a) Sample preparation: Required sample preparation depends on need to measure dissolved metals only or total metals.

If dissolved metals are to be determined, see Section 3030B for sample preparation. If total or acid-extractable metals are to be determined, see Sections 3030C through J. For all samples, make certain that the concentrations of acid and matrix modifiers are the same in both samples and standards.

When determining Ca or Mg, dilute and mix 100 mL sample or standard with 10 mL lanthanum solution (¶ 3f) before atomization. When determining Fe or Mn, mix 100 mL with 25 mL of Ca solution (¶ 3d) before aspirating. When determining Cr, mix 1 mL 30% H_2O_2 with each 100 mL before aspirating. Alternatively use proportionally smaller volumes.

b) Instrument operation: Because of differences between makes and models of atomic absorption spectrometers, it is not possible to formulate instructions applicable to every instrument. See manufacturer's operating manual. In general, proceed according to the following: Install a hollow-cathode lamp for the desired metal in the instrument and roughly set the wavelength dial according to Table 3111:I. Set slit width according to manufacturer's suggested setting for the element being measured. Turn on instrument, apply to the hollow-cathode lamp the current suggested by the manufacturer, and let instrument warm up until energy source stabilizes, generally about 10 to 20 min. Readjust current as necessary after warmup. Optimize wavelength by adjusting wavelength dial until optimum energy gain is obtained. Align lamp in accordance with manufacturer's instructions.

Install suitable burner head and adjust burner head position. Turn on air and adjust flow rate to that specified by manufacturer to give maximum sensitivity for the metal being measured. Turn on acetylene, adjust flow rate to value specified, and ignite flame. Let flame stabilize for a few minutes. Aspirate a blank consisting of either deionized water or an acid solution containing the same concentration of acid in standards and samples. Zero the instrument. Aspirate a standard solution and adjust aspiration rate of the nebulizer to obtain maximum sensitivity. Adjust burner both vertically and horizontally to obtain maximum response. Aspirate blank again and rezero the instrument. Aspirate a standard near the middle of the linear range. Record absorbance of this standard when freshly prepared and with a new hollow-cathode lamp. Refer to these data on subsequent determinations of the same element to check consistency of instrument setup and aging of hollow-cathode lamp and standard.

The instrument now is ready to operate. When analyses are finished, extinguish flame by turning off first acetylene and then air.

c) Standardization: Select at least three concentrations of each standard metal solution (prepared as in ¶ 3j above) to bracket the expected metal concentration of a sample. Aspirate blank and zero the instrument. Then aspirate each standard in turn into flame and record absorbance.

Prepare a calibration curve by plotting on linear graph paper absorbance of standards versus their concentrations. For instruments equipped with direct concentration readout, this step is unnecessary. With some instruments it may be necessary to convert percent absorption to absorbance by using a table generally provided by the manufacturer. Plot calibration curves for Ca and Mg based on original concentration of standards before dilution with lanthanum solution. Plot calibration curves for Fe and Mn based on original concentration of standards before dilution with Ca solution. Plot calibration curve for Cr based on original concentration of standard before addition of H_2O_2.

d. *Analysis of samples:* Rinse nebulizer by aspirating water containing 1.5 mL conc HNO_3/L. Atomize blank and zero instrument. Atomize sample and determine its absorbance.

5. Calculations

Calculate concentration of each metal ion, in micrograms per liter for trace elements, and in milligrams per liter for more common metals, by referring to the appropriate calibration curve prepared according to ¶ 4*c*. Alternatively, read concentration directly from the instrument readout if the instrument is so equipped. If the sample has been diluted, multiply by the appropriate dilution factor.

6. Bibliography

WILLIS, J.B. 1962. Determination of lead and other heavy metals in urine by atomic absorption spectrophotometry. *Anal. Chem.* 34:614.

Also see Section 3111A.8 and 9.

3111 C.   Extraction/Air-Acetylene Flame Method

1. General Discussion

This method is suitable for the determination of low concentrations of cadmium, chromium, cobalt, copper, iron, lead, manganese, nickel, silver, and zinc. The method consists of chelation with ammonium pyrrolidine dithiocarbamate (APDC) and extraction into methyl isobutyl ketone (MIBK), followed by aspiration into an air-acetylene flame.

2. Apparatus

a. Atomic absorption spectrometer and associated equipment: See Section 3111A.6.

b. Burner head, conventional. Consult manufacturer's operating manual for suggested burner head.

3. Reagents

a. Air: See 3111B.3*a.*

b. Acetylene: See 3111B.3*b.*

c. Metal-free water: See 3111B.3*c.*

d. Methyl isobutyl ketone (MIBK), reagent grade. For trace analysis, purify MIBK by redistillation or by sub-boiling distillation.

e. Ammonium pyrrolidine dithiocarbamate (APDC) solution: Dissolve 4 g APDC in 100 mL water. If necessary, purify APDC with an equal volume of MIBK. Shake 30 s in a separatory funnel, let separate, and withdraw lower portion. Discard MIBK layer.

f. Nitric acid, HNO_3, conc, ultrapure.

g. Standard metal solutions: See 3111B.3*j.*

h. Potassium permanganate solution, $KMnO_4$, 5% aqueous.

i. Sodium sulfate, Na_2SO_4, anhydrous.

j. Water-saturated MIBK: Mix one part purified MIBK with one part water in a separatory funnel. Shake 30 s and let separate. Discard aqueous layer. Save MIBK layer.

k. Hydroxylamine hydrochloride solution, 10%.

4. Procedure

a. Instrument operation: See Section 3111B.4*b*. After final adjusting of burner position, aspirate water-saturated MIBK into flame and gradually reduce fuel flow until flame is similar to that before aspiration of solvent.

b. Standardization: Select at least three concentrations of standard metal solutions (prepared as in 3111B.3*j*) to bracket expected sample metal concentration and to be, after extraction, in the optimum concentration range of the instrument. Adjust 100 mL of each standard and 100 mL of a metal-free water blank to pH 3 by adding 1*N* HNO₃ or 1*N* NaOH. For individual element extraction, use the following pH ranges to obtain optimum extraction efficiency:

Element	pH Range for Optimum Extraction
Ag	2–5 (complex unstable)
Cd	1–6
Co	2–10
Cr	3–9
Cu	0.1–8
Fe	2–5
Mn	2–4 (complex unstable)
Ni	2–4
Pb	0.1–6
Zn	2–6

NOTE: For Ag and Pb extraction the optimum pH value is 2.3 ± 0.2. The Mn complex deteriorates rapidly at room temperature, resulting in decreased instrument response. Chilling the extract to 0°C may preserve the complex for a few hours. If this is not possible and Mn cannot be analyzed immediately after extraction, use another analytical procedure.

Transfer each standard solution and blank to individual 200-mL volumetric flasks, add 1 mL APDC solution, and shake to mix. Add 10 mL MIBK and shake vigorously for 30 s. (The maximum volume ratio of sample to MIBK is 40.) Let contents of each flask separate into aqueous and organic layers, then carefully add water (adjusted to the same pH at which the extraction was carried out) down the side of each flask to bring the organic layer into the neck and accessible to the aspirating tube.

Aspirate organic extracts directly into the flame (zeroing instrument on a water-saturated MIBK blank) and record absorbance.

Prepare a calibration curve by plotting on linear graph paper absorbances of extracted standards against their concentrations before extraction.

c. Analysis of samples: Prepare samples in the same manner as the standards. Rinse atomizer by aspirating water-saturated MIBK. Aspirate organic extracts treated as above directly into the flame and record absorbances.

With the above extraction procedure only hexavalent chromium is measured. To determine total chromium, oxidize trivalent chromium to hexavalent chromium by bringing sample to a boil and adding sufficient KMnO₄ solution dropwise to give a persistent pink color while the solution is boiled for 10 min. Destroy excess KMnO₄ by adding 1 to 2 drops hydroxylamine hydrochloride solution to the boiling solution, allowing 2 min for the reaction to proceed. If pink color persists, add 1 to 2 more drops hydroxylamine hydrochloride solution and wait 2 min. Heat an additional 5 min. Cool, extract with MIBK, and aspirate.

During extraction, if an emulsion forms at the water-MIBK interface, add anhydrous Na₂SO₄ to obtain a homogeneous organic phase. In that case, also add Na₂SO₄ to all standards and blanks.

To avoid problems associated with instability of extracted metal complexes, determine metals immediately after extraction.

5. Calculations

Calculate the concentration of each metal ion in micrograms per liter by referring to the appropriate calibration curve.

6. Bibliography

ALLAN, J.E. 1961. The use of organic solvents in atomic absorption spectrophotometry. *Spectrochim. Acta* 17:467.

SACHDEV, S.L. & P.W. WEST. 1970. Concentration of trace metals by solvent extraction and their determination by atomic absorption spectrophotometry. *Environ. Sci. Technol.* 4:749.

3111 D. Direct Nitrous Oxide-Acetylene Flame Method

1. General Discussion

This method is applicable to the determination of aluminum, barium, beryllium, molybdenum, osmium, rhenium, silicon, thorium, titanium, and vanadium.

2. Apparatus

a. Atomic absorption spectrometer and associated equipment: See Section 3111A.6.

b. Nitrous oxide burner head: Use special burner head as suggested in manufacturer's manual. At roughly 20-min intervals of operation it may be necessary to dislodge the carbon crust that forms along the slit surface with a carbon rod or appropriate alternative.

c. T-junction valve or other switching valve for rapidly changing from nitrous oxide to air, so that flame can be turned on or off with air as oxidant to prevent flashbacks.

3. Reagents

a. Air: See 3111B.3*a*.

b. Acetylene: See 3111B.3*b*.

c. Metal-free water: See 3111B.3*c*.

d. Hydrochloric acid, HCl, 1*N,* 1+1, and conc.

e. Nitric acid, HNO$_3$, conc.

f. Sulfuric acid, H$_2$SO$_4$, 1%.

g. Hydrofluoric acid, HF, 1*N*.

h. Nitrous oxide, commercially available cylinders. Fit nitrous oxide cylinder with a special nonfreezable regulator or wrap a heating coil around an ordinary regulator to prevent flashback at the burner caused by reduction in nitrous oxide flow through a frozen regulator. (Some atomic absorption instruments have automatic gas control systems that will shut down a nitrous oxide-acetylene flame safely in the event of a reduction in nitrous oxide flow rate.)

i. Potassium chloride solution: Dissolve 250 g KCl in water and dilute to 1000 mL.

j. Aluminum nitrate solution: Dissolve 139 g Al(NO$_3$)$_3$·9H$_2$O in 150 mL water. Acidify slightly with conc HNO$_3$ to preclude possible hydrolysis and precipitation. Warm to dissolve completely. Cool and dilute to 200 mL.

k. Standard metal solutions: Prepare a series of standard metal solutions in the optimum concentration ranges by appropriate dilution of the following stock metal solutions with water containing 1.5 mL conc HNO$_3$/L:

1) *Aluminum:* Dissolve 0.100 g aluminum metal in an acid mixture of 4 mL 1 + 1 HCl and 1 mL conc HNO$_3$ in a beaker. Warm gently to effect solution. Transfer to a 1-L flask, add 10 mL 1 + 1 HCl, and dilute to 1000 mL with water; 1.00 mL = 100 μg Al.

2) *Barium:* Dissolve 0.1516 g BaCl$_2$ (dried at 250° for 2 h), in about 10 mL water with 1 mL 1 + 1 HCl. Add 10.0 mL

1 + 1 HCl and dilute to 1000 mL with water; 1.00 mL = 100 μg Ba.

3) *Beryllium: Do not dry.* Dissolve 1.966 g $BeSO_4 \cdot 4H_2O$ in water, add 10.0 mL conc HNO_3, and dilute to 1000 mL with water; 1.00 mL = 100 μg Be.

4) *Molybdenum:* Dissolve 0.2043 g $(NH_4)_2 MoO_4$ in water and dilute to 1000 mL; 1.00 mL = 100 μg Mo.

5) *Osmium:* Obtain standard $0.1M$ osmium tetroxide solution* and store in glass bottle; 1.00 mL = 19.02 mg Os. Make dilutions daily as needed using 1% (v/v) H_2SO_4. CAUTION: *OsO_4 is extremely toxic and highly volatile.*

6) *Rhenium:* Dissolve 0.1554 g potassium perrhenate, $KReO_4$, in 200 mL water. Dilute to 1000 mL with 1% (v/v) H_2SO_4; 1.00 mL = 100 μg Re.

7) *Silica: Do not dry.* Dissolve 0.4730 g $Na_2SiO_3 \cdot 9H_2O$ in water. Add 10.0 mL conc HNO_3 and dilute to 1000 mL with water. 1.00 mL = 100 μg Si. Store in polyethylene.

8) *Thorium:* Dissolve 0.238 g thorium nitrate, $Th(NO_3)_4 \cdot 4H_2O$ in 1000 mL water; 1.00 mL = 100 μg Th.

9) *Titanium:* Dissolve 0.3960 g pure (99.8 or 99.9%) titanium chloride, $TiCl_4$,† in a mixture of equal volumes of $1N$ HCl and $1N$ HF. Make up to 1000 mL with this acid mixture; 1.00 mL = 100 μg Ti.

10) *Vanadium:* Dissolve 0.2297 g ammonium metavanadate, NH_4VO_3, in a minimum amount of conc HNO_3. Heat to dissolve. Add 10 mL conc HNO_3, and dilute to 1000 mL with water; 1.00 mL = 100 μg V.

4. Procedure

a. Sample preparation: See Section 3111B.4*a.*

b. Instrument operation: See Section

3111B.4*b.* After adjusting wavelength, install a nitrous oxide burner head. Turn on acetylene (without igniting flame) and adjust flow rate to value specified by manufacturer for a nitrous oxide-acetylene flame. Turn off acetylene. With both air and nitrous oxide supplies turned on, set T-junction valve to nitrous oxide and adjust flow rate according to manufacturer's specifications. Turn switching valve to the air position and verify that flow rate is the same. Turn acetylene on and ignite to a bright yellow flame. With a rapid motion, turn switching valve to nitrous oxide. The flame should have a red cone above the burner. If it does not, adjust fuel flow to obtain red cone. After nitrous oxide flame has been ignited, let burner come to thermal equilibrium before beginning analysis.

Atomize water containing 1.5 mL conc HNO_3/L and check aspiration rate. Adjust if necessary to a rate between 3 and 5 mL/min. Atomize a standard of the desired metal with a concentration near the midpoint of the optimum concentration range and adjust burner (both horizontally and vertically) in the light path to obtain maximum response. The instrument now is ready to run standards and samples.

To extinguish flame, turn switching valve from nitrous oxide to air and turn off acetylene. This procedure eliminates the danger of flashback that may occur on direct ignition or shutdown of nitrous oxide and acetylene.

c. Standardization: Select at least three concentrations of standard metal solutions (prepared as in ¶ 3*k*) to bracket the expected metal concentration of a sample. Aspirate each in turn into the flame. Record absorbances. For Al, Ba, and Ti, add 2 mL KCl solution to 100 mL standard before aspiration. For Mo and V add 2 mL $Al(NO_3)_3 \cdot 9H_2O$ solution to 100 mL standard before aspiration.

Most modern instruments are equipped with microprocessors and digital readout which permit calibration in direct concen-

---

*GFS Chemical Co., P.O. Box 23214, Columbus, Ohio 43223, Cat. No. 64, or equivalent.

†Alpha Ventron, P.O. Box 299, 152 Andover St., Danvers, Mass. 01923, or equivalent.

tration terms. If instrument is not so equipped, prepare a calibration curve by plotting on linear graph paper absorbance of standards versus concentration. Plot calibration curves for Al, Ba, and Ti based on original concentration of standard before adding KCl solution. Plot calibration curves for Mo and V based on original concentration of standard before adding $Al(NO_3)_3$ solution.

d. *Analysis of samples:* Rinse atomizer by aspirating water containing 1.5 mL conc HNO_3/L and zero instrument. Atomize a sample and determine its absorbance.

When determining Al, Ba, and Ti, add 2 mL KCl solution to 100 mL sample before atomization. For Mo and V, add 2 mL $Al(NO_3)_3 \cdot 9H_2O$ solution to 100 mL sample before atomization.

5. Calculations

Calculate concentration of each metal ion in micrograms per liter by referring to the appropriate calibration curve prepared according to ¶ 4c.

Alternatively, read the concentration directly from the instrument readout if the instrument is so equipped. If sample has been diluted, multiply by the appropriate dilution factor.

6. Bibliography

WILLIS, J.B. 1965. Nitrous oxide-acetylene flame in atomic absorption spectroscopy. *Nature* 207:715.
Also see Section 3111A.8 and 9.

3111 E.   Extraction/Nitrous Oxide-Acetylene Flame Method

1. General Discussion

a. *Application:* This method is suitable for the determination of aluminum at concentrations less than 900 μg/L and beryllium at concentrations less than 30 μg/L. The method consists of chelation with 8-hydroxyquinoline, extraction with methyl isobutyl ketone (MIBK), and aspiration into a nitrous oxide-acetylene flame.

b. *Interferences:* Concentrations of Fe greater than 10 mg/L interfere by suppressing Al absorption. Iron interference can be masked by addition of hydroxylamine hydrochloride/1,10-phenanthroline. Mn concentrations up to 80 mg/L do not interfere if turbidity in the extract is allowed to settle. Mg forms an insoluble chelate with 8-hydroxyquinoline at pH 8.0 and tends to remove Al complex as a coprecipitate. However, the Mg complex forms slowly over 4 to 6 min; its interference can be avoided if the solution is extracted immediately after adding buffer.

2. Apparatus

Atomic absorption spectrometer and associated equipment: See Section 3111A.6.

3. Reagents

a. *Air:* See 3111B.3a.

b. *Acetylene:* See 3111B.3b.

c. *Ammonium hydroxide,* NH_4OH, conc.

d. *Buffer:* Dissolve 300 g ammonium acetate, $NH_4C_2H_3O_2$, in water, add 105 mL conc NH_4OH, and dilute to 1 L.

e. *Metal-free water:* See 3111B.2c.

f. *Hydrochloric acid,* HCl, conc.

g. *8-Hydroxyquinoline solution:* Dissolve 20 g 8-hydroxyquinoline in about 200 mL water, add 60 mL glacial acetic acid, and dilute to 1 L with water.

h. *Methyl isobutyl ketone:* See 3111C.3d.

i. *Nitric acid,* HNO_3, conc.

j. *Nitrous oxide:* See 3111D.3h.

k. *Standard metal solutions:* Prepare a series of standard metal solutions containing 5 to 1000 μg/L by appropriate dilution of the stock metal solutions prepared according to 3111D.3k.

l. Iron masking solution: Dissolve 1.3 g hydroxylamine hydrochloride and 6.58 g 1,10-phenanthroline monohydrate in about 500 mL water and dilute to 1 L with water.

4. Procedure

a. Instrumentation operation: See Sections 3111B.4b, C.4a, and D.4b. After final adjusting of burner position, aspirate MIBK into flame and gradually reduce fuel flow until flame is similar to that before aspiration of solvent. Adjust wavelength setting according to Table 3111:I.

b. Standardization: Select at least three concentrations of standard metal solutions (prepared as in ¶ 3k) to bracket the expected metal concentration of a sample and transfer 100 mL of each (and 100 mL water blank) to four different 200-mL volumetric flasks. Add 2 mL 8-hydroxyquinoline so-lution, 2 mL masking solution (if required), and 10 mL buffer to one flask, immediately add 10 mL MIBK, and shake vigorously. The duration of shaking affects the forms of aluminum complexed. A fast, 10-s shaking time favors monomeric Al, whereas 5 to 10 min of shaking also will complex polymeric species. Adjustment of the 8-hydroxyquinoline to sample ratio can improve recoveries of extremely high or low concentrations of aluminum. Treat each blank, standard, and sample in similar fashion. Continue as in Section 3111C.4b.

c. Analysis of samples: Rinse atomizer by aspirating water-saturated MIBK. Aspirate extracts of samples treated as above, and record absorbances.

5. Calculations

Calculate concentration of each metal in micrograms per liter by referring to the appropriate calibration curve prepared according to ¶ 4b.

3112   METALS BY COLD-VAPOR ATOMIC ABSORPTION SPECTROMETRY*

3112 A.   Introduction

For general introductory material on atomic absorption spectrometric methods, see Section 3111A.

---

* Approved by Standard Methods Committee, 1988.

3112 B.   Cold-Vapor Atomic Absorption Spectrometric Method

1. General Discussion

This method is applicable to the determination of mercury.

2. Apparatus

a. Atomic absorption spectrometer and associated equipment: See Section 3111A.6. Instruments and accessories specifically designed for measurement of mercury by the cold vapor technique are available commercially and may be substituted.

b. Absorption cell, a glass or plastic tube approximately 2.5 cm in diameter. An 11.4-cm-long tube has been found satisfactory but a 15-cm-long tube is preferred. Grind tube ends perpendicular to the longitudinal axis and cement quartz windows in place. Attach gas inlet and outlet ports (6.4 mm diam) 1.3 cm from each end.

c. Cell support: Strap cell to the flat nitrous-oxide burner head or other suitable support and align in light beam to give maximum transmittance.

d. Air pumps: Use any peristaltic pump with electronic speed control capable of delivering 2 L air/min. Any other regulated compressed air system or air cylinder also is satisfactory.

e. Flowmeter, capable of measuring an air flow of 2 L/min.

f. Aeration tubing, a straight glass frit having a coarse porosity for use in reaction flask.

g. Reaction flask, 250-mL erlenmeyer flask or a BOD bottle, fitted with a rubber stopper to hold aeration tube.

h. Drying tube, 150-mm × 18-mm-diam, containing 20 g Mg $(ClO_4)_2$. A 60-W light bulb with a suitable shade may be substituted to prevent condensation of moisture inside the absorption cell. Position bulb to maintain cell temperature at 10°C above ambient.

i. Connecting tubing, glass tubing to pass mercury vapor from reaction flask to absorption cell and to interconnect all other components. Clear vinyl plastic* tubing may be substituted for glass.

3. Reagents†

a. Metal-free water: See 3111B.3c.

b. Stock mercury solution: Dissolve 1.354 g mercuric chloride, $HgCl_2$, in about 700 mL water, add 10 mL conc HNO_3, and dilute to 1000 mL with water; 1.00 mL = 1.00 mg Hg.

c. Standard mercury solutions: Prepare a series of standard mercury solutions containing 0 to 5 μg/L by appropriate dilution of stock mercury solution with water containing 10 mL conc HNO_3/L. Prepare standards daily.

d. Nitric acid, HNO_3, conc.

e. Potassium permanganate solution: Dissolve 50 g $KMnO_4$ in water and dilute to 1 L.

f. Potassium persulfate solution: Dissolve 50 g $K_2S_2O_8$ in water and dilute to 1 L.

g. Sodium chloride-hydroxylamine sulfate solution: Dissolve 120 g NaCl and 120 g $(NH_2OH)_2 \cdot H_2SO_4$ in water and dilute to 1 L. A 10% hydroxylamine hydrochloride solution may be substituted for the hydroxylamine sulfate.

h. Stannous chloride solution: Dissolve 100 g $SnCl_2$ in water containing 200 mL conc HCl and dilute to 1 L. On aging, this

---

* Tygon or equivalent.
† Use specially prepared reagents low in mercury.

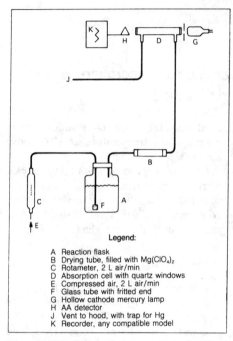

Legend:

A Reaction flask
B Drying tube, filled with Mg(ClO₄)₂
C Rotameter, 2 L air/min
D Absorption cell with quartz windows
E Compressed air, 2 L air/min
F Glass tube with fritted end
G Hollow cathode mercury lamp
H AA detector
J Vent to hood, with trap for Hg
K Recorder, any compatible model

Figure 3112:1. Schematic arrangement of equipment for measurement of mercury by cold-vapor atomic absorption technique.

solution decomposes. If a suspension forms, stir reagent continuously during use.

i. Sulfuric acid, H₂SO₄, conc.

4. Procedure

a. Instrument operation: See Section 3111B.4*b*. Install absorption cell and align in light path to give maximum transmission. Connect associated equipment to absorption cell with glass or vinyl plastic tubing as indicated in Figure 3112:1. Turn on air and adjust flow rate to 2 L/min. Allow air to flow continuously. Alternatively, follow manufacturer's directions for operation. NOTE: Fluorescent lighting may increase baseline noise.

b. Standardization: Transfer 100 mL of each of the 1.0, 2.0, and 5.0 μg/L Hg standard solutions and a blank of 100 mL water to 250-mL erlenmeyer reaction flasks. Add 5 mL conc H₂SO₄ and 2.5 mL conc HNO₃

to each flask. Add 15 mL KMnO₄ solution to each flask and let stand at least 15 min. Add 8 mL K₂S₂O₈ solution to each flask and heat for 2 h in a water bath at 95°C. Cool to room temperature.

Treating each flask individually, add enough NaCl-hydroxylamine sulfate solution to reduce excess KMnO₄, then add 5 mL SnCl₂ solution and immediately attach flask to aeration apparatus. As Hg is volatilized and carried into the absorption cell, absorbance will increase to a maximum within a few seconds. As soon as recorder returns approximately to the base line, remove stopper holding the frit from reaction flask, and replace with a flask containing water. Flush system for a few seconds and run the next standard in the same manner. Construct a standard curve by plotting peak height versus micrograms Hg.

c. Analysis of samples: Transfer 100 mL sample or portion diluted to 100 mL containing not more than 5.0 μg Hg/L to a reaction flask. Treat as in ¶ 4*b*. Seawaters, brines, and effluents high in chlorides require as much as an additional 25 mL KMnO₄ solution. During oxidation step, chlorides are converted to free chlorine, which absorbs at 253 nm. Remove all free chlorine before the Hg is reduced and swept into the cell by using an excess (25 mL) of hydroxylamine sulfate reagent.

Remove free chlorine by sparging sample gently with air or nitrogen after adding hydroxylamine reducing solution. Use a separate tube and frit to avoid carryover of residual stannous chloride, which could cause reduction and loss of mercury.

4. Calculation

Determine peak height of sample from recorder chart and read mercury value from standard curve prepared according to ¶ 4*b*.

TABLE 3112:I. INTERLABORATORY PRECISION AND BIAS
OF COLD-VAPOR ATOMIC ABSORPTION SPECTROMETRIC METHOD FOR MERCURY[1]

Form	Conc. μg/L	SD μg/L	Relative SD %	Relative Error %	No. of Participants
Inorganic	0.34	0.077	22.6	21.0	23
Inorganic	4.2	0.56	13.3	14.4	21
Organic	4.2	0.36	8.6	8.4	21

6. Precision and Bias

Data on interlaboratory precision and bias for this method are given in Table 3112:I.

7. Reference

1. KOPP, J.F., M.C. LONGBOTTOM & L.B. LOBRING. 1972. "Cold vapor" method for determining mercury. *J. Amer. Water Works Assoc.* 64:20.

8. Bibliography

HATCH, W.R. & W.L. OTT. 1968. Determination of submicrogram quantities of mercury by atomic absorption spectrophotometry. *Anal. Chem.* 40:2085.

UTHE, J.F., F.A.J. ARMSTRONG & M.P. STAINTON. 1970. Mercury determination in fish samples by wet digestion and flameless atomic absorption spectrophotometry. *J. Fish. Res. Board Can.* 27:805.

FELDMAN, C. 1974. Preservation of dilute mercury solutions. *Anal. Chem.* 46:99.

BOTHNER, M.H. & D.E. ROBERTSON. 1975. Mercury contamination of sea water samples

stored in polyethylene containers. *Anal. Chem.* 47:592.

HAWLEY, J.E. & J.D. INGLE, JR. 1975. Improvements in cold vapor atomic absorption determination of mercury. *Anal. Chem.* 47:719.

LO, J.M. & C.M. WAL. 1975. Mercury loss from water during storage: Mechanisms and prevention. *Anal. Chem.* 47:1869.

EL-AWADY, A.A., R.B. MILLER & M.J. CARTER. 1976. Automated method for the determination of total and inorganic mercury in water and wastewater samples. *Anal. Chem.* 48:110.

ODA, C.E. & J.D. INGLE, JR. 1981. Speciation of mercury by cold vapor atomic absorption spectrometry with selective reduction. *Anal. Chem.* 53:2305.

SUDDENDORF, R.F. 1981. Interference by selenium or tellurium in the determination of mercury by cold vapor generation atomic absorption spectrometry. *Anal. Chem.* 53:2234.

HEIDEN, R.W. & D.A. AIKENS. 1983. Humic acid as a preservative for trace mercury (II) solutions stored in polyolefin containers. *Anal. Chem.* 55:2327.

CHOU, H.N. & C.A. NALEWAY. 1984. Determination of mercury by cold vapor atomic absorption spectrometry. *Anal. Chem.* 56:1737.

3113   METALS BY ELECTROTHERMAL ATOMIC ABSORPTION SPECTROMETRY*

3113 A.   Introduction

1. Applications

Electrothermal atomic absorption permits determination of most metallic elements with sensitivities and detection limits from 20 to 1000 times better than those of conventional flame techniques without extraction or sample concentration. This increase in sensitivity results from the increased residence time of the ground-state atoms in the optical path, which is many times that of conventional flame atomic absorption. Many elements can be determined at concentrations as low as 1.0 μg/L. An additional advantage of electrothermal atomic absorption is that only a very small volume of sample is required.

Use the electrothermal technique only at concentration levels below the optimum range of direct flame atomic absorption because it is subject to more interferences than the flame procedure and requires increased analysis time. The method of standard additions often is required to insure validity of data. Because of the high sensitivity of this technique, exercise great care to avoid contamination errors.

2. Principle

Electrothermal atomic absorption spectroscopy is based on the same principle as direct flame atomization but an electrically heated atomizer or graphite furnace re-

places the standard burner head. A discrete sample volume is dispensed into the graphite sample tube (or cup). Typically, determinations are made by heating the sample in three or more stages. First, a low current heats the tube to dry the sample. The second, or charring stage, destroys organic matter and volatilizes other matrix components at an intermediate temperature. Finally, a high current heats the tube to incandescence and, in an inert atmosphere, atomizes the element being determined. Additional stages frequently are added to aid in drying and charring, and to clean and cool the tube between samples. The resultant ground-state atomic vapor absorbs monochromatic radiation from the source. A photoelectric detector measures the intensity of transmitted radiation, which is inversely proportional to the quantity of ground-state atoms in the optical path over a limited range.

3. Interference

Electrothermal atomization determinations are subject to significant interferences from molecular absorption as well as chemical and matrix effects. Molecular absorption may occur when components of the sample matrix volatilize during atomization, resulting in broadband absorption. Several background correction techniques are available commercially to compensate for this interference. A continuum source

---

*Approved by Standard Methods Committee, 1988.

such as a deuterium arc can correct for background up to absorbance levels of 0.8 or so. Zeeman effect background correctors can handle background absorbencies up to 1.5 to 2.0. The Smith-Hieftje correction technique can accommodate background absorbance levels as large as 2.5 to 3.0 (see Section 3111A.3). Use background correction when analyzing samples containing high concentrations of acid or dissolved solids and in determining elements for which an absorption line below 350 nm is used.

Matrix modification can be useful in minimizing interference. Accomplish this by adding various chemicals to the sample. Alternatively, program a modern autosampler to add matrix modifiers directly to the sample in the furnace chamber. Some matrix modifiers reduce volatility of the element being determined or increase its atomization efficiency by changing its chemical composition. This permits use of higher charring temperatures to volatilize interfering substances and increases sensitivity. Other matrix modifiers increase volatility of the matrix. Specific matrix modifiers are listed in Table 3113:I.

Temperature ramping, i.e., gradual heating, can be used to decrease background interferences and permits analysis of samples with complex matrices. Ramping permits a controlled, continuous increase of furnace temperature in any of the various

TABLE 3113:I. POTENTIAL MATRIX MODIFIERS FOR ELECTROTHERMAL ATOMIC ABSORPTION SPECTROMETRY[1]

Element	Matrix Modifiers For Interference Removal	Matrix Modifiers as Enhancers
Al	$Mg(NO_3)_2$	$Ca(NO_3)_2$, $Ca_3(PO_4)_2$, H_2SO_4
Sb	$Ni(NO_3)_2$ & $Mg(NO_3)_2$	—
As	$Mg(NO_3)_2$, $Ni(NO_3)_2$	—
Be	$Al(NO_3)_2$, $Mg(NO_3)_2$	$Ca(NO_3)_2$
Cd	$NH_4H_2PO_4$ & $Mg(NO_3)_2$, $(NH_4)_2HPO_4$ & $Mg(NO_3)_2$, $(NH_4)_2SO_4$, HNO_3, $(NH_4)_2S_2O_8$	
Cr	$Mg(NO_3)_2$	—
Co	$Mg(NO_3)_2$, $NH_4H_2PO_4$, ascorbic acid	
Cu	NH_4NO_3, ascorbic acid	$MgSO_4$, $LaNO_3$
Fe	NH_4NO_3	—
Pb	$NH_4H_2PO_4$, $(NH_4)_2HPO_4$, $Mg(NO_3)_2$, NH_4NO_3, ascorbic acid, oxalic acid, phosphoric acid, HNO_3, LaCl, $(NH_4)_2EDTA$	
Mn	Ascorbic acid, $Mg(NO_3)_2$, NH_4NO_3	—
Mo	—	HNO_3
Ni	$Mg(NO_3)_2$, $NH_4H_2PO_4$	—
Se	$Ni(NO_3)_2$, $Ni(NO_3)_2$ & $Mg(NO_3)_2$, $Ni(NO_3)_2$ & $Cu(NO_3)_2$, $AgNO_3$, $(NH_4)_6Mo_7O_{24}$, $Fe(NO_3)_3$ $Fe(NO_3)_3$ & $Cu(NO_3)_2$	—
Ag	$(NH_4)_2HPO_4$, $NH_4H_2PO_4$	
Sn	$(NH_4)_2HPO_4$ & $Mg(NO_3)_2$, $Ni(NO_3)_2$, ascorbic acid, NH_4NO_3	$Ca(NO_3)_2$

Source: SLAVIN, W. 1984. Graphite Furnace AAS—A Source Book. Perkin-Elmer Corp., Norwalk, Conn. Courtesy of the Perkin-Elmer Corporation.

steps of the temperature sequence. Use ramp drying for samples containing mixtures of solvents or for samples with a high salt content (to avoid spattering). Samples that contain a complex mixture of matrix components sometimes require ramp charring to effect controlled, complete thermal decomposition. Ramp atomization may minimize background absorption by permitting volatilization of the element being determined before the matrix. This is especially applicable in the determination of such volatile elements as cadmium and lead.

Use standard additions to compensate for matrix interferences. When making standard additions, determine whether the added species and the element being determined behave similarly under the specified conditions. [See Section 3113B.4d2)].

Chemical interaction of the graphite tube with various elements to form refractory carbides occurs at high charring and atomization temperatures. Elements that form carbides are barium, molybdenum, nickel, titanium, vanadium, and silicon. Carbide formation is characterized by broad, tailing atomization peaks and reduced sensitivity. Using pyrolytically coated tubes for these metals minimizes the problem. For the analysis of aluminum, thorium treated L'vov platforms provide sharper peaks at low concentrations and enhanced charring stability.

4. Sensitivity, Detection Limits, and Optimum Concentration Range

Estimated detection limits and optimum concentration ranges are listed in Table 3113:II. These values may vary with the chemical form of the element being determined, sample composition, or instrumental conditions.

For a given sample, increased sensitivity may be achieved by using a larger sample volume or by reducing flow rate of the purge gas or by using gas interrupt during atomization. Note, however, that these techniques also will increase the effects of any interferences present. Sensitivity can be decreased by diluting the sample, reducing sample volume, increasing purge-gas flow, or using a less sensitive wavelength. Use of argon, rather than nitrogen, as the purge gas generally improves sensitivity and reproducibility. Hydrogen mixed with the inert gas may suppress chemical interference and increase sensitivity by acting as a reducing agent, thereby aiding in producing more ground-state atoms. Using pyrolytically coated graphite tubes can increase sensitivity for the more refractory elements. The optical pyrometer/maximum power accessory available on some instruments also offers increased sensitivity with lower atomization temperatures for many elements.

Using the Stabilized Temperature Platform Furnace (STPF) technique, which is a combination of individual techniques, also offers significant interference reduction with improved sensitivity. Sensitivity changes with sample tube age. Discard graphite tubes when significant variations in sensitivity or poor reproducibility are observed. The use of high acid concentrations, brine samples, and matrix modifiers often drastically reduce tube life. Preferably use the L'vov platform in such situations.

5. Reference

1. SLAVIN, W. 1984. Graphite Furnace AAS—A Source Book. Perkin-Elmer Corp., Norwalk, Conn.

6. Bibliography

FERNANDEZ, F.J. & D.C. MANNING. 1971. Atomic absorption analyses of metal pollutants in water using a heated graphite atomizer. *Atomic Absorption Newsletter* 10:65.

SEGAR, D.A. & J.G. GONZALEZ. 1972. Evaluation of atomic absorption with a heated graphite atomizer for the direct determination of trace transition metals in sea water. *Anal. Chim. Acta* 58:7.

BARNARD, W.M. & M.J. FISHMAN. 1973. Eval-

TABLE 3113:II. DETECTION LEVELS AND CONCENTRATION RANGES FOR ELECTROTHERMAL
ATOMIZATION ATOMIC ABSORPTION SPECTROMETRY

Element	Wavelength nm	Estimated Detection Limit $\mu g/L$	Optimum Concentration Range $\mu g/L$
Al	309.3	3	20–200
Sb	217.6	3	20–300
As*	193.7	1	5–100
Ba†	553.6	2	10–200
Be	234.9	0.2	1–30
Cd	228.8	0.1	0.5–10
Cr	357.9	2	5–100
Co	240.7	1	5–100
Cu	324.7	1	5–100
Fe	248.3	1	5–100
Pb‡	283.3	1	5–100
Mn	279.5	0.2	1–30
Mo†	313.3	1	3–60
Ni†	232.0	1	5–100
Se*	196.0	2	5–100
Ag	328.1	0.2	1–25
Sn	224.6	5	20–300

* Gas interrupt utilized.
† Pyrolytic graphite tubes utilized.
‡ The more sensitive 217.0-nm wavelength is recommended for instruments with background correction capabilities.

uation of the use of heated graphite atomizer for the routine determination of trace metals in water. *Atomic Absorption Newsletter* 12:118.

KAHN, H.L. 1973. The detection of metallic elements in wastes and waters with the graphite furnace. *Int. J. Environ. Anal. Chem.* 3:121.

WALSH, P.R., J.L. FASCHING & R.A. DUCE. 1976. Matrix effects and their control during the flameless atomic absorption determination of arsenic. *Anal. Chem.* 48:1014.

HENN, E.L. 1977. Use of Molybdenum in Eliminating Matrix Interferences in Flameless Atomic Absorption. Spec. Tech. Publ. 618, American Soc. Testing & Materials, Philadelphia, Pa.

MARTIN, T.D. & J.F. KOPP. 1978. Methods for Metals in Drinking Water. U.S. Environmental Protection Agency, Environmental Monitoring and Support Lab., Cincinnati, Ohio.

HYDES, D.J. 1980. Reduction of matrix effects with a soluble organic acid in the carbon furnace atomic absorption spectrometric determination of cobalt, copper, and manganese in seawater. *Anal. Chem.* 52:289.

SOTERA, J.J. & H.L. KAHN. 1982. Background correction in AAS. *Amer. Lab.* 14:100.

SMITH, S.B. & G.M. HIEFTJE. 1983. A new background-correction method for atomic absorption spectrometry. *Appl. Spectrosc.* 37:419.

GROSSER, Z. 1985. Techniques in Graphite Furnace Atomic Absorption Spectrophotometry. Perkin-Elmer Corp., Ridgefield, Conn.

SLAVIN, W. & G.R. CARNICK. 1985. A survey of applications of the stabilized temperature platform furnace and Zeeman correction. *Atomic Spectrosc.* 6:157.

BRUEGGEMEYER, T. & F. FRICKE. 1986. Comparison of furnace & atomization behavior of aluminum from standard & thorium-treated L'vov platforms. *Anal. Chem.* 58:1143.

3113 B.   Electrothermal Atomic Absorption Spectrometric Method

1. General Discussion

This method is suitable for determination of micro quantities of aluminum, antimony, arsenic, barium, beryllium, cadmium, chromium, cobalt, copper, iron, lead, manganese, molybdenum, nickel, selenium, silver, and tin.

2. Apparatus

a. *Atomic absorption spectrometer:* See Section 3111A.6a. The instrument must have background correction capability.

b. *Source lamps:* See Section 3111A.6d.

c. *Graphite furnace:* Use an electrically heated device with electronic control circuitry designed to carry a graphite tube or cup through a heating program that provides sufficient thermal energy to atomize the elements of interest. Furnace heat controllers with only three heating steps are adequate only for fresh waters with low dissolved solids content. For salt waters, brines, and other complex matrices, use a furnace controller with up to seven individually programmed heating steps. Fit the furnace into the sample compartment of the spectrometer in place of the conventional burner assembly. Use argon as a purge gas to minimize oxidation of the furnace tube and to prevent the formation of metallic oxides. Use graphite tubes with L'vov platforms to minimize interferences and to improve sensitivity.

d. *Readout:* See Section 3111A.6c.

e. *Sample dispensers:* Use microliter pipets (5 to 100 μL) or an automatic sampling device designed for the specific instrument.

f. *Vent:* See Section 3111A.6f.

g. *Cooling water supply:* Cool with tap water flowing at 1 to 4 L/min or use a recirculating cooling device.

h. *Membrane filter apparatus:* Use an all-glass filtering device and 0.45-μm membrane filters. For trace analysis of aluminum, use device of polypropylene or TFE devices.

3. Reagents

a. *Metal-free water:* See Section 3111B.3c.

b. *Hydrochloric acid,* HCl, 1 + 1 and conc.

c. *Nitric acid,* HNO_3, 1 + 1 and conc.

d. *Matrix modifiers:*

1) *Ammonium nitrate,* 10% (w/v): Dissolve 100 g NH_4NO_3 in water. Dilute to 1000 mL with water.

2) *Ammonium phosphate,* 40%: Dissolve 40 g $(NH_4)_2HPO_4$ in water. Dilute to 100 mL with water.

3) *Calcium nitrate,* 20 000 mg Ca/L: Dissolve 11.8 g $Ca(NO_3)_2 \cdot 4H_2O$ in water. Dilute to 100 mL with water.

4) *Nickel nitrate,* 10 000 mg Ni/L: Dissolve 49.56 g $Ni(NO_3)_2 \cdot 6H_2O$ in water. Dilute to 1000 mL with water.

5) *Phosphoric acid,* 10% (v/v): Dilute 10 mL conc H_3PO_4 to 100 mL with water.

For preparation of other matrix modifiers, see references or follow manufacturers' instructions.

e. *Stock metal solutions:* Refer to Sections 3111B and 3114.

f. *Chelating resin:* 100 to 200 mesh* purified by heating at 60°C in 10N NaOH for 24 h. Cool resin and rinse 10 times each with alternating portions of 1N HCl, metal-free water, 1N NaOH, and metal-free water.

g. *Metal-free seawater (or brine):* Fill a 1.4-cm ID × 20-cm long borosilicate glass column to within 2 cm of the top with purified chelating resin. Elute resin with

---

*Chelex 100, or equivalent, available from Bio-Rad Laboratories, Richmond, Calif.

successive 50-mL portions of $1N$ HCl, metal-free water, $1N$ NaOH, and metal-free water at the rate of 5 mL/min just before use. Pass salt water or brine through the column at a rate of 5 mL/min to extract trace metals present. Discard the first 10 bed volumes (300 mL) of eluate.

4. Procedures

a. Sample pretreatment: Before analysis, pretreat all samples as indicated below. Rinse all glassware with $1 + 1$ HNO$_3$ and water. Carry out digestion procedures in a clean, dust-free laboratory area to avoid sample contamination. For digestion of trace aluminum, use polypropylene or TFE utensils to avoid leachable aluminum from glassware.

1) Dissolved metals—See Section 3030B. For samples requiring arsenic and/or selenium analysis add 3 mL 30% hydrogen peroxide and an appropriate concentration of nickel before analysis. For all other metals no further pretreatment is required except for adding an optional matrix modifier (see Table 3113:I).

2) Total recoverable metals (Al, Sb, Ba, Be, Cd, Cr, Co, Cu, Fe, Pb, Mn, Mo, Ni, Ag, and Sn)—NOTE: Sb and Sn are recovered unless HCl is used in the digestion. See Section 3030D. Quantitatively transfer digested sample to a 100-mL volumetric flask, add an appropriate amount of matrix modifier (if necessary, see Table 3113:I), and dilute to volume with water.

3) Total recoverable metals (As, Se)—Transfer 100 mL of shaken sample, 1 mL conc HNO$_3$, and 2 mL 30% H$_2$O$_2$ to a clean, acid-washed 250-mL beaker. Heat on a hot plate without allowing solution to boil until volume has been reduced to about 50 mL. Remove from hot plate and let cool to room temperature. Add an appropriate concentration of nickel (See Table 3113:I), and dilute to volume in a 100-mL volumetric flask with water. Simultaneously prepare a digested blank by substituting water for sample and proceed with digestion as described above.

b. Instrument operation: Mount and align furnace device according to manufacturer's instructions. Turn on instrument and strip-chart recorders. Select appropriate light source and adjust to recommended electrical setting. Select proper wavelength and set all conditions according to manufacturer's instructions, including background correction. Background correction is important when elements are determined at short wavelengths or when sample has a high level of dissolved solids. In general, background correction is usually not necessary at wavelengths longer than 350 nm. Above 350 nm deuterium arc background correction is not useful and other types must be used.

Select proper inert- or sheath-gas flow. In some cases, it is desirable to interrupt the inert-gas flow during atomization. Such interruption results in increased sensitivity by increasing residence time of the atomic vapor in the optical path. Gas interruption also increases background absorption and intensifies interference effects. Consider advantages and disadvantages of this option for each matrix when optimizing analytical conditions.

To optimize graphite furnace conditions, carefully adjust furnace temperature settings to maximize sensitivity and precision and to minimize interferences. Follow manufacturer's instructions.

Use drying temperatures slightly above the solvent boiling point to provide enough time and temperature for complete evaporation without boiling or spattering.

The charring temperature must be high enough to maximize volatilization of interfering matrix components yet too low to volatilize the element of interest. With the drying and atomization temperatures set to their optimum values, analyze a standard at a series of charring temperatures in increasing increments of 50 to 100°C. When the optimum charring temperature is exceeded, there will be a significant drop in sensitivity. Plot charring temperature versus sample absorbance: the optimum charring temperature is the highest temperature without reduced sensitivity.

Select atomization temperature by determining the temperature providing maximum sensitivity without significantly eroding precision. Optimize by a series of successive determinations at various atomization temperatures using a standard solution giving an absorbance of 0.2 to 0.5.

c. Instrument calibration: Prepare standards for instrument calibration by dilution of the metal stock solutions. Prepare standards fresh daily.

Prepare a blank and at least three calibration standards in the appropriate concentration range (See Table 3113:II) for correlating element concentration and instrument response. Match the matrix of the standard solutions to those of the samples as closely as possible. In most cases, this simply requires matching the acid background of the samples. For seawaters or brines, however, use the metal-free matrix (¶ 3g) as the standard solution diluent. In addition, add the same concentration of matrix modifier (if required for sample analysis) to the standard solutions.

Inject a suitable portion of each standard solution, in order of increasing concentration. Analyze each standard solution in triplicate to verify method precision.

Construct an analytical curve by plotting the average peak absorbencies or peak areas of the standard solution versus concentration on linear graph paper. Alternatively, use electronic instrument calibration if the instrument has this capability.

d. Sample analysis: Analyze all samples except those demonstrated to be free of matrix interferences (based on recoveries of 85%–115% for known additions) using the method of standard additions. Analyze all samples at least in duplicate or until reproducible results are obtained. A vari-

ation of $\leq 10\%$ is considered acceptable reproducibility. Average replicate values.

1) *Direct determination*—Inject a measured portion of pretreated sample into the graphite furnace. Use the same volume as was used to prepare the calibration curve. Dry, char, and atomize according to the preset program. Repeat until reproducible results are obtained.

Compare the average absorbance value or peak area to the calibration curve to determine concentration of the element of interest. Alternatively, read results directly if the instrument is equipped with this capability. If absorbance (or concentration) or peak area of the most concentrated sample is greater than absorbance (concentration) or peak area of the standard, dilute sample and reanalyze. If very large dilutions are required, another technique (e.g., flame AA or ICP) may be more suitable for this sample. Large dilution factors magnify small errors on final calculation. Keep acid background and concentration of matrix modifier (if required) constant. If sample is diluted with water, add acid and matrix modifier to restore the concentration of both to the original. Alternatively, dilute the sample in a blank solution of acid and matrix modifiers.

Proceed to ¶ 5a below.

2) *Method of standard additions*—Refer to ¶ 4c above. The method of standard additions is valid only when it falls in the linear portion of the calibration curve. Once instrument sensitivity has been optimized for the element of interest and the linear range for the element has been established, proceed with sample analyses.

Inject a measured volume of sample into furnace device. Dry, char or ash, and atomize samples according to preset program. Repeat until reproducible results are obtained. Record instrument response in absorbance or concentration as appropriate. Add a known concentration of the element of interest to a separate portion of sample so as not to change significantly the sample volume. Repeat the determination.

Add a known concentration (preferably twice that used in the first addition) to a separate sample portion. Mix well and repeat the determination.

Plot average absorbance or instrument response for the sample and the two portions with known additions on the vertical axis with the concentrations of element added on the horizontal axis of linear graph paper. Draw a straight line connecting the three points and extrapolate to zero absorbance. The intercept at the horizontal axis is the concentration of the sample. The concentration axis to the left of the origin should be a mirror image of the axis to the right.

5. Calculations

a. Direct determination:

$$\mu g \text{ metal}/L = C \times F$$

where:

C = metal concentration as read directly from the instrument or from the calibration curve, μg/L, and
F = dilution factor.

b. Method of additions:

$$\mu g \text{ metal}/L = C \times F$$

where:

C = metal concentration as read from the method of additions plot, μg/L, and
F = dilution factor.

6. Precision and Bias

Data typical of the precision and bias obtainable are presented in Tables 3113:III, IV, and V.

7. Quality Control

See Section 3020 for specific quality control procedures to be followed during analysis. Although previous indications were that very low optimum concentration ranges were attainable for most metals (see Table 3113:II), data in Table 3113:III using variations of these protocols show that this may not be so. Exercise extreme caution when applying this method to the lower concentration ranges. Verify analyst precision at the beginning of each analytical run by making triplicate analyses.

8. Reference

1. COPELAND, T.R. & J.P. MANEY. 1986. EPA Method Study 31: Trace Metals by Atomic Absorption (Furnace Techniques). EPA-600/S4-85-070, U.S. Environmental Protection Agency, Environmental Monitoring and Support Lab., Cincinnati, Ohio.

9. Bibliography

RENSHAW, G.D. 1973. The determination of barium by flameless atomic absorption spectrophotometry using a modified graphite tube atomizer. *Atomic Absorption Newsletter* 12:158.

YANAGISAWA, M., T. TAKEUCHI & M. SUZUKI. 1973. Flameless atomic absorption spectrometry of antimony. *Anal. Chim. Acta* 64:381.

RATTONETTI, A. 1974. Determination of soluble cadmium, lead, silver and indium in rainwater and stream water with the use of flameless atomic absorption. *Anal. Chem.* 46:739.

HENN, E.L. 1975. Determination of selenium in water and industrial effluents by flameless atomic absorption. *Anal. Chem.* 47:428.

MARTIN, T.D. & J.F. KOPP. 1975. Determining selenium in water, wastewater, sediment and sludge by flameless atomic absorption spectrometry. *Atomic Absorption Newsletter* 14:109.

MARUTA, T., K. MINEGISHI & G. SUDOH. 1976. The flameless atomic absorption spectrometric determination of aluminum with a carbon atomization system. *Anal. Chim. Acta* 81:313.

CRANSTON, R.E. & J.W. MURRAY. 1978. The determination of chromium species in natural waters. *Anal. Chim. Acta* 99:275.

HOFFMEISTER, W. 1978. Determination of iron in ultrapure water by atomic absorption spectroscopy. *Z. Anal. Chem.* 50:289.

LAGAS, P. 1978. Determination of beryllium, barium, vanadium and some other elements in water by atomic absorption spectrometry with electrothermal atomization. *Anal. Chim. Acta* 98:261.

CARRONDO, M.J.T., J.N. LESTER & R. PERRY. 1979. Electrothermal atomic absorption determination of total aluminum in waters and waste waters. *Anal. Chim. Acta* 111:291.

TABLE 3113:III. INTERLABORATORY SINGLE-ANALYST PRECISION DATA FOR ELECTROTHERMAL ATOMIZATION METHODS[1]

Element	Concentration $\mu g/L$	Lab Pure	Drinking Water	Surface Water	Effluent 1	Effluent 2	Effluent 3
Al	28	66	108	70	—	—	66
	125	27	35	24	—	—	34
	11 000	11	—	—	22	—	—
	58 300	27	—	—	19	—	—
	460	9	—	—	—	30	—
	2 180	28	—	—	—	4	—
	10.5	20	13	13	13	56	18
	230	10	18	13	21	94	14
As	9.78	40	25	15	74	23	11
	227	10	6	8	11	15	6
Ba	56.5	36	21	29	59	23	27
	418	14	12	20	24	24	18
Be	0.45	18	27	15	30	2	11
	10.9	14	4	9	7	12	12
Cd	0.43	72	49	1	121	35	27
	12	11	17	22	14	11	15
Cr	9.87	24	33	10	23	15	10
	236	16	7	11	13	16	7
Co	29.7	10	17	10	19	24	12
	420	8	11	13	14	9	5
Cu	10.1	49	47	17	17	—	30
	234	8	15	6	21	—	11
	300	6	—	—	—	11	—
	1 670	11	—	—	—	6	—
Fe	26.1	144	52	153	—	—	124
	455	48	37	45	—	—	31
	1 030	17	—	—	30	—	—
	5 590	6	—	—	32	—	—
	370	14	—	—	—	19	—
	2 610	9	—	—	—	18	—
Pb	10.4	6	19	17	21	19	33
	243	17	7	17	18	12	16
Mn	0.44	187	180	—	—	—	275
	14.8	32	19	—	—	—	18
	91.0	15	—	—	48	—	—
	484.0	4	—	—	12	—	—
	111.0	12	—	—	—	21	—
	666.0	6	—	—	—	20	—
Ni	26.2	20	26	25	24	18	9
	461.0	15	11	9	8	11	4
Se	10.0	12	27	16	35	41	13
	235.0	6	6	15	6	13	14
Ag	8.48	10	—	—	15	27	16
	56.5	14	—	—	7	16	23
	0.45	27	166	48	—	—	—
	13.6	15	4	10	—	—	—

TABLE 3113:IV. INTERLABORATORY OVERALL PRECISION DATA FOR ELECTROTHERMAL
ATOMIZATION METHODS[1]

Element	Concentration $\mu g/L$	Lab Pure	Drinking Water	Surface Water	Effluent 1	Effluent 2	Effluent 3
Al	28	99	114	124	—	—	131
	125	45	47	49	—	—	40
	11 000	19	—	—	43	—	—
	58 300	31	—	—	32	—	—
	460	20	—	—	—	47	—
	2 180	30	—	—	—	15	—
	10.5	37	19	22	50	103	39
	230	26	16	16	17	180	21
As	9.78	43	26	37	72	50	39
	227	18	12	13	20	15	14
Ba	56.5	68	38	43	116	43	65
	418	35	35	28	38	48	16
Be	0.45	28	31	15	67	50	35
	10.9	33	15	26	20	9	19
Cd	0.43	73	60	5	88	43	65
	12	19	25	41	26	20	27
Cr	9.87	30	53	24	60	41	23
	236	18	14	24	20	14	20
Co	29.7	13	26	17	18	21	17
	420	21	21	17	18	13	13
Cu	10.1	58	82	31	32	—	74
	234	12	33	19	21	—	26
	300	13	—	—	—	14	—
	1 670	12	—	—	—	13	—
Fe	26.1	115	93	306	—	—	204
	455	53	46	53	—	—	44
	1 030	32	—	—	25	—	—
	5 590	10	—	—	43	—	—
	370	28	—	—	—	22	—
	2 610	13	—	—	—	22	—
Pb	10.4	27	42	31	23	28	47
	243	18	19	17	19	19	25
Mn	0.44	299	272	—	—	—	248
	14.8	52	41	—	—	—	29
	91.0	16	—	—	45	—	—
	484.0	5	—	—	17	—	—
	111.0	15	—	—	—	17	—
	666.0	8	—	—	—	24	—
Ni	26.2	35	30	49	35	37	43
	461.0	23	22	15	12	21	17
Se	10.0	17	48	32	30	44	51
	235.0	16	18	18	17	22	34
Ag	8.48	23	—	—	16	35	34
	56.5	15	—	—	24	32	28
	0.45	57	90	368	—	—	—
	13.6	19	19	59	—	—	—

TABLE 3113:V. INTERLABORATORY RELATIVE ERROR DATA FOR ELECTROTHERMAL ATOMIZATION METHODS[1]

Element	Concentration μg/L	Relative Error %					
		Lab Pure Water	Drinking Water	Surface Water	Effluent 1	Effluent 2	Effluent 3
Al	28.0	86	150	54	—	—	126
	125.0	4	41	39	—	—	30
	11 000.0	2	—	—	14	—	—
	58 300.0	12	—	—	7	—	—
	460.0	2	—	—	—	11	—
	2 180.0	11	—	—	—	9	—
Sb	10.5	30	32	28	24	28	36
	230.0	35	14	19	13	73	39
As	9.78	36	1	22	106	13	16
	227.0	3	7	10	19	6	13
Ba	56.5	132	54	44	116	59	40
	418.0	4	0	0	13	6	60
Be	0.45	40	16	11	16	10	15
	10.9	13	2	9	7	8	8
Cd	0.43	58	45	37	66	16	19
	12.0	4	6	5	22	18	3
Cr	9.87	10	9	4	2	5	15
	236.0	11	0	9	13	5	8
Co	29.7	7	7	1	6	3	13
	420.0	12	8	8	11	5	18
Cu	10.1	16	48	2	5	—	15
	234.0	8	7	0	4	—	19
	300.0	4	—	—	—	21	—
	1 670.0	6	—	—	—	2	—
Fe	26.1	85	60	379	—	—	158
	455.0	43	22	31	—	—	18
	1 030.0	8	—	—	8	—	—
	5 590.0	2	—	—	12	—	—
	370.0	4	—	—	—	11	—
	2 610.0	35	—	—	—	2	—
Pb	10.4	16	10	17	1	34	14
	234.0	5	15	8	18	15	29
Mn	0.44	332	304	—	—	—	556
	14.8	10	1	—	—	—	36
	91.0	31	—	—	10	—	—
	484.0	42	—	—	4	—	—
	111.0	1	—	—	—	29	—
	666.0	6	—	—	—	23	—
Ni	26.2	9	16	10	7	33	54
	461.0	15	19	18	31	16	18
Se	10.0	12	9	6	36	17	37
	235.0	7	7	0	13	10	17
Ag	8.48	12	—	—	1	51	20
	56.5	16	—	—	8	51	22
	0.45	34	162	534	—	—	—
	13.6	3	12	5	—	—	—

NAKAHARA, T. & C.L. CHAKRABARTI. 1979. Direct determination of traces of molybdenum in synthetic sea water by atomic absorption spectrometry with electrothermal atomization and selective volatilization of the salt matrix. *Anal. Chim. Acta* 104:99.

TIMINAGA, M. & Y. UMEZAKI. 1979. Determination of submicrogram amounts of tin by atomic absorption spectrometry with electrothermal atomization. *Anal. Chim. Acta* 110:55.

3114 METALS BY HYDRIDE GENERATION/ATOMIC ABSORPTION SPECTROMETRY*

3114 A. Introduction

For general introductory material on atomic absorption spectrometric methods, see Section 3111A.

Two methods are presented in this section: A manual method and a continuous-flow method especially recommended for

---

*Approved by Standard Methods Committee, 1989.

selenium. Continuous-flow automated systems are preferable to manual hydride generators because the effect of sudden hydrogen generation on light-path transparency is removed and any blank response from contamination of the HCl reagent by the elements being determined is incorporated into the background base line.

3114 B. Manual Hydride Generation/Atomic Absorption Spectrometric Method

1. General Discussion

a. Principle: This method is applicable to the determination of arsenic and selenium by conversion to their hydrides by sodium borohydride reagent and aspiration into an atomic absorption atomizer.

Arsenous acid and selenous acid, the As(III) and Se(IV) oxidation states of arsenic and selenium, respectively, are instantaneously converted by sodium borohydride reagent in acid solution to their volatile hydrides. The hydrides are purged continuously by argon or nitrogen into an appropriate atomizer of an atomic absorption spectrometer and converted to the gas-phase atoms. The sodium borohydride reducing agent, by rapid generation

of the elemental hydrides in an appropriate reaction cell, minimizes dilution of the hydrides by the carrier gas and provides rapid, sensitive determinations of arsenic and selenium.

CAUTION: *Arsenic and selenium and their hydrides are toxic. Handle with care.*

At room temperature and solution pH values of 1 or less, arsenic acid, the As(V) oxidation state of arsenic, is reduced relatively slowly by sodium borohydride to As(III), which is then instantaneously converted to arsine. The arsine atomic absorption peaks commonly are decreased by one-fourth to one-third for As(V) when compared to As(III). Determination of total arsenic requires that all inorganic arsenic compounds be in the As(III) state. Organic and inorganic forms of arsenic are first oxidized to As(V) by acid digestion. The As(V) then is quantitatively reduced to As(III) with sodium or potassium iodide before reaction with sodium borohydride.

Selenic acid, the Se(VI) oxidation state of selenium, is not measurably reduced by sodium borohydride. To determine total selenium by atomic absorption and sodium borohydride, first reduce Se(VI) formed during the acid digestion procedure to Se(IV), being careful to prevent reoxidation by chlorine. Efficiency of reduction depends on temperature, reduction time, and HCl concentration. For $4N$ HCl, heat 1 h at 100°C. For $6N$ HCl, boiling for 10 min is sufficient.[1-3] Alternatively, autoclave samples in sealed containers at 121°C for 1 h. NOTE: Autoclaving in sealed containers may result in incomplete reduction, apparently due to the buildup of chlorine gas. To obtain equal instrument responses for reduced Se(VI) and Se (IV) solutions of equal concentrations, manipulate HCl concentration and heating time.

b. Equipment selection:

Certain atomic absorption atomizers and hydride reaction cells are available commercially for use with the sodium borohydride reagent. A functional system is presented in Figure 3114:1. Irrespective of the hydride reaction cell-atomizer system selected, it must meet the following quality-control considerations: (a) it must provide a precise and reproducible standard curve between 0 and 20 μg As or Se/L and an instrumental detection limit between 0.1 and 0.5 μg As or Se/L; (b) when carried through the entire procedure, oxidation state couples [As (III) - As (V) or Se (IV)-Se (VI)] must cause equal instrument response; and (c) sample digestion must yield 80% or greater recovery of added cacodylic acid (dimethyl arsinic acid) and 90% or greater recovery of added As(III), As(V), Se(VI), or Se(IV).

Three types of atomic absorption atomizers commonly are used in the measurement of arsenic and selenium. Most instrument manufacturers can provide a Boling-type burner for argon (or nitrogen)-air entrained-hydrogen flames. Alternatively use an externally heated quartz cell or a quartz cell with an internal fuel rich oxygen-hydrogen or air-hydrogen flame. Quartz atomization cells provide for the most sensitive arsenic and selenium hydride determinations and minimize background noise associated with the argon-air entrained-hydrogen flame.

c. Digestion techniques: Waters and wastewaters may contain varying amounts of organic arsenic compounds and inorganic compounds of As(III), As(V), Se(IV), and Se(VI). To measure total arsenic and selenium in these samples requires sample digestion to solubilize particulate forms and oxidize reduced forms of arsenic and selenium and to convert any organic compounds to inorganic ones. Organic selenium compounds rarely have been demonstrated in water. It is left to the experienced analyst's judgment whether sample digestion is required.

Two digestion procedures are provided in ¶ 4c below. Consider sulfuric-nitric-perchloric acid digestion or sulfuric-nitric acid digestion as providing a measure of total recoverable arsenic rather than total arsenic because they do not completely convert certain organic arsenic compounds to As(V). The sulfuric-nitric-perchloric acid digestion effectively destroys organics and most particulates in untreated wastewaters or solid samples. The potassium persulfate digestion (¶ 4d) is effective for converting organic arsenic and selenium compounds to As(V) and Se(VI) in potable and surface waters and in most wastewaters.[4]

The HCl-autoclave reduction of Se(VI) described above is an effective digestion procedure for total inorganic Se; however, it has not been found effective for con-

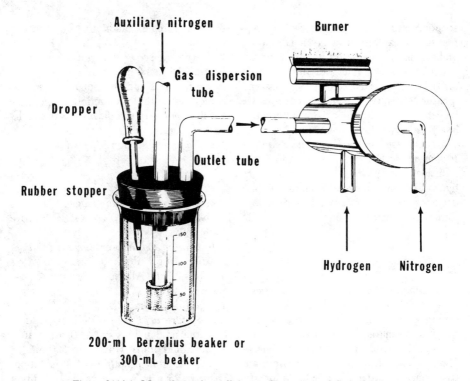

Figure 3114:1. Manual reaction cell for producing As and Se hydrides.

verting benzene substituted selenium compounds to inorganic selenium.

d. Interferences: Interferences are minimized because the As and Se hydrides are removed from the solution containing most potential interfering substances. Slight response variations occur when acid matrices are varied. Control these variations by treating standards and samples in the same manner. Low concentrations of noble metals (approximately 100 μg/L of Ag, Au, Pt, Pd, etc.), concentrations of copper, lead, and nickel at or greater than 1 mg/L, and concentrations between 0.1 and 1 mg/L of hydride-forming elements (Bi, Sb, Sn, and Te) may suppress the response of As and Se hydrides. Interference by transition metals depends strongly on HCl concentration. Interferences are less pronounced at 4 to 6N HCl than at lower concentrations.[5] The presence of As or Se

in each other's matrices can cause similar suppression. Reduced nitrogen oxides resulting from HNO_3 digestion and nitrite also can suppress instrumental response for both elements. Large concentrations of iodide interfere with the Se determination by reducing Se to its elemental form. Do not use any glassware for determining Se that has been used for iodide reduction of As(V).

To prevent chlorine gas produced in the reduction of Se(VI) to Se(IV) from reoxidizing the Se(IV), generate the hydride within a few hours of the reduction steps or purge the chlorine from the samples by sparging.[6]

Interferences depend on system design and defy quantitative description because of their synergistic effects. Certain waters and wastewaters can contain interferences in sufficient concentration to suppress absorption responses of As and Se. For representative samples in a given laboratory and for initial analyses of unknown wastewaters, add appropriate inorganic forms of As or Se to digested sample portions and measure recovery. If average recoveries are less than 90%, consider using alternative analytical procedures.

e. Detection limit and optimum concentration range: For both arsenic and selenium, analyzed by aspiration into a nitrogen-hydrogen flame after reduction, the method detection limit is 0.002 mg/L and the optimum concentration range 0.002 to 0.02 mg/L.

2. Apparatus

a. Atomic absorption spectrometer equipped with gas flow meters for argon (or nitrogen) and hydrogen, As and Se electrodeless discharge lamps with power supply, background correction at measurement wavelengths, and appropriate strip-chart recorder. A good-quality 10-mV recorder with high sensitivity and a fast response time is needed.

b. Atomizer: Use one of the following:

1) *Boling-type burner head* for argon (or nitrogen)-air entrained-hydrogen flame.

2) *Cylindrical quartz cell,* 10 to 20 cm long, electrically heated by external nichrome wire to 800 to 900°C.[7]

3) *Cylindrical quartz cell* with internal fuel rich hydrogen-oxygen (air) flame.[8]

The sensitivity of quartz cells deteriorates over several months of use. Sensitivity sometimes may be restored by treatment with 40% HF. CAUTION: *HF is extremely corrosive. Avoid all contact with exposed skin. Handle with care.*

c. Reaction cell for producing As or Se hydrides: See Figure 3114:1. A commercially available system is acceptable if it utilizes liquid sodium borohydride reagents; accepts samples digested in accordance with ¶s 4c, d, and e; accepts 4 to 6N HCl; and is efficiently and precisely stirred by the purging gas and/or a magnetic stirrer.

d. Eye dropper or syringe capable of delivering 0.5 to 3.0 mL sodium borohydride reagent. Exact and reproducible addition is required so that production of hydrogen gas does not vary significantly between determinations.

e. Vent: See Section 3111A.6f.

3. Reagents

a. Sodium borohydride reagent: Dissolve 8 g $NaBH_4$ in 200 mL 0.1N NaOH. Prepare fresh daily.

b. Sodium iodide prereductant solution: Dissolve 50 g NaI in 500 mL water. Prepare fresh daily. Alternatively use an equivalent KI solution.

c. Sulfuric acid, 18N.

d. Sulfuric acid, 2.5N: Cautiously add 35 mL conc H_2SO_4 to about 400 mL water, let cool, and adjust volume to 500 mL.

e. Potassium persulfate, 5% solution: Dissolve 25 g $K_2S_2O_8$ in water and dilute to 500 mL. Store in glass and refrigerate. Prepare weekly.

f. Nitric acid, HNO_3, conc.

g. Perchloric acid, $HClO_4$, conc.

h. Hydrochloric acid, HCl, conc.

i. Argon (or nitrogen), commercial grade.

j. Hydrogen, commercial grade.

k. Arsenic(III) solutions:

1) *Stock As(III) solution:* Dissolve 1.320 g arsenic trioxide, As_2O_3, in water containing 4 g NaOH. Dilute to 1 L; 1.00 mL = 1.00 mg As(III).

2) *Intermediate As(III) solution:* Dilute 10 mL stock As solution to 1000 mL with water containing 5 mL conc HCl; 1.00 mL = 10.0 µg As(III).

3) *Standard As(III) solution:* Dilute 10 mL intermediate As(III) solution to 1000 mL with water containing the same concentration of acid used for sample preservation (2 to 5 mL conc HNO_3); 1.00 mL = 0.100 µg As(III). Prepare diluted solutions daily.

l. Arsenic(V) solutions:

1) *Stock As(V) solution:* Dissolve 1.534 g arsenic pentoxide, As_2O_5, in distilled water containing 4 g NaOH. Dilute to 1 L; 1.00 mL = 1.00 mg As(V).

2) *Intermediate As(V) solution:* Prepare as for As(III) above; 1.00 mL = 10.0 μg As(V).

3) *Standard As(V) solution:* Prepare as for As(III) above; 1.00 mL = 0.100 μg As(V).

m. Organic arsenic solutions:

1) *Stock organic arsenic solution:* Dissolve 1.842 g dimethylarsinic acid (cacodylic acid), $(CH_3)_2AsOOH$, in water containing 4 g NaOH. Dilute to 1 L; 1.00 mL = 1.00 mg As. [NOTE: Check purity of cacodylic acid reagent against an intermediate arsenic standard (50 to 100 mg As/L) using flame atomic absorption.]

2) *Intermediate organic arsenic solution:* Prepare as for As(III) above; 1.00 mL = 10.0 μg As.

3) *Standard organic arsenic solution:* Prepare as for As(III) above; 1.00 mL = 0.100 μg As.

n. Selenium(IV) solutions:

1) *Stock Se(IV) solution:* Dissolve 2.190 g sodium selenite, Na_2SeO_3, in water containing 10 mL HCl and dilute to 1 L; 1.00 mL = 1.00 mg Se(IV).

2) *Intermediate Se(IV) solution:* Dilute 10 mL stock Se(IV) to 1000 mL with water containing 10 mL conc HCl; 1.00 mL = 10.0 μg Se(IV).

3) *Standard Se(IV) solution:* Dilute 10 mL intermediate Se(IV) solution to 1000 mL with water containing the same concentration of acid used for sample preservation (2 to 5 mL conc HNO_3). Prepare solution daily when checking the equivalency of instrument response for Se(IV) and Se(VI); 1.00 mL = 0.100 μg Se(IV).

o. Selenium(VI) solutions:

1) *Stock Se(VI) solution:* Dissolve 2.393 g sodium selenate, Na_2SeO_4, in water containing 10 mL conc HNO_3. Dilute to 1 L; 1.00 mL = 1.00 mg Se(VI).

2) *Intermediate Se(VI) solution:* Prepare as for Se(IV) above; 1.00 mL = 10.0 μg Se (VI).

3) *Standard Se(VI) solution:* Prepare as for Se(IV) above; 1.00 mL = 0.100 μg Se(VI).

4. Procedure

a. Apparatus setup: Either see Figure 3114:1 or follow manufacturer's instructions. Connect inlet of reaction cell with auxiliary purging gas controlled by flow meter. If a drying cell between the reaction cell and atomizer is necessary, use only anhydrous $CaCl_2$ but not $CaSO_4$ because it may retain SeH_2. Before using the hydride generation/analysis system, optimize operating parameters. Aspirate dilute aqueous solutions of As and Se directly into the flame to facilitate atomizer alignment. Align quartz atomizers for maximum absorbance. Aspirate a blank until memory effects are removed. Establish purging gas flow, concentration and rate of addition of sodium borohydride reagent, solution volume, and stirring rate for optimum instrument response for the chemical species to be analyzed. If a quartz atomizer is used, optimize cell temperature. If sodium borohyride reagent is added too quickly, rapid evolution of hydrogen will unbalance the system. If the volume of solution being purged is too large, the absorption signal will be decreased. Recommended wavelengths are 193.7 and 196.0 nm for As and Se, respectively.

b. Instrument calibration standards: Transfer 0.00, 1.00, 2.00, 5.00, 10.00, 15.00, and 20.00 mL standard solutions of As(III) or Se(IV) to 100-mL volumetric flasks and bring to volume with water containing the same acid concentration used for sample preservation (commonly 2 to 5 mL conc HNO_3/L). This yields blank and standard solutions of 0, 1, 2, 5, 10, 15, and 20 μg As or Se/L. Prepare fresh daily.

c. Preparation of samples and standards

for total recoverable arsenic and selenium: Follow general procedures of Section 3030F; alternatively, add 50 mL sample, As(III), or Se(IV) standard to 200-mL Berzelius beaker. (Alternatively, prepare standards by adding 100 μg/L standard As or Se solutions directly to the beaker and dilute to 50 mL in this beaker). Add 7 mL 18N H_2SO_4 and 5 mL conc HNO_3. Add a small boiling chip or glass beads if necessary. Evaporate to SO_3 fumes. Maintain oxidizing conditions at all times by adding small amounts of HNO_3 to prevent solution from darkening. Maintain an excess of HNO_3 until all organic matter is destroyed. Complete digestion usually is indicated by a light-colored solution. Cool slightly, add 25 mL water and 1 mL conc $HClO_4$ and again evaporate to SO_3 fumes to expel oxides of nitrogen. CAUTION: *See Section 3030H for cautions on use of $HClO_4$.* Monitor effectiveness of digestion procedure used by adding 5 mL of standard organic arsenic solution or 5 mL of a standard selenium solution to a 50-mL sample and measuring recovery, carrying standards through entire procedure. To report total recoverable arsenic as total arsenic, average recoveries of cacodylic acid must exceed 80%. Alternatively, use 100-mL microkjeldahl flasks for the digestion of total recoverable arsenic or selenium, thereby improving digestion effectiveness. After final evaporation of SO_3 fumes, dilute to 50 mL for arsenic measurements or to 30 mL for selenium measurements.

d. Preparation of samples and standards for total arsenic and selenium: Add 50 mL sample or standard to a 200-mL Berzelius beaker. Add 1 mL 2.5N H_2SO_4 and 5 mL 5% $K_2S_2O_8$. Boil gently on a pre-heated hot plate for approximately 30 to 40 min or until a final volume of 10 mL is reached. Do not let sample go to dryness. Alternatively heat in an autoclave at 121°C for 1 h in capped containers. After manual digestion, dilute to 50 mL for subsequent arsenic measurements and to 30 mL for

selenium measurements. Monitor effectiveness of digestion by measuring recovery of As or Se as above. If poor recovery of arsenic added as cacodylic acid is obtained, reanalyze using double the amount of $K_2S_2O_8$.

e. Determination of arsenic with sodium borohydride: To 50 mL digested standard or sample in a 200-mL Berzelius beaker (see Figure 3114:1) add 5 mL conc HCl and mix. Add 5 mL NaI prereductant solution, mix, and wait at least 30 min. (NOTE: The NaI reagent has not been found necessary for certain hydride reaction cell designs if a 20 to 30% loss in instrument sensitivity is not important and variables of solution acid conditions, temperatures, and volumes for production of As(V) and arsine can be controlled strictly. Such control requires an automated delivery system; see Section 3114C.)

Attach one Berzelius beaker at a time to the rubber stopper containing the gas dispersion tube for the purging gas, the sodium borohydride reagent inlet, and the outlet to the atomizer. Turn on strip-chart recorder and wait until the base line is established by the purging gas and all air is expelled from the reaction cell. Add 0.5 mL sodium borohydride reagent. After the instrument absorbance has reached a maximum and returned to the base line, remove beaker, rinse dispersion tube with water, and proceed to the next sample or standard. Periodically compare standard As(III) and As(V) curves for response consistency. Check for presence of chemical interferences that suppress instrument response for arsine by treating a digested sample with 10 μg/L As(III) or As(V) as appropriate. Average recoveries should be not less than 90%.

f. Determination of selenium with sodium borohydride: To 30 mL digested standard or sample, or to 30 mL undigested standard or sample in a 200-mL Berzelius beaker, add 15 mL conc HCl and mix. Heat for a predetermined period at 90 to 100°C. Alternatively autoclave at 121°C in capped containers for 60 min, or heat for a predetermined time in open test tubes using a 90 to 100°C hot water bath or an aluminum block digester. Check effectiveness of the selected heating by demonstrating equal instrument responses for calibration curves prepared either from standard Se(IV) or from Se(VI) solutions. Effective heat exposure for converting Se(VI) to Se(IV), with no loss of Se(IV), ranges between 5 and 60 min when open beakers or test tubes are used. Do not digest standard Se(IV) and Se(VI) solutions used for this check of equivalency. After prereduction of Se(VI) to Se(IV), attach Berzelius beakers, one at a time, to the purge apparatus. For each, turn on the strip-chart recorder and wait until the base line is established. Add 0.50 mL sodium borohydride reagent. After the instrument absorbance has reached a maximum and returned to the base line, remove beaker, rinse dispersion tube with water, and proceed to the next sample or stand-ard. Check for presence of chemical interferences that suppress selenium hydride instrument response by treating a digested sample with 10 μg Se (IV)/L. Average recoveries should be not less than 90%.

5. Calculation

Construct a standard curve by plotting peak heights or areas of standards versus concentration of standards. Measure peak heights or areas of samples and read concentrations from curve. If sample was diluted (or concentrated) before sample digestion, apply an appropriate factor. On instruments so equipped, read concentrations directly after standard calibration.

6. Precision and Bias

Single-laboratory, single-operator data were collected for As(III) and organic arsenic by both manual and automated methods, and for the manual determination of selenium. Recovery values (%) from seven replicates are given below:

	As(III)	Org As	Se(IV)	Se(VI)
Manual with digestion	91.8	87.3	—	—
Manual without digestion	109.4	19.4	100.6	110.8
Automated with digestion	99.8	98.4	—	—
Automated without digestion	92.5	10.4	—	—

7. References

1. VIJAN, P.N. & D. LEUNG. 1980. Reduction of chemical interference and speciation studies in the hydride generation-atomic absorption method for selenium. *Anal. Chim. Acta* 120:141.

2. VOTH-BEACH, L.M. & D.E. SHRADER. 1985. Reduction of interferences in the determination of arsenic and selenium by hydride generation. *Spectroscopy* 1:60.

3. JULSHAMN, K., O. RINGDAL, K.-E. SLINNING & O.R. BRAEKKAN. 1982. Optimization of the determination of selenium in marine samples by atomic absorption spectrometry: Comparison of a flameless graphite furnace atomic absorption system with a hydride generation atomic absorption system. *Spectrochim. Acta.* 37B:473.

4. NYGAARD, D.D. & J.H. LOWRY. 1982. Sample digestion procedures for simultaneous determination of arsenic, antimony, and selenium by inductively coupled argon plasma emission spectrometry with hydride generation. *Anal. Chem.* 54:803.

5. WELZ, B. & M. MELCHER. 1984. Mechanisms of transition metal interferences in hydride generation atomic-absorption spectrometry. Part 1. Influence of cobalt, copper, iron and nickel on selenium determination. *Analyst* 109:569.

6. KRIVAN, V., K. PETRICK, B. WELZ & M. MELCHER. 1985. Radiotracer error-diagnostic investigation of selenium determination by hydride-generation atomic absorption spectrometry involving treatment with hydrogen peroxide and hydrochloric acid. *Anal. Chem.* 57:1703.

7. Chu, R.C., G.P. Barron & P.A.W. Baumgarner. 1972. Arsenic determination at submicrogram levels by arsine evolution and flameless atomic absorption spectrophotometric technique. *Anal. Chem.* 44:1476.

8. Siemer, D.D., P. Koteel & V. Jariwala. 1976. Optimization of arsine generation in atomic absorption arsenic determinations. *Anal. Chem.* 48:836.

8. Bibliography

Fernandez, F.J. & D.C. Manning. 1971. The determination of arsenic at submicrogram levels by atomic absorption spectrophotometry. *Atomic Absorption Newsletter* 10:86.

Jarrel-Ash Corporation. 1971. High Sensitivity Arsenic Determination by Atomic Absorption. Jarrel-Ash Atomic Absorption Applications Laboratory Bull. No. As-3.

Manning, D.C. 1971. A high sensitivity arsenic-selenium sampling system for atomic absorption spectroscopy. *Atomic Absorption Newsletter* 10:123.

Braman, R.S. & C.C. Foreback. 1973. Methylated forms of arsenic in the environment. *Science* 182:1247.

Caldwell, J.S., R.J. Lishka & E.F. McFarren. 1973. Evaluation of a low-cost arsenic and selenium determination of microgram-per-liter levels. *J. Amer. Water Works Assoc.*, 65:731.

Aggett, J. & A.C. Aspell. 1976. The determination of arsenic (III) and total arsenic by atomic-absorption spectroscopy. *Analyst* 101:341.

Fiorino, J.A., J.W. Jones & S.G. Capar. 1976. Sequential determination of arsenic, selenium, antimony, and tellurium in foods via rapid hydride evolution and atomic absorption spectrometry. *Anal. Chem.* 48:120.

Cutter, G.A. 1978. Species determination of selenium in natural waters. *Anal. Chem. Acta* 98:59.

Godden, R.G. & D.R. Thomerson. 1980. Generation of covalent hydrides in atomic absorption spectroscopy. *Analyst* 105:1137.

Brown, R.M., Jr., R.C. Fry, J.L. Moyers, S.J. Northway, M.B. Denton & G.S. Wilson. 1981. Interference by volatile nitrogen oxides and transition-metal catalysis in the preconcentration of arsenic and selenium as hydrides. *Anal. Chem.* 53:1560.

Sinemus, H.W., M. Melcher & B. Welz. 1981. Influence of valence state on the determination of antimony, bismuth, selenium, and tellurium in lake water using the hydride AA technique. *Atomic Spectrosc.* 2:81.

Dedina, J. 1982. Interference of volatile hydride forming elements in selenium determination by atomic absorption spectrometry with hydride generation. *Anal. Chem.* 54:2097.

3114 C. Continuous Hydride Generation/Atomic Absorption Spectrometric Method (PROPOSED)

1. General Discussion

The continuous hydride generator, introduced recently, offers the advantages of simplicity in operation, excellent reproducibility, low detection limits, and high sample volume throughput for selenium analysis following preparations as described in 3500-Se.B or 3114B.4*c* and *d*. For further information on preparation procedures, see Section 3500-Se, 17th edition, *Standard Methods*.

a. Principle: See Section 3114B.

b. Interferences: Free chlorine in hydrochloric acid is a common but difficult-to-diagnose interference. (The amount of chlorine varies with manufacturer and with each lot from the same manufacturer). Chlorine oxidizes the hydride and can contaminate the hydride generator to prevent recoveries under any conditions. When interference is encountered, or preferably before using each new bottle of HCl, eliminate chlorine from a 2.3-L bottle of conc HCl by bubbling with helium (commercial grade, 100 mL/min) for 3 h.

Excess oxidant (peroxide, persulfate, or permanganate) from the total selenium digestion can oxidize the hydride. Follow procedures in 3500-Se.B.2, 3, or 4 to ensure removal of all oxidizing agents before hydride generation.

Nitrite is a common trace constituent in

natural and waste waters, and at levels as low as 10 μg/L nitrite can reduce the recovery of hydrogen selenide from Se(IV) by over 50%. Moreover, during the reduction of Se(VI) to Se(IV) by digestion with HCl (3500-Se.B.5), some nitrate is converted to nitrite, which subsequently interferes. When this interference is suspected, add sulfanilamide after sample acidification (or HCl digestion). The diazotization reaction between nitrite and sulfanilamide completely removes the interferent effect (i.e., the standard addition slope is normal).

2. Apparatus

a. Continuous hydride generator: The basic unit is composed of two parts: a precision peristaltic pump, which is used to meter and mix reagents and sample solutions, and the gas-liquid separator. At the gas-liquid separator a constant flow of argon strips out the hydrogen and metal hydride gases formed in the reaction and carries them to the heated quartz absorption cell (3114B.1*b* and 2*b*), which is supported by a metal bracket mounted on top of the regular air acetylene burner head.

The spent liquid flows out of the separator via a constant level side drain to a waste bucket. Schematics and operating parameters are shown in Figure 3114:2.

Check flow rates frequently to ensure a steady flow; an uneven flow in any tubing will cause an erratic signal. Remove tubings from pump rollers when not in use. Typical flow rates are: sample, 7 mL/min; acid, 1 mL/min; borohydride reagent, 1 mL/min. Argon flow usually is pre-fixed, typically at 90 mL/min.

b. Atomic absorption spectrometric equipment: See Section 3111A.6.

3. Reagents

a. Hydrochloric acid, HCl, 5 + 1: Handle conc HCl under a fume hood. If necessary, remove free Cl$_2$ by stripping conc HCl with helium as described above.

b. Borohydride reagent: Dissolve 0.6 g NaBH$_4$ and 0.5 g NaOH in 100 mL water. CAUTION: *Sodium borohydride is toxic, flammable, and corrosive.*

c. Selenium reference standard solution, 1000 mg/L: Use commercially available standard; verify that selenium is Se(IV).

d. Intermediate standard solution, 1 mg/L: Dilute 1 mL reference standard so-

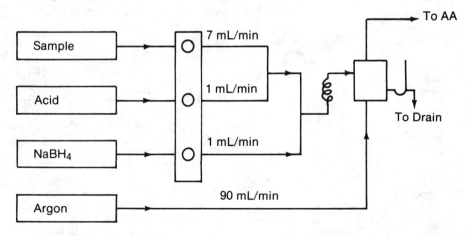

Figure 3114:2. Schematic of a continuous hydride generator.

lution to 1 L in a volumetric flask with distilled water.

e. *Working standard solutions,* 5, 10, 20, 30, and 40 µg/L: Dilute 0.5, 1.0, 2.0, 3.0, and 4.0 mL intermediate standard solution to 100 mL in a volumetric flask.

f. *Sulfanilamide solution:* Prepare a 2.5% (w/v) solution daily; add several drops conc HCl per 50 mL solution to facilitate dissolution.

4. Procedure

a. *Sample preparation:* See Section 3500-Se or 3114 B.4c and d for preparation steps for various Se fractions or total Se.

b. *Preconditioning hydride generator:* For newly installed tubing, turn on pump for at least 10 to 15 min before instrument calibration. Sample the highest standard for a few minutes to let volatile hydride react with the reactive sites in the transfer lines and on the quartz absorption cell surfaces.

c. *Instrument calibration:* Depending on total void volume in sample tubing, sampling time of 15 to 20 s generally is sufficient to obtain a steady signal. Between samples, submerge uptake tube in rinse water. Calibrate instrument daily after a 45-min lamp warmup time. Use either the hollow cathode or the electrodeless discharge lamp.

d. *Antifoaming agents:* Certain samples, particularly wastewater samples containing a high concentration of proteinaceous substances, can cause excessive foaming that could carry the liquid directly into the heated quartz absorption cell and cause splattering of salty deposits onto the windows of the spectrometer. Add a drop of antifoaming agent* to eliminate this problem.

e. *Nitrite removal:* After samples have been acidified, or after acid digestion, add 0.1 mL sulfanilamide solution per 10 mL sample and let react for 2 min.

f. *Analysis:* Follow manufacturer's instructions for operation of analytical equipment.

5. Calculation

Construct a calibration curve based on absorbance vs. standard concentration. Apply dilution factors on diluted samples.

6. Precision and Bias

Working standards were analyzed together with batches of water samples on a routine production basis. The standards were compounded using chemically pure sodium selenite and sodium selenate. The values of $Se(IV) + Se(VI)$ were determined by converting $Se(VI)$ to $Se(IV)$ by digestion with HCl. Results are tabulated below.

---

*Dow Corning or equivalent.

No. Analyses	Mean Se(IV) µg/L	Rel. Dev. %	Se(IV) + Se(VI) µg/L	Rel. Del. %
21	4.3	12	10.3	7
26	8.5	12	19.7	6
22	17.2	7	39.2	8
20	52.8	5	106.0	6

7. Bibliography

REAMER, D.C. & C. VEILOON. 1981. Preparation of biological materials for determination of selenium by hydride generation-AAS. *Anal. Chem.* 53:1192.

SINEMUS, H.W., M. MELCHER & B. WELZ. 1981. Influence of valence state on the determination of antimony, bismuth, selenium, and tellurium in lake water using the hydride AA technique. *Atomic Spectrosc.* 2:81.

RODEN, D.R. & D.E. TALLMAN. 1982. Determination of inorganic selenium species in groundwaters containing organic interferences by ion chromatography and hydride generation/atomic absorption spectrometry. *Anal. Chem.* 54:307.

CUTTER, G. 1983. Elimination of nitrite interference in the determination of selenium by hydride generation. *Anal. Chim. Acta* 149:391.

NARASAKI H. & M. IKEDA. 1984. Automated determination of arsenic and selenium by atomic absorption spectrometry with hydride generation. *Anal. Chem.* 56:2059.

WELZ, B. & M. MELCHER. 1985. Decomposition of marine biological tissues for determination of arsenic, selenium, and mercury using hydride-generation and cold-vapor atomic absorption spectrometries. *Anal. Chem.* 57:427.

EBDON, L. & S.T. SPARKES. 1987. Determination of arsenic and selenium in environmental samples by hydride generation-direct current plasma-atomic emission spectrometry. *Microchem. J.* 36:198.

EBDON, L. & J.R. WILKINSON. 1987. The determination of arsenic and selenium in coal by continuous flow hydride-generation atomic absorption spectroscopy and atomic fluorescence spectrometry. *Anal. Chim. Acta.* 194:177.

VOTH-BEACH, L.M. & D.E. SHRADER. 1985. Reduction of interferences in the determination of arsenic and selenium by hydride generation. *Spectroscopy* 1:60.

3120 METALS BY PLASMA EMISSION SPECTROSCOPY*

3120 A. Introduction

1. General Discussion

Emission spectroscopy using inductively coupled plasma (ICP) was developed in the mid-1960's[1,2] as a rapid, sensitive, and convenient method for the determination of metals in water and wastewater samples.[3-6] Dissolved metals are determined in filtered and acidified samples. Total metals are determined after appropriate digestion. Care must be taken to ensure that potential interferences are dealt with, especially when dissolved solids exceed 1500 mg/L.

2. References

1. GREENFIELD, S., I.L. JONES & C.T. BERRY. 1964. High-pressure plasma-spectroscopic emission sources. *Analyst* 89: 713.

2. WENDT, R.H. & V.A. FASSEL. 1965. Induction-coupled plasma spectrometric excitation source. *Anal. Chem.* 37:920.

3. U.S. ENVIRONMENTAL PROTECTION AGENCY. 1983. Method 200.7. Inductively coupled plasma-atomic emission spectrometric method for trace element analysis of water and wastes. Methods for Chemical Analysis of Water and Wastes. EPA-600/4-79-020, revised March 1983.

4. AMERICAN SOCIETY FOR TESTING AND MATERIALS. 1987. Annual Book of ASTM Standards, Vol. 11.01. American Soc. Testing & Materials, Philadelphia, Pa.

5. FISHMAN, M.J. & W.L. BRADFORD, eds. 1982. A Supplement to Methods for the Determination of Inorganic Substances in Water and Fluvial Sediments. Rep. No. 82-272, U.S. Geological Survey, Washington, D.C.

6. GARBARINO, J.R. & H.E. TAYLOR. 1985. Trace Analysis. Recent Developments and Applications of Inductively Coupled Plasma Emission Spectroscopy to Trace Elemental Analysis of Water. Volume 4. Academic Press, New York, N.Y.

---

*Approved by Standard Methods Committee, 1989.

3120 B.   Inductively Coupled Plasma (ICP) Method

1. General Discussion

a. Principle: An ICP source consists of a flowing stream of argon gas ionized by an applied radio frequency field typically oscillating at 27.1 MHz. This field is inductively coupled to the ionized gas by a water-cooled coil surrounding a quartz "torch" that supports and confines the plasma. A sample aerosol is generated in an appropriate nebulizer and spray chamber and is carried into the plasma through an injector tube located within the torch. The sample aerosol is injected directly into the ICP, subjecting the constituent atoms to temperatures of about 6000 to 8000°K.[1] Because this results in almost complete dissociation of molecules, significant reduction in chemical interferences is achieved. The high temperature of the plasma excites atomic emission efficiently. Ionization of a high percentage of atoms produces ionic emission spectra. The ICP provides an optically "thin" source that is not subject to self-absorption except at very high concentrations. Thus linear dynamic ranges of four to six orders of magnitude are observed for many elements.[2]

The efficient excitation provided by the ICP results in low detection limits for many elements. This, coupled with the extended dynamic range, permits effective multielement determination of metals.[3] The light emitted from the ICP is focused onto the entrance slit of either a monochromator or a polychromator that effects dispersion. A precisely aligned exit slit is used to isolate a portion of the emission spectrum for intensity measurement using a photomultiplier tube. The monochromator uses a single exit slit/photomultiplier and may use a computer-controlled scanning mechanism to examine emission wavelengths sequentially. The polychromator uses multiple fixed exit slits and corresponding photomultiplier tubes; it simultaneously monitors all configured wavelengths using a computer-controlled readout system. The sequential approach provides greater wavelength selection while the simultaneous approach can provide greater sample throughput.

b. Applicable metals and analytical limits: Table 3120:I lists elements for which this method applies, recommended analytical wavelengths, and typical estimated instrument detection limits using conventional pneumatic nebulization. Actual working detection limits are sample-dependent. Typical upper limits for linear calibration also are included in Table 3120:I.

c. Interferences: Interferences may be categorized as follows:

1) Spectral interferences—Light emission from spectral sources other than the element of interest may contribute to apparent net signal intensity. Sources of spectral interference include direct spectral line overlaps, broadened wings of intense spectral lines, ion-atom recombination continuum emission, molecular band emission, and stray (scattered) light from the emission of elements at high concentrations.[4] Avoid line overlaps by selecting alternate analytical wavelengths. Avoid or minimize other spectral interference by judicious choice of background correction positions. A wavelength scan of the element line region is useful for detecting potential spectral interferences and for selecting positions for background correction. Make corrections for residual spectral interference using empirically determined correction factors in conjunction with the computer

TABLE 3120:I. SUGGESTED WAVELENGTHS, ESTIMATED DETECTION LIMITS, ALTERNATE
WAVELENGTHS, CALIBRATION CONCENTRATIONS, AND UPPER LIMITS

Element	Suggested Wavelength nm	Estimated Detection Limit $\mu g/L$	Alternate Wavelength* nm	Calibration Concentration mg/L	Upper Limit Concentration mg/L
Aluminum	308.22	40	237.32	10.0	100
Antimony	206.83	30	217.58	10.0	100
Arsenic	193.70	50	189.04†	10.0	100
Barium	455.40	2	493.41	1.0	50
Beryllium	313.04	0.3	234.86	1.0	10
Boron	249.77	5	249.68	1.0	50
Cadmium	226.50	4	214.44	2.0	50
Calcium	317.93	10	315.89	10.0	100
Chromium	267.72	7	206.15	5.0	50
Cobalt	228.62	7	230.79	2.0	50
Copper	324.75	6	219.96	1.0	50
Iron	259.94	7	238.20	10.0	100
Lead	220.35	40	217.00	10.0	100
Lithium	670.78	4‡	—	5.0	100
Magnesium	279.08	30	279.55	10.0	100
Manganese	257.61	2	294.92	2.0	50
Molybdenum	202.03	8	203.84	10.0	100
Nickel	231.60	15	221.65	2.0	50
Potassium	766.49	100‡	769.90	10.0	100
Selenium	196.03	75	203.99	5.0	100
Silica (SiO_2)	212.41	20	251.61	21.4	100
Silver	328.07	7	338.29	2.0	50
Sodium	589.00	30‡	589.59	10.0	100
Strontium	407.77	0.5	421.55	1.0	50
Thallium	190.86†	40	377.57	10.0	100
Vanadium	292.40	8	—	1.0	50
Zinc	213.86	2	206.20	5.0	100

*Other wavelengths may be substituted if they provide the needed sensitivity and are corrected for spectral interference.
†Available with vacuum or inert gas purged optical path.
‡Sensitive to operating conditions.

software supplied by the spectrometer manufacturer or with the calculation detailed below. The empirical correction method cannot be used with scanning spectrometer systems if the analytical and interfering lines cannot be precisely and reproducibly located. In addition, if using a polychromator, verify absence of spectral interference from an element that could occur in a sample but for which there is no channel in the detector array. Do this by analyzing single-element solutions of 100 mg/L concentration and noting for each element channel the apparent concentration from the interfering substance that is greater than the element's instrument detection limit.

2) Nonspectral interferences

a) Physical interferences are effects associated with sample nebulization and transport processes. Changes in the physical properties of samples, such as viscosity and surface tension, can cause significant error. This usually occurs when samples containing more than 10% (by volume) acid or more than 1500 mg dissolved solids/L are analyzed using calibration standards containing $\leq$ 5% acid. Whenever a new or unusual sample matrix is encountered, use the test described in ¶ 4*g*. If physical interference is present, compensate for it by sample dilution, by using matrix-matched calibration standards, or by applying the method of standard addition (see ¶ 5*d* below).

High dissolved solids content also can contribute to instrumental drift by causing salt buildup at the tip of the nebulizer gas orifice. Using prehumidified argon for sample nebulization lessens this problem. Better control of the argon flow rate to the nebulizer using a mass flow controller improves instrument performance.

b) Chemical interferences are caused by molecular compound formation, ionization effects, and thermochemical effects associated with sample vaporization and atomization in the plasma. Normally these effects are not pronounced and can be minimized by careful selection of operating conditions (incident power, plasma observation position, etc.). Chemical interferences are highly dependent on sample matrix and element of interest. As with physical interferences, compensate for them by using matrix matched standards or by standard addition (¶ 5*d*). To determine the presence of chemical interference, follow instructions in ¶ 4*g*.

2. Apparatus

a. ICP source: The ICP source consists of a radio frequency (RF) generator capable of generating at least 1.1 KW of power, torch, tesla coil, load coil, impedance matching network, nebulizer, spray chamber, and drain. High-quality flow regulators are required for both the nebulizer argon and the plasma support gas flow. A peristaltic pump is recommended to regulate sample flow to the nebulizer. The type of nebulizer and spray chamber used may depend on the samples to be analyzed as well as on the equipment manufacturer. In general, pneumatic nebulizers of the concentric or cross-flow design are used. Viscous samples and samples containing particulates or high dissolved solids content (> 5000 mg/L) may require nebulizers of the Babington type.[5]

b. Spectrometer: The spectrometer may be of the simultaneous (polychromator) or sequential (monochromator) type with air-path, inert gas purged, or vacuum optics. A spectral bandpass of 0.05 nm or less is required. The instrument should permit examination of the spectral background surrounding the emission lines used for metals determination. It is necessary to be able to measure and correct for spectral background at one or more positions on either side of the analytical lines.

3. Reagents and Standards

Use reagents that are of ultra-high-purity grade or equivalent. Redistilled acids are acceptable. Except as noted, dry all salts at 105°C for 1 h and store in a desiccator before weighing. Use deionized water prepared by passing water through at least two stages of deionization with mixed bed cation/anion exchange resins.[6] Use deionized water for preparing all calibration standards, reagents, and for dilution.

a. Hydrochloric acid, HCl, conc and 1 + 1.

b. Nitric acid, HNO₃, conc.

c. Nitric acid, HNO₃, 1 + 1: Add 500 mL conc HNO₃ to 400 mL water and dilute to 1 L.

d. Standard stock solutions: See 3111B, 3111D, and 3114B. CAUTION: *Many metal salts are extremely toxic and may be fatal if swallowed. Wash hands thoroughly after handling.*

1) *Aluminum:* See 3111D.3k1).

2) *Antimony:* See 3111B.3j1).

3) *Arsenic:* See 3114B.3k1).

4) *Barium:* See 3111D.3k2).

5) *Beryllium:* See 3111D.3k3).

6) *Boron:* Do not dry but keep bottle tightly stoppered and store in a desiccator. Dissolve 0.5716 g anhydrous H_3BO_3 in water and dilute to 1000 mL; 1 mL = 100 μg B.

7) *Cadmium:* See 3111B.3j3).

8) *Calcium:* See 3111B.3j4).

9) *Chromium:* See 3111B.3j6).

10) *Cobalt:* See 3111B.3j7).

11) *Copper:* See 3111B.3j8).

12) *Iron:* See 3111B.3j11).

13) *Lead:* See 3111B.3j12).

14) *Lithium:* See 3111B.3j13).

15) *Magnesium:* See 3111B.3j14).

16) *Manganese:* See 3111B.3j15).

17) *Molybdenum:* See 3111D.3k4).

18) *Nickel:* See 3111B.3j16).

19) *Potassium:* See 3111B.3j19).

20) *Selenium:* See 3114B.3n1).

21) *Silica:* See 3111D.3k7).

22) *Silver:* See 3111B.3j22).

23) *Sodium:* See 3111B.3j23).

24) *Strontium:* See 3111B.3j24).

25) *Thallium:* See 3111B.3j25).

26) *Vanadium:* See 3111D.3k10).

27) *Zinc:* See 3111B.3j27).

e. Calibration standards: Prepare mixed calibration standards containing the concentrations shown in Table 3120:I by combining appropriate volumes of the stock solutions in 100-mL volumetric flasks. Add 2 mL 1+1 HNO_3 and 10 mL 1+1 HCl and dilute to 100 mL with water. Before preparing mixed standards, analyze each stock solution separately to determine possible spectral interference or the presence of impurities. When preparing mixed standards take care that the elements are compatible and stable. Store mixed standard solutions in an FEP fluorocarbon or unused polyethylene bottle. Verify calibration standards initially using the quality control standard; monitor weekly for sta-

bility. The following are recommended combinations using the suggested analytical lines in Table 3120:I. Alternative combinations are acceptable.

1) *Mixed standard solution I:* Manganese, beryllium, cadmium, lead, selenium, and zinc.

2) *Mixed standard solution II:* Barium, copper, iron, vanadium, and cobalt.

3) *Mixed standard solution III:* Molybdenum, silica, arsenic, strontium, and lithium.

4) *Mixed standard solution IV:* Calcium, sodium, potassium, aluminum, chromium, and nickel.

5) *Mixed standard solution V:* Antimony, boron, magnesium, silver, and thallium. If addition of silver results in an initial precipitation, add 15 mL water and warm flask until solution clears. Cool and dilute to 100 mL with water. For this acid combination limit the silver concentration to 2 mg/L. Silver under these conditions is stable in a tap water matrix for 30 d. Higher concentrations of silver require additional HCl.

f. Calibration blank: Dilute 2 mL 1+1 HNO_3 and 10 mL 1+1 HCl to 100 mL with water. Prepare a sufficient quantity to be used to flush the system between standards and samples.

g. Method blank: Carry a reagent blank through entire sample preparation procedure. Prepare method blank to contain the same acid types and concentrations as the sample solutions.

h. Instrument check standard: Prepare instrument check standards by combining compatible elements at a concentration of 2 mg/L.

i. Instrument quality control sample: Obtain a certified aqueous reference standard from an outside source and prepare according to instructions provided by the supplier. Use the same acid matrix as the calibration standards.

j. Method quality control sample: Carry the instrument quality control sample

(¶ 3*i*) through the entire sample preparation procedure.

k. Argon: Use technical or welder's grade. If gas appears to be a source of problems, use prepurified grade.

4. Procedure

a. Sample preparation: See Section 3030F.

b. Operating conditions: Because of differences among makes and models of satisfactory instruments, no detailed operating instructions can be provided. Follow manufacturer's instructions. Establish instrumental detection limit, precision, optimum background correction positions, linear dynamic range, and interferences for each analytical line. Verify that the instrument configuration and operating conditions satisfy the analytical requirements and that they can be reproduced on a day-to-day basis. An atom-to-ion emission intensity ratio [Cu(I) 324.75 nm/Mn(II) 257.61 nm] can be used to reproduce optimum conditions for multielement analysis precisely. The Cu/Mn intensity ratio may be incorporated into the calibration procedure, including specifications for sensitivity and for precision.[7] Keep daily or weekly records of the Cu and Mn intensities and/or the intensities of critical element lines. Also record settings for optical alignment of the polychromator, sample uptake rate, power readings (incident, reflected), photomultiplier tube attenuation, mass flow controller settings, and system maintenance.

c. Instrument calibration: Set up instrument as directed (¶ *b*). Warm up for 30 min. For polychromators, perform an optical alignment using the profile lamp or solution. Check alignment of plasma torch and spectrometer entrance slit, particularly if maintenance of the sample introduction system was performed. Make Cu/Mn or similar intensity ratio adjustment.

Calibrate instrument according to manufacturer's recommended procedure using calibration standards and blank. Aspirate each standard or blank for a minimum of 15 s after reaching the plasma before beginning signal integration. Rinse with calibration blank or similar solution for at least 60 s between each standard to eliminate any carryover from the previous standard. Use average intensity of multiple integrations of standards or samples to reduce random error.

Before analyzing samples, analyze instrument check standard. Concentration values obtained should not deviate from the actual values by more than ± 5% (or the established control limits, whichever is lower).

d. Analysis of samples: Begin each sample run with an analysis of the calibration blank, then analyze the method blank. This permits a check of the sample preparation reagents and procedures for contamination. Analyze samples, alternating them with analyses of calibration blank. Rinse for at least 60 s with dilute acid between samples and blanks. After introducing each sample or blank let system equilibrate before starting signal integration. Examine each analysis of the calibration blank to verify that no carry-over memory effect has occurred. If carry-over is observed, repeat rinsing until proper blank values are obtained. Make appropriate dilutions and acidifications of the sample to determine concentrations beyond the linear calibration range.

e. Instrumental quality control: Analyze instrument check standard once per 10 samples to determine if significant instrument drift has occurred. If agreement is not within ± 5% of the expected values (or within the established control limits, whichever is lower), terminate analysis of samples, correct problem, and recalibrate instrument. If the intensity ratio reference is used, resetting this ratio may restore calibration without the need for reanalyzing calibration standards. Analyze instrument check standard to confirm proper recalibration. Reanalyze one or more samples analyzed just before termination of the analytical run. Results should agree to within ± 5%, otherwise all samples analyzed after the last acceptable instrument check standard analysis must be reanalyzed.

Analyze instrument quality control sample within every run. Use this analysis to verify accuracy and stability of the calibration standards. If any result is not within ± 5% of the certified value, prepare a new calibration standard and recalibrate the instrument. If this does not correct the problem, prepare a new stock solution and a new calibration standard and repeat calibration.

f. Method quality control: Analyze the method quality control sample within every run. Results should agree to within ± 5% of the certified values. Greater discrepancies may reflect losses or contamination during sample preparation.

g. Test for matrix interference: When analyzing a new or unusual sample matrix verify that neither a positive nor negative nonlinear interference effect is operative. If the element is present at a concentration above 1 mg/L, use serial dilution with calibration blank. Results from the analyses of a dilution should be within ± 5% of the original result. Alternately, or if the concentration is either below 1 mg/L or not detected, use a post-digestion addition equal to 1 mg/L. Recovery of the addition should be either between 95% and 105% or within established control limits of ± 2 standard deviations around the mean. If a matrix effect causes test results to fall outside the critical limits, complete the analysis after either diluting the sample to eliminate the matrix effect while maintaining a detectable concentration of at least twice the detection limit or applying the method of standard additions.

5. Calculations and Corrections

a. Blank correction: Subtract result of an adjacent calibration blank from each sample result to make a baseline drift correction. (Concentrations printed out should include negative and positive values to compensate for positive and negative baseline drift. Make certain that the calibration blank used for blank correction has not been contaminated by carry-over.) Use the result of the method blank analysis to correct for reagent contamination. Alternatively, intersperse method blanks with appropriate samples. Reagent blank and baseline drift correction are accomplished in one subtraction.

b. Dilution correction: If the sample was diluted or concentrated in preparation, multiply results by a dilution factor (*DF*) calculated as follows:

$$DF = \frac{\text{Final weight or volume}}{\text{Initial weight or volume}}$$

c. Correction for spectral interference: Correct for spectral interference by using computer software supplied by the instrument manufacturer or by using the manual method based on interference correction factors. Determine interference correction factors by analyzing single-element stock solutions of appropriate concentrations under conditions matching as closely as possible those used for sample analysis. Unless analysis conditions can be reproduced accurately from day to day, or for longer periods, redetermine interference correction factors found to affect the results significantly each time samples are analyzed.[7, 8] Calculate interference correction factors (K_{ij}) from apparent concentrations observed in the analysis of the high-purity stock solutions:

$$K_{ij} = \frac{\text{Apparent concentration of element } i}{\text{Actual concentration of interfering element } j}$$

where the apparent concentration of element i is the difference between the observed concentration in the stock solution and the observed concentration in the blank. Correct sample concentrations observed for element i (already corrected for baseline drift), for spectral interferences from elements j, k, and l; for example:

Concentration of element i corrected for spectral interference

$$\begin{aligned} &= \begin{matrix} \text{Observed} \\ \text{concentration} \\ \text{of } i \end{matrix} - (K_{ij}) \begin{matrix} \text{Observed} \\ \text{concentration} \\ \text{of interfering} \\ \text{element } j \end{matrix} \\ &- (K_{ik}) \begin{matrix} \text{Observed} \\ \text{concentration} \\ \text{of interfering} \\ \text{element } k \end{matrix} - (K_{il}) \begin{matrix} \text{Observed} \\ \text{concentration} \\ \text{of interfering} \\ \text{element } l \end{matrix} \end{aligned}$$

Interference correction factors may be negative if background correction is used for element i. A negative K_{ij} can result where an interfering line is encountered at the background correction wavelength rather than at the peak wavelength. Determine concentrations of interfering elements j, k, and l within their respective linear ranges. Mutual interferences (i interferes with j and j interferes with i) require iterative or matrix methods for calculation.

d. Correction for nonspectral interference: If nonspectral interference correction is necessary, use the method of standard additions. It is applicable when the chemical and physical form of the element in the standard addition is the same as in the sample, *or* the ICP converts the metal in both sample and addition to the same form; the interference effect is independent of metal concentration over the concentration range of standard additions; and the analytical calibration curve is linear over the concentration range of standard additions.

Use an addition not less than 50% nor more than 100% of the element concentration in the sample so that measurement precision will not be degraded and interferences that depend on element/interferent ratios will not cause erroneous results.

Apply the method to all elements in the sample set using background correction at carefully chosen off-line positions. Multielement standard addition can be used if it has been determined that added elements are not interferents.

e. Reporting data: Report analytical data in concentration units of milligrams per liter using up to three significant figures. Report results below the determined detection limit as not detected less than the stated detection limit corrected for sample dilution.

6. Precision and Bias

As a guide to the generally expected precision and bias, see the linear regression equations in Table 3120:II.[9] Additional interlaboratory information is available.[10]

7. References

1. FAIRES, L.M., B.A. PALMER, R. ENGLEMAN, JR. & T.M. NIEMCZYK. 1984. Temperature determinations in the inductively coupled plasma using a Fourier transform spectrometer. *Spectrochim. Acta* 39B:819.
2. BARNES, R.M. 1978. Recent advances in emission spectroscopy: inductively coupled plasma discharges for spectrochemical analysis. *CRC Crit. Rev. Anal. Chem.* 7:203.
3. PARSONS, M.L., S. MAJOR & A.R. FORSTER. 1983. Trace element determination by atomic spectroscopic methods - State of the art. *Appl. Spectrosc.* 37:411.
4. LARSON, G.F., V.A. FASSEL, R. K. WINGE & R.N. KNISELEY. 1976. Ultratrace analysis by optical emission spectroscopy: The stray light problem. *Appl. Spectrosc.* 30:384.
5. GARBARINO, J.R. & H.E. TAYLOR. 1979. A Babington-type nebulizer for use in the analysis of natural water samples by inductively coupled plasma spectrometry. *Appl. Spectrosc.* 34:584.
6. AMERICAN SOCIETY FOR TESTING AND MATERIALS. 1988. Standard specification for reagent water, D1193-77 (reapproved 1983). Annual Book of ASTM Standards. American Soc. for Testing & Materials, Philadelphia, Pa.
7. BOTTO, R.I. 1984. Quality assurance in operating a multielement ICP emission spectrometer. *Spectrochim. Acta* 39B:95.

TABLE 3120:II. ICP PRECISION AND BIAS DATA

Element	Concentration Range $\mu g/L$	Total Digestion* $\mu g/L$		Recoverable Digestion* $\mu g/L$	
Aluminum	69–4792	X =	$0.9273C + 3.6$	X =	$0.9380C + 22.1$
		S =	$0.0559X + 18.6$	S =	$0.0873X + 31.7$
		SR =	$0.0507X + 3.5$	SR =	$0.0481X + 18.8$
Antimony	77–1406	X =	$0.7940C - 17.0$	X =	$0.8908C + 0.9$
		S =	$0.1556X - 0.6$	S =	$0.0982X + 8.3$
		SR =	$0.1081X + 3.9$	SR =	$0.0682X + 2.5$
Arsenic	69–1887	X =	$1.0437C - 12.2$	X =	$1.0175C + 3.9$
		S =	$0.1239X + 2.4$	S =	$0.1288X + 6.1$
		SR =	$0.0874X + 6.4$	SR =	$0.0643X + 10.3$
Barium	9–377	X =	$0.7683C + 0.47$	X =	$0.8380C + 1.68$
		S =	$0.1819X + 2.78$	S =	$0.2540X + 0.30$
		SR =	$0.1285X + 2.55$	SR =	$0.0826X + 3.54$
Beryllium	3–1906	X =	$0.9629C + 0.05$	X =	$1.0177C - 0.55$
		S =	$0.0136X + 0.95$	S =	$0.0359X + 0.90$
		SR =	$0.0203X - 0.07$	SR =	$0.0445X - 0.10$
Boron	19–5189	X =	$0.8807C + 9.0$	X =	$0.9676C + 18.7$
		S =	$0.1150X + 14.1$	S =	$0.1320X + 16.0$
		SR =	$0.0742X + 23.2$	SR =	$0.0743X + 21.1$
Cadmium	9–1943	X =	$0.9874C - 0.18$	X =	$1.0137C - 0.65$
		S =	$0.0557X + 2.02$	S =	$0.0585X + 1.15$
		SR =	$0.0300X + 0.94$	SR =	$0.0332X + 0.90$
Calcium	17–47 170	X =	$0.9182C - 2.6$	X =	$0.9658C + 0.8$
		S =	$0.1228X + 10.1$	S =	$0.0917X + 6.9$
		SR =	$0.0189X + 3.7$	SR =	$0.0327X + 10.1$
Chromium	13–1406	X =	$0.9544C + 3.1$	X =	$1.0049C - 1.2$
		S =	$0.0499X + 4.4$	S =	$0.0698X + 2.8$
		SR =	$0.0009X + 7.9$	SR =	$0.0571X + 1.0$
Cobalt	17–2340	X =	$0.9209C - 4.5$	X =	$0.9278C - 1.5$
		S =	$0.0436X + 3.8$	S =	$0.0498X + 2.6$
		SR =	$0.0428X + 0.5$	SR =	$0.0407X + 0.4$
Copper	8–1887	X =	$0.9297C - 0.30$	X =	$0.9647C - 3.64$
		S =	$0.0442X + 2.85$	S =	$0.0497X + 2.28$
		SR =	$0.0128X + 2.53$	SR =	$0.0406X + 0.96$
Iron	13–9359	X =	$0.8829C + 7.0$	X =	$0.9830C + 5.7$
		S =	$0.0683X + 11.5$	S =	$0.1024X + 13.0$
		SR =	$-0.0046X + 10.0$	SR =	$0.0790X + 11.5$
Lead	42–4717	X =	$0.9699C - 2.2$	X =	$1.0056C + 4.1$
		S =	$0.0558X + 7.0$	S =	$0.0799X + 4.6$
		SR =	$0.0353X + 3.6$	SR =	$0.0448X + 3.5$
Magnesium	34–13 868	X =	$0.9881C - 1.1$	X =	$0.9879C + 2.2$
		S =	$0.0607X + 11.6$	S =	$0.0564X + 13.2$
		SR =	$0.0298X + 0.6$	SR =	$0.0268X + 8.1$

TABLE 3120:II, CONT.

Element	Concentration Range $\mu g/L$	Total Digestion* $\mu g/L$		Recoverable Digestion* $\mu g/L$	
Manganese	4–1887	X =	$0.9417C + 0.13$	X =	$0.9725C + 0.07$
		S =	$0.0324X + 0.88$	S =	$0.0557X + 0.76$
		SR =	$0.0153X + 0.91$	SR =	$0.0400X + 0.82$
Molybdenum	17–1830	X =	$0.9682C + 0.1$	X =	$0.9707C - 2.3$
		S =	$0.0618X + 1.6$	S =	$0.0811X + 3.8$
		SR =	$0.0371X + 2.2$	SR =	$0.0529X + 2.1$
Nickel	17–47 170	X =	$0.9508C + 0.4$	X =	$0.9869C + 1.5$
		S =	$0.0604X + 4.4$	S =	$0.0526X + 5.5$
		SR =	$0.0425X + 3.6$	SR =	$0.0393X + 2.2$
Potassium	347–14 151	X =	$0.8669C - 36.4$	X =	$0.9355C - 183.1$
		S =	$0.0934X + 77.8$	S =	$0.0481X + 177.2$
		SR =	$-0.0099X + 144.2$	SR =	$0.0329X + 60.9$
Selenium	69–1415	X =	$0.9363C - 2.5$	X =	$0.9737C - 1.0$
		S =	$0.0855X + 17.8$	S =	$0.1523X + 7.8$
		SR =	$0.0284X + 9.3$	SR =	$0.0443X + 6.6$
Silicon	189–9434	X =	$0.5742C - 35.6$	X =	$0.9737C - 60.8$
		S =	$0.4160X + 37.8$	S =	$0.3288X + 46.0$
		SR =	$0.1987X + 8.4$	SR =	$0.2133X + 22.6$
Silver	8–189	X =	$0.4466C + 5.07$	X =	$0.3987C + 8.25$
		S =	$0.5055X - 3.05$	S =	$0.5478X - 3.93$
		SR =	$0.2086X - 1.74$	SR =	$0.1836X - 0.27$
Sodium	35–47 170	X =	$0.9581C + 39.6$	X =	$1.0526C + 26.7$
		S =	$0.2097X + 33.0$	S =	$0.1473X + 27.4$
		SR =	$0.0280X + 105.8$	SR =	$0.0884X + 50.5$
Thallium	79–1434	X =	$0.9020C - 7.3$	X =	$0.9238C + 5.5$
		S =	$0.1004X + 18.3$	S =	$0.2156X + 5.7$
		SR =	$0.0364X + 11.5$	SR =	$-0.0106X + 48.0$
Vanadium	13–4698	X =	$0.9615C - 2.0$	X =	$0.9551C + 0.4$
		S =	$0.0618X + 1.7$	S =	$0.0927X + 1.5$
		SR =	$0.0220X + 0.7$	SR =	$0.0472X + 0.5$
Zinc	7–7076	X =	$0.9356C - 0.30$	X =	$0.9500C + 1.22$
		S =	$0.0914X + 3.75$	S =	$0.0597X + 6.50$
		SR =	$-0.0130X + 10.07$	SR =	$0.0153X + 7.78$

*X = mean recovery, $\mu g/L$,
 C = true value, $\mu g/L$,
 S = multi-laboratory standard deviation, $\mu g/L$,
SR = single-analyst standard deviation, $\mu g/L$.

8. BOTTO, R.I. 1982. Long-term stability of spectral interference calibrations for inductively coupled plasma atomic emission spectrometry. *Anal. Chem.* 54:1654.

9. MAXFIELD, R. & B. MINDAK. 1985. EPA Method Study 27, Method 200. 7 (Trace Metals by ICP). EPA-600/S4-85/05. National Technical Information Serv., Springfield, Va.

10. GARBARINO, J.R., B.E. JONES, G. P. STEIN, W.T. BELSER & H.E. TAYLOR. 1985. Statistical evaluation of an inductively coupled plasma atomic emission spectrometric method for routine water quality testing. *Appl. Spectrosc.* 39:53.

*   *   *

3500-Ca   CALCIUM*

3500-Ca A.   Introduction

1. Occurrence and Significance

The presence of calcium (fifth among the elements in order of abundance) in water supplies results from passage through or over deposits of limestone, dolomite, gypsum, and gypsiferous shale. The calcium content may range from zero to several hundred milligrams per liter, depending on the source and treatment of the water. Small concentrations of calcium carbonate combat corrosion of metal pipes by laying down a protective coating. Appreciable calcium salts, on the other hand, precipitate on heating to form harmful scale in boilers, pipes, and cooking utensils. Calcium carbonate saturation is discussed in Section 2330.

---

*Approved by Standard Methods Committee, 1985.

Calcium contributes to the total hardness of water. Chemical softening treatment, reverse osmosis, electrodialysis, or ion exchange is used to reduce calcium and the associated hardness.

2. Selection of Method

The atomic absorption method and inductively coupled plasma method are accurate means of determining calcium. The permanganate and EDTA titration methods give good results for control and routine applications. The simplicity and rapidity of the EDTA titration procedure make it preferable to the permanganate method.

3. Storage of Samples

The customary precautions are sufficient if care is taken to redissolve any calcium carbonate that may precipitate on standing.

3500-Ca B.   Atomic Absorption Spectrometric Method

See flame atomic absorption spectrometric method, Section 3111B.

3500-Ca C.   Inductively Coupled Plasma Method

See Section 3120.

3500-Ca D.   EDTA Titrimetric Method

1. General Discussion

a. Principle: When EDTA (ethylenediaminetetraacetic acid or its salts) is added to water containing both calcium and magnesium, it combines first with the calcium.

Calcium can be determined directly, with EDTA, when the pH is made sufficiently high that the magnesium is largely precipitated as the hydroxide and an indicator is used that combines with calcium only. Several indicators give a color change when all of the calcium has been complexed by the EDTA at a pH of 12 to 13.

b. Interference: Under conditions of this test, the following concentrations of ions cause no interference with the calcium hardness determination: Cu^{2+}, 2 mg/L; Fe^{2+}, 20 mg/L; Fe^{3+}, 20 mg/L; Mn^{2+}, 10 mg/L; Zn^{2+}, 5 mg/L; Pb^{2+}, 5 mg/L; Al^{3+}, 5 mg/L; and Sn^{4+}, 5 mg/L. Orthophosphate precipitates calcium at the pH of the test. Strontium and barium give a positive interference and alkalinity in excess of 300 mg/L may cause an indistinct end point in hard waters.

2. Reagents

a. Sodium hydroxide, NaOH, 1*N.*

b. Indicators: Many indicators are available for the calcium titration. Some are described in the literature (see Bibliography); others are commercial preparations and also may be used. Murexide (ammonium purpurate) was the first indicator available for detecting the calcium end point, and directions for its use are presented in this procedure. Individuals who have difficulty recognizing the murexide end point may find the indicator Eriochrome Blue Black R (color index number 202) or Solochrome Dark Blue an improvement because of the color change from red to pure blue. Eriochrome Blue Black R is sodium-1-(2-hydroxy-1-naphthylazo)-2-naphthol-4-sulfonic acid. Other indicators specifically designed for use as end-point detectors in EDTA titration of calcium may be used.

1) *Murexide (ammonium purpurate) indicator:* This indicator changes from pink to purple at the end point. Prepare by dissolving 150 mg dye in 100 g absolute ethylene glycol. Water solutions of the dye are not stable for longer than 1 d. A ground mixture of dye powder and sodium chloride (NaCl) provides a stable form of the indicator. Prepare by mixing 200 mg murexide with 100 g solid NaCl and grinding

the mixture to 40 to 50 mesh. Titrate immediately after adding indicator because it is unstable under alkaline conditions. Facilitate end-point recognition by preparing a color comparison blank containing 2.0 mL NaOH solution, 0.2 g solid indicator mixture (or 1 to 2 drops if a solution is used), and sufficient standard EDTA titrant (0.05 to 0.10 mL) to produce an unchanging color.

2) *Eriochrome Blue Black R indicator:* Prepare a stable form of the indicator by grinding together in a mortar 200 mg powdered dye and 100 g solid NaCl to 40 to 50 mesh. Store in a tightly stoppered bottle. Use 0.2 g of ground mixture for the titration in the same manner as murexide indicator. During titration the color changes from red through purple to bluish purple to a pure blue with no trace of reddish or purple tint. The pH of some (not all) waters must be raised to 14 (rather than 12 to 13) by the use of 8*N* NaOH to get a good color change.

c. Standard EDTA titrant, 0.01*M:* Prepare standard EDTA titrant as described for the EDTA total-hardness method (Section 2340). Standard EDTA titrant, 0.0100*M*, is equivalent to 400.8 μg Ca/1.00 mL.

3. Procedure

a. Pretreatment of polluted water and wastewater samples: Follow the procedure described in Section 3030E or I.

b. Sample preparation: Because of the high pH used in this procedure, titrate immediately after adding alkali and indicator. Use 50.0 mL sample, or a smaller portion diluted to 50 mL so that the calcium content is about 5 to 10 mg. Analyze hard waters with alkalinity higher than 300 mg $CaCO_3$/L by taking a smaller portion and diluting to 50 mL, or by neutralizing the alkalinity with acid, boiling 1 min, and cooling before beginning the titration.

c. Titration: Add 2.0 mL NaOH solution

or a volume sufficient to produce a pH of 12 to 13. Stir. Add 0.1 to 0.2 g indicator mixture selected (or 1 to 2 drops if a solution is used). Add EDTA titrant slowly, with continuous stirring to the proper end point. When using murexide, check end point by adding 1 to 2 drops of titrant in excess to make certain that no further color change occurs.

4. Calculation

$$\text{mg Ca/L} = \frac{A \times B \times 400.8}{\text{mL sample}}$$

Calcium hardness as mg $CaCO_3/L$

$$= \frac{A \times B \times 1000}{\text{mL sample}}$$

where:

A = mL titrant for sample and
B = mg $CaCO_3$ equivalent to 1.00 mL EDTA titrant at the calcium indicator end point.

5. Precision and Bias

A synthetic sample containing 108 mg Ca/L, 82 mg Mg/L, 3.1 mg K/L, 19.9 mg Na/L, 241 mg Cl$^-$/L, 1.1 mg NO_3^--N/L, 0.25 mg NO_2^--N/L, 259 mg SO_4^{2-}/L and 42.5 mg total alkalinity/L (contributed by $NaHCO_3$) in distilled water was analyzed in 44 laboratories by the EDTA titrimetric method, with a relative standard deviation of 9.2% and a relative error of 1.9%.

6. Bibliography

DIEHL, H. & J.L. ELLINGBOE. 1956. Indicator for titration of calcium in the presence of magnesium using disodium dihydrogen ethylenediamine tetraacetate. *Anal. Chem.* 28:882.

PATTON, J. & W. REEDER. 1956. New indicator for titration of calcium with (ethylenedinitrilo) tetraacetate. *Anal. Chem.* 28:1026.

HILDEBRAND, G.P. & C.N. REILLEY. 1957. New indicator for complexometric titration of calcium in the presence of magnesium. *Anal. Chem.* 29:258.

SCHWARZENBACH, G. 1957. Complexometric Titrations. Interscience Publishers, New York, N.Y.

FURMAN, N.H. 1962. Standard Methods of Chemical Analysis, 6th ed. D. Van Nostrand Co., Inc., Princeton, N.J.

KATZ, H. & R. NAVONE. 1964. Method for simultaneous determination of calcium and magnesium. *J. Amer. Water Works Assoc.* 56:121.

3500-Ca E.   Permanganate Titrimetric Method

1. General Discussion

a. Principle: Ammonium oxalate precipitates calcium quantitatively as calcium oxalate. An excess of oxalate overcomes the adverse effects of magnesium. Optimum crystal formation and minimum occlusion are obtained only when the pH is brought slowly to the desired value. This is accomplished in two stages, with intervening digestion to promote seed crystal formation. The precipitated calcium oxalate is dissolved in acid and titrated with permanganate. The amount of permanganate required to oxidize the oxalate is proportional to the amount of calcium.

b. Interference: The sample should be free of interfering amounts of strontium, silica, aluminum, iron, manganese, phosphate, and suspended matter. Strontium may precipitate as the oxalate and cause high results. In such a case, determine strontium by flame photometry and apply the appropriate correction. Eliminate silica interference by the classical dehydration procedure. Precipitate aluminum, iron, and manganese by ammonium hydroxide after treatment with persulfate. Precipitate phosphate as the ferric salt. Remove suspended matter by centrifuging or by filtration through paper, sintered glass, or a cellulose acetate membrane (see Solids, Section 2540).

2. Apparatus

a. *Vacuum pump,* or other source of vacuum.

b. *Filter flasks.*

c. *Filter crucibles:* Medium-porosity, 30-mL crucibles are recommended. Use either glass or porcelain crucibles. Crucibles of all-porous construction are difficult to wash quantitatively.

3. Reagents

a. *Methyl red indicator solution:* Dissolve 0.1 g methyl red sodium salt and dilute to 100 mL with distilled water.

b. *Hydrochloric acid,* HCl, 1 + 1.

c. *Ammonium oxalate solution:* Dissolve 10 g $(NH_4)_2C_2O_4 \cdot H_2O$ in 250 mL distilled water. Filter if necessary.

d. *Ammonium hydroxide,* NH$_4$OH, 3N: Add 240 mL conc NH$_4$OH to about 700 mL distilled water and dilute to 1 L. Filter before use to remove suspended silica flakes.

e. *Ammonium hydroxide,* 1 + 99.

f. *Special reagents for removal of aluminum, iron, and manganese interference:*

1) *Ammonium persulfate,* solid.

2) *Ammonium chloride solution:* Dissolve 20 g NH$_4$Cl in 1 L distilled water. Filter if necessary.

g. *Sodium oxalate:* Use primary standard grade Na$_2$C$_2$O$_4$. Dry at 105°C overnight and store in a desiccator.

h. *Sulfuric acid,* H$_2$SO$_4$, 1 + 1.

i. *Standard potassium permanganate titrant,* 0.01M: Dissolve 1.6 g KMnO$_4$ in 1 L distilled water. Keep in a brown glass-stoppered bottle and age for at least 1 week. Carefully decant or pipet supernate without stirring up any sediment. Standardize this solution frequently by the following procedure (standard KMnO$_4$ solution, exactly 0.0100M, is equivalent to 1.002 mg Ca/1.00 mL):

Weigh to the nearest 0.1 mg several 100- to 200-mg samples of anhydrous Na$_2$C$_2$O$_4$ into 400-mL beakers. To each beaker, in turn, add 100 mL distilled water and stir to dissolve. Add 10 mL 1 + 1 H$_2$SO$_4$ and heat rapidly to 90 to 95°C. Titrate rapidly with permanganate solution to be standardized, while stirring, to a slight pink endpoint color that persists for at least 1 min. Do not let temperature fall below 85°C. If necessary, warm beaker contents during titration; 100 mg will consume about 30 mL solution. Run a blank on distilled water and H$_2$SO$_4$.

$$\text{Molarity of } KMnO_4 = \frac{\text{g } Na_2C_2O_4}{(A - B) \times 0.335\,05}$$

where:

A = mL titrant for sample and
B = mL titrant for blank.

Average the results of several titrations.

4. Procedure

a. *Pretreatment of polluted water and wastewater samples:* Follow procedure described in Section 3030E or I.

b. *Treatment of sample:* Use 200 mL sample, containing not more than 50 mg Ca (or a smaller portion diluted to 200 mL). If interfering substances are present, proceed as follows:

1) Removal of silica interference—Remove interfering amounts of silica by the gravimetric procedure described in Silica, Section 4500-Si. Discard silica precipitate and save filtrate for removing interfering amounts of combined oxides described in ¶ c below. If combined oxides are absent, proceed to ¶ d.

2) Removal of combined oxides interference—Remove interfering amounts of aluminum, iron, and manganese by concentrating filtrate from gravimetric silica determination to 120 to 150 mL. Add enough HCl so that filtrate from silica removal contains at least 10 mL conc HCl. Add 2 to 3 drops methyl red indicator and

$3N$ NH$_4$OH until indicator color turns yellow.

Add 1 g ammonium persulfate; when boiling begins, carefully add $3N$ NH$_4$OH until solution becomes slightly alkaline and the steam bears a distinct but not strong odor of ammonia. Test with litmus paper. Boil for 1 to 2 min and let stand 10 min, until the hydroxides coagulate, but no longer. Filter precipitate and wash three or four times with NH$_4$Cl solution. Treat filtrate as described in the following.

c. pH adjustment of sample: To 200 mL sample, containing not more than 50 mg Ca, or to a smaller portion diluted to 200 mL, add 2 or 3 drops methyl red indicator solution. Neutralize with 1 + 1 HCl and boil for 1 min. Add 50 mL (NH$_4$)$_2$C$_2$O$_4$·H$_2$O solution and if any precipitate forms, add just enough 1 + 1 HCl to redissolve.

d. Precipitation of calcium oxalate: Keeping solution just below boiling point, add $3N$ NH$_4$OH dropwise from a buret, stirring constantly. Continue addition until solution is quite turbid (about 5 mL are required.) Digest for 90 min at 90°C. Filter, preferably through a filter crucible, using suction. Wash at once with 1 + 99 NH$_4$OH. Although it is not necessary to transfer all of the precipitate to the filter crucible, remove all excess (NH$_4$)$_2$C$_2$O$_4$·H$_2$O from beaker. (If magnesium is to be determined gravimetrically, set aside combined filtrate and washings for this purpose.)

e. Titration of calcium oxalate: Place filter crucible on its side in beaker and cover with distilled water. Add 10 mL 1 + 1 H$_2$SO$_4$ and, while stirring, heat rapidly to 90 to 95°C. Titrate rapidly with KMnO$_4$ titrant to a slightly pink end point that persists for at least 1 min. Do not let temperature fall below 85°C; if necessary, warm beaker contents during titration. Agitate crucible sufficiently to insure reaction of all the oxalate. Run a blank, using a clean beaker and crucible, 10 mL 1 + 1 H$_2$SO$_4$, and about the same volume of distilled water used in titrating sample.

5. Calculation

$$\text{mg Ca/L} = \frac{(A - B) \times M \times 10\ 020}{\text{mL sample}}$$

where:

A = mL titrant for sample,
B = mL titrant for blank, and
M = molarity of KMnO$_4$.

6. Precision and Bias

A synthetic sample containing 108 mg Ca/L, 82 mg Mg/L, 3.1 mg K/L, 19.9 mg Na/L, 241 mg Cl$^-$/L, 1.1 mg NO$_3$$^-$-N/L, 0.25 mg NO$_2$$^-$-N/L, 259 mg SO$_4$$^{2-}$/L, and 42.5 mg total alkalinity/L (contributed by NaHCO$_3$) in distilled water was analyzed in six laboratories by the KMnO$_4$ titrimetric method, with a relative standard deviation of 3.5% and a relative error of 2.8%.

7. Bibliography

KOLTHOFF, I.M., E.J. MEEHAN, E.B. SANDELL & S. BRUCKENSTEIN. 1969. Quantitative Chemical Analysis, 4th ed. Macmillan Co., New York, N.Y.

* * *

3500-Fe   IRON*

3500-Fe A.   Introduction

1. Occurrence and Significance

In filtered samples of oxygenated surface waters iron concentrations seldom reach 1 mg/L. Some groundwaters and acid surface drainage may contain considerably more iron. Iron in water can cause staining of laundry and porcelain. A bittersweet astringent taste is detectable by some persons at levels above 1 mg/L.

Under reducing conditions, iron exists in the ferrous state. In the absence of complex-forming ions, ferric iron is not significantly soluble unless the pH is very low. On exposure to air or addition of oxidants, ferrous iron is oxidized to the ferric state and may hydrolyze to form insoluble hydrated ferric oxide.

In water samples iron may occur in true solution, in a colloidal state that may be peptized by organic matter, in inorganic or organic iron complexes, or in relatively coarse suspended particles. It may be either ferrous or ferric, suspended or dissolved.

Silt and clay in suspension may contain acid-soluble iron. Sometimes iron oxide particles are collected with a water sample as a result of flaking of rust from pipes. Iron may come from a metal cap used to close the sample bottle.

2. Selection of Method

Sensitivity and detection limits for the atomic absorption spectrometric proce-

dure, the inductively coupled plasma method, and the phenanthroline colorimetric procedure described here are similar and generally adequate for analysis of natural or treated waters. The complexing reagents used in the colorimetric procedures are specific for ferrous iron but the atomic absorption procedures are not. However, because of the instability of ferrous iron, which is changed easily to the ferric form in solutions in contact with air, determination of ferrous iron requires special precautions and may need to be done in the field at the time of sample collection.

The procedure for determining ferrous iron using 1,10-phenanthroline (¶ 3500-Fe.D.4c) has a somewhat limited applicability; long storage time or exposure of samples to light must be avoided. A rigorous quantitative distinction between ferrous and ferric iron can be obtained with a special procedure using bathophenanthroline. Spectrophotometric methods using bathophenanthroline[1-6] and other organic complexing reagents such as ferrozine[7] or TPTZ[8] are capable of determining iron concentrations as low as 1 μg/L. A chemiluminescence procedure[9] is stated to have a detection limit of 5 ng/L. Additional procedures are described elsewhere.[10-13]

3. Sampling and Storage

Plan in advance the methods of collecting, storing, and pretreating samples. Clean sample container with acid and rinse with

---

*Approved by Standard Methods Committee, 1985.

distilled water. Equipment for membrane filtration of samples in the field may be required to determine iron in solution (dissolved iron). Dissolved iron is considered to be that passing through a 0.45-μm membrane filter but colloidal iron may be included. The value of the determination depends greatly on the care taken to obtain a representative sample. Iron in well water or tap samples may vary in concentration and form with duration and degree of flushing before and during sampling. When taking a sample portion for determining iron in suspension, shake the sample bottle often and vigorously to obtain a uniform suspension of precipitated iron. Use particular care when colloidal iron adheres to the sample bottle. This problem can be acute with plastic bottles.

For a precise determination of total iron, use a separate container for sample collection. Treat with acid at the time of collection to place the iron in solution and prevent adsorption or deposition on the walls of the sample container. Take account of the added acid in measuring portions for analysis. The addition of acid to the sample may eliminate the need for adding acid before digestion (¶ 3500-Fe.D.4a).

4. References

1. LEE, G.F. & W. STUMM. 1960. Determination of ferrous iron in the presence of ferric iron using bathophenanthroline. *J. Amer. Water Works Assoc.* 52:1567.
2. GHOSH, M.M., J.T. O'CONNOR & R.S. EN-GELBRECHT. 1967. Bathophenanthroline method for the determination of ferrous iron. *J. Amer. Water Works Assoc.* 59:897.
3. BLAIR, D. & H. DIEHL. 1961. Bathophenanthroline-disulfonic acid and bathocuproinedisulfonic acid, water soluble reagents for iron and copper. *Talanta* 7:163.
4. SHAPIRO, J. 1966. On the measurement of ferrous iron in natural waters. *Limnol. Oceanogr.* 11:293.
5. McMAHON, J.W. 1967. The influence of light and acid on the measurement of ferrous iron in lake water. *Limnol. Oceanogr.* 12:437.
6. McMAHON, J.W. 1969. An acid-free bathophenanthroline method for measuring dissolved ferrous iron in lake water. *Water Res.* 3:743.
7. GIBBS, C. 1976. Characterization and application of ferrozine iron reagent as a ferrous iron indicator. *Anal. Chem.* 48:1197.
8. DOUGAN, W.K. & A. L. WILSON. 1973. Absorbtiometric determination of iron with TPTZ. *Water Treat. Exam.* 22:110.
9. SEITZ, W.R. & D.M. HERCULES. 1972. Determination of trace amounts of iron (II) using chemiluminescence analysis. *Anal. Chem.* 44:2143.
10. MOSS, M.L. & M.G. MELLON. 1942. Colorimetric determination of iron with 2,2'-bipyridine and with 2,2',2"-tripyridine. *Ind. Eng. Chem.*, Anal. Ed. 14:862.
11. WELCHER, F.J. 1947. Organic Analytical Reagents. D. Van Nostrand Co., Princeton, N.J., Vol. 3, pp. 100-104.
12. MORRIS, R.L. 1952. Determination of iron in water in the presence of heavy metals. *Anal. Chem.* 24:1376.
13. DOIG, M.T., III, & D.F. MARTIN. 1971. Effect of humic acids on iron analyses in natural water. *Water Res.* 5:689.

3500-Fe B. Atomic Absorption Spectrometric Method

See flame atomic absorption spectrometric method, Sections 3111B and C, and electrothermal atomic absorption spectrometric method, Section 3113.

3500-Fe C.   Inductively Coupled Plasma Method

See Section 3120.

3500-Fe D.   Phenanthroline Method

1. General Discussion

a. Principle: Iron is brought into solution, reduced to the ferrous state by boiling with acid and hydroxylamine, and treated with 1,10-phenanthroline at pH 3.2 to 3.3. Three molecules of phenanthroline chelate each atom of ferrous iron to form an orange-red complex. The colored solution obeys Beer's law; its intensity is independent of pH from 3 to 9. A pH between 2.9 and 3.5 insures rapid color development in the presence of an excess of phenanthroline. Color standards are stable for at least 6 months.

b. Interference: Among the interfering substances are strong oxidizing agents, cyanide, nitrite, and phosphates (polyphosphates more so than orthophosphate), chromium, zinc in concentrations exceeding 10 times that of iron, cobalt and copper in excess of 5 mg/L, and nickel in excess of 2 mg/L . Bismuth, cadmium, mercury, molybdate, and silver precipitate phenanthroline. The initial boiling with acid converts polyphosphates to orthophosphate and removes cyanide and nitrite that otherwise would interfere. Adding excess hydroxylamine eliminates errors caused by excessive concentrations of strong oxidizing reagents. In the presence of interfering metal ions, use a larger excess of phenanthroline to replace that complexed by the interfering metals. Where excessive concentrations of interfering metal ions are present, the extraction method may be used.

If noticeable amounts of color or organic matter are present, it may be necessary to evaporate the sample, gently ash the residue, and redissolve in acid. The ashing may be carried out in silica, porcelain, or platinum crucibles that have been boiled for several hours in 1 + 1 HCl. The presence of excessive amounts of organic matter may necessitate digestion before use of the extraction procedure.

c. Minimum detectable concentration: Dissolved or total concentrations of iron as low as 10 μg/L can be determined with a spectrophotometer using cells with a 5 cm or longer light path. Carry a blank through the entire procedure to allow for correction.

2. Apparatus

a. Colorimetric equipment: One of the following is required:

1) *Spectrophotometer,* for use at 510 nm, providing a light path of 1 cm or longer.

2) *Filter photometer,* providing a light path of 1 cm or longer and equipped with a green filter having maximum transmittance near 510 nm.

3) *Nessler tubes,* matched, 100-mL, tall form.

b. Acid-washed glassware: Wash all glassware with conc hydrochloric acid (HCl) and rinse with distilled water before use to remove deposits of iron oxide.

c. Separatory funnels: 125-mL, Squibb form, with ground-glass or TFE stopcocks and stoppers.

3. Reagents

Use reagents low in iron. Use iron-free distilled water in preparing standards and reagent solutions. Store reagents in glass-stoppered bottles. The HCl and ammonium acetate solutions are stable indefinitely if tightly stoppered. The hydroxylamine, phenanthroline, and stock iron solutions are stable for several months. The standard iron solutions are not stable; prepare daily as needed by diluting the stock solution. Visual standards in nessler tubes are stable for several months if sealed and protected from light.

a. Hydrochloric acid, HCl, conc, containing less than 0.000 05% iron.

b. Hydroxylamine solution: Dissolve 10 g $NH_2OH \cdot HCl$ in 100 mL water.

c. Ammonium acetate buffer solution: Dissolve 250 g $NH_4C_2H_3O_2$ in 150 mL water. Add 700 mL conc (glacial) acetic acid. Because even a good grade of $NH_4C_2H_3O_2$ contains a significant amount of iron, prepare new reference standards with each buffer preparation.

d. Sodium acetate solution: Dissolve 200 g $NaC_2H_3O_2 \cdot 3H_2O$ in 800 mL water.

e. Phenanthroline solution: Dissolve 100 mg 1,10-phenanthroline monohydrate, $C_{12}H_8N_2 \cdot H_2O$, in 100 mL water by stirring and heating to 80°C. Do not boil. Discard the solution if it darkens. Heating is unnecessary if 2 drops conc HCl are added to the water. (NOTE: One milliliter of this reagent is sufficient for no more than 100 μg Fe.)

f. Stock iron solution: Use metal (1) or salt (2) for preparing the stock solution.

1) Use electrolytic iron wire, or "iron wire for standardizing," to prepare the so-

lution. If necessary, clean wire with fine sandpaper to remove any oxide coating and to produce a bright surface. Weigh 200.0 mg wire and place in a 1000-mL volumetric flask. Dissolve in 20 mL 6N sulfuric acid (H_2SO_4) and dilute to mark with water; 1.00 mL = 200 μg Fe.

2) If ferrous ammonium sulfate is preferred, slowly add 20 mL conc H_2SO_4 to 50 mL water and dissolve 1.404 g $Fe(NH_4)_2(SO_4)_2 \cdot 6H_2O$. Add 0.1$N$ potassium permanganate ($KMnO_4$) dropwise until a faint pink color persists. Dilute to 1000 mL with water and mix; 1.00 mL = 200 μg Fe.

g. Standard iron solutions: Prepare daily for use.

1) Pipet 50.00 mL stock solution into a 1000-mL volumetric flask and dilute to mark with water; 1.00 mL = 10.0 μg Fe.

2) Pipet 5.00 mL stock solution into a 1000-mL volumetric flask and dilute to mark with water; 1.00 mL = 1.00 μg Fe.

h. Diisopropyl or isopropyl ether. CAUTION: *Ethers may form explosive peroxides; test before using.*

4. Procedure

a. Total iron: Mix sample thoroughly and measure 50.0 mL into a 125-mL erlenmeyer flask. If this sample volume contains more than 200 μg iron use a smaller accurately measured portion and dilute to 50.0 mL. Add 2 mL conc HCl and 1 mL $NH_2OH \cdot HCl$ solution. Add a few glass beads and heat to boiling. To insure dissolution of all the iron, continue boiling until volume is reduced to 15 to 20 mL. (If the sample is ashed, take up residue in 2 mL conc HCl and 5 mL water.) Cool to room temperature and transfer to a 50- or 100-mL volumetric flask or nessler tube. Add 10 mL $NH_4C_2H_3O_2$ buffer solution and 4 mL phenanthroline solution, and dilute to mark with water. Mix thoroughly and allow at least 10 to 15 min for maximum color development.

b. *Dissolved iron:* Immediately after collection filter sample through a 0.45-μm membrane filter into a vacuum flask containing 1 mL conc HCl/100 mL sample. Analyze filtrate for total dissolved iron (¶ 4a) and/or dissolved ferrous iron (¶ 4c). (This procedure also can be used in the laboratory with the understanding that normal sample exposure to air during shipment may result in precipitation of iron.)

Calculate suspended iron by subtracting dissolved from total iron.

c. *Ferrous iron:* Determine ferrous iron at sampling site because of the possibility of change in the ferrous-ferric ratio with time in acid solutions. To determine ferrous iron only, acidify a separate sample with 2 mL conc HCl/100 mL sample at time of collection. Fill bottle directly from sampling source and stopper. Immediately withdraw a 50-mL portion of acidified sample and add 20 mL phenanthroline solution and 10 mL $NH_4C_2H_3O_2$ solution with vigorous stirring. Dilute to 100 mL and measure color intensity within 5 to 10 min. Do not expose to sunlight. (Color development is rapid in the presence of excess phenanthroline. The phenanthroline volume given is suitable for less than 50 μg total iron; if larger amounts are present, use a correspondingly larger volume of phenanthroline or a more concentrated reagent. Excess phenanthroline is required because of the kinetics of the complexing process.)

Calculate ferric iron by subtracting ferrous from total iron.

d. *Color measurement:* Prepare a series of standards by accurately pipetting calculated volumes of standard iron solutions (use weaker solution to measure 1- to 10-μg portions) into 125-mL erlenmeyer flasks, diluting to 50 mL by adding measured volumes of water, and carrying out the steps in ¶ 4a.

For visual comparison, prepare a set of at least 10 standards, ranging from 1 to 100 μg Fe in the final 100-mL volume. Compare colors in 100-mL tall-form nessler tubes.

TABLE 3500-Fe:I. SELECTION OF LIGHT PATH LENGTH FOR VARIOUS IRON CONCENTRATIONS

Fe μg		
50-mL Final Volume	100-mL Final Volume	Light Path cm
50–200	100–400	1
25–100	50–200	2
10–40	20–80	5
5–20	10–40	10

For photometric measurement, use Table 3500-Fe:I as a rough guide for selecting proper light path at 510 nm. Read standards against distilled water set at zero absorbance and plot a calibration curve, including a blank (see ¶ 3c and General Introduction).

If samples are colored or turbid, carry a second set of samples through all steps of the procedure without adding phenanthroline. Instead of distilled water, use the prepared blanks to set photometer to zero absorbance and read each developed sample with phenanthroline against the corresponding blank without phenanthroline. Translate observed photometer readings into iron values by means of the calibration curve. This procedure does *not* compensate for interfering ions.

e. *Samples containing organic interferences:* Digest samples containing substantial amounts of organic substances according to the directions given in Sections 3030G and H.

1) If a digested sample has been prepared according to the directions given in Section 3030G or H, pipet 10.0 mL or other suitable portion containing 20 to 500 μg Fe into a 125-mL separatory funnel. If the volume taken is less than 10 mL, add distilled water to make up to 10 mL. To the separatory funnel add 15 mL conc HCl for

a 10-mL aqueous volume; or, if the portion taken was greater than 10.0 mL, add 1.5 mL conc HCl/mL of sample. Mix, cool, and proceed with 4e3) below.

2) To prepare a sample solely for determining iron, measure a suitable volume containing 20 to 500 μg Fe and carry it through either of the digestion procedures described in Sections 3030G and H. However, use only 5 mL H_2SO_4 or $HClO_4$ and omit H_2O_2. When digestion is complete, cool, dilute with 10 mL water, heat almost to boiling to dissolve slowly soluble salts, and, if the sample is still cloudy, filter through a glass-fiber, sintered-glass, or porcelain filter, washing with 2 to 3 mL water. Quantitatively transfer filtrate or clear solution to a 25-mL volumetric flask and make up to 25 mL with water. Empty flask into a 125-mL separatory funnel, rinse with 5 mL conc HCl that is added to the funnel, and add 25 mL conc HCl measured with the same graduate or flask. Mix and cool to room temperature.

3) Extract the iron from the HCl solution in the separatory funnel by shaking for 30 s with 25 mL isopropyl ether (CAUTION). Draw off lower acid layer into a second separatory funnel. Extract acid solution again with 25 mL isopropyl ether, drain acid layer into a suitable clean vessel, and combine the two portions of isopropyl ether. Pour acid layer back into second separatory funnel and re-extract with 25 mL isopropyl ether. Withdraw and discard acid layer and add ether layer to original funnel. Persistence of a yellow color in the HCl solution after three extractions does not signify incomplete separation of iron because copper, which is not extracted, gives a similar yellow color.

Shake combined ether extracts with 25 mL water to return iron to aqueous phase and transfer lower aqueous layer to a 100-mL volumetric flask. Repeat extraction with a second 25-mL portion of water, adding this to the first aqueous extract. Discard ether layer.

4) Add 1 mL $NH_2OH \cdot HCl$ solution, 10 mL phenanthroline solution, and 10 mL $NaC_2H_3O_2$ solution. Dilute to 100 mL with water, mix thoroughly, and let stand for 10 min. Measure absorbance at 510 nm using a 5-cm absorption cell for amounts of iron less than 100 μg or 1-cm cell for quantities from 100 to 500 μg. As reference, use either distilled water or a sample blank prepared by carrying the specified quantities of acids through the entire analytical procedure. If distilled water is used as reference, correct sample absorbance by subtracting absorbance of a sample blank.

Determine micrograms of iron in the sample from the absorbance (corrected, if necessary) by reference to the calibration curve prepared by using a suitable range of iron standards containing the same amounts of phenanthroline, hydroxylamine, and sodium acetate as the sample.

5. Calculation

When the sample has been treated according to 4a, b, c, or 4e2):

$$\text{mg Fe/L} = \frac{\mu g \text{ Fe (in 100 mL final volume)}}{\text{mL sample}}$$

When the sample has been treated according to 4e1):

$$\text{mg Fe/L} = \frac{\mu g \text{ Fe (in 100 mL final volume)}}{\text{mL sample}}$$

$$\times \frac{100}{\text{mL portion}}$$

Report details of sample collection, storage, and pretreatment if they are pertinent to interpretation of results.

6. Precision and Bias

Precision and bias depend on the method of sample collection and storage, the method of color measurement, the iron concentration, and the presence of interfering color, turbidity, and foreign ions. In general, optimum reliability of visual comparison in nessler tubes is not better than 5% and often only 10%, whereas, under optimum conditions, photometric measurement may be reliable to 3% or 3 μg, whichever is greater. The sensitivity limit for visual observation in nessler tubes is approximately 1 μg Fe. Sample variability and instability may affect precision and bias of this determination more than will the errors of analysis itself. Serious divergences have been found in reports of different laboratories because of variations in methods of collecting and treating samples.

A synthetic sample containing 300 μg Fe/L, 500 μg Al/L, 50 μg Cd/L, 110 μg Cr/L, 470 μg Cu/L, 70 μg Pb/L, 120 μg Mn/L, 150 μg Ag/L, and 650 μg Zn/L in distilled water was analyzed in 44 laboratories by the phenanthroline method, with a relative standard deviation of 25.5% and a relative error of 13.3%.

7. Bibliography

CHRONHEIM, G. & W. WINK. 1942. Determination of divalent iron (by o-nitrosophenol). *Ind. Eng. Chem.*, Anal. Ed. 14:447.

MEHLIG, R.P. & R. H. HULETT. 1942. Spectrophotometric determination of iron with o-phenanthroline and with nitro-o-phenanthroline. *Ind. Eng. Chem.*, Anal. Ed. 14:869.

CALDWELL, D.H. & R.B. ADAMS. 1946. Colorimetric determination of iron in water with o-phenanthroline. *J. Amer. Water Works Assoc.* 38:727.

WELCHER, F.J. 1947. Organic Analytical Reagents. D. Van Nostrand Co., Princeton, N.J., Vol. 3, pp. 85-93.

KOLTHOFF, I.M., T.S. LEE & D. L. LEUSSING. 1948. Equilibrium and kinetic studies on the formation and dissociation of ferroin and ferrin. *Anal. Chem.* 20:985.

RYAN, J.A. & G. H. BOTHAM. 1949. Iron in aluminum alloys: Colorimetric determination using 1,10-phenanthroline. *Anal. Chem.* 21:1521.

REITZ, L.K., A.S. O'BRIEN & T. L. DAVIS. 1950. Evaluation of three iron methods using a factorial experiment. *Anal. Chem.* 22:1470.

SANDELL, E.B. 1959. Colorimetric Determination of Traces of Metals, 3rd ed. Interscience Publishers, New York, N.Y. Chapter 22.

SKOUGSTAD, M.W., M.J. FISHMAN, L. C. FRIEDMAN, D. E. ERDMANN & S. S. DUNCAN. 1979. Methods for Determination of Inorganic Substances in Water and Fluvial Sediment. Chapter A1 *in* Book 5, Techniques of Water Resources Investigations of the United States Geological Survey. U.S. Geological Surv., Washington, D.C.

*   *   *

3500-Mg   MAGNESIUM*

3500-Mg A.   Introduction

1. Occurrence

Magnesium ranks eighth among the elements in order of abundance and is a common constituent of natural water. Important contributors to the hardness of a water, magnesium salts break down when

heated, forming scale in boilers. Concentrations greater than 125 mg/L also can have a cathartic and diuretic effect. Chemical softening, reverse osmosis, electrodialysis, or ion exchange reduces the magnesium and associated hardness to acceptable levels. The magnesium concentration may vary from zero to several hundred milligrams per liter, depending on the source and treatment of the water.

---

*Approved by Standard Methods Committee, 1985.

2. Selection of Method

The four methods presented are applicable to all natural waters. Direct determinations can be made with the atomic absorption spectrometric and inductively coupled plasma methods. Magnesium can be determined by the gravimetric method only after removal of calcium salts (see Section 3500-Ca). These methods can be applied to all concentrations by selection of suitable sample portions. Choice of method is largely a matter of personal preference and analyst experience.

3500-Mg B.   Atomic Absorption Spectrometric Method

See flame atomic absorption spectrometric method, Section 3111B.

3500-Mg C.   Inductively Coupled Plasma Method

See Section 3120.

3500-Mg D.   Gravimetric Method

1. General Discussion

a. Principle: Diammonium hydrogen phosphate quantitatively precipitates magnesium in ammoniacal solution as magnesium ammonium phosphate. The precipitate is ignited to, and weighed as, magnesium pyrophosphate. A choice is presented between: (*a*) destruction of ammonium salts and oxalate, followed by single precipitation of magnesium ammonium phosphate; and (*b*) double precipitation without pretreatment. Where time is not a factor, double precipitation is preferable because, while pretreatment is faster, it requires close attention to avoid mechanical loss.

b. Interference: The solution should be reasonably free from aluminum, calcium, iron, manganese, silica, strontium, and suspended matter. It should not contain more than about 3.5 g NH_4Cl.

2. Reagents

a. Nitric acid, HNO_3, conc.

b. Hydrochloric acid, HCl, conc; also 1 + 1, 1 + 9, and 1 + 99.

c. Methyl red indicator solution: Dissolve 100 mg methyl red sodium salt in distilled water and dilute to 100 mL.

d. Diammonium hydrogen phosphate solution: In distilled water, dissolve 30 g $(NH_4)_2HPO_4$ and make up to 100 mL.

e. Ammonium hydroxide, NH_4OH, conc; also 1 + 19.

3. Procedure

a. By removal of oxalate and ammonium salts: To the combined filtrate and washings from the calcium determination, containing not more than 60 mg Mg, or to a portion containing less than this amount in a 600- or 800-mL beaker, add 50 mL conc

HNO$_3$ and evaporate carefully to dryness on a hot plate. Do not let reaction become too violent during the latter part of the evaporation; stay in constant attendance to avoid losses through spattering. Moisten residue with 2 to 3 mL conc HCl; add 20 mL distilled water, warm, filter, and wash. To the filtrate add 3 mL conc HCl, 2 to 3 drops methyl red solution, and 10 mL (NH$_4$)$_2$HPO$_4$ solution. Cool and add conc NH$_4$OH, drop by drop, stirring constantly, until the color changes to yellow. Stir for 5 min, add 5 mL conc NH$_4$OH, and stir vigorously for 10 min more. Let stand overnight and filter through filter paper.* Wash with 1 + 19 NH$_4$OH. Transfer to an ignited, cooled, and weighed crucible. Dry precipitate thoroughly and burn paper off *slowly*, allowing circulation of air. Heat at about 500°C until residue is white. Ignite for 30-min periods at 1100°C to constant weight.

b. By double precipitation: To the combined filtrate and washings from the calcium determination, containing not more than 60 mg Mg, or to a portion containing less than this amount, add 2 to 3 drops methyl red solution; adjust volume to 150 mL and acidify with 1 + 1 HCl. Add 10 mL (NH$_4$)$_2$HPO$_4$ solution. Cool. Add conc NH$_4$OH, drop by drop, stirring constantly, until the color changes to yellow. Stir for 5 min, add 5 mL conc NH$_4$OH, and stir vigorously for 10 min more. Let stand overnight and then filter through filter paper.* Wash with 1 + 19 NH$_4$OH. Discard filtrate and washings. Dissolve precipitate with 50 mL warm 1 + 9 HCl and wash

---

*Carl Schleicher and Schuell Co., S & S No. 589 White Ribbon, or equivalent.

paper well with hot 1 + 99 HCl. Add 2 to 3 drops methyl red solution, adjust volume to 100 to 150 mL, add 1 to 2 mL (NH$_4$)$_2$HPO$_4$ solution, and precipitate as before. Let stand in a cool place for at least 4 h or preferably overnight. Filter through filter paper* and wash with 1 + 19 NH$_4$OH. Transfer to an ignited, cooled, and weighed crucible. Dry precipitate thoroughly and burn paper off *slowly*, allowing circulation of air. Heat at about 500°C until residue is white. Ignite for 30-min periods at 1100°C to constant weight.

4. Calculation

$$\text{mg Mg/L} = \frac{\text{mg Mg}_2\text{P}_2\text{O}_7 \times 218.4}{\text{mL sample}}$$

5. Precision and Bias

A synthetic sample containing 82 mg Mg/L, 108 mg Ca/L, 3.1 mg K/L, 19.9 mg Na/L, 241 mg Cl$^-$/L, 1.1 mg NO$_3^-$-N/L, 0.250 mg NO$_2^-$-N/L, 259 mg SO$_4^{2-}$/L, and 42.5 mg total alkalinity/L (contributed by NaHCO$_3$) was analyzed in eight laboratories by the gravimetric method, with a relative standard deviation of 6.3% and a relative error of 4.9%.

6. Bibliography

EPPERSON, A.W. 1928. The pyrophosphate method for the determination of magnesium and phosphoric anhydride. *J. Amer. Chem. Soc.* 50:321.

KOLTHOFF, I.M. & E.B. SANDELL. 1952. Textbook of Quantitative Inorganic Analysis, 3rd ed. Macmillan Co., New York, N.Y., Chapter 22.

HILLEBRAND, W.F. et al. 1953. Applied Inorganic Analysis, 2nd ed. John Wiley & Sons, New York, Chapter 41 and pp. 133-134.

3500-Mg E.   Calculation Method

Magnesium may be estimated as the difference between hardness and calcium as $CaCO_3$ if interfering metals are present in noninterfering concentrations in the calcium titration (Section 3500-Ca.D) and suitable inhibitors are used in the hardness titration (Section 2340C).

mg Mg/L = [total hardness (as mg $CaCO_3$/L) − calcium hardness (as mg $CaCO_3$/L)] × 0.243

*   *   *

PART 4000

DETERMINATION OF INORGANIC

NONMETALLIC CONSTITUENTS

4010 INTRODUCTION

The analytical methods included in this part make use of classical wet chemical techniques and their automated variations and such modern instrumental techniques as ion chromatography. Methods that measure various forms of chlorine, nitrogen, and phosphorus are presented. The procedures are intended for use in the assessment and control of receiving water quality, the treatment and supply of potable water, and the measurement of operation and process efficiency in wastewater treatment. The methods also are appropriate and applicable in evaluation of environmental water-quality concerns. The introduction to each procedure contains reference to special field sampling conditions, appropriate sample containers, proper procedures for sampling and storage, and the applicability of the method.

4020 QUALITY CONTROL

Detailed recommendations and general information concerning laboratory quality assurance, as well as specific details of applicable quality-control measures, are provided in Part 1000 and in individual methods. Also follow this general principle:

Keep in mind the overall purpose of the measurements. Can duplicates (replicates) adequately establish precision and can recovery of known additions determine bias? Are suitable standards, control charts, blanks, calibrations, and other necessary measures incorporated to assure the quality of data produced? Furthermore, can adequate documentation be presented to support these contentions? Obviously, the same degree of substantiation may not be necessary in all cases, e.g., requirements for an operational control determination may differ from those for data submitted for regulatory purposes. Therefore, the intended use of the data is an important factor in determining overall quality control as well as the accompanying quality assurance measures.

4110   DETERMINATION OF ANIONS BY ION CHROMATOGRAPHY*

4110 A.   Introduction

Determination of the common anions such as bromide, chloride, fluoride, nitrate, nitrite, phosphate, and sulfate often is desirable to characterize a water and/or to assess the need for specific treatment. Although conventional colorimetric, electrometric, or titrimetric methods are available

for determining individual anions, only ion chromatography provides a single instrumental technique that may be used for their rapid, sequential measurement. Ion chromatography eliminates the need to use hazardous reagents and it effectively distinguishes among the halides (Br^-, Cl^-, and F^-) and the oxides (SO_3^{2-}-SO_4^{2-} or NO_2^--NO_3^-).

---

*Approved by Standard Methods Committee, 1988.

4110 B.   Ion Chromatography with Chemical Suppression of Eluant Conductivity

1. General Discussion

a. Principle: A water sample is injected into a stream of carbonate-bicarbonate eluant and passed through a series of ion exchangers. The anions of interest are separated on the basis of their relative affinities for a low capacity, strongly basic anion exchanger (guard and separator columns). The separated anions are directed onto a strongly acidic cation exchanger (packed-bed suppressor) or through a hollow fiber of cation exchanger membrane (fiber suppressor) or micromembrane suppressor bathed in continuously flowing strongly acid solution (regenerant solution). In the suppressor the separated anions are converted to their highly conductive acid forms and the carbonate-bicarbonate

eluant is converted to weakly conductive carbonic acid. The separated anions in their acid forms are measured by conductivity. They are identified on the basis of retention time as compared to standards. Quantitation is by measurement of peak area or peak height.

b. Interferences: Any substance that has a retention time coinciding with that of any anion to be determined will interfere. For example, relatively high concentrations of low-molecular-weight organic acids interfere with the determination of chloride and fluoride. A high concentration of any one ion also interferes with the resolution of others. Sample dilution overcomes many interferences. To resolve uncertainties of identification or quantitation use the method of known additions. Spurious peaks may result from contaminants in reagent water, glassware, or sample processing apparatus. Because small sample volumes are used, scrupulously avoid contamination. The method is applicable to surface, ground, and drinking water, treated mixed wastewater, and some industrial process waters, such as boiler water and cooling water, subject to the provision for filtration through a 0.2-μm membrane filter to avoid plugging the columns. Modifications such as preconcentration of samples, gradient elution, or reinjection of portions of the eluted sample may alleviate some interferences but require individual validation for precision and bias.

c. *Minimum detectable concentration:* The minimum detectable concentration of an anion is a function of sample size and conductivity scale used. Generally, minimum detectable concentrations are near 0.1 mg/L for Br^-, Cl^-, NO_3^-, NO_2^-, PO_4^{3-}, and SO_4^{2-} with a 100-μL sample loop and a 10-μS/cm full-scale setting on the conductivity detector. Similar values may be achieved by using a higher scale setting and an electronic integrator.

d. *Limitations:* This method is not recommended for the routine determination of F^- because equivalency studies have indicated positive or negative bias and poor precision in some samples. F^- can be determined accurately by ion chromatography using special techniques such as dilute eluant or gradient elution with fiber suppressor or membrane suppressors.

2. Apparatus

a. *Ion chromatograph*, including an injection valve, a sample loop, guard, separator, and suppressor columns or membrane suppressors, a temperature-compensated small-volume conductivity cell (6 μL or less), and a strip-chart recorder capable of full-scale response of 2 s or less. An electronic peak integrator is optional. Use an ion chromatograph capable of delivering 2 to 5 mL eluant/min at a pressure of 1400 to 6900 kPa.

b. *Anion separator column*, with styrene divinylbenzene-based low-capacity pellicular anion-exchange resin capable of resolving Br^-, Cl^-, NO_3^-, NO_2^-, PO_4^{3-}, and SO_4^{2-}; 4 × 250 mm.*

c. *Guard column*, identical to separator column except 4 × 50 mm,† to protect separator column from fouling by particulates or organics.

d. *Suppressor:* Use either:

1) *Suppressor column*, high-capacity cation-exchange resin capable of converting eluant and separated anions to their acid forms.‡

2) *Fiber suppressor or membrane suppressor:*§ Cation-exchange membrane capable of continuously converting eluant and separated anions to their acid forms.

3. Reagents

a. *Deionized or distilled water* free from interferences at the minimum detection limit of each constituent and filtered through a 0.2-μm membrane filter to avoid plugging columns.

b. *Eluant solution*, sodium bicarbonate-sodium carbonate, 0.003M $NaHCO_3$-0.0024M Na_2CO_3: Dissolve 1.008 g $NaHCO_3$ and 1.0176 g Na_2CO_3 in water and dilute to 4 L.

c. *Regenerant solution 1*, H_2SO_4, 1N: Use this regenerant when suppressor is not a continuously regenerated one.

d. *Regenerant solution 2*, H_2SO_4, 0.025N: Dilute 2.8 mL conc H_2SO_4 to 4 L or 100 mL regenerant solution 1 to 4 L. Use this regenerant with continuous regeneration-fiber suppressor system.

---

*Dionex P/N 030827 (normal run) or P/N 030831 (fast run), or equivalent.
†Dionex P/N 030825 (normal run) or P/N 030830 (fast run), or equivalent.
‡No longer available commercially.
§Dionex P/N 037072 (micro membrane—high capacity/low volume—suppressor), or equivalent.

e. Standard anion solutions, 1000 mg/L: Prepare a series of standard anion solutions by weighing the indicated amount of salt, dried to a constant weight at 105°C, to 1000 mL. Store in plastic bottles in a refrigerator; these solutions are stable for at least 1 month. Verify stability.

Anion ‖	Salt	Amount g/L
Cl^-	NaCl	1.6485
Br^-	NaBr	1.2876
NO_3^-	$NaNO_3$	1.3707
NO_2^-	$NaNO_2$	1.4998#
PO_4^{3-}	KH_2PO_4	1.4330
SO_4^{2-}	K_2SO_4	1.8141

f. Combined working standard solution, high range: Combine 10 mL of the Cl^-, NO_3^-, NO_2^-, and PO_4^{3-} standard anion solutions, 1 mL of the Br^-, and 100 mL of the SO_4^{2-} standard solutions, dilute to 1000 mL, and store in a plastic bottle protected from light; contains 10 mg/L each of Cl^-, NO_3^-, NO_2^-, and PO_4^{3-}, 1 mg Br^-/L, and 100 mg SO_4^{2-}/L. Prepare fresh daily.

g. Combined working standard solution, low range: Dilute 100 mL combined working standard solution, high range, to 1000 mL and store in a plastic bottle protected from light; contains 1.0 mg/L each Cl^-, NO_3^-, NO_2^-, and PO_4^{3-}, 0.1 mg Br^-/L, and 10 mg SO_4^{2-}/L. Prepare fresh daily.

h. Alternative combined working standard solutions: Prepare appropriate combinations according to anion concentration to be determined. If NO_2^- and PO_4^{3-} are not included, the combined working standard is stable for 1 month.

4. Procedure

a. System equilibration: Turn on ion chromatograph and adjust eluant flow rate to approximate the separation achieved in

‖ Expressed as compound.
Do not oven-dry, but dry to constant weight in a desiccator.

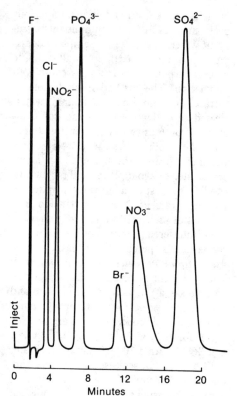

Figure 4110:1. **Typical inorganic anion separation using normal-run columns.** Conditions: 3mM $NaHCO_3$/2.4 mM Na_2CO_3 eluant; 2.0 mL/min flow.

Figures 4110:1 or 4110:2 (2 to 3 mL/min). Adjust detector to desired setting (usually 10 μS) and let system come to equilibrium (15 to 20 min). A stable base line indicates equilibrium conditions. Adjust detector offset to zero out eluant conductivity; with the fiber or membrane suppressor adjust the regeneration flow rate to maintain stability, usually 2.5 to 3 mL/min.

b. Calibration: Inject standards containing a single anion or a mixture and determine approximate retention times. Observed times vary with conditions but if standard eluant and anion separator column are used, retention always is in the order Cl^-, NO_2^-, HPO_4^{2-}, Br^-, NO_3^-, and SO_4^{2-}. Inject at least three different con-

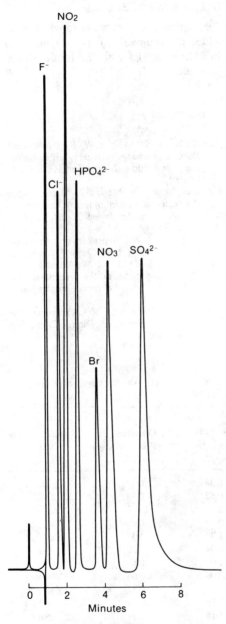

Figure 4110:2. Fast-run column separation. Conditions: 2.8 mM NaHCO$_3$/2.3 mM Na$_2$CO$_3$ eluant; 2.0 mL/min flow; 10-μL loop; 10 μS/cm full scale. Concentrations (mg/L): F$^-$, 3; Cl$^-$, 4; NO$_2^-$, 10; HPO$_4^{2-}$, 25; Br$^-$, 10; NO$_2^-$, 20; SO$_4^{2-}$, 25.

centrations for each anion to be measured and construct a calibration curve by plotting peak height or area against concentration on linear graph paper. Recalibrate whenever the detector setting is changed. With a system requiring suppressor regeneration, NO$_2^-$ interaction with the suppressor may lead to erroneous NO$_2^-$ results; make this determination only when the suppressor is at the same stage of exhaustion as during standardization or recalibrate frequently. In this type of system the water dip** may shift slightly during suppressor exhaustion and with a fast run column this may lead to slight interference for Cl$^-$. To eliminate this interference analyze standards that bracket the expected result or eliminate the water dip by diluting the sample with eluant or by adding concentrated eluant to the sample to give the same HCO$_3^-$/CO$_3^{2-}$ concentration as in the eluant. If sample adjustments are made, adjust standards and blanks identically.

If linearity is established for a given detector setting, single standard calibration is acceptable. Record peak height or area and retention time for calculation of the calibration factor, F. However, a calibration curve will result in better precision and bias.

c. Sample analysis: Remove sample particulates, if necessary, by filtering through a prewashed 0.2-μm-pore-diam membrane filter. Using a prewashed syringe of 1 to 10 mL capacity equipped with a male luer fitting inject sample or standard. Inject enough sample to flush sample loop several times: for 0.1 mL sample loop inject at least 1 mL. Switch ion chromatograph from load to inject mode and record peak heights and retention times on strip chart recorder. After the last peak (SO$_4^{2-}$) has appeared and the conductivity signal has returned to base line, another sample can be injected.

**Water dip occurs because water conductivity in sample is less than eluant conductivity (eluant is diluted by water).

d. Regeneration: For systems without fiber suppressor regenerate with $1N$ H_2SO_4 in accordance with the manufacturer's instructions when the conductivity base line exceeds 300 μS with the suppressor column on line.

5. Calculations

Calculate concentration of each anion, in milligrams per liter, by referring to the appropriate calibration curve. Alternatively, when the response is shown to be linear, use the following equation:

$$C = H \times F \times D$$

where:

C = mg anion/L,

H = peak height or area,

F = response factor = concentration of standard/height (or area) of standard, and

D = dilution factor for those samples requiring dilution.

6. Precision and Bias

Samples of reagent water to which were added the common anions were analyzed in 15 laboratories with the results shown in Table 4110:I.

7. Bibliography

SMALL, H., T. STEVENS & W. BAUMAN. 1975. Novel ion exchange chromatographic method using conductimetric detection. *Anal. Chem.* 47:1801.

FISHMAN, M. & G. S. PYEN. 1979. Determination of selected anions in water by ion chromatograph. Water Res. Invest. 79-101, U.S. Geological Survey.

JENKE, D. 1981. Anion peak migration in ion chromatography. *Anal. Chem.* 53:1536.

BYNUM, M.I., S. TYREE & W. WEISER. 1981. Effect of major ions on the determination of trace ions by ion chromatography. *Anal. Chem.* 53:1935.

WEISS, J. 1986. Handbook of Ion Chromatography. E. L. Johnson, ed. Dionex Corp., Sunnyvale, Calif.

TABLE 4110:I. PRECISION AND BIAS OBSERVED FOR ANIONS AT VARIOUS CONCENTRATION LEVELS IN REAGENT WATER*

Anion	Amount Added mg/L	Amount Found mg/L	Overall Precision mg/L	Single-Operator Precision mg/L	Significant Bias 95% Level
Cl^-	0.76	0.86	0.38	0.11	No
Cl^-	17	17.2	0.82	0.43	No
Cl^-	455	471	46	13	No
NO_2^-	0.45	0.09	0.09	0.04	Yes, neg
NO_2^-	21.8	19.4	1.9	1.3	Yes, neg
Br^-	0.25	0.25	0.04	0.02	No
Br^-	13.7	12.9	1.0	0.6	No
PO_4^{3-}	0.18	0.10	0.06	0.03	Yes, neg
PO_4^{3-}	0.49	0.34	0.15	0.17	Yes, neg
NO_3^-	0.50	0.33	0.16	0.03	No
NO_3^-	15.1	14.8	1.15	0.9	No
SO_4^{2-}	0.51	0.52	0.07	0.03	No
SO_4^{2-}	43.7	43.5	2.5	2.2	No

*Adopted, with permission, from the Annual Book of ASTM Standards. Part 31. Copyright: ASTM, 1916 Race Street, Philadelphia, Pa. 19103.

†These results were obtained with packed-column suppressors.

4500-CO$_2$ CARBON DIOXIDE*

4500-CO$_2$ A.   Introduction

1. Occurrence and Significance

Surface waters normally contain less than 10 mg free carbon dioxide (CO$_2$) per liter while some groundwaters may easily exceed that concentration. The CO$_2$ content of a water may contribute significantly to corrosion. Recarbonation of a supply during the last stages of water softening is a recognized treatment process. The subject of saturation with respect to calcium carbonate is discussed in Section 2330.

2. Selection of Method

A nomographic and a titrimetric method are described for the estimation of free CO$_2$ in drinking water. The titration may be performed potentiometrically or with phenolphthalein indicator. Properly conducted, the more rapid, simple indicator method is satisfactory for field tests and for control and routine applications if it is understood that the method gives, at best, only an approximation.

*Approved by Standard Methods Committee, 1985.

The nomographic method (B) usually gives a closer estimation of the total free CO$_2$ when the pH and alkalinity determinations are made immediately and correctly at the time of sampling. The pH measurement preferably should be made with an electrometric pH meter, properly calibrated with standard buffer solutions in the pH range of 7 to 8. The error resulting from inaccurate pH measurements grows with an increase in total alkalinity. For example, an inaccuracy of 0.1 in the pH determination causes a CO$_2$ error of 2 to 4 mg/L in the pH range of 7.0 to 7.3 and a total alkalinity of 100 mg CaCO$_3$/L. In the same pH range, the error approaches 10 to 15 mg/L when the total alkalinity is 400 mg as CaCO$_3$/L.

Under favorable conditions, agreement between the titrimetric and nomographic methods is reasonably good. When agreement is not precise and the CO$_2$ determination is of particular importance, state the method used.

The calculation of the total CO$_2$, free and combined, is given in Method D.

4500-CO$_2$ B.   Nomographic Determination of Free Carbon Dioxide and the Three Forms of Alkalinity*

1. General Discussion

Diagrams and nomographs enable the rapid calculation of the CO$_2$, bicarbonate, carbonate, and hydroxide content of natural and treated waters. These graphical

*See also Alkalinity, Section 2320.

presentations are based on equations relating the ionization equilibria of the carbonates and water. If pH, total alkalinity, temperature, and total mineral content are known, any or all of the alkalinity forms and CO$_2$ can be determined nomographically.

A set of charts, Figures 4500-CO$_2$:1-4,† is presented for use where their accuracy for the individual water supply is confirmed. The nomographs and the equations on which they are based are valid only when the salts of weak acids other than carbonic acid are absent or present in extremely small amounts.

Some treatment processes, such as superchlorination and coagulation, can affect significantly pH and total-alkalinity values of a poorly buffered water of low alkalinity and low total-dissolved-mineral content. In such instances the nomographs may not be applicable.

†Copies of the nomographs in Figures 4500-CO$_2$:1-4, enlarged to 2.5 times the size shown here, may be purchased as a set from The American Water Works Association, 6666 West Quincy Ave., Denver, Colorado 80235. Cat. No. 50007.

2. Precision and Bias

The precision possible with the nomographs depends on the size and range of the scales. With practice, the recommended nomographs can be read with a precision of 1%. However, the overall bias of the results depends on the bias of the analytical data applied to the nomographs and the validity of the theoretical equations and the numerical constants on which the nomographs are based. An approximate check of the bias of the calculations can be made by summing the three forms of alkalinity. Their sum should equal the total alkalinity.

3. Bibliography

MOORE, E.W. 1939. Graphic determination of carbon dioxide and the three forms of alkalinity. *J. Amer. Water Works Assoc.* 31:51.

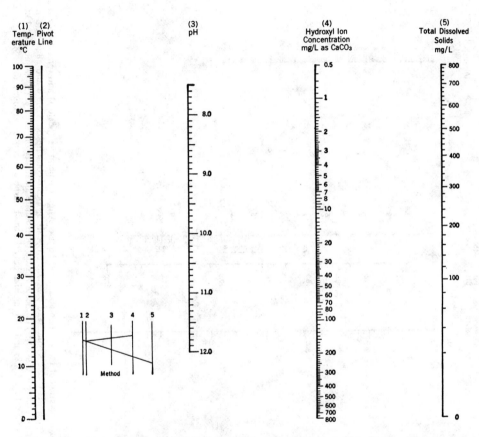

Figure 4500-CO₂:1. Nomograph for evaluation of hydroxide ion concentration. To use: Align temperature (Scale 1) and total dissolved solids (Scale 5); pivot on Line 2 to proper pH
(Scale 3); read hydroxide ion concentration, as mg CaCO₃/L, on Scale 4. (Example:
For 13°C temperature, 240 mg total dissolved solids/L, pH 9.8, the hydroxide ion
concentration is found to be 1.4 mg as CaCO₃/L.)

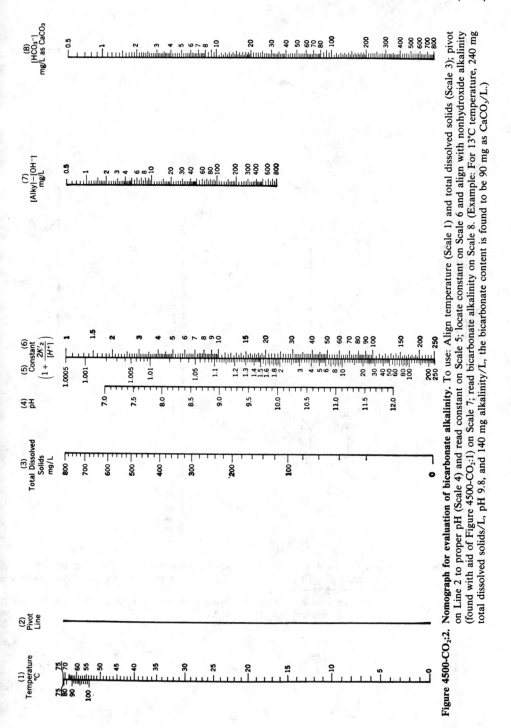

Figure 4500-CO₂:2. Nomograph for evaluation of bicarbonate alkalinity. To use: Align temperature (Scale 1) and total dissolved solids (Scale 3); pivot on Line 2 to proper pH (Scale 4) and read constant on Scale 5; locate constant on Scale 6 and align with nonhydroxide alkalinity (found with aid of Figure 4500-CO₂:1) on Scale 7; read bicarbonate alkalinity on Scale 8. (Example: For 13°C temperature, 240 mg total dissolved solids/L, pH 9.8, and 140 mg alkalinity/L, the bicarbonate content is found to be 90 mg as CaCO₃/L.)

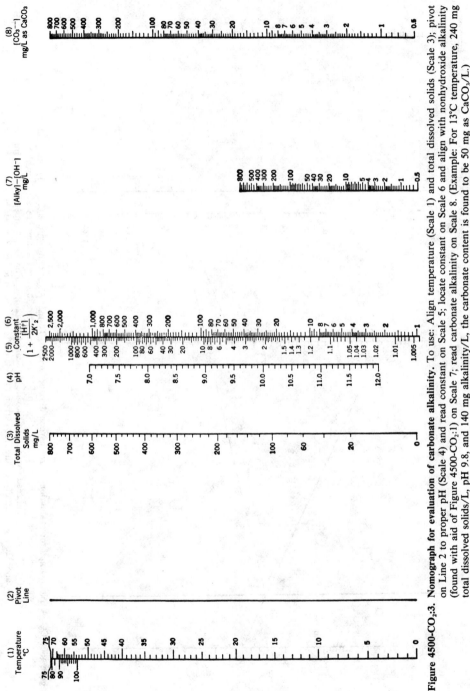

Figure 4500-CO₂:3. Nomograph for evaluation of carbonate alkalinity. To use: Align temperature (Scale 1) and total dissolved solids (Scale 3); pivot on Line 2 to proper pH (Scale 4) and read constant on Scale 5; locate constant on Scale 6 and align with nonhydroxide alkalinity (found with aid of Figure 4500-CO₂:1) on Scale 7; read carbonate alkalinity on Scale 8. (Example: For 13°C temperature, 240 mg total dissolved solids/L, pH 9.8, and 140 mg alkalinity/L, the carbonate content is found to be 50 mg as CaCO₃/L.)

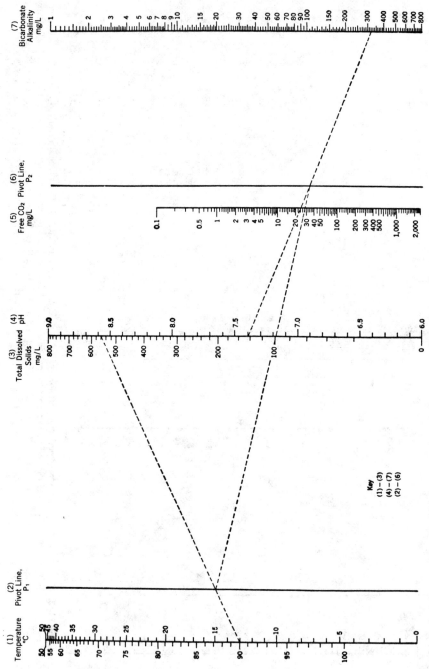

Figure 4500-CO₂:4. Nomograph for evaluation of free carbon dioxide content. To use: Align temperature (Scale 1) and total dissolved solids (Scale 3), which determines Point P_1 on Line 2; align pH (Scale 4) and bicarbonate alkalinity (Scale 7), which determines Points P_2 on Line 6; align P_1 and P_2 and read free carbon dioxide on Scale 5. (Example: For 13°C temperature, 560 mg total dissolved solids/L, pH 7.4, and 320 mg alkalinity/L, the free carbon dioxide content is found to be 28 mg/L.)

4500-CO$_2$ C. Titrimetric Method for Free Carbon Dioxide

1. General Discussion

a. Principle: Free CO$_2$ reacts with sodium carbonate or sodium hydroxide to form sodium bicarbonate. Completion of the reaction is indicated potentiometrically or by the development of the pink color characteristic of phenolphthalein indicator at the equivalence pH of 8.3. A 0.01N sodium bicarbonate (NaHCO$_3$) solution containing the recommended volume of phenolphthalein indicator is a suitable color standard until familiarity is obtained with the color at the end point.

b. Interference: Cations and anions that quantitatively disturb the normal CO$_2$-carbonate equilibrium interfere with the determination. Metal ions that precipitate in alkaline solution, such as aluminum, chromium, copper, and iron, contribute to high results. Ferrous ion should not exceed 1.0 mg/L. Positive errors also are caused by weak bases, such as ammonia or amines, and by salts of weak acids and strong bases, such as borate, nitrite, phosphate, silicate, and sulfide. Such substances should not exceed 5% of the CO$_2$ concentration. The titrimetric method for CO$_2$ is inapplicable to samples containing acid mine wastes and effluent from acid-regenerated cation exchangers. Negative errors may be introduced by high total dissolved solids, such as those encountered in seawater, or by addition of excess indicator.

c. Sampling and storage: Even with a careful collection technique, some loss in free CO$_2$ can be expected in storage and transit. This occurs more frequently when the gas is present in large amounts. Occasionally a sample may show an increase in free CO$_2$ content on standing. Consequently, determine free CO$_2$ immediately at the point of sampling. Where a field determination is impractical, fill completely a bottle for laboratory examination. Keep the sample, until tested, at a temperature lower than that at which the water was collected. Make the laboratory examination as soon as possible to minimize the effect of CO$_2$ changes.

2. Apparatus

See Section 2310B.2.

3. Reagents

See Section 2310B.3.

4. Procedure

Follow the procedure given in Section 2310B.4b, phenolphthalein, or 2310B.4d, using end-point pH 8.3.

5. Calculation

$$mg\ CO_2/L = \frac{A \times N \times 44\,000}{mL\ sample}$$

where:
  A = mL titrant and
  N = normality of NaOH.

6. Precision and Bias

Precision and bias of the titrimetric method are on the order of $\pm 10\%$ of the known CO$_2$ concentration.

4500-CO$_2$ D. Carbon Dioxide and Forms of Alkalinity by Calculation

1. General Discussion

When the total alkalinity of a water (Section 2320) is due almost entirely to hydroxides, carbonates, or bicarbonates, and the total dissolved solids (Section 2540) is not greater than 500 mg/L, the alkalinity forms and free CO$_2$ can be calculated from the sample pH and total alkalinity. The calculation is subject to the same limitations as the nomographic procedure given above and the additional restriction of using a single temperature, 25°C. The calculations are based on the ionization constants:

$$K_1 = \frac{[H^+][HCO_3^-]}{[H_2CO_3^*]} \quad (K_1 = 10^{-6.36})$$

and

$$K_2 = \frac{[H^+][CO_3^{2-}]}{[HCO_3^-]} \quad (K_2 = 10^{-10.33})$$

where:

$$[H_2CO_3^*] = [H_2CO_3] + [CO_2(aq)]$$

Activity coefficients are assumed equal to unity.

2. Calculation

Compute the forms of alkalinity and sample pH and total alkalinity using the following equations:

a. *Bicarbonate alkalinity:*

HCO_3^- as mg $CaCO_3/L$

$$= \frac{T - 5.0 \times 10^{(pH-10)}}{1 + 0.94 \times 10^{(pH-10)}}$$

where:

T = total alkalinity, mg $CaCO_3/L$.

b. *Carbonate alkalinity:*

CO_3^{2-} as mg $CaCO_3/L$
$$= 0.94 \times B \times 10^{(pH-10)}$$

where:

B = bicarbonate alkalinity, from a.

c. *Hydroxide alkalinity:*

OH^- as mg $CaCO_3/L = 5.0 \times 10^{(pH-10)}$

d. *Free carbon dioxide:*

mg $CO_2/L = 2.0 \times B \times 10^{(6-pH)}$

where:

B = bicarbonate alkalinity, from a.

e. *Total carbon dioxide:*

mg total $CO_2/L = A + 0.44 (2B + C)$

where:

A = mg free CO_2/L,
B = bicarbonate alkalinity from a, and
C = carbonate alkalinity from b.

3. Bibliography

DYE, J.F. 1958. Correlation of the two principal methods of calculating the three kinds of alkalinity. *J. Amer. Water Works Assoc.* 50:812.

4500-CN   CYANIDE*

4500-CN A.   Introduction

1. General Discussion

"Cyanide" refers to all of the CN groups in cyanide compounds that can be determined as the cyanide ion, CN^-, by the methods used. The cyanide compounds in which cyanide can be obtained as CN^- are classed as simple and complex cyanides.

Simple cyanides are represented by the formula $A(CN)_x$, where A is an alkali (sodium, potassium, ammonium) or a metal, and x, the valence of A, is the number of CN groups. In aqueous solutions of simple alkali cyanides, the CN group is present as

CN^- and molecular HCN, the ratio depending on pH and the dissociation constant for molecular HCN (p$K_a \simeq 9.2$). In most natural waters HCN greatly predominates.[1] In solutions of simple metal cyanides, the CN group may occur also in the form of complex metal-cyanide anions of varying stability. Many simple metal cyanides are sparingly soluble or almost insoluble [$CuCN$, $AgCN$, $Zn(CN)_2$], but they form a variety of highly soluble, complex metal cyanides in the presence of alkali cyanides.

Complex cyanides have a variety of formulae, but the alkali-metallic cyanides normally can be represented by $A_yM(CN)_x$. In

*Approved by Standard Methods Committee, 1985.

this formula, A represents the alkali present y times, M the heavy metal (ferrous and ferric iron, cadmium, copper, nickel, silver, zinc, or others), and x the number of CN groups; x is equal to the valence of A taken y times plus that of the heavy metal. Initial dissociation of each of these soluble, alkali-metallic, complex cyanides yields an anion that is the radical $M(CN)_x^{y-}$. This may dissociate further, depending on several factors, with the liberation of CN^- and consequent formation of HCN.

The great toxicity to aquatic life of molecular HCN is well known;[2-5] it is formed in solutions of cyanide by hydrolytic reaction of CN^- with water. The toxicity of CN^- is less than that of HCN; it usually is unimportant because most of the free cyanide (CN group present as CN^- or as HCN) exists as HCN,[2,5] as the pH of most natural waters is substantially lower than the pK_a for molecular HCN. The toxicity to fish of most tested solutions of complex cyanides is attributable mainly to the HCN resulting from dissociation of the complexes.[2,4,5] Analytical distinction between HCN and other cyanide species in solutions of complex cyanides is possible.[2,5-9,10]

The degree of dissociation of the various metallocyanide complexes at equilibrium, which may not be attained for a long time, increases with decreased concentration and decreased pH, and is inversely related to their highly variable stability.[2,4,5] The zinc- and cadmium-cyanide complexes are dissociated almost totally in very dilute solutions; thus these complexes can result in acute toxicity to fish at any ordinary pH. In equally dilute solutions there is much less dissociation for the nickel-cyanide complex and the more stable cyanide complexes formed with copper (I) and silver. Acute toxicity to fish of dilute solutions containing copper-cyanide or silver-cyanide complex anions can be due mainly or entirely to the toxicity of the undissociated ions, although the complex ions are much less toxic than HCN.[2,5]

The iron-cyanide complex ions are very stable and not materially toxic; in the dark, acutely toxic levels of HCN are attained only in solutions that are not very dilute and have been aged for a long time. However, these complexes are subject to extensive and rapid photolysis, yielding toxic HCN, on exposure of dilute solutions to direct sunlight.[2,11] The photodecomposition depends on exposure to ultraviolet radiation, and therefore is slow in deep, turbid, or shaded receiving waters. Loss of HCN to the atmosphere and its bacterial and chemical destruction concurrent with its production tend to prevent increases of HCN concentrations to harmful levels. Regulatory distinction between cyanide complexed with iron and that bound in less stable complexes, as well as between the complexed cyanide and free cyanide or HCN, can, therefore, be justified.

Historically, the generally accepted physicochemical technique for industrial waste treatment of cyanide compounds is alkaline chlorination:

$$NaCN + Cl_2 \rightarrow CNCl + NaCl \qquad (1)$$

The first reaction product on chlorination is cyanogen chloride (CNCl), a highly toxic gas of limited solubility. The toxicity of CNCl may exceed that of equal concentrations of cyanide.[2,3,12] At an alkaline pH, CNCl hydrolyzes to the cyanate ion (CNO^-), which has only limited toxicity.

There is no known natural reduction reaction that may convert CNO^- to CN^-.[13] On the other hand, breakdown of toxic CNCl is pH- and time-dependent. At pH 9, with no excess chlorine present, CNCl may persist for 24 h.[14,15]

$$CNCl + 2NaOH \rightarrow NaCNO \\ + NaCl + H_2O \qquad (2)$$

CNO^- can be oxidized further with chlorine at a nearly neutral pH to CO_2 and N_2:

$$2NaCNO + 4NaOH + 3Cl_2 \rightarrow 6NaCl$$
$$+ 2CO_2 + N_2 + 2H_2O \quad (3)$$

CNO^- also will be converted on acidification to NH_4^+:

$$2NaCNO + H_2SO_4$$
$$+ 4H_2O \rightarrow (NH_4)_2SO_4 + 2NaHCO_3 \quad (4)$$

The alkaline chlorination of cyanide compounds is relatively fast, but depends equally on the dissociation constant, which also governs toxicity. Metal cyanide complexes, such as nickel, cobalt, silver, and gold, do not dissociate readily. The chlorination reaction therefore requires more time and a significant chlorine excess.[16] Iron cyanides, because they do not dissociate to any degree, are not oxidized by chlorination. There is correlation between the refractory properties of the noted complexes, in their resistance to chlorination and lack of toxicity.

Thus, it is advantageous to differentiate between *total cyanide* and *cyanides amenable to chlorination*. When total cyanide is determined, the almost nondissociable cyanides, as well as cyanide bound in complexes that are readily dissociable and complexes of intermediate stability, are measured. Cyanide compounds that are amenable to chlorination include free cyanide as well as those complex cyanides that are potentially dissociable, almost wholly or in large degree, and therefore, potentially toxic at low concentrations, even in the dark. The chlorination test procedure is carried out under rigorous conditions appropriate for measurement of the more dissociable forms of cyanide.

Alternatively, the free and potentially dissociable cyanides also may be estimated when using the *weak acid dissociable* procedure. These methods depend on a rigorous distillation, but the solution is only slightly acidified, and elimination of iron cyanides is insured by the earlier addition of precipitation chemicals to the distillation

flask or by the avoidance of ultraviolet irradiation.

The *cyanogen chloride* procedure is common with the colorimetric test for cyanides amenable to chlorination. This test is based on the addition of chloramine-T and subsequent color complex formation with barbituric acid. Without the addition of chloramine-T, only existing CNCl is measured. CNCl is a gas that hydrolyzes to CNO^-; sample preservation is not possible. Because of this, spot testing of CNCl levels may be best. This procedure can be adapted and used when the sample is collected.

There may be analytical requirements for the determination of CNO^-, even though the reported toxicity level is low. On acidification, CNO^- decomposes to ammonia (NH_3).[3] Molecular ammonia and metal-ammonia complexes are highly toxic.[17]

Thiocyanate (SCN^-) is not very toxic to aquatic life.[2] However, upon chlorination, toxic CNCl is formed, as discussed above.[2,3,12] At least where subsequent chlorination is anticipated, the determination of SCN^- is desirable. Thiocyanate is biodegradable; ammonium is released in this reaction. Thiocyanate may be analyzed in samples properly preserved for determination of cyanide; however, thiocyanate also can be preserved in samples by acidification with H_2SO_4 to pH ≤ 2.

2. Cyanide in Solid Waste

a. Soluble cyanide: Determination of soluble cyanide requires sample leaching with distilled water until solubility equilibrium is established. One hour of stirring in distilled water should be satisfactory. Cyanide analysis is then performed on the leachate. Low cyanide concentration in the leachate may indicate presence of sparingly soluble metal cyanides. The cyanide content of the leachate is indicative of residual solubility of insoluble metal cyanides in the waste. High levels of cyanide in the leachate indicate soluble cyanide in the solid waste. When 500 mL distilled water are stirred into a 500-mg solid waste sample, the cyanide concentration (mg/L) of the leachate multiplied by 1000 will give the solubility level of the cyanide in the solid waste in milligrams per kilogram. The leachate may be analyzed for total cyanide and/or cyanide amenable to chlorination.

b. Insoluble cyanide: The insoluble cyanide of the solid waste can be determined with the total cyanide method by placing a 500-mg sample with 500 mL distilled water in the distillation flask and in general following the distillation procedure (Section 4500-CN.C). In calculating, multiply by 1000 to give the cyanide content of the solid sample in milligrams per kilogram. Insoluble iron cyanides in the solid can be leached out earlier by stirring a weighed sample for 12 to 16 h in a 10% NaOH solution. The leachate and wash waters of the solid waste will give the iron cyanide content with the distillation procedure. Prechlorination will have eliminated all cyanide amenable to chlorination. Do not expose sample to sunlight.

3. Selection of Method

a. Total cyanide after distillation: After removal of interfering substances, the metal cyanide is converted to HCN gas, which is distilled and absorbed in sodium hydroxide (NaOH) solution.[18] Because of the catalytic decomposition of cyanide in the presence of cobalt at high temperature in a strong acid solution,[19,20] cobalticyanide is not recovered completely. Indications are that cyanide complexes of the noble metals, i.e., gold, platinum, and palladium, are not recovered fully by this procedure either. Distillation also separates cyanide from other color-producing and possibly interfering organic or inorganic contaminants. Subsequent analysis is for the simple salt, sodium cyanide (NaCN). Some organic cyanide compounds, such as nitriles, are decomposed by the distillation. Aldehydes convert cyanide to nitrile. The absorption liquid is analyzed by either a titrimetric, colorimetric, or cyanide-ion-selective electrode procedure:

1) The titration method (D) is suitable for cyanide concentrations above 1 mg/L.

2) The colorimetric method (E) is suitable for cyanide concentrations to a lower limit of 20 μg/L. Analyze higher concentrations by diluting either the sample before distillation or the absorber solution before colorimetric measurement.

3) The ion-selective electrode method (F) using the cyanide ion electrode is applicable in the concentration range of 0.05 to 10 mg/L.

b. Cyanide amenable to chlorination:

1) Distillation of two samples is required, one that has been chlorinated to destroy all amenable cyanide present and the other unchlorinated. Analyze absorption liquids from both tests for total cyanide. The observed difference equals cyanides amenable to chlorination.

2) The colorimetric method, by conversion of amenable cyanide and SCN$^-$ to CNCl and developing the color complex with barbituric acid, is used for the determination of the total of these cyanides (H). Repeating the test with the cyanide masked by the addition of formaldehyde provides a measure of the SCN$^-$ content. When subtracted from the earlier results this provides an estimate of the amenable CN$^-$ content. This method is useful for natural and ground waters and clean metal finishing, heat treating, and sanitary effluents.

3) The *weak acid dissociable cyanides* procedure also measures the cyanide amenable to chlorination by freeing HCN from the dissociable cyanide. After being collected in a NaOH absorption solution, HCN may be determined by one of the three finishing procedures given for the total cyanide determination.

It should be noted that although cyanide amenable to chlorination and weak acid dissociable cyanide appear to be identical, certain industrial effluents (e.g., pulp and paper, petroleum refining industry effluents) contain some poorly understood substances that may produce interference. Application of the procedure for cyanide amenable to chlorination yields negative values. For natural waters and metal-finishing effluents, the direct colorimetric determination appears to be the simplest and most economical.

c. Cyanogen chloride: The colorimetric method for measuring cyanide amenable to chlorination may be used, but omit the chloramine-T addition. The spot test also may be used.

d. Spot test for sample screening: This procedure allows a quick sample screening to establish whether more than 50 µg/L cyanide amenable to chlorination is present. The test also may be used to estimate the CNCl content at the time of sampling.

e. Cyanate: CNO^- is converted to ammonium carbonate, $(NH_4)_2CO_3$, by acid hydrolysis at elevated temperature. Ammonia (NH_3) is determined before the conversion of the CNO^- and again afterwards. The CNO^- is estimated from the difference in NH_3 found in the two tests.[21-23] Measure NH_3 by either:

1) The selective electrode method, using the NH_3 gas electrode; or

2) The colorimetric method, using direct nesslerization or the phenate method for NH_3 (Section 4500-NH_3.C or D).

f. Thiocyanate: Use the colorimetric determination with ferric nitrate as a color-producing compound.

4. References

1. MILNE, D. 1950. Equilibria in dilute cyanide waste solutions. *Sewage Ind. Wastes* 23:904.
2. DOUDOROFF, P. 1976. Toxicity to fish of cyanides and related compounds. A review. EPA 600/3-76-038, U.S. Environmental Protection Agency, Duluth, Minn.
3. DOUDOROFF, P. & M. KATZ. 1950. Critical review of literature on the toxicity of industrial

wastes and their components to fish. *Sewage Ind. Wastes* 22:1432.
4. DOUDOROFF, P. 1956. Some experiments on the toxicity of complex cyanides to fish. *Sewage Ind. Wastes* 28:1020.
5. DOUDOROFF, P., G. LEDUC & C.R. SCHNEIDER. 1966. Acute toxicity to fish of solutions containing complex metal cyanides, in relation to concentrations of molecular hydrocyanic acid. *Trans. Amer. Fish. Soc.* 95:6.
6. SCHNEIDER, C.R. & H. FREUND. 1962. Determination of low level hydrocyanic acid. *Anal. Chem.* 34:69.
7. CLAEYS, R. & H. FREUND. 1968. Gas chromatographic separation of HCN. *Environ. Sci. Technol.* 2:458.
8. MONTGOMERY, H.A.C., D.K. GARDINER & J.G. GREGORY. 1969. Determination of free hydrogen cyanide in river water by a solvent-extraction method. *Analyst* 94:284.
9. NELSON, K.H. & L. LYSYJ. 1971. Analysis of water for molecular hydrogen cyanide. *J. Water Pollut. Control Fed.* 43:799.
10. BRODERIUS, S.J. Determination of hydrocyanic acid and free cyanide in aqueous solution. *Anal. Chem.* 53:1472.
11. BURDICK, G.E. & M. LIPSCHUETZ. 1948. Toxicity of ferro and ferricyanide solutions to fish. *Trans. Amer. Fish. Soc.* 78:192.
12. ZILLICH, J.A. 1972. Toxicity of combined chlorine residuals to freshwater fish. *J. Water Pollut. Control Fed.* 44:212.
13. RESNICK, J.D., W. MOORE & M.E. ETTINGER. 1958. The behavior of cyanates in polluted waters. *Ind. Eng. Chem.* 50:71.
14. PETTET, A.E.J. & G.C. WARE. 1955. Disposal of cyanide wastes. *Chem. Ind.* 1955:1232.
15. BAILEY, P.L. & E. BISHOP. 1972. Hydrolysis of cyanogen chloride. *Analyst* 97:691.
16. LANCY, L. & W. ZABBAN. 1962. Analytical methods and instrumentation for determining cyanogen compounds. Spec. Tech. Publ. 337, American Soc. Testing & Materials, Philadelphia, Pa.
17. CALAMARI, D. & R. MARCHETTI. 1975. Predicted and observed acute toxicity of copper and ammonia to rainbow trout. *Progr. Water Technol.* 7, 3-4:569.
18. SERFASS, E.J. & R.B. FREEMAN. 1952. Analytical method for the determination of cyanides in plating wastes and in effluents from treatment processes. *Plating* 39:267.

19. LESCHBER, R. & H. SCHLICHTING. 1969. Über die Zersetzlichkeit Komplexer Metall-cyanide bei der Cyanidbestimmung in Abwasser. *Z. Anal. Chem.* 245:300.

20. BASSETT, H., JR. & A.S. CORBET. 1924. The hydrolysis of potassium ferricyanide and potassium cobalticyanide by sulfuric acid. *J. Chem. Soc.* 125:1358.

21. DODGE, B.F. & W. ZABBAN. 1952. Analytical methods for the determination of cyanates in plating wastes. *Plating* 39:381.

22. GARDNER, D.C. 1956. The colorimetric determination of cyanates in effuents. *Plating* 43:743.

23. Procedures for Analyzing Metal Finishing Wastes. 1954. Ohio River Valley Sanitation Commission, Cincinnati, Ohio.

4500-CN B.   Preliminary Treatment of Samples

CAUTION—*Use care in manipulating cyanide-containing samples because of toxicity. Process in a hood or other well-ventilated area. Avoid contact, inhalation, or ingestion.*

1. General Discussion

The nature of the preliminary treatment will vary according to the interfering substance present. Sulfides, fatty acids, and oxidizing agents are removed by special procedures. Most other interfering substances are removed by distillation. The importance of the distillation procedure cannot be overemphasized.

2. Preservation of Samples

Oxidizing agents, such as chlorine, decompose most cyanides. Test by placing a drop of sample on a strip of potassium iodide (KI)-starch paper previously moistened with acetate buffer solution, pH 4 (Section 4500-Cl.C.3e). If a bluish discoloration is noted, add 0.1 g sodium arsenite (NaAsO$_2$)/L sample and retest. Repeat addition if necessary. Sodium thiosulfate also may be used, but avoid an excess greater than 0.1 g Na$_2$S$_2$O$_3$/L. Manganese dioxide, nitrosyl chloride, etc., if present, also may cause discoloration of the test paper. If possible, carry out this procedure before preserving sample as described below. If the following test indicates presence of sulfide, oxidizing compounds would not be expected.

Oxidized products of sulfide convert CN$^-$ to SCN$^-$ rapidly, especially at high pH.[1] Test for S^{2-} by placing a drop of sample on lead acetate test paper previously moistened with acetic acid buffer solution, pH 4 (Section 4500-Cl.C.3e). Darkening of the paper indicates presence of S^{2-}. Add lead acetate, or if the S^{2-} concentration is too high, add powdered lead carbonate [Pb(CO$_3$)$_2$] to avoid significantly reducing pH. Repeat test until a drop of treated sample no longer darkens the acidified lead acetate test paper. Filter sample before raising pH for stabilization. When particulate, metal cyanide complexes are suspected filter solution before removing S^{2-}. Reconstitute sample by returning filtered particulates to the sample bottle after S^{2-} removal. Homogenize particulates before analyses.

Aldehydes convert cyanide to cyanohydrin. Longer contact times between cyanide and the aldehyde and the higher ratios of aldehyde to cyanide both result in increasing losses of cyanide that are not reversible during analysis. If the presence of aldehydes is suspected, stabilize with NaOH at time of collection and add 2 mL 3.5% ethylenediamine solution per 100 mL of sample.

Because most cyanides are very reactive and unstable, analyze samples as soon as possible. If sample cannot be analyzed immediately, add NaOH pellets or a strong

NaOH solution to raise sample pH to 12 to 12.5 and store in a closed, dark bottle in a cool place.

To analyze for CNCl collect a separate sample and omit NaOH addition because CNCl is converted rapidly to CNO^- at high pH. Make colorimetric estimation immediately after sampling.

3. Interferences

a. Oxidizing agents may destroy most of the cyanide during storage and manipulation. Add $NaAsO_2$ or $Na_2S_2O_3$ as directed above; avoid excess $Na_2S_2O_3$.

b. Sulfide will distill over with cyanide and, therefore, adversely affect colorimetric, titrimetric, and electrode procedures. Test for and remove S^{2-} as directed above. Treat 25 mL more than required for the distillation to provide sufficient filtrate volume.

c. Fatty acids that distill and form soaps under alkaline titration conditions make the end point almost impossible to detect. Remove fatty acids by extraction.[2] Acidify sample with acetic acid (1 + 9) to pH 6.0 to 7.0. (CAUTION—*Perform this operation in a hood as quickly as possible*). Immediately extract with iso-octane, hexane, or $CHCl_3$ (preference in order named). Use a solvent volume equal to 20% of sample volume. One extraction usually is adequate to reduce fatty acid concentration below the interference level. Avoid multiple extractions or a long contact time at low pH to minimize loss of HCN. When extraction is completed, immediately raise pH to > 12 with NaOH solution.

d. Carbonate in high concentration may affect distillation by causing excessive gassing when acid is added. The carbon dioxide (CO_2) released also may reduce significantly the NaOH content in the absorber.

When sampling effluents such as coal gasification wastes, atmospheric emission scrub waters, and other high-carbonate wastes, use hydrated lime to stabilize the sample; slowly add with stirring to raise pH to 12 to 12.5. Decant sample into sample bottle after precipitate has settled.

e. Other possible interferences include substances that might contribute color or turbidity. In most cases, distillation will remove these.

Note, however, that distillation requires using sulfuric acid with various reagents. With certain wastes, these conditions may result in reactions that otherwise would not occur in the aqueous sample. As a quality control measure, periodically conduct addition and recovery tests with industrial waste samples.

f. Aldehydes convert cyanide to cyanohydrin, which forms nitrile under the distillation conditions. Only direct titration without distillation can be used, which reveals only non-complex cyanides. Formaldehyde interference is noticeable in concentrations exceeding 0.5 mg/L. Use the following spot test to establish absence or presence of aldehydes (detection limit 0.05 mg/L):[3-5]

1) Reagents

a) *MBTH indicator solution:* Dissolve 0.05 g 3-methyl, 2-benzothiazolone hydrazone hydrochloride in 100 mL water. Filter if turbid.

b) *Ferric chloride oxidizing solution:* Dissolve 1.6 g sulfamic acid and 1 g $FeCl_3 \cdot 6H_2O$ in 100 mL water.

c) *Ethylenediamine solution,* 3.5%: Dilute 3.5 mL pharmaceutical-grade anhydrous $NH_2CH_2CH_2NH_2$ to 100 mL with water.

2) Procedure—If the sample is alkaline, add 1 + 1 H_2SO_4 to 10 mL sample to adjust pH to less than 8. Place 1 drop of sample and 1 drop distilled water for a blank in separate cavities of a white spot plate. Add 1 drop MBTH solution and then 1 drop $FeCl_3$ oxidizing solution to each spot. Allow 10 min for color development. The color change will be from a faint green-yellow to a deeper green with blue-green

to blue at higher concentrations of aldehyde. The blank should remain yellow.

To minimize aldehyde interference, add 2 mL of 3.5% ethylenediamine solution/ 100 mL sample. This quantity overcomes the interference caused by up to 50 mg/L formaldehyde.

When using a known addition in testing, 100% recovery of the CN^- is not necessarily to be expected. Recovery depends on the aldehyde excess, time of contact, and sample temperature.

g. Glucose and other sugars, especially at the pH of preservation, lead to cyanohydrin formation by reaction of cyanide with aldose.[6] Reduce cyanohydrin to cyanide with ethylene diamine (see *f* above). MBTH is not applicable.

h. Nitrite may form HCN during distillation in Methods C, G, and L, by reacting with organic compounds.[7,8] Also, NO_3^- may reduce to NO_2^-, which interferes. To avoid NO_2^- interference, add 2 g sulfamic acid to the sample before distillation. *Nitrate* also may interfere by reacting with SCN^-.[9]

i. Some sulfur compounds may decompose during distillation, releasing S, H_2S, or SO_2. Sulfur compounds may convert cyanide to thiocyanate and also may interfere with the analytical procedures for CN^-. To avoid this potential interference, add 50 mg $PbCO_3$ to the absorption solution before distillation. Filter sample before proceeding with the colorimetric or titrimetric determination.

Absorbed SO_2 forms Na_2SO_3 which consumes chloramine-T added in the colorimetric determination. The volume of chloramine-T added is sufficient to overcome 100 to 200 mg SO_3^{2-}/L. Test for presence of chloramine-T after adding it by placing a drop of sample on KI-starch test paper; add more chloramine-T if the test paper remains blank, or use Method F.

Some wastewaters, such as those from coal gasification or chemical extraction mining, contain high concentrations of sulfites. Pretreat sample to avoid overloading the absorption solution with SO_3^{2-}. Titrate a suitable sample iodometrically (Section 4500-O) with dropwise addition of 30% H_2O_2 solution to determine volume of H_2O_2 needed for the 500 mL distillation sample. Subsequently, add H_2O_2 dropwise while stirring, but in only such volume that not more than 300 to 400 mg SO_3^{2-}/L will remain. Adding a lesser quantity than calculated is required to avoid oxidizing any CN^- that may be present.

4. References

1. LUTHY, R.G. & S. G. BRUCE, JR. 1979. Kinetics of reaction of cyanide and reduced sulfur species in aqueous solution. *Environ. Sci. Technol.* 13:1481.

2. KRUSE, J.M. & M.G. MELLON. 1951. Colorimetric determination of cyanides. *Sewage Ind. Wastes* 23:1402.

3. SAWICKI, E., T.W. STANLEY, T.R. HAUSER & W. ELBERT. 1961. The 3-methyl-2-benzothiazolone hydrazone test. Sensitive new methods for the detection, rapid estimation, and determination of aliphatic aldehydes. *Anal. Chem.* 33:93.

4. HAUSER, T.R. & R.L. CUMMINS. 1964. Increasing sensitivity of 3-methyl-2-benzothiazone hydrazone test for analysis of aliphatic aldehydes in air. *Anal. Chem.* 36:679.

5. Methods of Air Sampling and Analysis, 1st ed. 1972. Inter Society Committee, Air Pollution Control Assoc., pp. 199-204.

6. RAAF, S.F., W.G. CHARACKLIS, M.A. KESSICK & C.H. WARD. 1977. Fate of cyanide and related compounds in aerobic microbial systems. *Water Res.* 11:477.

7. RAPEAN, J.C., T. HANSON & R. A. JOHNSON. 1980. Biodegradation of cyanide-nitrate interference in the standard test for total cyanide. Proc. 35th Ind. Waste Conf., Purdue Univ., Lafayette, Ind., p. 430.

8. CASEY, J.P. 1980. Nitrosation and cyanohydrin decomposition artifacts in distillation test for cyanide. Extended Abs. American Chemical Soc., Div. Environmental Chemistry, Aug. 24-29, 1980, Las Vegas, Nev.

9. CSIKAI, N.J. & A.J. BARNARD, JR. 1983. Determination of total cyanide in thiocyanate-containing waste water. *Anal. Chem.* 55:1677.

4500-CN C. Total Cyanide after Distillation

1. General Discussion

Hydrogen cyanide (HCN) is liberated from an acidified sample by distillation and purging with air. The HCN gas is collected by passing it through an NaOH scrubbing solution. Cyanide concentration in the scrubbing solution is determined by titrimetric, colorimetric, or potentiometric procedures.

2. Apparatus

The apparatus is shown in Figure 4500-CN:1. It includes:

a. *Boiling flask,* 1 L, with inlet tube and provision for water-cooled condenser.

b. *Gas absorber,* with gas dispersion tube equipped with medium-porosity fritted outlet.

c. *Heating element,* adjustable.

d. *Ground glass ST joints,* TFE-sleeved or with an appropriate lubricant for the boiling flask and condenser. Neoprene stopper and plastic threaded joints also may be used.

3. Reagents

a. *Sodium hydroxide solution:* Dissolve 40 g NaOH in water and dilute to 1 L.

b. *Magnesium chloride reagent:* Dissolve 510 g $MgCl_2 \cdot 6H_2O$ in water and dilute to 1 L.

c. *Sulfuric acid,* H_2SO_4, 1 + 1.

d. *Lead carbonate,* $PbCO_3$, powdered.

e. *Sulfamic acid,* NH_2SO_3H.

4. Procedure

a. Add 500 mL sample, containing not more than 10 mg CN^-/L (diluted if necessary with distilled water) to the boiling flask. If a higher CN^- content is anticipated, use the spot test (4500-CN.K) to approximate the required dilution. Add 10 mL NaOH solution to the gas scrubber and dilute, if necessary, with distilled water to obtain an adequate liquid depth in the absorber. Do not use more than 225 mL total volume of absorber solution. When S^{2-} generation from the distilling flask is anticipated add 50 or more mg powdered $PbCO_3$ to the absorber solution to precipitate S^{2-}. Connect the train, consisting of boiling flask air inlet, flask, condenser, gas washer, suction flask trap, and aspirator. Adjust suction so that approximately 1 air bubble/s enters the boiling flask. This air rate will carry HCN gas from flask to absorber and usually will prevent a reverse flow of HCN through the air inlet. If this air rate does not prevent sample backup in the delivery tube, increase air-flow rate to 2 air bubbles/s. Observe air purge rate in the absorber where the liquid level should be raised not more than 6.5 to 10 mm. Maintain air flow throughout the reaction.

b. Add 2 g sulfamic acid through the air inlet tube and wash down with distilled water.

c. Add 50 mL 1 + 1 H_2SO_4 through the air inlet tube. Rinse tube with distilled water and let air mix flask contents for 3 min. Add 20 mL $MgCl_2$ reagent through air inlet and wash down with stream of water. A precipitate that may form redissolves on heating.

d. Heat with rapid boiling, but do not flood condenser inlet or permit vapors to rise more than halfway into condenser. Adequate refluxing is indicated by a reflux rate of 40 to 50 drops/min from the condenser lip. Reflux for at least 1 h. Discontinue heating but continue air flow. Cool for 15 min and drain gas washer contents into a separate container. Rinse connecting tube between condenser and gas washer with distilled water, add rinse water to drained liquid, and dilute to 250 mL in a volumetric flask.

e. Determine cyanide content by the titration method (D) if cyanide concentration exceeds 1 mg/L, by the colorimetric method (E) if the cyanide concentration is less, or by dilution to reduce the concentration into the applicable range (4500-

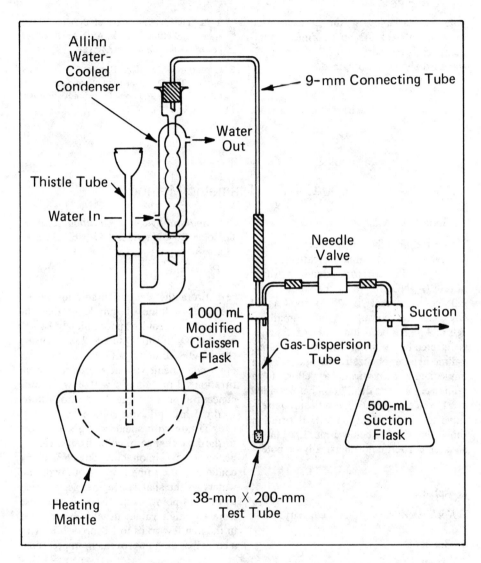

Figure 4500-CN:1. Cyanide distillation apparatus.

CN.E.4). Use titration, the electrode probe method, or the spot test to approximate CN^- content. Alternatively, use the cyanide-selective electrode in the concentration range 0.05 to 10 mg CN^-/L (Method F).

f. Distillation gives quantitative recovery of even refractory cyanides such as iron complexes. To obtain complete recovery of cobalticyanide use ultraviolet radiation pretreatment.[1,2] If incomplete recovery is suspected, distill again by refilling the gas washer with a fresh charge of NaOH solution and refluxing 1 h more. The cyanide from the second reflux, if any, will indicate completeness of recovery.

g. As a quality control measure, periodically test apparatus, reagents, and other potential variables in the concentration range of interest. As an example a minimum 98% recovery from 1 mg CN^-/L standard should be obtained.

5. References

1. CASAPIERI, P., R. SCOTT & E.A. SIMPSON.

1970. The determination of cyanide ions in waters and effluents by an Auto Analyzer procedure. *Anal. Chim. Acta* 49:188.

2. GOULDEN, P.D., K.A. BADAR & P. BROOKS-BANK. 1972. Determination of nanogram quantities of simple and complex cyanides in water. *Anal. Chem.* 44:1845.

4500-CN D.   Titrimetric Method

1. General Discussion

a. Principle: CN^- in the alkaline distillate from the preliminary treatment procedure is titrated with standard silver nitrate ($AgNO_3$) to form the soluble cyanide complex, $Ag(CN)_2^-$. As soon as all CN^- has been complexed and a small excess of Ag^+ has been added, the excess Ag^+ is detected by the silver-sensitive indicator, *p*-dimethylaminobenzalrhodanine, which immediately turns from a yellow to a salmon color.[1] The distillation has provided a 2:1 concentration. The indicator is sensitive to about 0.1 mg Ag/L. If titration shows that CN^- is below 1 mg/L, examine another portion colorimetrically or potentiometrically.

2. Apparatus

Koch microburet, 10-mL capacity.

3. Reagents

a. Indicator solution: Dissolve 20 mg *p*-dimethylaminobenzalrhodanine in 100 mL acetone.

b. Standard silver nitrate titrant: Dissolve 3.27 g $AgNO_3$ in 1 L distilled water. Standardize against standard NaCl solution, using the argentometric method with K_2CrO_4 indicator, as directed in Chloride, Section 4500-Cl^-.B.

Dilute 500 mL $AgNO_3$ solution according to the titer found so that 1.00 mL is equivalent to 1.00 mg CN^-.

c. Sodium hydroxide dilution solution: Dissolve 1.6 g NaOH in 1 L distilled water.

4. Procedure

a. From the absorption solution take a measured volume of sample so that the titration will require approximately 1 to 10 mL $AgNO_3$ titrant. Dilute to 250 mL using the NaOH dilution solution or to some other convenient volume to be used for all titrations. For samples with low cyanide concentration (≤ 5 mg/L) do not dilute. Add 0.5 mL indicator solution.

b. Titrate with standard $AgNO_3$ titrant to the first change in color from a canary yellow to a salmon hue. Titrate a blank containing the same amount of alkali and water. As the analyst becomes accustomed to the end point, blank titrations decrease from the high values usually experienced in the first few trials to 1 drop or less, with a corresponding improvement in precision.

5. Calculation

$$\text{mg } CN^-/L = \frac{(A - B) \times 1000}{\text{mL original sample}}$$
$$\times \frac{250}{\text{mL portion used}}$$

where:

A = mL standard $AgNO_3$ for sample and
B = mL standard $AgNO_3$ for blank.

6. Precision and Bias

For samples containing more than 1 mg CN^-/L that have been distilled or for relatively clear samples without significant interference, the coefficient of variation is 2%. Extraction and removal of S^{2-} or oxidizing agents tend to increase the coefficient of variation to a degree determined by the amount of manipulation and the type of sample. The limit of sensitivity is approximately 0.1 mg CN^-/L, but at this concentration the end point is indistinct. At 0.4 mg/L the coefficient of variation is four times that at CN^- concentration levels > 1.0 mg/L.

7. Reference

1. RYAN, J.A. & G.W. CULSHAW. 1944. The use of *p*-dimethylaminobenzylidene rhodanine as an indicator for the volumetric determination of cyanides. *Analyst* 69:370.

4500-CN E.   Colorimetric Method

1. General Discussion

a. Principle: CN^- in the alkaline distillate from preliminary treatment is converted to CNCl by reaction with chloramine-T at pH < 8 without hydrolyzing to CNO^-.[1] (CAUTION—*CNCl is a toxic gas; avoid inhalation.*) After the reaction is complete, CNCl forms a red-blue dye on addition of a pyridine-barbituric acid reagent. If the dye is kept in an aqueous solution, the absorbance is read at 578 nm. To obtain colors of comparable intensity, have the same salt content in sample and standards.

b. Interference: All known interferences are eliminated or reduced to a minimum by distillation.

2. Apparatus

Colorimetric equipment: One of the following is required:

a. Spectrophotometer, for use at 578 nm, providing a light path of 10 mm or longer.

b. Filter photometer, providing a light path of at least 10 mm and equipped with a red filter having maximum transmittance at 570 to 580 nm.

3. Reagents

a. Chloramine-T solution: Dissolve 1.0 g white, water-soluble powder in 100 mL water. Prepare weekly and store in refrigerator.

b. Stock cyanide solution: Dissolve approximately 1.6 g NaOH and 2.51 g KCN in 1 L distilled water. (CAUTION—*KCN is highly toxic; avoid contact or inhalation.*) Standardize against standard silver nitrate $(AgNO_3)$ titrant as described in Section 4500-CN.D.4, using 25 mL KCN solution. Check titer weekly because the solution gradually loses strength; 1 mL = 1 mg CN^-.

c. Standard cyanide solution: Based on the concentration determined for the KCN stock solution (¶ 3*b*) calculate volume required (approximately 10 mL) to prepare 1 L of a 10 µg CN^-/mL solution. Dilute with the NaOH dilution solution. Dilute 10 mL of the 10 µg CN^-/mL solution to 100 mL with the NaOH dilution solution; 1.0 mL = 1.0 µg CN^-. Prepare fresh daily and keep in a glass-stoppered bottle. (CAUTION—*Toxic; take care to avoid ingestion.*)

d. Pyridine-barbituric acid reagent: Place 15 g barbituric acid in a 250-mL volumetric flask and add just enough water to wash sides of flask and wet barbituric acid. Add

75 mL pyridine and mix. Add 15 mL conc hydrochloric acid (HCl), mix, and cool to room temperature. Dilute to mark with water and mix. This reagent is stable for up to 1 month; discard if a precipitate develops.

e. *Sodium dihydrogen phosphate, 1 M:* Dissolve 138 g $NaH_2PO_4 \cdot H_2O$ in 1 L distilled water. Refrigerate.

f. *Sodium hydroxide dilution solution:* Dissolve 1.6 g NaOH in 1 L distilled water.

4. Procedure

a. *Preparation of calibration curve:* Prepare a blank of NaOH dilution solution. From the standard KCN solution prepare a series of standards containing from 0.2 to 6 μg CN^- in 20 mL solution using the NaOH dilution solution for all dilutions. Treat standards in accordance with ¶ *b* below. Plot absorbance of standards against CN^- concentration (micrograms).

Recheck calibration curve periodically and each time a new reagent is prepared.

On the basis of the first calibration curve, prepare additional standards containing less than 0.2 and more than 6 μg CN^- to determine the limits measurable with the photometer being used.

b. *Color development:* Adjust photometer to zero absorbance each time using a blank consisting of the NaOH dilution solution and all reagents. Take a portion of absorption liquid obtained in Method C, such that the CN^- concentration falls in the measurable range, and dilute to 20 mL with NaOH dilution solution. Place in a 50-mL volumetric flask. Add 4 mL phosphate buffer and mix thoroughly. Add 2.0 mL chloramine-T solution and swirl to mix. *Immediately* add 5 mL pyridine-barbituric

acid solution and swirl gently. Dilute to mark with water; mix well by inversion.

Measure absorbance with the photometer at 578 nm after 8 min but within 15 min from the time of adding the pyridine-barbituric acid reagent. Even with the specified time of 8 to 15 min there is a slight change in absorbance. To minimize this, standardize time for all readings. Using the calibration curve and the formula in ¶ 5 below, determine CN^- concentration in original sample.

5. Calculations

$$CN^-,\ mg/L = \frac{A \times B}{C \times D}$$

where:

A = μg CN^- read from calibration curve (50 mL final volume),

B = total volume of absorbing solution from the distillation, mL,

C = volume of original sample used in the distillation, mL, and

D = volume of absorbing solution used in colorimetric test, mL.

6. Precision

The analysis of a mixed cyanide solution containing sodium, zinc, copper, and silver cyanides in tap water gave a precision within the designated range as follows:

$$S_T = 0.115X + 0.031$$

where:

S_T = overall precision and

X = CN^- concentration, mg/L.

7. Reference

1. AMUS, E.& H. GARSCHAGEN. 1953. Über die Verwendung der Barbitsäure für die photometrische Bestimmund von Cyanid und Rhodanid. *Z. Anal. Chem.* 138:414.

4500-CN F.   Cyanide-Selective Electrode Method

1. General Discussion

CN^- in the alkaline distillate from the preliminary treatment procedures can be determined potentiometrically by using a CN^--selective electrode in combination with a double-junction reference electrode and a pH meter having an expanded millivolt scale, or a specific ion meter. This method can be used to determine CN^- concentration in place of either the colorimetric or titrimetric procedures in the concentration range of 0.05 to 10 mg CN^-/L.[1-3] If the CN^--selective electrode method is used, the previously described titration screening step can be omitted.

2. Apparatus

a. Expanded-scale pH meter or specific-ion meter.

b. Cyanide-ion-selective electrode. *

c. Reference electrode, double-junction.

d. Magnetic mixer with TFE-coated stirring bar.

3. Reagents

a. Stock standard cyanide solution: See Section 4500-CN.E.3*b*.

b. Sodium hydroxide diluent: Dissolve 1.6 g NaOH in water and dilute to 1 L.

c. Intermediate standard cyanide solution: Dilute a calculated volume (approximately 100 mL) of stock KCN solution, based on the determined concentration, to 1000 mL with NaOH diluent. Mix thoroughly; 1 mL = 100 μg CN^-.

d. Dilute standard cyanide solution: Dilute 100.0 mL intermediate standard CN^- solution to 1000 mL with NaOH diluent; 1.00 mL = 10.0 μg CN^-. Prepare daily and keep in a dark, glass-stoppered bottle.

e. Potassium nitrate solution: Dissolve 100 g KNO_3 in water and dilute to 1 L. Adjust to pH 12 with KOH. This is the outer filling solution for the double-junction reference electrode.

4. Procedure

a. Calibration: Use the dilute and intermediate standard CN^- solutions and the NaOH diluent to prepare a series of three standards, 0.1, 1.0, and 10.0 mg CN^-/L. Transfer approximately 100 mL of each of these standard solutions into a 250-mL beaker prerinsed with a small portion of standard being tested. Immerse CN^- and double-junction reference electrodes. Mix well on a magnetic stirrer at 25°C, maintaining as closely as possible the same stirring rate for all solutions.

Always progress from the lowest to the highest concentration of standard because otherwise equilibrium is reached only slowly. The electrode membrane dissolves in solutions of high CN^- concentration; do not use with a concentration above 10 mg/L. After making measurements remove electrode and soak in water.

After equilibrium is reached (at least 5 min and not more than 10 min), record potential (millivolt) readings and plot CN^- concentrations versus readings on semilogarithmic graph paper. A straight line with a slope of approximately 59 mV per decade indicates that the instrument and electrodes are operating properly. Record slope of line obtained (millivolts/decade of concentration). The slope may vary somewhat from the theoretical value of 59.2 mV per decade because of manufacturing variation and reference electrode (liquid-junction) potentials. The slope should be a straight line and is the basis for calculating sample concentration.

b. Measurement of sample: Place 100 mL of absorption liquid obtained in Section 4500-CN.C.4*d* into a 250-mL beaker. When measuring low CN^- concentrations, first rinse beaker and electrodes with a small volume of sample. Immerse CN^- and dou-

*Orion Model 94-06A or equivalent.

ble-junction reference electrodes and mix on a magnetic stirrer at the same stirring rate used for calibration. After equilibrium is reached (at least 5 min and not more than 10 min), record values indicated on ion meter or found from graph prepared as above. Calculate concentration as directed below.

5. Calculations

$$\text{mg CN}^-/\text{L} = \frac{A \times B}{C}$$

where:

$A =$ mg CN^-/L found from meter reading or graph,

$B =$ total volume of absorption solution after dilution, mL, and

$C =$ volume of original sample used in the distillation, mL.

6. Precision

The precision of the CN^--ion-selective electrode method using the absorption so-lution from total cyanide distillation has been found in collaborative testing to be linear within its designated range and may be expressed as follows:

Reagent water: $S_T = 0.06X + 0.0016$
Water matrix: $S_T = 0.05X - 0.0176$

where:

$S_T =$ overall precision and
$X =$ concentration, mg CN^-/L.

The difference of overall precision from pooled single-operator precision was not statistically significant.

7. References

1. ORION RESEARCH, INC. 1975. Cyanide Ion Electrode Instruction Manual, Cambridge, Mass.

2. FRANT, M.S., J.W. ROSS & J. H. RISEMAN. 1972. An electrode indicator technique for measuring low levels of cyanide. *Anal. Chem.* 44:2227.

3. SEKERKA, J. & J.F. LECHNER. 1976. Potentiometric determination of low levels of simple and total cyanides. *Water Res.* 10:479.

4500-CN G.   Cyanides Amenable to Chlorination after Distillation

1. General Discussion

This method is applicable to the determination of cyanides amenable to chlorination, to determine the dissociable CN^- content of the sample.

After part of the sample is chlorinated to decompose the cyanides, both the chlorinated and the untreated sample are subjected to distillation as described in Section 4500-CN.C. The difference between the CN^- concentrations found in the two samples is expressed as cyanides amenable to chlorination.

The titration procedure may be used when it is known that the concentration of cyanides is more than 1 but less than 10 mg/L. With higher concentrations, use a smaller portion as described in 4500-CN.D.4a. Use a colorimetric determination when the cyanides are known to be 1 mg/L or less. The cyanide-selective electrode method is useful in the concentration range of 0.05 to 10 mg CN^-/L. For estimation of the concentration of cyanides amenable to chlorination use the spot test procedure (4500-CN.K).

Some unidentified organic chemicals may oxidize or form breakdown products during chlorination, giving higher results for cyanide after chlorination than before chlorination. This may lead to a negative value for cyanides amenable to chlorination after distillation for wastes from, for example, the steel industry, petroleum refining, and pulp and paper processing. Where such interferences are encountered use Method 4500-CN.I for determining dissociable cyanide.

2. Apparatus

a. Distillation apparatus: See Section 4500-CN.C.2

b. Apparatus for determining cyanide by either the titrimetric method, Section 4500-CN.D.2, the colorimetric method, Section 4500-CN.E.2, or the electrode method, Section 4500-CN.F.2.

3. Reagents

a. All reagents listed in Section 4500-CN.C.3.

b. All reagents listed in Section 4500-CN.D.3, 4500-CN.E.3, or 4500-CN.F.3, depending on method of estimation.

c. Calcium hypochlorite solution: Dissolve 5 g $Ca(OCl)_2$ in 100 mL distilled water. Store in an amber-colored glass bottle in the dark. Prepare monthly.

d. Potassium iodide(KI)-starch test paper.

4. Procedure

a. Divide sample into two equal parts and chlorinate one as in ¶ *b* below. Analyze both portions for CN^-. The difference in determined concentrations is the cyanide amenable to chlorination.

b. Add $Ca(OCl)_2$ solution dropwise to sample while agitating and maintaining pH between 11 and 12 by adding NaOH solution. Test for chlorine by placing a drop of treated sample on a strip of KI-starch paper. A distinct blue color indicates sufficient chlorine (approximately 50 to 100 mg Cl_2/L). Maintain excess residual chlorine for 1 h while agitating. If necessary, add more $Ca(OCl)_2$ and/or NaOH.

c. Add approximately 500 mg/L sodium thiosulfate ($Na_2S_2O_3$) as crystals to reduce residual chlorine. Test with KI-starch pa-

per; there should be no color change. Add approximately 0.1 g/L more $Na_2S_2O_3$ to ensure a slight excess.

d. Minimize sample exposure to ultraviolet radiation before distillation.

e. Distill both chlorinated and unchlorinated samples as in Section 4500-CN.C. Test according to Methods D, E, or F.

5. Calculation

mg CN^- amenable to chlorination/L
$$= G - H$$

where:

$G =$ mg CN^-/L found in unchlorinated portion of sample and

$H =$ mg CN^-/L found in chlorinated portion of sample.

For samples containing significant quantities of iron cyanides, it is possible that the second distillation will give a higher value for CN^- than the test for total cyanide, leading to a negative result. When the difference is within the precision limits of the method, report, "no determinable quantities of cyanide amenable to chlorination." If the difference is greater than the precision limit, ascertain the cause such as presence of interferences, manipulation of the procedure, etc., or use Method I.

6. Precision

Precision, with the titrimetric finish, for cyanides amenable to chlorination was determined from a mixed cyanide solution containing sodium, zinc, copper, and silver cyanides and sodium ferrocyanide. The precision of the method within its designated range may be expressed as follows:

$$S_T = 0.049X + 0.162$$

where:

$S_T =$ overall precision and
$X =$ CN^- concentration, mg/L.

4500-CN H.   Cyanides Amenable to Chlorination without Distillation (Short-Cut Method)

1. General Discussion

This method covers the determination of HCN and of CN complexes that are amenable to chlorination and also thiocyanates (SCN^-). The procedure does not measure cyanates (CNO^-) or iron cyanide complexes, but does determine cyanogen chloride (CNCl). This test requires neither lengthy distillation nor the chlorination of one sample before distillation. The recovery of CN^- from metal cyanide complexes will be comparable to that in Methods G and I.

The cyanides are converted to CNCl by chloramine-T after the sample has been heated. In the absence of nickel, copper, silver, and gold cyanide complexes or SCN^-, the CNCl may be developed at room temperature. The pyridine-barbituric acid reagent produces a red-blue color in the sample. The color can be estimated visually against standards or photometrically at 578 nm. The limits of the determination are 0.2 to 6 μg CN^-, representing 0.01 to 0.30 mg/L in a 20-mL sample. Higher CN^- concentrations may be determined by dilution. The dissolved salt content in the standards used for the development of the calibration curve should be near the salt content of the sample, including the added NaOH and phosphate buffer. See 4500-CN.E.1a.

The test sensitivity may be extended to the 5- to 150-μg/L level if a fresh, unstabilized sample is used. In these circumstances (pH < 9), add phosphate buffer dropwise to a pH of 6.5 (pH 6.0 to 6.6) and use a 40-mL sample, minimizing dilution before color development. Add 1 g sodium chloride (NaCl) to the 40-mL sample to make up for the salt content that would have been added if sodium hydroxide (NaOH) dilution solution and the re-quired amount of phosphate buffer had been added.

The method's usefulness is limited by thiocyanate interference. Although the procedure allows the specific determination of CN^- amenable to chlorination (see 4500-CN.H.2 and 5) by masking the CN^- content and thereby establishing a correction for the thiocyanide content, the ratio of SCN^- to CN^- should not exceed 3 to be applicable. In working with unknown samples, screen the sample for SCN^- by the spot test (4500-CN.K).

2. Interferences

a. Remove interfering agents as described in Section 4500-CN.B with the exception of NO_2^- and NO_3^- (4500-CN.B.3h).

b. The SCN^- ion reacts with chloramine-T to give a positive error equivalent to its concentration. The procedure allows the separate determination of SCN^- and subtraction of this value from the results for the total. Use the spot test (4500-CN.K) for SCN^- when its presence is suspected. If the SCN^- content is more than three times the CN^- content, use Method G or I.

c. Reducing chemical compounds, such as SO_3^{2-}, may interfere by consuming chlorine in the chloramine-T addition. A significant excess of chlorine is provided, but the procedure prescribes a test (4500-CN.H.5d) to avoid this interference.

d. Color and turbidity may interfere with the colorimetric determination. Overcome this interference by extraction with chloroform (4500-CN.B.3c) but omit reduction of the pH. Otherwise, use Method G or I.

3. Apparatus

a. *Apparatus listed in 4500-CN.E.2.*
b. *Hot water bath.*

4. Reagents

a. Reagents listed in Sections 4500-CN.B and E.3.

b. Sodium chloride, NaCl, crystals.

c. Sodium carbonate, Na_2CO_3, crystals.

d. Sulfuric acid solution, H_2SO_4, 1N.

e. EDTA solution, 0.05M: Dissolve 18.5 g disodium salt of ethylenediamine tetraacetic acid in water and dilute to 1 L.

f. Formaldehyde solution, 10%: Dilute 10 mL formaldehyde (37% pharmaceutical grade) 1 + 9 with water.

5. Procedure

a. Calibrate as directed in Section 4500-CN.E.1*a* and 4*a*. Adjust absorbance to zero, using the NaOH dilution solution to prepare the blank. For samples with more than 3000 mg total dissolved solids/ L, prepare a calibration curve from standards and blank NaOH solutions containing 6 g NaCl/L. Samples containing total dissolved solids exceeding 10 000 mg/L require appropriate standards and a new calibration curve.

b. If it is not in the desired range, adjust pH of a small amount of sample (50 mL) to 11.4 to 11.8. If this requires acid addition, first add a small amount (0.2 to 0.4 g) Na_2CO_3 and stir to dissolve. Then add the 1N H_2SO_4 slowly while stirring. If base addition is necessary to raise the pH, use 1N NaOH. Pipet 20 mL of pH-adjusted sample into a 50-mL volumetric flask. If more than 300 mg CN⁻/L is known to be present, use a smaller sample diluted to 20 mL with NaOH dilution solution.

c. To insure uniform color development, both in calibration and testing, maintain a uniform temperature. Immerse flask in a water bath held at 27 ± 1°C for 10 min before adding reagents and hold sample in water bath until all reagents have been added. Add 4 mL phosphate buffer and swirl to mix. Add 1 drop 0.1M EDTA solution. Hold in water bath for 1 min while swirling.

d. Add 2 mL chloramine-T solution and swirl to mix. Place a drop of solution on a strip of acidified starch-iodide test paper. The test paper should show the presence of chlorine. If reducing agents in the sample consume all the chloramine-T, add once more and recheck. If the test is again negative, the method is inapplicable; use Method G or I. After 1 min, add 5 mL pyridine-barbituric acid and swirl in water bath for 1 min.

e. Remove from water bath, dilute to 50.0 mL, and allow 7 min more for color development. Cool to room temperature, if necessary, and read absorbance at 578 nm within a total of 15 min from the time the pyridine-barbituric acid solution was added.

f. Standardize instrument with an appropriate blank each time it is used. Recheck calibration curve periodically using prepared standards and each time a new reagent is prepared.

g. If the presence of SCN⁻ is suspected (4500-CN.H.2*b*), take a second, pH-adjusted sample, add 3 drops formaldehyde solution, swirl to mix, and hold for 10 min. Place in water bath for an additional 10 min. The formaldehyde addition masks up to 0.3 mg CN⁻/L thereby providing a separate determination of SCN⁻. Follow the rest of the procedure ¶s 5*b-f*.

6. Calculation

Cyanide amenable to chlorination plus thiocyanate, mg CN⁻/L = A/B

where:

A = μg CN⁻ read from calibration curve (50 mL final volume) and

B = mL sample used.

Deduct SCN⁻ value from the results found when the CN⁻ has not been masked by formaldehyde addition (total) for cyanide content.

7. Precision

Collaborative testing of a mixed cyanide solution in both reagent and matrix water, containing sodium, copper, nickel, cadmium, and zinc metal cyanide complexes and additionally thiocyanate as an interference, gave a precision of the method within the designated range that is linear with concentration and may be expressed as follows:

Reagent water: $S_T = 0.0958X + 0.006$
$S_o = 0.0681X + 0.0048$

Matrix water: $S_T = 0.0973X + 0.0085$
$S_o = 0.0201X + 0.0064$

where:
S_T = overall precision, mg/L,
S_o = pooled single-operator precision, mg/L, and
X = concentration of cyanide, mg/L.

4500-CN I.   Weak and Dissociable Cyanide

1. General Discussion

Hydrogen cyanide (HCN) is liberated from a slightly acidified (pH 4.5 to 6.0) sample under the prescribed distillation conditions. The method does not recover CN^- from tight complexes that would not be amenable to oxidation by chlorine. The acetate buffer used contains zinc salts to precipitate iron cyanide as a further assurance of the selectivity of the method. In other respects the method is similar to 4500-CN.C.

2. Apparatus

See Section 4500-CN.C.2 and Figure 4500-CN:1, and also Section 4500-CN.D.2, 4500-CN.E.2, or 4500-CN.F.2, depending on method of estimation.

3. Reagents

a. Reagents listed in Section 4500-CN.C.3.

b. Reagents listed in Section 4500-CN.D.3, 4500-CN.E.3, or 4500-CN.F.3, depending on method of estimation.

c. Acetic acid, 1 + 9: Mix 1 volume of glacial acetic acid with 9 volumes of water.

d. Acetate buffer: Dissolve 410 g sodium acetate trihydrate ($NaC_2H_3O_2 \cdot 3H_2O$) in 500 mL water. Add glacial acetic acid to

yield a solution pH of 4.5 (approximately 500 mL).

e. Zinc acetate solution, 100 g/L: Dissolve 100 g $Zn(C_2H_3O_2)_2 \cdot H_2O$ in 500 mL water. Dilute to 1 L.

f. Methyl red indicator.

4. Procedure

Follow procedure described in 4500-CN.C.4, but with the following modifications:

a. Do not add sulfamic acid, because NO_2^- and NO_3^- do not interfere.

b. Instead of H_2SO_4 and $MgCl_2$ reagents, add 10 mL each of the acetate buffer and zinc acetate solutions through air inlet tube. Also add 2 to 3 drops methyl red indicator. Rinse air inlet tube with water and allow air to mix contents. If the solution is not pink, add acetic acid (1 + 9) dropwise through air inlet tube until a pink color persists.

c. Follow instructions beginning with 4500-CN.C.4d.

d. For determining CN^- in the absorption solution, use the preferred finish method (4500-CN.D, E, or F).

5. Precision

Collaborative testing of a mixed cyanide solution in both reagent and matrix water, using the electrode final determination, gave overall and pooled single-operator precisions that are linear within the designated range and may be expressed as follows:

Reagent water: $S_T = 0.085X + 0.0032$
$\quad\quad\quad\quad\quad\; S_o = 0.023X + 0.0093$

Water matrix: $S_T = 0.068X + 0.0039$
$\quad\quad\quad\quad\quad S_o = 0.017X + 0.0039$

where:

S_T = overall precision, mg/L,
S_o = pooled single-operator precision, mg/L, and
X = concentration, mg CN$^-$/L.

4500-CN J.   Cyanogen Chloride

1. General Discussion

Cyanogen chloride (CNCl) is the first reaction product when cyanide compounds are chlorinated. It is a volatile gas, only slightly soluble in water, but highly toxic even in low concentrations (CAUTION: *Avoid inhalation or contact*). A mixed pyridine-barbituric acid reagent produces a red-blue color with CNCl.

Because CNCl hydrolyzes to cyanate (CNO$^-$) at a pH of 12 or more, collect a separate sample for CNCl analysis (See Section 4500-CN.B.2) in a closed container without sodium hydroxide (NaOH). A quick test with a spot plate or comparator as soon as the sample is collected may be the only procedure for avoiding hydrolysis of CNCl due to time lapse between sampling and analysis.

If starch-iodide (KI) test paper indicates presence of chlorine or other oxidizing agents, add sodium thiosulfate (Na$_2$S$_2$O$_3$) immediately as directed in Section 4500-CN.B.2.

2. Apparatus

See Section 4500-CN.E.2.

3. Reagents

See Sections 4500-CN.E.3 and 4500-CN.H.4.

4. Procedure

Calibrate as directed in Sections 4500-CN.E.4 and 4500-CN.H.1, second paragraph. Add a portion of unstabilized sample, diluted if necessary, to contain 0.2 to 6 μg of CN$^-$/40 mL to a beaker. Add phosphate buffer to a pH of 6.5 (pH 6.0 to 6.6). Record exact volume of phosphate buffer required. Prepare a second sample as before and add to a 50-mL volumetric flask. Add phosphate buffer in the previously established volume. Add 5 mL pyridine-barbituric acid solution. Dilute to mark with distilled water and mix well by inversion. Allow 8 min for color development. Measure absorbance at 578 nm within 8 to 15 min from the addition of the pyridine-barbituric acid reagent. Using the calibration curve, determine the CNCl as CN$^-$.

5. Calculation

$$\text{mg CNCl (as CN}^-)/\text{L} = \frac{A}{B}$$

where:

A = μg CN$^-$ read from calibration curve (50 mL final volume) and
B = mL original unstabilized sample.

6. Precision

The instability of CNCl precludes round-robin testing procedures and a precision statement is not possible.

4500-CN K.   Spot Test for Sample Screening

1. General Discussion

The spot test procedure allows a quick screening of the sample to establish whether more than 50 μg/L of cyanide amenable to chlorination is present. The test also establishes the presence or absence of cyanogen chloride (CNCl). With practice and dilution, the test reveals the approximate concentration range of these compounds by the color development compared with that of similarly treated standards.

When chloramine-T is added to cyanides amenable to chlorination, CNCl is formed. CNCl forms a red-blue color with the mixed reagent pyridine-barbituric acid. When testing for CNCl omit the chloramine-T addition. (CAUTION: *CNCl is a toxic gas; avoid inhalation.*)

The presence of formaldehyde in excess of 0.5 mg/L interferes with the test. A spot test for the presence of aldehydes and a method for removal of this interference are given in Section 4500-CN.B.3.

Thiocyanate (SCN^-) reacts with chloramine-T, thereby creating a positive interference. The CN^- can be masked with formaldehyde and the sample retested. This makes the spot test specific for SCN^-. In this manner it is possible to determine whether the spot discoloration is due to the presence of CN^-, SCN^-, or both.

2. Apparatus

a. *Porcelain spot plate* with 6 to 12 cavities.

b. *Dropping pipets.*

c. *Glass stirring rods.*

3. Reagents

a. *Chloramine-T solution:* See Section 4500-CN.E.3a.

b. *Stock cyanide solution:* See Section 4500-CN.E.3b.

c. *Pyridine-barbituric acid reagent:* See Section 4500-CN.E.3d.

d. *Hydrochloric acid,* HCl, 1 + 9.

e. *Phenolphthalein indicator aqueous solution.*

f. *Sodium carbonate,* Na_2CO_3, anhydrous.

g. *Formaldehyde,* 37%, pharmaceutical grade.

4. Procedure

If the solution to be tested has a pH greater than 10, neutralize a 20- to 25-mL portion. Add about 250 mg Na_2CO_3 and swirl to dissolve. Add 1 drop phenolphthalein indicator. Add 1 + 9 HCl dropwise with constant swirling until the solution becomes colorless. Place 3 drops sample and 3 drops distilled water (for blanks) in separate cavities of the spot plate. To each cavity, add 1 drop chloramine-T solution and mix with a clean stirring rod. Add 1 drop pyridine-barbituric acid solution to each cavity and again mix. After 1 min, the sample spot will turn pink to red if 50 μg/L or more of CN^- are present. The blank spot will be faint yellow because of the color of the reagents. Until familiarity with the spot test is gained, use, in place of the water blank, a standard solution containing 50 μg CN^-/L for color comparison. This standard can be made by diluting the stock cyanide solution (¶ 3b).

If SCN^- is suspected, test a second sample pretreated as follows: Heat a 20- to 25-mL sample in a water bath at 50°C; add 0.1 mL formaldehyde and hold for 10 min. This treatment will mask up to 5 mg CN^-/L, if present. Repeat spot testing procedure. Color development indicates presence of SCN^-. Comparing color intensity in the two spot tests is useful in judging relative concentration of CN^- and SCN^-. If deep coloration is produced, serial dilution of sample and additional testing may allow closer approximation of the concentrations.

4500-CN L. Cyanates

1. General Discussion

Cyanate (CNO^-) may be of interest in analysis of industrial waste samples because the alkaline chlorination process used for the oxidation of cyanide yields cyanate in the second reaction.

Cyanate is unstable at neutral or low pH; therefore, stabilize the sample as soon as collected by adding sodium hydroxide (NaOH) to pH > 12. Remove residual chlorine by adding sodium thiosulfate ($Na_2S_2O_3$) (see Section 4500-CN.B.2).

a. Principle: Cyanate hydrolyzes to ammonia when heated at low pH.

$$2NaCNO + H_2SO_4 + 4H_2O \rightarrow (NH_4)_2SO_4 + 2NaHCO_3$$

The ammonia concentration must be determined on one sample portion before acidification. The ammonia content before and after hydrolysis of cyanate may be measured by direct nesslerization (4500-NH_3.C), phenate (4500-NH_3.D), or ammonia-selective electrode (4500-NH_3.F) method.[1] The test is applicable to cyanate compounds in natural waters and industrial waste.

b. Interferences:

1) Organic nitrogenous compounds may hydrolyze to ammonia (NH_3) upon acidification. To minimize this interference, control acidification and heating closely.

2) Metal compounds may precipitate or form colored complexes with nessler reagent. Adding Rochelle salt or EDTA in the determination of ammonia overcomes these interferences. Metal precipitates do not interfere with the ion-selective electrode method.

3) Reduce oxidants that oxidize cyanate to carbon dioxide and nitrogen with $Na_2S_2O_3$ (see Section 4500-CN.G).

4) Industrial waste containing organic material may contain unknown interferences.

c. Detection limit: 1 to 2 mg CNO^-/L.

2. Apparatus

a. Expanded-scale pH meter or selective-ion meter.

*b. Ammonia-selective electrode.**

c. Magnetic mixer, with TFE-coated stirring bar.

d. Heat barrier: Use a 3-mm-thick insulator under beaker to insulate against heat produced by stirrer motor.

3. Reagents

a. Stock ammonium chloride solution: See Section 4500-NH_3.C.3*d*.

b. Standard ammonium chloride solution: From the stock NH_4Cl solution prepare standard solutions containing 1.0, 10.0, and 100.0 mg NH_3-N/L by diluting with ammonia-free water.

c. Sodium hydroxide, 10N: Dissolve 400 g NaOH in water and dilute to 1 L.

d. Sulfuric acid solution, H_2SO_4, 1 + 1.

e. Ammonium chloride solution: Dissolve 5.4 g NH_4Cl in distilled water and dilute to 1 L. (Use only for soaking electrodes.)

4. Procedure

a. Calibration: Daily, calibrate the ammonia electrode as in 4500-NH_3.F.4*b* and *c* using standard NH_4Cl solutions.

b. Treatment of sample: Dilute sample, if necessary, so that the CNO^- concentration is 1 to 200 mg/L or NH_3-N is 0.5 to 100 mg/L. Take or prepare at least 200 mL. From this 200 mL, take a 100-mL portion and, following the calibration procedure, establish the potential (millivolts) developed from the sample. Check electrode reading with prepared standards and adjust instrument calibration setting daily. Record NH_3-N content of untreated sample (*B*).

---

*Orion Model 95-10, EIL Model 8002-2, Beckman Model 39565, or equivalent.

Acidify 100 mL of prepared sample by adding 0.5 mL 1 + 1 H_2SO_4 to a pH of 2.0 to 2.5. Heat sample to 90 to 95°C and maintain temperature for 30 min. Cool to room temperature and restore to original volume by adding ammonia-free water. Pour into a 150-mL beaker, immerse electrode, start magnetic stirrer, then add 1 mL 10N NaOH solution. With pH paper check that pH is greater than 11. If necessary, add more NaOH until pH 11 is reached.

After equilibrium has been reached (30 s) record the potential reading. Estimate NH_3-N content from calibration curve.

5. Calculations

mg NH_3-N derived from $CNO^-/L = A - B$

where:

A = mg NH_3-N/L found in the acidified and heated sample portion and
B = mg NH_3-N/L found in untreated portion.

$$mg\ CNO^-/L = 3.0 \times (A - B)$$

6. Precision

No data on precision of this method are available. See 4500-NH_3.F.6 for precision of ammonia-selective electrode method.

7. Reference

1. THOMAS, R.F. & R.L. BOOTH. 1973. Selective electrode determination of ammonia in water and wastes. *Environ. Sci. Technol.* 7:523.

4500-CN M. Thiocyanate

1. General Discussion

When wastewater containing thiocyanate (SCN^-) is chlorinated, highly toxic cyanogen chloride (CNCl) is formed. At an acidic pH, ferric ion (Fe^{3+}) and SCN^- form an intense red color suitable for colorimetric determination.

a. Interference:

1) Hexavalent chromium (Cr^{6+}) interferes and is removed by adding ferrous sulfate ($FeSO_4$) after adjusting to pH 1 to 2 with nitric acid (HNO_3). Raising the pH to 9 with 1N sodium hydroxide (NaOH) precipitates Fe^{3+} and Cr^{3+}, which are then filtered out.

2) Reducing agents that reduce Fe^{3+} to Fe^{2+}, thus preventing formation of ferric thiocyanate complex, are destroyed by adding a few drops of hydrogen peroxide (H_2O_2).

3) Industrial wastes may be highly colored or contain various interfering organic compounds. To eliminate these interferences,[1] use the pretreatment procedure given in ¶ 4c below. It is the analyst's re-

sponsibility to validate the method's applicability without pretreatment (¶ 4b). If in doubt, pretreat sample before proceeding with analysis (¶ 4c).

4) If sample contains cyanide amenable to chlorination and would be preserved for the cyanide determination at a high pH, sulfide could interfere by converting cyanide to SCN^-. To preserve SCN^- and CN^-, precipitate the sulfide by adding lead salts according to 4500-CN.B.2 before adding alkali; filter to remove precipitate.

5) Thiocyanate is biodegradable. Preserve samples that may contain bacteria at pH <2 by adding mineral acid and refrigerate.

b. Application: 0.1 to 2.0 mg SCN^-/L in natural or wastewaters. For higher concentrations, use a portion of diluted sample.

2. Apparatus

a. Spectrophotometer or filter photometer, for use at 460 nm, providing a light path of 5 cm.

b. Glass adsorption column: Use a 50-mL buret with a glass-wool plug, and pack with macroreticular resin (¶ 3*f*) approximately 40 cm high. For convenience, apply a powder funnel of the same diameter as the buret to the top with a short piece of plastic tubing.

3. Reagents

a. Ferric nitrate solution: Dissolve 404 g $Fe(NO_3)_3 \cdot 9H_2O$ in about 800 mL distilled water. Add 80 mL conc HNO_3 and dilute to 1 L.

b. Nitric acid solution, 0.1*N:* Mix 6.4 mL conc HNO_3 in about 800 mL distilled water and dilute to 1 L.

c. Stock thiocyanate solution: Dissolve 1.673 g potassium thiocyanate (KSCN) in distilled water and dilute to 1000 mL; 1.00 mL = 1.00 mg SCN⁻.

d. Standard thiocyanate solution: Dilute 10 mL stock solution to 1 L with distilled water; 1.00 mL = 0.01 mg SCN⁻.

e. Sodium hydroxide solution, 4 g/L: Dissolve 4 g NaOH in about 800 mL distilled water and dilute to 1 L.

f. Macroreticular resin, 18 to 50 mesh:* The resin now available is an experimental product and is not purified. Some samples have shown contamination with waxes and oil, giving poor permeability and adsorption. Purify as follows:

Place sufficient resin to fill the column or columns in a beaker and add 5 times the resin volume of acetone. Stir gently for 1 h. Pour off fines and acetone from settled resin and add 5 times the resin volume of hexane. Stir for 1 h. Pour off fines and hexane and add 5 times the resin volume of methanol. Stir for 15 min. Pour off methanol and add 3 times the resin volume of 0.1*N* NaOH. Stir for 15 min. Pour off NaOH solution and add 3 times the resin volume of 0.1*N* HNO_3. Stir for 15 min. Pour off HNO_3 solution and add 3 times

---

*Amberlite⁸ XAD-8, Rohm & Haas Company, or equivalent.

---

the resin volume of distilled water. Stir for 15 min. Drain excess water and use purified resin to fill the column. Store excess purified resin after covering it with distilled water. Keep in a closed jar.

g. Methyl alcohol.

4. Procedure

a. Preparation of calibration curve: Prepare a series of standards containing from 0.02 mg to 0.40 mg SCN⁻ by pipetting measured volumes of standard KSCN solution into 200-mL volumetric flasks and diluting with distilled water. Mix well. Develop color according to ¶ *b* below. Plot absorbance against SCN⁻ concentration expressed as mg/50 mL sample. The absorbance plot should be linear.

b. Color development: Use a filtered sample or portion from a diluted solution so that the concentration of SCN⁻ is between 0.1 and 2 mg/L. Adjust pH to 2 with conc HNO_3 added dropwise. Pipet 50-mL portion to a beaker, add 2.5 mL ferric nitrate, and mix.

Fill a 5-cm absorption cell and measure absorbance against a reagent blank at 460 nm or close to the maximum absorbance found with the instrument being used. Measure absorbance of the developed color against a reagent blank within 5 min from adding the reagent. (The color develops within 30 s and fades on standing in light.)

c. Sample pretreatment:

1) Color and various organic compounds interfere with absorbance measurement. At pH 2, macroreticular resin removes these interfering materials by adsorption without affecting thiocyanate.

2) To prepare the adsorption column, fill it with resin, rinse with 100 mL methanol, and follow by rinses with 100 mL 0.1*N* NaOH, 100 mL 0.1*N* HNO_3, and finally with 100 mL distilled water. If previously purified resin is used, omit these preparatory steps.

3) When washing, regenerating, or pass-

ing a sample through the column, as solution level approaches resin bed, add and drain five separate 5-mL volumes of solution or water (depending on which is used in next step) to approximate bed height. After last 5-mL volume, fill column with remaining liquid. This procedure prevents undue mixing of solutions and helps void the column of the previous solution.

4) Acidify 150 mL sample (or a dilution) to pH 2 by adding conc HNO_3 dropwise while stirring. Pass it through the column at a flow rate not to exceed 20 mL/min. If the resin becomes packed and the flow rate falls to 4 to 5 mL/min, use gentle pressure through a manually operated hand pump or squeeze bulb on the column. In this case, use a separatory funnel for the liquid reservoir instead of the powder funnel. Alternatively use a vacuum bottle as a receiver and apply gentle vacuum. Do not let liquid level drop below the adsorbent in the column.

5) When passing a sample through the column, measure 90 mL of sample in a graduated cylinder, and from this use the five 5-mL additions as directed in ¶ 3), then pour the remainder of the 90 mL into the column. Add rest of sample and collect 60 mL eluate to be tested after the first 60 mL has passed through the column.

6) Prepare a new calibration curve using standards prepared according to ¶ 4a, but acidify standards according to ¶ 4b, and pass them through the adsorption column. Develop color and measure absorbance according to ¶ 4b against a reagent blank prepared by passing acidified, distilled water through the adsorption column.

7) Pipet 50 mL from the collected eluate to a beaker, add 2.5 mL ferric nitrate solution, and mix. Measure absorbance according to ¶ 4b against a reagent blank [see ¶ 6) above].

8) From the measured absorbance value, determine thiocyanate content of the sample or dilution using the absorbance plot.

9) Each day the column is in use, test a mid-range standard to check absorption curve.

10) Regenerate column between samples by rinsing with 100 mL 0.1N NaOH; 50 mL 0.1N HNO_3; and 100 mL water. Insure that the water has rinsed empty glass section of the buret. Occasionally rinse with 100 mL methanol for complete regeneration. Adsorbed weak organic acids and thiocyanate residuals from earlier tests are eluted by the NaOH rinse. Leave the column covered with the last rinse water for storage.

5. Calculation

Calculate thiocyanate concentration as follows:

$$mg\ SCN^-/L = \frac{A \times 1000}{B}$$

where:

A = mg SCN^- from calibration curve and
B = milliliters sample used.

6. Precision

Based on the results of collaborative testing, the precision of the method, including sample pretreatment, within its designated range is linear with concentration and may be expressed as follows:

Reagent water: $S_T = 0.0930X + 0.0426$
$S_o = 0.045X + 0.010$

Water matrix: $S_T = 0.0547X + 0.0679$
$S_o = 0.0244X + 0.0182$

where:

S_T = overall precision, mg/L,
S_o = pooled single-operator precision, mg/L, and
X = thiocyanate concentration, mg/L.

7. Reference

1. SPENCER, R.R., J. LEENHEER, V.C. MARTI. 1980. Automated colorimetric determination of thiocyanate, thiosulfate and tetrathionate in water. 94th Annu. Meeting. Assoc. Official Agricultural Chemists, Washington, D.C. 1981.

4500-Cl   CHLORINE (RESIDUAL)*

4500-Cl A.   Introduction

1. Effects of Chlorination

The chlorination of water supplies and polluted waters serves primarily to destroy or deactivate disease-producing microorganisms. A secondary benefit, particularly in treating drinking water, is the overall improvement in water quality resulting from the reaction of chlorine with ammonia, iron, manganese, sulfide, and some organic substances.

Chlorination may produce adverse effects. Taste and odor characteristics of phenols and other organic compounds present in a water supply may be intensified. Potentially carcinogenic chloroorganic compounds such as chloroform may be formed. Combined chlorine formed on chlorination of ammonia- or amine-bearing waters adversely affects some aquatic life. To fulfill the primary purpose of chlorination and to minimize any adverse effects, it is essential that proper testing procedures be used with a foreknowledge of the limitations of the analytical determination.

2. Chlorine Forms and Reactions

Chlorine applied to water in its molecular or hypochlorite form initially undergoes hydrolysis to form free chlorine consisting of aqueous molecular chlorine, hypochlorous acid, and hypochlorite ion. The relative proportion of these free chlorine forms is pH- and temperature-dependent. At the pH of most waters, hypochlorous acid and hypochlorite ion will predominate.

Free chlorine reacts readily with ammonia and certain nitrogenous compounds to form combined chlorine. With ammonia, chlorine reacts to form the chloramines: monochloramine, dichloramine, and nitrogen trichloride. The presence and concentrations of these combined forms depend chiefly on pH, temperature, initial chlorine-to-nitrogen ratio, absolute chlorine demand, and reaction time. Both free and combined chlorine may be present simultaneously. Combined chlorine in water supplies may be formed in the treatment of raw waters containing ammonia or by the addition of ammonia or ammonium salts. Chlorinated wastewater effluents, as well as certain chlorinated industrial effluents, normally contain only combined chlorine. Historically, the principal analytical problem has been to distinguish between free and combined forms of chlorine.

3. Selection of Method

In two separate but related studies, samples were prepared and distributed to participating laboratories to evaluate chlorine methods. Because of poor accuracy and

---

*Approved by Standard Methods Committee, 1989.

precision and a high overall (average) total error in these studies, all orthotolidine procedures except one were dropped in the 14th edition of this work. The useful stabilized neutral orthotolidine method was deleted from the 15th edition because of the toxic nature of orthotolidine. The leuco crystal violet (LCV) procedure has been dropped from this edition because of its relative difficulty and the lack of comparative advantages.

a. *Natural and treated waters:* The iodometric methods (B and C) are suitable for measuring total chlorine concentrations greater than 1 mg/L, but the amperometric end point of Methods C and D gives greater sensitivity. All acidic iodometric methods suffer from interferences, generally in proportion to the quantity of potassium iodide (KI) and H^+ added.

The amperometric titration method (D) is a standard of comparison for the determination of free or combined chlorine. It is affected little by common oxidizing agents, temperature variations, turbidity, and color. The method is not as simple as the colorimetric methods and requires greater operator skill to obtain the best reliability. Loss of chlorine can occur because of rapid stirring in some commercial equipment. Clean and conditioned electrodes are necessary for sharp end points.

In this edition, a low-level amperometric titration procedure (E) has been added to determine total chlorine at levels below 0.2 mg/L. This method is recommended only when quantification of such low residuals is necessary. The interferences are similar to those found with the standard amperometric procedure (D). The DPD methods (Methods F and G) are operationally simpler for determining free chlorine than the amperometric titration. Procedures are given for estimating the separate mono- and dichloramine and combined fractions. High concentrations of monochloramine interfere with the free chlorine determination unless the reaction is stopped with arsenite or thioacetamide. In addition, the DPD methods are subject to interference by oxidized forms of manganese unless compensated for by a blank.

The amperometric and DPD methods are unaffected by dichloramine concentrations in the range of 0 to 9 mg Cl as Cl_2/L in the determination of free chlorine. Nitrogen trichloride, if present, may react partially as free chlorine in the amperometric, DPD, and FACTS methods. The extent of this interference in the DPD methods does not appear to be significant.

The free chlorine test, syringaldazine (FACTS, Method H) was developed specifically for free chlorine. It is unaffected by significant concentrations of monochloramine, dichloramine, nitrate, nitrite, and oxidized forms of manganese.[1]

Sample color and turbidity may interfere in all colorimetric procedures.

Organic contaminants may produce a false free chlorine reading in most colorimetric methods (see ¶ 3b below). Many strong oxidizing agents interfere in the measurement of free chlorine in all methods. Such interferences include bromine, chlorine dioxide, iodine, permanganate, hydrogen peroxide, and ozone. However, the reduced forms of these compounds—bromide, chloride, iodide, manganous ion, and oxygen, in the absence of other oxidants, do not interfere. Reducing agents such as ferrous compounds, hydrogen sulfide, and oxidizable organic matter generally do not interfere.

b. *Wastewaters:* The determination of total chlorine in samples containing organic matter presents special problems. Because of the presence of ammonia, amines, and organic compounds, particularly organic nitrogen, residual chlorine exists in a combined state. A considerable residual may exist in this form, but at the same time there may be appreciable unsatisfied chlorine demand. Addition of reagents in the determination may change these relationships so that residual chlorine is lost during the analysis. Only the DPD method for total chlorine is performed under neutral pH conditions. In wastewater, the differentiation between free chlorine and combined chlorine ordinarily is not made because wastewater chlorination seldom is carried far enough to produce free chlorine.

The determination of residual chlorine in industrial wastes is similar to that in domestic wastewater when the waste contains organic matter, but may be similar to the determination in water when the waste is low in organic matter.

None of these methods is applicable to estuarine or marine waters because the bromide is converted to bromine and bromamines, which are detected as free or total chlorine. A procedure for estimating this interference is available for the DPD method.

Although the methods given below are useful for the determination of residual chlorine in wastewaters and treated effluents, select the method in accordance with sample composition. Some industrial wastes, or mixtures of wastes with domestic wastewater, may require special precautions and modifications to obtain satisfactory results.

Determine free chlorine in wastewater by any of the methods provided that known interfering substances are absent or appropriate correction techniques are used. The amperometric method is the method of choice because it is not subject to interference from color, turbidity, iron, manganese, or nitrite nitrogen. The DPD method is subject to interference from high concentrations of monochloramine, which is avoided by adding thioacetamide immediately after reagent addition. Oxidized forms of manganese at all levels encountered in water will interfere in all methods except in the free chlorine measurement of amperometric titrations and FACTS, but a blank correction for manganese can be made in Methods F and G.

The FACTS method is unaffected by concentrations of monochloramine, dichloramine, nitrite, iron, manganese, and other interfering compounds normally found in domestic wastewaters.

For total chlorine in samples containing significant amounts of organic matter, use either the DPD methods (F and G), amperometric, or iodometric back titration method (C) to prevent contact between the full concentration of liberated iodine and the sample. With Method C, do not use the starch-iodide end point if the concentration is less than 1 mg/L. In the absence of interference, the amperometric and starch-iodide end points give concordant results. The amperometric end point is inherently more sensitive and is free of interference from color and turbidity, which can cause difficulty with the starch-iodide end point. On the other hand, certain metals, surface-active agents, and complex anions in some industrial wastes interfere in the amperometric titration and indicate the need for another method for such wastewaters. Silver in the form of soluble silver cyanide complex, in concentrations of 1.0 mg Ag/L, poisons the cell at pH 4.0 but not at 7.0. The silver ion, in the absence of the cyanide complex, gives extensive response in the current at pH 4.0 and gradually poisons the cell at all pH levels. Cuprous copper in the soluble copper cyanide ion, in concentrations of 5 mg Cu/L or less, poisons the cell at pH 4.0 and 7.0. Although iron and nitrite may interfere with this method, minimize the interference by buffering to pH 4.0 before adding KI. Oxidized forms of manganese interfere in all methods for total chlorine including amperometric titration. An unusually high content of organic matter may cause uncertainty in the end point.

Regardless of end-point detection, either phenylarsine oxide or thiosulfate may be used as the standard reducing reagent at pH 4. The former is more stable and is preferred.

The DPD titrimetric and colorimetric

methods (F and G, respectively) are applicable to determining total chlorine in polluted waters. In addition, both DPD procedures and the amperometric titration method allow for estimating monochloramine and dichloramine fractions. Because all methods for total chlorine depend on the stoichiometric production of iodine, waters containing iodine-reducing substances may not be analyzed accurately by these methods, especially where iodine remains in the solution for a significant time. This problem occurs in Methods B and D. The back titration procedure (C) and Methods F and G cause immediate reaction of the iodine generated so that it has little chance to react with other iodine-reducing substances.

In all colorimetric procedures, compensate for color and turbidity by using color and turbidity blanks.

A method (I) for total residual chlorine using a potentiometric iodide electrode is proposed. This method is suitable for analysis of chlorine residuals in natural and treated waters and wastewater effluents. No differentiation of free and combined chlorine is possible. This procedure is an adaptation of other iodometric techniques and is subject to the same inferences.

4. Sampling and Storage

Chlorine in aqueous solution is not stable, and the chlorine content of samples or solutions, particularly weak solutions, will decrease rapidly. Exposure to sunlight or other strong light or agitation will accelerate the reduction of chlorine. Therefore, start chlorine determinations immediately after sampling, avoiding excessive light and agitation. Do not store samples to be analyzed for chlorine.

5. Reference

1. COOPER, W.J., N.M. ROSCHER & R.A. SLIFER. 1982. Determining free available chlorine by DPD-colorimetric, DPD-steadifac (colorimetric) and FACTS procedures. *J. Amer. Water Works Assoc.* 74:362.

6. Bibliography

MARKS, H.C., D.B. WILLIAMS & G.U. GLASGOW. 1951. Determination of residual chlorine compounds. *J. Amer. Water Works Assoc.* 43:201.

NICOLSON, N.J. 1965. An evaluation of the methods for determining residual chlorine in water, Part 1. Free chlorine. *Analyst* 90:187.

WHITTLE, G.P. & A. LAPTEFF, JR. 1973. New analytical techniques for the study of water disinfection. *In* Chemistry of Water Supply, Treatment, and Distribution, p. 63. Ann Arbor Science Publishers, Ann Arbor, Mich.

GUTER, W.J., W.J. COOPER & C.A. SORBER. 1974. Evaluation of existing field test kits for determining free chlorine residuals in aqueous solutions. *J. Amer. Water Works Assoc.* 66:38.

4500-Cl B.   Iodometric Method I

1. General Discussion

a. Principle: Chlorine will liberate free iodine from potassium iodide (KI) solutions at pH 8 or less. The liberated iodine is titrated with a standard solution of sodium thiosulfate ($Na_2S_2O_3$) with starch as the indicator. Titrate at pH 3 to 4 because the reaction is not stoichiometric at neutral pH due to partial oxidation of thiosulfate to sulfate.

b. Interference: Oxidized forms of manganese and other oxidizing agents interfere. Reducing agents such as organic sulfides also interfere. Although the neutral titration minimizes the interfering effect of ferric and nitrite ions, the acid titration is preferred because some forms of combined chlorine do not react at pH 7. Use only acetic acid for the acid titration; sulfuric acid (H_2SO_4) will increase interferences;

never use hydrochloric acid (HCl). See Section A.3 for discussion of other interferences.

c. *Minimum detectable concentration:* The minimum detectable concentration approximates 40 μg Cl as Cl_2/L if $0.01N$ $Na_2S_2O_3$ is used with a 1000-mL sample. Concentrations below 1 mg/L cannot be determined accurately by the starch-iodide end point used in this method. Lower concentrations can be measured with the amperometric end point in Methods C and D.

2. Reagents

a. *Acetic acid,* conc (glacial).

b. *Potassium iodide,* KI, crystals.

c. *Standard sodium thiosulfate,* $0.1N$: Dissolve 25 g $Na_2S_2O_3 \cdot 5H_2O$ in 1 L freshly boiled distilled water and standardize against potassium bi-iodate or potassium dichromate after at least 2 weeks storage. This initial storage is necessary to allow oxidation of any bisulfite ion present. Use boiled distilled water and add a few milliliters chloroform ($CHCl_3$) to minimize bacterial decomposition.

Standardize $0.1N$ $Na_2S_2O_3$ by one of the following:

1) Iodate method—Dissolve 3.249 g anhydrous potassium bi-iodate, $KH(IO_3)_2$, primary standard quality, or 3.567 g KIO_3 dried at 103 $\pm$ 2°C for 1 h, in distilled water and dilute to 1000 mL to yield a $0.1000N$ solution. Store in a glass-stoppered bottle.

To 80 mL distilled water, add, with constant stirring, 1 mL conc H_2SO_4, 10.00 mL $0.1000N$ $KH(IO_3)_2$, and 1 g KI. Titrate immediately with $0.1N$ $Na_2S_2O_3$ titrant until the yellow color of the liberated iodine almost is discharged. Add 1 mL starch indicator solution and continue titrating until the blue color disappears.

2) Dichromate method—Dissolve 4.904 g anhydrous potassium dichromate, $K_2Cr_2O_7$, of primary standard quality, in distilled water and dilute to 1000 mL to

yield a $0.1000N$ solution. Store in a glass-stoppered bottle.

Proceed as in the iodate method, with the following exceptions: Substitute 10.00 mL $0.1000N$ $K_2Cr_2O_7$ for iodate and let reaction mixture stand 6 min in the dark before titrating with $0.1N$ $Na_2S_2O_3$ titrant.

$$\text{Normality } Na_2S_2O_3 = \frac{1}{\text{mL } Na_2S_2O_3 \text{ consumed}}$$

d. *Standard sodium thiosulfate titrant,* $0.01N$ *or* $0.025N$: Improve the stability of $0.01N$ or $0.025N$ $Na_2S_2O_3$ by diluting an aged $0.1N$ solution, made as directed above, with freshly boiled distilled water. Add 4 g sodium borate and 10 mg mercuric iodide/L solution. For accurate work, standardize this solution daily in accordance with the directions given above, using $0.01N$ or $0.025N$ iodate or $K_2Cr_2O_7$. Use sufficient volumes of these standard solutions so that their final dilution is not greater than 1 + 4. To speed up operations where many samples must be titrated use an automatic buret of a type in which rubber does not come in contact with the solution. Standard titrants, $0.0100N$ and $0.0250N$, are equivalent, respectively, to 354.5 μg and 886.3 μg Cl as Cl_2/1.00 mL.

e. *Starch indicator solution:* To 5 g starch (potato, arrowroot, or soluble), add a little cold water and grind in a mortar to a thin paste. Pour into 1 L of boiling distilled water, stir, and let settle overnight. Use clear supernate. Preserve with 1.25 g salicylic acid, 4 g zinc chloride, or a combination of 4 g sodium propionate and 2 g sodium azide/L starch solution. Some commercial starch substitutes are satisfactory.

f. *Standard iodine,* $0.1N$: See C.3g.

g. *Dilute standard iodine,* $0.0282N$: See C.3h.

3. Procedure

a. *Volume of sample:* Select a sample volume that will require no more than 20 mL $0.01N$ $Na_2S_2O_3$ and no less than 0.2 mL for the starch-iodide end point. For a chlorine range of 1 to 10 mg/L, use a 500-mL sample; above 10 mg/L, use proportionately less sample. Use smaller samples and volumes of titrant with the amperometric end point.

b. Preparation for titration: Place 5 mL acetic acid, or enough to reduce the pH to between 3.0 and 4.0, in a flask or white porcelain casserole. Add about 1 g KI estimated on a spatula. Pour sample in and mix with a stirring rod.

c. Titration: Titrate away from direct sunlight. Add $0.025N$ or $0.01N$ $Na_2S_2O_3$ from a buret until the yellow color of the liberated iodine almost is discharged. Add 1 mL starch solution and titrate until blue color is discharged.

If the titration is made with $0.025N$ $Na_2S_2O_3$ instead of $0.01N$, then, with a 1-L sample, 1 drop is equivalent to about 50 $\mu g/L$. It is not possible to discern the end point with greater accuracy.

d. Blank titration: Correct result of sample titration by determining blank contributed by oxidizing or reducing reagent impurities. The blank also compensates for the concentration of iodine bound to starch at the end point.

Take a volume of distilled water corresponding to the sample used for titration in ¶s *3a-c*, add 5 mL acetic acid, 1 g KI, and 1 mL starch solution. Perform blank titration as in 1) or 2) below, whichever applies.

1) If a blue color develops, titrate with $0.01N$ or $0.025N$ $Na_2S_2O_3$ to disappearance of blue color and record result. *B* (see ¶ 4, below) is negative.

2) If no blue color occurs, titrate with $0.0282N$ iodine solution until a blue color appears. Back-titrate with $0.01N$ or $0.025N$ $Na_2S_2O_3$ and record the difference. *B* is positive.

Before calculating the chlorine concentration, subtract the blank titration of ¶ 1) from the sample titration; or, if necessary, add the net equivalent value of the blank titration of ¶ 2).

4. Calculation

For standardizing chlorine solution for temporary standards:

$$\text{mg Cl as } Cl_2/mL = \frac{(A \pm B) \times N \times 35.45}{mL \text{ sample}}$$

For determining total available residual chlorine in a water sample:

$$\text{mg Cl as } Cl_2/L = \frac{(A \pm B) \times N \times 35\,450}{mL \text{ sample}}$$

where:
   A = mL titration for sample,
   B = mL titration for blank (positive or negative), and
   N = normality of $Na_2S_2O_3$.

5. Precision and Bias

Published studies[1,2] give the results of nine methods used to analyze synthetic water samples without interferences; variations of some of the methods appear in this edition. More current data are not now available.

6. References

1. Water Chlorine (Residual) No. 1. 1969. Analytical Reference Service Rep. No. 35, U.S. Environmental Protection Agency, Cincinnati, Ohio.
2. Water Chlorine (Residual) No. 2. 1971. Analytical Reference Service Rep. No. 40, U.S. Environmental Protection Agency, Cincinnati, Ohio.

7. Bibliography

LEA, C. 1933. Chemical control of sewage chlorination. The use and value of orthotolidine test. *J. Soc. Chem. Ind.* (London) 52:245T.
AMERICAN WATER WORKS ASSOCIATION. 1943. Committee report. Control of chlorination. *J. Amer. Water Works Assoc.* 35:1315.
MARKS, H.C., R. JOINER & F.B. STRANDSKOV.

1948. Amperometric titration of residual chlorine in sewage. *Water Sewage Works* 95:175.

STRANDSKOV, F.B. , H.C. MARKS & D.H. HOR-CHIFR. 1949. Application of a new residual chlorine method to effluent chlorination. *Sewage Works J.* 21:23.

NUSBAUM, I. & L.A. MEYERSON. 1951. Determination of chlorine demands and chlorine residuals in sewage. *Sewage Ind. Wastes* 23:968.

MARKS, H.C., & N.S. CHAMBERLIN. 1953. Determination of residual chlorine in metal finishing wastes. *Anal. Chem.* 24:1885.

4500-Cl C.   Iodometric Method II

1. General Discussion

a. *Principle:* In this method, used for wastewater analysis, the end-point signal is reversed because the unreacted standard reducing agent (phenylarsine oxide or thiosulfate) remaining in the sample is titrated with standard iodine or standard iodate, rather than the iodine released being titrated directly. This indirect procedure is necessary regardless of the method of end-point detection, to avoid contact between the full concentration of liberated iodine and the wastewater.

When iodate is used as a back titrant, use only phosphoric acid. Do not use acetate buffer.

b. *Interference:* Oxidized forms of manganese and other oxidizing agents give positive interferences. Reducing agents such as organic sulfides do not interfere as much as in Method B. Minimize iron and nitrite interference by buffering to pH 4.0 before adding potassium iodide (KI). An unusually high content of organic matter may cause some uncertainty in the end point. Whenever manganese, iron, and other interferences definitely are absent, reduce this uncertainty and improve precision by acidifying to pH 1.0. Control interference from more than 0.2 mg nitrite/L with phosphoric acid-sulfamic acid reagent. A larger fraction of organic chloramines will react at lower pH along with interfering substances. See Section A.3 for a discussion of other interferences.

2. Apparatus

For a description of the amperometric end-point detection apparatus and a discussion of its use, see D.2a.

3. Reagents

a. *Standard phenylarsine oxide solution,* 0.005 64N: Dissolve approximately 0.8 g phenylarsine oxide powder in 150 mL 0.3N NaOH solution. After settling, decant 110 mL into 800 mL distilled water and mix thoroughly. Bring to pH 6 to 7 with 6N HCl and dilute to 950 mL with distilled water. CAUTION: *Severe poison, cancer suspect agent.*

Standardization—Accurately measure 5 to 10 mL freshly standardized 0.0282N iodine solution into a flask and add 1 mL KI solution. Titrate with phenylarsine oxide solution, using the amperometric end point (Method D) or starch solution (see B.2e) as an indicator. Adjust to 0.005 64N and recheck against the standard iodine solution; 1.00 mL = 200 μg available chlorine. (CAUTION: *Toxic—take care to avoid ingestion.*)

b. *Standard sodium thiosulfate solution,* 0.1N: See B.2c.

c. *Standard sodium thiosulfate solution,* 0.005 64N: Prepare by diluting 0.1N $Na_2S_2O_3$. For maximum stability of the dilute solution, prepare by diluting an aged 0.1N solution with freshly boiled distilled water (to minimize bacterial action) and add 10 mg HgI_2 and 4 g $Na_4B_4O_7$/L. Standardize daily as directed in B.2c using 0.005

64N $K_2Cr_2O_7$, or iodate solution. Use sufficient volume of sample so that the final dilution does not exceed 1 + 2. Use an automatic buret of a type in which rubber does not come in contact with the solution. 1.00 mL = 200 μg available chlorine.

d. Potassium iodide, KI, crystals.

e. Acetate buffer solution, pH 4.0: Dissolve 146 g anhydrous $NaC_2H_3O_2$, or 243 g $NaC_2H_3O_2 \cdot 3H_2O$, in 400 mL distilled water, add 480 g conc acetic acid, and dilute to 1 L with chlorine-demand-free water.

f. Standard arsenite solution, 0.1N: Accurately weigh a stoppered weighing bottle containing approximately 4.95 g arsenic trioxide, As_2O_3. Transfer without loss to a 1-L volumetric flask and again weigh bottle. Do not attempt to brush out adhering oxide. Moisten As_2O_3 with water and add 15 g NaOH and 100 mL distilled water. Swirl flask contents gently to dissolve. Dilute to 250 mL with distilled water and saturate with CO_2, thus converting all NaOH to $NaHCO_3$. Dilute to mark, stopper, and mix thoroughly. This solution will preserve its titer almost indefinitely. (CAUTION: *Severe poison. Cancer suspect agent.*)

$$\text{Normality} = \frac{\text{g } As_2O_3}{49.455}$$

g. Standard iodine solution, 0.1N: Dissolve 40 g KI in 25 mL chlorine-demand-free water, add 13 g resublimed iodine, and stir until dissolved. Transfer to a 1-L volumetric flask and dilute to mark.

Standardization—Accurately measure 40 to 50 mL 0.1N arsenite solution into a flask and titrate with 0.1N iodine solution, using starch solution as indicator. To obtain accurate results, insure that the solution is saturated with CO_2 at end of titration by passing current of CO_2 through solution for a few minutes just before end point is reached, or add a few drops of HCl to liberate sufficient CO_2 to saturate solu-

tion. Alternatively standardize against $Na_2S_2O_3$; see B.2c1).

Optionally, prepare 0.1000N iodine solution directly as a standard solution by weighing 12.69 g primary standard resublimed iodine. Because I_2 may be volatilized and lost from both solid and solution, transfer the solid immediately to KI as specified above. Never let solution stand in open containers for extended periods.

h. Standard iodine titrant, 0.0282N: Dissolve 25 g KI in a little distilled water in a 1-L volumetric flask, add correct amount of 0.1N iodine solution exactly standardized to yield a 0.0282N solution, and dilute to 1 L with chlorine-demand-free water. For accurate work, standardize daily according to directions in ¶ 3g above, using 5 to 10 mL of arsenite or $Na_2S_2O_3$ solution. Store in amber bottles or in the dark; protect solution from direct sunlight at all times and keep from all contact with rubber.

i. Starch indicator: See B.2e.

j. Standard iodate titrant, 0.005 64N: Dissolve 201.2 mg primary standard grade KIO_3, dried for 1 h at 103°C, or 183.3 mg primary standard anhydrous potassium biiodate in distilled water and dilute to 1 L.

k. Phosphoric acid solution, H_3PO_4, 1 + 9.

l. Phosphoric acid-sulfamic acid solution: Dissolve 20 g NH_2SO_3H in 1 L 1 + 9 phosphoric acid.

m. Chlorine-demand-free water: Prepare chlorine-demand-free water from good-quality distilled or deionized water by adding sufficient chlorine to give 5 mg/L free chlorine. After standing 2 d this solution should contain at least 2 mg/L free chlorine; if not, discard and obtain better-quality water. Remove remaining free chlorine by placing container in sunlight or irradiating with an ultraviolet lamp. After several hours take sample, add KI, and measure total chlorine with a colorimetric method using a nessler tube to increase sensitivity. Do not use before last trace of free and combined chlorine has been removed.

Distilled water commonly contains ammonia and also may contain reducing agents. Collect good-quality distilled or deionized water in a sealed container from which water can be drawn by gravity. To the air inlet of the container add an H_2SO_4 trap consisting of a large test tube half filled with $1 + 1$ H_2SO_4 connected in series with a similar but empty test tube. Fit both test tubes with stoppers and inlet tubes terminating near the bottom of the tubes and outlet tubes terminating near the top of the tubes. Connect outlet tube of trap containing H_2SO_4 to the distilled water container, connect inlet tube to outlet of empty test tube. The empty test tube will prevent discharge to the atmosphere of H_2SO_4 due to temperature-induced pressure changes. Stored in such a container, chlorine-demand-free water is stable for several weeks unless bacterial growth occurs.

4. Procedure

a. Preparation for titration:

1) Volume of sample—For chlorine concentrations of 10 mg/L or less, titrate 200 mL. For greater chlorine concentrations, use proportionately less sample and dilute to 200 mL with chlorine-demand-free water. Use a sample of such size that not more than 10 mL phenylarsine oxide solution is required.

2) Preparation for titration—Measure 5 mL 0.005 64N phenylarsine oxide or thiosulfate for chlorine concentrations from 2 to 5 mg/L, and 10 mL for concentrations of 5 to 10 mg/L, into a flask or casserole for titration with standard iodine or iodate. Start stirring. For titration by amperometry or standard iodine, also add excess KI (approximately 1 g) and 4 mL acetate buffer solution or enough to reduce the pH to between 3.5 and 4.2.

b. Titration: Use one of the following:

1) Amperometric titration—Add 0.0282N iodine titrant in small increments from a 1-mL buret or pipet. Observe meter needle response as iodine is added: the pointer remains practically stationary until the end point is approached, whereupon each iodine increment causes a temporary deflection of the microammeter, with the pointer dropping back to its original position. Stop titration at end point when a small increment of iodine titrant gives a definite pointer deflection upscale and the pointer does not return promptly to its original position. Record volume of iodine titrant used to reach end point.

2) Colorimetric (iodine) titration—Add 1 mL starch solution and titrate with 0.0282N iodine to the first appearance of blue color that persists after complete mixing.

3) Colorimetric (iodate) titration—To suitable flask or casserole add 200 mL chlorine-demand-free water and add, with agitation, the required volume of reductant, an excess of KI (approximately 0.5 g), 2 mL 10% H_3PO_4 solution, and 1 mL starch solution in the order given, and titrate immediately* with 0.005 64N iodate solution to the first appearance of a blue color that persists after complete mixing. Designate volume of iodate solution used as A. Repeat procedure, substituting 200 mL sample for the 200 mL chlorine-demand-free water. If sample is colored or turbid, titrate to the first change in color, using for comparison another portion of sample with H_3PO_4 added. Designate this volume of iodate solution as B.

5. Calculation

a. Titration with standard iodine:

$$\text{mg Cl as Cl}_2/\text{L} = \frac{(A - 5B) \times 200}{C}$$

---

*Titration may be delayed up to 10 min without appreciable error if H_3PO_4 is not added until immediately before titration.

where:

A = mL 0.005 64 N reductant,
B = mL 0.0282 N I_2, and
C = mL sample.

b. Titration with standard iodate:

$$\text{mg Cl as Cl}_2/\text{L} = \frac{(A - B) \times 200}{C}$$

where:

A = mL $Na_2S_2O_3$,
B = mL iodate required to titrate $Na_2S_2O_3$, and
C = mL sample.

6. Bibliography

See B.7.

4500-Cl D.   Amperometric Titration Method

1. General Discussion

Amperometric titration requires a higher degree of skill and care than the colorimetric methods. Chlorine residuals over 2 mg/L are measured best by means of smaller samples or by dilution with water that has neither residual chlorine nor a chlorine demand. The method can be used to determine total chlorine and can differentiate between free and combined chlorine. A further differentiation into monochloramine and dichloramine fractions is possible by control of KI concentration and pH.

a. Principle: The amperometric method is a special adaptation of the polarographic principle. Free chlorine is titrated at a pH between 6.5 and 7.5, a range in which the combined chlorine reacts slowly. The combined chlorine, in turn, is titrated in the presence of the proper amount of KI in the pH range 3.5 to 4.5. When free chlorine is determined, the pH must not be greater than 7.5 because the reaction becomes sluggish at higher pH values, nor less than 6.5 because at lower pH values some combined chlorine may react even in the absence of iodide. When combined chlorine is determined, the pH must not be less than 3.5 because of increased interferences at lower pH values, nor greater than 4.5 because the iodide reaction is not quantitative at higher pH values. The tendency of monochlora-

mine to react more readily with iodide than does dichloramine provides a means for further differentiation. The addition of a small amount of KI in the neutral pH range enables estimation of monochloramine content. Lowering the pH into the acid range and increasing the KI concentration allows the separate determination of dichloramine.

Organic chloramines can be measured as free chlorine, monochloramine, or dichloramine, depending on the activity of the chlorine in the organic compound.

Phenylarsine oxide is stable even in dilute solution and each mole reacts with two equivalents of halogen. A special amperometric cell is used to detect the end point of the residual chlorine-phenylarsine oxide titration. The cell consists of a nonpolarizable reference electrode that is immersed in a salt solution and a readily polarizable noble-metal electrode that is in contact both with the salt solution and the sample being titrated. In some applications, endpoint selectivity is improved by adding +200 mV to the platinum electrode versus silver, silver chloride. Another approach to end-point detection uses dual platinum electrodes, a mercury cell with voltage divider to impress a potential across the electrodes, and a microammeter. If there is no chlorine residual in the sample, the microammeter reading will be comparatively low because of cell polarization. The greater the residual, the greater the microammeter reading. The meter acts merely as a null-point indicator—that is, the actual meter reading is not important, but rather the relative readings as the titration proceeds. The gradual addition of phenylarsine oxide causes the cell to become more and more polarized because of the decrease in chlorine. The end point is recognized when no further decrease in meter reading can be obtained by adding more phenylarsine oxide.

b. Interference: Accurate determinations of free chlorine cannot be made in the presence of nitrogen trichloride, NCl_3, or chlorine dioxide, which titrate partly as free chlorine. When present, NCl_3 can titrate partly as free chlorine and partly as dichloramine, contributing a positive error in both fractions at a rate of approximately 0.1%/min. Some organic chloramines also can be titrated in each step. Monochloramine can intrude into the free chlorine fraction and dichloramine can interfere in the monochloramine fraction, especially at high temperatures and prolonged titration times. Free halogens other than chlorine also will titrate as free chlorine. Combined chlorine reacts with iodide ions to produce iodine. When titration for free chlorine follows a combined chlorine titration, which requires addition of KI, erroneous results may occur unless the measuring cell is rinsed thoroughly with distilled water between titrations.

Interference from copper has been noted in samples taken from copper pipe or after heavy copper sulfate treatment of reservoirs, with metallic copper plating out on the electrode. Silver ions also poison the electrode. Interference occurs in some highly colored waters and in waters containing surface-active agents. Very low temperatures slow response of measuring cell and longer time is required for the titration, but precision is not affected. A reduction in reaction rate is caused by pH values above 7.5; overcome this by buffering all samples to pH 7.0 or less. On the other hand, some substances, such as manganese, nitrite, and iron, do not interfere. The violent stirring of some commercial titrators can lower chlorine values by volatilization. When dilution is used for samples containing high chlorine content, take care that the dilution water is free of chlorine and ammonia and possesses no chlorine demand.

See A.3 for a discussion of other interferences.

2. Apparatus

a. End-point detection apparatus, consisting of a cell unit connected to a microammeter, with necessary electrical accessories. The cell unit includes a noble-metal electrode of sufficient surface area, a salt bridge to provide an electrical connection without diffusion of electrolyte, and a reference electrode of silver-silver chloride in a saturated sodium chloride solution connected into the circuit by means of the salt bridge. Numerous commercial systems are available.

Keep platinum electrode free of deposits and foreign matter. Vigorous chemical cleaning generally is unnecessary. Occasional mechanical cleaning with a suitable abrasive usually is sufficient. Keep salt bridge in good operating condition; do not allow it to become plugged nor permit appreciable flow of electrolyte through it. Keep solution surrounding reference electrode free of contamination and maintain it at constant composition by insuring an adequate supply of undissolved salt at all times. A cell with two metal electrodes polarized by a small DC potential also may be used. (See Bibliography.)

b. Agitator, designed to give adequate agitation at the noble-metal electrode surface to insure proper sensitivity. Thoroughly clean agitator and exposed electrode system to remove all chlorine-consuming contaminants by immersing them in water containing 1 to 2 mg/L free chlorine for a few minutes. Add KI to the same water and let agitator and electrodes remain immersed for 5 min. After thorough rinsing with chlorine-demand-free water or the sample to be tested, sensitized electrodes and agitator are ready for use. Remove iodide reagent completely from cell.

c. Buret: Commercial titrators usually are equipped with suitable burets (1 mL). Manual burets are available.*

d. Glassware, exposed to water containing at least 10 mg/L chlorine for 3 h or more before use and rinsed with chlorine-demand-free water.

3. Reagents

a. Standard phenylarsine oxide titrant: See C.3a.

b. Phosphate buffer solution, pH 7: Dissolve 25.4 g anhydrous KH_2PO_4 and 34.1 g anhydrous Na_2HPO_4 in 800 mL distilled water. Add 2 mL sodium hypochlorite solution containing 1% chlorine and mix thoroughly. Protect from sunlight for 2 d. Determine that free chlorine still remains in the solution. Then expose to sunlight until no chlorine remains. If necessary, carry out the final dechlorination with an ultraviolet lamp. Determine that no total chlorine remains by adding KI and measuring with one of the colorimetric tests. Dilute to 1 L with distilled water and filter if any precipitate is present.

c. Potassium iodide solution: Dissolve 50 g KI and dilute to 1 L with freshly boiled and cooled distilled water. Store in the dark in a brown glass-stoppered bottle, preferably in the refrigerator. Discard when solution becomes yellow.

d. Acetate buffer solution, pH 4: See C.3e.

---

*Kimax 17110-F, 5 mL, Kimble Products, Box 1035, Toledo, Ohio, or equivalent.

4. Procedure

a. Sample volume: Select a sample volume requiring no more than 2 mL phenylarsine oxide titrant. Thus, for chlorine concentrations of 2 mg/L or less, take a 200-mL sample; for chlorine levels in excess of 2 mg/L, use 100 mL or proportionately less.

b. Free chlorine: Unless sample pH is known to be between 6.5 and 7.5, add 1 mL pH 7 phosphate buffer solution to produce a pH of 6.5 to 7.5. Titrate with standard phenylarsine oxide titrant, observing current changes on microammeter. Add titrant in progressively smaller increments until all needle movement ceases. Make successive buret readings when needle action becomes sluggish, signaling approach of end point. Subtract last very small increment that causes no needle response because of overtitration. Alternatively, use a system involving continuous current measurements and determine end point mathematically.

Continue titrating for combined chlorine as described in ¶ 4c below or for the separate monochloramine and dichloramine fractions as detailed in ¶s 4e and 4f.

c. Combined chlorine: To sample remaining from free-chlorine titration add 1.00 mL KI solution and 1 mL acetate buffer solution, in that order. Titrate with phenylarsine oxide titrant to the end point, as above. Do not refill buret but simply continue titration after recording figure for free chlorine. Again subtract last increment to give amount of titrant actually used in reaction with chlorine. (If titration was continued without refilling buret, this figure represents total chlorine. Subtracting free chlorine from total gives combined chlorine.) Wash apparatus and sample cell thoroughly to remove iodide ion to avoid inaccuracies when the titrator is used subsequently for a free chlorine determination.

d. Separate samples: If desired, determine total chlorine and free chlorine on separate samples. If sample pH is between 3.5 and 9.5 and total chlorine alone is required, treat sample immediately with 1 mL KI solution followed by 1 mL acetate buffer solution, and titrate with phenylarsine oxide titrant as described in ¶ 4c preceding.

e. Monochloramine: After titrating for free chlorine, add 0.2 mL KI solution to same sample and, without refilling buret, continue titration with phenylarsine oxide titrant to end point. Subtract last increment to obtain net volume of titrant consumed by monochloramine.

f. Dichloramine: Add 1 mL acetate buffer solution and 1 mL KI solution to same sample and titrate final dichloramine fraction as described above.

5. Calculation

Convert individual titrations for free chlorine, combined chlorine, total chlorine, monochloramine, and dichloramine by the following equation:

$$\text{mg Cl as Cl}_2/\text{L} = \frac{A \times 200}{\text{mL sample}}$$

where:

A = mL phenylarsine oxide titration.

6. Precision and Bias

See B.5.

7. Bibliography

FOULK, C.W. & A.T. BAWDEN. 1926. A new type of endpoint in electrometric titration and its application to iodimetry. *J. Amer. Chem. Soc.* 48:2045.

MARKS, H.C. & J. R. GLASS. 1942. A new method of determining residual chlorine. *J. Amer. Water Works Assoc.* 34:1227.

HALLER, J.F. & S.S. LISTEK. 1948. Determination of chloride dioxide and other active chlorine compounds in water. *Anal. Chem.* 20:639.

MAHAN, W.A. 1949. Simplified amperometric titration apparatus for determining residual chlorine in water. *Water Sewage Works* 96:171.

KOLTHOFF, I.M. & J.J. LINGANE. 1952. Polarography, 2nd ed. Interscience Publishers, New York, N.Y.

MORROW, J.J. 1966. Residual chlorine determination with dual polarizable electrodes. *J. Amer. Water Works Assoc.* 58:363.

4500-Cl E. Low-Level Amperometric Titration Method

1. General Discussion

Detection and quantification of chlorine residuals below 0.2 mg/L require special modifications to the amperometric titration procedure. With these modifications chlorine concentrations at the 10-μg/L level can be measured. It is not possible to differentiate between free and combined chlorine forms. Oxidizing agents that interfere with the amperometric titration method (D) will interfere.

a. Principle: This method modifies D by using a more dilute titrant and a graphical procedure to determine the end point.

b. Interference: See D.1b.

2. Apparatus

See D.2.

3. Reagents

a. Potassium bi-iodate, 0.002 256N: Dissolve 0.7332 g anhydrous potassium bi-iodate, KH(IO₃)₂, in 500 mL chlorine-free distilled water and dilute to 1000 mL. Dilute 10.00 mL to 100.0 mL with chlorine-free distilled water. Use only freshly prepared solution for the standardization of phenylarsine oxide.

b. Potassium iodide, KI crystals.

c. Low-strength phenylarsine oxide titrant, 0.000 564N: Dilute 10.00 mL of

0.005 64N phenylarsine oxide (see C.3a) to 100.0 mL with chlorine-demand-free water (see C.3m).

Standardization—Dilute 5.00 mL 0.002 256N potassium bi-iodate to 200 mL with chlorine-free water. Add approximately 1.5 g KI and stir to dissolve. Add 1 mL acetate buffer and let stand in the dark for 6 min. Titrate using the amperometric titrator and determine the equivalence point as indicated below.

Normality = 0.000 564 × 2.00/A

where A = mL phenylarsine oxide titrant required to reach the equivalence point of standard bi-iodate.

d. *Acetate buffer solution*, pH 4: See C.3e.

4. Procedure

Select a sample volume requiring no more than 2 mL phenylarsine oxide titrant. A 200-mL sample will be adequate for samples containing less than 0.2 mg total chlorine/L.

Before beginning titration, rinse buret with titrant several times. Rinse sample container with distilled water and then with sample. Add 200 mL sample to sample container and approximately 1.5 g KI. Dissolve, using a stirrer or mixer. Add 1 mL acetate buffer and place container in end-point detection apparatus. When the current signal stabilizes, record the reading. Initially adjust meter to a near full-scale deflection. Titrate by adding small,

known, volumes of titrant. After each addition, record cumulative volume added and current reading when the signal stabilizes. If meter reading falls to near or below 10% of full-scale deflection, record low reading, readjust meter to near full-scale deflection, and record difference between low amount and readjusted high deflection. Add this value to all deflection readings for subsequent titrant additions. Continue adding titrant until no further meter deflection occurs. If fewer than three titrant additions were made before meter deflection ceased, discard sample and repeat analysis using smaller titrant increments.

Determine equivalence point by plotting total meter deflection against titrant volume added. Draw straight line through the first several points in the plot and a second, horizontal straight line corresponding to the final total deflection in the meter. Read equivalence point as the volume of titrant added at the intersection of these two lines.

5. Calculation

$$\text{mg Cl as Cl}_2/\text{L} = \frac{A \times 200 \times N}{B \times 0.000\ 564}$$

where:

A = mL titrant at equivalence point,
B = sample volume, mL, and
N = phenylarsine oxide normality.

6. Bibliography

BROOKS, A. S. & G. L. SEEGERT. 1979. Low-level chlorine analysis by amperometric titration. *J. Water Pollut. Control Fed.* 51:2636.

4500-Cl F.   DPD Ferrous Titrimetric Method

1. General Discussion

a. *Principle:* N,N-diethyl-p-phenylenediamine (DPD) is used as an indicator in the titrimetric procedure with ferrous ammonium sulfate (FAS). Where complete differentiation of chlorine species is not required, the procedure may be simplified to give only free and combined chlorine or total chlorine.

In the absence of iodide ion, free chlorine reacts instantly with DPD indicator to produce a red color. Subsequent addition of a small amount of iodide ion acts catalytically to cause monochloramine to produce color. Addition of iodide ion to excess evokes a rapid response from dichloramine. In the presence of iodide ion, part of the nitrogen trichloride (NCl_3) is included with dichloramine and part with free chlorine. A supplementary procedure based on adding iodide ion before DPD permits estimating proportion of NCl_3 appearing with free chlorine.

Chlorine dioxide (ClO_2) appears, to the extent of one-fifth of its total chlorine content, with free chlorine. A full response from ClO_2, corresponding to its total chlorine content, may be obtained if the sample first is acidified in the presence of iodide ion and subsequently is brought back to an approximately neutral pH by adding bicarbonate ion. Bromine, bromamine, and iodine react with DPD indicator and appear with free chlorine.

Addition of glycine before determination of free chlorine converts free chlorine to unreactive forms, with only bromine and iodine residuals remaining. Subtractions of these residuals from the residual measured without glycine permits differentiation of free chlorine from bromine and iodine.

b. pH control: For accurate results careful pH control is essential. At the proper pH of 6.2 to 6.5, the red colors produced may be titrated to sharp colorless end points. *Titrate as soon as the red color is formed in each step.* Too low a pH in the first step tends to make the monochloramine show in the free-chlorine step and the dichloramine in the monochloramine step. Too high a pH causes dissolved oxygen to give a color.

c. Temperature control: In all methods for differentiating free chlorine from chloramines, higher temperatures increase the tendency for chloramines to react and lead to increased apparent free-chlorine results.

Higher temperatures also increase color fading. Complete measurements rapidly, especially at higher temperature.

d. Interference: The most significant interfering substance likely to be encountered in water is oxidized manganese. To correct for this, place 5 mL buffer solution and 0.5 mL sodium arsenite solution in the titration flask. Add 100 mL sample and mix. Add 5 mL DPD indicator solution, mix, and titrate with standard FAS titrant until red color is discharged. Subtract reading from Reading *A* obtained by the normal procedure as described in ¶ 3*a*1) of this method or from the total chlorine reading obtained in the simplified procedure given in ¶ 3*a*4). If the combined reagent in powder form (see below) is used, first add KI and arsenite to the sample and mix, then add combined buffer-indicator reagent.

As an alternative to sodium arsenite use a 0.25% solution of thioacetamide, adding 0.5 mL to 100 mL sample.

Interference by copper up to approximately 10 mg Cu/L is overcome by the EDTA incorporated in the reagents. EDTA enhances stability of DPD indicator solution by retarding deterioration due to oxidation, and in the test itself, provides suppression of dissolved oxygen errors by preventing trace metal catalysis.

Chromate in excess of 2 mg/L interferes with end-point determination. Add barium chloride to mask this interference by precipitation.

High concentrations of combined chlorine can break through into the free chlorine fraction. *If free chlorine is to be measured in the presence of more than 0.5 mg/L combined chlorine, use the thioacetamide modification.* If this modification is not used, a color-development time in excess of 1 min leads to progressively greater interference from monochloramine. Adding thioacetamide (0.5 mL 0.25% solution to 100 mL) immediately after mixing DPD reagent with sample completely stops further reaction with combined chlorine in the free chlorine measurement. Continue immediately with FAS titration to obtain free chlorine. Obtain total chlorine from the normal procedure, i.e., without thioacetamide.

Because high concentrations of iodide are used to measure combined chlorine and only traces of iodide greatly increase chloramine interference in free chlorine measurements, take care to avoid iodide contamination by rinsing between samples or using separate glassware.

See A.3 for a discussion of other interferences.

e. Minimum detectable concentration: Approximately 18 μg Cl as Cl_2/L. This detection limit is achievable under ideal conditions; normal working detection limits typically are higher.

2. Reagents

a. Phosphate buffer solution: Dissolve 24 g anhydrous Na_2HPO_4 and 46 g anhydrous KH_2PO_4 in distilled water. Combine with 100 mL distilled water in which 800 mg disodium ethylenediamine tetraacetate dihydrate (EDTA) have been dissolved. Dilute to 1 L with distilled water and add 20 mg $HgCl_2$ to prevent mold growth and interference in the free chlorine test caused by any trace amounts of iodide in the reagents. (CAUTION: *$HgCl_2$ is toxic—take care to avoid ingestion*).

b. N,N-Diethyl-p-phenylenediamine (DPD) indicator solution: Dissolve 1 g DPD oxalate,* or 1.5 g DPD sulfate pentahydrate,† or 1.1 g anhydrous DPD sulfate in chlorine-free distilled water containing 8 mL 1 + 3 H_2SO_4 and 200 mg disodium EDTA. Make up to 1 L, store in a brown glass-stoppered bottle in the dark, and discard when discolored. Periodically check solution blank for absorbance and discard

---

*Eastman chemical No. 7102 or equivalent.

†Available from Gallard-Schlesinger Chemical Mfg. Corp., 584 Mineola Avenue, Carle Place, N.Y. 11514, or equivalent.

when absorbance at 515 nm exceeds 0.002/ cm. (The buffer and indicator sulfate are available commercially as a combined reagent in stable powder form.) CAUTION: *The oxalate is toxic—take care to avoid ingestion.*

c. Standard ferrous ammonium sulfate (FAS) titrant: Dissolve 1.106 g $Fe(NH_4)_2(SO_4)_2 \cdot 6H_2O$ in distilled water containing 1 mL 1 + 3 H_2SO_4 and make up to 1 L with freshly boiled and cooled distilled water. This standard may be used for 1 month, and the titer checked by potassium dichromate. For this purpose add 10 mL 1 + 5 H_2SO_4, 5 mL conc H_3PO_4, and 2 mL 0.1% barium diphenylamine sulfonate indicator to a 100-mL sample of FAS and titrate with 0.100N primary standard potassium dichromate to a violet end point that persists for 30 s. The FAS titrant is equivalent to 100 μg Cl as Cl_2/ 1.00 mL.

d. Potassium iodide, KI, crystals.

e. Potassium iodide solution: Dissolve 500 mg KI and dilute to 100 mL, using freshly boiled and cooled distilled water. Store in a brown glass-stoppered bottle, preferably in a refrigerator. Discard when solution becomes yellow.

f. Potassium dichromate solution: See B.2c2).

g. Barium diphenylaminesulfonate, 0.1%: Dissolve 0.1 g $(C_6H_5NHC_6H_4\text{-}4\text{-} SO_3)_2Ba$ in 100 mL distilled water.

h. Sodium arsenite solution: Dissolve 5.0 g $NaAsO_2$ in distilled water and dilute to 1 L. (CAUTION: *Toxic—take care to avoid ingestion.*)

i. Thioacetamide solution: Dissolve 250 mg CH_3CSNH_2 in 100 mL distilled water. (CAUTION: *Cancer suspect agent. Take care to avoid skin contact or ingestion.*)

j. Chlorine-demand-free water: See C.3m.

k. Glycine solution: Dissolve 20 g glycine (aminoacetic acid) in sufficient chlorine-demand-free water to bring to 100 mL total volume. Store under refrigerated conditions and discard if cloudiness develops.

l. Barium chloride crystals, $BaCl_2 \cdot 2H_2O$.

3. Procedure

The quantities given below are suitable for concentrations of total chlorine up to 5 mg/L. If total chlorine exceeds 5 mg/L, use a smaller sample and dilute to a total volume of 100 mL. Mix usual volumes of buffer reagent and DPD indicator solution, or usual amount of DPD powder, with distilled water *before* adding sufficient sample to bring total volume to 100 mL. (If sample is added before buffer, test does not work.)

If chromate is present (> 2 mg/L) add and mix 0.2 g $BaCl_2 \cdot 2H_2O$/100 mL sample before adding other reagents. If, in addition, sulfate is > 500 mg/L, use 0.4 g $BaCl_2 \cdot 2H_2O$/100 mL sample.

a. Free chlorine or chloramine: Place 5 mL each of buffer reagent and DPD indicator solution in titration flask and mix (or use about 500 mg DPD powder). Add 100 mL sample, or diluted sample, and mix.

1) Free chlorine—Titrate rapidly with standard FAS titrant until red color is discharged (Reading *A*).

2) Monochloramine—Add one very small crystal of KI (about 0.5 mg) or 0.1 mL (2 drops) KI solution and mix. Continue titrating until red color is discharged again (Reading *B*).

3) Dichloramine—Add several crystals KI (about 1 g) and mix to dissolve. Let stand for 2 min and continue titrating until red color is discharged (Reading *C*). For dichloramine concentrations greater than 1 mg/L, let stand 2 min more if color drift-back indicates slightly incomplete reaction. When dichloramine concentrations are not expected to be high, use half the specified amount of KI.

4) Simplified procedure for free and combined chlorine or total chlorine—Omit 2) above to obtain monochloramine and dichloramine together as combined chlorine. To obtain total chlorine in one reading, add full amount of KI at the start, with the specified amounts of buffer reagent and DPD indicator, and titrate after 2 min standing.

b. Nitrogen trichloride: Place one very small crystal of KI (about 0.5 mg) or 0.1 mL KI solution in a titration flask. Add 100 mL sample and mix. Add contents to a second flask containing 5 mL each of buffer reagent and DPD indicator solution (or add about 500 mg DPD powder direct to the first flask). Titrate rapidly with standard FAS titrant until red color is discharged (Reading *N*).

c. Free chlorine in presence of bromine or iodine: Determine free chlorine as in ¶ 3*a*1). To a second 100-mL sample, add 1 mL glycine solution before adding DPD and buffer. Titrate according to ¶ 3*a*1). Subtract the second reading from the first to obtain Reading A.

4. Calculation

For a 100-mL sample, 1.00 mL standard FAS titrant = 1.00 mg Cl as Cl_2/L.

Reading	NCl_3 Absent	NCl_3 Present
A	Free Cl	Free Cl
B − A	NH_2Cl	NH_2Cl
C − B	$NHCl_2$	$NHCl_2 +$ $\frac{1}{2}NCl_3$
N	—	Free Cl + $\frac{1}{2}NCl_3$
2(*N − A*)	—	NCl_3
C − N	—	$NHCl_2$

In the event that monochloramine is present with NCl_3, it will be included in *N*, in which case obtain NCl_3 from 2(*N − B*).

Chlorine dioxide, if present, is included in *A* to the extent of one-fifth of its total chlorine content.

In the simplified procedure for free and combined chlorine, only *A* (free Cl) and *C* (total Cl) are required. Obtain combined chlorine from *C − A*.

The result obtained in the simplified total chlorine procedure corresponds to C.

5. Precision and Bias

See B.5.

6. Bibliography

PALIN, A.T. 1957. The determination of free and combined chlorine in water by the use of diethyl-p-phenylene diamine. *J. Amer. Water Works Assoc.* 49:873.

PALIN, A.T. 1960. Colorimetric determination of chlorine dioxide in water. *Water Sewage Works* 107:457.

PALIN, A.T. 1961. The determination of free residual bromine in water. *Water Sewage Works* 108:461.

NICOLSON, N.J. 1963, 1965, 1966. Determination of chlorine in water, Parts 1, 2, and 3. Water Res. Assoc. Tech. Pap. Nos. 29, 47, and 53.

PALIN, A.T. 1967. Methods for determination, in water, of free and combined available chlorine, chlorine dioxide and chlorite, bromine, iodine, and ozone using diethyl-p-phenylenediamine (DPD). *J. Inst. Water Eng.* 21:537.

PALIN, A.T. 1968. Determination of nitrogen trichloride in water. *J. Amer. Water Works Assoc.* 60:847.

PALIN, A.T. 1975. Current DPD methods for residual halogen compounds and ozone in water. *J. Amer. Water Works Assoc.* 67:32.

Methods for the Examination of Waters and Associated Materials. Chemical Disinfecting Agents in Water and Effluents, and Chlorine Demand. 1980. Her Majesty's Stationery Off., London, England.

4500-Cl G. DPD Colorimetric Method

1. General Discussion

a. Principle: This is a colorimetric version of the DPD method and is based on the same principles. Instead of titration with standard ferrous ammonium sulfate (FAS) solution as in the titrimetric method, a colorimetric procedure is used.

b. Interference: See A.3 and F.1d. Compensate for color and turbidity by using sample to zero photometer. Minimize chromate interference by using the thioacetamide blank correction.

c. Minimum detectable concentration: Approximately 10 μg Cl as Cl_2/L. This detection limit is achievable under ideal conditions; normal working detection limits typically are higher.

2. Apparatus

a. Photometric equipment: One of the following is required:

1) *Spectrophotometer,* for use at a wavelength of 515 nm and providing a light path of 1 cm or longer.

2) *Filter photometer,* equipped with a filter having maximum transmission in the wavelength range of 490 to 530 nm and providing a light path of 1 cm or longer.

b. Glassware: Use separate glassware, including separate spectrophotometer cells, for free and combined (dichloramine) measurements, to avoid iodide contamination in free chlorine measurement.

3. Reagents

See F.2a, b, c, d, e, h, i, and j.

4. Procedure

a. Calibration of photometric equipment: Calibrate instrument with chlorine or potassium permanganate solutions.

1) Chlorine solutions—Prepare chlorine standards in the range of 0.05 to 4 mg/L from about 100 mg/L chlorine water standardized as follows: Place 2 mL acetic acid and 10 to 25 mL chlorine-demand-free water in a flask. Add about 1 g KI. Measure into the flask a suitable volume of chlorine solution. In choosing a convenient volume, note that 1 mL 0.025N $Na_2S_2O_3$ titrant (see B.2d) is equivalent to about 0.9 mg chlo-

rine. Titrate with standardized $0.025N$ $Na_2S_2O_3$ titrant until the yellow iodine color almost disappears. Add 1 to 2 mL starch indicator solution and continue titrating to disappearance of blue color.

Determine the blank by adding identical quantities of acid, KI, and starch indicator to a volume of chlorine-demand-free water corresponding to the sample used for titration. Perform blank titration A or B, whichever applies, according to B.3d.

$$\text{mg Cl as Cl}_2/\text{mL} = \frac{(A + B) \times N \times 35.45}{\text{mL sample}}$$

where:
  N = normality of $Na_2S_2O_3$,
  A = mL titrant for sample,
  B = mL titrant for blank (to be added or subtracted according to required blank titration. See B.3d).

Use chlorine-demand-free water and glassware to prepare these standards. Develop color by first placing 5 mL phosphate buffer solution and 5 mL DPD indicator reagent in flask and then adding 100 mL chlorine standard with thorough mixing as described in b and c below. Fill photometer or colorimeter cell from flask and read color at 515 nm. Return cell contents to flask and titrate with standard FAS titrant as a check on chlorine concentration.

2) Potassium permanganate solutions—Prepare a stock solution containing 891 mg $KMnO_4$/1000 mL. Dilute 10.00 mL stock solution to 100 mL with distilled water in a volumetric flask. When 1 mL of this solution is diluted to 100 mL with distilled water, a chlorine equivalent of 1.00 mg/L will be produced in the DPD reaction. Prepare a series of $KMnO_4$ standards covering the chlorine equivalent range of 0.05 to 4 mg/L. Develop color by first placing 5 mL phosphate buffer and 5 mL DPD indicator reagent in flask and adding 100 mL standard with thorough mixing as described in b and c below. Fill photometer or colorimeter cell from flask and read

color at 515 nm. Return cell contents to flask and titrate with FAS titrant as a check on any absorption of permanganate by distilled water.

Obtain all readings by comparison to color standards or the standard curve before use in calculation.

b. *Volume of sample:* Use a sample volume appropriate to the photometer or colorimeter. The following procedure is based on using 10-mL volumes; adjust reagent quantities proportionately for other sample volumes. Dilute sample with chlorine-demand-free water when total chlorine exceeds 4 mg/L.

c. *Free chlorine:* Place 0.5 mL each of buffer reagent and DPD indicator reagent in a test tube or photometer cell. Add 10 mL sample and mix. Read color immediately (Reading A).

d. *Monochloramine:* Continue by adding one very small crystal of KI (about 0.1 mg) and mix. If dichloramine concentration is expected to be high, instead of small crystal add 0.1 mL (2 drops) freshly prepared KI solution (0.1 g/100 mL). Read color immediately (Reading B).

e. *Dichloramine:* Continue by adding several crystals of KI (about 0.1 g) and mix to dissolve. Let stand about 2 min and read color (Reading C).

f. *Nitrogen trichloride:* Place a very small crystal of KI (about 0.1 mg) in a clean test tube or photometer cell. Add 10 mL sample and mix. To a second tube or cell add 0.5 mL each of buffer and indicator reagents; mix. Add contents to first tube or cell and mix. Read color immediately (Reading N).

g. *Chromate correction using thioacetamide:* Add 0.5 mL thioacetamide solution (F.2i) to 100 mL sample. After mixing, add buffer and DPD reagent. Read color immediately. Add several crystals of KI (about 0.1 g) and mix to dissolve. Let stand about 2 min and read color. Subtract the first reading from Reading A and the second reading from Reading C and use in calculations.

5. Calculation

Reading	NCl₃ Absent	NCl₃ Present
A	Free Cl	Free Cl
$B - A$	NH_2Cl	NH_2Cl
$C - B$	$NHCl_2$	$NHCl_2 + \frac{1}{2}NCl_3$
N	—	Free Cl $+ \frac{1}{2}NCl_3$
$2(N - A)$	—	NCl_3
$C - N$	—	$NHCl_2$

In the event that monochloramine is present with NCl₃, it will be included in Reading N, in which case obtain NCl₃ from $2(N - B)$.

6. Bibliography

See F.6.

4500-Cl H.   Syringaldazine (FACTS) Method

1. General Discussion

a. Principle: The free (available) chlorine test, syringaldazine (FACTS) measures free chlorine over the range of 0.1 to 10 mg/L. A saturated solution of syringaldazine (3,5-dimethoxy-4-hydroxybenzaldazine) in 2-propanol is used. Syringaldazine is oxidized by free chlorine on a 1:1 molar basis to produce a colored product with an absorption maximum of 530 nm. The color product is only slightly soluble in water; therefore, at chlorine concentrations greater than 1 mg/L, the final reaction mixture must contain 2-propanol to prevent product precipitation and color fading.

The optimum color and solubility (minimum fading) are obtained in a solution having a pH between 6.5 and 6.8. At a pH less than 6, color development is slow and reproducibility is poor. At a pH greater than 7, the color develops rapidly but fades quickly. A buffer is required to maintain the reaction mixture pH at approximately 6.7. Take care with waters of high acidity or alkalinity to assure that the added buffer maintains the proper pH.

Temperature has a minimal effect on the color reaction. The maximum error observed at temperature extremes of 5 and 35°C is ± 10%.

b. Interferences: Interferences common to other methods for determining free chlorine do not affect the FACTS procedure. Monochloramine concentrations up to 18 mg/L, dichloramine concentrations up to 10 mg/L, and manganese concentrations (oxidized forms) up to 1 mg/L do not interfere. Trichloramine at levels above 0.6 mg/L produces an apparent free chlorine reaction. Very high concentrations of monochloramine (≥ 35 mg/L) and oxidized manganese (≥ 2.6 mg/L) produce a color with syringaldazine slowly. Ferric iron can react with syringaldazine; however, concentrations up to 10 mg/L do not interfere. Nitrite (≤ 250 mg/L), nitrate (≤ 100 mg/L), sulfate (≤ 1000 mg/L), and chloride (≤ 1000 mg/L) do not interfere. Waters with high hardness (≥ 500 mg/L) will produce a cloudy solution that can be compensated for by using a blank. Oxygen does not interfere.

Other strong oxidizing agents, such as iodine, bromine, and ozone, will produce a color.

c. Minimum detectable concentration: The FACTS procedure is sensitive to free chlorine concentrations of 0.1 mg/L or less.

2. Apparatus

Colorimetric equipment: One of the following is required:

a. Filter photometer, providing a light path of 1 cm for chlorine concentrations ≤ 1 mg/L or a light path from 1 to 10 mm for chlorine concentrations above 1 mg/L; also equipped with a filter having a band pass of 500 to 560 nm.

b. Spectrophotometer, for use at 530 nm, providing the light paths noted above.

3. Reagents

a. Chlorine-demand-free water: See C.3*m.* Use to prepare reagent solutions and sample dilutions.

b. Syringaldazine indicator: Dissolve 115 mg 3,5-dimethoxy-4-hydroxybenzaldazine* in 1 L 2-propanol.

c. 2-Propanol: To aid in dissolution use ultrasonic agitation or gentle heating and stirring. Redistill reagent-grade 2-propanol to remove chlorine demand. Use a 30.5-cm Vigreux column and take the middle 75% fraction. Alternatively, chlorinate good-quality 2-propanol to maintain a free residual overnight; then expose to UV light or sunlight to dechlorinate. CAUTION: *2-Propanol is extremely flammable.*

d. Buffer: Dissolve 17.01 g KH_2PO_4 in 250 mL water; pH should be 4.4. Dissolve 17.75 g Na_2HPO_4 in 250 mL water; the pH should be 9.9. Mix equal volumes of these solutions to obtain FACTS buffer, pH 6.6. Verify pH with pH meter. For waters containing considerable hardness or high al-

kalinity other pH 6.6 buffers can be used, for example, 23.21 g maleic acid and 16.5 mL 50% NaOH per liter of water.

e. Hypochlorite solution: Dilute household hypochlorite solution, which contains about 30 000 to 50 000 mg Cl equivalent/ L, to a strength between 100 and 1000 mg/ L. Standardize as directed in G.4*a*1).

4. Procedure

a. Calibration of photometer: Prepare a calibration curve by making dilutions of a standardized hypochlorite solution (¶ 3*e*). Develop and measure colors as described in ¶ 4*b*, below. Check calibration regularly, especially as reagent ages.

b. Free chlorine analysis: Add 3 mL sample and 0.1 mL buffer to a 5-mL-capacity test tube. Add 1 mL syringaldazine indicator, cap tube, and invert twice to mix. Transfer to a photometer tube or spectrophotometer cell and measure absorbance. Compare absorbance value obtained with calibration curve and report corresponding value as milligrams free chlorine per liter.

5. Bibliography

BAUER, R. & C. RUPE. 1971. Use of syringaldazine in a photometric method for estimating "free" chlorine in water. *Anal. Chem.* 43:421.

COOPER, W.J., C.A. SORBER & E.P. MEIER. 1975. A rapid, free, available chlorine test with syringaldazine (FACTS). *J. Amer. Water Works Assoc.* 67:34.

COOPER, W.J., P.H. GIBBS, E.M. OTT & P. PATEL. 1983. Equivalency testing of procedures for measuring free available chlorine: amperometric titration, DPD, and FACTS. *J. Amer. Water Works Assoc.* 75:625.

---

*Aldrich No. 17, 753-9, Aldrich Chemical Company, Inc., Cedar Knolls, N.J. 07927, or equivalent.

4500-Cl I. Iodometric Electrode Technique

1. General Discussion

a. Principle: This method involves the direct potentiometric measurement of iodine released on the addition of potassium iodide to an acidified sample. A platinum-

iodide electrode pair is used in combination with an expanded-scale pH meter.

b. Interference: All oxidizing agents that interfere with other iodometric procedures interfere. These include oxidized manganese and iodate, bromine, and cupric ions. Silver and mercuric ions above 10 and 20 mg/L interfere.

2. Apparatus

a. Electrodes: Use either a combination electrode consisting of a platinum electrode and an iodide ion-selective electrode or two individual electrodes. Both systems are available commercially.

b. pH/millivolt meter: Use an expanded-scale pH/millivolt meter with 0.1 mV readability or a direct-reading selective ion meter.

3. Reagents

a. pH 4 buffer solution: See C.3e.

b. Chlorine-demand-free water: See C.3m.

c. Potassium iodide solution: Dissolve 42 g KI and 0.2 g Na_2CO_3 in 500 mL chlorine-demand-free, distilled water. Store in a dark bottle.

d. Standard potassium iodate 0.002 81N: Dissolve 0.1002 g KIO_3 in chlorine-demand-free, distilled water and dilute to 1000 mL. Each 1.0 mL, when diluted to 100 mL, produces a solution equivalent to 1 mg/L as Cl_2.

4. Procedure

a. Standardization: Pipet into three 100-mL stoppered volumetric flasks 0.20, 1.00, and 5.00 mL standard iodate solution. Add to each flask, and a fourth flask to be used as a reagent blank, 1 mL each of acetate buffer solution and KI solution. Stopper, swirl to mix, and let stand 2 min before dilution. Dilute each standard to 100 mL with chlorine-demand-free distilled water. Stopper, invert flask several times to mix, and pour into separate 150-mL beakers. Stir gently without turbulence, using a magnetic stirrer, and immerse electrode(s) in the 0.2-mg/L (0.2-mL) standard. Wait for the potential to stabilize and record potential in mV. Rinse electrodes with

chlorine-demand-free water and repeat for each standard and for the reagent blank. Prepare a calibration curve by plotting, on semilogarithmic paper, potential (linear axis) against concentration. Determine apparent chlorine concentration in the reagent blank from this graph (Reading B).

b. Analysis: Select a volume of sample containing no more than 0.5 mg chlorine. Pipet 1 mL acetate buffer solution and 1 mL KI into a 100-mL glass-stoppered volumetric flask. Stopper, swirl and let stand for at least 2 min. Adjust sample pH to 4 to 5, if necessary (mid-range pH paper is adequate for pH measurement), by adding acetic acid. Add pH-adjusted sample to volumetric flask and dilute to mark. Stopper and mix by inversion several times. Let stand for 2 min. Pour into a 150-mL beaker, immerse the electrode(s), wait for the potential to stabilize, and record. If the mV reading is greater than that recorded for the 5-mg/L standard, repeat analysis with a smaller volume of sample.

5. Calculation

Determine chlorine concentration (mg/L) corresponding to the recorded mV reading from the standard curve. This is Reading A. Determine total residual chlorine from the following:

$$\text{Total residual chlorine} = A \times 100/V$$

where V = sample volume, mL. If total residual chlorine is below 0.2 mg/L, subtract apparent chlorine in reagent blank (Reading B) to obtain the true total residual chlorine value.

6. Bibliography

DIMMOCK, N.A. & D. MIDGLEY. 1981. Determination of Total Residual Chlorine in Cooling Water with the Orion 97-70 Ion Selective Electrode. Central Electricity Generating Board (U.K.) Report RD/L/2159N81.

JENKINS, R.L. & R.B. BAIRD. 1979. Determination of total chlorine residual in treated wastewaters by electrode. *Anal. Letters* 12:125.

SYNNOTT, J.C. & A.M. SMITH. 1985. Total Residual Chlorine by Ion-Selective Electrode—

from Bench Top to Continuous Monitor. Paper presented at 5th International Conf. on Chemistry for Protection of the Environment, Leuven, Belgium.

4500-Cl⁻   CHLORIDE*

4500-Cl⁻ A.   Introduction

1. Occurrence

Chloride, in the form of chloride (Cl^-) ion, is one of the major inorganic anions in water and wastewater. In potable water, the salty taste produced by chloride concentrations is variable and dependent on the chemical composition of water. Some waters containing 250 mg Cl^-/L may have a detectable salty taste if the cation is sodium. On the other hand, the typical salty taste may be absent in waters containing as much as 1000 mg/L when the predominant cations are calcium and magnesium.

The chloride concentration is higher in wastewater than in raw water because sodium chloride (NaCl) is a common article of diet and passes unchanged through the digestive system. Along the sea coast, chloride may be present in high concentrations because of leakage of salt water into the sewerage system. It also may be increased by industrial processes.

A high chloride content may harm metallic pipes and structures, as well as growing plants.

2. Selection of Method

Five methods are presented for the determination of chloride. Because the first two are similar in most respects, selection is largely a matter of personal preference. The argentometric method (B) is suitable for use in relatively clear waters when 0.15 to 10 mg Cl^- are present in the portion titrated. The end point of the mercuric nitrate method (C) is easier to detect. The potentiometric method (D) is suitable for colored or turbid samples in which color-indicated end points might be difficult to observe. The potentiometric method can be used without a pretreatment step for samples containing ferric ions (if not present in an amount greater than the chloride concentration), chromic, phosphate, and ferrous and other heavy-metal ions. The ferricyanide method (E) is an automated technique. Ion chromatography (F) also may be used for chloride determinations.

3. Sampling and Storage

Collect representative samples in clean, chemically resistant glass or plastic bottles. The maximum sample portion required is 100 mL. No special preservative is necessary if the sample is to be stored.

---

*Approved by Standard Methods Committee, 1985.

4500-Cl⁻ B.   Argentometric Method

1. General Discussion

a. Principle: In a neutral or slightly alkaline solution, potassium chromate can indicate the end point of the silver nitrate titration of chloride. Silver chloride is precipitated quantitatively before red silver chromate is formed.

b. Interference: Substances in amounts normally found in potable waters will not interfere. Bromide, iodide, and cyanide register as equivalent chloride concentrations. Sulfide, thiosulfate, and sulfite ions interfere but can be removed by treatment with hydrogen peroxide. Orthophosphate in excess of 25 mg/L interferes by precipitating as silver phosphate. Iron in excess of 10 mg/L interferes by masking the end point.

2. Apparatus

a. Erlenmeyer flask, 250-mL.
b. Buret, 50-mL.

3. Reagents

a. Potassium chromate indicator solution: Dissolve 50 g K_2CrO_4 in a little distilled water. Add $AgNO_3$ solution until a definite red precipitate is formed. Let stand 12 h, filter, and dilute to 1 L with distilled water.

b. Standard silver nitrate titrant, $0.0141M$ $(0.0141N)$: Dissolve 2.395 g $AgNO_3$ in distilled water and dilute to 1000 mL. Standardize against NaCl by the procedure described in ¶ *4b* below; 1.00 mL = 500 µg Cl⁻. Store in a brown bottle.

c. Standard sodium chloride, $0.0141M$ $(0.0141N)$: Dissolve 824.0 mg NaCl (dried at 140°C) in distilled water and dilute to 1000 mL; 1.00 mL = 500 µg Cl⁻.

d. Special reagents for removal of interference:

1) *Aluminum hydroxide suspension:* Dissolve 125 g aluminum potassium sulfate or aluminum ammonium sulfate, $AlK(SO_4)_2 \cdot 12H_2O$ or $AlNH_4(SO_4)_2 \cdot 12H_2O$, in 1 L distilled water. Warm to 60°C and add 55 mL conc ammonium hydroxide (NH_4OH) slowly with stirring. Let stand about 1 h, transfer to a large bottle, and wash precipitate by successive additions, with thorough mixing and decanting with distilled water, until free from chloride. When freshly prepared, the suspension occupies a volume of approximately 1 L.

2) *Phenolphthalein indicator solution.*
3) *Sodium hydroxide,* NaOH, 1N.
4) *Sulfuric acid,* H_2SO_4, 1N.
5) *Hydrogen peroxide,* H_2O_2, 30%.

4. Procedure

a. Sample preparation: Use a 100-mL sample or a suitable portion diluted to 100 mL. If the sample is highly colored, add 3 mL $Al(OH)_3$ suspension, mix, let settle, and filter.

If sulfide, sulfite, or thiosulfate is present, add 1 mL H_2O_2 and stir for 1 min.

b. Titration: Directly titrate samples in the pH range 7 to 10. Adjust sample pH to 7 to 10 with H_2SO_4 or NaOH if it is not in this range. Add 1.0 mL K_2CrO_4 indicator solution. Titrate with standard $AgNO_3$ titrant to a pinkish yellow end point. Be consistent in end-point recognition.

Standardize $AgNO_3$ titrant and establish reagent blank value by the titration method outlined above. A blank of 0.2 to 0.3 mL is usual.

5. Calculation

$$\text{mg Cl}^-/\text{L} = \frac{(A - B) \times N \times 35\,450}{\text{mL sample}}$$

where:

A = mL titration for sample,
B = mL titration for blank, and
N = normality of $AgNO_3$.

$$\text{mg NaCl}/\text{L} = (\text{mg Cl}^-/\text{L}) \times 1.65$$

6. Precision and Bias

A synthetic sample containing 241 mg Cl^-/L, 108 mg Ca/L, 82 mg Mg/L; 3.1 mg K/L, 19.9 mg Na/L, 1.1 mg NO_3^--N/ L, 0.25 mg NO_2^-- N/L, 259 mg SO_4^{2-}/L, and 42.5 mg total alkalinity/L (contributed by $NaHCO_3$) in distilled water was analyzed in 41 laboratories by the argentometric method, with a relative standard deviation of 4.2% and a relative error of 1.7%.

7. Bibliography

HAZEN, A. 1889. On the determination of chlorine in water. *Amer. Chem. J.* 11:409.

KOLTHOFF, I.M. & V.A. STENGER. 1947. Volumetric Analysis, 2nd ed. Vol. 2. Interscience Publishers, New York, N.Y., pp. 242-245, 256-258.

4500-Cl⁻ C.   Mercuric Nitrate Method

1. General Discussion

a. Principle: Chloride can be titrated with mercuric nitrate, $Hg(NO_3)_2$, because of the formation of soluble, slightly dissociated mercuric chloride. In the pH range 2.3 to 2.8, diphenylcarbazone indicates the titration end point by formation of a purple complex with the excess mercuric ions. Xylene cyanol FF serves as a pH indicator and end-point enhancer. Increasing the strength of the titrant and modifying the indicator mixtures extend the range of measurable chloride concentrations.

b. Interference: Bromide and iodide are titrated with $Hg(NO_3)_2$ in the same manner as chloride. Chromate, ferric, and sulfite ions interfere when present in excess of 10 mg/L.

2. Apparatus

a. Erlenmeyer flask, 250-mL.

b. Microburet, 5-mL with 0.01-mL graduation intervals.

3. Reagents

a. Standard sodium chloride, 0.0141M (0.0141N): See Method B, ¶ 3c above.

b. Nitric acid, HNO_3, 0.1N.

c. Sodium hydroxide, NaOH, 0.1N.

d. Reagents for chloride concentrations below 100 mg/L:

1) *Indicator-acidifier reagent:* The HNO_3 concentration of this reagent is an important factor in the success of the determination and can be varied as indicated in a) or b) to suit the alkalinity range of the sample. Reagent a) contains sufficient HNO_3 to neutralize a total alkalinity of 150 mg as $CaCO_3$/L to the proper pH in a 100-mL sample. Adjust amount of HNO_3 to accommodate samples of alkalinity different from 150 mg/L.

a) Dissolve, in the order named, 250 mg s-diphenylcarbazone, 4.0 mL conc HNO_3, and 30 mg xylene cyanol FF in 100 mL 95% ethyl alcohol or isopropyl alcohol. Store in a dark bottle in a refrigerator. This reagent is not stable indefinitely. Deterioration causes a slow end point and high results.

b) Because pH control is critical, adjust pH of highly alkaline or acid samples to 2.5 ± 0.1 with 0.1N HNO_3 or NaOH, not with sodium carbonate (Na_2CO_3). Use a pH meter with a nonchloride type of reference electrode for pH adjustment. If only the usual chloride-type reference electrode is available for pH adjustment, determine amount of acid or alkali required to obtain a pH of 2.5 ± 0.1 and discard this sample portion. Treat a separate sample portion with the determined amount of acid or alkali and continue analysis. Under these circumstances, omit HNO_3 from indicator reagent.

2) *Standard mercuric nitrate titrant,* 0.007 05 M (0.0141N): Dissolve 2.3 g $Hg(NO_3)_2$ or 2.5 g $Hg(NO_3)_2 \cdot H_2O$ in 100 mL distilled water containing 0.25 mL conc HNO_3. Dilute to just under 1 L. Make a preliminary standardization by following the procedure described in ¶ 4*a*. Use replicates containing 5.00 mL standard NaCl solution and 10 mg sodium bicarbonate (NaHCO$_3$) diluted to 100 mL with distilled water. Adjust titrant to 0.0141N and make a final standardization; 1.00 mL = 500 μg Cl$^-$. Store away from light in a dark bottle.

e. Reagent for chloride concentrations greater than 100 mg/L:

1) *Mixed indicator reagent:* Dissolve 0.50 g diphenylcarbazone powder and 0.05 g bromphenol blue powder in 75 mL 95% ethyl or isopropyl alcohol and dilute to 100 mL with the same alcohol.

2) *Strong standard mercuric nitrate titrant,* 0.0705 M (0.141N) Dissolve 25 g $Hg(NO_3)_2 \cdot H_2O$ in 900 mL distilled water containing 5.0 mL conc HNO_3. Dilute to just under 1 L and standardize by following the procedure described in ¶ 4*b*. Use replicates containing 25.00 mL standard NaCl solution and 25 mL distilled water. Adjust titrant to 0.141N and make a final standardization; 1.00 mL = 5.00 mg Cl$^-$.

4. Procedure

a. Titration of chloride concentrations less than 100 mg/L: Use a 100-mL sample or smaller portion so that the chloride content is less than 10 mg.

Add 1.0 mL indicator-acidifier reagent. (The color of the solution should be green-blue at this point. A light green indicates pH less than 2.0; a pure blue indicates pH more than 3.8.) For most potable waters, the pH after this addition will be 2.5 ± 0.1. For highly alkaline or acid waters, adjust pH to about 8 before adding indicator-acidifier reagent.

Titrate with 0.0141N $Hg(NO_3)_2$ titrant

to a definite purple end point. The solution turns from green-blue to blue a few drops before the end point.

Determine blank by titrating 100 mL distilled water containing 10 mg NaHCO$_3$.

b. Titration of chloride concentrations greater than 100 mg/L: Use a sample portion (5 to 50 mL) requiring less than 5 mL titrant to reach the end point. Measure into a 150-mL beaker. Add approximately 0.5 mL mixed indicator reagent and mix well. The color should be purple. Add 0.1N HNO_3 dropwise until the color just turns yellow. Titrate with strong $Hg(NO_3)_2$ titrant to first permanent dark purple. Titrate a distilled water blank using the same procedure.

5. Calculation

$$mg \ Cl^-/L = \frac{(A - B) \times N \times 35\,450}{mL \ sample}$$

where:

A = mL titration for sample,
B = mL titration for blank, and
N = normality of $Hg(NO_3)_2$.

$$mg \ NaCl/L = (mg \ Cl^-/L) \times 1.65$$

6. Precision and Bias

A synthetic sample containing 241 mg Cl$^-$/L, 108 mg Ca/L, 82 mg Mg/L, 3.1 mg K/L, 19.9 mg Na/L, 1.1 mg NO$_3$$^-$-N/L, 0.25 mg NO$_2$$^-$-N/L, 259 mg SO$_4$$^{2-}$/L, and 42.5 mg total alkalinity/L (contributed by NaHCO$_3$) in distilled water was analyzed in 10 laboratories by the mercurimetric method, with a relative standard deviation of 3.3% and a relative error of 2.9%.

7. Bibliography

KOLTHOFF, I.M. & V.A. STENGER. 1947. Volumetric Analysis, 2nd ed. Vol. 2. Interscience Publishers, New York, N.Y., pp. 334-335.

DOMASK, W.C. & K.A. KOBE. 1952. Mercurimetric determination of chlorides and water-soluble chlorohydrins. *Anal. Chem.* 24:989.

GOLDMAN, E. 1959. New indicator for the mercurimetric chloride determination in potable water. *Anal. Chem.* 31:1127.

4500-Cl⁻ D. Potentiometric Method

1. General Discussion

a. Principle: Chloride is determined by potentiometric titration with silver nitrate solution with a glass and silver-silver chloride electrode system. During titration an electronic voltmeter is used to detect the change in potential between the two electrodes. The end point of the titration is that instrument reading at which the greatest change in voltage has occurred for a small and constant increment of silver nitrate added.

b. Interference: Iodide and bromide also are titrated as chloride. Ferricyanide causes high results and must be removed. Chromate and dichromate interfere and should be reduced to the chromic state or removed. Ferric iron interferes if present in an amount substantially higher than the amount of chloride. Chromic ion, ferrous ion, and phosphate do not interfere.

Grossly contaminated samples usually require pretreatment. Where contamination is minor, some contaminants can be destroyed simply by adding nitric acid.

2. Apparatus

a. Glass and silver-silver chloride electrodes: Prepare in the laboratory or purchase a silver electrode coated with AgCl for use with specified instruments. Instructions on use and care of electrodes are supplied by the manufacturer.

b. Electronic voltmeter, to measure potential difference between electrodes: A pH meter may be converted to this use by substituting the appropriate electrode.

c. Mechanical stirrer, with plastic-coated or glass impeller.

3. Reagents

a. Standard sodium chloride solution, $0.0141M$ $(0.0141N)$: See ¶ 4500-Cl⁻.B.3c.

b. Nitric acid, HNO_3, conc.

c. Standard silver nitrate titrant, $0.0141M$ $(0.0141N)$: See ¶ 4500-Cl⁻.B.3b.

d. Pretreatment reagents:

1) *Sulfuric acid,* H_2SO_4, $1 + 1$.

2) *Hydrogen peroxide,* H_2O_2, 30%.

3) *Sodium hydroxide,* NaOH, $1N$.

4. Procedure

a. Standardization: The various instruments that can be used in this determination differ in operating details; follow the manufacturer's instructions. Make necessary mechanical adjustments. Then, after allowing sufficient time for warmup (10 min), balance internal electrical components to give an instrument setting of 0 mV or, if a pH meter is used, a pH reading of 7.0.

1) Place 10.0 mL standard NaCl solution in a 250-mL beaker, dilute to about 100 mL, and add 2.0 mL conc HNO_3. Immerse stirrer and electrodes.

2) Set instrument to desired range of millivolts or pH units. Start stirrer.

3) Add standard $AgNO_3$ titrant, recording scale reading after each addition. At the start, large increments of $AgNO_3$ may be added; then, as the end point is approached, add smaller and equal increments (0.1 or 0.2 mL) at longer intervals, so that the exact end point can be determined. Determine volume of $AgNO_3$ used at the point at which there is the greatest change in instrument reading per unit addition of $AgNO_3$.

4) Plot a differential titration curve if the exact end point cannot be determined by inspecting the data. Plot change in instrument reading for equal increments of $AgNO_3$ against volume of $AgNO_3$ added, using average of buret readings before and after each addition. The procedure is illustrated in Figure 4500-Cl⁻:1.

b. Sample analysis:

1) Pipet 100.0 mL sample, or a portion containing not more than 10 mg Cl⁻, into a 250-mL beaker. In the absence of interfering substances, proceed with ¶ 3) below.

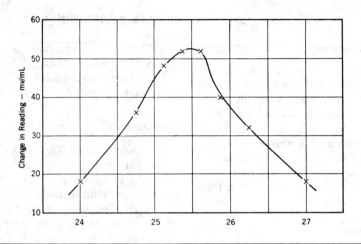

Experimental Data Plotted Above								
Volume, mL	23.50	24.50	25.00	25.25	25.50	25.75	26.00	26.50	27.50
Change, mV/mL	18	36	48	52	52	40	32	18

Figure 4500-Cl⁻:1. Example of differential titration curve (end point is 25.5 mL).

2) In the presence of organic compounds, sulfite, or other interferences (such as large amounts of ferric iron, cyanide, or sulfide) acidify sample with H_2SO_4, using litmus paper. Boil for 5 min to remove volatile compounds. Add more H_2SO_4, if necessary, to keep solution acidic. Add 3 mL H_2O_2 and boil for 15 min, adding chloride-free distilled water to keep the volume above 50 mL. Dilute to 100 mL, add NaOH solution dropwise until alkaline to litmus, then 10 drops in excess. Boil for 5 min, filter into a 250-mL beaker, and wash precipitate and paper several times with hot distilled water.

3) Add conc HNO_3 dropwise until acidic to litmus paper, then 2.0 mL in excess. Cool and dilute to 100 mL if necessary. Immerse stirrer and electrodes and start stirrer. Make any necessary adjustments according to the manufacturer's instructions and set selector switch to appropriate setting for measuring the difference of potential between electrodes.

4) Complete determination by titrating according to ¶ 4a4). If an end-point reading has been established from previous determinations for similar samples and conditions, use this predetermined end point. For the most accurate work, make a blank titration by carrying chloride-free distilled water through the procedure.

5. Calculation

$$\text{mg Cl}^-/\text{L} = \frac{(A - B) \times N \times 35\,450}{\text{mL sample}}$$

where:

A = mL $AgNO_3$,
B = mL blank, and
N = normality of titrant.

6. Precision and Bias

In the absence of interfering substances, the precision and bias are estimated to be about 0.12 mg for 5 mg Cl⁻, or 2.5% of the amount present. When pretreatment is required to remove interfering substances, the precision and bias are reduced to about

0.25 mg for 5 mg Cl⁻, or 5% of amount present.

7. Bibliography

KOLTHOFF, I.M. & N.H. FURMAN. 1931. Potentiometric Titrations, 2nd ed. John Wiley & Sons, New York, N.Y.

REFFENBURG, H.B. 1935. Colorimetric determination of small quantities of chlorides in water. *Ind. Eng. Chem.*, Anal. Ed. 7:14.

CALDWELL, J.R. & H.V. MEYER. 1935. Chloride determination. *Ind. Eng. Chem.*, Anal. Ed. 7:38.

SERFASS, E.J. & R.F. MURACA. 1954. Procedures for Analyzing Metal-Finishing Wastes. Ohio River Valley Water Sanitation Commission, Cincinnati, Ohio, p. 80.

FURMAN, N.H., ed. 1962. Standard Methods of Chemical Analysis, 6th ed. D. Van Nostrand Co., Princeton, N.J., Vol. I.

WALTON, H.F. 1964. Principles and Methods of Chemical Analysis. Prentice-Hall, Inc., Englewood Cliffs, N.J.

WILLARD, H.H., L.L. MERRITT & J.A. DEAN. 1965. Instrumental Methods of Analysis, 4th ed. D. Van Nostrand Co., Princeton, N.J.

4500-Cl⁻ E.   Automated Ferricyanide Method

1. General Discussion

a. Principle: Thiocyanate ion is liberated from mercuric thiocyanate by the formation of soluble mercuric chloride. In the presence of ferric ion, free thiocyanate ion forms a highly colored ferric thiocyanate, of which the intensity is proportional to the chloride concentration.

b. Interferences: None of significance. However, use a continuous filter on turbid samples.

c. Application: The method is applicable to potable, surface, and saline waters, and domestic and industrial wastewaters. The concentration range can be varied by using the colorimeter controls.

2. Apparatus

a. Automated analytical equipment: The required continuous-flow analytical instrument* consists of the interchangeable components shown in Figure 4500-Cl⁻:2.

b. Filters, 480-nm.

3. Reagents

a. Stock mercuric thiocyanate solution: Dissolve 4.17 g Hg(SCN)₂ in about 500 mL methanol, dilute to 1000 mL with methanol, mix, and filter through filter paper.

b. Stock ferric nitrate solution: Dissolve 202 g Fe(NO₃)₃·9H₂O in about 500 mL distilled water, then carefully add 21 mL conc HNO₃. Dilute to 1000 mL with distilled water and mix. Filter through paper and store in an amber bottle.

c. Color reagent: Add 150 mL stock Hg(SCN)₂ solution to 150 mL stock Fe(NO₃)₃ solution. Mix and dilute to 1000 mL with distilled water. Add 0.5 mL polyoxyethylene 23 lauryl ether.†

d. Stock chloride solution: Dissolve 1.6482 g NaCl, dried at 140°C, in distilled water and dilute to 1000 mL; 1.00 mL + 1.00 mg Cl⁻.

e. Standard chloride solutions: Prepare chloride standards in the desired concentration range, such as 1 to 200 mg/L, using stock chloride solution.

4. Procedure

Set up manifold as shown in Figure 4500-Cl⁻:2 and follow general procedure described by the manufacturer.

---

*Technicon™ Autoanalyzer™ II or equivalent.

†Brij 35, available from ICI Americas, Wilmington, Del., Technicon Instruments Corporation, Tarrytown, N.Y. 10591, or equivalent.

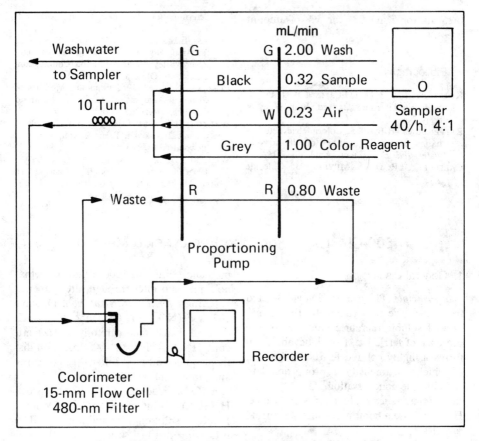

Figure 4500-Cl⁻:2. Flow scheme for automated chloride analysis.

5. Calculation

Prepare standard curves by plotting peak heights of standards processed through the manifold against chloride concentrations in standards. Compute sample chloride concentration by comparing sample peak height with standard curve.

6. Precision and Bias

With an automated system in a single laboratory six samples were analyzed in septuplicate. At a concentration ranging from about 1 to 50 mg Cl⁻/L the average standard deviation was 0.39 mg/L. The coefficient of variation was 2.2%. In two samples with added chloride, recoveries were 104% and 97%.

7. Bibliography

ZALL, D.M., D. FISHER & M.D. GARNER. 1956. Photometric determination of chlorides in water. *Anal. Chem.* 28:1665.

O'BRIEN, J.E. 1962. Automatic analysis of chlorides in sewage. *Wastes Eng.* 33:670.

4500-Cl⁻ F. Ion Chromatography Method

See Section 4110.

4500-ClO₂ CHLORINE DIOXIDE*

4500-ClO₂ A.   Introduction

Because the physical and chemical properties of chlorine dioxide resemble those of chlorine in many respects, read the entire discussion of Residual Chlorine (Section 4500-Cl) before attempting a chlorine dioxide determination.

1. Occurrence and Significance

Chlorine dioxide, ClO₂, has been used widely as a bleaching agent in the paper and pulp industry. It has been applied to water supplies to combat tastes and odors due to phenolic-type wastes, actinomycetes, and algae, as well as to oxidize soluble iron and manganese to a more easily removable form. It is a disinfectant, and some results suggest that it may be stronger than free chlorine or hypochlorite.

Chlorine dioxide is a deep yellow, volatile, unpleasant-smelling gas that is toxic and under certain conditions may react explosively. It should be handled with care in a vented area. There are several methods of generating ClO₂; for laboratory purposes the acidification of a solution of sodium chlorite followed by suitable scrubbing is the most practical.

2. Selection of Method

The iodometric method (B) gives a very precise measure of total available strength of a solution in terms of its ability to lib-

erate iodine from iodide. However, ClO₂, chlorine, chlorite, and hypochlorite are not distinguished easily by this technique. It is designed primarily, and best used, for standardizing ClO₂ solutions needed for preparation of temporary standards. It often is inapplicable to industrial wastes.

The amperometric methods (C and E) are useful when a knowledge of the various chlorine fractions in a water sample is desired. They distinguish various chlorine compounds of interest with good accuracy and precision, but require specialized equipment and considerable analytical skill.

The N,N-diethyl-p-phenylenediamine (DPD) method (D) has the advantages of a relatively easy-to-perform colorimetric test with the ability to distinguish between ClO₂ and various forms of chlorine. This technique is not as accurate as the amperometric method, but should yield results adequate for most common applications.

3. Sampling and Storage

Determine ClO₂ promptly after collecting the sample. Do not expose sample to sunlight or strong artificial light and do not aerate to mix. Minimum ClO₂ losses occur when the determination is completed immediately at the site of sample collection.

---

*Approved by Standard Methods Committee, 1988.

4. Bibliography

INGOLS, R.S. & G.M. RIDENOUR. 1948. Chemical properties of chlorine dioxide in water treatment. *J. Amer. Water Works Assoc.* 40:1207.

PALIN, A.T. 1948. Chlorine dioxide in water treatment. *J. Inst. Water Eng.* 11:61.

HODGDEN, H.W. & R.S. INGOLS. 1954. Direct colorimetric method for determination of chlorine dioxide in water. *Anal. Chem.* 26:1224.

FEUSS, J.V. 1964. Problems in determination of chlorine dioxide residuals. *J. Amer. Water Works Assoc.* 56:607.

MASSCHELEIN, W. 1966. Spectrophotometric determination of chlorine dioxide with acid chrome violet K. *Anal. Chem.* 38:1839.

MASSCHELEIN, W. 1969. Les Oxydes de Chlore et le Chlorite de Sodium. Dunod, Paris, Chapter XI.

4500-ClO₂ B. Iodometric Method

1. General Discussion

a. Principle: A pure solution of ClO_2 is prepared by slowly adding dilute H_2SO_4 to a sodium chlorite ($NaClO_2$) solution. Contaminants such as chlorine are removed by a $NaClO_2$ scrubber and passing the gas into distilled water in a steady stream of air.

ClO_2 releases free iodine from a KI solution acidified with acetic acid or H_2SO_4. The liberated iodine is titrated with a standard solution of sodium thiosulfate ($Na_2S_2O_3$), with starch as the indicator.

b. Interference: There is little interference in this method, but temperature and strong light affect solution stability. Minimize ClO_2 losses by storing stock ClO_2 solution in a dark refrigerator and by preparing and titrating dilute ClO_2 solutions for standardization purposes at the lowest practicable temperature and in subdued light.

c. Minimum detectable concentration: One drop (0.05 mL) of 0.01N $Na_2S_2O_3$ is equivalent to 20 µg ClO_2/L (or 40 µg/L in terms of available chlorine) when a 500-mL sample is titrated.

2. Reagents

All reagents listed for the determination of residual chlorine in Section 4500-Cl.B.2*a-g* are required. Also needed are the following:

a. Stock chlorine dioxide solution: Prepare a gas generating and absorbing system as illustrated in Figure 4500-ClO₂:1. Connect aspirator flask (A), 500-mL capacity, with rubber tubing to a source of compressed air. Let air bubble through a layer of 300 mL distilled water in flask and then pass through a glass tube ending within 5 mm of the bottom of the 1-L gas-generating bottle (B). Conduct evolved gas via glass tubing through a scrubber bottle (C) containing saturated $NaClO_2$ solution or a tower packed with flaked $NaClO_2$, and finally, via glass tubing, into a 2-L borosilicate glass collecting bottle (D) where the gas is absorbed in 1500 mL distilled water. Provide an air outlet tube on collecting bottle (D) for escape of air. Select for gas generation a bottle constructed of strong borosilicate glass and having a mouth wide enough to permit insertion of three separate glass tubes: the first leading almost to the bottom for admitting air, the second reaching below the liquid surface for gradual introduction of H_2SO_4, and the third near the top for exit of evolved gas and air. Fit to second tube a graduated cylindrical separatory funnel (E) to contain H_2SO_4. Locate this system in a fume hood with an adequate shield.

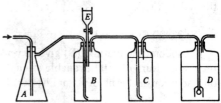

Figure 4500-ClO₂:1. Chlorine dioxide generation and absorption system.

Dissolve 10 g NaClO₂ in 750 mL distilled water and place in generating bottle (B). Carefully add 2 mL conc H₂SO₄ to 18 mL distilled water and mix. Transfer to funnel. Connect flask to generating bottle, generating bottle to scrubber, and the latter to collecting bottle. Pass a smooth current of air through the system, as evidenced by the bubbling rate in all bottles.

Introduce 5-mL increments of H₂SO₄ from funnel into generating bottle at 5-min intervals. Continue air flow for 30 min after last portion of acid has been added.

Store yellow stock solution in glass-stoppered dark-colored bottle in a dark refrigerator. The concentration of ClO₂ thus prepared varies between 250 and 600 mg/L, corresponding to approximately 500 to 1200 mg free chlorine/L.

b. Standard chlorine dioxide solution: Use this solution for preparing temporary ClO₂ standards. Dilute required volume of stock ClO₂ solution to desired strength with chlorine-demand-free water (see Section 4500-Cl.C.3m). Standardize solution by titrating with standard 0.01N or 0.025N Na₂S₂O₃ titrant in the presence of KI, acid, and starch indicator by following the procedure given in ¶ 3 below. A full or nearly full bottle of chlorine or ClO₂ solution retains its titer longer than a partially full one. When repeated withdrawals reduce volume to a critical level, standardize diluted solution at the beginning, midway in the series of withdrawals, and at the end of the series. Shake contents thoroughly before drawing off needed solution from middle of the glass-stoppered dark-colored bottle. Prepare this solution frequently.

3. Procedure

Select volume of sample, prepare for titration, and titrate sample and blank as described in Section 4500-Cl.B.3. The only exception is the following: *Let ClO₂ react in the dark with acid and KI for 5 min before starting titration.*

4. Calculations

Express ClO₂ concentrations in terms of ClO₂ or as free chlorine content. Free chlorine is defined as the total oxidizing power of ClO₂ measured by titrating iodine released by ClO₂ from an acidic solution of KI. Calculate result in terms of chlorine itself.

For standardizing ClO₂ solution:

$$\text{mg ClO}_2/\text{mL} = \frac{(A \pm B) \times N \times 13.49}{\text{mL sample titrated}}$$

$$\text{mg ClO}_2 \text{ as Cl}_2/\text{mL} = \frac{(A \pm B) \times N \times 35.45}{\text{mL sample titrated}}$$

For determining ClO₂ temporary standards:

$$\text{mg ClO}_2/\text{L} = \frac{(A \pm B) \times N \times 13\,490}{\text{mL sample}}$$

$$\text{mg ClO}_2 \text{ as Cl}_2/\text{L} = \frac{(A \pm B) \times N \times 35\,453}{\text{mL sample}}$$

where:

A = mL titration for sample,
B = mL titration for blank (positive or negative, see 4500-Cl.B.3d), and
N = normality of Na₂S₂O₃.

5. Bibliography

POST, M.A. & W.A. MOORE. 1959. Determination of chlorine dioxide in treated surface waters. *Anal. Chem.* 31:1872.

4500-ClO₂ C.   Amperometric Method I

1. General Discussion

a. Principle: The amperometric titration of ClO_2 is an extension of the amperometric method for chlorine. By performing four titrations with phenylarsine oxide, free chlorine (including hypochlorite and hypochlorous acid), chloramines, chlorite, and ClO_2 may be determined separately. The first titration step consists of conversion of ClO_2 to chlorite and chlorate through addition of sufficient NaOH to produce a pH of 12, followed by neutralization to a pH of 7 and titration of free chlorine. In the second titration KI is added to a sample that has been treated similarly with alkali and had the pH readjusted to 7; titration yields free chlorine and monochloramine. The third titration involves addition of KI and pH adjustment to 7, followed by titration of free chlorine, monochloramine, and one-fifth of the available ClO_2. In the fourth titration, addition of sufficient H_2SO_4 to lower the pH to 2 enables all available ClO_2 and chlorite, as well as the total free chlorine, to liberate an equivalent amount of iodine from the added KI and thus be titrated.

b. Interference: The interferences described in Section 4500-Cl.D.1*b* apply also to determination of ClO_2.

2. Apparatus

The apparatus required is given in Sections 4500-Cl.D.2*a* through *d*.

3. Reagents

All reagents listed for the determination of chlorine in Section 4500-Cl.D.3 are required. Also needed are the following:

a. Sodium hydroxide, NaOH, 6*N*.

b. Sulfuric acid, H_2SO_4, 6*N*, 1 + 5.

4. Procedure

Minimize effects of pH, time, and temperature of reaction by standardizing all conditions.

a. Titration of free available chlorine (hypochlorite and hypochlorous acid): Add sufficient 6*N* NaOH to raise sample pH to 12. After 10 min, add 6*N* H_2SO_4 to lower pH to 7. Titrate with standard phenylarsine oxide titrant to the amperometric end point as given in Section 4500-Cl.D. Record result as *A*.

b. Titration of free available chlorine and chloramine: Add 6*N* NaOH to raise sample pH to 12. After 10 min, add 6*N* H_2SO_4 to reduce pH to 7. Add 1 mL KI solution. Titrate with standard phenylarsine oxide titrant to the amperometric end point. Record result as *B*.

c. Titration of free available chlorine, chloramine, and one-fifth of available ClO_2: Adjust sample pH to 7 with pH 7 phosphate buffer solution. Add 1 mL KI solution. Titrate with standard phenylarsine oxide titrant to the amperometric end point. Record result as *C*.

d. Titration of free available chlorine, chloramines, ClO_2, and chlorite: Add 1 mL KI solution to sample. Add sufficient 6*N* H_2SO_4 to lower pH to 2. After 10 min, add sufficient 6*N* NaOH to raise pH to 7. Titrate with standard phenylarsine oxide titrant to the amperometric end point. Record result as *D*.

5. Calculation

Convert individual titrations (*A, B, C,* and *D*) into chlorine concentration by the following equation:

$$\text{mg Cl as Cl}_2/\text{L} = \frac{E \times 200}{\text{mL sample}}$$

where:

E = mL phenylarsine oxide titration for each individual sample *A, B, C,* or *D*.

Calculate ClO₂ and individual chlorine fractions as follows:

$$\text{mg ClO}_2 \text{ as ClO}_2/\text{L} = 1.9 \ (C - B)$$
$$\text{mg ClO}_2 \text{ as Cl}_2/\text{L} = 5 \ (C - B)$$
$$\text{mg free available chlorine}/\text{L} = A$$

$$\text{mg chloramine}/\text{L as chlorine} = B - A$$
$$\text{mg chlorite}/\text{L as chlorine} = 4B - 5C + D$$

6. Bibliography

HALLER, J.F. & S.S. LISTEK. 1948. Determination of chlorine dioxide and other active chlorine compounds in water. *Anal. Chem.* 20:639.

4500-ClO₂ D. DPD Method

1. General Discussion

a. Principle: This method is an extension of the *N,N*-diethyl-*p*-phenylenediamine (DPD) method for determining free chlorine and chloramines in water. ClO₂ appears in the first step of this procedure but only to the extent of one-fifth of its total available chlorine content corresponding to reduction of ClO₂ to chlorite ion. If the sample is then acidified in the presence of iodide the chlorite also reacts. When neutralized by subsequent addition of bicarbonate, the color thus produced corresponds to the total available chlorine content of the ClO₂. If chlorite is present in the sample, this will be included in the step involving acidification and neutralization. Chlorite that did not result from ClO₂ reduction by the procedure will cause a positive error equal to twice this chlorite concentration. In evaluating mixtures of these various chloro-compounds, it is necessary to suppress free chlorine by adding glycine before reacting the sample with DPD reagent. Differentiation is based on the fact that glycine converts free chlorine instantaneously into chloroaminoacetic acid but has no effect on ClO₂.

b. Interference: The interference by oxidized manganese described in Section 4500-Cl.F.1*d* applies also to ClO₂ determination. Manganese interference appears as an increase in the first titrations after addition of DPD, with or without KI, and irrespective of whether there has been prior addition of glycine. Titration readings must

be corrected suitably. Interference by chromate in wastewaters may be corrected similarly.

Iron contributed to the sample by adding ferrous ammonium sulfate (FAS) titrant may activate chlorite so as to interfere with the first end point of the titration. Suppress this effect with additional EDTA, disodium salt.

2. Reagents

Reagents required in addition to those for the DPD free-combined chlorine method as listed in Section 4500-Cl.F.2 are as follows:

a. Glycine solution: Dissolve 10 g NH₂CH₂COOH in 100 mL distilled water.

b. Sulfuric acid solution: Dilute 5 mL conc H₂SO₄ to 100 mL with distilled water.

c. Sodium bicarbonate solution: Dissolve 27.5 g NaHCO₃ in 500 mL distilled water.

d. EDTA: Disodium salt of ethylenediamine tetraacetic acid, solid.

3. Procedure

For samples containing more than 5 mg/L total available chlorine follow the dilution procedure given in Section 4500-Cl.F.3.

a. Chlorine dioxide: Add 2 mL glycine solution to 100 mL sample and mix. Place 5 mL each of buffer reagent and DPD indicator solution in a separate titration flask and mix (or use about 500 mg DPD powder). Add about 200 mg EDTA, disodium salt. Then add glycine-treated sample and mix. Titrate rapidly with standard FAS titrant until red color is discharged (Reading G).

b. *Free available chlorine and chloramine:* Using a second 100-mL sample follow the procedures of Section 4500-Cl.F.3a adding about 200 mg EDTA, disodium salt, initially with the DPD reagents (Readings A, B, and C).

c. *Total available chlorine including chlorite:* After obtaining Reading C add 1 mL H_2SO_4 solution to the same sample in titration flask, mix, and let stand about 2 min. Add 5 mL $NaHCO_3$ solution, mix, and titrate (Reading D).

d. *Colorimetric procedure:* Instead of titration with standard FAS solution, colorimetric procedures may be used to obtain the readings at each stage. Calibrate colorimeters with standard permanganate solution as directed in Section 4500-Cl.G.4a. Use of additional EDTA, disodium salt, with the DPD reagents is not required in colorimetric procedures.

4. Calculations

For 100 mL sample, 1 mL FAS solution = 1 mg available chlorine/L.

In the absence of chlorite:

$$\text{Chlorine dioxide} = 5G \text{ (or } 1.9G \text{ expressed as } ClO_2\text{)}$$
$$\text{Free available chlorine} = A - G$$
$$\text{Monochloramine} = B - A$$
$$\text{Dichloramine} = C - B$$
$$\text{Total available chlorine} = C + 4G$$

If the step leading to Reading B is omitted, monochloramine and dichloramine are obtained together when:

$$\text{Combined available chlorine} = C - A$$

If it is desired to check for presence of chlorite in sample, obtain Reading D. Chlorite is indicated if D is greater than $C + 4G$.

In the presence of chlorite:

$$\text{Chlorine dioxide} = 5G \text{ (or } 1.9G \text{ expressed as } ClO_2\text{)}$$
$$\text{Chlorite} = D - (C + 4G)$$
$$\text{Free available chlorine} = A - G$$
$$\text{Monochloramine} = B - A$$
$$\text{Dichloramine} = C - B$$
$$\text{Total available chlorine} = D$$

If B is omitted,

$$\text{Combined available chlorine} = C - A$$

5. Bibliography

PALIN, A.T. 1960. Colorimetric determination of chlorine dioxide in water. *Water Sewage Works* 107:457.

PALIN, A.T. 1967. Methods for the determination, in water, of free and combined available chlorine, chlorine dioxide and chlorite, bromine, iodine, and ozone using diethyl-p-phenylenediamine (DPD). *J. Inst. Water Eng.* 21:537.

PALIN, A.T. 1974. Analytical control of water disinfection with special reference to differential DPD methods for chlorine, chlorine dioxide, bromine, iodine and ozone. *J. Inst. Water Eng.* 28:139.

PALIN, A.T. 1975. Current DPD methods for residual halogen compounds and ozone in water. *J. Amer. Water Works Assoc.* 67:32.

4500-ClO$_2$ E.   Amperometric Method II (PROPOSED)

1. General Discussion

a. *Principle:*   Like   Amperometric Method I (Section 4500-ClO$_2$.C), this procedure entails successive titrations of combinations of chlorine species. Subsequent calculations determine the concentration of each species. The equilibrium for reduction of the chlorine species of interest by iodide is pH-dependent.

The analysis of a sample for chlorine,

chlorine dioxide, chlorite, and chlorate requires the following steps: determination of all of the chlorine (free plus combined) and one-fifth of the chlorine dioxide at pH 7; lowering sample pH to 2 and determination of the remaining four-fifths of the ClO$_2$ and all of the chlorite (the chlorite measured in this step comes from the chlorite originally present in the sample and that formed in the first titration); preparation of a second sample by purging with nitrogen to remove ClO$_2$ and by reacting with iodide at pH 7 to remove any chlorine remaining; lowering latter sample pH to 2 and determination of all chlorite present (this chlorite only comes from the chlorite originally present in the sample); and, in a third sample, determination of all of the relevant, oxidized chlorine species—chlorine, chlorine dioxide, chlorite, and chlorate—after reduction in hydrochloric acid.[1]

This procedure can be applied to concentrated solutions (10 to 100 mg/L) or dilute solutions (0.1 to 10 mg/L) by appropriate selection of titrant concentration and sample size.

b. Interferences: At pH values above 4, significant iodate formation is possible if iodine is formed in the absence of iodide;[2] this results in a negative bias in titrating the first and second samples. Acidification of these samples causes reduction of iodate to iodine and a positive bias. To prevent formation of iodate add 1 g KI granules to stirred sample.

A positive bias results from oxidation of iodide to iodine by dissolved oxygen in strongly acidic solutions.[1] To minimize this bias, use bromide as the reducing agent in titrating the third sample (bromide is not oxidized by oxygen under these conditions). After reaction is completed, add iodide, which will be oxidized to iodine by the bromine formed from the reduction of the original chlorine species. Add iodide carefully so that bromine gas is not lost. Rapid dilution of the sample with sodium phosphate decreases sample acidity and

minimizes oxidation of iodide by oxygen. The pH of the solution to be titrated should be between 1.0 and 2.0. Carry a blank through the procedure as a check on iodide oxidation.

The potential for interferences from manganese, copper, and nitrate are minimized by buffering the sample to pH ≥ 4.[3,4] For the method presented here, the low pH required for the chlorite and chlorate analyses provides conditions favorable to manganese, copper, and nitrite interferences.

2. Apparatus

a. Titrators: See Section 4500-Cl.D.2*a* through *d*. Amperometric titrators with a platinum-platinum electrode system are more stable and require less maintenance. (NOTE: Chlorine dioxide may attack adhesives used to connect the platinum plate to the electrode, resulting in poor readings.)

If a potentiometric titrator is used, provide a platinum sensing electrode and a silver chloride reference electrode for endpoint detection.

b. Glassware: Store glassware used in this method separately from other laboratory glassware and do not use for other purposes because ClO$_2$ reacts with glass to form a hydrophobic surface coating. To satisfy any ClO$_2$ demand, before first use immerse all glassware in a strong ClO$_2$ solution (200 to 500 mg/L) for 24 h and rinse only with water between uses.

c. Sampling: ClO$_2$ is volatile and will vaporize easily from aqueous solution. When sampling a liquid stream, minimize contact with air by placing a flexible sample line to reach the bottom of the sample container, letting several container volumes overflow, slowly removing sample line, and capping container with minimum headspace. Protect from sunlight. Remove sample portions with a volumetric pipet with pipet tip placed at bottom of container. Drain pipet by placing its tip below the surface of reagent or dilution water.

3. Reagents

a. *Standard sodium thiosulfate,* 0.100*N*: See Section 4500-Cl.B.2*c*.

b. *Standard phenylarsine oxide,* 0.005 64*N*: See Section 4500-Cl.C.3*a*.

c. *Phosphate buffer solution,* pH 7: See Section 4500-Cl.D.3*b*.

d. *Potassium iodide,* KI, granules.

e. *Saturated sodium phosphate solution:* Prepare a saturated solution of $Na_2HPO_4 \cdot 12H_2O$ with cold deionized-distilled water.

f. *Potassium bromide solution,* 5%: Dissolve 5 g KBr and dilute to 100 mL. Store in a brown glass-stoppered bottle. Make fresh weekly.

g. *Hydrochloric acid,* HCl, conc.

h. *Hydrochloric acid,* HCl, 2.5*N*: Cautiously add 200 mL conc HCl, with mixing, to distilled water, diluting to 1000 mL.

i. *Purge gas:* Use nitrogen gas for purging ClO_2 from samples. Assure that gas is free of contaminants and pass it through a 5% KI scrub solution. Discard solution at first sign of color.

4. Procedure

Use either sodium thiosulfate or phenylarsine oxide as titrant. Select concentration on basis of concentration range expected. The total mass of oxidant species should be no greater than about 15 mg. Make appropriate sample dilutions if necessary. A convenient volume for titration is 200 to 300 mL. Preferably analyze all samples and blanks in triplicate.

Minimize effects of pH, time, and temperature of reaction by standardizing all conditions.

a. *Titration of residual chlorine and one-fifth of available* ClO_2: Place 1 mL pH 7 phosphate buffer in beaker and add distilled-deionized dilution water if needed. Introduce sample with minimum aeration and add 1 g KI granules while stirring. Titrate to end point (see Section 4500-

Cl.D). Record reading A = mL titrant/mL sample.

b. *Titration of four-fifths of available* ClO_2 *and chlorite:* Continuing with same sample, add 2 mL 2.5*N* HCl. Let stand in the dark for 5 min. Titrate to end point. Record reading B = mL titrant/mL sample.

c. *Titration of nonvolatilized chlorine:* Place 1 mL pH 7 phosphate buffer in purge vessel and add distilled-deionized dilution water if needed. Add sample and purge with nitrogen gas for 15 min. Use a gas-dispersion tube to give good gas-liquid contact. Add 1 g KI granules while stirring and titrate to end point. Record reading C = mL titrant/mL sample.

d. *Titration of chlorite:* Continuing with same sample, add 2 mL 2.5*N* HCl. Let stand in the dark for 5 min. Titrate to end point, and record reading D = mL titrant/mL sample.

e. *Titration of chlorine,* ClO_2, *chlorate, and chlorite:* Add 1 mL KBr and 10 mL conc HCl to 50-mL reaction flask and mix. Carefully add 15 mL sample, with minimum aeration. Mix and stopper immediately. Let stand in the dark for 20 min. Rapidly add 1 g KI granules and shake vigorously for 5 s. Rapidly transfer to titration flask containing 25 mL saturated Na_2HPO_4 solution. Rinse reaction flask thoroughly and add rinse water to titration flask. Final titration volume should be about 200 to 300 mL. Titrate to end point.

Repeat procedure of preceding paragraph using distilled-deionized water in place of sample to determine blank value.

Record reading E = (mL titrant sample − mL titrant blank)/mL sample.

NOTE: The 15-mL sample volume can be adjusted to provide an appropriate dilution, but maintain the ratio of sample to HCl.

5. Calculations

Because the combining power of the titrants is pH-dependent, all calculations are

TABLE 4500-ClO₂:I. EQUIVALENT WEIGHTS FOR CALCULATING CONCENTRATIONS ON THE BASIS OF MASS

pH	Species	Molecular Weight mg/mol	Electrons Transferred	Equivalent Weight mg/eq
7	Chlorine dioxide	67 452	1	67 452
2, 0.1	Chlorine dioxide	67 452	5	13 490
7, 2, 0.1	Chlorine	70 906	2	35 453
2, 0.1	Chlorite	67 452	4	16 863
0.1	Chlorate	83 451	6	13 909

based on the equivalents of reducing titrant required to react with equivalents of oxidant present. Use Table 4500-ClO₂:I to obtain the equivalent weights to be used in the calculations.

In the following equations, N is the normality of the titrant used in equivalents per liter and A through E are as defined previously.

Chlorite, mg $ClO_2^-/L = D \times N \times 16\ 863$
Chlorate, mg ClO_2^{2-}/L
$$= [E - (A + B)] \times N \times 13\ 909$$
Chlorine dioxide, mg ClO_2/L
$$= (5/4) \times (B - D) \times N \times 13\ 490$$
Chlorine, mg Cl_2/L
$$= \{A - [(B - D)/4]\} \times N \times 35\ 453$$

6. References

1. AIETA, E.M., P.V. ROBERTS & M. HERNANDEZ. 1984. Determination of chlorine dioxide, chlorine, chlorite, and chlorate in water. *J. Amer. Water Works Assoc.* 76:64.

2. WONG, G. 1982. Factors affecting the amperometric determination of trace quantities of total residual chlorine in seawater. *Environ. Sci. Technol.* 16:11.

3. WHITE, G. 1972. Handbook of Chlorination. Van Nostrand Reinhold Co., New York, N.Y.

4. JOLLEY, R. & J. CARPENTER. 1982. Aqueous Chemistry of Chlorine: Chemistry, Analysis, and Environmental Fate of Reactive Oxidant Species. ORNL/TM-788, Oak Ridge National Lab., Oak Ridge, Tenn.

7. Bibliography

AIETA, E.M. 1985. Amperometric analysis of chlorine dioxide, chlorine and chlorite in aqueous solution. Presented at American Water Works Assoc. Water Quality Technology Conf. 13, Houston, Texas.

GORDON, G. 1982. Improved methods of analysis for chlorate, chlorite, and hypochlorite ions. Presented at American Water Works Assoc. Water Quality Technology Conf., Nashville, Tenn.

TANG, T. F. & G. GORDON. 1980. Quantitative determination of chloride, chlorite, and chlorate ions in a mixture by successive potentiometric titrations. *Anal. Chem.* 52:1430.

4500-F⁻   FLUORIDE*

4500-F⁻ A.   Introduction

A fluoride concentration of approximately 1.0 mg/L in drinking water effectively reduces dental caries without harmful effects on health. Fluoride may occur naturally in water or it may be added in controlled amounts. Some fluorosis may occur when the fluoride level exceeds the recommended limits. In rare instances the naturally occurring fluoride concentration may approach 10 mg/L; such waters should be defluoridated.

Accurate determination of fluoride has increased in importance with the growth of the practice of fluoridation of water supplies as a public health measure. Maintenance of an optimal fluoride concentration is essential in maintaining effectiveness and safety of the fluoridation procedure.

1. Preliminary Treatment

Among the methods suggested for determining fluoride ion (F⁻) in water, the electrode and colorimetric methods are the most satisfactory. Because both methods are subject to errors due to interfering ions (Table 4500-F⁻:I), it may be necessary to distill the sample as directed in Section 4500-F⁻.B before making the determination. When interfering ions are not present in excess of the tolerances of the method, the fluoride determination may be made directly without distillation.

2. Selection of Method

The electrode method (Method C) is suitable for fluoride concentrations from 0.1 to more than 10 mg/L. Adding the prescribed buffer frees the electrode method from most interferences that adversely affect the SPADNS colorimetric method and necessitate preliminary distillation. Some substances in industrial wastes, such as fluoborates, may be sufficiently concentrated to present problems in electrode measurements. Fluoride measurements can be made with a specific ion electrode and either an expanded-scale pH meter or a specific ion meter, usually without distillation, in the time necessary for electrode equilibration.

The SPADNS method (D) has an analytical range of 0 to 1.40 mg F⁻/L with virtually instantaneous color development. Color determinations are made photometrically, using either a filter photometer or a spectrophotometer. A curve developed from standards is used for determining the fluoride concentration of a sample.

Fluoride also may be determined by the automated complexone method, Method E.

Ion chromatography (Section 4110) may be an acceptable method if weaker eluants are used to separate fluoride from interfering peaks.

3. Sampling and Storage

Preferably use polyethylene bottles for collecting and storing samples for fluoride analysis. Glass bottles are satisfactory if previously they have not contained high-fluoride solutions. Always rinse bottle with a portion of sample.

Never use an excess of dechlorinating agent. Dechlorinate with sodium arsenite rather than sodium thiosulfate when using the SPADNS method because the latter may produce turbidity that causes erroneous readings.

---

*Approved by Standard Methods Committee, 1988.

TABLE 4500-F⁻:1. CONCENTRATION OF SOME SUBSTANCES CAUSING 0.1-MG/L ERROR AT
1.0 MG F/L IN FLUORIDE METHODS

Substance	Method C (Electrode)		Method D (SPADNS)	
	Conc mg/L	Type of Error*	Conc mg/L	Type of Error*
Alkalinity ($CaCO_3$)	7 000	+	5 000	−
Aluminum (Al^{3+})	3.0	−	0.1†	−
Chloride (Cl^-)	20 000		7 000	+
Chlorine	5 000		Remove completely with arsenite	
Color & turbidity			Remove or compensate for	
Iron	200	−	10	−
Hexametaphosphate ($[NaPO_3]_6$)	50 000		1.0	+
Phosphate (PO_4^{3-})	50 000		16	+
Sulfate (SO_4^{2-})	50 000	−	200	−

* + denotes positive error
   − denotes negative error
  Blank denotes no measurable error.
† On immediate reading. Tolerance increases with time: after 2 h, 3.0; after 4 h, 30.

4500-F⁻ B. Preliminary Distillation Step

1. Discussion

Fluoride can be separated from other nonvolatile constituents in water by conversion to hydrofluoric or fluosilicic acid and subsequent distillation. The conversion is accomplished by using a strong, high-boiling acid. To protect against glassware etching, hydrofluoric acid is converted to fluosilicic acid by using soft glass beads. Quantitative fluoride recovery is approached by using a relatively large sample. Acid and sulfate carryover are minimized by distilling over a controlled temperature range.

Distillation will separate fluoride from most water samples. Some tightly bound fluoride, such as that in biological materials, may require digestion before distillation, but water samples seldom require such drastic treatment. Distillation produces a distillate volume equal to that of the original water sample so that usually it is not necessary to incorporate a dilution factor when expressing analytical results. The distillate will be essentially free of substances that might interfere with the fluoride determination if the apparatus used is adequate and distillation has been carried out properly. The only common volatile constituent likely to cause interference with colorimetric analysis of the distillate is chloride. When the concentration of chloride is high enough to interfere, add silver sulfate to the sulfuric acid distilling mixture to minimize the volatilization of hydrogen chloride.

Heating an acid-water mixture can be hazardous if precautions are not taken: *Mix acid and water thoroughly before heating.* Use of a quartz heating mantle and a magnetic stirrer in the distillation apparatus simplifies the mixing step.

2. Apparatus

a. Distillation apparatus consisting of a 1-L round-bottom long-neck borosilicate glass boiling flask, a connecting tube, an efficient condenser, a thermometer adapter, and a thermometer that can be read to 200°C. Use standard taper joints for all connections in the direct vapor path. Position the thermometer so that the bulb always is immersed in boiling mixture. The apparatus should be disassembled easily to permit adding sample. Substituting a thermoregulator and necessary circuitry for the thermometer is acceptable and provides some automation.

Alternative types of distillation apparatus may be used. Carefully evaluate any apparatus for fluoride recovery and sulfate carryover. The critical points are obstructions in the vapor path and trapping of liquid in the adapter and condenser. (The condenser should have a vapor path with minimum obstruction. A double-jacketed condenser, with cooling water in the outer jacket and the inner spiral tube, is ideal, but other condensers are acceptable if they have minimum obstructions. Avoid using Graham-type condensers.) Avoid using an open flame as a heat source if possible, because heat applied to the boiling flask above the liquid level causes superheating of vapor and subsequent sulfate carryover.

CAUTION: *Regardless of apparatus used, provide for thorough mixing of sample and acid; heating a non-homogenous acid-water*

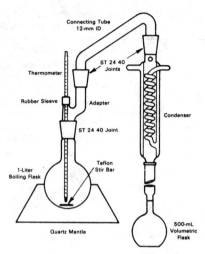

Figure 4500-F⁻:1. Direct distillation apparatus for fluoride.

mixture will result in bumping or possibly a violent explosion.

The preferred apparatus is illustrated in Figure 4500-F⁻:1.

b. Quartz hemispherical heating mantle, for full-voltage operation.

c. Magnetic stirrer, with TFE-coated stirring bar.

d. Soft glass beads.

3. Reagents

a. Sulfuric acid, H_2SO_4, conc, reagent grade.

b. Silver sulfate, Ag_2SO_4, crystals, reagent grade.

4. Procedure

a. Place 400 mL distilled water in the distilling flask and, with the magnetic stirrer operating, carefully add 200 mL conc H_2SO_4. Keep stirrer in operation throughout distillation. Add a few glass beads and connect the apparatus as shown in Figure 4500-F⁻:1, making sure all joints are tight. Begin heating and continue until flask contents reach 180°C (because of heat retention by the mantle, it is necessary to discontinue heating when the temperature reaches

178°C to prevent overheating). Discard distillate. This process removes fluoride contamination and adjusts the acid-water ratio for subsequent distillations.

b. After the acid mixture remaining in the steps outlined in ¶ 4*a*, or previous distillations, has cooled to 80°C or below, add 300 mL sample, with stirrer operating, and distill until the temperature reaches 180°C. To prevent sulfate carryover, turn off heat before 178°C. Retain the distillate for analysis.

c. Add Ag_2SO_4 to the distilling flask at the rate of 5 mg/mg Cl^- when the chloride concentration is high enough to interfere (see Table 4500-F⁻:I).

d. Use H_2SO_4 solution in the flask repeatedly until contaminants from samples accumulate to such an extent that recovery is affected or interferences appear in the distillate. Check acid suitability periodically by distilling standard fluoride samples

and analyzing for both fluoride and sulfate. After distilling samples containing more than 3 mg F⁻/L, flush still by adding 300 mL distilled water, redistill, and combine the two fluoride distillates. If necessary, repeat flushing until the fluoride content of the last distillate is at a minimum. Include additional fluoride recovered with that of the first distillation. After periods of inactivity, similarly flush still and discard distillate.

5. Interpretation of Results

The recovery of fluoride is quantitative within the accuracy of the methods used for its measurement.

6. Bibliography

BELLACK, E. 1958. Simplified fluoride distillation method. *J. Amer. Water Works Assoc.* 50:530.
BELLACK, E. 1961. Automatic fluoride distillation. *J. Amer. Water Works Assoc.* 53:98.
ZEHNPFENNIG, R.G. 1976. Letter to the editor. *Environ. Sci. Technol.* 10:1049.

4500-F⁻ C. Ion-Selective Electrode Method

1. General Discussion

a. Principle: The fluoride electrode is an ion-selective sensor. The key element in the fluoride electrode is the laser-type doped lanthanum fluoride crystal across which a potential is established by fluoride solutions of different concentrations. The crystal contacts the sample solution at one face and an internal reference solution at the other. The cell may be represented by:

Ag|AgCl, Cl⁻(0.3*M*), F⁻(0.001*M*)|LaF₃| test
solution|reference electrode

The fluoride electrode can be used with a standard calomel reference electrode and almost any modern pH meter having an expanded millivolt scale.

The fluoride electrode measures the ion activity of fluoride in solution rather than concentration. Fluoride ion activity depends on the solution total ionic strength and pH, and on fluoride complexing species. Adding an appropriate buffer provides a nearly uniform ionic strength background, adjusts pH, and breaks up complexes so that, in effect, the electrode measures concentration.

b. Interference: Table 4500-F⁻:I lists common interferences. Fluoride forms complexes with several polyvalent cations, notably aluminum and iron. The extent to which complexation takes place depends on solution pH, relative levels of fluoride, and complexing species. However, CDTA (cyclohexylenediaminetetraacetic acid), a component of the buffer, preferentially will complex interfering cations and release free fluoride ions. Concentrations of aluminum, the most common interference, up to 3.0 mg/L can be complexed preferentially. In acid solution, F^- forms a poorly ionized $HF \cdot HF$ complex but the buffer maintains a pH above 5 to minimize hydrogen fluoride complex formation. In alkaline solution hydroxide ion also can interfere with electrode response to fluoride ion whenever the hydroxide ion concentration is greater than one-tenth the concentration of fluoride ion. At the pH maintained by the buffer, no hydroxide interference occurs.

Fluoborates are widely used in industrial processes. Dilute solutions of fluoborate or fluoboric acid hydrolyze to liberate fluoride ion but in concentrated solutions, as in electroplating wastes, hydrolysis does not occur completely. Distill such samples or measure fluoborate with a fluoborate-selective electrode. Also distill the sample if the dissolved solids concentration exceeds 10 000 mg/L.

2. Apparatus

a. Expanded-scale or digital pH meter or ion-selective meter.

b. Sleeve-type reference electrode: Do not use fiber-tip reference electrodes because they exhibit erratic behavior in very dilute solutions.

c. Fluoride electrode.

d. Magnetic stirrer, with TFE-coated stirring bar.

e. Timer.

3. Reagents

a. Stock fluoride solution: Dissolve 221.0 mg anhydrous sodium fluoride, NaF, in distilled water and dilute to 1000 mL; 1.00 mL = 100 μg F^-.

b. Standard fluoride solution: Dilute 100 mL stock fluoride solution to 1000 mL with distilled water; 1.00 mL = 10.0 μg F^-.

c. Fluoride buffer: Place approximately 500 mL distilled water in a 1-L beaker and add 57 mL glacial acetic acid, 58 g NaCl,

and 4.0 g 1,2 cyclohexylenediaminetetraacetic acid (CDTA).* Stir to dissolve. Place beaker in a cool water bath and add slowly 6N NaOH (about 125 mL) with stirring, until pH is between 5.3 and 5.5. Transfer to a 1-L volumetric flask and add distilled water to the mark. This buffer, as well as a more concentrated version, is available commercially. In using the concentrated buffer follow the manufacturer's directions.

4. Procedure

a. Instrument calibration: No major adjustment of any instrument normally is required to use electrodes in the range of 0.2 to 2.0 mg F^-/L. For those instruments with zero at center scale adjust calibration control so that the 1.0 mg F^-/L standard reads at the center zero (100 mV) when the meter is in the expanded-scale position. This cannot be done on some meters that do not have a millivolt calibration control. To use a selective-ion meter follow the manufacturer's instructions.

b. Preparation of fluoride standards: Prepare a series of standards by diluting with distilled water 5.0, 10.0, and 20.0 mL of standard fluoride solution to 100 mL with distilled water. These standards are equivalent to 0.5, 1.0, and 2.0 mg F^-/L.

c. Treatment of standards and sample: In 100-mL beakers or other convenient containers add by volumetric pipet from 10 to 25 mL standard or sample. Bring standards and sample to same temperature, preferably room temperature. Add an equal volume of buffer. The total volume should be sufficient to immerse the electrodes and permit operation of the stirring bar.

d. Measurement with electrode: Immerse electrodes in each of the fluoride standard solutions and measure developed potential while stirring on a magnetic stirrer. Avoid stirring before immersing electrodes be-

---

*Also known as 1,2 cyclohexylenedinitrilotetraacetic acid.

cause entrapped air around the crystal can produce erroneous readings or needle fluctuations. Let electrodes remain in the solution 3 min (or until reading is constant) before taking a final millivolt reading. A layer of insulating material between stirrer and beaker minimizes solution heating. Withdraw electrodes, rinse with distilled water, and *blot dry* between readings. (CAUTION: Blotting may poison electrode if not done gently.) Repeat measurements with samples.

When using an expanded-scale pH meter or selective-ion meter, frequently recalibrate the electrode by checking potential reading of the 1.00-mg F^-/L standard and adjusting the calibration control, if necessary, until meter reads as before.

If a direct-reading instrument is not used, plot potential measurement of fluoride standards against concentration on two-cycle semilogarithmic graph paper. Plot milligrams F^- per liter on the logarithmic axis (ordinate), with the lowest concentration at the bottom of the graph. Plot millivolts on the abscissa. From the potential measurement for each sample, read the corresponding fluoride concentration from the standard curve.

The known-additions method may be substituted for the calibration method described. Follow the directions of the instrument manufacturer.

Selective-ion meters may necessitate using a slightly altered procedure, such as preparing 1.00 and 10.0 mg F^-/L standards or some other concentration. Follow the manufacturer's directions. Commercial standards, often already diluted with buffer, frequently are supplied with the meter. Verify the stated fluoride concentration of these standards by comparing them with standards prepared by the analyst.

5. Calculation

$$\text{mg } F^-/L = \frac{\mu g \ F^-}{mL \ \text{sample}}$$

6. Precision and Bias

A synthetic sample containing 0.850 mg F^-/L in distilled water was analyzed in 111 laboratories by the electrode method, with a relative standard deviation of 3.6% and a relative error of 0.7%.

A second synthetic sample containing 0.750 mg F^-/L, 2.5 mg $(NaPO_3)_6/L$, and 300 mg alkalinity/L added as $NaHCO_3$, was analyzed in 111 laboratories by the electrode method, with a relative standard deviation of 4.8% and a relative error of 0.2%.

A third synthetic sample containing 0.900 mg F^-/L, 0.500 mg Al/L, and 200 mg SO_4^{2-}/L was analyzed in 13 laboratories by the electrode method, with a relative standard deviation of 2.9% and a relative error of 4.9%.

7. Bibliography

FRANT, M.S. & J.W. ROSS, JR. 1968. Use of total ionic strength adjustment buffer for electrode determination of fluoride in water supplies. *Anal. Chem.* 40:1169.

HARWOOD, J.E. 1969. The use of an ion-selective electrode for routine analysis of water samples. *Water Res.* 3:273.

4500-F⁻ D.   SPADNS Method

1. General Discussion

a. Principle: The SPADNS colorimetric method is based on the reaction between fluoride and a zirconium-dye lake. Fluoride reacts with the dye lake, dissociating a portion of it into a colorless complex anion (ZrF_6^{2-}); and the dye. As the amount of fluoride increases, the color produced becomes progressively lighter.

The reaction rate between fluoride and zirconium ions is influenced greatly by the acidity of the reaction mixture. If the proportion of acid in the reagent is increased, the reaction can be made almost instantaneous. Under such conditions, however, the effect of various ions differs from that in the conventional alizarin methods. The selection of dye for this rapid fluoride method is governed largely by the resulting tolerance to these ions.

b. Interference: Table 4500-F⁻:I lists common interferences. Because these are neither linear in effect nor algebraically additive, mathematical compensation is impossible. Whenever any one substance is present in sufficient quantity to produce an error of 0.1 mg/L or whenever the total interfering effect is in doubt, distill the sample. Also distill colored or turbid samples. In some instances, sample dilution or adding appropriate amounts of interfering substances to the standards may be used to compensate for the interference effect. If alkalinity is the only significant interference, neutralize it with either hydrochloric or nitric acid. Chlorine interferes and provision for its removal is made.

Volumetric measurement of sample and reagent is extremely important to analytical accuracy. Use samples and standards at the same temperature or at least within 2°C. Maintain constant temperature throughout the color development period. Prepare different calibration curves for different temperature ranges.

2. Apparatus

Colorimetric equipment: One of the following is required:

a. Spectrophotometer, for use at 570 nm, providing a light path of at least 1 cm.

b. Filter photometer, providing a light path of at least 1 cm and equipped with a greenish yellow filter having maximum transmittance at 550 to 580 nm.

3. Reagents

a. Standard fluoride solution: Prepare as directed in the electrode method, Section 4500-F⁻.C.3*b*.

b. SPADNS solution: Dissolve 958 mg SPADNS, sodium 2-(parasulfophenylazo)-1,8-dihydroxy-3,6-naphthalene disulfonate, also called 4,5-dihydroxy-3-(parasulfophenylazo)-2,7-naphthalenedisulfonic acid trisodium salt, in distilled water and dilute to 500 mL. This solution is stable for at least 1 year if protected from direct sunlight.

c. Zirconyl-acid reagent: Dissolve 133 mg zirconyl chloride octahydrate, $ZrOCl_2 \cdot 8H_2O$, in about 25 mL distilled water. Add 350 mL conc HCl and dilute to 500 mL with distilled water.

d. Acid zirconyl-SPADNS reagent: Mix equal volumes of SPADNS solution and zirconyl-acid reagent. The combined reagent is stable for at least 2 years.

e. Reference solution: Add 10 mL SPADNS solution to 100 mL distilled water. Dilute 7 mL conc HCl to 10 mL and add to the diluted SPADNS solution. The resulting solution, used for setting the instrument reference point (zero), is stable for at least 1 year. Alternatively, use a prepared standard of 0 mg F⁻/L as a reference.

f. Sodium arsenite solution: Dissolve 5.0 g $NaAsO_2$ and dilute to 1 L with distilled water. (CAUTION: *Toxic—avoid ingestion.*)

4. Procedure

a. Preparation of standard curve: Prepare fluoride standards in the range of 0 to 1.40 mg F⁻/L by diluting appropriate quantities of standard fluoride solution to 50 mL with distilled water. Pipet 5.00 mL each of SPADNS solution and zirconyl-acid reagent, or 10.00 mL mixed acid-zirconyl-SPADNS reagent, to each standard and mix well. Avoid contamination. Set photometer to zero absorbance with the reference solution and obtain absorbance readings of standards. Plot a curve of the milligrams fluoride-absorbance relationship. Prepare a new standard curve whenever a fresh reagent is made or a different standard temperature is desired. As an alternative to using a reference, set photometer at some convenient point (0.300 or 0.500 absorbance) with the prepared 0 mg F^-/L standard.

b. Sample pretreatment: If the sample contains residual chlorine, remove it by adding 1 drop (0.05 mL) $NaAsO_2$ solution/0.1 mg residual chlorine and mix. (Sodium arsenite concentrations of 1300 mg/L produce an error of 0.1 mg/L at 1.0 mg F^-/L.)

c. Color development: Use a 50.0-mL sample or a portion diluted to 50 mL with distilled water. Adjust sample temperature to that used for the standard curve. Add 5.00 mL each of SPADNS solution and zirconyl-acid reagent, or 10.00 mL acid-zirconyl-SPADNS reagent; mix well and read absorbance, first setting the reference point of the photometer as above. If the absorbance falls beyond the range of the standard curve, repeat using a diluted sample.

5. Calculation

$$\text{mg } F^-/L = \frac{A}{\text{mL sample}} \times \frac{B}{C}$$

where:

A = μg F^- determined from plotted curve,
B = final volume of diluted sample, mL, and
C = volume of diluted sample used for color development, mL.

When the prepared 0 mg F^-/L standard is used to set the photometer, alternatively calculate fluoride concentration as follows:

$$\text{mg } F^-/L = \frac{A_0 - A_x}{A_0 - A_1}$$

where:

A_0 = absorbance of the prepared 0 mg F^-/L standard,
A_1 = absorbance of a prepared 1.0 mg F^-/L standard, and
A_x = absorbance of the prepared sample.

6. Precision and Bias

A synthetic sample containing 0.830 mg F^-/L and no interference in distilled water was analyzed in 53 laboratories by the SPADNS method, with a relative standard deviation of 8.0% and a relative error of 1.2%. After direct distillation of the sample, the relative standard deviation was 11.0% and the relative error 2.4%.

A synthetic sample containing 0.570 mg F^-/L, 10 mg Al/L, 200 mg SO_4^{2-}/L, and 300 mg total alkalinity/L was analyzed in 53 laboratories by the SPADNS method without distillation, with a relative standard deviation of 16.2% and a relative error of 7.0%. After direct distillation of the sample, the relative standard deviation was 17.2% and the relative error 5.3%.

A synthetic sample containing 0.680 mg F^-/L, 2 mg Al/L, 2.5 mg $(NaPO_3)_6/L$, 200 mg SO_4^{2-}/L, and 300 mg total alkalinity/L was analyzed in 53 laboratories by direct distillation and SPADNS methods with a relative standard deviation of 2.8% and a relative error of 5.9%.

7. Bibliography

BELLACK, E. & P.J. SCHOUBOE. 1968. Rapid photometric determination of fluoride with SPADNS-zirconium lake. *Anal. Chem.* 30:2032.

4500-F⁻ E. Complexone Method

1. General Discussion

a. Principle: The sample is distilled in the automated system, and the distillate is reacted with alizarin fluorine blue-lanthanum reagent to form a blue complex that is measured colorimetrically at 620 nm.

b. Interferences: Interferences normally associated with the determination of fluoride are removed by distillation.

c. Application: This method is applicable to potable, surface, and saline waters as well as domestic and industrial wastewaters. The range of the method, which can be modified by using the adjustable colorimeter, is 0.1 to 2.0 mg F⁻/L.

2. Apparatus

The required continuous-flow analytical instrument* consists of the interchangeable components in the number and manner indicated in Figure 4500-F⁻:2.

3. Reagents

a. Standard fluoride solution: Prepare in appropriate concentrations from 0.10 to 2.0 mg F⁻/L using the stock fluoride solution (see Section 4500-F⁻.C.3a).

b. Distillation reagent: Add 50 mL conc H_2SO_4 to about 600 mL distilled water. Add 10.00 mL stock fluoride solution (see Section 4500-F⁻.C.3a; 1.00 mL = 100 μg F⁻) and dilute to 1000 mL.

c. Acetate buffer solution: Dissolve 60 g anhydrous sodium acetate, $NaC_2H_3O_2$, in about 600 mL distilled water. Add 100 mL conc (glacial) acetic acid and dilute to 1 L.

d. Alizarin fluorine blue stock solution: Add 960 mg alizarin fluorine,† $C_{14}H_7O_4 \cdot CH_2N(CH_2 \cdot COOH)_2$, to 100 mL distilled water. Add 2 mL conc NH_4OH

and mix until dye is dissolved. Add 2 mL conc (glacial) acetic acid, dilute to 250 mL and store in an amber bottle in the refrigerator.

e. Lanthanum nitrate stock solution: Dissolve 1.08 g $La(NO_3)_3$ in about 100 mL distilled water, dilute to 250 mL, and store in refrigerator.

f. Working color reagent: Mix in the following order: 300 mL acetate buffer solution, 150 mL acetone, 50 mL tertiary butanol, 36 mL alizarin fluorine blue stock solution, 40 mL lanthanum nitrate stock solution, and 2 mL polyoxyethylene 23 lauryl ether.‡ Dilute to 1 L with distilled water. This reagent is stable for 2 to 4 d.

4. Procedure

No special handling or preparation of sample is required.

Set up manifold as shown in Figure 4500-F⁻:2 and follow the manufacturer's instructions.

5. Calculation

Prepare standard curves by plotting peak heights of standards processed through the manifold against constituent concentrations in standards. Compute sample concentrations by comparing sample peak height with standard curve.

6. Precision and Bias

In a single laboratory four samples of natural water containing from 0.40 to 0.82

---

*Technicon™ Autoanalyzer™ II or equivalent.
†J.T. Baker Catalog number J-112 or equivalent.

‡Brij-35, available from ICI Americas, Wilmington, Del. or Technicon Instruments Corp., Tarrytown, N.Y., or equivalent.

mg F⁻/L were analyzed in septuplicate. Average precision was ± 0.03 mg F⁻/L. To two of the samples, additions of 0.20 and 0.80 mg F⁻/L were made. Average recovery of the additions was 98%.

7. Bibliography

WEINSTEIN, L.H., R.H. MANDL, D.C. MCCUNE, J.S. JACOBSON & A.E. HITCHCOCK. 1963. A semi-automated method for the determination of fluorine in air and plant tissues. *Boyce Thompson Inst.* 22:207.

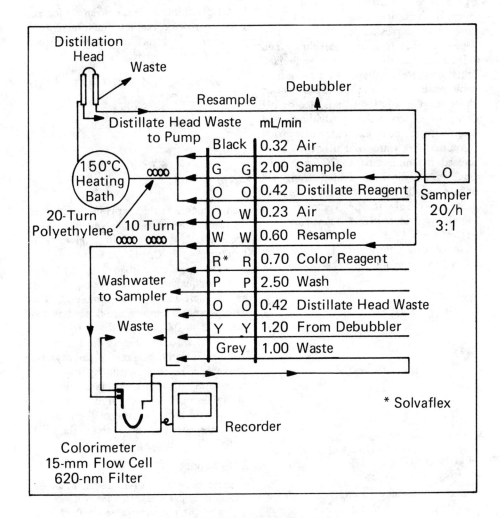

Figure 4500-F⁻:2. Fluoride manifold.

4500-H⁺   pH VALUE*

4500-H⁺ A.   Introduction

1. Principles

Measurement of pH is one of the most important and frequently used tests in water chemistry. Practically every phase of water supply and wastewater treatment, e.g., acid-base neutralization, water softening, precipitation, coagulation, disinfection, and corrosion control, is pH-dependent. pH is used in alkalinity and carbon dioxide measurements and many other acid-base equilibria. At a given temperature the *intensity* of the acidic or basic character of a solution is indicated by pH or hydrogen ion activity. Alkalinity and acidity are the acid- and base-neutralizing capacities of a water and usually are expressed as milligrams $CaCO_3$ per liter. Buffer capacity is the amount of strong acid or base, usually expressed in moles per liter, needed to change the pH value of a 1-L sample by 1 unit. pH as defined by Sorenson[1] is $-\log [H^+]$; it is the "intensity" factor of acidity. Pure water is very slightly ionized and at equilibrium the ion product is

$$[H^+][OH^-] = K_w$$

$$= 1.01 \times 10^{-14} \text{ at } 25°C \quad (1)$$

and

$$[H^+] = [OH^-]$$

$$= 1.005 \times 10^{-7}$$

where:

$[H^+]$ = activity of hydrogen ions, moles/L,
$[OH^-]$ = activity of hydroxyl ions, moles/L, and
K_w = ion product of water.

Because of ionic interactions in all but very dilute solutions, it is necessary to use the "activity" of an ion and not its molar concentration. Use of the term pH assumes that the activity of the hydrogen ion, a_{H^+}, is being considered. The *approximate* equivalence to molarity, $[H^+]$ can be presumed only in very dilute solutions (ionic strength <0.1).

A logarithmic scale is convenient for expressing a wide range of ionic activities. Equation 1 in logarithmic form and corrected to reflect activity is:

$$(-\log_{10} a_{H^+}) + (-\log_{10} a_{OH^-}) = 14 \quad (2)$$

or

$$pH + pOH = pK_w$$

where:

pH† $= -\log_{10} a_{H^+}$ and
pOH $= -\log_{10} a_{OH^-}$.

Equation 2 states that as pH increases pOH decreases correspondingly and vice versa because pK_w is constant for a given temperature. At 25°C, pH 7.0 is neutral, the activities of the hydrogen and hydroxyl ions are equal, and each corresponds to an approximate activity of 10^{-7} moles/L. The neutral point is temperature-dependent and is pH 7.5 at 0°C and pH 6.5 at 60°C.

The pH value of a highly dilute solution is approximately the same as the negative common logarithm of the hydrogen ion concentration. Natural waters usually have pH values in the range of 4 to 9, and most are slightly basic because of the presence of bicarbonates and carbonates of the alkali and alkaline earth metals.

2. Reference

1. SORENSON, S. 1909. Über die Messung und die Bedeutung der Wasserstoff ionen Konzentration bei Enzymatischen Prozessen. *Biochem. Z.* 21: 131.

---

*Approved by Standard Methods Committee, 1985.

†p designates $-\log_{10}$ of a number.

4500-H⁺ B. Electrometric Method

1. General Discussion

a. Principle: The basic principle of electrometric pH measurement is determination of the activity of the hydrogen ions by potentiometric measurement using a standard hydrogen electrode and a reference electrode. The hydrogen electrode consists of a platinum electrode across which hydrogen gas is bubbled at a pressure of 101 kPa. Because of difficulty in its use and the potential for poisoning the hydrogen electrode, the glass electrode commonly is used. The electromotive force (emf) produced in the glass electrode system varies linearly with pH. This linear relationship is described by plotting the measured emf against the pH of different buffers. Sample pH is determined by extrapolation.

Because single ion activities such as a_{H^+} cannot be measured, pH is defined operationally on a potentiometric scale. The pH measuring instrument is calibrated potentiometrically with an indicating (glass) electrode and a reference electrode using National Institute of Standards and Technology (NIST, formerly National Bureau of Standards) buffers having assigned values so that:

$$pH_B = - \log_{10} a_{H^+}$$

where:

pH_B = assigned pH of NIST buffer.

The operational pH scale is used to measure sample pH and is defined as:

$$pH_x = pH_B \pm \frac{F(E_x - E_s)}{2.303\ RT}$$

where:

pH_x = potentiometrically measured sample pH,

F = Faraday: 9.649×10^4 coulomb/mole,
E_x = sample emf, V,
E_s = buffer emf, V,
R = gas constant; 8.314 joule/(mole °K), and
T = absolute temperature, °K.

NOTE: Although the equation for pH_x appears in the literature with a plus sign, the sign of emf readings in millivolts for most pH meters manufactured in the U.S. is negative. The choice of negative sign is consistent with the IUPAC Stockholm convention concerning the sign of electrode potential.[1,2]

The activity scale gives values that are higher than those on Sorenson's scale by 0.04 units:

$$pH\ (activity) = pH\ (Sorenson) + 0.04$$

The equation for pH_x assumes that the emf of the cells containing the sample and buffer is due solely to hydrogen ion activity unaffected by sample composition. In practice, samples will have varying ionic species and ionic strengths, both affecting H^+ activity. This imposes an experimental limitation on pH measurement; thus, to obtain meaningful results, the differences between E_x and E_s should be minimal. Samples must be dilute aqueous solutions of simple solutes ($< 0.2M$). (Choose buffers to bracket the sample.) Determination of pH cannot be made accurately in nonaqueous media, suspensions, colloids, or high-ionic-strength solutions.

b. Interferences: The glass electrode is relatively free from interference from color, turbidity, colloidal matter, oxidants, reductants, or high salinity, except for a sodium error at pH > 10. Reduce this error by using special "low sodium error" electrodes.

pH measurements are affected by temperature in two ways: mechanical effects that are caused by changes in the properties of the electrodes and chemical effects caused by equilibrium changes. In the first instance, the Nernstian slope increases with increasing temperature and electrodes take time to achieve thermal equilibrium. This can cause long-term drift in pH. Because chemical equilibrium affects pH, standard pH buffers have a specified pH at indicated temperatures.

Always report temperature at which pH is measured.

2. Apparatus

a. pH meter consisting of potentiometer, a glass electrode, a reference electrode, and a temperature-compensating device. A circuit is completed through the potentiometer when the electrodes are immersed in the test solution. Many pH meters are capable of reading pH or millivolts and some have scale expansion that permits reading to 0.001 pH unit, but most instruments are not that precise.

For routine work use a pH meter accurate and reproducible to 0.1 pH unit with a range of 0 to 14 and equipped with a temperature-compensation adjustment.

Although manufacturers provide operating instructions, the use of different descriptive terms may be confusing. For most instruments, there are two controls: intercept (set buffer, asymmetry, standardize) and slope (temperature, offset); their functions are shown diagramatically in Figures 4500-H$^+$:1 and 2. The intercept control shifts the response curve laterally to pass through the isopotential point with no change in slope. This permits bringing the instrument on scale (0 mV) with a pH 7 buffer that has no change in potential with temperature.

The slope control rotates the emf/pH slope about the isopotential point (0 mV/pH 7). To adjust slope for temperature without disturbing the intercept, select a buffer that brackets the sample with pH 7 buffer and adjust slope control to pH of this buffer. The instrument will indicate correct millivolt change per unit pH at the test temperature.

b. Reference electrode consisting of a half cell that provides a constant electrode potential. Commonly used are calomel and silver: silver-chloride electrodes. Either is available with several types of liquid junctions.

The liquid junction of the reference electrode is critical because at this point the

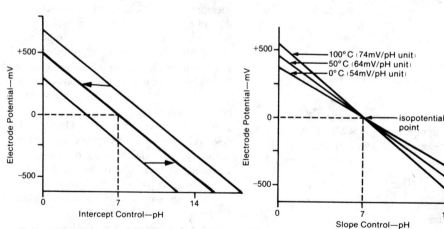

Figure 4500-H$^+$:1. Electrode potential vs. pH. Intercept control shifts response curve laterally.

Figure 4500-H$^+$:2. Typical pH electrode response as a function of temperature.

electrode forms a salt bridge with the sample or buffer and a liquid junction potential is generated that in turn affects the potential produced by the reference electrode. Reference electrode junctions may be annular ceramic, quartz, or asbestos fiber, or the sleeve type. The quartz type is most widely used. The asbestos fiber type is not recommended for strongly basic solutions. Follow the manufacturer's recommendation on use and care of the reference electrode.

Refill nonsealed electrodes with the correct electrolyte to proper level and make sure junction is properly wetted.

c. Glass electrode: The sensor electrode is a bulb of special glass containing a fixed concentration of HCl or a buffered chloride solution in contact with an internal reference electrode. Upon immersion of a new electrode in a solution the outer bulb surface becomes hydrated and exchanges sodium ions for hydrogen ions to build up a surface layer of hydrogen ions. This, together with the repulsion of anions by fixed, negatively charged silicate sites, produces at the glass-solution interface a potential that is a function of hydrogen ion activity in solution.

Several types of glass electrodes are available. Combination electrodes incorporate the glass and reference electrodes into a single probe. Use a "low sodium error" electrode that can operate at high temperatures for measuring pH over 10 because standard glass electrodes yield erroneously low values. For measuring pH below 1 standard glass electrodes yield erroneously high values; use liquid membrane electrodes instead.

d. Beakers: Preferably use polyethylene or TFE* beakers.

e. Stirrer: Use either a magnetic, TFE-coated stirring bar or a mechanical stirrer with inert plastic-coated impeller.

f. Flow chamber: Use for continuous flow measurements or for poorly buffered solutions.

3. Reagents

a. General preparation: Calibrate the electrode system against standard buffer solutions of known pH. Because buffer solutions may deteriorate as a result of mold growth or contamination, prepare fresh as needed for accurate work by weighing the amounts of chemicals specified in Table 4500-H$^+$:I, dissolving in distilled water at 25°C, and diluting to 1000 mL. This is particularly important for borate and carbonate buffers.

Boil and cool distilled water having a conductivity of less than 2 μmhos/cm. To 50 mL add 1 drop of saturated KCl solution suitable for reference electrode use. If the pH of this test solution is between 6.0 and 7.0, use it to prepare all standard solutions.

Dry KH$_2$PO$_4$ at 110 to 130°C for 2 h before weighing but do not heat unstable hydrated potassium tetroxalate above 60°C nor dry the other specified buffer salts.

Although ACS-grade chemicals generally are satisfactory for preparing buffer solutions, use certified materials available from the National Institute of Standards and Technology when the greatest accuracy is required. For routine analysis, use commercially available buffer tablets, powders, or solutions of tested quality. In preparing buffer solutions from solid salts, insure complete solution.

As a rule, select and prepare buffer solutions classed as primary standards in Table 4500-H$^+$:I; reserve secondary standards for extreme situations encountered in wastewater measurements. Consult Table 4500-H$^+$:II for accepted pH of standard buffer solutions at temperatures other than 25°C. In routine use, store buffer solutions and samples in polyethylene bottles. Replace buffer solutions every 4 weeks.

---

*Teflon or equivalent.

TABLE 4500-H$^+$:I. PREPARATION OF pH STANDARD SOLUTIONS[3]

Standard Solution (molality)	pH at 25°C	Weight of Chemicals Needed/1000 mL Aqueous Solution at 25°C
Primary standards:		
Potassium hydrogen tartrate (saturated at 25°C)	3.557	> 7 g $KHC_4H_4O_6$*
0.05 potassium dihydrogen citrate	3.776	11.41 g $KH_2C_6H_5O_7$
0.05 potassium hydrogen phthalate	4.004	10.12 g $KHC_8H_4O_4$
0.025 potassium dihydrogen phosphate + 0.025 disodium hydrogen phosphate	6.863	3.387 g KH_2PO_4 + 3.533 g Na_2HPO_4†
0.008 695 potassium dihydrogen phosphate + 0.030 43 disodium hydrogen phosphate	7.415	1.179 g KH_2PO_4 + 4.303 g Na_2HPO_4†
0.01 sodium borate decahydrate (borax)	9.183	3.80 g $Na_2B_4O_7$ · $10H_2O$†
0.025 sodium bicarbonate + 0.025 sodium carbonate	10.014	2.092 g $NaHCO_3$ + 2.640 g Na_2CO_3
Secondary standards:		
0.05 potassium tetroxalate dihydrate	1.679	12.61 g $KH_3C_4O_8$ · $2H_2O$
Calcium hydroxide (saturated at 25°C)	12.454	> 2 g $Ca(OH)_2$*

* Approximate solubility.
† Prepare with freshly boiled and cooled distilled water (carbon-dioxide-free).

TABLE 4500-H⁺:II. STANDARD pH VALUES[3]

Temperature °C	Tartrate (Saturated)	Citrate (0.05 M)	Phthalate (0.05 M)	Phosphate (1:1)	Phosphate (1:3.5)	Borax (0.01 M)	Bicarbonate-Carbonate (0.025 M)	Tetroxalate (0.05 M)	Calcium Hydroxide (Saturated)
				Primary Standards				Secondary Standards	
0			4.003	6.982	7.534	9.460	10.321	1.666	
5			3.998	6.949	7.501	9.392	10.248	1.668	
10			3.996	6.921	7.472	9.331	10.181	1.670	
15			3.996	6.898	7.449	9.276	10.120	1.672	
20			3.999	6.878	7.430	9.227	10.064	1.675	
25	3.557	3.776	4.004	6.863	7.415	9.183	10.014	1.679	12.454
30	3.552		4.011	6.851	7.403	9.143	9.968	1.683	
35	3.549		4.020	6.842	7.394	9.107	9.928	1.688	
37			4.024	6.839	7.392	9.093			
40	3.547		4.030	6.836	7.388	9.074	9.891	1.694	
45	3.547		4.042	6.832	7.385	9.044	9.859	1.700	
50	3.549		4.055	6.831	7.384	9.017	9.831	1.707	
55	3.554		4.070					1.715	
60	3.560		4.085					1.723	
70	3.580		4.12					1.743	
80	3.609		4.16					1.766	
90	3.650		4.19					1.792	
95	3.674		4.21					1.806	

b. Saturated potassium hydrogen tartrate solution: Shake vigorously an excess (5 to 10 g) of finely crystalline $KHC_4H_4O_6$ with 100 to 300 mL distilled water at 25°C in a glass-stoppered bottle. Separate clear solution from undissolved material by decantation or filtration. Preserve for 2 months or more by adding one thymol crystal (8 mm diam) per 200 mL solution.

c. Saturated calcium hydroxide solution: Calcine a well-washed, low-alkali grade $CaCO_3$ in a platinum dish by igniting for 1 h at 1000°C. Cool, hydrate by slowly adding distilled water with stirring, and heat to boiling. Cool, filter, and collect solid $Ca(OH)_2$ on a fritted glass filter of medium porosity. Dry at 110°C, cool, and pulverize to uniformly fine granules. Vigorously shake an excess of fine granules with distilled water in a stoppered polyethylene bottle. Let temperature come to 25°C after mixing. Filter supernatant under suction through a sintered glass filter of medium porosity and use filtrate as the buffer solution. Discard buffer solution when atmospheric CO_2 causes turbidity to appear.

d. Auxiliary solutions: 0.1N NaOH, 0.1N HCl, 5N HCl (dilute five volumes 6N HCl with one volume distilled water), and acid potassium fluoride solution (dissolve 2 g KF in 2 mL conc H_2SO_4 and dilute to 100 mL with distilled water).

4. Procedure

a. Instrument calibration: In each case follow manufacturer's instructions for pH meter and for storage and preparation of electrodes for use. Recommended solutions for short-term storage of electrodes vary with type of electrode and manufacturer, but generally have a conductivity greater than 4000 μmhos/cm. Tap water is a better substitute than distilled water, but pH 4 buffer is best for the single glass electrode and saturated KCl is preferred for a calomel and Ag/AgCl reference electrode. Saturated KCl is the preferred solution for a combination electrode. Keep electrodes wet by returning them to storage solution whenever pH meter is not in use.

Before use, remove electrodes from storage solution, rinse, blot dry with a soft tissue, place in initial buffer solution, and set the isopotential point (¶ *2a* above). Select a second buffer within 2 pH units of sample pH and bring sample and buffer to same temperature, which may be the room temperature, a fixed temperature such as 25°C, or the temperature of a fresh sample. Remove electrodes from first buffer, rinse thoroughly with distilled water, blot dry, and immerse in second buffer. Record temperature of measurement and adjust temperature dial on meter so that meter indicates pH value of buffer at test temperature (this is a slope adjustment).

Use the pH value listed in the tables for the buffer used at the test temperature. Remove electrodes from second buffer, rinse thoroughly with distilled water and dry electrodes as indicated above. Immerse in a third buffer below pH 10, approximately 3 pH units different from the second; the reading should be within 0.1 unit for the pH of the third buffer. If the meter response shows a difference greater than 0.1 pH unit from expected value, look for trouble with the electrodes or potentiometer (see ¶s *5a* and *b* below).

The purpose of standardization is to adjust the response of the glass electrode to the instrument. When only occasional pH measurements are made standardize instrument before each measurement. When frequent measurements are made and the instrument is stable, standardize less frequently. If sample pH values vary widely, standardize for each sample with a buffer having a pH within 1 to 2 pH units of the sample.

b. Sample analysis: Establish equilibrium between electrodes and sample by stirring sample to insure homogeneity; stir gently to minimize carbon dioxide entrainment. For buffered samples or those of high ionic strength, condition electrodes after cleaning by dipping them into sample for 1 min. Blot dry, immerse in a fresh portion of the same sample, and read pH.

With dilute, poorly buffered solutions, equilibrate electrodes by immersing in three or four successive portions of sample. Take a fresh sample to measure pH.

5. Trouble Shooting

a. Potentiometer: To locate trouble source disconnect electrodes and, using a short-circuit strap, connect reference electrode terminal to glass electrode terminal. Observe change in pH when instrument calibration knob is adjusted. If potentiometer is operating properly, it will respond rapidly and evenly to changes in calibration over a wide scale range. A faulty potentiometer will fail to respond, will react erratically, or will show a drift upon adjustment. Switch to the millivolt scale on which the meter should read zero. If inexperienced, do not attempt potentiometer repair other than maintenance as described in instrument manual.

b. Electrodes: If potentiometer is functioning properly, look for the instrument fault in the electrode pair. Substitute one electrode at a time and cross-check with two buffers that are about 4 pH units apart. A deviation greater than 0.1 pH unit indicates a faulty electrode. Glass electrodes fail because of scratches, deterioration, or accumulation of debris on the glass surface. Rejuvenate electrode by alternately immersing it three times each in $0.1N$ HCl and $0.1N$ NaOH. If this fails, immerse tip in KF solution for 30 s. After rejuvenation, soak in pH 7.0 buffer overnight. Rinse and store in pH 7.0 buffer. Rinse again with distilled water before use. Protein coatings can be removed by soaking glass electrodes in a 10% pepsin solution adjusted to pH 1 to 2.

To check reference electrode, oppose the emf of a questionable reference electrode against another one of the same type that is known to be good. Using an adapter, plug good reference electrode into glass electrode jack of potentiometer; then plug questioned electrode into reference electrode jack. Set meter to read millivolts and take readings with both electrodes immersed in the same electrolyte (KCl) solution and then in the same buffer solution. The millivolt readings should be $0 \pm 5\,mV$ for both solutions. If different electrodes are used, i.e., silver: silver-chloride against calomel or vice versa, the reading will be $44 \pm 5\,mV$ for a good reference electrode.

Reference electrode troubles generally are traceable to a clogged junction. Interruption of the continuous trickle of electrolyte through the junction causes increase in response time and drift in reading. Clear a clogged junction by applying suction to the tip or by boiling tip in distilled water until the electrolyte flows freely when suction is applied to tip or pressure is applied to the fill hole. Replaceable junctions are available commercially.

6. Precision and Bias

By careful use of a laboratory pH meter with good electrodes, a precision of ± 0.02 pH unit and an accuracy of ± 0.05 pH unit can be achieved. However, ± 0.1 pH unit represents the limit of accuracy under normal conditions, especially for measurement of water and poorly buffered solutions. For this reason, report pH values to the nearest 0.1 pH unit. A synthetic sample of a Clark and Lubs buffer solution of pH 7.3 was analyzed electrometrically by 30 laboratories with a standard deviation of ± 0.13 pH unit.

7. References

1. BATES, R.G. 1978. Concept and determination of pH. *In* I.M. Kolthoff & P.J. Elving, eds. Treatise on Analytical Chemistry. Part 1, Vol. 1, p. 821. Wiley-Interscience, New York, N.Y.

2. LICHT, T.S. & A.J. DE BETHUNE. 1957. Recent developments concerning the signs of electrode potentials. *J. Chem. Educ.* 34:433.

3. DURST, R.A. 1975. Standard Reference Ma-

terials: Standardization of pH Measurements. NBS Spec. Publ. 260-53, National Bur. Standards, Washington, D.C.

8. Bibliography

CLARK, W.M. 1928. The Determination of Hydrogen Ions, 3rd ed. Williams & Wilkins Co., Baltimore, Md.

DOLE, M. 1941. The Glass Electrode. John Wiley & Sons, New York, N.Y.

BATES, R.G. & S.F. ACREE. 1945. pH of aqueous mixtures of potassium dihydrogen phosphate and disodium hydrogen phosphate at 0 to 60°C. J. Res. Nat. Bur. Standards 34:373.

LANGELIER, W.F. 1946. Effect of temperature on the pH of natural water. J. Amer. Water Works Assoc. 38:179.

FELDMAN, I. 1956. Use and abuse of pH measurements. Anal. Chem. 28:1859.

BRITTON, H.T.S. 1956. Hydrogen Ions, 4th ed. D. Van Nostrand Co., Princeton, N.J.

KOLTHOFF, I.M. & H.A. LAITINEN. 1958. pH and Electrotitrations. John Wiley & Sons, New York, N.Y.

KOLTHOFF, I.M. & P.J. ELVING. 1959. Treatise on Analytical Chemistry. Part I, Vol. 1, Chapter 10. Wiley-Interscience, New York, N.Y.

BATES, R.G. 1962. Revised standard values for pH measurements from 0 to 95°C. J. Res. Nat. Bur. Standards 66A:179.

AMERICAN WATER WORKS ASSOCIATION. 1964. Simplified Procedures for Water Examination. Manual M12, American Water Works Assoc., New York, N.Y.

WINSTEAD, M. 1967. Reagent Grade Water: How, When and Why? American Soc. Medical Technologists, The Steck Company, Austin, Tex.

STAPLES, B.R. & R.G. BATES. 1969. Two new standards for the pH scale. J. Res. Nat. Bur. Standards 73A:37.

BATES, R.G. 1973. Determination of pH, Theory and Practice, 2nd ed. John Wiley & Sons, New York, N.Y.

*   *   *

4500-N   NITROGEN*

In waters and wastewaters the forms of nitrogen of greatest interest are, in order of decreasing oxidation state, nitrate, nitrite, ammonia, and organic nitrogen. All these forms of nitrogen, as well as nitrogen gas (N_2), are biochemically interconvertible and are components of the nitrogen cycle. They are of interest for many reasons.

Organic nitrogen is defined functionally as organically bound nitrogen in the trinegative oxidation state. It does not include all organic nitrogen compounds. Analytically, organic nitrogen and ammonia can be determined together and have been referred to as "kjeldahl nitrogen," a term that reflects the technique used in their determination. Organic nitrogen includes such natural materials as proteins and peptides, nucleic acids and urea, and numerous synthetic organic materials. Typical organic nitrogen concentrations vary from a few hundred micrograms per liter in some lakes to more than 20 mg/L in raw sewage.

Total oxidized nitrogen is the sum of nitrate and nitrite nitrogen. Nitrate generally occurs in trace quantities in surface water but may attain high levels in some groundwater. In excessive amounts, it contributes to the illness known as methemoglobinemia in infants. A limit of 10 mg

---

*Approved by Standard Methods Committee, 1988.

nitrate as nitrogen/L has been imposed on drinking water to prevent this disorder. Nitrate is found only in small amounts in fresh domestic wastewater but in the effluent of nitrifying biological treatment plants nitrate may be found in concentrations of up to 30 mg nitrate as nitrogen/L. It is an essential nutrient for many photosynthetic autotrophs and in some cases has been identified as the growth-limiting nutrient.

Nitrite is an intermediate oxidation state of nitrogen, both in the oxidation of ammonia to nitrate and in the reduction of nitrate. Such oxidation and reduction may occur in wastewater treatment plants, water distribution systems, and natural waters. Nitrite can enter a water supply system through its use as a corrosion inhibitor in industrial process water. Nitrite is the actual etiologic agent of methemoglobinemia. Nitrous acid, which is formed from nitrite in acidic solution, can react with secondary amines (RR′NH) to form nitrosamines (RR′N-NO), many of which are known to be carcinogens. The toxicologic significance of nitrosation reactions in vivo and in the natural environment is the subject of much current concern and research.

Ammonia is present naturally in surface and wastewaters. Its concentration generally is low in groundwaters because it adsorbs to soil particles and clays and is not leached readily from soils. It is produced largely by deamination of organic nitrogen-containing compounds and by hydrolysis of urea. At some water treatment plants ammonia is added to react with chlorine to form a combined chlorine residual.

In the chlorination of wastewater effluents containing ammonia, virtually no free residual chlorine is obtained until the ammonia has been oxidized. Rather, the chlorine reacts with ammonia to form mono- and dichloramines. Ammonia concentrations encountered in water vary from less than 10 μg ammonia nitrogen/L in some natural surface and groundwaters to more than 30 mg/L in some wastewaters.

In this manual, organic nitrogen is referred to as organic N, nitrate nitrogen as NO_3^--N, nitrite nitrogen as NO_2^--N, and ammonia nitrogen as NH_3-N.

4500-NH₃   NITROGEN (AMMONIA)*

4500-NH₃ A.   Introduction

1. Selection of Method

The two major factors that influence selection of the method to determine ammonia are concentration and presence of interferences. In general, direct manual determination of low concentrations of ammonia is confined to drinking waters, clean surface water, and good-quality nitrified wastewater effluent. In other instances, and where interferences are present and greater precision is necessary, a preliminary distillation step (B) is required. For high ammonia concentrations a distillation and titration technique is preferred. The data presented in ¶ 4 below and Table 4500-NH₃:I should be helpful in selecting the appropriate method of analysis.

Two manual colorimetric techniques—the nesslerization (C) and phenate (D) methods—and one titration method (E) are presented. An ammonia-selective electrode method (F), which may be used either with

*Approved by Standard Methods Committee, 1985.

TABLE 4500-NH₃:I. PRECISION AND BIAS DATA FOR AMMONIA METHODS

Number of Laboratories	Ammonia Nitrogen Concentration μg/L	Relative Standard Deviation					Relative Error				
		Direct Nesslerization %	Direct Manual Phenate Method %	Distillation Plus			Direct Nesslerization %	Direct Manual Phenate Method %	Distillation Plus		
				Nessler Method %	Manual Phenate Method %	Titrimetric Method %			Nessler Method %	Manual Phenate Method %	Titrimetric Method %
20	200	38.1	—	—	—	—	0	—	—	—	—
44	200	—	—	46.3	—	—	—	—	10.0	—	—
21	200	—	—	—	—	69.8	—	—	—	—	20.0
20	800	11.2	—	—	—	—	0	—	—	—	—
42	800	—	—	21.2	—	—	—	—	8.7	—	—
20	800	—	—	—	—	28.6	—	—	—	—	5.0
21	1500	11.6	—	—	—	—	0.6	—	—	—	—
42	1500	—	—	18.0	—	—	—	—	4.0	—	—
21	1500	—	—	—	—	21.6	—	—	—	—	2.6
70	200	—	39.2	—	—	—	—	2.4	—	—	—
3	200	—	—	—	15.1	—	—	—	—	16.7	—
9	200	22.0	—	—	—	—	8.3	—	—	—	—
5	200	—	—	15.7	—	—	—	—	2.0	—	—
66	800	—	15.8	—	—	—	—	1.5	—	—	—
3	800	—	—	—	16.6	—	—	—	—	1.7	—
9	800	16.1	—	—	—	—	0.3	—	—	—	—
6	800	—	—	16.3	—	—	—	—	3.1	—	—
71	1500	—	26.0	—	—	—	—	10.0	—	—	—
3	1500	—	—	—	7.3	—	—	—	—	0.4	—
8	1500	5.3	—	—	—	—	1.2	—	—	—	—
6	1500	—	—	7.5	—	—	—	—	3.6	—	—

or without prior sample distillation, an ammonia-selective electrode method using a known addition (G), and an automated version of the phenate method (H) also are included. While the stated maximum concentration ranges for the manual methods are not rigorous limits, titration is preferred at concentrations higher than the stated maximum levels for the photometric procedure.

The nessler method is sensitive to 20 μg NH₃-N/L under optimum conditions and may be used for up to 5 mg NH₃-N/L. Turbidity, color, and substances precipitated by hydroxyl ion, such as magnesium and calcium, interfere and may be removed by preliminary distillation or, less satisfactorily, by precipitation with zinc sulfate and alkali.

The manual phenate method has a sensitivity of 10 μg NH₃-N/L and is useful for up to 500 μg NH₃-N/L. Preliminary distillation is required if the alkalinity exceeds 500 mg CaCO₃/L, if color or turbidity is present, or if the sample has been preserved with acid.

The distillation and titration procedure is used especially for NH₃-N concentrations greater than 5 mg/L.

Distillation into sulfuric acid (H₂SO₄) absorbent is mandatory for the phenate method when interferences are present. Boric acid must be the absorbent following distillation if the distillate is to be nesslerized or titrated.

The ammonia-selective electrode method is applicable over the range from 0.03 to 1400 mg NH₃-N/L.

2. Interferences

Glycine, urea, glutamic acid, cyanates, and acetamide hydrolyze very slowly in solution on standing but, of these, only urea and cyanates will hydrolyze on distillation at pH of 9.5. Hydrolysis amounts to about 7% at this pH for urea and about 5% for cyanates. Glycine, hydrazine, and some amines will react with nessler reagent to give the characteristic yellow color in the time required for the test. Similarly, volatile alkaline compounds such as hydrazine and amines will influence titrimetric results. Some organic compounds such as ketones, aldehydes, alcohols, and some amines may cause a yellowish or greenish off-color or a turbidity on nesslerization following distillation. Some of these, such as formaldehyde, may be eliminated by boiling off at a low pH before nesslerization. Remove residual chlorine by sample pretreatment.

3. Storage of Samples

Most reliable results are obtained on fresh samples. Destroy residual chlorine immediately after sample collection to prevent its reaction with ammonia. If prompt analysis is impossible, preserve samples with 0.8 mL conc H₂SO₄/L sample and store at 4°C. The pH of the acid-preserved samples should be between 1.5 and 2. Some wastewaters may require more conc H₂SO₄ to achieve this pH. If acid preservation is used, neutralize samples with NaOH or KOH immediately before making the determination.

4. Precision and Bias

Six synthetic samples containing ammonia and other constituents dissolved in distilled water were analyzed by five procedures. The first three samples were subjected to direct nesslerization alone, distillation followed by nesslerization, and distillation followed by titration. Samples 4 through 6 were analyzed by direct nesslerization, by distillation followed by nesslerization, by the phenate method alone, and by distillation followed by the phenate method. Results obtained by the participating laboratories are summarized in Table 4500-NH₃:I.

Sample 1 contained the following additional constituents: 10 mg Cl⁻/L, 1.0 mg

NO_3^--N/L, 1.5 mg organic N/L, 10.0 mg PO_4^{3-}/L, and 5.0 mg silica/L.

Sample 2 contained the following constituents: 200 mg Cl^-/L, 1.0 mg NO_3^--N/L, 0.8 mg organic N/L, 5.0 mg PO_4^{3-}/L, and 15.0 mg silica/L.

Sample 3 contained the following additional constituents: 400 mg Cl^-/L, 1.0 mg NO_3^--N/L, 0.2 mg organic N/L, 0.5 mg PO_4^{3-}/L, and 30.0 mg silica/L.

Sample 4 contained the following additional constituents: 400 mg Cl^-/L, 0.05 mg NO_3^--N/L, 0.23 mg organic phosphorus/L added in the form of adenylic acid, 7.00 mg orthophosphate phosphorus/L, and 3.00 mg polyphosphate phosphorus/L added as sodium hexametaphosphate.

Sample 5 contained the following additional constituents: 400 mg Cl^-/L, 5.00 mg NO_3^--N/L, 0.09 mg organic phosphorus/L added in the form of adenylic acid, 0.6 mg orthophosphate phosphorus/L, and 0.3 mg polyphosphate phosphorus/L added as sodium hexametaphosphate.

Sample 6 contained the following additional constituents: 400 mg Cl^-/L, 0.4 mg NO_3^--N/L, 0.03 mg organic phosphorus/L added in the form of adenylic acid, 0.1

mg orthophosphate phosphorus/L, and 0.08 mg polyphosphate phosphorus/L added as sodium hexametaphosphate.

For the ammonia-selective electrode in a single laboratory using surface water samples at concentrations of 1.00, 0.77, 0.19, and 0.13 mg NH_3-N/L, standard deviations were ±0.038, ±0.017, ±0.007, and ±0.003, respectively. In a single laboratory using surface water samples at concentrations of 0.10 and 0.13 NH_3-N/L, recoveries were 96% and 91%, respectively. The results of an interlaboratory study involving 12 laboratories using the ammonia-selective electrode† on distilled water and effluents are summarized in Table 4500-NH_3:II.

For an automated phenate system‡ in a single laboratory using surface water samples at concentrations of 1.41, 0.77, 0.59, and 0.43 mg NH_3-N/L, the standard deviation was ±0.005, and at concentrations of 0.16 and 1.44 mg NH_3-N/L, recoveries were 107 and 99%, respectively.

---

†American Society for Testing and Materials, ASTM Method 1426-79.
‡AutoAnalyzer™ I, Technicon Instrument Corp., Tarrytown, N.Y. 10591.

TABLE 4500-NH_3:II. PRECISION AND BIAS OF AMMONIA-SELECTIVE ELECTRODE

Level mg/L	Matrix	Mean Recovery %	Precision	
			Overall, S_T	Operator, S_O
0.04	Distilled water	200	0.05	0.01
	Effluent water	100	0.03	0.00
0.10	Distilled water	180	0.05	0.01
	Effluent water	470	0.61	0.01
0.80	Distilled water	105	0.11	0.04
	Effluent water	105	0.30	0.06
20	Distilled water	95	2	1
	Effluent water	95	3	2
100	Distilled water	98	5	2
	Effluent water	97	—	—
750	Distilled water	97	78	12
	Effluent water	99	106	10

4500-NH$_3$ B.   Preliminary Distillation Step

1. General Discussion

The sample is buffered at pH 9.5 with a borate buffer to decrease hydrolysis of cyanates and organic nitrogen compounds. It is distilled into a solution of boric acid when nesslerization or titration is to be used or into H$_2$SO$_4$ when the phenate method is used. The ammonia in the distillate can be determined either colorimetrically by nesslerization or the phenate method or titrimetrically with standard H$_2$SO$_4$ and a mixed indicator or a pH meter. The choice between the colorimetric and the acidimetric method depends on the concentration of ammonia. Ammonia in the distillate also can be determined by the ammonia-selective electrode method, using 0.04N H$_2$SO$_4$ to trap the distillate.

2. Apparatus

a. Distillation apparatus: Arrange a borosilicate glass flask of 800- to 2000-mL capacity attached to a vertical condenser so that the outlet tip may be submerged below the surface of the receiving acid solution. Use an all-borosilicate-glass apparatus or one with condensing units constructed of block tin or aluminum tubes.

b. pH meter.

3. Reagents

a. Ammonia-free water: Prepare by ion-exchange or distillation methods:

1) Ion exchange—Prepare ammonia-free water by passing distilled water through an ion-exchange column containing a strongly acidic cation-exchange resin mixed with a strongly basic anion-exchange resin. Select resins that will remove organic compounds that interfere with the ammonia determination. Some anion-exchange resins tend to release ammonia. If this occurs, prepare ammonia-free water with a strongly acidic cation-exchange resin. Regenerate the column according to the manufacturer's instructions. Check ammonia-free water for the possibility of a high blank value.

2) Distillation—Eliminate traces of ammonia in distilled water by adding 0.1 mL conc H$_2$SO$_4$ to 1 L distilled water and redistilling. Alternatively, treat distilled water with sufficient bromine or chlorine water to produce a free halogen residual of 2 to 5 mg/L and redistill after standing at least 1 h. Discard the first 100 mL distillate. Check redistilled water for the possibility of a high blank.

It is very difficult to store ammonia-free water in the laboratory without contamination from gaseous ammonia. However, if storage is necessary, store in a tightly stoppered glass container to which is added about 10 g ion-exchange resin (preferably a strongly acidic cation-exchange resin) per liter ammonia-free water. For use, let resin settle and decant ammonia-free water. If a high blank value is produced, replace the resin or prepare fresh ammonia-free water.

Use ammonia-free distilled water for preparing all reagents, rinsing, and sample dilution.

b. Borate buffer solution: Add 88 mL 0.1N NaOH solution to 500 mL approximately 0.025M sodium tetraborate (Na$_2$B$_4$O$_7$) solution (9.5 g Na$_2$B$_4$O$_7$·10 H$_2$O/L) and dilute to 1 L.

c. Sodium hydroxide, 6N: Dissolve 240 g NaOH in water and dilute to 1 L.

d. Dechlorinating agent: Use 1 mL of any

of the following reagents to remove 1 mg/ L residual chlorine in 500 mL sample.

1) *Sodium sulfite:* Dissolve 0.9 g Na_2SO_3 in water and dilute to 1 L. Prepare fresh daily.

2) *Sodium thiosulfate:* Dissolve 3.5 g $Na_2S_2O_3 \cdot 5H_2O$ in water and dilute to 1 L. Prepare fresh weekly.

3) *Phenylarsine oxide:* Dissolve 1.2 g C_6H_5AsO in 200 mL $0.3N$ NaOH solution, filter if necessary, and dilute to 1 L with water. (CAUTION: *Toxic—take care to avoid ingestion.*)

4) *Sodium arsenite:* Dissolve 0.93 g $NaAsO_2$ in water and dilute to 1 L. (CAUTION: *Toxic—take care to avoid ingestion.*) Prepare fresh weekly.

e. *Neutralization agent:* Prepare with ammonia-free water.

1) *Sodium hydroxide,* NaOH, $1N$.

2) *Sulfuric acid,* H_2SO_4, $1N$.

f. *Absorbent solution, plain boric acid:* Dissolve 20 g H_3BO_3 in water and dilute to 1 L.

g. *Indicating boric acid solution:* See Section 4500-NH_3.E.3a and b.

h. *Sulfuric acid,* $0.04N$: Dilute 1.0 mL conc H_2SO_4 to 1 L.

4. Procedure

a. *Preparation of equipment:* Add 500 mL water and 20 mL borate buffer to a distillation flask and adjust pH to 9.5 with $6N$ NaOH solution. Add a few glass beads or boiling chips and use this mixture to steam out the distillation apparatus until distillate shows no traces of ammonia.

b. *Sample preparation:* Use 500 mL dechlorinated sample or a portion diluted to 500 mL with water. When NH_3-N concentration is less than 100 µg/L, use a sample volume of 1000 mL. Remove residual chlorine by adding, at the time of collection, dechlorinating agent equivalent to the chlorine residual. If necessary, neutralize

to approximately pH 7 with dilute acid or base, using a pH meter.

Add 25 mL borate buffer solution and adjust to pH 9.5 with $6N$ NaOH using a pH meter.

c. *Distillation:* To minimize contamination, leave distillation apparatus assembled after steaming out and until just before starting sample distillation. Disconnect steaming-out flask and immediately transfer sample flask to distillation apparatus. Distill at a rate of 6 to 10 mL/min with the tip of the delivery tube below the surface of acid receiving solution. Collect distillate in a 500-mL erlenmeyer flask containing 50 mL plain boric acid solution for nesslerization method. Use 50 mL indicating boric acid solution for titrimetric method. Distill ammonia into 50 mL $0.04N$ H_2SO_4 for the phenate method and for the ammonia-selective electrode method. Collect at least 200 mL distillate. Lower collected distillate free of contact with delivery tube and continue distillation during the last minute or two to cleanse condenser and delivery tube. Dilute to 500 mL with water.

When the phenate method is used for determining NH_3-N, neutralize distillate with $1N$ NaOH solution.

d. *Ammonia determination:* Determine ammonia by the nesslerization method (C), the phenate method (D), the titrimetric method (E) or the ammonia-selective electrode method (F).

5. Bibliography

NICHOLS, M.S. & M.E. FOOTE. 1931. Distillation of free ammonia from buffered solutions. *Ind. Eng. Chem.,* Anal. Ed. 3:311.

GRIFFIN, A.E. & N.S. CHAMBERLIN. 1941. Relation of ammonia nitrogen to breakpoint chlorination. *Amer. J. Pub. Health* 31:803.

PALIN, A.T. 1950. Symposium on the sterilization of water. Chemical aspects of chlorination. *J. Inst. Water Eng.* 4:565.

TARAS, M.J. 1953. Effect of free residual chlorination of nitrogen compounds in water. *J. Amer. Water Works Assoc.* 45:47.

4500-NH₃ C.   Nesslerization Method
(Direct and Following Distillation)

1. General Discussion

Use direct nesslerization only for purified drinking waters, natural water, and highly purified wastewater effluents, all of which should be low in color and have NH_3-N concentrations exceeding 20 μg/L. Apply the direct nesslerization method to domestic wastewaters only when errors of 1 to 2 mg/L are acceptable. Use this method only after it has been established that it yields results comparable to those obtained after distillation. Check validity of direct nesslerization measurements periodically.

Pretreatment before direct nesslerization with zinc sulfate and alkali precipitates calcium, iron, magnesium, and sulfide, which form turbidity when treated with nessler reagent. The floc also removes suspended matter and sometimes colored matter. Addition of EDTA or Rochelle salt solution inhibits precipitation of residual calcium and magnesium ions in the presence of the alkaline nessler reagent. However, use of EDTA demands an extra amount of nessler reagent to insure a sufficient nessler reagent excess for reaction with the ammonia.

The graduated yellow to brown colors produced by the nessler-ammonia reaction absorb strongly over a wide wavelength range. The yellow color characteristic of low ammonia nitrogen concentration (0.4 to 5 mg/L) can be measured with acceptable sensitivity in the wavelength region from 400 to 425 nm when a 1-cm light path is available. A light path of 5 cm extends measurements into the nitrogen concentration range of 5 to 60 μg/L. The reddish brown hues typical of ammonia nitrogen levels approaching 10 mg/L may be measured in the wavelength region of 450 to 500 nm. A judicious selection of light path and wavelength thus permits the photometric determination of ammonia nitrogen concentrations over a considerable range.

Departures from Beer's law may be evident when photometers equipped with broad-band color filters are used. For this reason, prepare the calibration curve under conditions identical with those adopted for the samples.

A carefully prepared nessler reagent may respond under optimum conditions to as little as 1 μg NH_3-N/50 mL. In direct nesslerization, this represents 20 μg/L. However, reproducibility below 100 μg/L may be erratic.

2. Apparatus

a. Colorimetric equipment: One of the following is required:

1) *Spectrophotometer,* for use at 400 to 500 nm and providing a light path of 1 cm or longer.

2) *Filter photometer,* providing a light path of 1 cm or longer and equipped with a violet filter having maximum transmittance at 400 to 425 nm. A blue filter can be used for higher NH_3-N concentrations.

3) *Nessler tubes,* matched, 50-mL, tall form.

b. pH meter, equipped with a high-pH electrode.

3. Reagents

Use ammonia-free water for preparing all reagents, rinsing, and making dilutions. All the reagents listed in Preliminary Distillation (4500-NH₃.B above), except the borate buffer and absorbent solution, are required, plus the following:

a. Zinc sulfate solution: Dissolve 100 g $ZnSO_4 \cdot 7H_2O$ and dilute to 1 L with water.

b. Stabilizer reagent: Use either EDTA or Rochelle salt to prevent calcium or magnesium precipitation in undistilled samples after addition of alkaline nessler reagent.

1) *EDTA reagent:* Dissolve 50 g disodium ethylenediamine tetraacetate dihydrate in 60 mL water containing 10 g NaOH. If necessary, apply gentle heat to complete dissolution. Cool to room temperature and dilute to 100 mL.

2) *Rochelle salt solution:* Dissolve 50 g potassium sodium tartrate tetrahydrate, $KNaC_4H_4O_6 \cdot 4H_2O$, in 100 mL water. Remove ammonia usually present in the salt by boiling off 30 mL of solution. After cooling, dilute to 100 mL.

c. *Nessler reagent:* Dissolve 100 g HgI_2 and 70 g KI in a small quantity of water and add this mixture slowly, with stirring, to a cool solution of 160 g NaOH dissolved in 500 mL water. Dilute to 1 L. Store in rubber-stoppered borosilicate glassware and out of sunlight to maintain reagent stability for up to a year under normal laboratory conditions. Check reagent to make sure that it yields the characteristic color with 0.1 mg NH_3-N/L within 10 min after addition and does not produce a precipitate with small amounts of ammonia within 2 h. (CAUTION: *Toxic—take care to avoid ingestion.*)

d. *Stock ammonium solution:* Dissolve 3.819 g anhydrous NH_4Cl, dried at 100°C, in water, and dilute to 1000 mL; 1.00 mL = 1.00 mg N = 1.22 mg NH_3.

e. *Standard ammonium solution:* Dilute 10.00 mL stock ammonium solution to 1000 mL with water; 1.00 mL = 10.00 μg N = 12.2 μg NH_3.

f. *Permanent color solutions:*

1) *Potassium chloroplatinate solution:* Dissolve 2.0 g K_2PtCl_6 in 300 to 400 mL water; add 100 mL conc HCl and dilute to 1 L.

2) *Cobaltous chloride solution:* Dissolve 12.0 g $CoCl_2 \cdot 6H_2O$ in 200 mL water. Add 100 mL conc HCl and dilute to 1 L.

4. Procedure

a. *Treatment of undistilled samples:* If necessary, remove residual chlorine from the freshly collected sample by adding an equivalent amount of dechlorinating agent. (Do not store chlorinated samples without prior dechlorination.) Add 1 mL $ZnSO_4$ solution to 100 mL sample and mix thoroughly. Add 0.4 to 0.5 mL 6N NaOH solution to obtain a pH of 10.5, as determined with a pH meter and a high-pH glass electrode, and mix gently. Let treated sample stand for a few minutes, whereupon a heavy flocculent precipitate should fall, leaving a clear and colorless supernate. Clarify by centrifuging or filtering. Pretest any filter paper used to be sure no ammonia is present as a contaminant. Do this by running water through the filter and testing the filtrate by nesslerization. Filter sample, discarding first 25 mL filtrate. (CAUTION: Samples containing more than about 10 mg NH_3-N/L may lose ammonia during this treatment of undistilled samples because of the high pH. Dilute such samples to the sensitive range for nesslerization before pretreatment.)

b. *Color development:*

1) Undistilled samples—Use 50.0 mL sample or a portion diluted to 50.0 mL with water. If the undistilled portion contains sufficient concentrations of calcium, magnesium, or other ions that produce turbidity or precipitate with nessler reagent, add 1 drop (0.05 mL) EDTA reagent or 1 to 2 drops (0.05 to 0.1 mL) Rochelle salt solution. Mix well. Add 2.0 mL nessler reagent if EDTA reagent is used or 1.0 mL nessler reagent if Rochelle salt is used.

2) Distilled samples—Neutralize the boric acid used for absorbing the ammonia distillate by adding either 2 mL nessler reagent, an excess that raises the pH to the desired high level, or alternatively, neutralizing the boric acid with NaOH before adding 1 mL nessler reagent.

3) Mix samples by capping nessler tubes with clean rubber stoppers (washed thoroughly with water) and then inverting tubes at least six times. Keep such conditions as temperature and reaction time the same in blank, samples, and standards. Let reaction proceed for at least 10 min after

adding nessler reagent. Measure color in sample and standards. If NH_3-N is very low, use a 30-min contact time for sample, blank, and standards. Measure color either photometrically or visually as directed in ¶s *c* or *d* below.

c. Photometric measurement: Measure absorbance or transmittance with a spectrophotometer or filter photometer. Prepare calibration curve at the same temperature and reaction time used for samples. Measure transmittance readings against a reagent blank and run parallel checks frequently against standards in the nitrogen range of the samples. Redetermine complete calibration curve for each new batch of nessler reagent.

For distilled samples, prepare standard curve under the same conditions as the samples. Distill reagent blank and appropriate standards, each diluted to 500 mL, in the same manner as the samples. Dilute 300 mL distillate plus 50 mL boric acid absorbent to 500 mL with water and take a 50-mL portion for nesslerization.

d. Visual comparison: Compare colors produced in sample against those of ammonia standards. Prepare temporary or permanent standards as follows:

1) Temporary standards—Prepare a series of visual standards in nessler tubes by adding the following volumes of standard NH_4Cl solution and diluting to 50 mL with water: 0, 0.2, 0.4, 0.7, 1.0, 1.4, 1.7, 2.0, 2.5, 3.0, 3.5, 4.0, 4.5, 5.0, and 6.0 mL. Nesslerize standards and portions of distillate by adding 1.0 mL nessler reagent to each tube and mixing well.

2) Permanent standards—Measure into 50-mL nessler tubes the volumes of K_2PtCl_6 and $CoCl_2$ solutions indicated in Table 4500-NH₃:III, dilute to mark, and mix thoroughly. The values given in the table are *approximate;* actual equivalents of the ammonium standards will differ with the quality of nessler reagent, the kind of illumination used, and the color sensitivity of the analyst's eye. Therefore, compare color standards with nesslerized temporary

TABLE 4500-NH₃:III. PREPARATION OF PERMANENT COLOR STANDARDS FOR VISUAL DETERMINATION OF AMMONIA NITROGEN

Value in Ammonia Nitrogen μg	Approximate Volume of Platinum Solution mL*	Approximate Volume of Cobalt Solution mL*
0	1.2	0.0
2	2.8	0.0
4	4.7	0.1
7	5.9	0.2
10	7.7	0.5
14	9.9	1.1
17	11.4	1.7
20	12.7	2.2
25	15.0	3.3
30	17.3	4.5
35	19.0	5.7
40	19.7	7.1
45	19.9	8.7
50	20.0	10.4
60	20.0	15.0

*In matched 50-mL nessler tubes.

ammonia standards and modify the tints as necessary. Make such comparisons for each newly prepared nessler reagent and satisfy each analyst as to the aptness of the color match. Protect standards from dust to extend their usefulness for several months. Compare either 10 or 30 min after nesslerization, depending on reaction time used in preparing nesslerized ammonium standards against which they were matched.

5. Calculation

a. Deduct amount of NH_3-N in water used for diluting original sample before computing final nitrogen value.

b. Deduct also reagent blank for volume of borate buffer and 6N NaOH solutions used with sample.

c. Compute total NH_3-N by the following equation:

mg NH$_3$-N/L (51 mL final volume)

$$= \frac{A}{\text{mL sample}} \times \frac{B}{C}$$

where:

A = μg NH$_3$-N (51 mL final volume),
B = total volume distillate collected, mL, including acid absorbent, and
C = volume distillate taken for nesslerization, mL.

The ratio B/C applies only to distilled samples; ignore in direct nesslerization.

6. Precision and Bias

See Section 4500-NH$_3$.A.4 and Table 4500-NH$_3$:I.

7. Bibliography

JACKSON, D.D. 1900. Permanent standards for use in the analysis of water. *Mass. Inst. Technol. Quart.* 13:314.

SAWYER, C.N. 1953. pH adjustment for determination of ammonia nitrogen. *Anal. Chem.* 25:816.

JENKINS, D. 1967. The differentiation, analysis and preservation of nitrogen and phosphorus forms in natural waters. *In* Trace Inorganics in Water. American Chemical Soc., Washington, D.C.

BOLTZ, D.F. & J.A. HOWELL, EDS. 1978. Colorimetric Determination of Nonmetals. Wiley Interscience, New York, N.Y.

4500-NH$_3$ D.   Phenate Method

1. General Discussion

a. Principle: An intensely blue compound, indophenol, is formed by the reaction of ammonia, hypochlorite, and phenol catalyzed by a manganous salt.

b. Interference: Alkalinity over 500 mg as CaCO$_3$/L, acidity over 100 mg as CaCO$_3$/L, and turbidity interfere. Remove these interferences by preliminary distillation.

2. Apparatus

a. Colorimetric equipment: One of the following is required:

1) *Spectrophotometer,* for use at 630 nm with a light path of approximately 1 cm.

2) *Filter photometer,* equipped with a red-orange filter having a maximum transmittance near 630 nm and providing a light path of approximately 1 cm.

b. Magnetic stirrer.

3. Reagents

a. Ammonia-free water: Prepare as directed in Section 4500-NH$_3$.B.3a. Use for making all reagents.

b. Hypochlorous acid reagent: To 40 mL water add 10 mL 5% NaOCl solution prepared from commercial bleach. Adjust pH to 6.5 to 7.0 with HCl. Prepare this unstable reagent weekly.

c. Manganous sulfate solution, 0.003 M: Dissolve 50 mg MnSO$_4$·H$_2$O in 100 mL water.

d. Phenate reagent: Dissolve 2.5 g NaOH and 10 g phenol, C$_6$H$_5$OH, in 100 mL water. Because this reagent darkens on standing, prepare weekly. (CAUTION: *Handle phenol with care.*)

e. Stock ammonium solution: Dissolve 381.9 mg anhydrous NH$_4$Cl, dried at 100°C, in water, and dilute to 1000 mL; 1.00 mL = 100 μg N = 122 μg NH$_3$.

f. Standard ammonium solution: Dilute 5.00 mL stock ammonium solution to 1000 mL with water; 1.00 mL = 0.500 μg N = 0.607 μg NH$_3$.

4. Procedure

a. Treatment of sample: To a 10.0-mL sample in a 50-mL beaker, add 1 drop (0.05 mL) MnSO$_4$ solution. Place on a magnetic stirrer and add 0.5 mL hypochlorous acid reagent. Immediately add, a drop at a time, 0.6 mL phenate reagent. Add reagent without delay using a bulb pipet or a buret for convenient delivery. Mark pipet for hypochlorous acid at the 0.5-mL level and deliver the phenate reagent from a pipet or a buret that has been calibrated by counting the number of drops previously found to be equivalent to 0.6 mL. Stir vigorously during addition of reagents. Because color intensity is affected by age of reagents, carry a blank and a standard through the procedure with each batch of samples. Measure absorbance using reagent blank to zero the spectrophotometer. Color formation is complete in 10 min and is stable for at least 24 h. Although the blue color has a maximum absorbance at 630 nm, satisfactory measurements can be made in the 600- to 660-nm region.

b. Preparation of standards: Prepare a calibration curve in the NH_3-N range of 0.1 to 5 μg, treating standards exactly as the sample. Beer's Law governs.

5. Calculation

Calculate ammonia concentration as follows:

mg NH_3-N/L (11.1 mL final volume)

$$= \frac{A \times B}{C \times S} \times \frac{D}{E}$$

where:

A = absorbance of sample,
B = NH_3-N in standard, μg,
C = absorbance of standard,
S = volume of sample used, mL,
D = volume of total distillate collected, mL, including acid absorbent, neutralizing agent, and ammonia-free water added, and
E = volume of distillate used for color development, mL.

The ratio D/E applies only to distilled samples.

6. Precision and Bias

See Section 4500-NH₃.A.4 and Table 4500-NH₃:I.

7. Bibliography

Rossum, J.R. & P.A. Villarruz. 1963. Determination of ammonia by the indophenol method. *J. Amer. Water Works Assoc.* 55:657.
Weatherburn, M.W. 1967. Phenolhypochlorite reaction for determination of ammonia. *Anal. Chem.* 39:971.

4500-NH₃ E.   Titrimetric Method

1. General Discussion

The titrimetric method is used only on samples that have been carried through preliminary distillation (see Section 4500-NH₃.B). The following table is useful in selecting sample volume for the distillation and titration method.

Ammonia Nitrogen in Sample *mg/L*	Sample Volume *mL*
5–10	250
10–20	100
20–50	50.0
50–100	25.0

2. Apparatus

Distillation apparatus: See Section 4500-NH₃.B.2*a* and *b*.

3. Reagents

Use ammonia-free water in making all reagents and dilutions.

a. Mixed indicator solution: Dissolve 200 mg methyl red indicator in 100 mL 95% ethyl or isopropyl alcohol. Dissolve 100 mg methylene blue in 50 mL 95% ethyl or isopropyl alcohol. Combine solutions. Prepare monthly.

b. Indicating boric acid solution: Dissolve

20 g H_3BO_3 in ammonia-free distilled water, add 10 mL mixed indicator solution, and dilute to 1 L. Prepare monthly.

c. Standard sulfuric acid titrant, 0.02N: Prepare and standardize as directed in Alkalinity, Section 2320B.3c. For greatest accuracy, standardize titrant against an amount of Na_2CO_3 that has been incorporated in the indicating boric acid solution to reproduce the actual conditions of sample titration; 1.00 mL = 280 μg N.

4. Procedure

a. Proceed as described in Section 4500-NH_3.B using indicating boric acid solution as absorbent for the distillate.

b. Sludge or sediment samples: Rapidly weigh to within $\pm 1\%$ an amount of wet sample, equivalent to approximately 1 g dry weight, in a weighing bottle or crucible. Wash sample into a 500-mL kjeldahl flask with water and dilute to 250 mL. Proceed as in ¶ 4a but add a piece of paraffin wax to distillation flask and collect only 100 mL distillate.

c. Titrate ammonia in distillate with standard 0.02N H_2SO_4 titrant until indicator turns a pale lavender.

d. Blank: Carry a blank through all steps

of the procedure and apply the necessary correction to the results.

5. Calculation

a. Liquid samples:

$$mg\ NH_3\text{-}N/L = \frac{(A - B) \times 280}{mL\ sample}$$

b. Sludge or sediment samples:

$$mg\ NH_3\text{-}N/kg = \frac{(A - B) \times 280}{g\ dry\ wt\ sample}$$

where:
A = volume of H_2SO_4 titrated for sample, mL, and
B = volume of H_2SO_4 titrated for blank, mL.

6. Precision and Bias

See Section 4500-NH_3.A.4 and Table 4500-NH_3:I.

7. Bibliography

MEEKER, E.W. & E.C. WAGNER. 1933. Titration of ammonia in the presence of boric acid. *Ind. Eng. Chem.,* Anal. Ed. 5:396.
WAGNER, E.C. 1940. Titration of ammonia in the presence of boric acid. *Ind. Eng. Chem.,* Anal. Ed. 12:711.

4500-NH_3 F.   Ammonia-Selective Electrode Method

1. General Discussion

a. Principle: The ammonia-selective electrode uses a hydrophobic gas-permeable membrane to separate the sample solution from an electrode internal solution of ammonium chloride. Dissolved ammonia ($NH_{3(aq)}$ and NH_4^+) is converted to $NH_{3(aq)}$ by raising pH to above 11 with a strong base. $NH_{3(aq)}$ diffuses through the membrane and changes the internal solution pH that is sensed by a pH electrode. The fixed level of chloride in the internal solution is sensed by a chloride ion-selective electrode

that serves as the reference electrode. Potentiometric measurements are made with a pH meter having an expanded millivolt scale or with a specific ion meter.

b. Scope and application: This method is applicable to the measurement of 0.03 to 1400 mg NH_3-N/L in potable and surface waters and domestic and industrial wastes. High concentrations of dissolved ions affect the measurement, but color and turbidity do not. Sample distillation is unnecessary. Use standard solutions and samples that have the same temperature and contain about the same total level of dissolved species. The ammonia-selective electrode responds slowly below 1 mg NH_3-N/L; hence, use longer times of electrode immersion (5 to 10 min) to obtain stable readings.

c. Interference: Amines are a positive interference. Mercury and silver interfere by complexing with ammonia.

d. Sample preservation: Do not use $HgCl_2$ as a sample preservative. Refrigerate at 4°C for samples to be analyzed within 24 h. Preserve samples high in organic and nitrogenous matter, and any other samples for a prolonged period, by lowering pH to 2 or less with conc H_2SO_4.

2. Apparatus

a. Electrometer: A pH meter with expanded millivolt scale capable of 0.1 mV resolution between -700 mV and $+700$ mV or a specific ion meter.

*b. Ammonia-selective electrode.**

c. Magnetic stirrer, thermally insulated, with TFE-coated stirring bar.

3. Reagents

a. Ammonia-free water: See Section 4500-NH₃.B.3a. Use for making all reagents.

b. Sodium hydroxide, 10N: Dissolve 400 g NaOH in 800 mL water. Cool and dilute to 1000 mL with water.

c. Stock ammonium chloride solution: See Section 4500-NH₃.C.3d.

d. Standard ammonium chloride solutions: See ¶ 4a below.

4. Procedure

a. Preparation of standards: Prepare a series of standard solutions covering the concentrations of 1000, 100, 10, 1, and 0.1 mg NH₃-N/L by making decimal dilutions of stock NH_4Cl solution with water.

b. Electrometer calibration: Place 100 mL of each standard solution in a 150-mL beaker. Immerse electrode in standard of

lowest concentration and mix with a magnetic stirrer. Do not stir so rapidly that air bubbles are sucked into the solution because they will become trapped on the electrode membrane. Maintain the same stirring rate and a temperature of about 25°C throughout calibration and testing procedures. Add a sufficient volume of 10N NaOH solution (1 mL usually is sufficient) to raise pH above 11. Keep electrode in solution until a stable millivolt reading is obtained. CAUTION: Check electrode sensing element performance according to manufacturer's instructions to make sure that electrode is operating properly. Do not add NaOH solution before immersing electrode, because ammonia may be lost from a basic solution. Repeat procedure with remaining standards, proceeding from lowest to highest concentration. Wait for at least 5 min before recording millivolts for standards and samples containing $\leq$ 1 mg NH₃-N/L.

c. Preparation of standard curve: Using semilogarithmic graph paper, plot ammonia concentration in milligrams NH₃-N per liter on the log axis vs. potential in millivolts on the linear axis starting with the lowest concentration at the bottom of the scale. If the electrode is functioning properly a tenfold change of NH₃-N concentration produces a potential change of 59 mV.

d. Calibration of specific ion meter: Refer to manufacturer's instructions and proceed as in ¶s 4a and b.

e. Measurement of samples: Dilute if necessary to bring NH₃-N concentration to within calibration curve range. Place 100 mL sample in 150-mL beaker and follow procedure in ¶ 4b above. Record volume of 10N NaOH added in excess of 1 mL. Read NH₃-N concentration from standard curve.

5. Calculation

---

*Orion Model 95-10 or 95-12, EIL Model 8002-2, Beckman Model 39565, or equivalent.

$$\text{mg NH}_3\text{-N/L} = A \times B \times \left[\frac{101 + C}{101} \right]$$

where:

A = dilution factor,

B = concentration of NH_3-N/L, mg/L, from calibration curve, and

C = volume of added $10N$ NaOH in excess of 1 mL, mL.

6. Precision and Bias

See Section 4500-NH_3.A.4.

7. Bibliography

BANWART, W.L., J.M. BREMNER & M.A. TABATABAI. 1972. Determination of ammonium in soil extracts and water samples by an ammonia electrode. *Comm. Soil Sci. Plant Anal.* 3:449.

MIDGLEY, C. & K. TERRANCE. 1972. The determination of ammonia in condensed steam and boiler feed-water with a potentiometric ammonia probe. *Analyst* 97:626.

BOOTH, R.L. & R.F. THOMAS. 1973. Selective electrode determination of ammonia in water and wastes. *Environ. Sci. Technol.* 7:523.

U.S. ENVIRONMENTAL PROTECTION AGENCY. 1979. Methods for Chemical Analysis of Water and Wastes. EPA-600/4-79-020, National Environmental Research Center, Cincinnati, Ohio.

4500-NH_3 G.   Ammonia-Selective Electrode Method Using Known Addition

1. General Discussion

a. Principle: When a linear relationship exists between concentration and response, known addition is convenient for measuring occasional samples because no calibration is needed. Because an accurate measurement requires that the concentration approximately double as a result of the addition, sample concentration must be known within a factor of three. Total concentration of ammonia can be measured in the absence of complexing agents down to 0.8 mg NH_3-N/L or in the presence of a large excess (50 to 100 times) of complexing agent. Known addition is a convenient check on the results of direct measurement.

b. See Section 4500-NH_3.F.1 for further discussion.

2. Apparatus

Use apparatus specified in Section 4500-NH_3.F.2.

3. Reagents

Use reagents specified in Section 4500-NH_3.F.3.

Add standard ammonium chloride solution approximately 10 times as concentrated as samples being measured.

4. Procedure

a. Dilute 1000 mg/L stock solution to make a standard solution about 10 times as concentrated as the sample concentrate.

b. Add 1 mL $10N$ NaOH to each 100 mL sample and immediately immerse electrode. When checking a direct measurement, leave electrode in 100 mL of sample solution. Use magnetic stirring throughout. Measure mV reading and record as E_1.

c. Pipet 10 mL of standard solution into sample. Thoroughly stir and immediately record new mV reading as E_2.

5. Calculation

a. $\Delta E = E_1 - E_2$.

b. From Table 4500-NH_3:IV find the concentration ratio, Q, corresponding to change in potential, ΔE. To determine original total sample concentration, multiply Q by the concentration of the added standard:

$$C_0 = Q C_s$$

TABLE 4500-NH$_3$:IV.* VALUES OF Q VS. ΔE (59 MV SLOPE) FOR 10% VOLUME CHANGE

ΔE	Q	ΔE	Q	ΔE	Q	ΔE	Q	ΔE	Q
5.0	0.297	9.0	0.178	16.0	0.0952	24.0	0.0556	32.0	0.0354
5.1	0.293	9.1	0.176	16.2	0.0938	24.2	0.0549	32.2	0.0351
5.2	0.288	9.2	0.174	16.4	0.0924	24.4	0.0543	32.4	0.0347
5.3	0.284	9.3	0.173	16.6	0.0910	24.6	0.0536	32.6	0.0343
5.4	0.280	9.4	0.171	16.8	0.0897	24.8	0.0530	32.8	0.0340
5.5	0.276	9.5	0.169	17.0	0.0884	25.0	0.0523	33.0	0.0335
5.6	0.272	9.6	0.167	17.2	0.0871	25.2	0.0517	33.2	0.0333
5.7	0.268	9.7	0.165	17.4	0.0858	25.4	0.0511	33.4	0.0329
5.8	0.264	9.8	0.164	17.6	0.0846	25.6	0.0505	33.6	0.0326
5.9	0.260	9.9	0.162	17.8	0.0834	25.8	0.0499	33.8	0.0336
6.0	0.257	10.0	0.160	18.0	0.0822	26.0	0.0494	34.0	0.0319
6.1	0.253	10.2	0.157	18.2	0.0811	26.2	0.0488	34.2	0.0316
6.2	0.250	10.4	0.154	18.4	0.0799	26.4	0.0482	34.4	0.0313
6.3	0.247	10.6	0.151	18.6	0.0788	26.6	0.0477	34.6	0.0310
6.4	0.243	10.8	0.148	18.8	0.0777	26.8	0.0471	34.8	0.0307
6.5	0.240	11.0	0.145	19.0	0.0767	27.0	0.0466	35.0	0.0304
6.6	0.237	11.2	0.143	19.2	0.0756	27.2	0.0461	36.0	0.0289
6.7	0.234	11.4	0.140	19.4	0.0746	27.4	0.0456	37.0	0.0275
6.8	0.231	11.6	0.137	19.6	0.0736	27.6	0.0450	38.0	0.0261
6.9	0.228	11.8	0.135	19.8	0.0726	27.8	0.0445	39.0	0.0249
7.0	0.225	12.0	0.133	20.0	0.0716	28.0	0.0440	40.0	0.0237
7.1	0.222	12.2	0.130	20.2	0.0707	28.2	0.0435	41.0	0.0226
7.2	0.219	12.4	0.128	20.4	0.0698	28.4	0.0431	42.0	0.0216
7.3	0.217	12.6	0.126	20.6	0.0689	28.6	0.0426	43.0	0.0206
7.4	0.214	12.8	0.123	20.8	0.0680	28.8	0.0421	44.0	0.0196
7.5	0.212	13.0	0.121	21.0	0.0671	29.0	0.0417	45.0	0.0187
7.6	0.209	13.2	0.119	21.2	0.0662	29.2	0.0412	46.0	0.0179
7.7	0.207	13.4	0.117	21.4	0.0654	29.4	0.0408	47.0	0.0171
7.8	0.204	13.6	0.115	21.6	0.0645	29.6	0.0403	48.0	0.0163
7.9	0.202	13.8	0.113	21.8	0.0637	29.8	0.0399	49.0	0.0156
8.0	0.199	14.0	0.112	22.0	0.0629	30.0	0.0394	50.0	0.0149
8.1	0.197	14.2	0.110	22.2	0.0621	30.2	0.0390	51.0	0.0143
8.2	0.195	14.4	0.108	22.4	0.0613	30.4	0.0386	52.0	0.0137
8.3	0.193	14.6	0.106	22.6	0.0606	30.6	0.0382	53.0	0.0131
8.4	0.190	14.8	0.105	22.8	0.0598	30.8	0.0378	54.0	0.0125
8.5	0.188	15.0	0.103	23.0	0.0591	31.0	0.0374	55.0	0.0120
8.6	0.186	15.2	0.1013	23.2	0.0584	31.2	0.0370	56.0	0.0115
8.7	0.184	15.4	0.0997	23.4	0.0576	31.4	0.0366	57.0	0.0110
8.8	0.182	15.6	0.0982	23.6	0.0569	31.6	0.0362	58.0	0.0105
8.9	0.180	15.8	0.0967	23.8	0.0563	31.8	0.0358	59.0	0.0101

*Orion Research Inc. Instruction Manual, Ammonia Electrode, Mode 95-10, Cambridge, Mass.

where:

   C_0 = total sample concentration, mg/L,
   Q = reading from known-addition table, and
   C_s = concentration of added standard, mg/L.

c. To check a direct measurement, compare results of the two methods. If they agree within ±4%, the measurements probably are good. If the known-addition result is much larger than the direct measurement, the sample may contain complexing agents.

6. Precision and Bias

In 38 water samples analyzed by both the phenate and the known-addition ammonia-selective electrode method, the electrode method yielded a mean recovery of 102% of the values obtained by the phenate method when the NH_3-N concentrations varied between 0.30 and 0.78 mg/L. In 57 wastewater samples similarly compared, the electrode method yielded a mean recovery of 108% of the values obtained by the phenate method using distillation when the NH_3-N concentrations varied between 10.2 and 34.7 mg N/L. In 20 instances in which two to four replicates of these samples were analyzed, the mean standard deviation was 1.32 mg N/L. In three measurements at a sewer outfall, distillation did not change statistically the value obtained by the electrode method. In 12 studies using standards in the 2.5- to 30-mg N/L range, average recovery by the phenate method was 97% and by the electrode method 101%.

4500-NH₃ H.   Automated Phenate Method

1. General Discussion

a. Principle: Alkaline phenol and hypochlorite react with ammonia to form indophenol blue that is proportional to the ammonia concentration. The blue color formed is intensified with sodium nitroprusside.

b. Interferences: Seawater contains calcium and magnesium ions in sufficient concentrations to cause precipitation during analysis. Adding EDTA and sodium potassium tartrate reduces the problem. Eliminate any marked variation in acidity or alkalinity among samples because intensity of measured color is pH-dependent. Likewise, insure that pH of wash water and standard ammonia solutions approximates that of sample. For example, if sample has been preserved with 0.8 mL conc H_2SO_4/L, include 0.8 mL conc H_2SO_4/L in wash water and standards. Mercuric chloride used as a preservative gives a negative interference by complexing with ammonia.

Overcome this effect by adding a comparable amount of $HgCl_2$ to the ammonia standards. Remove interfering turbidity by filtration. Color in the samples that absorbs in the photometric range used for analysis interferes.

c. Application: Ammonia nitrogen can be determined in potable, surface, and saline waters as well as domestic and industrial wastewaters over a range of 0.02 to 2.0 mg/L when photometric measurement is made at 630 to 660 nm in a 15- or 50-mm tubular flow cell. Determine higher concentrations by diluting the sample.

2. Apparatus

Automated analytical equipment. The required continuous-flow analytical instrument* consists of the interchangeable components shown in Figure 4500-NH₃:1.

---

*Technicon™ Autoanalyzer™ II or equivalent.

A 50-mm flow cell and a filter for use at 630 nm may be used.

3. Reagents

a. Ammonia-free distilled water: See Section 4500-NH₃.B.3*a*. Use for preparing all reagents and dilutions.

b. Sulfuric acid, H₂SO₄, 5N, air scrubber solution: Carefully add 139 mL conc H₂SO₄ to approximately 500 mL water, cool to room temperature, and dilute to 1 L.

c. Sodium phenate solution: In a 1-L erlenmeyer flask, dissolve 83 g phenol in 500 mL water. In small increments and with agitation, cautiously add 32 g NaOH. Cool flask under running water and dilute to 1 L.

d. Sodium hypochlorite solution: Dilute 250 mL bleach solution containing 5.25% NaOCl to 500 mL with water.

e. EDTA reagent: Dissolve 50 g disodium ethylenediamine tetraacetate and approximately six pellets NaOH in 1 L water. For salt-water samples where EDTA reagent does not prevent precipitation of cations, use sodium potassium tartrate solution prepared as follows:

Sodium potassium tartrate solution: To 900 mL water add 100 g NaKC₄H₄O₆ · 4H₂O, two pellets NaOH, and a few boiling chips, and boil gently for 45 min. Cover, cool, and dilute to 1 L. Adjust pH to 5.2 ± 0.05 with H₂SO₄. Let settle overnight in a cool place and filter to remove precipitate. Add 0.5 mL polyoxyethylene 23 lauryl ether† solution and store in stoppered bottle.

---

†Brij-35, available from ICI Americas, Wilmington, Del. or Technicon Instrument Corp., Tarrytown, N.Y. 10591.

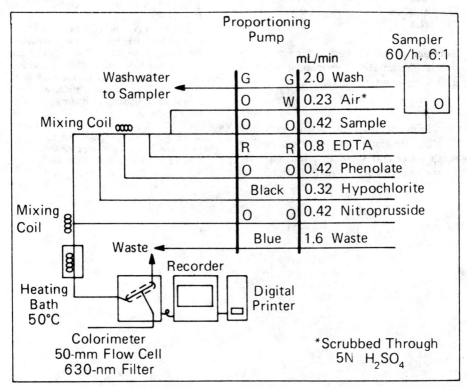

Figure 4500-NH₃:1. Ammonia manifold.

f. Sodium nitroprusside solution: Dissolve 0.5 g $Na_2(NO)Fe(CN)_5 \cdot 2H_2O$ in 1 L water.

g. Ammonia standard solutions: See Sections 4500-NH₃.D.3e and *f*. Use standard ammonia solution and water to prepare the calibration curve in the appropriate ammonia concentration range. To analyze saline waters use substitute ocean water of the following composition to prepare calibration standards:

Constituent	Concentration g/L
NaCl	24.53
MgCl₂	5.20
CaCl₂	1.16
KCl	0.70
SrCl₂	0.03
Na₂SO₄	4.09
NaHCO₃	0.20
KBr	0.10
H₃BO₃	0.03
NaF	0.003

Subtract blank background response of substitute seawater from standards before preparing standard curve.

4. Procedure

a. Eliminate marked variation in acidity or alkalinity among samples. Adjust pH of wash water and standard ammonia solutions to approximately that of sample.

b. Set up manifold and complete system as shown in Figure 4500-NH₃:1.

c. Obtain a stable base line with all reagents, feeding water through sample line.

d. Use a 60/h, 6:1 cam with a common wash.

5. Calculation

Prepare standard curves by plotting peak heights of standards processed through the manifold against NH₃-N concentrations in standards. Compute sample NH₃-N concentration by comparing sample peak height with standard curve.

6. Precision and Bias

See Section 4500-NH₃.A.4.

7. Bibliography

HILLER, A. & D. VAN SLYKE. 1933. Determination of ammonia in blood. *J. Biol. Chem.* 102:499.

FIORE, J. & J.E. O'BRIEN. 1962. Ammonia determination by automatic analysis. *Wastes Eng.* 33:352.

AMERICAN SOCIETY FOR TESTING AND MATERIALS. 1966. Manual on Industrial Water and Industrial Waste Water, 2nd ed. American Soc. Testing & Materials, Philadelphia, Pa.

O'CONNOR, B., R. DOBBS, B. VILLIERS & R. DEAN. 1967. Laboratory distillation of municipal waste effluents. *J. Water Pollut. Control Fed.* 39:25.

BOOTH, R.L. & L.B. LOBRING. 1973. Evaluation of the AutoAnalyzer II: A progress report. *In* Advances in Automated Analysis: 1972 Technicon International Congress, Vol. 8, p.7. Mediad Inc., Tarrytown, N.Y.

4500-NO$_2^-$ NITROGEN (NITRITE)*

4500-NO$_2^-$ A.   Introduction

1. Occurrence and Significance

For a discussion of the chemical characteristics, sources, and effects of nitrite nitrogen, see Section 4500-N.

---

*Approved by Standard Methods Committee, 1988.

2. Selection of Method

The colorimetric method (B) is suitable for concentrations of 5 to 1000 μg NO$_2^-$-N/L (See ¶ B.1a). Nitrite values can be obtained by the automated method given in Section 4500-NO$_3^-$.E with the Cu-Cd reduction step omitted. Additionally, nitrite nitrogen can be determined by ion chromatography (C).

4500–NO$_2^-$ B.   Colorimetric Method

1. General Discussion

a. *Principle:* Nitrite (NO$_2^-$) is determined through formation of a reddish purple azo dye produced at pH 2.0 to 2.5 by coupling diazotized sulfanilamide with N-(1-naphthyl)-ethylenediamine dihydrochloride (NED dihydrochloride). The applicable range of the method for spectrophotometric measurements is 10 to 1000 μg NO$_2^-$-N/L. Photometric measurements can be made in the range 5 to 50 μg N/L if a 5-cm light path and a green color filter are used. The color system obeys Beer's law up to 180 μg N/ L with a 1-cm light path at 543 nm. Higher NO$_2^-$ concentrations can be determined by diluting a sample.

b. *Interferences:* Chemical incompatibility makes it unlikely that NO$_2^-$, free chlorine, and nitrogen trichloride (NCl$_3$) will coexist. NCl$_3$ imparts a false red color when color reagent is added. The following ions interfere because of precipitation under test conditions and should be absent: Sb^{3+}, Au^{3+}, Bi^{3+}, Fe^{3+}, Pb^{2+}, Hg^{2+}, Ag$^+$, chloroplatinate (PtCl$_6^{2-}$), and metavanadate (VO$_3^{2-}$). Cupric ion may cause low results by catalyzing decomposition of the diazon-ium salt. Colored ions that alter the color system also should be absent. Remove suspended solids by filtration.

c. *Storage of sample:* Never use acid preservation for samples to be analyzed for NO$_2^-$. Make the determination promptly on fresh samples to prevent bacterial conversion of NO$_2^-$ to NO$_3^-$ or NH$_3$. For short-term preservation for 1 to 2 d, freeze at $-20°$C or store at 4°C.

2. Apparatus

Colorimetric equipment: One of the following is required:

a. *Spectrophotometer,* for use at 543 nm, providing a light path of 1 cm or longer.

b. *Filter photometer,* providing a light path of 1 cm or longer and equipped with a green filter having maximum transmittance near 540 nm.

3. Reagents

a. *Nitrite-free water:* If it is not known that the distilled or demineralized water is free from NO$_2^-$, use either of the following procedures to prepare nitrite-free water:

1) Add to 1 L distilled water one small crystal each of $KMnO_4$ and either $Ba(OH)_2$ or $Ca(OH)_2$. Redistill in an all-borosilicate-glass apparatus and discard the initial 50 mL of distillate. Collect the distillate fraction that is free of permanganate; a red color with DPD reagent (Section 4500-Cl.F.2b), indicates the presence of permanganate.

2) Add 1 mL conc H_2SO_4 and 0.2 mL $MnSO_4$ solution (36.4 g $MnSO_4$ H_2O/100 mL distilled water) to each 1 L distilled water, and make pink with 1 to 3 mL KMnO4 solution (400 mg $KMnO_4$/L distilled water). Redistill as described in the preceding paragraph.

Use nitrite-free water in making all reagents and dilutions.

b. Color reagent: To 800 mL water add 100 mL 85% phosphoric acid and 10 g sulfanilamide. After dissolving sulfanilamide completely, add 1 g *N*-(1-naphthyl)-ethylenediamine dihydrochloride. Mix to dissolve, then dilute to 1 L with water. Solution is stable for about a month when stored in a dark bottle in refrigerator.

c. Sodium oxalate, 0.025*M* (0.05*N*): Dissolve 3.350 g $Na_2C_2O_4$, primary standard grade, in water and dilute to 1000 mL.

d. Ferrous ammonium sulfate, 0.05*M* (0.05*N*): Dissolve 19.607 g $Fe(NH_4)_2$ $(SO_4)_2 \cdot 6H_2O$ plus 20 mL conc H_2SO_4 in water and dilute to 1000 mL. Standardize as in Section 5220B.3*d*.

e. Stock nitrite solution: Commercial reagent-grade $NaNO_2$ assays at less than 99%. Because NO_2^- is oxidized readily in the presence of moisture, use a fresh bottle of reagent for preparing the stock solution and keep bottles tightly stoppered against the free access of air when not in use. To determine $NaNO_2$ content, add a known excess of standard 0.05*M* (0.05*N*) $KMnO_4$ solution prepared (with 8.0 g $KMnO_4$) and standardized as described in 3500-Ca.C.3*i*, discharge permanganate color with a known quantity of standard reductant

such as 0.025*M* $Na_2C_2O_4$ or 0.05*M* $Fe(NH_4)_2(SO_4)_2$, and back-titrate with standard permanganate solution.

1) Preparation of stock solution—Dissolve 1.232 g $NaNO_2$ in water and dilute to 1000 mL; 1.00 mL = 250 μg N. Preserve with 1 mL $CHCl_3$.

2) Standardization of stock nitrite solution—Pipet, in order, 50.00 mL standard 0.05*M* $KMnO_4$, 5 mL conc H_2SO_4, and 50.00 mL stock NO_2^- solution into a glass-stoppered flask or bottle. Submerge pipet tip well below surface of permanganate-acid solution while adding stock NO_2^- solution. Shake gently and warm to 70 to 80°C on a hot plate. Discharge permanganate color by adding sufficient 10-mL portions of standard 0.025*M* $Na_2C_2O_4$. Titrate excess $Na_2C_2O_4$ with 0.05*M* $KMnO_4$ to the faint pink end point. Carry a water blank through the entire procedure and make the necessary corrections in the final calculation as shown in the equation below.

If standard 0.05*M* ferrous ammonium sulfate solution is substituted for $Na_2C_2O_4$, omit heating and extend reaction period between $KMnO_4$ and Fe^{2+} to 5 min before making final $KMnO_4$ titration.

Calculate NO_2^--N content of stock solution by the following equation:

$$A = \frac{[(B \times C) - (D \times E)] \times 7}{F}$$

where:

A = mg NO_2^--N/mL in stock $NaNO_2$ solution,
B = total mL standard $KMnO_4$ used,
C = normality of standard $KMnO_4$,
D = total mL standard reductant added,
E = normality of standard reductant, and
F = mL stock $NaNO_2$ solution taken for titration.

Each 1.00 mL 0.05*M* $KMnO_4$ consumed by the $NaNO_2$ solution corresponds to 1750 μg NO_2^--N.

f. Intermediate nitrite solution: Calculate the volume, G, of stock NO_2^- solution required for the intermediate NO_2^- solution from $G = 12.5/A$. Dilute the volume G (approximately 50 mL) to 250 mL with water; 1.00 mL = 50.0 μg N. Prepare daily.

g. *Standard nitrite solution:* Dilute 10.00 mL intermediate NO_2^- solution to 1000 mL with water; 1.00 mL = 0.500 μg N. Prepare daily.

4. Procedure

a. *Removal of suspended solids:* If sample contains suspended solids, filter through a 0.45-μm-pore-diam membrane filter.

b. *Color development:* If sample pH is not between 5 and 9, adjust to that range with 1N HCl or NH₄OH as required. To 50.0 mL sample, or to a portion diluted to 50.0 mL, add 2 mL color reagent and mix.

c. *Photometric measurement:* Between 10 min and 2 h after adding color reagent to samples and standards, measure absorbance at 543 nm. As a guide use the following light paths for the indicated NO_2^--N concentrations:

Light Path Length cm	NO_2^--N $\mu g/L$
1	2–25
5	2–6
10	<2

5. Calculation

Prepare a standard curve by plotting absorbance of standards against NO_2^--N concentration. Compute sample concentration directly from curve.

6. Precision and Bias

In a single laboratory using wastewater samples at concentrations of 0.04, 0.24, 0.55, and 1.04 mg NO^-_3 + NO_2^--N/L, the standard deviations were ±0.005, ± 0.004, ± 0.005, and ± 0.01, respectively. In a single laboratory using wastewater samples at concentrations of 0.24, 0.55, and 1.05 mg NO_3^- + NO_2^--N/L, the recoveries were 100%, 102%, and 100%, respectively.[1]

7. Reference

1. U.S. ENVIRONMENTAL PROTECTION AGENCY. 1979. Methods for Chemical Analysis of Water and Wastes. Method 353.3 U.S. Environmental Protection Agency, Washington, D.C.

8. Bibliography

BOLTZ, D.F., ed. 1958. Colorimetric Determination of Nonmetals. Interscience Publishers, New York, N.Y.
NYDAHL, F. 1976. On the optimum conditions for the reduction of nitrate by cadmium. *Talanta* 23:349.

4500-NO₂⁻ C.   Ion Chromatographic Method

See Section 4110.

4500-NO₃⁻   NITROGEN (NITRATE)*

4500-NO₃⁻   A. Introduction

1. Selection of Method

Determination of nitrate (NO_3^-) is difficult because of the relatively complex pro-

cedures required, the high probability that interfering constituents will be present, and the limited concentration ranges of the various techniques.

---

* Approved by Standard Methods Committee, 1988.

An ultraviolet (UV) technique (Method B) that measures the absorbance of NO_3^- at 220 nm is suitable for screening uncontaminated water (low in organic matter).

Screen a sample; if necessary, then select a method suitable for its concentration range and probable interferences. Nitrate may be determined by ion chromatography (C). Applicable ranges for other methods are: nitrate electrode method (D), 0.14 to 1400 mg NO_3^--N/L; cadmium reduction method (E), 0.01 to 1.0 mg NO_3^--N/L; titanous chloride method (G), 0.01 to 10 mg NO_3^--N/L; hydrazine reduction method (H), 0.01 to 10 mg NO_3^--N/L; automated cadmium reduction method (F),

0.5 to 10 mg NO_3^--N/L. For higher NO_3^--N concentrations, dilute into the range of the selected method.

Colorimetric methods require an optically clear sample. Filter turbid sample through 0.45-μm-pore-diam membrane filter. Test filters for nitrate contamination.

2. Storage of Samples

Start NO_3^- determinations promptly after sampling. If storage is necessary, store for up to 24 h at 4°C; for longer storage, preserve with 2 mL conc H_2SO_4/L and store at 4°C. NOTE: When sample is preserved with acid, NO_3^- and NO_2^- cannot be determined as individual species.

4500-NO_3^- B.   Ultraviolet Spectrophotometric Screening Method

1. General Discussion

a. Principle: Use this technique only for screening samples that have low organic matter contents, i.e., uncontaminated natural waters and potable water supplies. The NO_3^- calibration curve follows Beer's law up to 11 mg N/L.

Measurement of UV absorption at 220 nm enables rapid determination of NO_3^-. Because dissolved organic matter also may absorb at 220 nm and NO_3^- does not absorb at 275 nm, a second measurement made at 275 nm may be used to correct the NO_3^- value. The extent of this empirical correction is related to the nature and concentration of organic matter and may vary from one water to another. Consequently, this method is not recommended if a significant correction for organic matter absorbance is required, although it may be useful in monitoring NO_3^- levels within a water body with a constant type of organic matter. Correction factors for organic matter absorbance can be established by the method of additions in combination with analysis of the original NO_3^- content by another method. Sample filtration is in-

tended to remove possible interference from suspended particles. Acidification with $1N$ HCl is designed to prevent interference from hydroxide or carbonate concentrations up to 1000 mg $CaCO_3$/L. Chloride has no effect on the determination.

b. Interference: Dissolved organic matter, surfactants, NO_2^-, and Cr^{6+} interfere. Various inorganic ions not normally found in natural water, such as chlorite and chlorate, may interfere. Inorganic substances can be compensated for by independent analysis of their concentrations and preparation of individual correction curves. For turbid samples, see ¶ A.1.

2. Apparatus

Spectrophotometer, for use at 220 nm and 275 nm with matched silica cells of 1-cm or longer light path.

3. Reagents

a. Nitrate-free water: Use redistilled or distilled, deionized water of highest purity to prepare all solutions and dilutions.

b. Stock nitrate solution: Dry potassium

nitrate (KNO₃) in an oven at 105°C for 24 h. Dissolve 0.7218 g in water and dilute to 1000 mL; 1.00 mL = 100 μg NO_3^--N. Preserve with 2 mL CHCl₃/L. This solution is stable for at least 6 months.

c. *Intermediate nitrate solution:* Dilute 100 mL stock nitrate solution to 1000 mL with water; 1.00 mL = 10.0 μg NO_3^--N. Preserve with 2 mL CHCl₃/L. This solution is stable for 6 months.

d. *Hydrochloric acid solution,* HCl, 1N.

4. Procedure

a. *Treatment of sample:* To 50 mL clear sample, filtered if necessary, add 1 mL HCl solution and mix thoroughly.

b. *Preparation of standard curve:* Prepare NO_3^- calibration standards in the range 0 to 7 mg NO_3^--N/L by diluting to 50 mL the following volumes of intermediate nitrate solution: 0, 1.00, 2.00, 4.00, 7.00 . . . 35.0 mL. Treat NO_3^- standards in same manner as samples.

c. *Spectrophotometric measurement:* Read absorbance or transmittance against redistilled water set at zero absorbance or 100% transmittance. Use a wavelength of 220 nm to obtain NO_3^- reading and a wavelength of 275 nm to determine interference due to dissolved organic matter.

5. Calculation

For samples and standards, subtract two times the absorbance reading at 275 nm from the reading at 220 nm to obtain absorbance due to NO_3^-. Construct a standard curve by plotting absorbance due to NO_3^- against NO_3^--N concentration of standard. Using corrected sample absorbances, obtain sample concentrations directly from standard curve. NOTE: If correction value is more than 10% of the reading at 220 nm, do not use this method.

6. Bibliography

HOATHER, R.C. & R.F. RACKMAN. 1959. Oxidized nitrogen and sewage effluents observed by ultraviolet spectrophotometry. *Analyst* 84:549.

GOLDMAN, E. & R. JACOBS. 1961. Determination of nitrates by ultraviolet absorption. *J. Amer. Water Works Assoc.* 53:187.

ARMSTRONG, F.A.J. 1963. Determination of nitrate in water by ultraviolet spectrophotometry. *Anal. Chem.* 35:1292.

NAVONE, R. 1964. Proposed method for nitrate in potable waters. *J. Amer. Water Works Assoc.* 56:781.

4500-NO₃⁻ C. Ion Chromatographic Method

See Section 4110.

4500-NO₃⁻ D. Nitrate Electrode Method

1. General Discussion

a. *Principle:* The NO_3^- ion electrode is a selective sensor that develops a potential across a thin, porous, inert membrane that holds in place a water-immiscible liquid ion exchanger. The electrode responds to NO_3^- ion activity between about 10^{-5} and 10^{-1} M (0.14 to 1400 mg NO_3^--N/L). The lower limit of detection is determined by the small but finite solubility of the liquid ion exchanger.

b. *Interferences:* Chloride and bicarbonate ions interfere when their weight ratios to NO_3^--N are > 10 or > 5, respectively. Ions that are potential interferences but do not normally occur at significant levels in potable waters are NO_2^-, CN^-, S^{2-}, Br^-, I^-, ClO_3^-, and ClO_4^-. Although the electrodes function satisfactorily in buffers over the range pH 3 to 9, erratic responses have been noted where pH is not held constant. Because the electrode responds to NO_3^- activity rather than concentration, ionic strength must be constant in all samples and standards. Minimize these problems by using a buffer solution containing Ag_2SO_4 to remove Cl^-, Br^-, I^-, S^{2-}, and CN^-, sulfamic acid to remove NO_2^-, a buffer at pH 3 to eliminate HCO_3^- and to maintain a constant pH and ionic strength, and $Al_2(SO_4)_3$ to complex organic acids.

2. Apparatus

a. *pH meter, expanded-scale or digital,* capable of 0.1 mV resolution.

b. *Double-junction reference electrode.** Fill outer chamber with $(NH_4)_2SO_4$ solution.

c. *Nitrate ion electrode:†* Carefully follow manufacturer's instructions regarding care and storage.

d. *Magnetic stirrer:* TFE-coated stirring bar.

3. Reagents

a. *Nitrate-free water:* Prepare as described in ¶ B.3a. Use for all solutions and dilutions.

b. *Stock nitrate solution:* Prepare as described in ¶ B.3b.

c. *Standard nitrate solutions:* Dilute 1.0, 10, and 50 mL stock nitrate solution to 100 mL with water to obtain standard solutions of 1.0, 10, and 50 mg NO_3^--N/L, respectively.

d. *Buffer solution:* Dissolve 17.32 g

$Al_2(SO_4)_3 \cdot 18H_2O$, 3.43 g Ag_2SO_4, 1.28 g H_3BO_3, and 2.52 g sulfamic acid (H_2NSO_3H), in about 800 mL water. Adjust to pH 3.0 by slowly adding $0.10N$ NaOH. Dilute to 1000 mL and store in a dark glass bottle.

e. *Sodium hydroxide,* NaOH, $0.1N$.

f. *Reference electrode filling solution:* Dissolve 0.53 g $(NH_4)_2SO_4$ in water and dilute to 100 mL.

4. Procedure

a. *Preparation of calibration curve:* Transfer 10 mL of 1 mg NO_3^--N/L standard to a 50-mL beaker, add 10 mL buffer, and stir with a magnetic stirrer. Immerse tips of electrodes and record millivolt reading when stable (after about 1 min). Remove electrodes, rinse, and blot dry. Repeat for 10-mg NO_3^--N/L and 50-mg NO_3^--N/L standards. Plot potential measurements against NO_3^--N concentration on semilogarithmic graph paper, with NO_3^--N concentration on the logarithmic axis (abscissa) and potential (in millivolts) on the linear axis (ordinate). A straight line with a slope of $+ 57 \pm 3$ mV/decade at 25°C should result. Recalibrate electrodes several times daily by checking potential reading of the 10 mg NO_3^--N standard and adjusting the calibration control until the reading plotted on the calibration curve is displayed again.

b. *Measurement of sample:* Transfer 10 mL sample to a 50-mL beaker, add 10 mL buffer solution, and stir (for about 1 min) with a magnetic stirrer. Measure standards and samples at about the same temperature. Immerse electrode tips in sample and record potential reading when stable (after about 1 min). Read concentration from calibration curve.

5. Precision

Over the range of the method, precision of ± 0.4 mV, corresponding to 2.5% in concentration, is expected.

---

* Orion Model 90-02, or equivalent.
† Orion Model 93-07, Corning Model 476134, or equivalent.

6. Bibliography

LANGMUIR, D. & R.I. JACOBSON. 1970. Specific ion electrode determination of nitrate in some fresh waters and sewage effluents. *Environ. Sci. Technol.* 4:835.

KEENEY, D.R., B.H. BYRNES & J.J. GENSON. 1970. Determination of nitrate in waters with nitrate-selective ion electrode. *Analyst* 95:383.

MILHAM, P.J., A.S. AWAD, R.E. PAUL & J.H.

BULL. 1970. Analysis of plants, soils and waters for nitrate by using an ion-selective electrode. *Analyst* 95:751.

SYNNOTT, J.C., S.J. WEST & J.W. ROSS. 1984. Comparison of ion-selective electrode and gas-sensing electrode technique for measurement of nitrate in environmental samples. *In* Pawlowski et al., eds., Studies in Environmental Science, No. 23, Chemistry for Protection of the Environment, Elsevier Press, New York, N.Y.

4500-NO₃⁻ E.   Cadmium Reduction Method

1. General Discussion

a. Principle: NO_3^- is reduced almost quantitatively to nitrite (NO_2^-) in the presence of cadmium (Cd). This method uses commercially available Cd granules treated with copper sulfate ($CuSO_4$) and packed in a glass column.

The NO_2^- produced thus is determined by diazotizing with sulfanilamide and coupling with N-(1-naphthyl)-ethylenediamine dihydrochloride to form a highly colored azo dye that is measured colorimetrically. A correction may be made for any NO_2^- present in the sample by analyzing without the reduction step. The applicable range of this method is 0.01 to 1.0 mg NO_3^--N/L. The method is recommended especially for NO_3^- levels below 0.1 mg N/L where other methods lack adequate sensitivity.

b. Interferences: Suspended matter in the column will restrict sample flow. For turbid samples, see ¶ A.1. Concentrations of iron, copper, or other metals above several milligrams per liter lower reduction efficiency. Add EDTA to samples to eliminate this interference. Oil and grease will coat the Cd surface. Remove by pre-extraction with an organic solvent (see Section 5520). Residual chlorine can interfere by oxidizing the Cd column, reducing its efficiency. Check samples for residual chlorine (see DPD methods in Section 4500-Cl). Remove residual chlorine by adding

sodium thiosulfate ($Na_2S_2O_3$) solution [Section 4500-NH₃.B.3*d*4)]. Sample color that absorbs at about 540 nm interferes.

2. Apparatus

a. Reduction column: Purchase or construct the column* (Figure 4500-NO₃⁻:1) from a 100-mL volumetric pipet by removing the top portion. The column also can be constructed from two pieces of tubing joined end to end: join a 10-cm length of 3-cm-ID tubing to a 25-cm length of 3.5-mm-ID tubing. Add a TFE stopcock with metering valve[1] to control flow rate.

b. Colorimetric equipment: One of the following is required:

1) *Spectrophotometer,* for use at 543 nm, providing a light path of 1 cm or longer.

2) *Filter photometer*, with light path of 1 cm or longer and equipped with a filter having maximum transmittance near 540 nm.

3. Reagents

a. Nitrate-free water: See ¶ B.3*a*. The absorbance of a reagent blank prepared with this water should not exceed 0.01. Use for all solutions and dilutions.

b. Copper-cadmium granules: Wash 25

---

* Tudor Scientific Glass Co., 555 Edgefield Road, Belvedere, S.C. 29841, Cat. TP-1730, or equivalent.

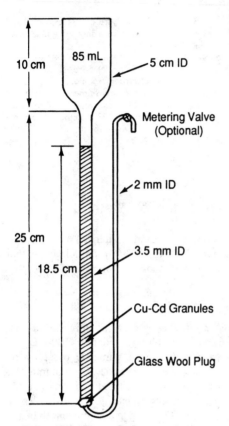

Figure 4500-NO$_3^-$:1. Reduction column.

g new or used 40- to 60-mesh Cd granules†
with 6N HCl and rinse with water. Swirl
Cd with 100 mL 2% CuSO$_4$ solution for
5 min or until blue color partially fades.
Decant and repeat with fresh CuSO$_4$ until
a brown colloidal precipitate begins to develop. Gently flush with water to remove
all precipitated Cu.

c. *Color reagent:* Prepare as directed in
Section 4500-NO$_2^-$ B.3b.

d. *Ammonium chloride-EDTA solution:*
Dissolve 13 g NH$_4$Cl and 1.7 g disodium
ethylenediamine tetraacetate in 900 mL
water. Adjust to pH 8.5 with conc NH$_4$OH
and dilute to 1 L.

† EM Laboratories, Inc., 500 Exec. Blvd., Elmsford,
N.Y., Cat. 2001, or equivalent.

e. *Dilute ammonium chloride-EDTA solution:* Dilute 300 mL NH$_4$Cl-EDTA solution to 500 mL with water.

f. *Hydrochloric acid, HCl, 6N.*

g. *Copper sulfate solution, 2%:* Dissolve
20 g CuSO$_4$.5H$_2$O in 500 mL water and
dilute to 1 L.

h. *Stock nitrate solution:* Prepare as directed in ¶ B.3b.

i. *Intermediate nitrate solution:* Prepare
as directed in ¶ B.3c.

j. *Stock nitrite solution:* See Section
4500-NO$_2^-$.B.3e.

k. *Intermediate nitrite solution:* See Section 4500-NO$_2^-$.B.3f.

l. *Working nitrite solution:* Dilute 50.0
mL intermediate nitrite solution to 500 mL
with nitrite-free water; 1.00 mL = 5 μg
NO$_2^-$-N.

4. Procedure

a. *Preparation of reduction column:* Insert a glass wool plug into bottom of reduction column and fill with water. Add
sufficient Cu-Cd granules to produce a column 18.5 cm long. Maintain water level
above Cu-Cd granules to prevent entrap-
ment of air. Wash column with 200 mL
dilute NH$_4$Cl-EDTA solution. Activate
column by passing through it, at 7 to 10
mL/min, at least 100 mL of a solution
composed of 25% 1.0 mg NO$_3^-$-N/L
standard and 75% NH$_4$Cl-EDTA solution.

b. *Treatment of sample:*

1) Turbidity removal—For turbid samples, see ¶ A.1.

2) pH adjustment—Adjust pH to between 7 and 9, as necessary, using a pH
meter and dilute HCl or NaOH. This insures a pH of 8.5 after adding NH$_4$Cl-
EDTA solution.

3) Sample reduction—To 25.0 mL sample or a portion diluted to 25.0 mL, add
75 mL NH$_4$Cl-EDTA solution and mix.
Pour mixed sample into column and collect
at a rate of 7 to 10 mL/min. Discard first
25 mL. Collect the rest in original sample

flask. There is no need to wash columns between samples, but if columns are not to be reused for several hours or longer, pour 50 mL dilute NH_4Cl-EDTA solution on to the top and let it pass through the system. Store Cu-Cd column in this solution and never let it dry.

4) *Color development and measurement*—As soon as possible, and not more than 15 min after reduction, add 2.0 mL color reagent to 50 mL sample and mix. Between 10 min and 2 h afterward, measure absorbance at 543 nm against a distilled water-reagent blank. NOTE: If NO_3^- concentration exceeds the standard curve range (about 1 mg N/L), use remainder of reduced sample to make an appropriate dilution and analyze again.

c. Standards: Using the intermediate NO_3^--N solution, prepare standards in the range 0.05 to 1.0 mg NO_3^--N/L by diluting the following volumes to 100 mL in volumetric flasks: 0.5, 1.0, 2.0, 5.0, and 10.0 mL. Carry out reduction of standards exactly as described for samples. Compare at least one NO_2^- standard to a reduced NO_3^- standard at the same concentration to verify reduction column efficiency. Reactivate Cu-Cd granules as described in ¶ 3*b* above when efficiency of reduction falls below about 75%.

5. Calculation

Obtain a standard curve by plotting absorbance of standards against NO_3^--N concentration. Compute sample concentra-

tions directly from standard curve. Report as milligrams oxidized N per liter (the sum of NO_3^--N plus NO_2^--N) unless the concentration of NO_2^--N is separately determined and subtracted.

6. Precision and Bias

In a single laboratory using wastewater samples at concentrations of 0.04, 0.24, 0.55, and 1.04 mg NO_3^- + NO_2^--N/L, the standard deviations were ±0.005, ±0.004, ±0.005, and ±0.01, respectively. In a single laboratory using wastewater with additions of 0.24, 0.55, and 1.05 mg NO_3^- + NO_2^--N/L, the recoveries were 100%, 102%, and 100%, respectively.[2]

7. References

1. WOOD, E.D., F.A.J. ARMSTRONG & F.A. RICHARDS. 1967. Determination of nitrate in sea water by cadmium-copper reduction to nitrite. *J. Mar. Biol. Assoc. U.K.* 47:23.
2. U.S. ENVIRONMENTAL PROTECTION AGENCY. 1979. Methods for Chemical Analysis of Water and Wastes, Method 353.3. U.S. Environmental Protection Agency, Washington, D.C.

8. Bibliography

STRICKLAND, J.D.H. & T.R. PARSONS. 1972. A Practical Handbook of Sea Water Analysis, 2nd ed. Bull. No. 167, Fisheries Research Board Canada, Ottawa, Ont.
NYDAHL, F. 1976. On the optimum conditions for the reduction of nitrate by cadmium. *Talanta* 23:349.
AMERICAN SOCIETY FOR TESTING AND MATERIALS. 1987. Annual Book of ASTM Standards, Vol. 11.01. American Soc. Testing & Materials, Philadelphia, Pa.

4500-NO₃⁻ F. Automated Cadmium Reduction Method

1. General Discussion

a. Principle: See ¶ E.1*a*.

b. Interferences: Sample turbidity may interfere. Remove by filtration before analysis. Sample color that absorbs in the pho-

tometric range used for analysis also will interfere.

c. Application: Nitrate and nitrite, singly or together in potable, surface, and saline waters and domestic and industrial wastewaters, can be determined over a range of 0.5 to 10 mg N/L.

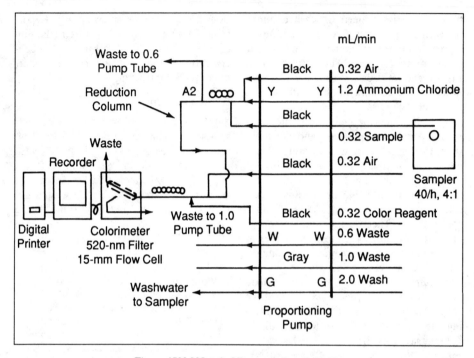

Figure 4500-NO₃⁻:2. Nitrate-nitrite manifold.

2. Apparatus

Automated analytical equipment: The required continuous-flow analytical instrument* consists of the components shown in Figure 4500-NO₃⁻:2.

3. Reagents

a. Deionized distilled water: See ¶ B.3a.

b. Copper sulfate solution: Dissolve 20 g $CuSO_4 \cdot 5H_2O$ in 500 mL water and dilute to 1 L.

c. Wash solution: Use water for unpreserved samples. For samples preserved with H_2SO_4, add 2 mL conc H_2SO_4/L wash water.

d. Copper-cadmium granules: See ¶ E.3b.

e. Hydrochloric acid, HCl, conc.

f. Ammonium hydroxide, NH_4OH, conc.

g. Color reagent: To approximately 800 mL water, add, while stirring, 100 mL conc H_3PO_4, 40 g sulfanilamide, and 2 g *N*-(1-naphthyl)-ethylenediamine dihydrochloride. Stir until dissolved and dilute to 1 L. Store in brown bottle and keep in the dark when not in use. This solution is stable for several months.

h. Ammonium chloride solution: Dissolve 85 g NH_4Cl in water and dilute to 1 L. Add 0.5 mL polyoxyethylene 23 lauryl ether.†

i. Stock nitrate solution: See ¶ B.3b.

---

* AutoAnalyzer™II: Technicon Instrument Corp., Tarrytown, N.Y., or equivalent.

† Brij-35, available from ICI Americas, Inc., Wilmington, Del., or Technicon Instruments Corp., Tarrytown, N.Y., or equivalent.

j. Intermediate nitrate solution: See ¶ B.3c.

k. Standard nitrate solutions: Using intermediate NO_3^--N solution and water, prepare standards for calibration curve in appropriate nitrate range. Compare at least one NO_2^- standard to a NO_3^- standard at the same concentration to verify column reduction efficiency. To examine saline waters prepare standard solutions with the substitute ocean water described in Section 4500-NH₃.G.3g.

l. Standard nitrite solution: See 4500-NH₃.3g.

4. Procedure

Set up manifold as shown in Figure 4500-NO₃⁻:2 and follow general procedure described by the manufacturer.

If sample pH is below 5 or above 9, adjust to between 5 and 9 with either conc HCl or conc NH_4OH.

5. Calculation

Prepare standard curves by plotting peak heights of standards processed through the manifold against NO_3^--N concentration in standards. Compute sample NO_3^--N concentration by comparing sample peak height with standard curve.

6. Precision and Bias

Data obtained in three laboratories with an automated system based on identical chemical principles but having slightly different configurations‡ are given in the table

‡ Automated System I, described in the 16th edition of this publication, Section 418F.

below. Analyses were conducted on four natural water samples containing exact increments of inorganic nitrate:

Increment as NO_3^--N µg/L	Standard Deviation µg N/L	Bias %	Bias µg N/L
290	12	+5.75	+17
350	92	+18.10	+63
2310	318	+4.47	+103
2480	176	−2.69	−67

In a single laboratory using surface water samples at concentrations of 100, 200, 800, and 2100 µg N/L, the standard deviations were 0, ±40, ±50, and ±50 µg/L, respectively, and at concentrations of 200 and 2200 µg N/L, recoveries were 100 and 96%, respectively.

Precision and bias for the system described herein are believed to be comparable.

7. Bibliography

FIORE, J. & J.E. O'BRIEN. 1962. Automation in sanitary chemistry—Parts 1 and 2. Determination of nitrates and nitrites. *Wastes Eng.* 33:128 & 238.

ARMSTRONG, F.A., C.R. STEARNS & J.D. STRICKLAND. 1967. The measurement of upwelling and subsequent biological processes by means of the Technicon AutoAnalyzer and associated equipment. *Deep Sea Res.* 14:381.

U.S. ENVIRONMENTAL PROTECTION AGENCY. 1979. Methods for Chemical Analysis of Water and Wastes. U.S. Environmental Protection Agency, Washington, D.C.

AMERICAN SOCIETY FOR TESTING AND MATERIALS. 1987. Annual Book of ASTM Standards, Vol. 11.01. American Soc. Testing & Materials, Philadelphia, Pa.

4500-NO$_3^-$ G.   Titanous Chloride Reduction Method (PROPOSED)

1. General Discussion

a. Principle: NO$_3^-$ is determined potentiometrically using an NH$_3$ gas-sensing electrode after reduction of the NO$_3^-$ to NH$_3$. Reduction is accomplished by use of titanous chloride reagent. The electrode is calibrated with NO$_3^-$ solutions and the concentrations of samples are determined in the same background solution containing sodium hydroxide and titanous chloride.

This method is applicable to the determination of NO$_3^-$ in water containing 0.1 to 20 mg NO$_3^-$-N/L. The concentration range can be extended by appropriate sample dilution.

b. Interferences: NH$_3$ and NO$_2^-$, if present, are measured with NO$_3^-$. If either concentration is significant, relative to the NO$_3^-$ concentration, measure separately and subtract.

2. Apparatus

a. pH meter, with 0.1 mV resolution, or a specific ion meter.

b. NH$_3$ gas-sensing electrode*.

c. Magnetic stirrer, with a TFE-coated stirring bar.

3. Reagents

a. Titanous chloride reagent solution, TiCl$_3$, practical grade, 20%.

b. Sodium hydroxide solution, NaOH, 10N: Dissolve 400 g reagent-grade NaOH pellets and dilute to 1000 mL with water.

c. Stock nitrate solution: See ¶ B.3*b*.

d. NH$_3$ electrode filling solution, NH$_4$Cl and NaNO$_3$: Dissolve 0.535 g NH$_4$Cl and 8.500 g NaNO$_3$ and dilute to 100 mL with distilled water. Add 0.3 mL 0.1M AgNO$_3$. Solution will be slightly cloudy.

* Orion Model 95-12, or equivalent.

4. Procedure

a. Preparation of calibration curve: Assemble and check NH$_3$ electrode according to manufacturer's instructions, but use the filling solution prepared in ¶ 3*d*. By serial dilution of the NO$_3^-$ stock solution, prepare NO$_3^-$ standards at 0.1, 1.0, and 10.0 mg/L. Transfer 100 mL 0.1 mg/L standard into a 150-mL beaker, add a stirring bar, and stir moderately. Add 10 mL 10N NaOH and 2 mL TiCl$_3$ reagent. Immerse electrode in stirring solution, let potential stabilize, and record the reading in millivolts. Plot as 0.1 mg NO$_3^-$-N/L and repeat for each remaining standard. Prepare a calibration curve by plotting smoothly, on semilogarithmic graph paper, the potential observed on the linear axis (ordinate) and the NO$_3^-$-N concentration on the logarithmic axis (abscissa). NOTE: Volume corrections are incorporated into calibration, so that readings can be made directly from the graph.

b. Measurement of samples: Transfer 100 mL sample to a 150-mL beaker, add a stirring bar, and stir moderately. Add 10 mL 10N NaOH and 2 mL TiCl$_3$ reagent. Immerse electrode in stirring solution, let potential stabilize, and use the voltage to read NO$_3^-$/L directly from the calibration curve. Rinse electrode with distilled water between samples.

5. Precision

Over the range of the method, precision of ±0.6 mV or less, corresponding to about ±3.0% in concentration, is expected.

6. Bibliography

BRAUNSTEIN, L., K. HOCHMULLER & K. SPENGLER. 1980. Combined ammonium/nitrate analysis using an ion-selective electrode. Special printing from *Vom Wasser*, 54, Verlag Chemie GmbH.

4500-NO$_3^-$ H. Automated Hydrazine Reduction Method (PROPOSED)

1. General Discussion

a. Principle: NO$_3^-$ is reduced to NO$_2^-$ with hydrazine sulfate. The NO$_2^-$ (originally present plus reduced NO$_3^-$) is determined by diazotization with sulfanilamide and coupling with *N*-(1-naphthyl)-ethylenediamine dihydrochloride to form a highly colored azo dye that is measured colorimetrically.

b. Interferences: Sample color that absorbs in the photometric range used will interfere. Concentrations of sulfide ion of less than 10 mg/L cause variations of NO$_3^-$ and NO$_2^-$ concentrations of ± 10%.

c. Application: NO$_3^-$ + NO$_2^-$ in potable and surface water and in domestic and industrial wastes can be determined over a range of 0.01 to 10 mg N/L.

2. Apparatus

Automated analytical equipment: The required continuous-flow analytical instrument* consists of the components shown in Figure 4500-NO$_3^-$:3.

3. Reagents

a. Color developing reagent: To approximately 500 mL water add 200 mL conc phosphoric acid and 10 g sulfanilamide. After sulfanilamide is dissolved completely, add 0.8 g *N*-(1-naphthyl)-ethylenediamine dihydrochloride. Dilute to 1 L with water, store in a dark bottle, and refrigerate. Solution is stable for approximately 1 month.

b. Copper sulfate stock solution: Dissolve 2.5 g CuSO$_4 \cdot$5H$_2$O in water and dilute to 1 L.

c. Copper sulfate dilute solution: Dilute 20 mL stock solution to 2 L.

d. Sodium hydroxide stock solution, 10N: Dissolve 400 g NaOH in 750 mL water, cool, and dilute to 1 L.

e. Sodium hydroxide, 1.0N: Dilute 100 mL stock NaOH solution to 1 L.

f. Hydrazine sulfate stock solution: Dissolve 27.5 g N$_2$H$_4 \cdot$H$_2$SO$_4$ in 900 mL water and dilute to 1 L. This solution is stable for approximately 6 months. CAUTION: *Toxic if ingested. Mark container with appropriate warning.*

g. Hydrazine sulfate dilute solution: Dilute 22 mL stock solution to 1 L.

h. Stock nitrate solution: See ¶ B.3*b*.

i. Intermediate nitrate solution: See ¶ B.3*c*.

j. Standard nitrate solutions: Prepare NO$_3^-$ calibration standards in the range 0 to 10 mg/L by diluting to 100 mL the following volumes of stock nitrate solution: 0, 0.5, 1.0, 2.0...10.0 mL. For standards in the range of 0.01 mg/L use intermediate nitrate solution. Compare at least one nitrite standard to a nitrate standard at the same concentration to verify the efficiency of the reduction.

k. Standard nitrite solution: See ¶s B.3*e, f,* and *g.*

4. Procedure

Set up manifold as shown in Figure 4500-NO$_3^-$:3 and follow general procedure described by manufacturer. Run a 2.0-mg NO$_3^-$-N/L and a 2.0-mg NO$_2^-$-N/L

---

* AutoAnalyzer II: Technicon Instrument Corp., Tarrytown. N.Y., or equivalent.

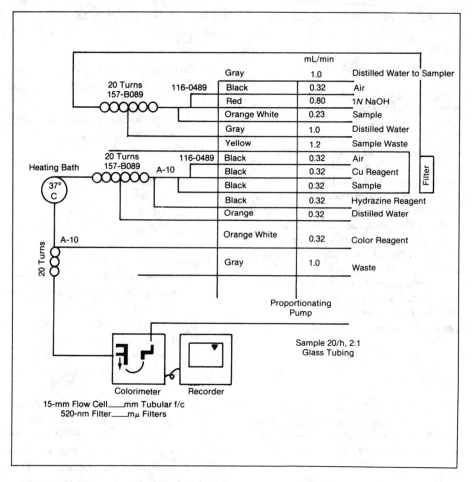

Figure 4500-NO₃⁻:3. Nitrate-nitrite manifold.

standard through the system to check for 100% reduction of nitrate to nitrite. The two peaks should be of equal height; if not, adjust concentration of the hydrazine sulfate solution: If the NO_3^- peak is lower than the NO_2^- peak, increase concentration of hydrazine sulfate until they are equal; if the NO_3^- peak is higher than the NO_2^- reduce concentration of hydrazine sulfate. When correct concentration has

been determined, no further adjustment should be necessary.

5. Calculation

Prepare a standard curve by plotting peak heights of processed standards against known concentrations. Compute concentrations of samples by comparing peak heights with standard curve.

6. Precision and Bias

In a single laboratory using drinking water, surface water, and industrial waste at concentrations of 0.39, 1.15, 1.76, and 4.75 mg NO_3^--N/L, the standard deviations were ±0.02, ±0.01, ±0.02, and ±0.03, respectively. In a single laboratory using drinking water at concentrations of 0.75 and 2.97 the recoveries were 99% and 101%.[1]

7. Reference

1. U.S. ENVIRONMENTAL PROTECTION AGENCY. 1979. Methods for Chemical Analysis of Water and Wastes. U.S. Environmental Protection Agency, Washington, D.C.

8. Bibliography

KAMPHAKE, L., S. HANNAH & J. COHEN. 1967. Automated analysis for nitrate by hydrazine reduction. *Water Res.* 1:205.

4500-N$_{org}$ NITROGEN (ORGANIC)*

4500-N$_{org}$ A. Introduction

1. Selection of Method

The major factor that influences the selection of a macro- or semi-micro-kjeldahl method to determine organic nitrogen is the concentration of organic nitrogen. The macro-kjeldahl method is applicable for samples containing either low or high concentrations of organic nitrogen but requires a relatively large sample volume for low concentrations. In the semi-micro-kjeldahl method, which is applicable to samples containing high concentrations of organic nitrogen, the sample volume should be chosen to contain organic plus ammonia nitrogen (kjeldahl nitrogen) in the range of 0.2 to 2 mg.

2. Storage of Samples

The most reliable results are obtained on fresh samples. If an immediate analysis is not possible, preserve samples by acidifying to pH 1.5 to 2.0 with concentrated H_2SO_4 and storing at 4°C. Do not use $HgCl_2$ be-

cause it will interfere with ammonia removal.

3. Interferences

a. Nitrate: During digestion, nitrate in excess of 10 mg/L can oxidize a portion of the ammonia released from the digested organic nitrogen, producing N_2O and resulting in a negative interference. When sufficient organic matter in a low state of oxidation is present, nitrate can be reduced to ammonia, resulting in a positive interference. The conditions under which significant interferences occur are not well defined and there is no proven way to eliminate the interference in conjunction with the methods described herein.

b. Inorganic salts and solids: The acid and salt content of the digestion reagent is intended to produce a digestion temperature of about 360 to 370°C. If the sample contains a very large quantity of salt or inorganic solids that dissolve during digestion, the temperature may rise above 400°C, at which point pyrolytic loss of nitrogen

---

*Approved by Standard Methods Committee, 1985.

begins to occur. To prevent an excessive digestion temperature, add more H_2SO_4 to maintain the acid-salt balance. Not all salts cause precisely the same temperature rise, but adding of 1 mL H_2SO_4/g salt in the sample gives reasonable results. Add the extra acid and the digestion reagent to both sample and reagent blank. Too much acid will lower the digestion temperature below 360°C and result in incomplete digestion and recovery. If necessary, add more sodium hydroxide-sodium thiosulfate before the final distillation step to neutralize the excess acid.

Large amounts of salt or solids also may cause bumping during distillation. If this occurs, add more dilution water to the samples after digestion.

c. *Organic matter:* During digestion, H_2SO_4 oxidizes organic matter to CO_2 and H_2O. If a large amount of organic matter is present, a large amount of acid will be consumed, the ratio of salt to acid will increase, and the digestion temperature will increase. If enough organic matter is present, the temperature will rise above 400°C, resulting in pyrolytic loss of nitrogen. To prevent this, add to the digestion flask 10 mL conc H_2SO_4/3 g COD. (For most organic substances, 3 g COD equals about 1 g organic matter). Alternately, add 50 mL more of digestion reagent/g COD. Additional sodium hydroxide-sodium thiosulfate reagent may be necessary to keep the distillation pH high. Because reagents may contain traces of ammonia, treat the reagent blank identically with the samples.

4. Use of a Catalyst

Although it generally is desirable to avoid using mercury because of its toxicity and the problems associated with disposal of residues, mercury is the catalyst of choice. Only selenium is as effective as mercury, but selenium is highly toxic and there are potential interferences associated with its use. Digestion of some samples may be complete or nearly complete without the use of a catalyst or with the use of a less toxic catalyst, such as copper. If copper is substituted for mercury, add 10 mL of a solution containing 25.115 g $CuSO_4$/L to each macro-kjeldahl digestion flask with 50 mL digestion reagent from which the HgO has been omitted. Use 2 mL of $CuSO_4$ solution for the semi-micro method. If the mercury catalyst is omitted, report this deviation and indicate, if possible, the percentage recovery relative to the results for similar samples analyzed using the mercury catalyst.

4500-N$_{org}$ B.   Macro-Kjeldahl Method

1. General Discussion

The kjeldahl method determines nitrogen in the trinegative state. It fails to account for nitrogen in the form of azide, azine, azo, hydrazone, nitrate, nitrite, nitrile, nitro, nitroso, oxime, and semi-carbazone. If ammonia nitrogen is not removed in the initial phase (¶ 4b below) of the procedure, the term "kjeldahl nitrogen" is applied to the result. Should kjeldahl nitrogen and ammonia nitrogen be determined individually, "organic nitrogen" can be obtained by difference.

a. *Principle:* In the presence of H_2SO_4, potassium sulfate (K_2SO_4), and mercuric sulfate ($HgSO_4$) catalyst, amino nitrogen of many organic materials is converted to ammonium sulfate [$(NH_4)_2SO_4$]. Free ammonia and ammonium-nitrogen also are converted to $(NH_4)_2SO_4$. During sample digestion, a mercury ammonium complex is formed and then decomposed by sodium thiosulfate (Na$_2$S$_2$O$_3$). After decomposition the ammonia is distilled from an alkaline medium and absorbed in boric or sulfuric acid. The ammonia is determined colorimetrically or by titration with a standard mineral acid.

b. Selection of ammonia measurement method: The sensitivity of colorimetric methods makes them particularly useful for determining organic nitrogen levels below 5 mg/L. The titrimetric and selective electrode methods of measuring ammonia in the distillate are suitable for determining a wide range of organic nitrogen concentrations.

2. Apparatus

a. Digestion apparatus: Kjeldahl flasks with a total capacity of 800 mL yield the best results. Digest over a heating device adjusted so that 250 mL water at an initial temperature of 25°C can be heated to a rolling boil in approximately 5 min. For testing, preheat heaters for 10 min if gas or 30 min if electric. A heating device meeting this specification should provide the temperature range of 365 to 370°C for effective digestion.

b. Distillation apparatus: See Section 4500-NH$_3$.B.2*a*.

c. Apparatus for ammonia determination: See Sections 4500-NH$_3$.C.2, D.2, E.2, or F.2.

3. Reagents

Prepare all reagents and dilutions in ammonia-free water.

All of the reagents listed for the determination of Nitrogen (Ammonia), Sections 4500-NH$_3$.C.3, D.3, E.3, or F.3, are required, plus the following:

a. Mercuric sulfate solution: Dissolve 8 g red mercuric oxide, HgO, in 100 mL 6*N* H$_2$SO$_4$.

b. Digestion reagent: Dissolve 134 g K$_2$SO$_4$ in 650 mL water and 200 mL conc H$_2$SO$_4$. Add, with stirring, 25 mL mercuric

sulfate solution. Dilute the combined solution to 1 L with water. Keep at a temperature close to 20°C to prevent crystallization.

c. Sodium hydroxide-sodium thiosulfate reagent: Dissolve 500 g NaOH and 25 g Na$_2$S$_2$O$_3$·5H$_2$O in water and dilute to 1 L.

d. Borate buffer solution: See Section 4500-NH$_3$.B.3*b*.

e. Sodium hydroxide, NaOH, 6*N*.

4. Procedure

a. Selection of sample volume and sample preparation: Place a measured volume of sample in an 800-mL kjeldahl flask. Select sample size from the following tabulation:

Organic Nitrogen in Sample mg/L	Sample Size mL
0–1	500
1–10	250
10–20	100
20–50	50.0
50–100	25.0

If necessary, dilute sample to 300 mL, neutralize to pH 7, and dechlorinate as described in Section 4500-NH$_3$.B.4*b*.

b. Ammonia removal: Add 25 mL borate buffer and then 6*N* NaOH until pH 9.5 is reached. Add a few glass beads or boiling chips and boil off 300 mL. If desired, distill this fraction and determine ammonia nitrogen. Alternately, if ammonia has been determined by the distillation method, use residue in distilling flask for organic nitrogen determination.

For sludge and sediment samples, weigh wet sample in a crucible or weighing bottle, transfer contents to a kjeldahl flask, and determine kjeldahl nitrogen. Follow a similar procedure for ammonia nitrogen and organic nitrogen determined by difference. Determinations of organic and kjeldahl nitrogen on dried sludge and sediment samples are not accurate because drying results in loss of ammonium salts. Measure dry weight of sample on a separate portion.

c. Digestion: Cool and add carefully 50 mL digestion reagent (or substitute 10 mL conc H_2SO_4, 6.7 g K_2SO_4, and 1.25 mL $HgSO_4$ solution) to distillation flask. Add a few glass beads and, after mixing, heat under a hood or with suitable ejection equipment to remove acid fumes. Boil briskly until the volume is greatly reduced (to about 25 to 50 mL) and copious white fumes are observed (fumes may be dark for samples high in organic matter). Then continue to digest for an additional 30 min. As digestion continues, colored or turbid samples will turn clear or straw-colored. After digestion, let flask and contents cool, dilute to 300 mL with water, and mix. Tilt flask and carefully add 50 mL hydroxide-thiosulfate reagent to form an alkaline layer at flask bottom. Connect flask to steamed-out distillation apparatus and shake flask to insure complete mixing. A black precipitate, HgS, will form, and the pH should exceed 11.0.

d. Distillation: Distill and collect 200 mL distillate below surface of 50 mL absorbent solution. Use plain boric acid solution when ammonia is to be determined by nesslerization and use indicating boric acid for a titrimetric finish. Use 50 mL 0.04N H_2SO_4 solution for collecting distillate for manual phenate, nesslerization, or electrode methods. Extend tip of condenser well below level of absorbent solution and do not let temperature in condenser rise above 29°C. Lower collected distillate free of contact with delivery tube and continue distillation during last 1 or 2 min to cleanse condenser.

e. Final ammonia measurement: Use the nesslerization, manual phenate, titration, or ammonia-selective electrode method, Sections 4500-NH₃.C, D, E, and F, respectively.

f. Blank: Carry a reagent blank through all steps of the procedure and apply necessary corrections to the results.

5. Calculation

See Section 4500-NH₃.C.5, D.5, E.5, or F.5.

6. Precision and Bias

Three synthetic samples containing various organic nitrogen concentrations and other constituents were analyzed by three procedural modifications of the macro-kjeldahl method: kjeldahl-nessler finish, kjeldahl-titrimetric finish, and calculation of the difference between kjeldahl nitrogen and ammonia nitrogen, both determined by a nessler finish. The results obtained by participating laboratories are summarized in Table 4500-N$_{org}$:I.

No data on the precision of the macro-kjeldahl-phenate method are available.

Sample 1 contained the following additional constituents: 400 mg Cl^-/L, 1.50 mg NH_3-N/L, 1.0 mg NO_3^--N/L, 0.5 mg PO_4^{3-}/L, and 30.0 mg SiO_2/L.

Sample 2 contained the following additional constituents: 200 mg Cl^-/L, 0.8 mg NH_3-N/L, 1.0 mg NO_3^--N/L, 5.0 mg PO_4^{3-}/L, and 15.0 mg SiO_2/L.

Sample 3 contained the following additional constituents: 10 mg Cl^-/L, 0.2 mg NH_3-N/L, 1.0 mg NO_3^--N/L, 10.0 mg PO_4^{3-}/L, and 5.0 mg SiO_2/L.

7. Bibliography

KJELDAHL, J. 1883. A new method for the determination of nitrogen in organic matter. *Z. Anal. Chem.* 22:366.

PHELPS, E.B. 1905. The determination of organic nitrogen in sewage by the Kjeldahl process. *J. Infect. Dis.* (Suppl.) 1:225.

MEEKER, E.W. & E.C. WAGNER. 1933. Titration of ammonia in the presence of boric acid. *Ind. Eng. Chem.,* Anal. Ed. 5:396.

WAGNER, E.C. 1940. Titration of ammonia in the presence of boric acid. *Ind. Eng. Chem.,* Anal. Ed. 12:771.

McKENZIE, H.A. & H.S. WALLACE. 1954. The

TABLE 4500-N$_{org}$:I. PRECISION AND BIAS DATA FOR ORGANIC NITROGEN, MACRO-KJELDAHL PROCEDURE

			Relative Standard Deviation			Relative Error		
Sample	No. of Labora-tories	Organic Nitrogen Concen-tration $\mu g/L$	Nessler Finish %	Titri-metric Finish %	Calculation of Total Kjeldahl N Minus NH$_3$-N %	Nessler Finish %	Titri-metric Finish %	Calculation of Total Kjeldahl N Minus NH$_3$-N %
1	26	200	94.8	—	—	55.0	—	—
	29	200	—	104.4	—	—	70.0	—
	15	200	—	—	68.8	—	—	70.0
2	26	800	52.1	—	—	12.5	—	—
	31	800	—	44.8	—	—	3.7	—
	16	800	—	—	52.6	—	—	8.7
3	26	1500	43.1	—	—	9.3	—	—
	30	1500	—	54.7	—	—	22.6	—
	16	1500	—	—	45.9	—	—	4.0

Kjeldahl determination of nitrogen: A critical study of digestion conditions. *Aust. J. Chem.* 7:55.

MORGAN, G.B., J.B. LACKEY & F.W. GILCREAS. 1957. Quantitative determination of organic nitrogen in water, sewage, and industrial wastes. *Anal. Chem.* 29:833.

BOLTZ, D.F., ed. 1978. Colorimetric Determination of Nonmetals. Interscience Publishers, New York, N.Y.

4500-N$_{org}$ C. Semi-Micro-Kjeldahl Method

1. General Discussion

See Section 4500-N$_{org}$.B.1.

2. Apparatus

a. Digestion apparatus: Use kjeldahl flasks with a capacity of 100 mL in a semi-micro-Kjeldahl digestion apparatus* equipped with heating elements to accomodate kjeldahl flasks and a suction outlet to vent fumes. The heating elements should provide the temperature range of 365 to 380°C for effective digestion.

b. Distillation apparatus: Use an all-glass unit equipped with a steam-generating vessel containing an immersion heater† (Figure 4500-N$_{org}$:1).

c. pH meter.

3. Reagents

All of the reagents listed for the determination of Nitrogen (Ammonia) (Section 4500-NH$_3$.B.3) and Nitrogen (Organic) macro-kjeldahl (Section 4500-N$_{org}$.B.3) are required. Prepare all reagents and dilutions with ammonia-free water.

---

*Rotary kjeldahl digestion unit, Kontes, Model K551100, or equivalent.

†ASTM E-147 or equivalent.

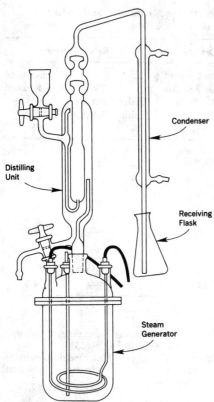

Figure 4500-N$_{org}$:1. Micro-kjeldahl distillation apparatus.

4. Procedure

a. Selection of sample volume: Determine the sample size from the following tabulation:

Organic Nitrogen in Sample mg/L	Sample Size mL
4–40	50
8–80	25
20–200	10
40–400	5

For sludge and sediment samples weigh a portion of wet sample containing between 0.2 and 2 mg organic nitrogen in a crucible

or weighing bottle. Transfer sample quantitatively to a 100-mL beaker by diluting it and rinsing the weighing dish several times with small quantities of water. Make the transfer using as small a quantity of water as possible and do not exceed a total volume of 50 mL. Measure dry weight of sample on a separate portion.

b. Ammonia removal: Pipet 50 mL sample or an appropriate volume diluted to 50 mL with water into a 100-mL beaker. Add 3 mL borate buffer and adjust to pH 9.5 with 6N NaOH, using a pH meter. Quantitatively transfer sample to a 100-mL kjeldahl flask and boil off 30 mL.

Alternatively, if ammonia removal is not required, digest samples directly as described in ¶ *c* below. Distillation following this direct digestion yields kjeldahl nitrogen concentration rather than organic nitrogen.

c. Digestion: Carefully add 10 mL digestion reagent to kjeldahl flask containing sample. Add 5 or 6 glass beads (3- to 4-mm size) to prevent bumping during digestion. Set each heating unit on the micro-kjeldahl digestion apparatus to its medium setting and heat flasks under a hood or with suitable ejection equipment to remove fumes of SO$_3$. Continue to boil briskly until solution clears (becomes colorless or a pale straw color) and copious fumes are observed. Then turn each heating unit up to its maximum setting and digest for an additional 30 min. Cool. Quantitatively transfer digested sample by diluting and rinsing several times into micro-kjeldahl distillation apparatus so that total volume in distillation apparatus does not exceed 30 mL. Add 10 mL hydroxide-thiosulfate reagent and turn on steam.

d. Distillation: Control rate of steam generation to boil contents in distillation unit so that neither escape of steam from tip of condenser nor bubbling of contents in receiving flask occurs. Distill and collect 30 to 40 mL distillate below surface of 10 mL boric acid solution contained in a 125-mL erlenmeyer flask. Use plain boric acid solution when ammonia is to be determined by nesslerization and use indicating boric acid for a titrimetric finish. Use 10 mL 0.04N H$_2$SO$_4$ solution for collecting distillate for the phenate, nessler, or electrode methods. Extend tip of condenser well below level of boric acid solution and do not let temperature in condenser rise above 29°C. Lower collected distillate free of contact with delivery tube and continue distillation during last 1 or 2 min to cleanse condenser.

e. Blank: Carry a reagent blank through all steps of procedure and apply necessary correction to results.

f. Final ammonia measurement: Determine ammonia by nesslerization, manual phenate, titration, or ammonia-selective electrode method.

5. Calculation

See Section 4500-NH$_3$.C.5, D.5, E.5, or F.5.

6. Precision and Bias

No data on the precision and bias of the semi-micro-kjeldahl method are available.

7. Bibliography

See Section 4500-N$_{org}$.B.7.

4500-O   OXYGEN (DISSOLVED)*

4500-O A.   Introduction

1. Significance

Dissolved oxygen (DO) levels in natural and wastewaters depend on the physical, chemical, and biochemical activities in the water body. The analysis for DO is a key test in water pollution and waste treatment process control.

2. Selection of Method

Two methods for DO analysis are described: the Winkler or iodometric method and its modifications and the electrometric method using membrane electrodes. The

iodometric method[1] is a titrimetric procedure based on the oxidizing property of DO while the membrane electrode procedure is based on the rate of diffusion of molecular oxygen across a membrane.[2] The choice of procedure depends on the interferences present, the accuracy desired, and, in some cases, convenience or expedience.

3. References

1. WINKLER, L.W. 1888. The determination of dissolved oxygen in water. *Berlin. Deut. Chem. Ges.* 21:2843.
2. MANCY, K.H. & T. JAFFE. 1966. Analysis of Dissolved Oxygen in Natural and Waste Waters. Publ. No. 999-WP-37, U.S. Public Health Serv., Washington, D.C.

*Approved by Standard Methods Committee, 1988.

4500-O B.   Iodometric Methods

1. Principle

The iodometric test is the most precise and reliable titrimetric procedure for DO analysis. It is based on the addition of divalent manganese solution, followed by strong alkali, to the sample in a glass-stoppered bottle. DO rapidly oxidizes an equivalent amount of the dispersed divalent manganous hydroxide precipitate to hydroxides of higher valency states. In the presence of iodide ions in an acidic solution, the oxidized manganese reverts to the divalent state, with the liberation of iodine equivalent to the original DO content. The iodine is then titrated with a standard solution of thiosulfate.

The titration end point can be detected visually, with a starch indicator, or electrometrically, with potentiometric or dead-stop techniques.[1] Experienced analysts can maintain a precision of ±50 µg/L with visual end-point detection and a precision of ±5 µg/L with electrometric end-point detection.[1,2]

The liberated iodine also can be determined directly by simple absorption spectrophotometers.[3] This method can be used on a routine basis to provide very accurate estimates for DO in the microgram-per-liter range provided that interfering particulate matter, color, and chemical interferences are absent.

2. Selection of Method

Before selecting a method consider the effect of interferences, particularly oxidizing or reducing materials that may be present in the sample. Certain oxidizing agents liberate iodine from iodides (positive interference) and some reducing agents reduce iodine to iodide (negative interference). Most organic matter is oxidized partially when the oxidized manganese precipitate is acidified, thus causing negative errors.

Several modifications of the iodometric method are given to minimize the effect of interfering materials.[2] Among the more commonly used procedures are the azide modification,[4] the permanganate modification,[5] the alum flocculation modification,[6] and the copper sulfate-sulfamic acid flocculation modification.[7,8] The azide modification (C) effectively removes interference caused by nitrite, which is the most common interference in biologically treated effluents and incubated BOD samples. Use the permanganate modification (D) in the presence of ferrous iron. When the sample contains 5 or more mg ferric iron salts/L, add potassium fluoride (KF) as the first reagent in the azide modification or after the permanganate treatment for ferrous iron. Alternately, eliminate Fe(III) interference by using 85 to 87% phosphoric acid (H_3PO_4) instead of sulfuric acid (H_2SO_4) for acidification. This procedure has not been tested for Fe(III) concentrations above 20 mg/L.

Use the alum flocculation modification (E) in the presence of suspended solids that cause interference and the copper sulfate-sulfamic acid flocculation modification (F) on activated-sludge mixed liquor.

3. Collection of Samples

Collect samples very carefully. Methods of sampling are highly dependent on source to be sampled and, to a certain extent, on method of analysis. Do not let sample remain in contact with air or be agitated, because either condition causes a change in its gaseous content. Samples from any depth in streams, lakes, or reservoirs, and samples of boiler water, need special precautions to eliminate changes in pressure and temperature. Procedures and equipment have been developed for sampling waters under pressure and unconfined waters (e.g., streams, rivers, and reservoirs). Sampling procedures and equipment needed are described in American Society for Testing and Materials Special Technical

Publication No. 148-1 and in U.S. Geological Survey Water Supply Paper No. 1454.

Collect surface water samples in narrow-mouth glass-stoppered BOD bottles of 300-mL capacity with tapered and pointed ground-glass stoppers and flared mouths. Avoid entraining or dissolving atmospheric oxygen. In sampling from a line under pressure, attach a glass or rubber tube to the tap and extend to bottom of bottle. Let bottle overflow two or three times its volume and replace stopper so that no air bubbles are entrained.

Suitable samplers for streams, ponds, or tanks of moderate depth are of the APHA type shown in Figure 4500-O:1. Use a Kemmerer-type sampler for samples collected from depths greater than 2 m. Bleed sample from bottom of sampler through a tube extending to bottom of a 250- to 300-mL BOD bottle. Fill bottle to overflowing (overflow for approximately 10 s), and prevent turbulence and formation of bubbles while filling. Record sample temperature to nearest degree Celsius or more precisely.

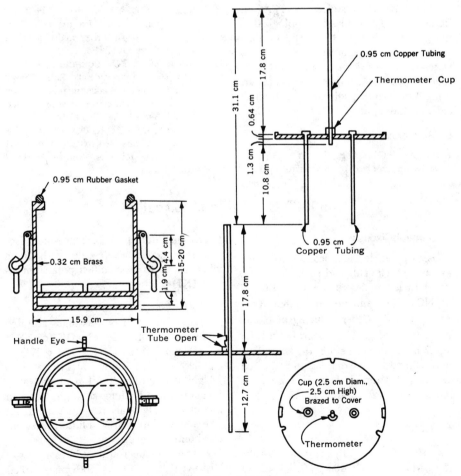

Figure 4500-O:1. DO and BOD sampler assembly.

4. Preservation of Samples

Determine DO immediately on all samples containing an appreciable oxygen or iodine demand. Samples with no iodine demand may be stored for a few hours without change after adding manganous sulfate ($MnSO_4$) solution, alkali-iodide solution, and H_2SO_4, followed by shaking in the usual way. Protect stored samples from strong sunlight and titrate as soon as possible.

For samples with an iodine demand, preserve for 4 to 8 h by adding 0.7 mL conc H_2SO_4 and 1 mL sodium azide solution (2 g NaN_3/100 mL distilled water) to the BOD bottle. This will arrest biological activity and maintain DO if the bottle is stored at the temperature of collection or water-sealed and kept at 10 to 20°C. As soon as possible, complete the procedure, using 2 mL $MnSO_4$ solution, 3 mL alkali-iodide solution, and 2 mL conc H_2SO_4.

5. References

1. POTTER, E.C. & G.E. EVERITT. 1957. Advances in dissolved oxygen microanalysis. *J. Appl. Chem.* 9:642.
2. MANCY, K.H. & T. JAFFE. 1966. Analysis of Dissolved Oxygen in Natural and Waste Waters. Publ. No. 99-WP-37, U.S. Public Health Serv., Washington, D.C.
3. OULMAN, C.S. & E.R. BAUMANN. 1956. A colorimetric method for determining dissolved oxygen. *Sewage Ind. Wastes* 28:1461.
4. ALSTERBERG, G. 1925. Methods for the determination of elementary oxygen dissolved in water in the presence of nitrite. *Biochem. Z.* 159:36.
5. RIDEAL, S. & G.G. STEWART. 1901. The determination of dissolved oxygen in waters in the presence of nitrites and of organic matter. *Analyst* 26:141.
6. RUCHHOFT, C.C. & W.A. MOORE. 1940. The determination of biochemical oxygen demand and dissolved oxygen of river mud suspensions. *Ind. Eng. Chem.*, Anal. Ed. 12:711.
7. PLACAK, O.R. & C.C. RUCHHOFT. 1941. Comparative study of the azide and Rideal-Stewart modifications of the Winkler method in the determination of biochemical oxygen demand. *Ind. Eng. Chem.*, Anal. Ed. 13:12.
8. RUCHHOFT, C.C. & O.R. PLACAK. 1942. Determination of dissolved oxygen in activated-sludge sewage mixtures. *Sewage Works J.* 14:638.

4500-O C. Azide Modification

1. General Discussion

Use the azide modification for most wastewater, effluent, and stream samples, especially if samples contain more than 50 μg NO_2^--N/L and not more than 1 mg ferrous iron/L. Other reducing or oxidizing materials should be absent. If 1 mL KF solution is added before the sample is acidified and there is no delay in titration, the method is applicable in the presence of 100 to 200 mg ferric iron/L.

2. Reagents

a. Manganous sulfate solution: Dissolve 480 g $MnSO_4 \cdot 4H_2O$, 400 g $MnSO_4 \cdot 2H_2O$, or 364 g $MnSO_4 \cdot H_2O$ in distilled water, filter, and dilute to 1 L. The $MnSO_4$ solution should not give a color with starch when added to an acidified potassium iodide (KI) solution.

b. Alkali-iodide-azide reagent:
1) For saturated or less-than-saturated samples—Dissolve 500 g NaOH (or 700 g KOH) and 135 g NaI (or 150 g KI) in distilled water and dilute to 1 L. Add 10 g NaN_3 dissolved in 40 mL distilled water. Potassium and sodium salts may be used interchangeably. This reagent should not give a color with starch solution when diluted and acidified.
2) For supersaturated samples—Dissolve 10 g NaN_3 in 500 mL distilled water. Add 480 g sodium hydroxide

(NaOH) and 750 g sodium iodide (NaI), and stir until dissolved. There will be a white turbidity due to sodium carbonate (Na_2CO_3), but this will do no harm. CAUTION—*Do not acidify this solution because toxic hydrazoic acid fumes may be produced.*

c. Sulfuric acid, H_2SO_4, conc: One milliliter is equivalent to about 3 mL alkali-iodide-azide reagent.

d. Starch: Use either an aqueous solution or soluble starch powder mixtures.

To prepare an aqueous solution, dissolve 2 g laboratory-grade soluble starch and 0.2 g salicylic acid, as a preservative, in 100 mL hot distilled water.

e. Standard sodium thiosulfate titrant: Dissolve 6.205 g $Na_2S_2O_3 \cdot 5H_2O$ in distilled water. Add 1.5 mL 6N NaOH or 0.4 g solid NaOH and dilute to 1000 mL. Standardize with bi-iodate solution.

f. Standard potassium bi-iodate solution, 0.0021M: Dissolve 812.4 mg $KH(IO_3)_2$ in distilled water and dilute to 1000 mL.

Standardization—Dissolve approximately 2 g KI, free from iodate, in an erlenmeyer flask with 100 to 150 mL distilled water. Add 1 mL 6N H_2SO_4 or a few drops of conc H_2SO_4 and 20.00 mL standard bi-iodate solution. Dilute to 200 mL and titrate liberated iodine with thiosulfate titrant, adding starch toward end of titration, when a pale straw color is reached. When the solutions are of equal strength, 20.00 mL 0.025M $Na_2S_2O_3$ should be required. If not, adjust the $Na_2S_2O_3$ solution to 0.025M.

g. Potassium fluoride solution: Dissolve 40 g $KF \cdot 2H_2O$ in distilled water and dilute to 100 mL.

3. Procedure

a. To the sample collected in a 250- to 300-mL bottle, add 1 mL $MnSO_4$ solution, followed by 1 mL alkali-iodide-azide reagent. If pipets are dipped into sample, rinse them before returning them to reagent bottles. Alternatively, hold pipet tips just above liquid surface when adding reagents. Stopper carefully to exclude air bubbles and mix by inverting bottle a few times. When precipitate has settled sufficiently (to approximately half the bottle volume) to leave clear supernate above the manganese hydroxide floc, add 1.0 mL conc H_2SO_4. Restopper and mix by inverting several times until dissolution is complete. Titrate a volume corresponding to 200 mL original sample after correction for sample loss by displacement with reagents. Thus, for a total of 2 mL (1 mL each) of $MnSO_4$ and alkali-iodide-azide reagents in a 300-mL bottle, titrate $200 \times 300/(300 - 2) = 201$ mL.

b. Titrate with 0.025M $Na_2S_2O_3$ solution to a pale straw color. Add a few drops of starch solution and continue titration to first disappearance of blue color. If end point is overrun, back-titrate with 0.0021M bi-iodate solution added dropwise, or by adding a measured volume of treated sample. Correct for amount of bi-iodate solution or sample. Disregard subsequent recolorations due to the catalytic effect of nitrite or to traces of ferric salts that have not been complexed with fluoride.

4. Calculation

a. For titration of 200 mL sample, 1 mL 0.025M $Na_2S_2O_3$ = 1 mg DO/L.

b. To express results as percent saturation at 101.3 kPa, use the solubility data in Table 4500-O:I. Equations for correcting solubilities to barometric pressures other than mean sea level and for various chlorinities are given below the table.

5. Precision and Bias

DO can be determined with a precision, expressed as a standard deviation, of about 20 μg/L in distilled water and about 60 μg/L in wastewater and secondary effluents. In the presence of appreciable interference, even with proper modifications,

TABLE 4500-O:I. SOLUBILITY OF OXYGEN IN WATER EXPOSED TO WATER-SATURATED AIR AT ATMOSPHERIC PRESSURE (101.3 KPA)[1]

Temperature °C	Oxygen Solubility mg/L					
	Chlorinity: 0	5.0	10.0	15.0	20.0	25.0
0.0	14.621	13.728	12.888	12.097	11.355	10.657
1.0	14.216	13.356	12.545	11.783	11.066	10.392
2.0	13.829	13.000	12.218	11.483	10.790	10.139
3.0	13.460	12.660	11.906	11.195	10.526	9.897
4.0	13.107	12.335	11.607	10.920	10.273	9.664
5.0	12.770	12.024	11.320	10.656	10.031	9.441
6.0	12.447	11.727	11.046	10.404	9.799	9.228
7.0	12.139	11.442	10.783	10.162	9.576	9.023
8.0	11.843	11.169	10.531	9.930	9.362	8.826
9.0	11.559	10.907	10.290	9.707	9.156	8.636
10.0	11.288	10.656	10.058	9.493	8.959	8.454
11.0	11.027	10.415	9.835	9.287	8.769	8.279
12.0	10.777	10.183	9.621	9.089	8.586	8.111
13.0	10.537	9.961	9.416	8.899	8.411	7.949
14.0	10.306	9.747	9.218	8.716	8.242	7.792
15.0	10.084	9.541	9.027	8.540	8.079	7.642
16.0	9.870	9.344	8.844	8.370	7.922	7.496
17.0	9.665	9.153	8.667	8.207	7.770	7.356
18.0	9.467	8.969	8.497	8.049	7.624	7.221
19.0	9.276	8.792	8.333	7.896	7.483	7.090
20.0	9.092	8.621	8.174	7.749	7.346	6.964
21.0	8.915	8.456	8.021	7.607	7.214	6.842
22.0	8.743	8.297	7.873	7.470	7.087	6.723
23.0	8.578	8.143	7.730	7.337	6.963	6.609
24.0	8.418	7.994	7.591	7.208	6.844	6.498
25.0	8.263	7.850	7.457	7.083	6.728	6.390
26.0	8.113	7.711	7.327	6.962	6.615	6.285
27.0	7.968	7.575	7.201	6.845	6.506	6.184
28.0	7.827	7.444	7.079	6.731	6.400	6.085
29.0	7.691	7.317	6.961	6.621	6.297	5.990
30.0	7.559	7.194	6.845	6.513	6.197	5.896
31.0	7.430	7.073	6.733	6.409	6.100	5.806
32.0	7.305	6.957	6.624	6.307	6.005	5.717
33.0	7.183	6.843	6.518	6.208	5.912	5.631
34.0	7.065	6.732	6.415	6.111	5.822	5.546
35.0	6.950	6.624	6.314	6.017	5.734	5.464
36.0	6.837	6.519	6.215	5.925	5.648	5.384
37.0	6.727	6.416	6.119	5.835	5.564	5.305
38.0	6.620	6.316	6.025	5.747	5.481	5.228
39.0	6.515	6.217	5.932	5.660	5.400	5.152
40.0	6.412	6.121	5.842	5.576	5.321	5.078
41.0	6.312	6.026	5.753	5.493	5.243	5.005
42.0	6.213	5.934	5.667	5.411	5.167	4.933
43.0	6.116	5.843	5.581	5.331	5.091	4.862
44.0	6.021	5.753	5.497	5.252	5.017	4.793
45.0	5.927	5.665	5.414	5.174	4.944	4.724

TABLE 4500-O:I, CONT.

| Temperature °C | Oxygen Solubility mg/L | | | | | |
	Chlorinity: 0	5.0	10.0	15.0	20.0	25.0
46.0	5.835	5.578	5.333	5.097	4.872	4.656
47.0	5.744	5.493	5.252	5.021	4.801	4.589
48.0	5.654	5.408	5.172	4.947	4.730	4.523
49.0	5.565	5.324	5.094	4.872	4.660	4.457
50.0	5.477	5.242	5.016	4.799	4.591	4.392

NOTE:

1. The table provides three decimal places to aid interpolation. When computing saturation values to be used with measured values, such as in computing DO deficit in a receiving water, precision of measured values will control choice of decimal places to be used.

2. Equations are available to compute DO concentration in fresh water[1-3] and in seawater[1] at equilibrium with water-saturated air. Figures and tables also are available.[3]

Calculate the equilibrium oxygen concentration, $C*$, from the equation:

$$\ln C* = -139.344\ 11 + (1.575\ 701 \times 10^5/T) - (6.642\ 308$$
$$\times 10^7/T^2) + (1.243\ 800 \times 10^{10}/T^3)$$
$$- (8.621\ 949 \times 10^{11}/T^4) - \text{Chl}\,[(3.1929) \times 10^{-2}$$
$$- (1.9428 \times 10^1/T) + (3.8673 \times 10^3/T^2)]$$

where:

$C*$ = equilibrium oxygen concentration at 101.325 kPa, mg/L,

T = temperature (°K) = °C + 273.150, (°C is between 0.0 and 40.0 in the equation; the table is accurate up to 50.0), and

Chl = chlorinity (see definition in Note 4, below).

Example 1: At 20°C and 0.000 Chl, $\ln C*$ = 2.207 442 and
$\quad\quad C*$ = 9.092 mg/L;

Example 2: At 20°C and 15.000 Chl,
$\quad\quad \ln C*$ = (2.207 442) − 15.000 (0.010 657)
$\quad\quad$ = 2.0476 and $C*$ = 7.749 mg/L.

When salinity is used, replace the chlorinity term (−Chl[...]) by:
$-S\,(1.7674 \times 10^{-2}) - (1.0754 \times 10^1/T)$
$+ (2.1407 \times 10^3/T^2)$

where:

S = salinity (see definition in Note 4, below).

3. For nonstandard conditions of pressure:

$$C_p = C* P \left[\frac{(1 - P_{wv}/P)\,(1 - \theta P)}{(1 - P_{wv})\,(1 - \theta)}\right]$$

where:

C_p = equilibrium oxygen concentration at nonstandard pressure, mg/L,

$C*$ = equilibrium oxygen concentration at standard pressure of 1 atm, mg/L.

P = nonstandard pressure, atm,

P_{wv} = partial pressure of water vapor, atm, computed from: $\ln P_{wv} = 11.8571 - (3840.70/T) - (216\ 961/T^2)$,

T = temperature, °K,

$\theta = 0.000\,975 - (1.426 \times 10^{-5}t) + (6.436 \times 10^{-8}t^2)$, and

t = temperature, °C.

N.B.: Although not explicit in the above, the quantity in brackets in the equation for C_p has dimensions of atm^{-1} per Reference 4, so that P multiplied by this quantity is dimensionless.

Also, the equation for ln P_{wv} is strictly valid for fresh water only, but for practical purposes no error is made by neglecting the effect of salinity. An equation for P_{wv} that includes the salinity factor may be found in Reference 1.

Example 3: At 20°C, 0.000 Chl, and 0.700 atm,

$$C_p = C^* P (0.990\,092) = 6.30 \text{ mg/L.}$$

4. Definitions:

Salinity: Although salinity has been defined traditionally as the total solids in water after all carbonates have been converted to oxides, all bromide and iodide have been replaced by chloride, and all organic matter has been oxidized (see Section 2520), the new scale used to define salinity is based on the electrical conductivity of seawater relative to a specified solution of KCl in water.[5] The scale is dimensionless and the traditional dimension of parts per thousand (i.e., g/kg of solution) no longer applies.

Chlorinity: Chlorinity is defined in relation to salinity as follows:

$$\text{Salinity} = 1.806\,55 \times \text{chlorinity}$$

Although chlorinity is not equivalent to chloride concentration, the factor for converting a chloride concentration in seawater to include bromide, for example, is only 1.0045 (based on the relative molecular weights and amounts of the two ions). Therefore, for practical purposes, chloride concentration (in g/kg of solution) is nearly equal to chlorinity in seawater. For wastewater, it is necessary to know the ions responsible for the solution's electrical conductivity to correct for their effect on oxygen solubility and use of the tabular value. If this is not done, the equation is inappropriate unless the relative composition of the wastewater is similar to that of seawater.

the standard deviation may be as high as 100 µg/L. Still greater errors may occur in testing waters having organic suspended solids or heavy pollution. Avoid errors due to carelessness in collecting samples, prolonging the completion of test, or selecting an unsuitable modification.

6. References

1. BENSON, B.B. & D. KRAUSE, JR. 1984. The concentration and isotopic fractionation of oxygen dissolved in freshwater and seawater in equilibrium with the atmosphere. *Limnol. Oceanogr.* 29:620.

2. BENSON, B.B. & D. KRAUSE, JR. 1980. The concentration and isotopic fractionation of gases dissolved in fresh water in equilibrium with the atmosphere: I. Oxygen. *Limnol. Oceanogr.* 25:662.

3. MORTIMER, C.H. 1981. The oxygen content of air-saturated fresh waters over ranges of temperature and atmospheric pressure of limnological interest. *Int. Assoc. Theoret. Appl. Limnol.*, Communication No. 22, Stuttgart, West Germany.

4. SULZER, F. & W.M. WESTGARTH. 1962. Continuous D. O. recording in activated sludge. *Water Sewage Works* 109: 376.

5. UNITED NATIONS EDUCATIONAL, SCIENTIFIC & CULTURAL ORGANIZATION. 1981. Background Papers and Supporting Data on the Practical Salinity Scale 1978. Tech. Paper Mar. Sci. No. 37.

4500-O D. Permanganate Modification

1. General Discussion

Use the permanganate modification only on samples containing ferrous iron. Interference from high concentrations of ferric iron (up to several hundred milligrams per liter), as in acid mine water, may be overcome by the addition of 1 mL potassium fluoride (KF) and azide, provided that the final titration is made immediately after acidification.

This procedure is ineffective for oxidation of sulfite, thiosulfate, polythionate, or the organic matter in wastewater. The error with samples containing 0.25% by volume of digester waste from the manufacture of sulfite pulp may amount to 7 to 8 mg DO/L. With such samples, use the alkali-hypochlorite modification.[1] At best, however, the latter procedure gives low results, the deviation amounting to 1 mg/L for samples containing 0.25% digester wastes.

2. Reagents

All the reagents required for Method C, and in addition:

a. Potassium permanganate solution: Dissolve 6.3 g $KMnO_4$ in distilled water and dilute to 1 L.

b. Potassium oxalate solution: Dissolve 2 g $K_2C_2O_4 \cdot H_2O$ in 100 mL distilled water; 1 mL will reduce about 1.1 mL permanganate solution.

3. Procedure

a. To a sample collected in a 250- to 300-mL bottle add, below the surface, 0.70 mL conc H_2SO_4, 1 mL $KMnO_4$ solution, and 1 mL KF solution. Stopper and mix by inverting. Never add more than 0.7 mL conc H_2SO_4 as the first step of pretreatment. Add acid with a 1-mL pipet graduated to 0.1 mL. Add sufficient $KMnO_4$ solution to obtain a violet tinge that persists for 5 min. If the permanganate color is destroyed in a shorter time, add additional $KMnO_4$ solution, but avoid large excesses.

b. Remove permanganate color completely by adding 0.5 to 1.0 mL $K_2C_2O_4$ solution. Mix well and let stand in the dark to facilitate the reaction. Excess oxalate causes low results; add only enough $K_2C_2O_4$ to decolorize the $KMnO_4$ completely without an excess of more than 0.5 mL. Complete decolorization in 2 to 10 min. If it is impossible to decolorize the sample without adding a large excess of oxalate, the DO result will be inaccurate.

c. From this point the procedure closely parallels that in Section 4500-O.C.3. Add 1 mL $MnSO_4$ solution and 3 mL alkali-iodide-azide reagent. Stopper, mix, and let precipitate settle a short time; acidify with 2 mL conc H_2SO_4. When 0.7 mL acid, 1 mL $KMnO_4$ solution, 1 mL $K_2C_2O_4$ solution, 1 mL $MnSO_4$ solution, and 3 mL alkali-iodide-azide (or a total of 6.7 mL reagents) are used in a 300-mL bottle, take $200 \times 300/(300 - 6.7) = 205$ mL for titration.

This correction is slightly in error because the $KMnO_4$ solution is nearly saturated with DO and 1 mL would add about 0.008 mg oxygen to the DO bottle. However, because precision of the method (standard deviation, 0.06 mL thiosulfate titration, or 0.012 mg DO) is 50% greater than this error, a correction is unnecessary. When substantially more $KMnO_4$ solution is used routinely, use a solution several times more concentrated so that 1 mL will satisfy the permanganate demand.

4. Reference

1. THERIAULT, E.J. & P.D. MCNAMEE. 1932. Dissolved oxygen in the presence of organic matter, hypochlorites, and sulfite wastes. *Ind. Eng. Chem.*, Anal. Ed. 4:59.

4500-O E.   Alum Flocculation Modification

1. General Discussion

Samples high in suspended solids may consume appreciable quantities of iodine in acid solution. The interference due to solids may be removed by alum flocculation.

2. Reagents

All the reagents required for the azide modification (Section 4500-O.C.2) and in addition:

a. *Alum solution:* Dissolve 10 g aluminum potassium sulfate, $AlK(SO_4)_2 \cdot 12H_2O$, in distilled water and dilute to 100 mL.

b. *Ammonium hydroxide,* NH_4OH, conc.

3. Procedure

Collect sample in a glass-stoppered bottle of 500 to 1000 mL capacity, using the same precautions as for regular DO samples. Add 10 mL alum solution and 1 to 2 mL conc NH_4OH. Stopper and invert gently for about 1 min. Let sample settle for about 10 min and siphon clear supernate into a 250- to 300-mL DO bottle until it overflows. Avoid sample aeration and keep siphon submerged at all times. Continue sample treatment as in Section 4500-O.C.3 or an appropriate modification.

4500-O F.   Copper Sulfate-Sulfamic Acid Flocculation Modification

1. General Discussion

This modification is used for biological flocs such as activated sludge mixtures, which have high oxygen utilization rates.

2. Reagents

All the reagents required for the azide modification (Section 4500-O.C.2) and, in addition:

Copper sulfate-sulfamic acid inhibitor solution: Dissolve 32 g technical-grade NH_2SO_2OH without heat in 475 mL distilled water. Dissolve 50 g $CuSO_4 \cdot 5H_2O$ in

500 mL distilled water. Mix the two solutions and add 25 mL conc acetic acid.

3. Procedure

Add 10 mL $CuSO_4$-NH_2SO_2OH inhibitor to a 1-L glass-stoppered bottle. Insert bottle in a special sampler designed so that bottle fills from a tube near bottom and overflows only 25 to 50% of bottle capacity. Collect sample, stopper, and mix by inverting. Let suspended solids settle and siphon relatively clear supernatant liquor into a 250- to 300-mL DO bottle. Continue sample treatment as rapidly as possible by the azide (Section 4500-O.C.3) or other appropriate modification.

4500-O G.   Membrane Electrode Method

1. General Discussion

Various modifications of the iodometric method have been developed to eliminate

or minimize effects of interferences; nevertheless, the method still is inapplicable to a variety of industrial and domestic wastewaters.[1] Moreover, the iodometric method is not suited for field testing and cannot be adapted easily for continuous monitoring or for DO determinations in situ.

Polarographic methods using the dropping mercury electrode or the rotating platinum electrode have not been reliable always for the DO analysis in domestic and industrial wastewaters because impurities in the test solution can cause electrode poisoning or other interferences.[2,3] With membrane-covered electrode systems these problems are minimized, because the sensing element is protected by an oxygen-permeable plastic membrane that serves as a diffusion barrier against impurities.[4-6] Under steady-state conditions the current is directly proportional to the DO concentration.*

Membrane electrodes of the polarographic[4] as well as the galvanic[5] type have been used for DO measurements in lakes and reservoirs,[8] for stream survey and control of industrial effluents,[9,10] for continuous monitoring of DO in activated sludge units,[11] and for estuarine and oceanographic studies.[12] Being completely submersible, membrane electrodes are suited for analysis in situ. Their portability and ease of operation and maintenance make them particularly convenient for field applications. In laboratory investigations, membrane electrodes have been used for continuous DO analysis in bacterial cultures, including the BOD test.[5,13]

Membrane electrodes provide an excellent method for DO analysis in polluted waters, highly colored waters, and strong waste effluents. They are recommended for use especially under conditions that are unfavorable for use of the iodometric method, or when that test and its modifications are subject to serious errors caused by interferences.

a. *Principle:* Oxygen-sensitive membrane electrodes of the polarographic or galvanic type are composed of two solid metal electrodes in contact with supporting electrolyte separated from the test solution by a selective membrane. The basic difference between the galvanic and the polarographic systems is that in the former the electrode reaction is spontaneous (similar to that in a fuel cell), while in the latter an external source of applied voltage is needed to polarize the indicator electrode. Polyethylene and fluorocarbon membranes are used commonly because they are permeable to molecular oxygen and are relatively rugged.

Membrane electrodes are commercially available in some variety. In all these instruments the "diffusion current" is linearly proportional to the concentration of molecular oxygen. The current can be converted easily to concentration units (e.g., milligrams per liter) by a number of calibration procedures.

Membrane electrodes exhibit a relatively high temperature coefficient largely due to changes in the membrane permeability.[6] The effect of temperature on the electrode sensitivity, ϕ (microamperes per milligram per liter), can be expressed by the following simplified relationship:[6]

$$\log \phi = 0.43\, mt + b$$

where:

t = temperature, °C,
m = constant that depends on the membrane material, and
b = constant that largely depends on membrane thickness.

If values of ϕ and m are determined for one temperature (ϕ_0 and t_0), it is possible to calculate the sensitivity at any desired temperature (ϕ and t) as follows:

$$\log \phi = \log \phi_0 + 0.43\, m\, (t - t_0)$$

---

*Fundamentally, the current is directly proportional to the activity of molecular oxygen.[7]

Nomographic charts for temperature correction can be constructed easily[7] and are available from some manufacturers. An example is shown in Figure 4500-O:2, in which, for simplicity, sensitivity is plotted versus temperature on semilogarithmic coordinates. Check one or two points frequently to confirm original calibration. If calibration changes, the new calibration should be parallel to the original, provided that the same membrane material is used.

Temperature compensation also can be made automatically by using thermistors in the electrode circuit.[4] However, thermistors may not compensate fully over a wide temperature range. For certain applications where high accuracy is required, use calibrated nomographic charts to correct for temperature effect.

To use the DO membrane electrode in estuarine waters or in wastewaters with varying ionic strength, correct for effect of salting-out on electrode sensitivity.[6,7] This effect is particularly significant for large changes in salt content. Electrode sensitivity varies with salt concentration according to the following relationship:

$$\log \phi_s = 0.43 \, m_s C_s + \log \phi_0$$

where:

ϕ_s, ϕ_0 = sensitivities in salt solution and distilled water, respectively,

C_s = salt concentration (preferably ionic strength), and

m_s = constant (salting-out coefficient).

If ϕ_0 and m_s are determined, it is possible to calculate sensitivity for any value of C_s. Conductivity measurements can be used to approximate salt concentration (C_s). This is particularly applicable to estuarine waters. Figure 4500-O:3 shows calibration curves for sensitivity of varying salt solutions at different temperatures.

b. Interference: Plastic films used with membrane electrode systems are permeable to a variety of gases besides oxygen, although none is depolarized easily at the indicator electrode. Prolonged use of membrane electrodes in waters containing such gases as hydrogen sulfide (H_2S) tends to lower cell sensitivity. Eliminate this interference by frequently changing and calibrating the membrane electrode.

c. Sampling: Because membrane electrodes offer the advantage of analysis in situ they eliminate errors caused by sample handling and storage. If sampling is required, use the same precautions suggested for the iodometric method.

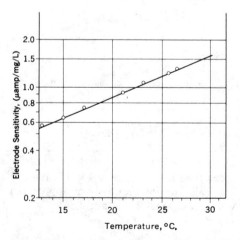

Figure 4500-O:2. Effect of temperature on electrode sensitivity.

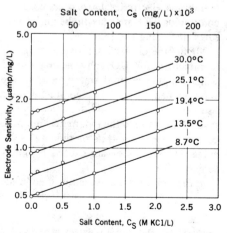

Figure 4500-O:3. The salting-out effect at different temperatures.

2. Apparatus

Oxygen-sensitive membrane electrode, polarographic or galvanic, with appropriate meter.

3. Procedure

a. Calibration: Follow manufacturer's calibration procedure exactly to obtain guaranteed precision and accuracy. Generally, calibrate membrane electrodes by reading against air or a sample of known DO concentration (determined by iodometric method) as well as in a sample with zero DO. (Add excess sodium sulfite, Na_2SO_3, and a trace of cobalt chloride, $CoCl_2$, to bring DO to zero.) Preferably calibrate with samples of water under test. Avoid an iodometric calibration where interfering substances are suspected. The following illustrate the recommended procedures:

1) Fresh water—For unpolluted samples where interfering substances are absent, calibrate in the test solution or distilled water, whichever is more convenient.

2) Salt water—Calibrate directly with samples of seawater or waters having a constant salt concentration in excess of 1000 mg/L.

3) Fresh water containing pollutants or interfering substances—Calibrate with distilled water because erroneous results occur with the sample.

4) Salt water containing pollutants or interfering substances—Calibrate with a sample of clean water containing the same salt content as the sample. Add a concentrated potassium chloride (KCl) solution (see Conductivity, Section 2510 and Table 2510:I) to distilled water to produce the same specific conductance as that in the sample. For polluted ocean waters, calibrate with a sample of unpolluted seawater.

5) Estuary water containing varying quantities of salt—Calibrate with a sample of uncontaminated seawater or distilled or tap water. Determine sample chloride or salt concentration and revise calibration to account for change of oxygen solubility in the estuary water.[7]

b. Sample measurement: Follow all precautions recommended by manufacturer to insure acceptable results. Take care in changing membrane to avoid contamination of sensing element and also trapping of minute air bubbles under the membrane, which can lead to lowered response and high residual current. Provide sufficient sample flow across membrane surface to overcome erratic response (see Figure 4500-O:4 for a typical example of the effect of stirring).

c. Validation of temperature effect: Check frequently one or two points to verify temperature correction data.

4. Precision and Bias

With most commercially available membrane electrode systems an accuracy of ±0.1 mg DO/L and a precision of ±0.05 mg DO/L can be obtained.

5. References

1. MCKEOWN, J.J., L.C. BROWN & G.W. GOVE. 1967. Comparative studies of dissolved oxygen analysis methods. *J. Water Pollut. Control Fed.* 39:1323.

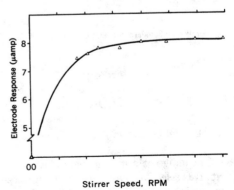

Figure 4500-O:4. **Typical trend of effect of stirring on electrode response.**

2. LYNN, W.R. & D.A. OKUN. 1955. Experience with solid platinum electrodes in the determination of dissolved oxygen. *Sewage Ind. Wastes* 27:4.

3. MANCY, K.H. & D.A. OKUN. 1960. Automatic recording of dissolved oxygen in aqueous systems containing surface active agents. *Anal. Chem.* 32:108.

4. CARRITT, D.E. & J.W. KANWISHER. 1959. An electrode system for measuring dissolved oxygen. *Anal. Chem.* 31:5.

5. MANCY, K.H. & W.C. WESTGARTH. 1962. A galvanic cell oxygen analyzer. *J. Water Pollut. Control Fed.* 34:1037.

6. MANCY, K.H., D.A. OKUN & C.N. REILLEY. 1962. A galvanic cell oxygen analyzer. *J. Electroanal. Chem.* 4:65.

7. MANCY, K.H. & T. JAFFE. 1966. Analysis of Dissolved Oxygen in Natural and Waste Waters. Publ. No. 999-WP-37, U.S. Public Health Serv., Washington, D.C.

8. WEISS, C.M. & R.T. OGLESBY. 1963. Instrumentation for monitoring water quality in reservoirs. American Water Works Assoc. 83rd Annual Conf., New York, N.Y.

9. CLEARY, E.J. 1962. Introducing the ORSANCO robot monitor. *Proc. Water Quality Meas. Instrum.* Publ. No. 108, U.S. Public Health Serv., Washington, D.C.

10. MACKERETH, F.J.H. 1964. An improved galvanic cell for determination of oxygen concentrations in fluids. *J. Sci. Instrum.* 41:38.

11. SULZER, F. & W.M. WESTGARTH. 1962. Continuous D.O. recording in activated sludge. *Water Sewage Works* 109:376.

12. DUXBURY, A.C. 1963. Calibration and use of a galvanic type oxygen electrode in field work. *Limnol. Oceanogr.* 8:483.

13. LIPNER, H.J., L.R. WITHERSPOON & V.C. CHAMPEAUS. 1964. Adaptation of a galvanic cell for microanalysis of oxygen. *Anal. Chem.* 36:204.

4500-O₃   OZONE (RESIDUAL)* (PROPOSED)

4500-O₃ A.   Introduction

Ozone, a potent germicide, is used also as an oxidizing agent for the destruction of

---

*Approved by Standard Methods Committee, 1988.

organic compounds producing taste and odor in drinking water, for the destruction of organic coloring matter, and for the oxidation of reduced iron or manganese salts to insoluble oxides.

4500-O₃ B.   Indigo Colorimetric Method

1. General Discussion

The indigo colorimetric method is quantitative, selective, and simple; it replaces methods based on the measurement of total oxidant. The method is applicable to lake water, river infiltrate, manganese-contain-

ing groundwaters, extremely hard groundwaters, and even biologically treated domestic wastewaters.

a. Principle: In acidic solution, ozone rapidly decolorizes indigo. The decrease in absorbance is linear with increasing concentration. The proportionality constant at

600 nm is 0.42 ± 0.01/cm/mg/L ($\Delta\epsilon$ = 20 000/$M \cdot$cm) compared to the ultraviolet absorption of pure ozone of ϵ = 2950/$M \cdot$cm at 258 nm).[1]

b. Interferences: Hydrogen peroxide (H_2O_2) and organic peroxides decolorize the indigo reagent very slowly. H_2O_2 does not interfere if ozone is measured in less than 6 h after adding reagents. Organic peroxides may react more rapidly. Fe(III) does not interfere. Mn(II) does not interfere but it is oxidized by ozone to forms that decolorize the reagent. Correct for this interference by making the measurement relative to a blank in which the ozone has been destroyed selectively. Without the corrective procedure, 0.1 mg/L ozonated manganese gives a response of about 0.08 mg/L apparent ozone. Chlorine also interferes but it can be masked by malonic acid. Bromine, which can be formed by oxidation of Br⁻, interferes (1 mole HOBr corresponds to 0.4 mole ozone).

c. Minimum detectable concentration: For the spectrophotometric procedure using thermostated cells and a high-quality photometer, the low-range procedure will measure down to 2 μg O₃/L. For the visual method the detection limit is 10 μg/L.

2. Apparatus

a. Photometer: Spectrophotometer or filter colorimeter for use at 600 ± 5 nm.

b. Glass cylinders (for visual procedure): 100-mL graduated glass cylinders, preferably with flat bottoms.

3. Reagents

a. Indigo stock solution: Add about 500 mL distilled water and 1 mL conc phosphoric acid to a 1-L volumetric flask. With stirring, add 770 mg potassium indigo trisulfonate, $C_{16}H_7N_2O_{11}S_3K_3$ (commercially available at about 80 to 85% purity). Fill to mark with distilled water. A 1:100 dilution exhibits an absorbance of 0.20 ± 0.010 cm at 600 nm. The stock solution is

stable for about 4 months when stored in the dark. Discard when absorbance of a 1:100 dilution falls below 0.16/cm.

b. Indigo reagent I: To a 1-L volumetric flask add 20 mL indigo stock solution, 10 g sodium dihydrogen phosphate (NaH_2PO_4), and 7 mL conc phosphoric acid. Dilute to mark. Prepare solution fresh when its absorbance decreases to less than 80% of its initial value, typically within a week.

c. Indigo reagent II: Proceed as with indigo reagent I, but add 100 mL indigo stock solution instead of 20 mL.

d. Malonic acid reagent: Dissolve 5 g malonic acid in water and dilute to 100 mL.

e. Glycine reagent: Dissolve 7 g glycine in water and dilute to 100 mL.

4. Procedure

a. Spectrophotometric procedure:

1) Concentration range 0.01 to 0.1 mg O₃/L—Add 10.0 mL indigo reagent I to two 100-mL volumetric flasks. Fill one flask (blank) to mark with distilled water. Fill other flask to mark with sample. Add sample so that completely decolorized zones are eliminated quickly by stirring but no ozone degassing occurs. Measure absorbance of both solutions at 600 ± 5 nm as soon as possible but at least within 4 h. Preferably use 10-cm cells. Calculate the ozone concentration from the difference between the absorbances found in sample and blank (¶ 5a below). (NOTE: A maximum delay of 4 h before spectrophotometric reading can be tolerated only for drinking water samples. For other sample types test the time drift.)

2) Range 0.05 to 0.5 mg O₃/L—Proceed as above using 10.0 mL indigo reagent II instead of reagent I. Preferably measure absorbance in 4- or 5-cm cells.

3) Concentrations greater than 0.3 mg O₃/L—Proceed using indigo reagent II, but for these higher ozone concentrations

use a correspondingly smaller sample volume. Dilute resulting mixture to 100 mL with distilled water. Use a glass pipet for dosing sample; let sample flow through an erlenmeyer flask for at least 1 min without generating bubbles. Rinse pipet with sample and add measured amount to flask while keeping the pipet tip below the surface.

4) Control of interferences—In presence of chlorine, place 1 mL malonic acid reagent in both flasks before adding sample and/or filling to mark. Measure absorbance as soon as possible, within 60 min (Br⁻, Br_2, and HOBr are only partially masked by malonic acid).

In presence of manganese prepare a blank solution using sample, in which ozone is selectively destroyed by addition of glycine. Place 0.1 mL glycine reagent in 100-mL volumetric flask (blank) and 10.0 mL indigo reagent II in second flask (sample). Pipet exactly the same volume of sample into each flask. Adjust dose so that decolorization in second flask is easily visible but complete bleaching does not result (maximum 80 mL).

Insure that pH of glycine/sample mixture in blank flask (before adding indigo) is not below 6 because reaction between ozone and glycine becomes very slow at low pH. Stopper flasks and mix by carefully inverting. Add 10.0 mL indigo reagent II to blank flask only 30 to 60 s after sample addition. Fill both flasks to the mark with ozone-free water and mix thoroughly. Measure absorbance of both solutions at comparable contact times of approximately 30 to 60 min (after this time, residual manganese oxides further discolor indigo only slowly and the drift of absorbance in blank and sample become comparable). Reduced absorbance in blank flask results from manganese oxides while that in sample flask is due to ozone plus manganese oxide.

5) Calibration—Because ozone is unstable, base measurements on known and constant loss of absorbance of the indigo

reagent ($f = 0.42 \pm 0.01$/cm/mg O_3/L). For maximum accuracy analyze the lot of potassium indigo trisulfonate (no commercial lot has been found to deviate from $f = 0.42$) using the iodometric procedure.

When using a filter photometer, readjust the conversion factor, f, by comparing photometer sensitivity with absorbance at 600 nm by an accurate spectrophotometer.

b. *Visual procedure*:

1) Concentration range 0.01 to 0.1 mg O_3/L—Add 10.0 mL indigo reagent I to each of two identical 100-mL graduated glass cylinders. Fill reference cylinder (blank) to the mark with distilled water and other cylinder with sample. Add sample to cylinder so that completely decolorized zones are eliminated quickly by mixing but no degassing occurs. Pour off blank by portions until liquid height gives the same apparent color intensity as the sample when viewed from top. Record volume in blank cylinder. Color comparisons may be made up to 4 h after sample addition.

2) Concentrations greater than 0.1 mg O_3/L—Proceed as above, adding either 30 or 45 mL of sample and dilute to the mark.

3) Manganese-containing waters—The visual method is not suitable for these waters when the manganese concentration is comparable to that of the ozone because the difference measurement becomes too inaccurate.

5. Calculations

a. *Spectrophotometric procedure*:

$$\text{mg } O_3/L = \frac{100 \times \Delta A}{f \times b \times V}$$

where:

ΔA = difference in absorbance between sample and blank,
b = path length of cell, cm,
V = volume of sample, mL (normally 90 mL), and
f = 0.42.

The factor f is based on a sensitivity factor of 20 000/cm for the change of absorbance (600 nm) per mole of added ozone per liter. It was calibrated by iodometric titration. The UV absorbance of ozone in pure water may serve as a secondary standard: the factor $f = 0.42$ corresponds to an absorption coefficient for aqueous ozone, $\epsilon = 2950/M \cdot$ cm at 258 nm.

b. Visual procedure:

$$\text{mg O}_3/\text{L} = \frac{(100 - V) \times k}{100}$$

where:

V = volume of reference solution in blank cylinder, mL, and

k = conversion factor for indigo stock solution, calibrated by a spectrophotometric analysis of ozone. The value is about 0.10 mg O₃/L if the 1:100 dilution gives an absorbance of 0.19/cm.

When adding only 45 or 30 mL of sample, the conversion factor becomes $2k$ or $3k$, respectively.

6. Precision and Bias

a. Spectrophotometric procedure: In the absence of interferences, the relative error is less than 5% without special sampling setups. In laboratory testing this may be reduced to 1%.

Because this method is based on the differences in absorbance between the sample and blank (ΔA) the method is not applicable in the presence of chlorine. If the manganese content exceeds the ozone, precision is reduced. If the ratio of manganese to ozone is less than 10:1, ozone concentrations above 0.02 mg/L may be determined with a relative error of less than 20%.

b. Visual procedure: Duplicate determinations gave an average deviation of 1 to 1.5% within the pair. If the manganese concentration is comparable to that of ozone, this method is not applicable.

7. Reference

1. HOIGNÉ, J. & H. BADER. 1980. Bestimmung von Ozon und Chlordioxid im Wasser mit der Indigo-Methode. *Vom Wasser* 55:261.

8. Bibliography

THÉNARD, A. & P. THÉNARD. 1872. Mémoire sur l'action comparée de l'ozone sur le sulfate d'indigo et l'acide arsénieux. *Comptes Rend. Acad. Sci.* 75:458.

BADER, H. & J. HOIGNÉ. 1981. Determination of ozone in water by the indigo method. *Water Res.* 15:449.

BADER, H. & J. HOIGNÉ. 1982. Colorimetric method for the measurement of aqueous ozone based on the decolorization of indigo derivatives. *In* W.J. Masschelein, ed. Ozonization Manual for Water and Wastewater Treatment. John Wiley & Sons, New York, N.Y.

BADER, H. & J. HOIGNÉ. 1982. Determination of ozone in water by the indigo method: A submitted standard method. *Ozone: Sci. Eng.* 4:169.

GILBERT, E. & J. HOIGNÉ. 1983. Messung von Ozon in Wasserwerken; Vergleich der DPD- und Indigo-Methode. *GWF-Wasser/Abwasser* 124:527.

HAAG, W.R. & J. HOIGNÉ. 1983. Ozonation of bromide-containing waters: kinetics of formation of hypobromous acid and bromate. *Environ. Sci. Technol.* 17:261.

STRAKA, M.R., G.E. PACEY & G. GORDON. 1984. Residual ozone determination by flow injection analysis. *Anal. Chem.* 56:1973.

STRAKA, M.R., G. GORDON & G.E. PACEY. 1985. Residual aqueous ozone determination by gas diffusion flow injection analysis. *Anal. Chem.* 57:1799.

GORDON, G. & G.E. PACEY. 1986. An introduction to the chemical reactions of ozone pertinent to its analysis. *In* R.G. Rice, L.J. Bollyky & W.J. Lacy, eds. Analytical Aspects of Ozone Treatment of Water and Wastewater—A Monograph. Lewis Publishers, Inc., Chelsea, Mich.

4500-P   PHOSPHORUS*

4500-P   A.   Introduction

1. Occurrence

Phosphorus occurs in natural waters and in wastewaters almost solely as phosphates. These are classified as orthophosphates, condensed phosphates (pyro-, meta-, and other polyphosphates), and organically bound phosphates. They occur in solution, in particles or detritus, or in the bodies of aquatic organisms.

These forms of phosphate arise from a variety of sources. Small amounts of certain condensed phosphates are added to some water supplies during treatment. Larger quantities of the same compounds may be added when the water is used for laundering or other cleaning, because these materials are major constituents of many commercial cleaning preparations. Phosphates are used extensively in the treatment of boiler waters. Orthophosphates applied to agricultural or residential cultivated land as fertilizers are carried into surface waters with storm runoff and to a lesser extent with melting snow. Organic phosphates are formed primarily by biological processes. They are contributed to sewage by body wastes and food residues, and also may be formed from orthophosphates in biological treatment processes or by receiving water biota.

Phosphorus is essential to the growth of organisms and can be the nutrient that limits the primary productivity of a body of water. In instances where phosphate is a growth-limiting nutrient, the discharge of raw or treated wastewater, agricultural drainage, or certain industrial wastes to that water may stimulate the growth of photosynthetic aquatic micro- and macro-organisms in nuisance quantities.

Phosphates also occur in bottom sediments and in biological sludges, both as precipitated inorganic forms and incorporated into organic compounds.

2. Definition of Terms

Phosphorus analyses embody two general procedural steps: (a) conversion of the phosphorus form of interest to dissolved orthophosphate, and (b) colorimetric determination of dissolved orthophosphate. The separation of phosphorus into its various forms is defined analytically but the analytical differentiations have been selected so that they may be used for interpretive purposes.

Filtration through a 0.45-μm-pore-diam membrane filter separates dissolved from suspended forms of phosphorus. No claim is made that filtration through 0.45-μm filters is a true separation of suspended and dissolved forms of phosphorus; it is merely a convenient and replicable analytical technique designed to make a gross separation.

Membrane filtration is selected over depth filtration because of the greater likelihood of obtaining a consistent separation of particle sizes. Prefiltration through a glass fiber filter may be used to increase the filtration rate.

Phosphates that respond to colorimetric tests without preliminary hydrolysis or oxidative digestion of the sample are termed "reactive phosphorus." While reactive phosphorus is largely a measure of orthophosphate, a small fraction of any condensed phosphate present usually is hydrolyzed unavoidably in the procedure. Reactive phosphorus occurs in both dissolved and suspended forms.

Acid hydrolysis at boiling-water temperature converts dissolved and particulate condensed phosphates to dissolved ortho-

---

*Approved by Standard Methods Committee, 1988.

phosphate. The hydrolysis unavoidably releases some phosphate from organic compounds, but this may be reduced to a minimum by judicious selection of acid strength and hydrolysis time and temperature. The term "acid-hydrolyzable phosphorus" is preferred over "condensed phosphate" for this fraction.

The phosphate fractions that are converted to orthophosphate only by oxidation destruction of the organic matter present are considered "organic" or "organically bound" phosphorus. The severity of the oxidation required for this conversion depends on the form—and to some extent on the amount—of the organic phosphorus present. Like reactive phosphorus and acid-hydrolyzable phosphorus, organic phosphorus occurs both in the dissolved and suspended fractions.

The total phosphorus as well as the dissolved and suspended phosphorus fractions each may be divided analytically into the three chemical types that have been described: reactive, acid-hydrolyzable, and organic phosphorus. Figure 4500-P:1 shows the steps for analysis of individual phosphorus fractions. As indicated, determinations usually are conducted only on the unfiltered and filtered samples. Suspended fractions generally are determined by difference.

3. Selection of Method

a. Digestion methods: Because phosphorus may occur in combination with organic matter, a digestion method to determine total phosphorus must be able to oxidize organic matter effectively to release phosphorus as orthophosphate. Three digestion methods are given in Section 4500-P.B.3, 4, and 5. The perchloric acid method, the most drastic and time-consuming method, is recommended only for particularly difficult samples such as sediments. The nitric acid-sulfuric acid method is recommended for most samples. By far the simplest method is the persulfate oxidation technique. It is recommended that this method be checked against one or more of the more drastic digestion techniques and be adopted if identical recoveries are obtained.

After digestion, determine liberated orthophosphate by Method C, D, or E. The colorimetric method used, rather than the digestion procedure, governs in matters of interference and minimum detectable concentration.

b. Colorimetric methods: Three methods of orthophosphate determination are described. Selection depends largely on the concentration range of orthophosphate. The vanadomolybdophosphoric acid method (C) is most useful for routine analyses in the range of 1 to 20 mg P/L. The stannous chloride method (D) or the ascorbic acid method (E) is more suited for the range of 0.01 to 6 mg P/L. An extraction step is recommended for the lower levels of this range and when interferences must be overcome. An automated version of the ascorbic acid method F also is presented.

4. Precision and Bias

To aid in method selection, Table 4500-P:I presents the results of various combinations of digestions, hydrolysis, and colorimetric techniques for three synthetic samples of the following compositions:

Sample 1: 100 μg orthophosphate phosphorus (PO_4^{3-}-P)/L, 80 μg condensed phosphate phosphorus/L (sodium hexametaphosphate), 30 μg organic phosphorus/L (adenylic acid), 1.5 mg NH_3-N/L, 0.5 mg NO_3-N/L, and 400 mg Cl^-/L.

Sample 2: 600 μg PO_4^{3-}-P/L, 300 μg condensed phosphate phosphorus/L (sodium hexametaphosphate), 90 μg organic phosphorus/L (adenylic acid), 0.8 mg NH_3-N/L, 5.0 mg NO^-_3-N/L, and 400 mg Cl^-/L.

Sample 3: 7.00 mg PO_4^{3-}-P/L, 3.00 mg condensed phosphate phosphorus/L (sodium hexametaphosphate), 0.230 mg organic phosphorus/L (adenylic acid), 0.20 mg NH_3-N/L, 0.05 mg NO_3^--N/L, and 400 mg Cl^-/L.

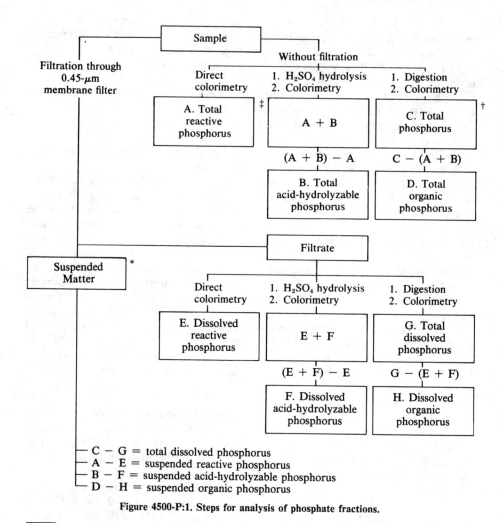

C − G = total dissolved phosphorus
A − E = suspended reactive phosphorus
B − F = suspended acid-hydrolyzable phosphorus
D − H = suspended organic phosphorus

Figure 4500-P:1. Steps for analysis of phosphate fractions.

_____

*Direct determination of phosphorus on the membrane filter containing suspended matter will be required where greater precision than that obtained by difference is desired. Digest filter with HNO₃ and follow by perchloric acid. Then perform colorimetry.

†Total phosphorus measurements on highly saline samples may be difficult because of precipitation of large quantities of salt as a result of digestion techniques that drastically reduce sample volume. For total phosphorus analyses on such samples, directly determine total dissolved phosphorus and total suspended phosphorus and add the results.

‡In determination of total dissolved or total suspended reactive phosphorus, anomalous results may be obtained on samples containing large amounts of suspended sediments. Very often results depend largely on the degree of agitation and mixing to which samples are subjected during analysis because of a time-dependent desorption of orthophosphate from the suspended particles.

5. Sampling and Storage

If phosphorus forms are to be differentiated, filter sample immediately after collection. Preserve by freezing at or below −10°C. Add 40 mg HgCl₂/L to the samples, especially when they are to be stored for long periods. CAUTION: *HgCl₂ is a hazardous substance; take appropriate precautions in disposal.* Do not add either acid or

TABLE 4500-P:I. PRECISION AND BIAS DATA FOR MANUAL PHOSPHORUS METHODS

Method	Phosphorus Concentration			No. of Laboratories	Relative Standard Deviation %	Relative Error %
	Ortho-phosphate $\mu g/L$	Poly-phosphate $\mu g/L$	Total $\mu g/L$			
Vanadomolybdophosphoric	100			45	75.2	21.6
acid	600			43	19.6	10.8
	7000			44	8.6	5.4
Stannous chloride	100			45	25.5	28.7
	600			44	14.2	8.0
	7000			45	7.6	4.3
Ascorbic acid	100			3	9.1	10.0
	600			3	4.0	4.4
	7000			3	5.2	4.9
Acid hydrolysis +		80		37	106.8	7.4
vanadomolybdophosphoric		300		38	66.5	14.0
acid		3000		37	36.1	23.5
Acid hydrolysis + stannous		80		39	60.1	12.5
chloride		300		36	47.6	21.7
		3000		38	37.4	22.8
Persulfate +			210	32	55.8	1.6
vanadomolybdophosphoric			990	32	23.9	2.3
acid			10 230	31	6.5	0.3
Sulfuric-nitric acids +			210	23	65.6	20.9
vanadomolybdophosphoric			990	22	47.3	0.6
acid			10 230	20	7.0	0.4
Perchloric acid +			210	4	33.5	45.2
vanadomolybdophosphoric			990	5	20.3	2.6
acid			10 230	6	11.7	2.2
Persulfate + stannous			210	29	28.1	9.2
chloride			990	30	14.9	12.3
			10 230	29	11.5	4.3
Sulfuric-nitric acids +			210	20	20.8	1.2
stannous chloride			990	17	8.8	3.2
			10 230	19	7.5	0.4

$CHCl_3$ as a preservative when phosphorus forms are to be determined. If total phosphorus alone is to be determined, add 1 mL conc HCl/L or freeze without any additions.

Do not store samples containing low concentrations of phosphorus in plastic bottles unless kept in a frozen state because phosphates may be adsorbed onto the walls of plastic bottles.

Rinse all glass containers with hot dilute HCl, then rinse several times in distilled water. Never use commercial detergents containing phosphate for cleaning glassware used in phosphate analysis.

6. Bibliography

BLACK, C.A., D.D. EVANS, J.L. WHITE, L.E. ENSMINGER & F.E. CLARK, eds. 1965. Methods of Soil Analysis, Part 2. Chemical and Microbiological Properties. American Soc. Agronomy, Madison, Wisc.

JENKINS, D. 1965. A study of methods suitable for the analysis and preservation of phosphorus forms in an estuarine environment. SERL Rep. No. 65-18, Sanitary Engineering Research Lab., Univ. California, Berkeley.

LEE, G.F. 1967. Analytical chemistry of plant nutrients. *In* Proc. Int. Conf. Eutrophication, Madison, Wisc.

FITZGERALD, G.P. & S.L. FAUST. 1967. Effect of water sample preservation methods on the release of phosphorus from algae. *Limnol. Oceanogr.* 12:332.

4500-P B.   Sample Preparation

For information on selection of digestion method (¶s 3 through 5 below), see 4500-P.A.3 *a*.

1. Preliminary Filtration

Filter samples for determination of dissolved reactive phosphorus, dissolved acid-hydrolyzable phosphorus, and total dissolved phosphorus through 0.45-μm membrane filters. A glass fiber filter may be used to prefilter hard-to-filter samples.

Wash membrane filters by soaking in distilled water before use because they may contribute significant amounts of phosphorus to samples containing low concentrations of phosphate. Use one of two washing techniques: (*a*) soak 50 filters in 2 L distilled water for 24 h; (*b*) soak 50 filters in 2 L distilled water for 1 h, change distilled water, and soak filters an additional 3 h. Membrane filters also may be washed by running several 100-mL portions of distilled water through them. This procedure requires more frequent determination of blank values to ensure consistency in washing and to evaluate different lots of filters.

2. Preliminary Acid Hydrolysis

The acid-hydrolyzable phosphorus content of the sample is defined operationally as the difference between reactive phosphorus as measured in the untreated sample and phosphate found after mild acid hydrolysis. Generally, it includes condensed phosphates such as pyro-, tripoly-, and higher-molecular-weight species such as hexametaphosphate. In addition, some natural waters contain organic phosphate compounds that are hydrolyzed to orthophosphate under the test conditions. Polyphosphates generally do not respond to reactive phosphorus tests but can be hydrolyzed to orthophosphate by boiling with acid.

After hydrolysis, determine reactive phosphorus by a colorimetric method (C, D, or E). Interferences, precision, bias, and sensitivity will depend on the colorimetric method used.

a. Apparatus:

Autoclave or pressure cooker, capable of operating at 98 to 137 kPa.

b. Reagents:

1) *Phenolphthalein indicator aqueous solution.*

2) *Strong acid solution:* Slowly add 300 mL conc H_2SO_4 to about 600 mL distilled water. When cool, add 4.0 mL conc HNO_3 and dilute to 1 L.

3) *Sodium hydroxide,* NaOH, 6*N*.

c. Procedure: To 100-mL sample or a portion diluted to 100 mL, add 0.05 mL (1 drop) phenolphthalein indicator solution. If a red color develops, add strong acid solution dropwise, to just discharge the color. Then add 1 mL more.

Boil gently for at least 90 min, adding distilled water to keep the volume between 25 and 50 mL. Alternatively, heat for 30 min in an autoclave or pressure cooker at 98 to 137 kPa. Cool, neutralize to a faint pink color with NaOH solution, and restore to the original 100-mL volume with distilled water.

Prepare a calibration curve by carrying a series of standards containing orthophosphate (see colorimetric method C, D, or E) through the hydrolysis step. Do not use orthophosphate standards without hydrolysis, because the salts added in hydrolysis cause an increase in the color intensity in some methods.

Determine reactive phosphorus content of treated portions, using Method C, D, or E. This gives the sum of polyphosphate and orthophosphate in the sample. To calculate its content of acid-hydrolyzable phosphorus, determine reactive phosphorus in a sample portion that has not been hydrolyzed, using the same colorimetric method as for treated sample, and subtract.

3. Perchloric Acid Digestion

a. Apparatus:

1) *Hot plate:* A 30- $\times$ 50-cm heating surface is adequate.

2) *Safety shield.*

3) *Safety goggles.*

4) *Erlenmeyer flasks,* 125-mL, acid-washed and rinsed with distilled water.

b. Reagents:

1) *Nitric acid,* HNO_3, conc.

2) *Perchloric acid,* $HClO_4 \cdot 2H_2O$, purchased as 70 to 72% $HClO_4$, reagent-grade.

3) *Sodium hydroxide,* NaOH, 6*N*.

4) *Methyl orange indicator solution.*

5) *Phenolphthalein indicator aqueous solution.*

c. Procedure: CAUTION—*Heated mixtures of $HClO_4$ and organic matter may explode violently. Avoid this hazard by taking the following precautions: (a) Do not add $HClO_4$ to a hot solution that may contain organic matter. (b) Always initiate digestion of samples containing organic matter with HNO_3. Complete digestion using the mixture of HNO_3 and $HClO_4$. (c) Do not fume with $HClO_4$ in ordinary hoods. Use hoods especially constructed for $HClO_4$ fuming or a glass fume eradicator* connected to a water pump. (d) Never let samples being digested with $HClO_4$ evaporate to dryness.*

Measure sample containing the desired amount of phosphorus (this will be determined by whether Method C, D, or E is to be used) into a 125-mL erlenmeyer flask. Acidify to methyl orange with conc HNO_3, add another 5 mL conc HNO_3, and evaporate on a steam bath or hot plate to 15 to 20 mL.

Add 10 mL each of conc HNO_3 and $HClO_4$ to the 125-mL conical flask, cooling the flask between additions. Add a few boiling chips, heat on a hot plate, and evaporate gently until dense white fumes of $HClO_4$ just appear. If solution is not clear, cover neck of flask with a watch glass and keep solution barely boiling until it clears. If necessary, add 10 mL more HNO_3 to aid oxidation.

Cool digested solution and add 1 drop aqueous phenolphthalein solution. Add 6*N*

---

*GFS Chemical Co., Columbus, Ohio, or equivalent.

NaOH solution until the solution just turns pink. If necessary, filter neutralized solution and wash filter liberally with distilled water. Make up to 100 mL with distilled water.

Determine the PO_4^{3-}-P content of the treated sample by Method C, D, or E.

Prepare a calibration curve by carrying a series of standards containing orthophosphate (see Method C, D, or E) through digestion step. Do not use orthophosphate standards without treatment.

4. Sulfuric Acid-Nitric Acid Digestion

a. Apparatus:

1) *Digestion rack:* An electrically or gas-heated digestion rack with provision for withdrawal of fumes is recommended. Digestion racks typical of those used for micro-kjeldahl digestions are suitable.

2) *Micro-kjeldahl flasks.*

b. Reagents:

1) *Sulfuric acid,* H_2SO_4, conc.

2) *Nitric acid,* HNO_3, conc.

3) *Phenolphthalein indicator aqueous solution.*

4) *Sodium hydroxide,* NaOH, 1*N*.

c. Procedure: Into a micro-kjeldahl flask, measure a sample containing the desired amount of phosphorus (this is determined by the colorimetric method used). Add 1 mL conc H_2SO_4 and 5 mL conc HNO_3.

Digest to a volume of 1 mL and then continue until solution becomes colorless to remove HNO_3.

Cool and add approximately 20 mL distilled water, 0.05 mL (1 drop) phenolphthalein indicator, and as much 1*N* NaOH solution as required to produce a faint pink tinge. Transfer neutralized solution, filtering if necessary to remove particulate material or turbidity, into a 100-mL volumetric flask. Add filter washings to flask and adjust sample volume to 100 mL with distilled water.

Determine phosphorus by Method C, D,

or E, for which a separate calibration curve has been constructed by carrying standards through the acid digestion procedure.

5. Persulfate Digestion Method

a. Apparatus:

1) *Hot plate:* A 30- × 50-cm heating surface is adequate.

2) *Autoclave:* An autoclave or pressure cooker capable of developing 98 to 137 kPa may be used in place of a hot plate.

3) *Glass scoop,* to hold required amounts of persulfate crystals.

b. Reagents:

1) *Phenolphthalein indicator aqueous solution.*

2) *Sulfuric acid solution:* Carefully add 300 mL conc H_2SO_4 to approximately 600 mL distilled water and dilute to 1 L with distilled water.

3) *Ammonium persulfate,* $(NH_4)_2S_2O_8$, solid, or potassium persulfate, $K_2S_2O_8$, solid.

4) *Sodium hydroxide,* NaOH, 1*N*.

c. Procedure: Use 50 mL or a suitable portion of thoroughly mixed sample. Add 0.05 mL (1 drop) phenolphthalein indicator solution. If a red color develops, add H_2SO_4 solution dropwise to just discharge the color. Then add 1 mL H_2SO_4 solution and either 0.4 g solid $(NH_4)_2S_2O_8$ or 0.5 g solid $K_2S_2O_8$.

Boil gently on a preheated hot plate for 30 to 40 min or until a final volume of 10 mL is reached. Organophosphorus compounds such as AMP may require as much as 1.5 to 2 hr for complete digestion. Cool, dilute to 30 mL with distilled water, add 0.05 mL (1 drop) phenolphthalein indicator solution, and neutralize to a faint pink color with NaOH. Alternatively, heat for 30 min in an autoclave or pressure cooker at 98 to 137 kPa. Cool, add 0.05 mL (1 drop) phenolphthalein indicator solution, and neutralize to a faint pink color with NaOH. Make up to 100 mL with distilled water. In some samples a precipitate may form at this stage, but do not filter. For any subsequent subdividing of the sample, shake well. The precipitate (which is possibly a calcium phosphate) redissolves under the acid conditions of the colorimetric reactive phosphorus test. Determine phosphorus by Method C, D, or E, for which a separate calibration curve has been constructed by carrying standards through the persulfate digestion procedure.

6. Bibliography

LEE, G.F., N.L. CLESCERI & G.P. FITZGERALD. 1965. Studies on the analysis of phosphates in algal cultures. *J. Air Water Pollut.* 9:715.

SHANNON, J.E. & G.F. LEE. 1966. Hydrolysis of condensed phosphates in natural waters. *J. Air Water Pollut.* 10:735.

GALES, M.E., JR., E.C. JULIAN & R.C. KRONER. 1966. Method for quantitative determination of total phosphorus in water. *J. Amer. Water Works Assoc.* 58:1363.

4500-P C.   Vanadomolybdophosphoric Acid Colorimetric Method

1. General Discussion

a. Principle: In a dilute orthophosphate solution, ammonium molybdate reacts under acid conditions to form a heteropoly acid, molybdophosphoric acid. In the presence of vanadium, yellow vanadomolybdophosphoric acid is formed. The intensity of the yellow color is proportional to phosphate concentration.

b. Interference: Positive interference is caused by silica and arsenate only if the sample is heated. Negative interferences are caused by arsenate, fluoride, thorium, bismuth, sulfide, thiosulfate, thiocyanate, or excess molybdate. Blue color is caused by ferrous iron but this does not affect results if ferrous iron concentration is less than 100 mg/L. Sulfide interference may be removed by oxidation with bromine water. Ions that do not interfere in concentrations up to 1000 mg/L are Al^{3+}, Fe^{3+}, Mg^{2+}, Ca^{2+}, Ba^{2+}, Sr^{2+}, Li^+, Na^+, K^+, NH_4^+, Cd^{2+}, Mn^{2+}, Pb^{2+}, Hg^+, Hg^{2+}, Sn^{2+}, Cu^{2+}, Ni^{2+}, Ag^+, U^{4+}, Zr^{4+}, AsO_3^-, Br^-, CO_3^{2-}, ClO_4^-, CN^-, IO_3^-, SiO_4^{4-}, NO_3^-, NO_2^-, SO_4^{2-}, SO_3^{2-}, pyrophosphate, molybdate, tetraborate, selenate, benzoate, citrate, oxalate, lactate, tartrate, formate, and salicylate. If HNO_3 is used in the test, Cl^- interferes at 75 mg/L.

c. Minimum detectable concentration: The minimum detectable concentration is 200 μg P/L in 1-cm spectrophotometer cells.

2. Apparatus

a. Colorimetric equipment: One of the following is required:

1) *Spectrophotometer,* for use at 400 to 490 nm.

2) *Filter photometer,* provided with a blue or violet filter exhibiting maximum transmittance between 400 and 470 nm.

The wavelength at which color intensity is measured depends on sensitivity desired, because sensitivity varies tenfold with wavelengths 400 to 490 nm. Ferric iron causes interference at low wavelengths, particularly at 400 nm. A wavelength of 470 nm usually is used. Concentration ranges for different wavelengths are:

P Range *mg/L*	Wavelength *nm*
1.0– 5.0	400
2.0–10	420
4.0–18	470

b. Acid-washed glassware: Use acid-washed glassware for determining low concentrations of phosphorus. Phosphate contamination is common because of its absorption on glass surfaces. Avoid using commercial detergents containing phosphate. Clean all glassware with hot dilute HCl and rinse well with distilled water. Preferably, reserve the glassware only for phosphate determination, and after use, wash and keep filled with water until needed. If this is done, acid treatment is required only occasionally.

c. *Filtration apparatus and filter paper.**

3. Reagents

a. *Phenolphthalein indicator aqueous solution.*

b. *Hydrochloric acid,* HCl, 1 + 1. H_2SO_4, $HClO_4$, or HNO_3 may be substituted for HCl. The acid concentration in the determination is not critical but a final sample concentration of $0.5N$ is recommended.

c. *Activated carbon.†* Remove fine particles by rinsing with distilled water.

d. *Vanadate-molybdate reagent:*

1) *Solution A:* Dissolve 25 g ammonium molybdate, $(NH_4)_6Mo_7O_{24} \cdot 4H_2O$, in 300 mL distilled water.

2) *Solution B:* Dissolve 1.25 g ammonium metavanadate, NH_4VO_3, by heating to boiling in 300 mL distilled water. Cool and add 330 mL conc HCl. Cool Solution B to room temperature, pour Solution A into Solution B, mix, and dilute to 1 L.

e. *Standard phosphate solution:* Dissolve in distilled water 219.5 mg anhydrous KH_2PO_4 and dilute to 1000 mL; 1.00 mL = 50.0 μg PO_4^{3-}-P.

4. Procedure

a. *Sample pH adjustment:* If sample pH is greater than 10, add 0.05 mL (1 drop) phenolphthalein indicator to 50.0 mL sample and discharge the red color with 1 + 1 HCl before diluting to 100 mL.

b. *Color removal from sample:* Remove excessive color in sample by shaking about 50 mL with 200 mg activated carbon in an erlenmeyer flask for 5 min and filter to remove carbon. Check each batch of car-

bon for phosphate because some batches produce high reagent blanks.

c. *Color development in sample:* Place 35 mL or less of sample, containing 0.05 to 1.0 mg P, in a 50-mL volumetric flask. Add 10 mL vanadate-molybdate reagent and dilute to the mark with distilled water. Prepare a blank in which 35 mL distilled water is substituted for the sample. After 10 min or more, measure absorbance of sample versus a blank at a wavelength of 400 to 490 nm, depending on sensitivity desired (see ¶ 2a above). The color is stable for days and its intensity is unaffected by variation in room temperature.

d. *Preparation of calibration curve:* Prepare a calibration curve by using suitable volumes of standard phosphate solution and proceeding as in ¶ 4c. When ferric ion is low enough not to interfere, plot a family of calibration curves of one series of standard solutions for various wavelengths. This permits a wide latitude of concentrations in one series of determinations. Analyze at least one standard with each set of samples.

5. Calculation

$$mg\ P/L = \frac{mg\ P\ (in\ 50\ mL\ final\ volume) \times 1000}{mL\ sample}$$

6. Precision and Bias

See Table 4500-P:I.

7. Bibliography

KITSON, R.E. & M.G. MELLON. 1944. Colorimetric determination of phosphorus as molybdovanadophosphoric acid. *Ind. Eng. Chem.*, Anal. Ed. 16:379.

BOLTZ, D.F. & M.G. MELLON. 1947. Determination of phosphorus, germanium, silicon, and arsenic by the heteropoly blue method. *Ind. Eng. Chem.*, Anal. Ed. 19:873.

GREENBERG, A.E., L.W. WEINBERGER & C.N. SAWYER. 1950. Control of nitrite interference in colorimetric determination of phosphorus. *Anal. Chem.* 22:499.

---

*Whatman No. 42 or equivalent.
†Darco G60 or equivalent.

YOUNG, R.S. & A. GOLLEDGE. 1950. Determination of hexametaphosphate in water after threshold treatment. *Ind. Chem.* 26:13.

GRISWOLD, B.L., F.L. HUMOLLER & A.R. MCINTYRE. 1951. Inorganic phosphates and phosphate esters in tissue extracts. *Anal. Chem.* 23:192.

BOLTZ, D.F., ed. 1958. Colorimetric Determination of Nonmetals. Interscience Publishers, New York, N.Y.

AMERICAN WATER WORKS ASSOCIATION. 1958. Committee report. Determination of ortho-

phosphate, hydrolyzable phosphate, and total phosphate in surface waters. *J. Amer. Water Works Assoc.* 50:1563.

JACKSON, M.L. 1958. Soil Chemical Analysis. Prentice-Hall, Englewood Cliffs, N.J.

ABBOT, D.C., G.E. EMSDEN & J.R. HARRIS. 1963. A method for determining orthophosphate in water. *Analyst* 88:814.

GOTTFRIED, P. 1964. Determination of total phosphorus in water and wastewater as molybdovanadophosphoric acid. *Limnologica* 2:407.

4500-P D. Stannous Chloride Method

1. General Discussion

a. Principle: Molybdophosphoric acid is formed and reduced by stannous chloride to intensely colored molybdenum blue. This method is more sensitive than Method C and makes feasible measurements down to 7 μg P/L by use of increased light path length. Below 100 μg P/L an extraction step may increase reliability and lessen interference.

b. Interference: See Section 4500-P.C.1*b*.

c. Minimum detectable concentration: The minimum detectable concentration is about 3 μg P/L. The sensitivity at 0.3010 absorbance is about 10 μg P/L for an absorbance change of 0.009.

2. Apparatus

The same apparatus is required as for Method C, except that a pipetting bulb is required for the extraction step. Set spectrophotometer at 625 nm in the measurement of benzene-isobutanol extracts and at 690 nm for aqueous solutions. If the instrument is not equipped to read at 690 nm, use a wavelength of 650 nm for aqueous solutions, with somewhat reduced sensitivity and precision.

3. Reagents

a. Phenolphthalein indicator aqueous solution.

b. Strong-acid solution: Prepare as directed in Section 4500-P.B.2*b*2).

c. Ammonium molybdate reagent I: Dissolve 25 g $(NH_4)_6Mo_7O_{24} \cdot 4H_2O$ in 175 mL distilled water. Cautiously add 280 mL conc H_2SO_4 to 400 mL distilled water. Cool, add molybdate solution, and dilute to 1 L.

d. Stannous chloride reagent I: Dissolve 2.5 g fresh $SnCl_2 \cdot 2H_2O$ in 100 mL glycerol. Heat in a water bath and stir with a glass rod to hasten dissolution. This reagent is stable and requires neither preservatives nor special storage.

e. Standard phosphate solution: Prepare as directed in Section 4500-P.C.3*e*.

f. Reagents for extraction:

1) *Benzene-isobutanol solvent:* Mix equal volumes of benzene and isobutyl alcohol. (CAUTION—*This solvent is highly flammable.*)

2) *Ammonium molybdate reagent II:* Dissolve 40.1 g $(NH_4)_6Mo_7O_{24} \cdot 4H_2O$ in approximately 500 mL distilled water. Slowly add 396 mL ammonium molybdate reagent I. Cool and dilute to 1 L.

3) *Alcoholic sulfuric acid solution:* Cautiously add 20 mL conc H_2SO_4 to 980 mL methyl alcohol with continuous mixing.

4) *Dilute stannous chloride reagent II:* Mix 8 mL stannous chloride reagent I with

50 mL glycerol. This reagent is stable for at least 6 months.

4. Procedure

a. Preliminary sample treatment: To 100 mL sample containing not more than 200 μg P and free from color and turbidity, add 0.05 mL (1 drop) phenolphthalein indicator. If sample turns pink, add strong acid solution dropwise to discharge the color. If more than 0.25 mL (5 drops) is required, take a smaller sample and dilute to 100 mL with distilled water after first discharging the pink color with acid.

b. Color development: Add, with thorough mixing after each addition, 4.0 mL molybdate reagent I and 0.5 mL (10 drops) stannous chloride reagent I. Rate of color development and intensity of color depend on temperature of the final solution, each 1°C increase producing about 1% increase in color. Hence, hold samples, standards, and reagents within 2°C of one another and in the temperature range between 20 and 30°C.

c. Color measurement: After 10 min, but before 12 min, using the same specific interval for all determinations, measure color photometrically at 690 nm and compare with a calibration curve, using a distilled water blank. Light path lengths suitable for various concentration ranges are as follows:

Approximate P Range mg/L	Light Path cm
0.3–2	0.5
0.1–1	2
0.007–0.2	10

Always run a blank on reagents and distilled water. Because the color at first develops progressively and later fades, maintain equal timing conditions for samples and standards. Prepare at least one standard with each set of samples or once

each day that tests are made. The calibration curve may deviate from a straight line at the upper concentrations of the 0.3 to 2.0-mg/L range.

d. Extraction: When increased sensitivity is desired or interferences must be overcome, extract phosphate as follows: Pipet a 40-mL sample, or one diluted to that volume, into a 125-mL separatory funnel. Add 50.0 mL benzene-isobutanol solvent and 15.0 mL molybdate reagent II. Close funnel at once and shake vigorously for exactly 15 s. If condensed phosphate is present, any delay will increase its conversion to orthophosphate. Remove stopper and withdraw 25.0 mL of separated organic layer, using a pipet with safety bulb. Transfer to a 50-mL volumetric flask, add 15 to 16 mL alcoholic H_2SO_4 solution, swirl, add 0.50 mL (10 drops) dilute stannous chloride reagent II, swirl, and dilute to the mark with alcoholic H_2SO_4. Mix thoroughly. After 10 min, but before 30 min, read against the blank at 625 nm. Prepare blank by carrying 40 mL distilled water through the same procedure used for the sample. Read phosphate concentration from a calibration curve prepared by taking known phosphate standards through the same procedure used for samples.

5. Calculation

Calculate as follows:

a. Direct procedure:

$$\text{mg P/L} = \frac{\text{mg P (in approximately 104.5 mL final volume)} \times 1000}{\text{mL sample}}$$

b. Extraction procedure:

$$\text{mg P/L} = \frac{\text{mg P (in 50 mL final volume)} \times 1000}{\text{mL sample}}$$

6. Precision and Bias

See Table 4500-P:I.

4500-P E.   Ascorbic Acid Method

1. General Discussion

a. Principle: Ammonium molybdate and potassium antimonyl tartrate react in acid medium with orthophosphate to form a heteropoly acid—phosphomolybdic acid—that is reduced to intensely colored molybdenum blue by ascorbic acid.

b. Interference: Arsenates react with the molybdate reagent to produce a blue color similar to that formed with phosphate. Concentrations as low as 0.1 mg As/L interfere with the phosphate determination. Hexavalent chromium and NO_2^- interfere to give results about 3% low at concentrations of 1 mg/L and 10 to 15% low at 10 mg/L. Sulfide (Na_2S) and silicate do not interfere at concentrations of 1.0 and 10 mg/L.

c. Minimum detectable concentration: Approximately 10 μg P/L. P ranges are as follows:

Approximate P Range mg/L	Light Path cm
0.30–2.0	0.5
0.15–1.30	1.0
0.01–0.25	5.0

2. Apparatus

a. Colorimetric equipment: One of the following is required:

1) *Spectrophotometer,* with infrared phototube for use at 880 nm, providing a light path of 2.5 cm or longer.

2) *Filter photometer,* equipped with a red color filter and a light path of 0.5 cm or longer.

b. Acid-washed glassware: See Section 4500-P.C.2b.

3. Reagents

a. Sulfuric acid, H_2SO_4, 5N: Dilute 70 mL conc H_2SO_4 to 500 mL with distilled water.

b. Potassium antimonyl tartrate solution: Dissolve 1.3715 g $K(SbO)C_4H_4O_6 \cdot 1/2H_2O$ in 400 mL distilled water in a 500-mL volumetric flask and dilute to volume. Store in a glass-stoppered bottle.

c. Ammonium molybdate solution: Dissolve 20 g $(NH_4)_6Mo_7O_{24} \cdot 4H_2O$ in 500 mL distilled water. Store in a glass-stoppered bottle.

d. Ascorbic acid, 0.01M: Dissolve 1.76 g ascorbic acid in 100 mL distilled water. The solution is stable for about 1 week at 4°C.

e. Combined reagent: Mix the above reagents in the following proportions for 100 mL of the combined reagent: 50 mL 5N H_2SO_4, 5 mL potassium antimonyl tartrate solution, 15 mL ammonium molybdate solution, and 30 mL ascorbic acid solution. *Mix after addition of each reagent.* Let all reagents reach room temperature before they are mixed and mix in the order given. If turbidity forms in the combined reagent, shake and let stand for a few minutes until turbidity disappears before proceeding. The reagent is stable for 4 h.

f. Stock phosphate solution: See Section 4500-P.C.3e.

g. Standard phosphate solution: Dilute 50.0 mL stock phosphate solution to 1000 mL with distilled water; 1.00 mL = 2.50 μg P.

4. Procedure

a. Treatment of sample: Pipet 50.0 mL sample into a clean, dry test tube or 125-mL erlenmeyer flask. Add 0.05 mL (1 drop) phenolphthalein indicator. If a red color develops add 5N H_2SO_4 solution dropwise to just discharge the color. Add 8.0 mL combined reagent and mix thoroughly. After at least 10 min but no more than 30 min, measure absorbance of each sample at 880 nm, using reagent blank as the reference solution.

b. Correction for turbidity or interfering color: Natural color of water generally does not interfere at the high wavelength used.

TABLE 4500-P:II. COMPARISON OF PRECISION AND BIAS OF ASCORBIC ACID METHODS

Ascorbic Acid Method	Phosphorus Concentration, Dissolved Orthophosphate $\mu g/L$	No. of Laboratories	Relative Standard Deviation %		Relative Error %	
			Distilled Water	River Water	Distilled Water	River Water
13th Edition[1]	228	8	3.87	2.17	4.01	2.08
Current method[2]	228	8	3.03	1.75	2.38	1.39

For highly colored or turbid waters, prepare a blank by adding all reagents except ascorbic acid and antimonyl potassium tartrate to the sample. Subtract blank absorbance from absorbance of each sample.

c. *Preparation of calibration curve:* Prepare individual calibration curves from a series of six standards within the phosphate ranges indicated in ¶ 1c above. Use a distilled water blank with the combined reagent to make photometric readings for the calibration curve. Plot absorbance vs. phosphate concentration to give a straight line passing through the origin. Test at least one phosphate standard with each set of samples.

5. Calculation

$$\text{mg P/L} = \frac{\text{mg P (in approximately 58 mL final volume)} \times 1000}{\text{mL sample}}$$

6. Precision and Bias

The precision and bias values given in Table 4500-P:I are for a single-solution procedure given in the 13th edition. The present procedure differs in reagent-to-sample ratios, no addition of solvent, and acidity conditions. It is superior in precision and bias to the previous technique in the analysis of both distilled water and river water at the 228-μg P/L level (Table 4500-P:II).

7. References

1. EDWARDS, G.P., A.H. MOLOF & R.W. SCHNEEMAN. 1965. Determination of orthophosphate in fresh and saline waters. *J. Amer. Water Works Assoc.* 57:917.
2. MURPHY, J. & J. RILEY. 1962. A modified single solution method for the determination of phosphate in natural waters. *Anal. Chim. Acta* 27:31.

8. Bibliography

SLETTEN, O. & C.M. BACH. 1961. Modified stannous chloride reagent for orthophosphate determination. *J. Amer. Water Works Assoc.* 53:1031.
STRICKLAND, J.D.H. & T.R. PARSONS. 1965. A Manual of Sea Water Analysis, 2nd ed. Fisheries Research Board of Canada, Ottawa.

4500-P F.   Automated Ascorbic Acid Reduction Method

1. General Discussion

a. *Principle:* Ammonium molybdate and potassium antimonyl tartrate react with orthophosphate in an acid medium to form an antimony-phosphomolybdate complex, which, on reduction with ascorbic acid, yields an intense blue color suitable for photometric measurement.

b. *Interferences:* As much as 50 mg

Fe^{3+}/L, 10 mg Cu/L, and 10 mg SiO_2/L can be tolerated. High silica concentrations cause positive interference.

In terms of phosphorus, the results are high by 0.005, 0.015, and 0.025 mg/L for silica concentrations of 20, 50, and 100 mg/L, respectively. Salt concentrations up to 20% (w/v) cause an error of less than 1%. Arsenate (AsO_4^{3-}) is a positive interference.

Eliminate interference from NO_2^- and S^{2-} by adding an excess of bromine water or a saturated potassium permanganate ($KMnO_4$) solution. Remove interfering turbidity by filtration before analysis. Filter samples for total or total hydrolyzable phosphorus only after digestion. Sample color that absorbs in the photometric range used for analysis also will interfere. See also Section 4500-P.E.1b.

c. *Application:* Orthophosphate can be determined in potable, surface, and saline waters as well as domestic and industrial wastewaters over a range of 0.001 to 10.0 mg P/L when photometric measurements are made at 650 to 660 or 880 nm in a 15-mm or 50-mm tubular flow cell. Determine higher concentrations by diluting sample. Although the automated test is designed for orthophosphate only, other phosphorus compounds can be converted to this reactive form by various sample pretreatments described in Section 4500-P.B.1, 2, and 5.

2. Apparatus

a. *Automated analytical equipment:* The required continuous-flow analytical instrument† consists of the interchangeable components shown in Figure 4500-P:2. A flow cell of 15 or 50 mm and a filter of 650 to 660 or 880 nm may be used.

b. *Hot plate or autoclave.*

c. *Acid-washed glassware:* See Section 4500-P.C.2b.

†AutoAnalyzer™ II, Technicon Instrument Co., Tarrytown, N.Y. 10591, or equivalent.

3. Reagents

a. *Potassium antimonyl tartrate solution:* Dissolve 0.3 g $K(SbO)C_2H_4O_6 \cdot 1/2H_2O$ in approximately 50 mL distilled water and dilute to 100 mL. Store at 4°C in a dark, glass-stoppered bottle.

b. *Ammonium molybdate solution:* Dissolve 4 g $(NH_4)_6Mo_7O_{24} \cdot 4H_2O$ in 100 mL distilled water. Store in a plastic bottle at 4°C.

c. *Ascorbic acid solution:* See Section 4500-P.E.3d.

d. *Combined reagent:* See Section 4500-P.E.3e.

e. *Dilute sulfuric acid solution:* Slowly add 140 mL conc H_2SO_4 to 600 mL distilled water. When cool, dilute to 1 L.

f. *Ammonium persulfate,* $(NH_4)_2S_2O_8$, crystalline.

g. *Phenolphthalein indicator aqueous solution.*

h. *Stock phosphate solution:* Dissolve 439.3 mg anhydrous KH_2PO_4, dried for 1 h at 105°C, in distilled water and dilute to 1000 mL; 1.00 mL = 100 μg P.

i. *Intermediate phosphate solution:* Dilute 100.0 mL stock phosphate solution to 1000 mL with distilled water; 1.00 mL = 10.0 μg P.

j. *Standard phosphate solutions:* Prepare a suitable series of standards by diluting appropriate volumes of intermediate phosphate solution.

4. Procedure

Set up manifold as shown in Figure 4500-P:2 and follow the general procedure described by the manufacturer.

Add 0.05 mL (1 drop) phenolphthalein indicator solution to approximately 50 mL sample. If a red color develops, add H_2SO_4 (¶ 3e) dropwise to just discharge the color.

5. Calculation

Prepare standard curves by plotting peak heights of standards processed through the manifold against P concentration in stand-

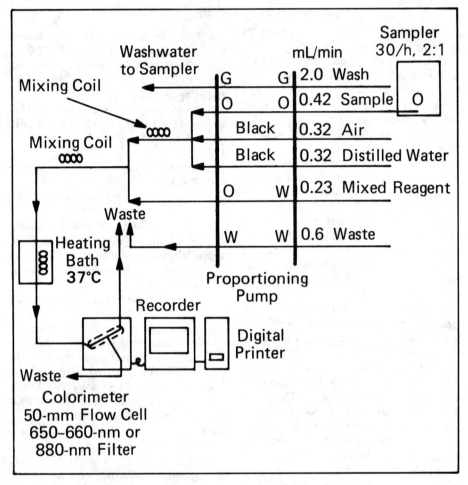

Figure 4500-P:2. Phosphate manifold for automated analytical system.

ards. Compute sample P concentration by comparing sample peak height with standard curve.

6. Precision and Bias

Six samples were analyzed in a single laboratory in septuplicate. At an average PO_4^{3-} concentration of 0.340 mg/L, the average deviation was 0.015 mg/L. The coefficient of variation was 6.2%. In two samples with added PO_4^{3-}, recoveries were 89 and 96%.

7. Bibliography

HENRIKSEN, A. 1966. An automatic method for determining orthophosphate in sewage and highly polluted waters. *Analyst* 91:652.

LOBRING, L.B. & R.L. BOOTH. 1973. Evaluation of the AutoAnalyzer II; A progress report. *In* Advances in Automated Analysis: 1972 Technicon International Congress. Vol. 8, p. 7. Mediad, Inc., Tarrytown, N.Y.

U.S. ENVIRONMENTAL PROTECTION AGENCY. 1979. Methods for Chemical Analysis of Water and Wastes. EPA-600/4-79-020, National Environmental Research Center, Cincinnati, Ohio.

U.S. ENVIRONMENTAL PROTECTION AGENCY. MDQARL Method Study 4, Automated Methods. National Environmental Research Center, Cincinnati, Ohio (in preparation).

4500-Si SILICA*

4500-Si A. Introduction

1. Occurrence and Significance

Silicon ranks next to oxygen in abundance in the earth's crust. It appears as the oxide (silica) in quartz and sand and is combined with metals in the form of many complex silicate minerals, particularly igneous rocks. Degradation of silica-containing rocks results in the presence of silica in natural waters as suspended particles, in a colloidal or polymeric state, and as silicic acids or silicate ions. Volcanic and geothermally heated waters often contain an abundance of silica.

A more complete discussion of the occurrence and chemistry of silica in natural waters is available.[1]

The silica (SiO_2) content of natural water most commonly is in the 1- to 30-mg/L range, although concentrations as high as 100 mg/L are not unusual and concentrations exceeding 1000 mg/L are found in some brackish waters and brines.

Silica in water is undesirable for a number of industrial uses because it forms difficult-to-remove silica and silicate scales in equipment, particularly on high-pressure steam-turbine blades. Silica is removed most often by the use of strongly basic anion-exchange resins in the deionization process, by distillation, or by reverse osmosis. Some plants use precipitation with magnesium oxide in either the hot or cold lime softening process.

2. Selection of Method

Method C determines total silica. Methods D, E, and F determine molybdate-reactive silica. As noted in Section 4500-Si.D.4, it is possible to convert other forms of silica to the molybdate-reactive form for determination by these methods. Method B, like Method C, determines more than one form of silica. It will determine all dissolved silica and some colloidally dispersed silica. The determination of silica present in micrometer and submicrometer particles will depend on the size distribution, composition, and structure of the particles; thus Method B cannot be said to determine total silica.

Use Method C to standardize sodium silicate solutions used as standards for Methods D, E, and F. Do not use Method C for water samples that contain less than 20 mg SiO_2/L. Method D is recommended for relatively pure waters containing from 0.4 to 25 mg SiO_2/L. As with most colorimetric methods, the range can be extended, if necessary, by diluting, by concentrating, or by varying the light path. Interferences due to tannin, color, and turbidity are more severe with this method than with Method E. Moreover, the yellow color produced by Method D has a limited stability and attention to timing is necessary. When applicable, however, it offers

---

*Approved by Standard Methods Committee, 1988.

greater speed and simplicity than Method E because one reagent fewer is used; one timing step is eliminated; and many natural waters can be analyzed without dilution, which is not often the case with Method E. Method E is recommended for the low range, from 0.04 to 2 mg SiO_2/L. This range also can be extended if necessary. Such extension may be desirable if interference is expected from tannin, color, or turbidity. A combination of factors renders Methods E and F less susceptible than Method D to those interferences; also, the blue color in Methods E and F is more stable than the yellow color in Method D. However, many samples will require dilution because of the high sensitivity of the method. Permanent artificial color standards are not available for the blue color developed in Method E.

The yellow color produced by Method D and the blue color produced by Methods E and F are affected by high concentrations of salts. With sea water the yellow color intensity is decreased by 20 to 25% and the blue color intensity is increased by 10 to 15%. When waters of high ionic strength are analyzed by these methods, use silica standards of approximately the same ionic strengths.[2]

Method F may be used where large numbers of samples are analyzed regularly. Method B is recommended for broad-range use. Although Method B is usable from 1 to 300 mg SiO_2/L, optimal results are obtained from about 20 to 300 mg/L. The range can be extended upward by dilution if necessary. This method is rapid and does not require any timing step.

The inductively coupled plasma method (G) also may be used in analyses for silica.

3. Sampling and Storage

Collect samples in bottles of polyethylene, other plastic, or hard rubber, especially if there will be a delay between collection and analysis. Borosilicate glass is a less desirable choice, particularly with waters of pH above 8 or with seawater, in which cases a significant amount of silica in the glass can dissolve. Freezing to preserve samples for analysis of other constituents can lower soluble silica values by as much as 20 to 40% in waters that have a pH below 6. Do not acidify samples for preservation because silica precipitates in acidic solutions.

4. References

1. HEM, J.D. 1959. Study and interpretation of the chemical characteristics of natural water. U.S. Geol. Surv. Water Supply Pap. No. 1473.
2. FANNING, K.A. & M.E.Q. PILSON. 1973. On the spectrophotometric determination of dissolved silica in natural waters. *Anal. Chem.* 45:136.

5. Bibliography

ROY, C.J. 1945. Silica in natural waters. *Amer. J. Sci.* 243:393.
VAIL, J.G. 1952. The Soluble Silicates, Their Properties and Uses. Reinhold Publishing Corp., New York, N.Y. Vol. 1, pp. 95-97, 100-161.

4500-Si B.   Atomic Absorption Spectrometric Method

See Section 3111D.

4500-Si C.   Gravimetric Method

1. General Discussion

a. Principle: Hydrochloric acid decomposes silicates and dissolved silica, forming silicic acids that are precipitated as partially dehydrated silica during evaporation and baking. Ignition completes dehydration of the silica, which is weighed and then volatilized as silicon tetrafluoride, leaving any impurities behind as nonvolatile residue. The residue is weighed and silica is determined as loss on volatilization. Perchloric acid ($HClO_4$) may be used to dehydrate the silica instead of HCl. A single fuming with $HClO_4$ will recover more silica than one with HCl, although for complete silica recovery two dehydrations with either acid are necessary. The use of $HClO_4$ lessens the tendency to spatter, yields a silica precipitate that is easier to filter, and shortens the time required for the determination.

b. Interference: Because glassware may contribute silica, avoid its use as much as possible. Use reagents and distilled or deionized water low in silica. Carry out a blank determination to correct for silica introduced by the reagents and apparatus.

2. Apparatus

a. Platinum crucibles, with covers.

b. Platinum evaporating dishes, 200-mL. In dehydration steps, acid-leached glazed porcelain evaporating dishes free from etching may be substituted for platinum, but for greatest accuracy, platinum is preferred.

3. Reagents

For maximum accuracy, set aside batches of chemicals low in silica for this method. Store all reagents in plastic containers and run blanks.

a. Hydrochloric acid, HCl, 1 + 1 and 1 + 50.

b. Sulfuric acid, H_2SO_4, 1 + 1.

c. Hydrofluoric acid, HF, 48%.

d. Perchloric acid, $HClO_4$, 72%.

4. Procedure

Before determining silica, test H_2SO_4 and HF for interfering nonvolatile matter by carrying out the procedure of ¶ 4a5) below. Use a clean empty platinum crucible. If any increase in weight is observed, make a correction in the silica determinations.

a. HCl dehydration:

1) Sample evaporation—To a clear sample containing at least 10 mg silica, add 5 mL 1 + 1 HCl. Evaporate to dryness in a 200-mL platinum or acid-leached glazed porcelain evaporating dish, in several portions if necessary, on a water bath or suspended on an asbestos ring over a hot plate. Protect against contamination by atmospheric dust. During evaporation, add a total of 15 mL 1 + 1 HCl in several portions. Dry dish and place it in a 110°C oven or over a hot plate to bake for 30 min.

2) First filtration—Add 5 mL 1 + 1 HCl, warm, and add 50 mL hot distilled water. While mixture is hot, filter through an ashless medium-texture filter paper, decanting as much liquid as possible. Wash dish and residue with hot 1 + 50 HCl and then with a minimum volume of distilled water until washings are chloride-free. Save all washings. Set aside filter paper with its residue.

3) Second filtration—Evaporate filtrate and washings from the above operation to dryness in the original platinum dish. Bake residue in a 110°C oven or over a hot plate for 30 min. Repeat steps in ¶ 2) above. Use a separate filter paper and a rubber policeman to aid in transferring residue from dish to filter. Take special care with porcelain dishes because silica adheres to the dish.

4) Ignition—Transfer the two filter papers (one if dehydrated by 4b) and residues to a covered platinum crucible, dry at 110°C, and ignite at 1200°C to constant weight. Avoid mechanical loss of residue when first charring and burning off the pa-

per by gradual heating at minimum temperature. Too rapid heating may form black silicon carbide. Cool in desiccator, weigh, and repeat ignition and weighing until constant weight is attained. Record weight of crucible and contents.

5) Volatilization with HF—Thoroughly moisten weighed residue with distilled water. Add 4 drops 1 + 1 H_2SO_4, followed by 10 mL HF, measuring the latter in a plastic graduated cylinder or pouring an estimated 10 mL directly from the reagent bottle. Slowly evaporate to dryness over an air bath or hot plate in a hood and avoid loss by splattering. Ignite crucible to constant weight at 1200°C. Record weight of crucible and contents.

b. HClO₄ dehydration: Follow procedure in ¶ 4*a*1) above until all but 50 mL of sample has been evaporated. Add 5 mL $HClO_4$ and evaporate until dense white fumes appear. (CAUTION: *Explosive— Place a shield between analyst and fuming dish.*)

Continue dehydration for 10 min. Cool, add 5 mL 1 + 1 HCl and 50 mL hot distilled water. Bring to a boil and filter through an ashless quantitative filter paper. Wash thoroughly ten times with hot distilled water and proceed as directed in ¶s 4*a*4) and 5) preceding. For many purposes, the silica precipitate often is sufficiently

pure for the purpose intended and may be weighed directly, omitting HF volatilization. Make an initial check against the longer procedure, however, to be sure that the result is within the limits of accuracy required.

5. Calculation

Subtract weight of crucible and contents after HF treatment from the corresponding weight before HF treatment. The difference, *A*, in milligrams is "loss on volatilization" and represents silica:

$$\text{mg SiO}_2/\text{L} = \frac{A \times 1000}{\text{mL sample}}$$

6. Precision and Bias

The accuracy is limited both by the finite solubility of silica in water under the conditions of analysis and by the analytical balance sensitivity. Under optimum conditions, an experienced analyst can obtain a precision of approximately ±0.2 mg SiO_2.

7. Bibliography

HILLEBRAND, W.F. et al. 1953. Applied Inorganic Analysis, 2nd ed. John Wiley & Sons, New York, N.Y. Chapter 43.
KOLTHOFF, I.M., E.J. MEEHAN, E.B. SANDELL & S. BRUCKENSTEIN. 1969. Quantitative Chemical Analysis, 4th ed. Macmillan Co., New York, N.Y.

4500-Si D.   Molybdosilicate Method

1. General Discussion

a. Principle: Ammonium molybdate at pH approximately 1.2 reacts with silica and any phosphate present to produce heteropoly acids. Oxalic acid is added to destroy the molybdophosphoric acid but not the molybdosilicic acid. Even if phosphate is known to be absent, the addition of oxalic acid is highly desirable and is a mandatory step in both this method and Method E.

The intensity of the yellow color is proportional to the concentration of "molybdate-reactive" silica. In at least one of its forms, silica does not react with molybdate even though it is capable of passing through filter paper and is not noticeably turbid. It is not known to what extent such "unreactive" silica occurs in waters. Terms such as "colloidal," "crystalloidal," and "ionic" have been used to distinguish among various forms of silica but such terminology cannot be substantiated. "Molybdate-unreactive" silica can be converted to the "molybdate-reactive" form by heating or fusing with alkali. Molybdate-reactive or unreactive does not imply reactivity, or lack of it, toward *other* reagents or processes.

b. Interference: Because both apparatus and reagents may contribute silica, avoid using glassware as much as possible and use reagents low in silica. Also, make a blank determination to correct for silica so introduced. In both this method and Method E, tannin, large amounts of iron, color, turbidity, sulfide, and phosphate interfere. Treatment with oxalic acid eliminates interference from phosphate and decreases interference from tannin. If necessary, use photometric compensation to cancel interference from color or turbidity.

c. Minimum detectable concentration: Approximately 1 mg SiO_2/L can be detected in 50-mL nessler tubes.

2. Apparatus

a. Platinum dishes, 100-mL.

b. Colorimetric equipment: One of the following is required:

1) *Spectrophotometer,* for use at 410 nm, providing a light path of 1 cm or longer. See Table 4500-Si:I for light path selection.

2) *Filter photometer,* providing a light path of 1 cm or longer and equipped with a violet filter having maximum transmittance near 410 nm.

3) *Nessler tubes,* matched, 50-mL, tall form.

3. Reagents

For best results, set aside and use batches of chemicals low in silica. Store all reagents in plastic containers to guard against high blanks.

a. Sodium bicarbonate, $NaHCO_3$, powder.

b. Sulfuric acid, H_2SO_4, 1N.

c. Hydrochloric acid, HCl, 1 + 1.

TABLE 4500-Si:I. SELECTION OF LIGHT PATH LENGTH FOR VARIOUS SILICA CONCENTRATIONS

	Method D	Method E	
		Silica in 55 mL Final Volume μg	
Light Path *cm*	Silica in 55 mL Final Volume μg	650 nm Wavelength	815 nm Wavelength
1	200–1300	40–300	20–100
2	100–700	20–150	10–50
5	40–250	7–50	4–20
10	20–130	4–30	2–10

d. Ammonium molybdate reagent: Dissolve 10 g $(NH_4)_6Mo_7O_{24} \cdot 4H_2O$ in distilled water, with stirring and gentle warming, and dilute to 100 mL. Filter if necessary. Adjust to pH 7 to 8 with silica-free NH_4OH or NaOH and store in a polyethylene bottle to stabilize. (If the pH is not adjusted, a precipitate gradually forms. If the solution is stored in glass, silica may leach out and cause high blanks.) If necessary, prepare silica-free NH_4OH by passing gaseous NH_3 into distilled water contained in a plastic bottle.

e. Oxalic acid solution: Dissolve 7.5 g $H_2C_2O_4 \cdot H_2O$ in distilled water and dilute to 100 mL.

f. Stock silica solution: Dissolve 4.73 g sodium metasilicate nonahydrate, $Na_2SiO_3 \cdot 9H_2O$, in distilled water and dilute to 1000 mL. Analyze 100.0-mL portions by Method C to determine concentration. Store in a tightly stoppered plastic bottle.

g. Standard silica solution: Dilute 10.00 mL stock solution to 1000 mL with distilled water; 1.00 mL = 10.0 μg SiO_2. Calculate exact concentration from concentration of stock silica solution. Store in a tightly stoppered plastic bottle.

h. Permanent color solutions:

1) *Potassium chromate solution:* Dissolve 630 mg K_2CrO_4 in distilled water and dilute to 1 L.

2) *Borax solution:* Dissolve 10 g sodium borate decahydrate, $Na_2B_4O_7 \cdot 10H_2O$, in distilled water and dilute to 1 L.

4. Procedure

a. Color development: To 50.0 mL sample add in rapid succession 1.0 mL 1 + 1 HCl and 2.0 mL ammonium molybdate reagent. Mix by inverting at least six times and let stand for 5 to 10 min. Add 2.0 mL oxalic acid solution and mix thoroughly. Read color after 2 min but before 15 min, measuring time from addition of oxalic acid. Because the yellow color obeys Beer's law, measure photometrically or visually.

b. To detect the presence of molybdate-unreactive silica, digest sample with $NaHCO_3$ before color development. This digestion is not necessarily sufficient to convert all molybdate-unreactive silica to the molybdate-reactive form. Complex silicates and higher silica polymers may require extended fusion with alkali at high temperatures or digestion under pressure for complete conversion. Omit digestion if all the silica is known to react with molybdate.

Prepare a clear sample by filtration if necessary. Place 50.0 mL, or a smaller portion diluted to 50 mL, in a 100-mL platinum dish. Add 200 mg silica-free $NaHCO_3$ and digest on a steam bath for 1 h. Cool and add slowly, with stirring, 2.4 mL $1N$ H_2SO_4. Do not interrupt analysis but proceed *at once* with remaining steps. Transfer quantitatively to a 50-mL nessler tube and make up to mark with distilled water. (Tall-form 50-mL nessler tubes are convenient for mixing even if the solution subsequently is transferred to an absorption cell for photometric measurement.)

c. Preparation of standards: If $NaHCO_3$ pretreatment is used, add to the standards (approximately 45 mL total volume) 200 mg $NaHCO_3$ and 2.4 mL $1N$ H_2SO_4, to compensate both for the slight amount of silica introduced by the reagents and for the effect of the salt on color intensity. Dilute to 50.0 mL.

d. Correction for color or turbidity: Prepare a special blank for every sample that needs such correction. Carry two identical portions of each such sample through the procedure, including $NaHCO_3$ treatment if this is used. To one portion add all reagents as directed in ¶ 4a preceding. To the other portion add HCl and oxalic acid but no molybdate. Adjust photometer to zero absorbance with the blank containing no molybdate before reading absorbance of molybdate-treated sample.

e. Photometric measurement: Prepare a calibration curve from a series of approximately six standards to cover the optimum ranges cited in Table 4500-Si:I. Follow directions of ¶ 4a above on suitable portions of standard silica solution diluted to 50.0 mL in nessler tubes. Set photometer at zero absorbance with distilled water and read all standards, including a reagent blank, against distilled water. Plot micrograms silica in the final (55 mL) developed solution against photometer readings. Run a reagent blank and at least one standard with each group of samples to confirm that the calibration curve previously established has not shifted.

f. Visual comparison: Make a set of permanent artificial color standards, using K_2CrO_4 and borax solutions. Mix liquid volumes specified in Table 4500-Si:II and place them in well-stoppered, appropriately labeled 50-mL nessler tubes. Verify correctness of these permanent artificial standards by comparing them visually against standards prepared by analyzing portions of the standard silica solution. Use permanent artificial color standards only for visual comparison.

TABLE 4500-Si:II. PREPARATION OF
PERMANENT COLOR STANDARDS FOR VISUAL
DETERMINATION OF SILICA

Value in Silica μg	Potassium Chromate Solution mL	Borax Solution mL	Water mL
0	0.0	25	30
100	1.0	25	29
200	2.0	25	28
400	4.0	25	26
500	5.0	25	25
750	7.5	25	22
1000	10.0	25	20

5. Calculation

$$mg\ SiO_2/L = \frac{\mu g\ SiO_2\ (in\ 55\ mL\ final\ volume)}{mL\ sample}$$

Report whether $NaHCO_3$ digestion was used.

6. Precision and Bias

A synthetic sample containing 5.0 mg SiO_2/L, 10 mg Cl^-/L, 0.20 mg NH_3-N/L, 1.0 mg NO_3^--N/L, 1.5 mg organic N/L, and 10.0 mg PO_4^{3-}/L in distilled water was analyzed in 19 laboratories by the molybdosilicate method with a relative standard deviation of 14.3% and a relative error of 7.8%.

Another synthetic sample containing 15.0 mg SiO_2/L, 200 mg Cl^-/L, 0.800 mg NH_3-N/L, 1.0 mg NO_3^--N/L, 0.800 mg organic N/L, and 5.0 mg PO_4^{3-}/L in distilled water was analyzed in 19 laboratories by the molybdosilicate method, with a relative standard deviation of 8.4% and a relative error of 4.2%.

A third synthetic sample containing 30.0 mg SiO_2/L, 400 mg Cl^-/L, 1.50 mg NH_3-N/L, 1.0 mg NO_3^--N/L, 0.200 mg organic N/L, and 0.500 mg PO_4^{3-}/L, in distilled water was analyzed in 20 laboratories by the molybdosilicate method, with a relative standard deviation of 7.7% and a relative error of 9.8%.

All results were obtained after sample digestion with $NaHCO_3$.

7. Bibliography

DIENERT, F.& F. WANDENBULCKE. 1923. On the determination of silica in waters. *Bull. Soc. Chim. France* 33:1131, *Compt. Rend.* 176:1478.

DIENERT, F. & F. WANDENBULCKE. 1924. A study of colloidal silica. *Compt. Rend.* 178:564.

SWANK, H.W. & M.G. MELLON. 1934. Colorimetric standards for silica. *Ind. Eng. Chem.*, Anal. Ed. 6:348.

TOURKY, A.R. & D.H. BANGHAM. 1936. Colloidal silica in natural waters and the "silicomolybdate" colour test. *Nature* 138:587.

BIRNBAUM, N. & G.H. WALDEN. 1938. Co-precipitation of ammonium silicomolybdate and ammonium phosphomolybdate. *J. Amer. Chem. Soc.* 60:66.

KAHLER, H.L. 1941. Determination of soluble silica in water: A photometric method. *Ind. Eng. Chem.*, Anal. Ed. 13:536.

NOLL, C.A. & J.J. MAGUIRE. 1942. Effect of container on soluble silica content of water samples. *Ind. Eng. Chem.*, Anal. Ed. 14:569.

SCHWARTZ, M.C. 1942. Photometric determination of silica in the presence of phosphates. *Ind. Eng. Chem.*, Anal. Ed. 14:893.

GUTTER, H. 1945. Influence of pH on the composition and physical aspects of the ammonium molybdates. *Compt. Rend.* 220:146.

MILTON, R.F. 1951. Formation of silicomolybdate. *Analyst* 76:431.

KILLEFFER, D.H. & A. LINZ. 1952. Molybdenum Compounds, Their Chemistry and Technology. Interscience Publishers, New York, N.Y. pp. 1-2, 42-45, 67-82, 87-92.

STRICKLAND, J.D.H. 1952. The preparation and properties of silicomolybdic acid. *J. Amer. Chem. Soc.* 74:862, 868, 872.

CHOW, D.T.W. & R.J. ROBINSON. 1953. The forms of silicate available for colorimetric determination. *Anal. Chem.* 25:646.

4500-Si E.   Heteropoly Blue Method

1. General Discussion

a. Principle: The principles outlined under Method D, ¶ 1*a*, also apply to this method. The yellow molybdosilicic acid is reduced by means of aminonaphthol-sulfonic acid to heteropoly blue. The blue color is more intense than the yellow color of Method D and provides increased sensitivity.

b. Interference: See Section 4500-Si.D.1*b*.

c. Minimum detectable concentration: Approximately 20 μg SiO_2/L can be detected in 50-mL nessler tubes and 50 μg SiO_2/L spectrophotometrically with a 1-cm light path at 815 nm.

2. Apparatus

a. Platinum dishes, 100-mL.

b. Colorimetric equipment: One of the following is required:

1) *Spectrophotometer,* for use at approximately 815 nm. The color system also obeys Beer's law at 650 nm, with appreciably reduced sensitivity. Use light path of 1 cm or longer. See Table 4500-Si:I for light path selection.

2) *Filter photometer,* provided with a red filter exhibiting maximum transmittance in the wavelength range of 600 to 815 nm. Sensitivity improves with increasing wavelength. Use light path of 1 cm or longer.

3) *Nessler tubes,* matched, 50-mL, tall form.

3. Reagents

For best results, set aside and use batches of chemicals low in silica. Store all reagents in plastic containers to guard against high blanks. Use distilled water that does not contain detectable silica after storage in glass.

All of the reagents listed in Section 4500-Si.D.3 are required, and in addition:

Reducing agent: Dissolve 500 mg 1-amino-2-naphthol-4-sulfonic acid and 1 g

Na_2SO_3 in 50 mL distilled water, with gentle warming if necessary; add this to a solution of 30 g $NaHSO_3$ in 150 mL distilled water. Filter into a plastic bottle. Discard when solution becomes dark. Prolong reagent life by storing in a refrigerator and away from light. Do not use amino-naphtholsulfonic acid that is incompletely soluble or that produces reagents that are dark even when freshly prepared.*

4. Procedure

a. Color development: Proceed as in ¶ 4500-Si.D.4*a* up to and including the words, "Add 2.0 mL oxalic acid solution and mix thoroughly." Measuring time from the moment of adding oxalic acid, wait at least 2 min but not more than 15 min, add 2.0 mL reducing agent, and mix thoroughly. After 5 min, measure blue color photometrically or visually. If $NaHCO_3$ pretreatment is used, follow ¶ 4500-Si.D.4*b*.

b. Photometric measurement: Prepare a calibration curve from a series of approximately six standards to cover the optimum range indicated in Table 4500-Si:I. Carry out the steps described above on suitable portions of standard silica solution diluted to 50.0 mL in nessler tubes; pretreat standards if $NaHCO_3$ digestion is used (see 4500-Si.D.4*b*). Adjust photometer to zero absorbance with distilled water and read all standards, including a reagent blank, against distilled water. If necessary to correct for color or turbidity in a sample, see ¶ 4500-Si.D.4*d*. To the special blank add HCl and oxalic acid, but no molybdate or reducing agent. Plot micrograms silica in the final 55 mL developed solution against absorbance. Run a reagent blank and at least one standard with each group of samples to check the calibration curve.

c. Visual comparison: Prepare a series of

---

*Eastman No. 360 has been found satisfactory.

not less than 12 standards, covering the range 0 to 120 μg SiO_2, by placing the calculated volumes of standard silica solution in 50-mL nessler tubes, diluting to mark with distilled water, and developing color as described in ¶ *a* preceding.

5. Calculation

$$mg\ SiO_2/L = \frac{\mu g\ SiO_2\ (in\ 55\ mL\ final\ volume)}{mL\ sample}$$

Report whether $NaHCO_3$ digestion was used.

6. Precision and Bias

A synthetic sample containing 5.0 mg SiO_2/L, 10 mg Cl^-/L, 0.200 mg NH_3-N/L, 1.0 mg NO_3^--N/L, 1.5 mg organic N/L, and 10.0 mg PO_4^{3-}/L in distilled water was analyzed in 11 laboratories by the heteropoly blue method, with a relative standard deviation of 27.2% and a relative error of 3.0%.

A second synthetic sample containing 15 mg SiO_2/L, 200 mg Cl^-/L, 0.800 mg NH_3-N/L, 1.0 mg NO_3^--N/L, 0.800 mg organic N/L, and 5.0 mg PO_4^{3-}/L in distilled water was analyzed in 11 laboratories by

the heteropoly blue method, with a relative standard deviation of 18.0% and a relative error of 2.9%.

A third synthetic sample containing 30.0 mg SiO_2/L, 400 mg Cl^-/L, 1.50 mg NH_3-N/L, 1.0 mg NO_3^--N/L, 0.200 mg organic N/L, and 0.500 mg PO_4^{3-}/L in distilled water was analyzed in 10 laboratories by the heteropoly blue method with a relative standard deviation of 4.9% and a relative error of 5.1%.

All results were obtained after sample digestion with $NaHCO_3$.

7. Bibliography

BUNTING, W.E. 1944. Determination of soluble silica in very low concentrations. *Ind. Eng. Chem.*, Anal. Ed. 16:612.
STRAUB, F.G. & H. GRABOWSKI. 1944. Photometric determination of silica in condensed steam in the presence of phosphates. *Ind. Eng. Chem.*, Anal. Ed. 16:574.
BOLTZ, D.F. & M.G. MELLON. 1947. Determination of phosphorus, germanium, silicon, and arsenic by the heteropoly blue method. *Ind. Eng. Chem.*, Anal. Ed. 19:873.
MILTON, R.F. 1951. Estimation of silica in water. *J. Appl. Chem.* (London) 1: (Supplement No. 2) 126.
CARLSON, A.B. & C.V. BANKS. 1952. Spectrophotometric determination of silicon. *Anal. Chem.* 24:472.

4500-Si F.   Automated Method for Molybdate-Reactive Silica

1. General Discussion

a. Principle: This method is an adaptation of the heteropoly blue method (Method E) utilizing a continuous-flow analytical instrument.

b. Interferences: See Section 4500-Si.D.1*b*. If particulate matter is present, filter sample or use a continuous filter as an integral part of the system.

c. Application: This method is applicable to potable, surface, domestic, and other waters containing 0 to 20 mg SiO_2/L. The range of concentration can be broadened

to 0 to 80 mg/L by substituting a 15-mm flow cell for the 50-mm flow cell shown in Figure 4500-Si:1.

2. Apparatus

Automated analytical equipment: The required continuous-flow analytical instrument* consists of the interchangeable components shown in Figure 4500-Si:1.

---

*Technicon™ Autoanalyzer™ or equivalent.

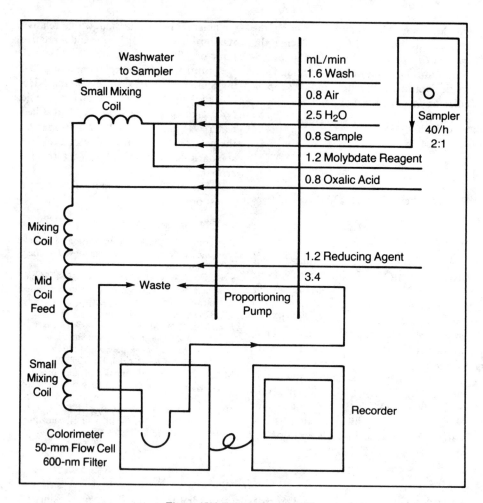

Figure 4500-Si:1. Silica manifold.

3. Reagents

a. Sulfuric acid, H_2SO_4, 0.1N.

b. Ammonium molybdate reagent: Dissolve 10 g $(NH_4)_6Mo_7O_{24} \cdot 4H_2O$ in 1 L 0.1N H_2SO_4. Filter and store in an amber plastic bottle.

c. Oxalic acid solution: Dissolve 50 g oxalic acid in 900 mL distilled water and dilute to 1 L.

d. Reducing agent: Dissolve 120 g $NaHSO_3$ and 4 g Na_2SO_3 in 800 mL warm distilled water. Add 2 g 1-amino-2-naphthol-4-sulfonic acid, mix well, and dilute to 1 L. Filter into amber plastic bottle for storage.

To prepare working reagent, dilute 100 mL to 1 L with distilled water. Make working reagent daily.

e. Standard silica solution: See 4500-Si.C.3*f.*

4. Procedure

Set up manifold as shown in Figure 4500-Si:1 and follow the general procedure described by the manufacturer. Determine absorbance at 660 nm.

5. Calculation

Prepare standard curves by plotting peak heights of standards processed through the manifold against SiO_2 concentration in standards. Compute sample SiO_2 concentration by comparing sample peak height with standard curve.

6. Precision and Bias

For 0 to 20 mg SiO_2/L, when a 50-mm flow cell was used at 40 samples/h, the detection limit was 0.1 mg/L, sensitivity (concentration giving 0.398 absorbance) was 7.1 mg/L, and the coefficient of variation (95% confidence level at 7.1 mg/L) was 1.6%. For 0 to 80 mg SiO_2/L, when a 15-mm flow cell was used at 50 samples/h, detection limit was 0.5 mg/L, sensitivity was 31 mg/L, and coefficient of variation at 31 mg/L was 1.5%.

4500-Si G. Inductively Coupled Plasma Method

See Section 3120.

4500-S²⁻ SULFIDE*

4500-S²⁻ A. Introduction

1. Occurrence and Significance

Sulfide often is present in groundwater, especially in hot springs. Its common presence in wastewaters comes partly from the decomposition of organic matter, sometimes from industrial wastes, but mostly from the bacterial reduction of sulfate. Hydrogen sulfide escaping into the air from sulfide-containing wastewater causes odor nuisances. The threshold odor concentration of H_2S in clean water is between 0.025 and 0.25 µg/L. H_2S is very toxic and has claimed the lives of numerous workers in sewers. It attacks metals directly and indirectly has caused serious corrosion of concrete sewers because it is oxidized biologically to H_2SO_4 on the pipe wall.

*Approved by Standard Methods Committee, 1988.

2. Categories of Sulfides

From an analytical standpoint, three categories of sulfide in water and wastewater are distinguished:

a. *Total sulfide* includes dissolved H_2S and HS^-, as well as acid-soluble metallic sulfides present in suspended matter. The S^{2-} is negligible, amounting to less than 0.5% of the dissolved sulfide at pH 12, less than 0.05% at pH 11, etc. Copper and silver sulfides are so insoluble that they do not respond in ordinary sulfide determinations; they can be ignored for practical purposes.

b. *Dissolved sulfide* is that remaining after suspended solids have been removed by flocculation and settling.

c. *Un-ionized hydrogen sulfide* may be

calculated from the concentration of dissolved sulfide, the sample pH, and the practical ionization constant of H_2S.

3. Sampling and Storage

Take samples with minimum aeration. To preserve a sample for a total sulfide determination put zinc acetate solution into bottle before filling it with sample. Use 4 drops of $2N$ zinc acetate solution per 100 mL sample. Fill bottle completely and stopper.

4. Qualitative Tests

A qualitative test for sulfide often is useful. It is advisable in the examination of industrial wastes containing interfering substances that may give a false negative result in the methylene blue procedure.

a. Antimony test: To about 200 mL sample, add 0.5 mL saturated solution of potassium antimony tartrate and 0.5 mL $6N$ HCl in excess of phenolphthalein alkalinity.

Yellow antimony sulfide (Sb_2S_3) is discernible at a sulfide concentration of 0.5 mg/L. Comparisons with samples of known sulfide concentration make the technique roughly quantitative. The only known interferences are metallic ions such as lead, which hold the sulfide so firmly that it does not produce Sb_2S_3, and dithionite, which decomposes in acid solution to produce sulfide.

b. Silver-silver sulfide electrode test: The potential of a silver-silver sulfide electrode assembly relative to a reference electrode varies with the activity of the sulfide ion in solution. By correcting for the ion activity coefficient and pH, this potential estimates sulfide concentration. Standardize electrode frequently against a sulfide solution of known strength. An electrode of this type can be used as an end-point indicator for titrating dissolved sulfide with a standard solution of a silver or lead salt, but slow response always is a problem.

c. Lead acetate paper and silver foil tests: Confirm odors attributed to H_2S with lead acetate paper. On exposure to the vapor of a slightly acidified sample, the paper becomes blackened by formation of PbS. A strip of silver foil is more sensitive than lead acetate paper. Clean the silver by dipping in NaCN solution and rinse. Silver is suitable particularly for long-time exposure in the vicinity of possible H_2S sources because black Ag_2S is permanent whereas PbS slowly oxidizes.

5. Selection of Quantitative Methods

Iodine reacts with sulfide in acid solution, oxidizing it to sulfur. A titration based on this reaction is an accurate method for determining sulfide at concentrations above 1 mg/L if interferences are absent and if loss of H_2S is avoided. The iodometric method (E) is useful for standardizing the methylene blue colorimetric method and is suitable for analyzing samples freshly taken from wells or springs. The method can be used for wastewater and partly oxidized water from sulfur springs if interfering substances are removed first.

The methylene blue method (D) is based on the reaction of sulfide, ferric chloride, and dimethyl-*p*-phenylenediamine to produce methylene blue. Ammonium phosphate is added after color development to remove ferric chloride color. The procedure is applicable at sulfide concentrations up to 20 mg/L.

Potentiometric methods utilizing a silver electrode may be suitable. From the potential of the electrode relative to a reference electrode an estimate can be made of the sulfide concentration, but careful attention to details of procedures and frequent standardizations are needed to secure good results. The electrode is useful particularly as an end-point indicator for titration of dissolved sulfide with silver nitrate.

Figure 4500-S^{2-}:1 shows analytical flow

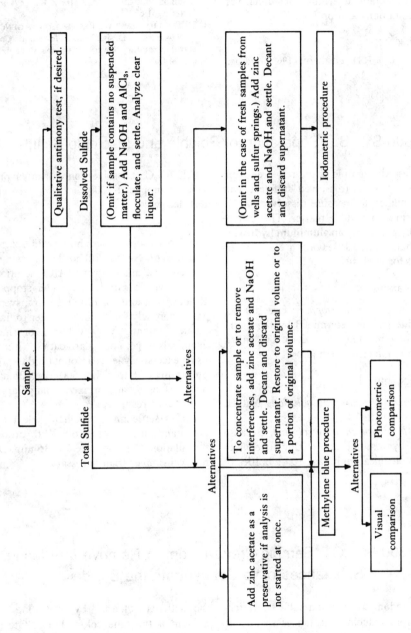

Figure 4500-S^{2-}:1. Analytical flow paths for sulfide determinations.

paths for sulfide determinations under various conditions and options.

5. Bibliography

CRUSE, H. & R.D. POMEROY. 1969. Hydrogen sulfide odor threshold. *J. Amer. Water Works Assoc.* 61:677.

U.S. ENVIRONMENTAL PROTECTION AGENCY. 1974. Process Design Manual for Sulfide Control in Sanitary Sewerage Systems. Publ. 625/1-74-005.

4500-S²⁻ B.   Separation of Soluble and Insoluble Sulfides

Unless the sample is entirely free from suspended solids (dissolved sulfide equals total sulfide), to measure dissolved sulfide first remove insoluble matter. This can be done by producing an aluminum hydroxide floc that is settled, leaving a clear supernatant for analysis.

1. Apparatus

Glass bottles with stoppers: Use 100 mL if sulfide will be determined by the methylene blue method and 500 to 1000 mL if by the iodometric method.

2. Reagents

a. *Sodium hydroxide solution,* NaOH, 6N.

b. *Aluminum chloride solution:* Because of the hygroscopic and caking tendencies of this chemical, purchase 100-g bottles of AlCl₃·6H₂O. Dissolve contents of a previously unopened 100-g bottle in 144 mL distilled water.

3. Procedure

a. To a 100-mL glass bottle add 0.2 mL (4 drops) 6N NaOH. Fill bottle with sample and add 0.2 mL (4 drops) AlCl₃ solution. Stopper bottle with no air under stopper. Rotate back and forth about a transverse axis vigorously for 1 min or longer to flocculate contents. Vary volumes of these chemicals to get good clarification without using excessively large amounts and to produce a pH of 6 to 9. If a 500- or 1000-mL bottle is used, add proportionally larger amounts of reagents.

b. Let settle until reasonably clear supernatant can be drawn off. With proper flocculation, this may take 5 to 15 min. Do not wait longer than necessary.

4500-S²⁻ C.   Sample Pretreatment to Remove Interfering Substances or to Concentrate the Sulfide

The iodometric method suffers interference from reducing substances that react with iodine, including thiosulfate, sulfite, and various organic compounds, both solid and dissolved.

Strong reducing agents also interfere in the methylene blue test by preventing formation of the blue color. Thiosulfate at concentrations above 10 mg/L may retard color formation or completely prevent it. Sulfide itself prevents the reaction if its concentration is very high, in the range of several hundred milligrams per liter. To avoid the possibility of false negative results, use the antimony method to obtain a qualitative result in industrial wastes likely to contain sulfide but showing no color by the methylene blue method. Iodide, which is likely to be present in oil-field wastewaters, may diminish color formation if its concentration exceeds 2 mg/L. Ferrocyanide produces a blue color.

Eliminate interferences due to sulfite, thiosulfate, iodide, and many other soluble substances, but not ferrocyanide, by first precipitating ZnS, removing the supernatant, and replacing it with distilled water. Use the same procedure, even when not needed for removal of interferences, to concentrate sulfide.

1. Apparatus

Glass bottles with stoppers: See Section 4500-S^{2-}.B.1.

2. Reagents

a. Zinc acetate solution: Dissolve 220 g $Zn(C_2H_3O_2)_2 \cdot 2H_2O$ in 870 mL water; this makes 1 L solution.

b. Sodium hydroxide solution, NaOH, 6N.

3. Procedure

a. Put 0.15 mL (3 drops) zinc acetate solution into a 100-mL glass bottle, fill with sample, and add 0.10 mL (2 drops) 6N NaOH solution. Stopper with no air bubbles under stopper and mix by rotating

back and forth vigorously about a transverse axis. For the iodometric procedure, use a 500-mL bottle or other convenient size, with proportionally larger volumes of reagents. Vary volume of reagents added according to sample so that the resulting precipitate is not excessively bulky and settles readily. Add enough NaOH to produce a pH above 9. Let precipitate settle for 30 min. The treated sample is relatively stable and can be held for several hours. However, if much iron is present, oxidation may be fairly rapid.

b. If the iodometric method is to be used, filter precipitate through glass fiber filter paper and continue at once with titration according to the procedure of Method E. If the methylene blue method is used, let precipitate settle for 30 min and decant as much supernatant as possible without loss of precipitate. Refill bottle with distilled water, resuspend precipitate, and withdraw a sample. If interfering substances are present in high concentration, settle, decant, and refill a second time. If sulfide concentration is known to be low, add only enough water to bring volume to one-half or one-fifth of original volume. Use this technique for analyzing samples of very low sulfide concentrations. After determining the sulfide concentration colorimetrically, multiply the result by the ratio of final to initial volume.

Cadmium salts sometimes are used instead of zinc, but CdS is more susceptible to oxidation than ZnS.

4500-S^{2-} D. Methylene Blue Method

1. Apparatus

a. Matched test tubes, approximately 125 mm long and 15 mm OD.

b. Droppers, delivering 20 drops/mL methylene blue solution. To obtain uniform

drops hold dropper in a vertical position and let drops form slowly.

c. If photometric rather than visual color determination will be used, either:

1) *Spectrophotometer,* for use at a wavelength of 664 nm with cells providing light paths of 1 cm and 1 mm, or

2) *Filter photometer,* with a filter providing maximum transmittance near 600 nm.

2. Reagents

a. Amine-sulfuric acid stock solution: Dissolve 27 g N,N- dimethyl-*p*-phenylenediamine oxalate* in a cold mixture of 50 mL conc H_2SO_4 and 20 mL distilled water. Cool and dilute to 100 mL with distilled water. Use fresh oxalate because an old supply may be oxidized and discolored to a degree that results in interfering colors in the test. Store in a dark glass bottle. When this stock solution is diluted and used in the procedure with a sulfide-free sample, it first will be pink but then should become colorless within 3 min.

b. Amine-sulfuric acid reagent: Dilute 25 mL amine-sulfuric acid stock solution with 975 mL 1 + 1 H_2SO_4. Store in a dark glass bottle.

c. Ferric chloride solution: Dissolve 100 g $FeCl_3 \cdot 6H_2O$ in 40 mL water.

d. Sulfuric acid solution, H_2SO_4, 1 + 1.

e. Diammonium hydrogen phosphate solution: Dissolve 400 g $(NH_4)_2HPO_4$ in 800 mL distilled water.

f. Methylene blue solution I: Use USP grade dye or one certified by the Biological Stain Commission. The dye content should be reported on the label and should be 84% or more. Dissolve 1.0 g in distilled water and make up to 1 L. This solution will be approximately the correct strength, but because of variation between different lots of dye, standardize against sulfide solutions of known strength and adjust its concentration so that 0.05 mL (1 drop) = 1.0 mg sulfide/L.

Standardization—Put several grams of clean, washed crystals of $Na_2S \cdot 9H_2O$ into a small beaker. Add somewhat less than enough water to cover crystals. Stir occasionally for a few minutes, then pour so-

lution into another vessel. This solution reacts slowly with oxygen but the change is unimportant within a few hours. Make solution daily. To 1 L distilled water add 1 drop of solution and mix. Immediately determine sulfide concentration by the methylene blue procedure and by the iodometric procedure. Repeat, using more than 1 drop Na_2S solution or smaller volumes of water, until at least five tests have been made, with a range of sulfide concentrations between 1 and 8 mg/L. Calculate average percent error of the methylene blue result as compared to the iodometric result. If the average error is negative, that is, methylene blue results are lower than iodometric results, dilute methylene blue solution by the same percentage, so that a greater volume will be used in matching colors. If methylene blue results are high, increase solution strength by adding more dye.

g. Methylene blue solution II: Dilute 10.00 mL of adjusted methylene blue solution I to 100 mL.

3. Procedure

a. Color development: Transfer 7.5 mL sample to each of two matched test tubes, using a special wide-tip pipet or filling to marks on test tubes. Add to Tube A 0.5 mL amine-sulfuric acid reagent and 0.15 mL (3 drops) $FeCl_3$ solution. Mix immediately by inverting slowly, only once. (Excessive mixing causes low results by loss of H_2S as a gas before it has had time to react). To Tube B add 0.5 mL 1 + 1 H_2SO_4 and 0.15 mL (3 drops) $FeCl_3$ solution and mix. The presence of S^{2-} will be indicated by the appearance of blue color in Tube A. Color development usually is complete in about 1 min, but a longer time often is required for fading out of the initial pink color. Wait 3 to 5 min and add 1.6 mL $(NH_4)_2HPO_4$ solution to each tube. Wait 3 to 15 min and make color comparisons. If

---

*Eastman catalog No. 5672 has been found satisfactory for this purpose.

zinc acetate was used, wait at least 10 min before making a visual color comparison.

b. Color determination:

1) Visual color estimation—Add methylene blue solution I or II, depending on sulfide concentration and desired accuracy, dropwise, to the second tube, until color matches that developed in first tube. If the concentration exceeds 20 mg/L, repeat test with a portion of sample diluted to one tenth.

With methylene blue solution I, adjusted so that 0.05 mL (1 drop) = 1.0 mg S^{2-}/L when 7.5 mL of sample are used:

mg S^{2-}/L = no. drops solution I
+ 0.1 (no. drops solution II)

2) Photometric color measurement—A cell with a light path of 1 cm is suitable for measuring sulfide concentrations from 0.1 to 2.0 mg/L. Use shorter or longer light paths for higher or lower concentrations.

The upper limit of the method is 20 mg/L. Zero instrument with a portion of treated sample from Tube B. Prepare calibration curves on basis of colorimetric tests made on Na$_2$S solutions simultaneously analyzed by the iodometric method, plotting concentration vs. absorbance. A straight-line relationship between concentration and absorbance can be assumed from 0 to 1.0 mg/L.

Read sulfide concentration from calibration curve.

4. Precision and Bias

The accuracy is about ±10%. The standard deviation has not been determined.

5. Bibliography

POMEROY, R.D. 1936. The determination of sulfides in sewage. *Sewage Works J.* 8:572.

NUSBAUM, I. 1965. Determining sulfides in water and waste water. *Water Sewage Works* 112:113.

4500-S^{2-} E. Iodometric Method

1. Reagents

a. Hydrochloric acid, HCl, 6*N.*

b. Standard iodine solution, 0.0250*N:* Dissolve 20 to 25 g KI in a little water and add 3.2 g iodine. After iodine has dissolved, dilute to 1000 mL and standardize against 0.0250*N* Na$_2$S$_2$O$_3$, using starch solution as indicator.

c. Standard sodium thiosulfate solution, 0.0250*N:* See Section 4500-O.C.2*e.*

d. Starch solution: See Section 4500-O.C.2*d.*

2. Procedure

a. Measure from a buret into a 500-mL flask an amount of iodine solution esti-

mated to be an excess over the amount of sulfide present. Add distilled water, if necessary, to bring volume to about 20 mL. Add 2 mL 6*N* HCl. Pipet 200 mL sample into flask, discharging sample under solution surface. If iodine color disappears, add more iodine so that color remains. Back-titrate with Na$_2$S$_2$O$_3$ solution, adding a few drops of starch solution as end point is approached, and continuing until blue color disappears.

b. If sulfide was precipitated with zinc and ZnS filtered out, return filter with precipitate to original bottle and add about 100 mL water. Add iodine solution and HCl and titrate as in ¶ 2*a* above.

3. Calculation

One milliliter $0.0250N$ iodine solution reacts with 0.4 mg S^{2-}:

$$\text{mg } S^{2-}/L = \frac{[(A \times B) - (C \times D)] \times 16\,000}{\text{mL sample}}$$

where:

A = mL iodine solution,
B = normality of iodine solution,
C = mL $Na_2S_2O_3$ solution, and
D = normality of $Na_2S_2O_3$ solution.

4. Precision

The precision of the end point varies with the sample. In clean waters it should be determinable within 1 drop, which is equivalent to 0.1 mg/L in a 200-mL sample.

4500-S^{2-} F. Calculation of Un-ionized Hydrogen Sulfide

1. Calculation

Hydrogen sulfide and HS^-, which together constitute dissolved sulfide, are in equilibrium with hydrogen ions:

$$H_2S \rightleftarrows H^+ + HS^-$$

The ionization constant of H_2S is used to calculate the distribution of dissolved sulfide between the two forms. The practical constant written in logarithmic form, pK', is used. The constant varies with temperature and ionic strength of the solution. The ionic strength effect can be estimated most easily from the conductivity. Because the effect of ionic strength is not large, values that are sufficiently dependable generally can be assumed if the nature of the sample is known. Table 4500-S^{2-}:I gives approximate pK' values for various temperatures and conductivities. The temperature effect is practically linear from 15°C to 35°C; interpolations or extrapolations can be used. The last line of Table 4500-S^{2-}:I corresponds approximately to seawater.

From sample pH and appropriate value of pK', calculate pH − pK'. From Figure 4500-S^{2-}:2 read proportions of dissolved sulfide present as H_2S (left-side scale of Figure 4500-S^{2-}:2). Let this proportion equal J,

TABLE 4500-S^{2-}:I. VALUES OF pK', LOGARITHM OF PRACTICAL IONIZATION CONSTANT FOR HYDROGEN SULFIDE

Conductivity at 25°C $\mu mhos/cm$	pK' at Given Temperature		
	20°C	25°C	30°C
0	—	7.03*	—
100	7.08	7.01	6.94
200	7.07	7.00	6.93
400	7.06	6.99	6.92
700	7.05	6.98	6.91
1 200	7.04	6.97	6.90
2 000	7.03	6.96	6.89
3 000	7.02	6.95	6.88
4 000	7.01	6.94	6.87
5 200	7.00	6.93	6.86
7 200	6.99	6.92	6.85
10 000	6.98	6.91	6.84
14 000	6.97	6.90	6.83
22 000	6.96	6.89	6.82
50 000	6.95	6.88	6.81

*Theoretical.

$J \times$ (dissolved sulfide)
= un-ionized H_2S expressed as S^{2-}

2. Bibliography

PLATFORD, R.F. 1965. The activity coefficient of sodium chloride in seawater. *J. Mar. Res.* 23:55.

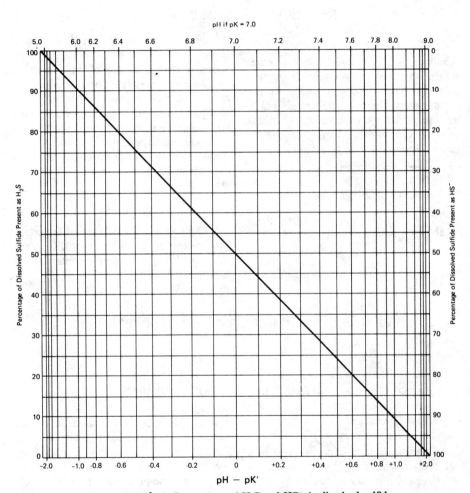

Figure 4500-S²⁻:2. Proportions of H₂S and HS⁻ in dissolved sulfide.

4500-SO_4^{2-} SULFATE*

4500-SO_4^{2-} A.   Introduction

1. Occurrence

Sulfate (SO_4^{2-}) is widely distributed in nature and may be present in natural waters in concentrations ranging from a few to several thousand milligrams per liter. Mine drainage wastes may contribute large amounts of SO_4^{2-} through pyrite oxidation. Sodium and magnesium sulfate exert a cathartic action.

2. Selection of Method

The ion chromatographic method (B) is suitable for sulfate concentrations above

---

*Approved by Standard Methods Committee, 1985.

0.1 mg/L. The gravimetric methods (C and D) are suitable for SO_4^{2-} concentrations above 10 mg/L; use one of these methods for accurate results. The turbidimetric method (E) is applicable in the range of 1 to 40 mg SO_4^{2-}/L. The automated methylthymol blue method (F) is the procedure for analyzing large numbers of samples for sulfate alone when the equipment is available; about 30 samples can be analyzed per hour.

3. Sampling and Storage

In the presence of organic matter certain bacteria may reduce SO_4^{2-} to S^{2-}. To avoid this, store heavily polluted or contaminated samples at 4°C.

4500-SO_4^{2-} B.   Ion Chromatographic Method

See Section 4110.

4500-SO_4^{2-} C.   Gravimetric Method with Ignition of Residue

1. General Discussion

a. Principle: Sulfate is precipitated in a hydrochloric acid (HCl) solution as barium sulfate ($BaSO_4$) by the addition of barium chloride ($BaCl_2$).

The precipitation is carried out near the boiling temperature, and after a period of digestion the precipitate is filtered, washed with water until free of Cl^-, ignited or dried, and weighed as $BaSO_4$.

b. Interference: The gravimetric determination of SO_4^{2-} is subject to many errors, both positive and negative. In potable waters where the mineral concentration is low, these may be of minor importance.

1) Interferences leading to high results—Suspended matter, silica, $BaCl_2$ pre-

cipitant, NO_3^-, SO_3^{2-} and occluded mother liquor in the precipitate are the principal factors in positive errors. Suspended matter may be present in both the sample and the precipitating solution; soluble silicate may be rendered insoluble and SO_3^{2-} may be oxidized to SO_4^{2-} during analysis. Barium nitrate [$Ba(NO_3)_2$], $BaCl_2$, and water are occluded to some extent with the $BaSO_4$ although water is driven off if the temperature of ignition is sufficiently high.

2) Interferences leading to low results—Alkali metal sulfates frequently yield low results. This is true especially of alkali hydrogen sulfates. Occlusion of alkali sulfate with $BaSO_4$ causes substitution of an element of lower atomic weight than

barium in the precipitate. Hydrogen sulfates of alkali metals act similarly and, in addition, decompose on being heated. Heavy metals, such as chromium and iron, cause low results by interfering with the complete precipitation of SO$_4^{2-}$ and by formation of heavy metal sulfates. BaSO$_4$ has small but significant solubility, which is increased in the presence of acid. Although an acid medium is necessary to prevent precipitation of barium carbonate and phosphate, it is important to limit its concentration to minimize the solution effect.

2. Apparatus

a. Steam bath.

b. Drying oven, equipped with thermostatic control.

c. Muffle furnace, with temperature indicator.

d. Desiccator.

e. Analytical balance, capable of weighing to 0.1 mg.

f. Filter: Use one of the following:

1) *Filter paper,* acid-washed, ashless hard-finish, sufficiently retentive for fine precipitates.

2) *Membrane filter,* with a pore size of about 0.45 μm.

g. Filtering apparatus, appropriate to the type of filter selected. (Coat membrane filter holder with silicone fluid to prevent precipitate from adhering.)

3. Reagents

a. Methyl red indicator solution: Dissolve 100 mg methyl red sodium salt in distilled water and dilute to 100 mL.

b. Hydrochloric acid, HCl, 1 + 1.

c. Barium chloride solution: Dissolve 100 g BaCl$_2$·2H$_2$O in 1 L distilled water. Filter through a membrane filter or hard-finish filter paper before use; 1 mL is capable of precipitating approximately 40 mg SO$_4^{2-}$.

d. Silver nitrate-nitric acid reagent: Dissolve 8.5 g AgNO$_3$ and 0.5 mL conc HNO$_3$ in 500 mL distilled water.

e. Silicone fluid. *

4. Procedure

a. Removal of silica: If the silica concentration exceeds 25 mg/L, evaporate sample nearly to dryness in a platinum dish on a steam bath. Add 1 mL HCl, tilt, and rotate dish until the acid comes in complete contact with the residue. Continue evaporation to dryness. Complete drying in an oven at 180°C and if organic matter is present, char over flame of a burner. Moisten residue with 2 mL distilled water and 1 mL HCl, and evaporate to dryness on a steam bath. Add 2 mL HCl, take up soluble residue in hot water, and filter. Wash insoluble silica with several small portions of hot distilled water. Combine filtrate and washings. Discard residue.

b. Precipitation of barium sulfate: Adjust volume of clarified sample to contain approximately 50 mg SO$_4^{2-}$ in a 250-mL volume. Lower concentrations of SO$_4^{2-}$ may be tolerated if it is impracticable to concentrate sample to the optimum level, but in such cases limit total volume to 150 mL. Adjust pH with HCl to pH 4.5 to 5.0, using a pH meter or the orange color of methyl red indicator. Add 1 to 2 mL HCl. Heat to boiling and, while stirring gently, slowly add warm BaCl$_2$ solution until precipitation appears to be complete; then add about 2 mL in excess. If amount of precipitate is small, add a total of 5 mL BaCl$_2$ solution. Digest precipitate at 80 to 90°C, preferably overnight but for not less than 2 h.

c. Filtration and weighing: Mix a small amount of ashless filter paper pulp with the BaSO$_4$, quantitatively transfer to a filter, and filter at room temperature. The pulp aids filtration and reduces the tendency of the precipitate to creep. Wash precipitate with small portions of warm distilled water until washings are free of Cl$^-$ as indicated by testing with AgNO$_3$-HNO$_3$ reagent.

---

*"Desicote" (Beckman), or equivalent.

Place filter and precipitate in a weighed platinum crucible and ignite at 800°C for 1 h. *Do not let filter paper flame.* Cool in desiccator and weigh.

5. Calculation

$$mg\ SO_4^{2-}/L = \frac{mg\ BaSO_4 \times 411.6}{mL\ sample}$$

6. Precision and Bias

A synthetic sample containing 259 mg SO_4^{2-}/L, 108 mg Ca^{2+}/L, 82 mg Mg^{2+}/L, 3.1 mg K^+/L, 19.9 mg Na^+/L, 241 mg Cl^-/L, 0.250 mg NO_2^--N/L, 1.1 mg NO_3^--N/L, and 42.5 mg total alkalinity/L (contributed by $NaHCO_3$) was analyzed in 32 laboratories by the gravimetric method, with a relative standard deviation of 4.7% and a relative error of 1.9%.

7. Bibliography

HILLEBRAND, W.F. et al. 1953. Applied Inorganic Analysis, 2nd ed. John Wiley & Sons, New York, N.Y.

KOLTHOFF, I.M., E.J. MEEHAN, E.B. SANDELL & S. BRUCKENSTEIN. 1969. Quantitative Chemical Analysis, 4th ed. Macmillan Co., New York, N.Y.

4500-SO$_4^{2-}$ D. Gravimetric Method with Drying of Residue

1. General Discussion

See Method C, preceding.

2. Apparatus

With the exception of the filter paper, all of the apparatus cited in Section 4500-SO_4^{2-}.C.2 is required, plus the following:

a. *Filters:* Use one of the following:

1) *Fritted-glass filter,* fine ("F") porosity, with a maximum pore size of 5 μm.

2) *Membrane filter,* with a pore size of about 0.45 μm.

b. *Vacuum oven.*

3. Reagents

All the reagents listed in Section 4500-SO_4^{2-}.C.3 are required.

4. Procedure

a. *Removal of interference:* See Section 4500-SO_4^{2-}.C.4a.

b. *Precipitation of barium sulfate:* See Section 4500-SO_4^{2-}.C.4b.

c. *Preparation of filters:*

1) Fritted glass filter—Dry to constant weight in an oven maintained at 105°C or higher, cool in desiccator, and weigh.

2) Membrane filter—Place filter on a piece of filter paper or a watch glass and dry to constant weight* in a vacuum oven at 80°C, while maintaining a vacuum of at least 85 kPa or in a conventional oven at a temperature of 103 to 105°C. Cool in desiccator and weigh membrane only.

d. *Filtration and weighing:* Filter $BaSO_4$ at room temperature. Wash precipitate with several small portions of warm distilled water until washings are free of Cl^-, as indicated by testing with $AgNO_3$-HNO_3 reagent. If a membrane filter is used add a few drops of silicone fluid to the suspension before filtering, to prevent adherence of precipitate to holder. Dry filter and precipitate by the same procedure used in preparing filter. Cool in a desiccator and weigh.

5. Calculation

$$mg\ SO_4^{2-}/L = \frac{mg\ BaSO_4 \times 411.6}{mL\ sample}$$

6. Bibliography

See Section 4500-SO_4^{2-}.C.7.

---

*Constant weight is defined as a change of not more than 0.5 mg in two successive operations consisting of heating, cooling in desiccator, and weighing.

4500-SO$_4^{2-}$ E.   Turbidimetric Method

1. General Discussion

a. *Principle:* Sulfate ion (SO$_4^{2-}$) is precipitated in an acetic acid medium with barium chloride (BaCl$_2$) so as to form barium sulfate (BaSO$_4$) crystals of uniform size. Light absorbance of the BaSO$_4$ suspension is measured by a photometer and the SO$_4^{2-}$ concentration is determined by comparison of the reading with a standard curve.

b. *Interference:* Color or suspended matter in large amounts will interfere. Some suspended matter may be removed by filtration. If both are small in comparison with the SO$_4^{2-}$ concentration, correct for interference as indicated in ¶ 4*d* below. Silica in excess of 500 mg/L will interfere, and in waters containing large quantities of organic material it may not be possible to precipitate BaSO$_4$ satisfactorily.

In potable waters there are no ions other than SO$_4^{2-}$ that will form insoluble compounds with barium under strongly acid conditions. Make determination at room temperature; variation over a range of 10°C will not cause appreciable error.

c. *Minimum detectable concentration:* Approximately 1 mg SO$_4^{2-}$/L.

2. Apparatus

a. *Magnetic stirrer:* Use a constant stirring speed. It is convenient to incorporate a fixed resistance in series with the motor operating the magnetic stirrer to regulate stirring speed. Use magnets of identical shape and size. The exact speed of stirring is not critical, but keep it constant for each run of samples and standards and adjust it to prevent splashing.

b. *Photometer:* One of the following is required, with preference in the order given:

1) *Nephelometer.*

2) *Spectrophotometer,* for use at 420 nm, providing a light path of 2.5 to 10 cm.

3) *Filter photometer,* equipped with a violet filter having maximum transmittance near 420 nm and providing a light path of 2.5 to 10 cm.

c. *Stopwatch or electric timer.*

d. *Measuring spoon,* capacity 0.2 to 0.3 mL.

3. Reagents

a. *Buffer solution A:* Dissolve 30 g magnesium chloride, MgCl$_2$·6H$_2$O, 5 g sodium acetate, CH$_3$COONa·3H$_2$O, 1.0 g potassium nitrate, KNO$_3$, and 20 mL acetic acid, CH$_3$COOH (99%), in 500 mL distilled water and make up to 1000 mL.

b. *Buffer solution B* (required when the sample SO$_4^{2-}$ concentration is less than 10 mg/L): Dissolve 30 g MgCl$_2$·6H$_2$O, 5 g CH$_3$COONa·3H$_2$O, 1.0 g KNO$_3$, 0.111 g sodium sulfate, Na$_2$SO$_4$, and 20 mL acetic acid (99%) in 500 mL distilled water and make up to 1000 mL.

c. *Barium chloride,* BaCl$_2$, crystals, 20 to 30 mesh. In standardization, uniform turbidity is produced with this mesh range and the appropriate buffer.

d. *Standard sulfate solution:* Prepare a standard sulfate solution as described in 1) or 2) below; 1.00 mL = 100 µg SO$_4^{2-}$.

1) Dilute 10.4 mL standard 0.0200*N* H$_2$SO$_4$ titrant specified in Alkalinity, Section 2320B.3*c*, to 100 mL with distilled water.

2) Dissolve 0.1479 g anhydrous Na$_2$SO$_4$ in distilled water and dilute to 1000 mL.

4. Procedure

a. *Formation of barium sulfate turbidity:* Measure 100 mL sample, or a suitable portion made up to 100 mL, into a 250-mL erlenmeyer flask. Add 20 mL buffer solution and mix in stirring apparatus. While stirring, add a spoonful of $BaCl_2$ crystals and begin timing immediately. Stir for 60 $\pm$ 2 s at constant speed.

b. Measurement of barium sulfate turbidity: After stirring period has ended, pour solution into absorption cell of photometer and measure turbidity at 5 $\pm$ 0.5 min.

c. Preparation of calibration curve: Estimate SO_4^{2-} concentration in sample by comparing turbidity reading with a calibration curve prepared by carrying SO_4^{2-} standards through the entire procedure. Space standards at 5-mg/L increments in the 0- to 40-mg/L SO_4^{2-} range. Above 40 mg/L accuracy decreases and $BaSO_4$ suspensions lose stability. Check reliability of calibration curve by running a standard with every three or four samples.

d. Correction for sample color and turbidity: Correct for sample color and turbidity by running blanks to which $BaCl_2$ is not added.

5. Calculation

$$\text{mg } SO_4^{2-}/L = \frac{\text{mg } SO_4^{2-} \times 1000}{\text{mL sample}}$$

If buffer solution A was used, determine SO_4^{2-} concentration directly from the cal-

ibration curve after subtracting sample absorbance before adding $BaCl_2$. If buffer solution B was used subtract SO_4^{2-} concentration of blank from apparent SO_4^{2-} concentration as determined above; because the calibration curve is not a straight line, this is not equivalent to subtracting blank absorbance from sample absorbance.

6. Precision and Bias

With a turbidimeter,* in a single laboratory with a sample having a mean of 7.45 mg SO_4^{2-}/L, a standard deviation of 0.13 mg/L and a coefficient of variation of 1.7% were obtained. Two samples dosed with sulfate gave recoveries of 85 and 91%.

7. Bibliography

SHEEN, R.T., H.L. KAHLER & E.M. ROSS. 1935. Turbidimetric determination of sulfate in water. *Ind. Eng. Chem.*, Anal. Ed. 7:262.

THOMAS, J.F. & J.E. COTTON. 1954. A turbidimetric sulfate determination. *Water Sewage Works* 101:462.

ROSSUM, J.R. & P. VILLARRUZ. 1961. Suggested methods for turbidimetric determination of sulfate in water. *J. Amer. Water Works Assoc.* 53:873.

---

*Hach 2100 A.

4500-SO_4^{2-} F.   Automated Methylthymol Blue Method

1. General Discussion

a. Principle: Barium sulfate is formed by the reaction of the SO_4^{2-} with barium chloride ($BaCl_2$) at a low pH. At high pH excess barium reacts with methylthymol blue to produce a blue chelate. The un-

complexed methylthymol blue is gray. The amount of gray uncomplexed methylthymol blue indicates the concentration of SO_4^{2-}.

b. Interferences: Because many cations interfere, use an ion-exchange column to remove interferences.

c. Application: This method is applicable to potable, surface, and saline waters as well as domestic and industrial wastewaters over a range from about 10 to 300 mg SO_4^{2-}/L.

2. Apparatus

a. Automated analytical equipment: The required continuous-flow analytical instrument* consists of the interchangeable components shown in Figure 4500-SO₄²⁻:1.

b. Ion-exchange column: Fill a piece of 2-mm-ID glass tubing about 20 cm long with the ion-exchange resin.† To simplify filling column put resin in distilled water

---

*Technicon™ Autoanalyzer™ or equivalent.
†Ion-exchange resin Bio-Rex 70, 20-50 mesh, sodium form, available from Bio-Rad Laboratories, Richmond, Calif. 94804, or equivalent.

and aspirate it into the tubing, which contains a glass-wool plug. After filling, plug other end of tube with glass wool. Avoid trapped air in the column.

3. Reagents

a. Barium chloride solution: Dissolve 1.526 g $BaCl_2 \cdot 2H_2O$ in 500 mL distilled water and dilute to 1 L. Store in a polyethylene bottle.

b. Methylthymol blue reagent: Dissolve 118.2 mg methylthymol blue‡ in 25 mL $BaCl_2$ solution. Add 4 mL 1N HCl and 71 mL distilled water and dilute to 500 mL with 95% ethanol. Store in a brown glass bottle. Prepare fresh daily.

---

‡Eastman Organic Chemicals, Rochester, N.Y. 14615. No. 8068 3',3" bis [N,N-bis(carboxymethyl)-aminolmethyl] thymolsulfonphthalein pentasodium salt.

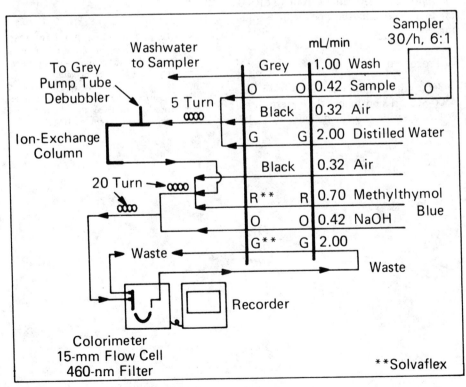

Figure 4500-SO₄²⁻:1. Sulfate manifold.

c. Buffer solution, pH 10.1: Dissolve 6.75 g NH_4Cl in 500 mL distilled water. Add 57 mL conc NH_4OH and dilute to 1 L with distilled water. Adjust pH to 10.1 and store in a polyethylene bottle. Prepare fresh monthly.

d. EDTA reagent: Dissolve 40 g tetrasodium ethylenediaminetetraacetate in 500 mL pH 10.1 buffer solution. Dilute to 1 L with pH 10.1 buffer solution and store in a polyethylene bottle.

e. Sodium hydroxide solution, 0.36N: Dissolve 7.2 g NaOH in 500 mL distilled water. Cool and make up to 1 L with distilled water.

f. Stock sulfate solution: Dissolve 1.479 g anhydrous Na_2SO_4 in 500 mL distilled water and dilute to 1000 mL; 1.00 mL = 1.00 mg SO_4^{2-}.

g. Standard sulfate solutions: Prepare in appropriate concentrations from 10 to 300 mg SO_4^{2-}/L, using the stock sulfate solution.

4. Procedure

Set up the manifold as shown in Figure 4500-SO_4^{2-}:1 and follow the general procedure described by the manufacturer.

After use, rinse methylthymol blue and NaOH reagent lines in water for a few minutes, rinse them in the EDTA solution for 10 min, and then rinse in distilled water.

5. Calculation

Prepare standard curves by plotting peak heights of standards processed through the manifold against SO_4^{2-} concentrations in standards. Compute sample SO_4^{2-} concentration by comparing sample peak height with standard curve.

6. Precision and Bias

With a Technicon Autoanalyzer II in a single laboratory a sample with an average concentration of about 28 mg SO_4^{2-}/L had a standard deviation of 0.68 mg/L and a coefficient of variation of 2.4%. In two samples with added SO_4^{2-}, recoveries were 91% and 100%.

7. Bibliography

LAZRUS, A.L., K.C. HILL & J. P. LODGE. 1965. A new colorimetric microdetermination of sulfate ion. *In* Automation in Analytical Chemistry. Technicon Symposium.

COLOROS, E., M. R. PANESAR & F.P. PERRY. 1976. Linearizing the calibration curve in determination of sulfate by the methylthymol blue method. *Anal. Chem.* 48:1693.

PART 5000

DETERMINATION OF

AGGREGATE ORGANIC CONSTITUENTS

5010 INTRODUCTION

5010 A. General Discussion

Analyses for organic matter in water and wastewater can be classified into two general types of measurements: those that quantify an aggregate amount of organic matter comprising organic constituents with a common characteristic and those that quantify individual organic compounds. The latter can be found in Part 6000. The former, described here in Part 5000, have been grouped into four categories: oxygen-demanding substances, organically bound elements, classes of compounds, and formation potentials.

Methods for total organic carbon and chemical oxygen demand are used to assess the total amount of organics present. Gross fractions of the organic matter can be identified analytically, as in the measurement of BOD, which is an index of the biodegradable organics present, oil and grease, which represents material extractable from a sample by a nonpolar solvent, or total organic halide (TOX), which measures organically bound halogens. Trihalomethane formation potential is an aggregate measure of the total concentration of trihalomethanes formed upon chlorination of a water sample.

Analyses of organics are made to assess the concentration and general composition of organic matter in raw water supplies, wastewaters, treated effluents, and receiving waters; and to determine the efficiency of treatment processes.

5010 B. Sample Collection and Preservation

The sampling, field treatment, preservation, and storage of samples taken for organic matter analysis are covered in detail in the individual introductions to the methods. If possible, analyze samples immediately because preservatives often interfere with the tests. Otherwise, store at a low temperature (4°C) immediately after collection to preserve most samples. Use chemical preservatives only when they are shown not to interfere with the examinations to be made (see Section 1060). Never use preservatives for samples to be analyzed for BOD. When preservatives are used, add them to the sample bottle initially so that all portions are preserved as soon as collected. No single method of preservation is entirely satisfactory; choose the preservative with due regard to the determinations that are to be made. All methods of preservation may be inadequate when applied to samples containing significant amounts of suspended matter.

5020   QUALITY CONTROL

Part 1000 contains important information relevant to analyses included in Part 5000. Give particular attention to Sections 1020B (Quality Control), 1060 (Collection and Preservation of Samples), 1080 (Reagent-Grade Water), and 1090 (Safety), all of which are critical for many of the Part 5000 methods.

Take special precautions when analyses are performed by independent laboratories. Reliable use of independent laboratories deserves the same quality assurance procedures observed for in-house analyses: replicate samples, samples with known additions, and blanks.

Preparation of samples with known ad-

ditions may not be feasible for certain analyses. In such cases, consider using a mixture, in varying ratios, of several samples. Use the reported concentrations in the samples and the proportions in which they were mixed to calculate the expected concentration in the mixture. Examine laboratory performance using externally prepared standards and check samples (see Section 1020B).

Type I reagent water (Section 1080) should give satisfactory results for most of the analyses in Part 5000, but additional purification steps may be needed for certain methods, such as total organic halide (TOX) and trihalomethane formation potential (THMFP).

5210   BIOCHEMICAL OXYGEN DEMAND (BOD)*

5210 A.   Introduction

1. General Discussion

The biochemical oxygen demand (BOD) determination is an empirical test in which standardized laboratory procedures are used to determine the relative oxygen requirements of wastewaters, effluents, and polluted waters. The test has its widest application in measuring waste loadings to treatment plants and in evaluating the BOD-removal efficiency of such treatment systems. The test measures the oxygen utilized during a specified incubation period for the biochemical degradation of organic material (carbonaceous demand) and the oxygen used to oxidize inorganic material such as sulfides and ferrous iron. It also may measure the oxygen used to oxidize reduced forms of nitrogen (nitrogenous de-

mand) unless their oxidation is prevented by an inhibitor. The seeding and dilution procedures provide an estimate of the BOD at pH 6.5 to 7.5.

Although only the 5-d BOD (BOD_5) is described here, many variations of oxygen demand measurements exist. These include using shorter and longer incubation periods, tests to determine rates of oxygen uptake, and continuous oxygen-uptake measurements by respirometric techniques. Alternative seeding, dilution, and incubation conditions can be chosen to mimic receiving-water conditions, thereby providing an estimate of the environmental effects of wastewaters and effluents.

2. Carbonaceous Versus Nitrogenous BOD

Oxidation of reduced forms of nitrogen, mediated by microorganisms, exerts nitrog-

*Approved by Standard Methods Committee, 1988.

enous demand. Nitrogenous demand historically has been considered an interference in the determination of BOD, as clearly evidenced by the inclusion of ammonia in the dilution water. The interference from nitrogenous demand can now be prevented by an inhibitory chemical.[1] If an inhibiting chemical is not used, the oxygen demand measured is the sum of carbonaceous and nitrogenous demands.

Measurements that include nitrogenous demand generally are not useful for assessing the oxygen demand associated with organic material. Nitrogenous demand can be estimated directly from ammonia nitrogen (Section 4500-NH$_3$); and carbonaceous demand can be estimated by subtracting the theoretical equivalent of the reduced nitrogen oxidation from uninhibited test results. However, this method is cumbersome and is subject to considerable error. Chemical inhibition of nitrogenous demand provides a more direct and more reliable measure of carbonaceous demand.

The extent of oxidation of nitrogenous compounds during the 5-d incubation period depends on the presence of microorganisms capable of carrying out this oxidation. Such organisms usually are not present in raw sewage or primary effluent in sufficient numbers to oxidize significant quantities of reduced nitrogen forms in the 5-d BOD test. Many biological treatment plant effluents contain significant numbers of nitrifying organisms. Because oxidation of nitrogenous compounds can occur in such samples, inhibition of nitrification as directed in ¶ B.4e6) is recommended for samples of secondary effluent, for samples seeded with secondary effluent, and for samples of polluted waters.

Report results as CBOD$_5$ when inhibiting the nitrogenous oxygen demand. When nitrification is not inhibited, report results as BOD$_5$.

3. Dilution Requirements

The BOD concentration in most wastewaters exceeds the concentration of dissolved oxygen (DO) available in an air-saturated sample. Therefore, it is necessary to dilute the sample before incubation to bring the oxygen demand and supply into appropriate balance. Because bacterial growth requires nutrients such as nitrogen, phosphorus, and trace metals, these are added to the dilution water, which is buffered to ensure that the pH of the incubated sample remains in a range suitable for bacterial growth. Complete stabilization of a sample may require a period of incubation too long for practical purposes; therefore, 5 d has been accepted as the standard incubation period.

If the dilution water is of poor quality, effectively, dilution water will appear as sample BOD. This effect will be amplified by the dilution factor. A positive bias will result. The method included below contains both a dilution-water check and a dilution-water blank. Seeded dilution waters are checked further for acceptable quality by measuring their consumption of oxygen from a known organic mixture, usually glucose and glutamic acid.

The source of dilution water is not restricted and may be distilled, tap, or receiving-stream water free of biodegradable organics and bioinhibitory substances such as chlorine or heavy metals. Distilled water may contain ammonia or volatile organics; deionized waters often are contaminated with soluble organics leached from the resin bed. Use of copper-lined stills or copper fittings attached to distilled water lines may produce water containing excessive amounts of copper.

4. Reference

1. YOUNG, J.C. 1973. Chemical methods for nitrification control. *J. Water Pollut. Control Fed.* 45:637.

5. Bibliography

THERIAULT, E.J., P.D. MCNAMEE & C.T. BUT-
TERFIELD. 1931. Selection of dilution water
for use in oxygen demand tests. *Pub. Health
Rep.* 46:1084.

LEA, W.L. & M.S. NICHOLS. 1937. Influence of
phosphorus and nitrogen on biochemical oxygen demand. *Sewage Works J.* 9:34.

RUCHHOFT, C.C. 1941. Report on the cooperative
study of dilution waters made for the Standard Methods Committee of the Federation of
Sewage Works Associations. *Sewage Works
J.* 13:669.

MOHLMAN, F.W., E. HURWITZ, G.R. BARNETT
& H.K. RAMER. 1950. Experience with modified methods for BOD. *Sewage Ind. Wastes*
22:31.

5210 B.　5-Day BOD Test

1. General Discussion

a. Principle: The method consists of filling with sample, to overflowing, an airtight
bottle of the specified size and incubating
it at the specified temperature for 5 d. Dissolved oxygen is measured initially and
after incubation, and the BOD is computed
from the difference between initial and final
DO. Because the initial DO is determined
immediately after the dilution is made, all
oxygen uptake, including that occurring
during the first 15 min, is included in the
BOD measurement.

b. Sampling and storage: Samples for
BOD analysis may degrade significantly
during storage between collection and analysis, resulting in low BOD values. Minimize reduction of BOD by analyzing
sample promptly or by cooling it to near-
freezing temperature during storage. However, even at low temperature, keep holding
time to a minimum. Warm chilled samples
to 20°C before analysis.

1) *Grab samples*—If analysis is begun
within 2 h of collection, cold storage is
unnecessary. If analysis is not started
within 2 h of sample collection, keep sample at or below 4°C from the time of collection. Begin analysis within 6 h of
collection; when this is not possible because
the sampling site is distant from the laboratory, store at or below 4°C and report
length and temperature of storage with the
results. In no case start analysis more than

24 h after grab sample collection. When
samples are to be used for regulatory purposes make every effort to deliver samples
for analysis within 6 h of collection.

2) *Composite samples*—Keep samples
at or below 4°C during compositing. Limit
compositing period to 24 h. Use the same
criteria as for storage of grab samples, starting the measurement of holding time from
end of compositing period. State storage
time and conditions as part of the results.

2. Apparatus

a. Incubation bottles, 250- to 300-mL capacity. Clean bottles with a detergent, rinse
thoroughly, and drain before use. As a precaution against drawing air into the dilution bottle during incubation, use a water-
seal. Obtain satisfactory water seals by
inverting bottles in a water bath or by adding water to the flared mouth of special
BOD bottles. Place a paper or plastic cup
or foil cap over flared mouth of bottle to
reduce evaporation of the water seal during
incubation.

b. Air incubator or water bath, thermo-
statically controlled at 20 ± 1°C. Exclude
all light to prevent possibility of photosynthetic production of DO.

3. Reagents

a. Phosphate buffer solution: Dissolve
8.5 g KH_2PO_4, 21.75 g K_2HPO_4, 33.4 g
$Na_2HPO_4 \cdot 7H_2O$, and 1.7 g NH_4Cl in about

about 500 mL distilled water and dilute to 1 L. The pH should be 7.2 without further adjustment. Discard reagent (or any of the following reagents) if there is any sign of biological growth in the stock bottle.

b. *Magnesium sulfate solution:* Dissolve 22.5 g $MgSO_4 \cdot 7H_2O$ in distilled water and dilute to 1 L.

c. *Calcium chloride solution:* Dissolve 27.5 g $CaCl_2$ in distilled water and dilute to 1 L.

d. *Ferric chloride solution:* Dissolve 0.25 g $FeCl_3 \cdot 6H_2O$ in distilled water and dilute to 1 L.

e. *Acid and alkali solutions,* $1N$, for neutralization of caustic or acidic waste samples.

1) Acid—Slowly and while stirring, add 28 mL conc sulfuric acid to distilled water. Dilute to 1 L.

2) Alkali—Dissolve 40 g sodium hydroxide in distilled water. Dilute to 1 L.

f. *Sodium sulfite solution:* Dissolve 1.575 g Na_2SO_3 in 1000 mL distilled water. This solution is not stable; prepare daily.

g. *Nitrification inhibitor,* 2-chloro-6-(trichloro methyl) pyridine.*

h. *Glucose-glutamic acid solution:* Dry reagent-grade glucose and reagent-grade glutamic acid at 103°C for 1 h. Add 150 mg glucose and 150 mg glutamic acid to distilled water and dilute to 1 L. Prepare fresh immediately before use.

i. *Ammonium chloride solution:* Dissolve 1.15 g NH_4Cl in about 500 mL distilled water, adjust pH to 7.2 with NaOH solution, and dilute to 1 L. Solution contains 0.3 mg N/mL.

4. Procedure

a. *Preparation of dilution water:* Place desired volume of water in a suitable bottle and add 1 mL each of phosphate buffer, $MgSO_4$, $CaCl_2$, and $FeCl_3$ solutions/L of water. Seed dilution water, if desired, as

---

*Nitrification Inhibitor 2579-24 (2.2% TCMP), Hach Co., or equivalent.

described in ¶ 4d. Test and store dilution water as described in ¶s 4b and c so that water of assured quality always is on hand.

Before use bring dilution water temperature to 20°C. Saturate with DO by shaking in a partially filled bottle or by aerating with organic-free filtered air. Alternatively, store in cotton-plugged bottles long enough for water to become saturated with DO. Protect water quality by using clean glassware, tubing, and bottles.

b. *Dilution water check:* Use this procedure as a rough check on quality of dilution water.

If the oxygen depletion of a candidate water exceeds 0.2 mg/L obtain a satisfactory water by improving purification or from another source. Alternatively, if nitrification inhibition is used, store the dilution water, seeded as prescribed below, in a darkened room at room temperature until the oxygen uptake is sufficiently reduced to meet the dilution-water check criteria. Check quality of stored dilution water on use, but do not add seed to dilution water stored for quality improvement. Storage is not recommended when BODs are to be determined without nitrification inhibition because nitrifying organisms may develop during storage. Check stored dilution water to determine whether sufficient ammonia remains after storage. If not, add ammonium chloride solution to provide a total of 0.45 mg ammonia/L as nitrogen. If dilution water has not been stored for quality improvement, add sufficient seeding material to produce a DO uptake of 0.05 to 0.1 mg/L in 5 d at 20°C. Incubate a BOD bottle full of dilution water for 5 d at 20°C. Determine initial and final DO as in ¶s 4g and j. The DO uptake in 5 d at 20°C should not be more than 0.2 mg/L and preferably not more than 0.1 mg/L.

c. *Glucose-glutamic acid check:* Because the BOD test is a bioassay its results can be influenced greatly by the presence of toxicants or by use of a poor seeding material. Distilled waters frequently are contaminated with copper; some sewage seeds are relatively inactive. Low results always are obtained with such seeds and waters. Periodically check dilution water quality, seed effectiveness, and analytical technique by making BOD measurements on pure organic compounds and samples with known additions. In general, for BOD determinations not requiring an adapted seed, use a mixture of 150 mg glucose/L and 150 mg glutamic acid/L as a "standard" check solution. Glucose has an exceptionally high and variable oxidation rate but when it is used with glutamic acid, the oxidation rate is stabilized and is similar to that obtained with many municipal wastes. Alternatively, if a particular wastewater contains an identifiable major constituent that contributes to the BOD, use this compound in place of the glucose-glutamic acid.

Determine the 5-d 20°C BOD of a 2% dilution of the glucose-glutamic acid standard check solution using the techniques outlined in ¶s 4d-j. Evaluate data as described in ¶ 6, Precision and Bias.

d. Seeding:

1) Seed source—It is necessary to have present a population of microorganisms capable of oxidizing the biodegradable organic matter in the sample. Domestic wastewater, unchlorinated or otherwise-undisinfected effluents from biological waste treatment plants, and surface waters receiving wastewater discharges contain satisfactory microbial populations. Some samples do not contain a sufficient microbial population (for example, some untreated industrial wastes, disinfected wastes, high-temperature wastes, or wastes with extreme pH values). For such wastes seed the dilution water by adding a population of microorganisms. The preferred seed is effluent from a biological treatment system processing the waste. Where this is not available, use supernatant from domestic wastewater after settling at room temperature for at least 1 h but no longer

than 36 h. When effluent from a biological treatment process is used, inhibition of nitrification is recommended.

Some samples may contain materials not degraded at normal rates by the microorganisms in settled domestic wastewater. Seed such samples with an adapted microbial population obtained from the undisinfected effluent of a biological process treating the waste. In the absence of such a facility, obtain seed from the receiving water below (preferably 3 to 8 km) the point of discharge. When such seed sources also are not available, develop an adapted seed in the laboratory by continuously aerating a sample of settled domestic wastewater and adding small daily increments of waste. Optionally use a soil suspension or activated sludge, or a commercial seed preparation to obtain the initial microbial population. Determine the existence of a satisfactory population by testing the performance of the seed in BOD tests on the sample. BOD values that increase with time of adaptation to a steady high value indicate successful seed adaptation.

2) Seed control—Determine BOD of the seeding material as for any other sample. This is the *seed control*. From the value of the seed control and a knowledge of the seeding material dilution (in the dilution water) determine seed DO uptake. Ideally, make dilutions of seed such that the largest quantity results in at least 50% DO depletion. A plot of DO depletion, in milligrams per liter, versus milliliters seed should present a straight line for which the slope indicates DO depletion per milliliter of seed. The DO-axis intercept is oxygen depletion caused by the dilution water and should be less than 0.1 mg/L (¶ 4h). To determine a sample DO uptake subtract seed DO uptake from total DO uptake. The DO uptake of seeded dilution water should be between 0.6 and 1.0 mg/L.

Techniques for adding seeding material to dilution water are described for two sample dilution methods (¶ 4f).

e. Sample pretreatment:

1) Samples containing caustic alkalinity or acidity— Neutralize samples to pH 6.5 to 7.5 with a solution of sulfuric acid (H_2SO_4) or sodium hydroxide (NaOH) of such strength that the quantity of reagent does not dilute the sample by more than 0.5%. The pH of seeded dilution water should not be affected by the lowest sample dilution.

2) Samples containing residual chlorine compounds—If possible, avoid samples containing residual chlorine by sampling ahead of chlorination processes. If the sample has been chlorinated but no detectable chlorine residual is present, seed the dilution water. If residual chlorine is present, dechlorinate sample and seed the dilution water (¶ 4*f*). Do not test chlorinated/dechlorinated samples without seeding the dilution water. In some samples chlorine will dissipate within 1 to 2 h of standing in the light. This often occurs during sample transport and handling. For samples in which chlorine residual does not dissipate in a reasonably short time, destroy chlorine residual by adding Na_2SO_3 solution. Determine required volume of Na_2SO_3 solution on a 100- to 1000-mL portion of neutralized sample by adding 10 mL of 1 + 1 acetic acid or 1 + 50 H_2SO_4, 10 mL potassium iodide (KI) solution (10 g/100 mL), and titrating with Na_2SO_3 solution to the starch-iodine end point for residual. Add to neutralized sample the relative volume of Na_2SO_3 solution determined by the above test, mix, and after 10 to 20 min check sample for residual chlorine. (NOTE: Excess Na_2SO_3 exerts an oxygen demand and reacts slowly with certain organic chloramine compounds that may be present in chlorinated samples).

3) Samples containing other toxic substances—Certain industrial wastes, for example, plating wastes, contain toxic metals. Such samples often require special study and treatment.

4) Samples supersaturated with DO—

Samples containing more than 9 mg DO/L at 20°C may be encountered in cold waters or in water where photosynthesis occurs. To prevent loss of oxygen during incubation of such samples, reduce DO to saturation at 20°C by bringing sample to about 20°C in partially filled bottle while agitating by vigorous shaking or by aerating with clean, filtered compressed air.

5) Sample temperature adjustment— Bring samples to 20 ± 1°C before making dilutions.

6) Nitrification inhibition—If nitrification inhibition is desired add 3 mg 2-chloro-6-(trichloro methyl) pyridine (TCMP) to each 300-mL bottle before capping or add sufficient amounts to the dilution water to make a final concentration of 10 mg/L. (NOTE: Pure TCMP may dissolve slowly and can float on top of the sample. Some commercial formulations dissolve more readily but are not 100% TCMP; adjust dosage accordingly.) Samples that may require nitrification inhibition include, but are not limited to, biologically treated effluents, samples seeded with biologically treated effluents, and river waters. Note the use of nitrogen inhibition in reporting results.

f. Dilution technique: Dilutions that result in a residual DO of at least 1 mg/L and a DO uptake of at least 2 mg/L after 5 d incubation produce the most reliable results. Make several dilutions of prepared sample to obtain DO uptake in this range. Experience with a particular sample will permit use of a smaller number of dilutions. A more rapid analysis, such as COD, may be correlated approximately with BOD and serve as a guide in selecting dilutions. In the absence of prior knowledge, use the following dilutions: 0.0 to 1.0% for strong industrial wastes, 1 to 5% for raw and settled wastewater, 5 to 25% for biologically treated effluent, and 25 to 100% for polluted river waters.

Prepare dilutions either in graduated cylinders and then transfer to BOD bottles or prepare directly in BOD bottles. Either dilution method can be combined with any DO measurement technique. The number of bottles to be prepared for each dilution depends on the DO technique and the number of replicates desired.

When using graduated cylinders to prepare dilutions, and when seeding is necessary, add seed either directly to dilution water or to individual cylinders before dilution. Seeding of individual cylinders avoids a declining ratio of seed to sample as increasing dilutions are made. When dilutions are prepared directly in BOD bottles and when seeding is necessary, add seed directly to dilution water or directly to the BOD bottles.

1) Dilutions prepared in graduated cylinders—If the azide modification of the titrimetric iodometric method (Section 4500-O.C) is used, carefully siphon dilution water, seeded if necessary, into a 1- to 2-L-capacity graduated cylinder. Fill cylinder half full without entraining air. Add desired quantity of carefully mixed sample and dilute to appropriate level with dilution water. Mix well with a plunger-type mixing rod; avoid entraining air. Siphon mixed dilution into two BOD bottles. Determine initial DO on one of these bottles. Stopper the second bottle tightly, water-seal, and incubate for 5 d at 20°C. If the membrane electrode method is used for DO measurement, siphon dilution mixture into one BOD bottle. Determine initial DO on this bottle and replace any displaced contents with sample dilution to fill the bottle. Stopper tightly, water-seal, and incubate for 5 d at 20°C.

2) Dilutions prepared directly in BOD bottles—Using a wide-tip volumetric pipet, add the desired sample volume to individual BOD bottles of known capacity. Add appropriate amounts of seed material to the individual BOD bottles or to the dilution water. Fill bottles with enough dilution water, seeded if necessary, so that insertion of stopper will displace all air, leaving no

bubbles. For dilutions greater than 1:100 make a primary dilution in a graduated cylinder before making final dilution in the bottle. When using titrimetric iodometric methods for DO measurement, prepare two bottles at each dilution. Determine initial DO on one bottle. Stopper second bottle tightly, water-seal, and incubate for 5 d at 20°C. If the membrane electrode method is used for DO measurement, prepare only one BOD bottle for each dilution. Determine initial DO on this bottle and replace any displaced contents with dilution water to fill the bottle. Stopper tightly, water-seal, and incubate for 5 d at 20°C. Rinse DO electrode between determinations to prevent cross-contamination of samples.

g. Determination of initial DO: If the sample contains materials that react rapidly with DO, determine initial DO immediately after filling BOD bottle with diluted sample. If rapid initial DO uptake is insignificant, the time period between preparing dilution and measuring initial DO is not critical.

Use the azide modification of the iodometric method (Section 4500-O.C) or the membrane electrode method (Section 4500-O.G) to determine initial DO on all sample dilutions, dilution water blanks, and where appropriate, seed controls.

h. Dilution water blank: Use a dilution water blank as a rough check on quality of unseeded dilution water and cleanliness of incubation bottles. Together with each batch of samples incubate a bottle of unseeded dilution water. Determine initial and final DO as in ¶s 4g and j. The DO uptake should not be more than 0.2 mg/L and preferably not more than 0.1 mg/L.

i. Incubation: Incubate at 20°C ± 1°C BOD bottles containing desired dilutions, seed controls, dilution water blanks, and glucose-glutamic acid checks. Water-seal bottles as described in ¶ 4f.

j. Determination of final DO: After 5 d

incubation determine DO in sample dilutions, blanks, and checks as in ¶ 4g.

5. Calculation

When dilution water is not seeded:

$$BOD_5, \text{ mg/L} = \frac{D_1 - D_2}{P}$$

When dilution water is seeded:

$$BOD_5, \text{ mg/L} = \frac{(D_1 - D_2) - (B_1 - B_2) f}{P}$$

where:

D_1 = DO of diluted sample immediately after preparation, mg/L,

D_2 = DO of diluted sample after 5 d incubation at 20°C, mg/L,

P = decimal volumetric fraction of sample used,

B_1 = DO of seed control before incubation, mg/L (¶ 4d),

B_2 = DO of seed control after incubation mg/L (¶ 4d), and

f = ratio of seed in diluted sample to seed in seed control = (% seed in diluted sample)/(% seed in seed control).

If seed material is added directly to sample or to seed control bottles:

$$f = \text{(volume of seed in diluted sample)/(volume of seed in seed control)}$$

Report results as $CBOD_5$ if nitrification is inhibited.

If more than one sample dilution meets the criteria of a residual DO of at least 1 mg/L and a DO depletion of at least 2 mg/L and there is no evidence of toxicity at higher sample concentrations or the existence of an obvious anomaly, average results in the acceptable range.

In these calculations, do not make corrections for DO uptake by the dilution water blank during incubation. This correction is unnecessary if dilution water meets the blank criteria stipulated above. If the dilution water does not meet these criteria, proper corrections are difficult and results become questionable.

6. Precision and Bias

There is no measurement for establishing bias of the BOD procedure. The glucose-glutamic acid check prescribed in ¶ 4c is intended to be a reference point for evaluation of dilution water quality, seed effectiveness, and analytical technique. Single-laboratory tests using a 300-mg/L mixed glucose-glutamic acid solution provided the following results:[1]

Number of months: 14
Number of triplicates: 421
Average monthly recovery: 204 mg/L
Average monthly
standard deviation: 10.4 mg/L

In a series of interlaboratory studies,[2] each involving 2 to 112 laboratories (and as many analysts and seed sources), 5-d BOD measurements were made on synthetic water samples containing a 1:1 mixture of glucose and glutamic acid in the total concentration range of 3.3 to 231 mg/L. The regression equations for mean value, $\overline{X}$, and standard deviation, S, from these studies were:

$$\overline{X} = 0.658 \text{ (added level, mg/L)} + 0.280 \text{ mg/L}$$
$$S = 0.100 \text{ (added level, mg/L)} + 0.547 \text{ mg/L}$$

For the 300-mg/L mixed primary standard, the average 5-d BOD would be 198 mg/L with a standard deviation of 30.5 mg/L.

a. *Control limits:* Because of many factors affecting BOD tests in multilaboratory studies and the resulting extreme variability in test results, one standard deviation, as determined by interlaboratory tests, is recommended as a control limit for individual laboratories. Alternatively, for each laboratory, establish its control limits by performing a minimum of 25 glucose-glutamic acid checks (¶ 4c) over a period of several weeks or months and calculating the mean and standard deviation. Use the mean $\pm$ 3 standard deviations as the control limit for future glucose-glutamic acid checks. Compare calculated control limits to the single-laboratory tests presented above and to interlaboratory results. If control limits are outside the range of 198 $\pm$ 30.5, re-evaluate the control limits and investigate source of the problem. If measured BOD for a glucose-glutamic acid check is outside the accepted control limit range, reject tests made with that seed and dilution water.

b. Working range and detection limit: The working range is equal to the difference between the maximum initial DO (7 to 9 mg L) and minimum DO residual of 1 mg/L multiplied by the dilution factor. A lower detection limit of 2 mg/L is established by the requirement for a minimum DO depletion of 2 mg/L.

7. References

1. KENNEY, W. & J. RESNICK. 1987. Personal communication with J. C. Young. Water Pollution Control Plant, Davenport, Iowa.

2. U.S. ENVIRONMENTAL PROTECTION AGENCY, OFFICE OF RESEARCH AND DEVELOPMENT. 1986. Method-by-Method Statistics from Water Pollution (WP) Laboratory Performance Evaluation Studies. Quality Assurance Branch, Environmental Monitoring and Support Lab., Cincinnati, Ohio.

8. Bibliography

SAWYER, C.N. & L. BRADNEY. 1946. Modernization of the BOD test for determining the efficiency of the sewage treatment process. *Sewage Works J.* 18:1113.
RUCHHOFT, C.C., O.R. PLACAK, J. KACHMAR & C.E. CALBERT. 1948. Variations in BOD velocity constant of sewage dilutions. *Ind. Eng. Chem.* 40:1290.
ABBOTT, W.E. 1948. The bacteriostatic effects of methylene blue on the BOD test. *Water Sewage Works* 95:424.
SAWYER, C.N., P. CALLEJAS, M. MOORE & A.Q.Y. TOM. 1950. Primary standards for BOD work. *Sewage Ind. Wastes* 22:26.
YOUNG, J.C., G.N. McDERMOTT & D. JENKINS. 1981. Alterations in the BOD procedure for the 15th edition of Standard Methods for the Examination of Water and Wastewater. *J. Water Pollut. Control Fed.* 53:1253.

5220   CHEMICAL OXYGEN DEMAND (COD)*

5220 A.   Introduction

The chemical oxygen demand (COD) is used as a measure of the oxygen equivalent of the organic matter content of a sample that is susceptible to oxidation by a strong chemical oxidant. For samples from a specific source, COD can be related empirically to BOD, organic carbon, or organic matter. The test is useful for monitoring

and control after correlation has been established. The dichromate reflux method is preferred over procedures using other oxidants because of superior oxidizing ability, applicability to a wide variety of samples, and ease of manipulation. Oxidation of most organic compounds is 95 to 100% of the theoretical value. Pyridine and related compounds resist oxidation and vol-

*Approved by Standard Methods Committee, 1985.

atile organic compounds are oxidized only to the extent that they remain in contact with the oxidant. Ammonia, present either in the waste or liberated from nitrogen-containing organic matter, is not oxidized in the absence of significant concentration of free chloride ions.

1. Selection of Method

The open reflux method (B) is suitable for a wide range of wastes where a large sample size is preferred. The closed reflux methods (C and D) are more economical in the use of metallic salt reagents, but require homogenization of samples containing suspended solids to obtain reproducible results. Ampules and culture tubes with premeasured reagents are available commercially. Follow instructions furnished by the manufacturer.

Determine COD values of > 50 mg $O_2/$ L by using procedures 5220B.4a, C.4, or D.4. Use procedure 5220B.4b to determine, with lesser accuracy, COD values from 5 to 50 mg $O_2/$L.

2. Interferences and Limitations

Volatile straight-chain aliphatic compounds are not oxidized to any appreciable extent. This failure occurs partly because volatile organics are present in the vapor space and do not come in contact with the oxidizing liquid. Straight-chain aliphatic compounds are oxidized more effectively when silver sulfate (Ag_2SO_4) is added as a catalyst. However, Ag_2SO_4 reacts with chloride, bromide, and iodide to produce precipitates that are oxidized only partially. The difficulties caused by the presence of the halides can be overcome largely, though not completely, by complexing with mercuric sulfate ($HgSO_4$) before the refluxing procedure. Although 1 g $HgSO_4$ is specified for 50 mL sample, a lesser amount may be used where sample chloride concentration is known to be less than 2000

mg/L, as long as a 10:1 ratio of $HgSO_4:Cl^-$ is maintained. Do not use the test for samples containing more than 2000 mg $Cl^-/$ L. Techniques designed to measure COD in saline waters are available.[1,2]

Nitrite (NO_2^-) exerts a COD of 1.1 mg $O_2/$mg NO_2^--N. Because concentrations of NO_2^- in waters rarely exceed 1 or 2 mg NO_2^--N/L, the interference is considered insignificant and usually is ignored. To eliminate a significant interference due to NO_2^-, add 10 mg sulfamic acid for each mg NO_2^--N present in the sample volume used; add the same amount of sulfamic acid to the reflux vessel containing the distilled water blank.

Reduced inorganic species such as ferrous iron, sulfide, manganous manganese, etc., are oxidized quantitatively under the test conditions. For samples containing significant levels of these species, stoichiometric oxidation can be assumed from known initial concentration of the interfering species and corrections can be made to the COD value obtained.

3. Sampling and Storage

Preferably collect samples in glass bottles. Test unstable samples without delay. If delay before analysis is unavoidable, preserve sample by acidification to pH ≤ 2 using conc H_2SO_4. Blend samples containing settleable solids with a homogenizer to permit representative sampling. Make preliminary dilutions for wastes containing a high COD to reduce the error inherent in measuring small sample volumes.

4. References

1. BURNS, E.R. & C. MARSHALL. 1965. Correction for chloride interference in the chemical oxygen demand test. *J. Water Pollut. Control Fed.* 37:1716.
2. BAUMANN, F.I. 1974. Dichromate reflux chemical oxygen demand: A proposed method for chloride correction in highly saline waters. *Anal. Chem.* 46:1336.

5220 B.   Open Reflux Method

1. General Discussion

a. Principle: Most types of organic matter are oxidized by a boiling mixture of chromic and sulfuric acids. A sample is refluxed in strongly acid solution with a known excess of potassium dichromate ($K_2Cr_2O_7$). After digestion, the remaining unreduced $K_2Cr_2O_7$ is titrated with ferrous ammonium sulfate to determine the amount of $K_2Cr_2O_7$ consumed and the oxidizable organic matter is calculated in terms of oxygen equivalent. Keep ratios of reagent weights, volumes, and strengths constant when sample volumes other than 50 mL are used. The standard 2-h reflux time may be reduced if it has been shown that a shorter period yields the same results.

2. Apparatus

Reflux apparatus, consisting of 500- or 250-mL erlenmeyer flasks with ground-glass 24/40 neck* and 300-mm jacket Liebig, West, or equivalent condenser† with 24/40 ground-glass joint, and a hot plate having sufficient power to produce at least 1.4 W/cm^2 of heating surface, or equivalent.

3. Reagents

a. Standard potassium dichromate solution, 0.0417M: Dissolve 12.259 g $K_2Cr_2O_7$, primary standard grade, previously dried at 103°C for 2 h, in distilled water and dilute to 1000 mL.

b. Sulfuric acid reagent: Add Ag_2SO_4, reagent or technical grade, crystals or powder, to conc H_2SO_4 at the rate of 5.5 g Ag_2SO_4/kg H_2SO_4. Let stand 1 to 2 d to dissolve Ag_2SO_4.

c. Ferroin indicator solution: Dissolve 1.485 g 1,10-phenanthroline monohydrate and 695 mg $FeSO_4 \cdot 7H_2O$ in distilled water and dilute to 100 mL. This indicator so-

lution may be purchased already prepared.‡

d. Standard ferrous ammonium sulfate (FAS) titrant, approximately 0.25M: Dissolve 98 g $Fe(NH_4)_2(SO_4)_2 \cdot 6H_2O$ in distilled water. Add 20 mL conc H_2SO_4, cool, and dilute to 1000 mL. Standardize this solution daily against standard $K_2Cr_2O_7$ solution as follows:

Dilute 10.0 mL standard $K_2Cr_2O_7$ to about 100 mL. Add 30 mL conc H_2SO_4 and cool. Titrate with FAS titrant using 0.10 to 0.15 mL (2 to 3 drops) ferroin indicator.

Molarity of FAS solution

$$= \frac{\text{Volume } 0.0417M \text{ } K_2Cr_2O_7}{\text{Volume FAS used in titration, mL}} \times 0.25$$

e. Mercuric sulfate, $HgSO_4$, crystals or powder.

f. Sulfamic acid: Required only if the interference of nitrites is to be eliminated (see 5220A.2 above).

g. Potassium hydrogen phthalate (KHP) standard: Lightly crush and then dry potassium hydrogen phthalate ($HOOCC_6H_4COOK$) to constant weight at 120°C. Dissolve 425 mg in distilled water and dilute to 1000 mL. KHP has a theoretical COD[1] of 1.176 mg O_2/mg and this solution has a theoretical COD of 500 μg O_2/mL. This solution is stable when refrigerated for up to 3 months in the absence of visible biological growth.

4. Procedure

a. Treatment of samples with COD of > 50 mg O_2/L: Place 50.0 mL sample (for samples with COD of > 900 mg O_2/L, use smaller sample portion diluted to 50.0 mL) in a 500-mL refluxing flask. Add 1 g $HgSO_4$, several glass beads, and very slowly add 5.0 mL sulfuric acid reagent, with mix-

---

*Corning 5000 or equivalent.
†Corning 2360, 91548, or equivalent.

‡GFS Chemical Co., Columbus, Ohio.

ing to dissolve $HgSO_4$. Cool while mixing to avoid possible loss of volatile materials. Add 25.0 mL 0.0417M $K_2Cr_2O_7$ solution and mix. Attach flask to condenser and turn on cooling water. Add remaining sulfuric acid reagent (70 mL) through open end of condenser. Continue swirling and mixing while adding the sulfuric acid reagent. CAUTION: *Mix reflux mixture thoroughly before applying heat to prevent local heating of flask bottom and a possible blowout of flask contents.*

Cover open end of condenser with a small beaker to prevent foreign material from entering refluxing mixture and reflux for 2 h. Cool and wash down condenser with distilled water. Disconnect reflux condenser and dilute mixture to about twice its volume with distilled water. Cool to room temperature and titrate excess $K_2Cr_2O_7$ with FAS, using 0.10 to 0.15 mL (2 to 3 drops) ferroin indicator. Although the quantity of ferroin indicator is not critical, use the same volume for all titrations. Take as the end point of the titration the first sharp color change from blue-green to reddish brown. The blue-green may reappear. In the same manner, reflux and titrate a blank containing the reagents and a volume of distilled water equal to that of sample.

b. Alternate procedure for low-COD samples: Follow procedure of ¶ 4*a*, with two exceptions: (*i*) use standard 0.00417M $K_2Cr_2O_7$, and (*ii*) titrate with 0.025M FAS. Exercise extreme care with this procedure because even a trace of organic matter on the glassware or from the atmosphere may cause gross errors. If a further increase in sensitivity is required, concentrate a larger volume of sample before digesting under reflux as follows: Add all reagents to a sample larger than 50 mL and reduce total volume to 150 mL by boiling in the refluxing flask open to the atmosphere without the condenser attached. Compute amount of $HgSO_4$ to be added (before concentration) on the basis of a weight ratio

of 10:1, $HgSO_4$:Cl^-, using the amount of Cl^- present in the original volume of sample. Carry a blank reagent through the same procedure. This technique has the advantage of concentrating the sample without significant losses of easily digested volatile materials. Hard-to-digest volatile materials such as volatile acids are lost, but an improvement is gained over ordinary evaporative concentration methods.

c. Determination of standard solution: Evaluate the technique and quality of reagents by conducting the test on a standard potassium hydrogen phthalate solution.

5. Calculation

$$\text{COD as mg } O_2/L = \frac{(A - B) \times M \times 8000}{\text{mL sample}}$$

where:

  A = mL FAS used for blank,
  B = mL FAS used for sample, and
  M = molarity of FAS.

6. Precision and Bias

A set of synthetic samples containing potassium hydrogen phthalate and NaCl was tested by 74 laboratories. At a COD of 200 mg O_2/L in the absence of chloride, the standard deviation was ±13 mg/L (coefficient of variation, 6.5%). At COD of 160 mg O_2/L and 100 mg Cl^-/L, the standard deviation was ±14 mg/L (coefficient of variation, 10.8%).

7. Reference

1. PITWELL, L.R. 1983. Standard COD. *Chem. Brit.* 19:907.

8. Bibliography

MOORE, W.A., R.C. KRONER & C.C. RUCHHOFT. 1949. Dichromate reflux method for determination of oxygen consumed. *Anal. Chem.* 21:953.
MEDALIA, A.I. 1951. Test for traces of organic matter in water. *Anal. Chem.* 23:1318.
MOORE, W.A., F.J. LUDZACK & C.C. RUCHHOFT.

1951. Determination of oxygen-consumed values of organic wastes. *Anal. Chem.* 23:1297.

DOBBS, R.A. & R.T. WILLIAMS. 1963. Elimination of chloride interference in the chemical oxygen demand test. *Anal. Chem.* 35:1064.

5220 C.　Closed Reflux, Titrimetric Method

1. General Discussion

a. Principle: See 5220B.1*a*.

b. Interferences and limitations: See 5220A.2. Volatile organic compounds are more completely oxidized in the closed system because of longer contact with the oxidant. Before each use inspect culture-tube caps for breaks in the TFE liner. Select culture-tube size for the degree of sensitivity desired. Use the 25- × 150-mm tube for samples with low COD content because a larger volume sample can be treated.

2. Apparatus

a. Digestion vessels: Preferably use borosilicate culture tubes, 16- × 100-mm, 20- × 150-mm, or 25- × 150-mm, with TFE-lined screw caps. Alternatively, use borosilicate ampules, 10-mL capacity, 19- to 20-mm diam.

b. Heating block, cast aluminum, 45 to 50 mm deep, with holes sized for close fit of culture tubes or ampules.

c. Block heater or oven, to operate at 150 ± 2°C. NOTE: Severe damage of most culture tube closures from oven digestion introduces a potential source of contamination and increases the probability of leakage. Use an oven for culture-tube digestion only when it has been determined that 2 h exposure at 150°C will not damage the caps.

d. Ampule sealer: Use only a mechanical sealer to insure strong, consistent seals.

3. Reagents

a. Standard potassium dichromate digestion solution, 0.0167*M*: Add to about 500 mL distilled water 4.913 g $K_2Cr_2O_7$, pri-

mary standard grade, previously dried at 103°C for 2 h, 167 mL conc H_2SO_4, and 33.3 g $HgSO_4$. Dissolve, cool to room temperature, and dilute to 1000 mL.

b. Sulfuric acid reagent: See Section 5220B.3*b*.

c. Ferroin indicator solution: See Section 5220B.3*c*.

d. Standard ferrous ammonium sulfate titrant (FAS), approximately 0.10*M*: Dissolve 39.2 g $Fe(NH_4)_2(SO_4)_2 \cdot 6H_2O$ in distilled water. Add 20 mL conc H_2SO_4, cool, and dilute to 1000 mL. Standardize solution daily against standard $K_2Cr_2O_7$ digestion solution as follows:

Add reagents according to Table 5220:I to a culture tube containing the correct volume of distilled water substituted for sample. Cool tube to room temperature and add 0.05 to 0.10 mL (1 to 2 drops) ferroin indicator and titrate with FAS titrant.

Molarity of FAS solution

$$= \frac{\text{Volume } 0.0167M \text{ } K_2Cr_2O_7 \text{ solution titrated, mL}}{\text{Volume FAS used in titration, mL}} \times 0.10$$

e. Sulfamic acid: See Section 5220B.3*f*.

f. Potassium hydrogen phthalate standard: See Section 5220B.3*g*.

4. Procedure

Wash culture tubes and caps with 20% H_2SO_4 before first use to prevent contamination. Refer to Table 5220:I for proper sample and reagent volumes. Place sample in culture tube or ampule and add digestion solution. Carefully run sulfuric acid reagent down inside of vessel so an acid layer

TABLE 5220:I. SAMPLE AND REAGENT QUANTITIES FOR VARIOUS DIGESTION VESSELS

Digestion Vessel	Sample mL	Digestion Solution mL	Sulfuric Acid Reagent mL	Total Final Volume mL
Culture tubes:				
16 × 100 mm	2.5	1.5	3.5	7.5
20 × 150 mm	5.0	3.0	7.0	15.0
25 × 150 mm	10.0	6.0	14.0	30.0
Standard 10-mL				
ampules	2.5	1.5	3.5	7.5

is formed under the sample-digestion solution layer. Tightly cap tubes or seal ampules, and invert each several times to mix completely. CAUTION: *Wear face shield and protect hands from heat produced when contents of vessels are mixed. Mix thoroughly before applying heat to prevent local heating of vessel bottom and possible explosive reaction.*

Place tubes or ampules in block digester or oven preheated to 150°C and reflux for 2 h. Cool to room temperature and place vessels in test tube rack. Remove culture tube caps and add small TFE-covered magnetic stirring bar. If ampules are used, transfer contents to a larger container for titrating. Add 0.05 to 0.10 mL (1 to 2 drops) ferroin indicator and stir rapidly on magnetic stirrer while titrating with 0.10M FAS. The end point is a sharp color change from blue-green to reddish brown, although the blue-green may reappear within minutes. In the same manner reflux and titrate a blank containing the reagents and a volume of distilled water equal to that of the sample.

5. Calculation

$$\text{COD as mg O}_2/\text{L} = \frac{(A - B) \times M \times 8000}{\text{mL sample}}$$

where:
  A = mL FAS used for blank,
  B = mL FAS used for sample, and
  M = molarity of FAS.

6. Precision and Bias

Sixty synthetic samples containing potassium hydrogen phthalate and NaCl were tested by six laboratories. At an average COD of 195 mg O_2/L in the absence of chloride, the standard deviation was ±11 mg O_2/L (coefficient of variation, 5.6%). At an average COD of 208 mg O_2/L and 100 mg Cl^-/L, the standard deviation was ±10 mg O_2/L (coefficient of variation, 4.8%).

5220 D.   Closed Reflux, Colorimetric Method

1. General Discussion

a. Principle: See Section 5220B.1*a*. Colorimetric reaction vessels are sealed glass ampules or capped culture tubes. Oxygen consumed is measured against standards at 600 nm with a spectrophotometer.

b. Interferences and limitations: See Section 5220C.1*b*.

2. Apparatus

a. See Section 5220C.2.

b. Spectrophotometer, for use at 600 nm with access opening adapter for ampule or 16-, 20-, or 25-mm tubes.

3. Reagents

a. Digestion solution: Add to about 500 mL distilled water 10.216 g $K_2Cr_2O_7$, primary standard grade, previously dried at 103°C for 2 h, 167 mL conc H_2SO_4, and 33.3 g $HgSO_4$. Dissolve, cool to room temperature, and dilute to 1000 mL.

b. Sulfuric acid reagent: See 5220B.3*b*.

c. Sulfamic acid: See Section 5220B.3*f.*

d. Potassium hydrogen phthalate standard: See Section 5220B.3*g.*

4. Procedure

a. Treatment of samples: Measure suitable volume of sample and reagents into tube or ampule as indicated in Table 5220:I. Prepare, digest, and cool samples, blank, and one or more standards as directed in Section 5220C.4.

b. Measurement of dichromate reduction: Invert cooled samples, blank, and standards several times and allow solids to settle before measuring absorbance. Dislodge solids that adhere to container wall by gentle tapping and settling. Insert unopened tube or ampule through access door into light path of spectrophotometer set at 600 nm. Read absorbance and compare to calibration curve. Use optically matched culture tubes or ampules for greater sensitivity; discard scratched or blemished glassware.

c. Preparation of calibration curve: Prepare at least five standards from potassium hydrogen phthalate solution with COD equivalents from 20 to 900 mg O_2/L. Make up to volume with distilled water; use same reagent volumes, tube, or ampule size, and digestion procedure as for samples. Prepare calibration curve for each new lot of tubes or ampules or when standards prepared in ¶ 4*a* differ by $\geq 5\%$ from calibration curve.

5. Calculation

COD as mg O_2/L

$$= \frac{\text{mg } O_2 \text{ in final volume} \times 1000}{\text{mL sample}}$$

6. Precision and Bias

Forty-eight synthetic samples containing potassium hydrogen phthalate and NaCl were tested by five laboratories. At an average COD of 193 mg O_2/L in the absence of chloride, the standard deviation was ± 17 mg O_2/L (coefficient of variation 8.7%). At an average COD of 212 mg O_2/L and 100 mg Cl^-/L, the standard deviation was ± 20 mg O_2/L (coefficient of variation, 9.6%).

7. Bibliography

JIRKA, A.M. & M.J. CARTER. 1975. Micro semi-automated analysis of surface and wastewaters for chemical oxygen demand. *Anal. Chem.* 47:1397.

HIMEBAUGH, R.R. & M.J. SMITH. 1979. Semi-micro tube method for chemical oxygen demand. *Anal. Chem.* 51:1085.

5310   TOTAL ORGANIC CARBON (TOC)*

5310 A.   Introduction

1. General Discussion

The organic carbon in water and wastewater is composed of a variety of organic compounds in various oxidation states. Some of these carbon compounds can be oxidized further by biological or chemical processes, and the biochemical oxygen demand (BOD) and chemical oxygen demand (COD) may be used to characterize these fractions. The presence of organic carbon that does not respond to either the BOD or COD test makes them unsuitable for the measurement of total organic carbon. Total organic carbon (TOC) is a more convenient and direct expression of total organic content than either BOD or COD, but does not provide the same kind of information. If a repeatable empirical relationship is established between TOC and BOD or COD, then TOC can be used to estimate the accompanying BOD or COD. This relationship must be established independently for each set of matrix conditions, such as various points in a treatment process. Unlike BOD or COD, TOC is independent of the oxidation state of the organic matter and does not measure other organically bound elements, such as nitrogen and hydrogen, and inorganics that can contribute to the oxygen demand measured by BOD and COD. TOC measurement does not replace BOD and COD testing.

To determine the quantity of organically bound carbon, the organic molecules must be broken down to single carbon units and converted to a single molecular form that can be measured quantitatively. TOC

*Approved by Standard Methods Committee, 1985.

methods utilize heat and oxygen, ultraviolet irradiation, chemical oxidants, or combinations of these oxidants to convert organic carbon to carbon dioxide (CO_2). The CO_2 may be measured directly by a nondispersive infrared analyzer, it may be reduced to methane and measured with a flame ionization detector, or CO_2 may be titrated chemically.

2. Fractions of Total Carbon

The methods and instruments used in measuring TOC analyze fractions of total carbon (TC) and measure TOC by two or more determinations. These fractions of total carbon are defined as: inorganic carbon (IC)—the carbonate, bicarbonate, and dissolved CO_2; total organic carbon (TOC)—all carbon atoms covalently bonded in organic molecules; dissolved organic carbon (DOC)—the fraction of TOC that passes through a 0.45-μm-pore-diam filter; nondissolved organic carbon (NDOC)—also referred to as particulate organic carbon, the fraction of TOC retained by a 0.45-μm filter; purgeable organic carbon (POC)—also referred to as volatile organic carbon, the fraction of TOC removed from an aqueous solution by gas stripping under specified conditions; and nonpurgeable organic carbon (NPOC)—the fraction of TOC not removed by gas stripping.

In most water samples, the IC fraction is many times greater than the TOC fraction. Eliminating or compensating for IC interferences requires multiple determinations to measure true TOC. IC interference can be eliminated by acidifying samples to pH 2 or less to convert IC species to CO_2. Subsequently, purging the sample with a purified gas removes the CO_2 by volatilization. Sample purging also removes POC so that the organic carbon measurement made after eliminating IC interferences is actually a NPOC determination; determine POC to measure true TOC. In many surface and ground waters the POC contribution to TOC is negligible. Therefore, in practice, the NPOC determination is substituted for TOC.

Alternatively, IC interference may be compensated for by separately measuring total carbon (TC) and inorganic carbon. The difference between TC and IC is TOC.

The purgeable fraction of TOC is a function of the specific conditions and equipment employed. Sample temperature and salinity, gas-flow rate, type of gas diffuser, purging-vessel dimensions, volume purged, and purging time affect the division of TOC into purgeable and nonpurgeable fractions. When separately measuring POC and NPOC on the same sample, use identical conditions for purging during the POC measurement as in purging to prepare the NPOC portion for analysis. Consider the conditions of purging when comparing POC or NPOC data from different laboratories or different instruments.

3. Selection of Method

The combustion-infrared method (B) is suitable for samples with TOC ≥ 1 mg/L.

For lower concentrations, use the persulfate-ultraviolet oxidation method (C) or the wet-oxidation method (D). See 5310B.1, C.1, and D.1.

4. Bibliography

FORD, D.L. 1968. Total organic carbon as a wastewater parameter. *Pub. Works* 99:89.

FREDERICKS, A.D. 1968. Concentration of organic carbon in the Gulf of Mexico. Off. Naval Res. Rep. 68-27T.

WILLIAMS, P.M. 1969. The determination of dissolved organic carbon in seawater: A comparison of two methods. *Limnol. Oceanogr.* 14:297.

CROLL, B.T. 1972. Determination of organic carbon in water. *Chem. Ind.* (London), 110:386.

SHARP, J. 1973. Total organic carbon in seawater—comparison of measurements using persulfate oxidation and high temperature combustion. *Mar. Chem.* 1:211.

BORTLIJZ, J. 1976. Instrumental TOC analysis. *Vom Wasser* 46:35.

VAN STEENDEREN, R.A. 1976. Parameters which influence the organic carbon determination in water. *Water SA* 2:156.

TAKAHASHI, Y. 1979. Analysis Techniques for Organic Carbon and Organic Halogen. Proc. EPA/NATO-CCMS Conf. on Adsorption Techniques, Reston, Va.

STANDING COMMITTEE OF ANALYSIS, DEPARTMENT OF THE ENVIRONMENT, NATIONAL WATER COUNCIL. 1980. The instrumental determination of total organic carbon, total oxygen demand and related determinants, 1979. Her Majesty's Stationery Off., London.

WERSHAW, R.L., M.J. FISHMAN, R.R. GRABBE & L.E. LOWE, eds. 1983. Methods for the Determination of Organic Substances in Water and Fluvial Sediments. U.S. Geological Survey Techniques of Water-Resources Investigations, Book 5, Laboratory Analysis, Chapter A3.

5310 B.   Combustion-Infrared Method

1. General Discussion

The combustion-infrared method has been used for a wide variety of samples, but its accuracy is dependent on particle size reduction because it uses small-orifice syringes.

a. Principle: The sample is homogenized

and diluted as necessary and a microportion is injected into a heated reaction chamber packed with an oxidative catalyst such as cobalt oxide. The water is vaporized and the organic carbon is oxidized to CO_2 and H_2O. The CO_2 from oxidation of organic and inorganic carbon is transported in the carrier-gas streams and is measured by means of a nondispersive infrared analyzer.

Because total carbon is measured, IC must be measured separately and TOC obtained by difference.

Measure IC by injecting the sample into a separate reaction chamber packed with phosphoric acid-coated quartz beads. Under the acidic conditions, all IC is converted to CO_2, which is measured. Under these conditions organic carbon is not oxidized and only IC is measured.

Alternatively, convert inorganic carbonates to CO_2 with acid and remove the CO_2 by purging before sample injection. The sample contains only the NPOC fraction of total carbon; a POC determination also is necessary to measure true TOC.

b. Interference: Removal of carbonate and bicarbonate by acidification and purging with purified gas results in the loss of volatile organic substances. The volatiles also can be lost during sample blending, particularly if the temperature is allowed to rise. Another important loss can occur if large carbon-containing particles fail to enter the needle used for injection. Filtration, although necessary to eliminate particulate organic matter when only DOC is to be determined, can result in loss or gain of DOC, depending on the physical properties of the carbon-containing compounds and the adsorption of carbonaceous material on the filter, or its desorption from it. Check filters for their contribution to DOC by analyzing a filtered blank. Note that any contact with organic material may contaminate a sample. Avoid contaminated glassware, plastic containers, and rubber tubing. Analyze treatment, system, and reagent blanks.

c. Minimum detectable concentration: 1 mg carbon/L. This can be achieved with most combustion-infrared analyzers although instrument performance varies. The minimum detectable concentration may be reduced by concentrating the sample, or by increasing the portion taken for analysis.

d. Sampling and storage: Collect and store samples in amber glass bottles with TFE-lined cap. Before use, wash bottles with acid, seal with aluminum foil, and bake at 400°C for at least 1 h. Wash TFE septa with detergent, rinse repeatedly with organic-free water, wrap in aluminum foil, and bake at 100°C for 1 h. Preferably use thick silicone rubber-backed TFE septa with open ring caps to produce a positive seal. Because the detection limit is relatively high, less rigorous cleaning may be acceptable; use bottle blanks with each set of samples. Use a Kemmerer or similar type sampler for collecting samples from a depth exceeding 2 m. Preserve samples that cannot be examined promptly by holding at 4°C with minimal exposure to light and atmosphere. Acidification with phosphoric or sulfuric acid to a pH ≤ 2 may be used only if inorganic carbon subsequently is purged. Under any conditions, minimize storage time.

2. Apparatus

a. Total organic carbon analyzer.*

b. Syringes: 0 to 50-μL, 0 to 200-μL, 0 to 500-μL, and 0 to 1-mL capacity.†

c. Sample blender or homogenizer.

d. Magnetic stirrer and TFE-coated stirring bars.

e. Filtering apparatus and 0.45-μm-pore-diam filters.

---

*Beckman Instruments Model No. 915B or equivalent.
†Hamilton No. 705 N or 750 N: CR-700-20 or CR-700-200 with needle point style No. 3, or equivalent. Spring-loaded syringe may improve reproducibility.

3. Reagents

a. Reagent water: Prepare blanks and standard solutions from carbon-free water; preferably use carbon-filtered, redistilled water.

b. Phosphoric acid, H_3PO_4, conc. Alternatively use sulfuric acid, H_2SO_4, but not hydrochloric acid.

c. Organic carbon stock solution: Dissolve 2.1254 g anhydrous potassium biphthalate, $C_8H_5KO_4$, in carbon-free water and dilute to 1000 mL; 1.00 mL = 1.00 mg carbon. Alternatively, use any other organic-carbon-containing compound of adequate purity, stability, and water solubility. Preserve by acidifying with H_3PO_4 or H_2SO_4 to pH ≤ 2.

d. Inorganic carbon stock solution: Dissolve 4.4122 g anhydrous sodium carbonate, Na_2CO_3, in water, add 3.497 g anhydrous sodium bicarbonate, $NaHCO_3$, and dilute to 1000 mL; 1.00 mL = 1.00 mg carbon. Alternatively, use any other inorganic carbonate compound of adequate purity, stability, and water solubility. Keep tightly stoppered. Do not acidify.

e. Carrier gas: Purified oxygen or air, CO_2-free and containing less than 1 ppm hydrocarbon (as methane).

f. Purging gas: Any gas free of CO_2 and hydrocarbons.

4. Procedure

a. Instrument operation: Follow manufacturer's instructions for analyzer assembly, testing, calibration, and operation. Adjust to optimum combustion temperature (900°C) before using instrument; monitor temperature to insure stability.

b. Sample treatment: If a sample contains gross solids or insoluble matter, homogenize until satisfactory replication is obtained. Analyze a homogenizing blank consisting of reagent water carried through the homogenizing treatment.

If inorganic carbon must be removed before analysis, transfer a representative portion of 10 to 15 mL to a 30-mL beaker, add conc H_3PO_4 to reduce pH to 2 or less, and purge with gas for 10 min. Do not use plastic tubing. Inorganic carbon also may be removed by stirring the acidified sample in a beaker while directing a stream of purified gas into the beaker. Because volatile organic carbon will be lost during purging of the acidified solution, report organic carbon as total nonpurgeable organic carbon.

If the available instrument provides for a separate determination of inorganic carbon (carbonate, bicarbonate, free CO_2) and total carbon, omit decarbonation and proceed according to the manufacturer's directions to determine TOC by difference between TC and IC.

If dissolved organic carbon is to be determined, filter sample through 0.45-μm-pore-diam filter with vacuum; analyze a filtering blank.

c. Sample injection: Withdraw a portion of prepared sample using a syringe fitted with a blunt-tipped needle. Select sample volume according to manufacturer's direction. Stir samples containing particulates with a magnetic stirrer. Select needle size consistent with sample particulate size. Inject samples and standards into analyzer according to manufacturer's directions and record response. Repeat injection until consecutive peaks are obtained that are reproducible to within $\pm 10\%$.

d. Preparation of standard curve: Prepare standard organic and inorganic carbon series by diluting stock solutions to cover the expected range in samples. Inject and record peak height of these standards and a dilution water blank. Plot carbon concentration in milligrams per liter against corrected peak height in millimeters on rectangular coordinate paper. This is unnecessary for instruments provided with a digital readout of concentration. If desirable, prepare a standard curve having concentrations of 1 to 10 mg/L by making appropriate dilutions of the standards.

With most TOC analyzers, it is not possible to determine separate blanks for reagent water, reagents, and the entire system. In addition, some TOC analyzers produce a variable and erratic blank that cannot be corrected reliably. In many laboratories, reagent water is the major contributor to the blank value. Correcting only the peak heights of standards (which contain reagent water + reagents + system blank) creates a positive error, while also correcting samples (which contain only reagents and system blank contributions) for the reagent water blank creates a negative error. Minimize errors by using reagent water and reagents low in carbon.

Inject samples and procedural blanks (consisting of reagent water taken through any pre-analysis steps—values are typically higher than those for reagent water) and determine sample organic carbon concentrations by comparing corrected peak heights to the calibration curve.

5. Calculations

a. When reagent water is a major portion of the total blank:

1) Calculate corrected peak height of standards by subtracting the reagent-water blank peak height from the standard peak heights.

2) Prepare a standard curve of corrected peak height vs. TOC concentration.

3) Subtract the procedural blank from each sample peak height and compare to the standard curve to determine carbon content.

NOTE: There will be a positive error if the TOC of the reagent water is significant in comparison to the TOC of the sample. Make a special effort to obtain carbon-free reagent water.

4) Apply the appropriate dilution factor when necessary.

5) Subtract the inorganic carbon from the total carbon when TOC is determined by difference.

b. When reagent water is a minor portion of the total blank:

1) Calculate corrected peak height of standards and samples by subtracting the reagent-water blank peak height from the standard and sample peak heights.

2) Prepare a standard curve of corrected peak height vs. TOC concentration.

3) Subtract the procedural blank from each sample peak height and compare to the standard curve to determine the carbon content. Values will have a negative error equal to the blank contribution from the reagent water.

4) Apply the appropriate dilution factor when necessary.

5) Subtract the inorganic carbon from the total carbon when TOC is determined by difference.

NOTE: If the TOC analyzer design permits isolation of each of the contributions to the total blank, apply appropriate blank corrections to peak heights of standards (reagent blank, water blank, system blank) and sample (reagent blank and system blank).

6. Precision

The difficulty of sampling particulate matter on unfiltered samples limits the precision of the method to approximately 5 to 10%. On clear samples or on those that have been filtered before analysis, precision approaches 1 to 2% or ± 1 to 2 mg carbon/L, whichever is greater.

7. Bibliography

KATZ, J., S. ABRAHAN & N. BAKER. 1954. Analytical procedure using a combined combustion-diffusion vessel: Improved method for combustion of organic compounds in aqueous solution. *Anal. Chem.* 26:1503.

VAN HALL, C.E., J. SAFRANKO & V. A. STENGER. 1963. Rapid combustion method for the determination of organic substances in aqueous solutions. *Anal. Chem.* 35:315.

SCHAFFER, R.B. et al. 1965. Application of a carbon analyzer in waste treatment. *J. Water Pollut. Control Fed.* 37:1545.

VAN HALL, C.E., D. BARTH & V. A. STENGER. 1965. Elimination of carbonates from aqueous solutions prior to organic carbon determinations. *Anal. Chem.* 37:769.

BUSCH, A.W. 1966. Energy, total carbon and oxygen demand. *Water Resour. Res.* 2:59.

BLACKMORE, R.H. & D. VOSHEL. 1967. Rapid determination of total organic carbon (TOC) in sewage. *Water Sewage Works* 114:398.

WILLIAMS, R.T. 1967. Water-pollution instrumentation—Analyzer looks for organic carbon. *Instrum. Technol.* 14:63.

5310 C.　Persulfate-Ultraviolet Oxidation Method

1. General Discussion

Many instruments utilizing persulfate oxidation of organic carbon are available. They depend either on heat or ultraviolet irradiation activation of the reagents. The persulfate-ultraviolet oxidation method is a rapid, precise method for the measurement of trace levels of organic carbon in water and is of particular interest to the electronic, pharmaceutical, and steampower-generation industries where even trace concentrations of organic compounds may degrade ion-exchange capacity, serve as a nutrient source for biological growth, or be detrimental to the process for which the water is being utilized.

a. Principle: Organic carbon is oxidized to carbon dioxide, CO_2, by persulfate in the presence of ultraviolet light. The CO_2 produced may be measured directly by a nondispersive infrared analyzer, be reduced to methane and measured by a flame ionization detector, or be chemically titrated.

Instruments are available that utilize an ultraviolet lamp submerged in a continuously gas-purged reactor that is filled with a constant-feed persulfate solution. The samples are introduced serially into the reactor by an autosampler or they are injected manually. The CO_2 produced is sparged continuously from the solution and is carried in the gas stream to an infrared analyzer that is specifically tuned to the absorptive wavelength of CO_2. The instrument's microprocessor calculates the area of the peaks produced by the analyzer, compares them to the peak area of the calibration standard stored in its memory, and prints out a calibrated organic carbon value in milligrams per liter.

b. Interferences: See Section 5310B.1. Excessive acidification of sample, producing a reduction in pH of the persulfate solution to 1 or less, can result in sluggish and incomplete oxidation of organic carbon.

The intensity of the ultraviolet light reaching the sample matrix may be reduced by highly turbid samples or with aging of the ultraviolet source, resulting in sluggish or incomplete oxidation. Large organic particles or very large or complex organic molecules such as tannins, lignins, and humic acid may be oxidized slowly because persulfate oxidation is rate-limited. Because the efficiency of conversion of organic carbon to CO_2 may be affected by many factors, check efficiency of oxidation with selected model compounds representative of the sample matrix.

Persulfate oxidation of organic molecules is slowed in samples containing significant concentrations of chloride by the preferential oxidation of chloride; at a concentration of 0.1%, chloride oxidation of organic matter may be inhibited completely. To remove this interference add mercuric nitrate to the persulfate solution.

With any organic carbon measurement, contamination during sample handling and treatment is a likely source of interference. This is especially true of trace analysis. Take extreme care in sampling, handling, and analysis of samples below 1 mg TOC/L.

c. *Minimum detectable concentration:* Concentration of 0.05 mg organic carbon/L can be measured if scrupulous attention is given to minimizing sample contamination and method background. Use the combustion-infrared method (B) for high concentrations of TOC.

d. *Sampling and storage:* See Section 5310B.1d.

2. Apparatus

a. *Total organic carbon analyzer.**

b. *Syringes:* 0 to 50-μL, 0 to 250-μL, and 0 to 1-mL capacity, fitted with a blunt-tipped needle.

3. Reagents

See Section 5310B.3.

4. Procedure

a. *Instrument operation:* Follow manufacturer's instructions for assembly, testing, calibration, and operation.

b. *Sample preparation:* If a sample contains gross particulates or insoluble matter, homogenize until a representative portion can be withdrawn through the syringe needle or autosampler tubing.

If dissolved organic carbon is to be determined, filter sample and a reagent water blank through 0.45-μm glass fiber filter with vacuum. Pretreat filter by submerging overnight in a 1:1 solution of HNO_3 and reagent water and collect in an acid-washed, baked flask. Use a clean filter and flask for each sample.

To determine NPOC, transfer 15 to 30 mL sample to a flask or test tube and acidify to a pH of 2. Purge according to manufacturer's recommendations.

c. *Sample injection:* See Section 5310B.4c.

d. *Standard curve preparation:* Prepare an organic carbon standard series over the range of organic carbon concentrations in the samples. Inject standards and blanks and record analyzer's response. Determine peak area for each standard and blank. Determinations based on peak height may be inadequate because of differences in the rate of oxidation of standards and samples. Correct peak area of standards by subtracting reagent water blank and plot organic carbon concentration in milligrams per liter against corrected peak area. For instruments providing a digital readout of concentration, this is not necessary.

Inject samples, treatment blanks, if applicable, and instrument blank. Subtract appropriate blank's peak area from each sample's peak area and determine organic carbon from the standard curve.

5. Calculation

See Section 5310B.5, but use peak area rather than peak height.

6. Precision and Bias

See Table 5310:I.

7. Bibliography

BEATTIE, J., C. BRICKER & D. GARVIN. 1961. Photolytic determination of trace amounts of organic material in water. *Anal. Chem.* 33:1890.

ARMSTRONG, F.A.J., P.M. WILLIAMS & J.D.H. STRICKLAND. 1966. Photooxidation of organic matter in sea water by ultraviolet radiation, analytical and other applications. *Nature* 211:481.

BRAMER, H.C., M.J. WALSH & S.C. CARUSO. 1966. Instrument for monitoring trace organic compounds in water. *Water Sewage Works* 113:275.

DOBBS, R.A., R. H. WISE & R. B. DEAN. 1967. Measurement of organic carbon in water using the hydrogen flame ionization detector. *Anal. Chem.* 39:1255.

MONTGOMERY, H.A.C. & N.S. THOM. 1967. The determination of low concentrations of organic carbon in water. *Analyst* 87:689.

ARMSTRONG, F.A.J. & S. TIBBITS. 1968. Photochemical combustion of organic matter in seawater for nitrogen, phosphorus and carbon

---

*Xertex-Dohrmann DC-80 or equivalent.

TABLE 5310:I. PRECISION AND BIAS FOR TOTAL ORGANIC CARBON (TOC) BY PERSULFATE-ULTRAVIOLET OXIDATION

Characteristic of Analysis	Spring Water	Spring Water +0.15 mg/L KHP*	Tap Water	Tap Water +10 mg/L KHP*	Municipal Wastewater Effluent
Concentration determined, mg/L:					
Replicate 1	0.402	0.559	2.47	11.70	5.88
Replicate 2	0.336	0.491	2.49	11.53	5.31
Replicate 3	0.340	0.505	2.47	11.70	5.21
Replicate 4	0.341	0.523	2.47	11.64	5.17
Replicate 5	0.355	0.542	2.46	11.55	5.10
Replicate 6	0.366	0.546	2.46	11.68	5.33
Replicate 7	0.361	0.548	2.42	11.55	5.35
Mean, mg/L	0.35	0.53	2.46	11.53	5.32
Standard deviation:					
mg/L	0.02	0.03	0.02	0.21	0.23
%	6	6	1	2	4
Actual value, mg/L	—	0.50	—	12.46	—
Recovery, %	—	106	—	93	—
Error, %	—	6	—	7	—

*KHP = potassium acid phthalate.

determination. *J. Mar. Biol. Assoc. U.K.* 48:143.

JONES, R.H. & A.F. DAGEFORD. 1968. Application of a high sensitivity total organic carbon analyzer. *Proc. Instr. Soc. Amer.* 6:43.

TAKAHASHI, Y., R.T. MOORE & R.J. JOYCE. 1972. Direct determination of organic carbon in water by reductive pyrolysis. *Amer. Lab.* 4:31.

COLLINS, K.J. & P.J. LEB. WILLIAMS. 1977. An automated photochemical method for the determination of dissolved organic carbon in sea and estuarine waters. *Mar. Chem.* 5:123.

GRAVELET-BLONDIN, L.R., H.R. VAN VLIET & P.A. MYNHARDT. 1980. An automated method for the determination of dissolved organic carbon in fresh water. *Water SA* 6:138.

OAKE, R.J. 1981. A Review of Photo-Oxidation for the Determination of Total Organic Carbon in Water. Water Research Center, Technical Rep. (TR 160), Medmenham, England.

VAN STEENDEREN, R.A. & J.S. LIN. 1981. Determination of dissolved organic carbon in water. *Anal. Chem.* 53:521.

5310 D.   Wet-Oxidation Method

1. General Discussion

The wet-oxidation method is suitable for the analyses of water, water-suspended sediment mixtures, brines, and wastewaters containing at least 0.1 mg nonpurgeable organic carbon (NPOC)/L. The method is not suitable for the determination of volatile organic constituents.

a. Principle: The sample is acidified, purged to remove inorganic carbon, and oxidized with persulfate in an autoclave at temperatures from 116 to 130°C. The resultant carbon dioxide (CO_2) is measured by nondispersive infrared spectrometry.

b. Interferences: See Section 5310B.1 and C.1.

c. Minimum detectable concentrations: High concentrations of reducing agents may interfere. Concentration of 0.10 mg organic carbon/L can be measured if scrupulous attention is given to minimizing sample contamination and method background. Use the combustion-infrared method (B) for high concentrations of TOC.

d. Sampling and storage: See Section 5310B.1*d*.

2. Apparatus

a. Ampules, precombusted, 10-mL, glass.*

b. Ampule purging and sealing unit. *

c. Autoclave. *

d. Carbon analyzer. *

e. Homogenizer.†

3. Reagents

In addition to the reagents specified in Section 5310B.3*a, c, e,* and *f,* the following reagents are required:

a. Phosphoric acid solution, H_3PO_4, 1.2*N:* Add 83 mL H_3PO_4 (85%) to water and dilute to 1 L with water. Store in a tightly stoppered glass bottle.

b. Potassium persulfate, reagent-grade, granular. Avoid using finely divided forms.

4. Procedure

a. Instrument operation: Follow manufacturer's instructions for assembly, testing calibration, and operation. Add 0.2 g po-

tassium persulfate using a dipper calibrated to deliver 0.2 g and 0.5 mL 1.2*N* H_3PO_4 solution to precombusted ampules.

To analyze for dissolved organic carbon, pass sample and reagent water blank under vacuum through a separate 0.45-μm glass fiber filter that was pretreated by submerging overnight in a 1:1 solution of HNO_3 and reagent water and collect in acid-washed, baked flasks. Use clean filter and flask for each sample.

Homogenize sample to produce a uniform suspension. Rinse homogenizer with reagent water after each use. Pipet water sample (10.0 mL maximum) into an ampule. Adjust smaller volumes to 10 mL with reagent water. Prepare one reagent blank (10 mL reagent water plus acid and oxidant) for every 15 to 20 water samples. Prepare standards covering the range of 0.1 to 40 mg carbon/L by diluting the carbon standard solution. Immediately place filled ampules on purging and sealing unit and purge them at rate of 60 mL/min for 6 min with purified oxygen. Seal samples according to the manufacturer's instructions. Place sealed samples, blanks, and a set of standards in ampule racks in an autoclave and digest 4 h at temperature between 116 and 130°C.

Set sensitivity range of carbon analyzer by adjusting the zero and span controls in accordance with the manufacturer's instructions. Break combusted ampules in the cutter assembly of the carbon analyzer, sweep CO_2 into the infrared cell with nitrogen gas, and record area of each CO_2 peak. CAUTION: *Because combusted ampules are under positive pressure, handle with care to prevent explosion.*

5. Calculations

Prepare an analytical standard curve by plotting peak area of each standard versus concentration (mg/L) of organic carbon standards. The relationship between peak

---

*Oceanographics International Corp. or equivalent.
†Willems Polytron PT-105T, Brinkman Inst., or equivalent.

area and carbon concentration is curvilinear. Define operating curves each day samples are analyzed.

Report nonpurgeable organic carbon concentration (NPOC) as follows: 0.1 mg/L to 0.9 mg/L, one significant figure; 1.0 mg/L and above, two significant figures.

Number of Replicates	Mean mg/L	Relative Standard Deviation %
9	2.2	5.9
10	5.3	2.8
10	9.9	1.1
10	38.0	3.7

6. Precision and Bias

Multiple determinations of four different concentrations of aqueous potassium acid phthalate samples at 2.00, 5.00, 10.0, and 40.0 mg carbon/L resulted in mean values of 2.2, 5.3, 9.9, and 38 mg/L and standard deviations of 0.13, 0.15, 0.11, and 1.4, respectively.

Precision also may be expressed in terms of percent relative standard deviation as follows:

7. Bibliography

WILLIAMS, P.M. 1969. The determination of dissolved organic carbon in seawater: A comparison of two methods. *Limnol. Oceanogr.* 14:297.

OCEANOGRAPHY INTERNATIONAL CORP. 1970. The total carbon system operating manual. College Station, Tex.

MACKINNON, M.D. 1981. The measurement of organic carbon in seawater. *In* E.K. Duursma & R. Dawson, eds. Marine Organic Chemistry: Evolution, Composition, Interactions and Chemistry of Organic Matter in Seawater. Elsevier Scientific Publishing Co., New York, N.Y.

5320   DISSOLVED ORGANIC HALOGEN*

5320 A.   Introduction

Dissolved organic halogen (DOX) is a measurement used to estimate the total quantity of dissolved halogenated organic material in a water sample. This is similar to previous literature references to "TOX." The presence of halogenated organic molecules is indicative of synthetic chemical contamination. Halogenated compounds that contribute to a DOX result include, but are not limited to: the trihalomethanes (THMs); organic solvents such as trichloroethene, tetrachloroethene, and other halogenated alkanes and alkenes; chlorinated and brominated pesticides and herbicides; polychlorinated biphenyls (PCBs); chlorinated aromatics such as hexachlorobenzene and 2,4-dichlorophenol; and high-molecular-weight, partially chlorinated aquatic humic substances. Compound-specific methods such as gas chromatography typically are more sensitive than DOX measurements.

The adsorption-pyrolysis-titrimetric method for DOX measures only the total molar amount of dissolved organically bound halogen retained on the carbon adsorbent; it yields no information about the structure or nature of the organic compounds to which the halogens are bound or about the individual halogens present. It is sensitive to organic chloride, bromide, and iodide, but does not detect fluorinated organics.

DOX measurement is an inexpensive

---

* Approved by Standard Methods Committee, 1988.

and useful method for screening large numbers of samples before specific (and often more complex) analyses; for extensive field surveying for pollution by certain classes of synthetic organic compounds in natural waters; for mapping the extent of organohalide contamination in groundwater; for monitoring the breakthrough of some synthetic organic compounds in water treatment processes; and for estimating the level of formation of chlorinated organic by-products after disinfection with chlorine. When used as a screening tool, a large positive (i.e., above background measurements) DOX test result indicates the need for identifying and quantifying specific substances. In saline or brackish waters the high inorganic halogen concentrations interfere. The possibility of overestimating DOX concentration because of inorganic halide interference always should be considered when interpreting results.

5320 B.   Adsorption-Pyrolysis-Titrimetric Method

1. General Discussion

a. Principle: The method consists of four processes. First, dissolved organic material is separated from inorganic halides and concentrated from aqueous solution by adsorption onto activated carbon. Second, inorganic halides present on the activated carbon are removed by competitive displacement by nitrate ions. Third, the activated carbon with adsorbed organic material is introduced into a furnace that pyrolyzes organic carbon to carbon dioxide (CO_2) and the bound halogens to hydrogen halide (HX). Fourth, the HX is transported in a carrier gas stream to a microcoulometric titration cell where the amount of halide is quantified by measuring the current produced by silver-ion precipitation of the halides. The microcoulometric detector operates by maintaining a constant silver-ion concentration in a titration cell. An electric potential is applied to a solid silver electrode to produce silver ions in the cell solution. As hydrogen halide from the pyrolysis furnace enters the cell in the carrier gas, it is partitioned into the acetic acid solution where it precipitates as silver halide. The current that is produced is integrated over the period of the pyrolysis. The integrated area under the curve is proportional to the number of moles of halogen recovered. The mass concentration of organic halides is reported as an equivalent concentration of organically bound chloride in micrograms per liter.

When a sample is purged with inert gas before activated carbon adsorption, analysis of that sample determines the nonpurgeable dissolved organic halogen (NPDOX) fraction of DOX. The purgeable organic halogen concentration (POX) may be calculated by subtracting the NPDOX value from the DOX value. Alternatively, the POX fraction may be determined directly by purging the sample with carrier gas and introducing that gas stream and the volatilized organics directly into the pyrolysis furnace. From the analysis of POX and DOX, NPDOX may be determined by difference.

b. Interferences: The method is applicable only to aqueous samples free of particulate matter. Inorganic substances such as chloride, chlorite, chlorate, bromide, and iodide will adsorb on activated carbon to an extent dependent on their original concentration in the aqueous solution and the volume of sample adsorbed. Positive interference will result if inorganic halides are not removed. Treating the activated carbon with a concentrated aqueous solution of nitrate ion causes competitive desorption from the activated carbon of inorganic halide species and washes inorganic halides from other surfaces. However, if the inorganic halide concentration is greater than 20 000 times the concentration of organic halides, the DOX results may be affected significantly. In general, this procedure may not be applicable to samples with inorganic halide concentrations above 500 mg Cl⁻/L, based on carbon quality testing results. Therefore, consider both the results of mineral analysis for inorganic halides and the results of the carbon quality test (see ¶ 5, below) when interpreting results.

Halogenated organic compounds that are weakly adsorbed on activated carbon are recovered only partially. These include certain alcohols and acids (e.g., chloroethanol), and such compounds as chloroacetic acid, that can be removed from activated carbon by the nitrate ion wash. However, for most halogenated organic molecules, recovery is very good; the activated carbon adsorbable organic halide (CAOX) therefore is a good estimate of true DOX.

Failure to acidify samples with nitric acid may result in reduced adsorption efficiency for some halogenated organic compounds and may intensify the inorganic halide interference. Further, if the water contains residual chlorine, reduce it before adsorption to eliminate positive interference resulting from continued chlorination reactions with organic compounds adsorbed on the activated carbon surface or with the activated carbon surface itself. The sulfite dechlorinating agent may cause decomposition of a small fraction of the DOX; do not add in great excess.

Highly volatile components of the POX fraction may be lost during sampling, shipment, sample storage, sample handling, and sample preparation, or during sample adsorption. A laboratory quality-control program to insure sample integrity from time of sampling until analysis is vital. During sample filtration for the analysis of samples containing undissolved solids major losses of POX are to be expected. Therefore, analyze for POX before sample filtration and analyze for NPDOX after filtration; the sum of POX and NPDOX is the true DOX. In preparing samples for DOX analysis, process a blank and a standard solution to determine effect of this procedure on DOX measurement. If an insignificant loss of POX occurs during the removal of particulate matter by filtration, DOX may be measured directly.

Granular activated carbon used to concentrate organic material from the sample is a major source of variability in the analysis and it has a dramatic effect on the minimum detectable concentration. Ideally, activated carbon should have a low halide content, readily release adsorbed inorganic halides on nitrate washing, be homogeneous, and readily adsorb *all* organic halide compounds even in the presence of large excesses of other organic material. An essential element of quality control for DOX requires testing and monitoring of activated carbon (see ¶ 5 below). Nonhomogeneous activated carbon or activated carbon with a high background value affects the method reliability at low concentrations of DOX. A high and/or variable blank value raises the minimum detectable concentration. Random positive bias, in part due to the ease of carbon contamination during use, necessitates analyzing duplicates of each sample. Because activated carbon from different sources may vary widely in the ease of releasing inorganic halides, test for this quality before using activated carbon. Proper quantification also may be affected by the adsorptive capacity of the activated carbon. If excessive organic loading occurs, some DOX may break through and not be recovered. For this reason, make serial adsorptions of each sample portion and individual analyses.

c. *Sampling and storage:* Collect and store samples in amber glass bottles with TFE-lined caps. If amber bottles are not available, store samples in the dark. To prepare sample bottles acid wash, rinse with deionized water, seal with aluminum foil, and bake at 400°C for at least 1 h. If bottle blanks without baking show no detectable DOX, baking may be omitted. Wash septa with detergent, rinse repeatedly in organic-free, deionized water, wrap in aluminum foil, and bake for 1 h at 100°C. Preferably use thick silicone rubber-backed TFE septa and open ring caps to produce a positive seal that prevents loss of POX and contamination. Store sealed sample bottles in a clean environment until use. Completely fill sample bottles but take care not to volatilize any organic halogen compounds. Preserve samples that cannot be analyzed promptly by acidifying with conc nitric acid to pH 2. Refrigerate samples at 4°C with minimal exposure to light. Reduce any residual chlorine by adding sodium sulfite crystals (minimum: 5 mg/L). NOTE: Some organic chloramines are not completely dechlorinated by sodium sulfite, particularly at pH > 7. This may affect reported concentrations.[1] Analyze all samples within 14 d.

d. *Minimum detectable concentration:* For nonsaline waters free of particulate matter, 5 μg organic Cl⁻/L is considered a typical minimum detection limit. The minimum detectable concentration may be influenced by the analytical repeatability, equipment used, activated carbon quality, and the operator. Determine the detection limit for each procedure, instrument, and operator.

2. Apparatus

a. *Adsorption assembly,* including gas-tight sample reservoir, activated carbon-packed adsorption columns, column housings, and nitrate solution reservoir. In particular, note the following:

1) *Noncombustible insulating material (microcolumn method only):* Form into plugs to hold activated carbon in columns. CAUTION: *Do not touch with fingers.*

2) *Activated carbon columns (microcolumn method only):* Pack 40 ± 5 mg activated carbon (¶ 3k) into dry glass tubing approximately 2 to 3 mm ID × 6 mm OD × 40 to 50 mm long. CAUTION: *Protect these columns from all sources of halogenated organic vapors.* Clean glass tubes before use with a small-diameter pipe cleaner to remove residual carbon, then soak in chromate cleaning solution for 15 min and dry at 400°C. Rinse between steps with deionized water.

b. *Analyzer assembly,* including carrier gas source, boat sampler, and pyrolysis furnace, that can oxidatively pyrolyze halogenated organics at a temperature of 800°C ± 25°C to produce hydrogen halides and deliver them to the titration cell with a minimum overall efficiency of 90% for 2,4,6-trichlorophenol; including a micro-coulometric titration system with integrator, digital display, and chart recorder connection; including (optional) purging apparatus (see Figure 5320:1).

c. *Chart recorder.*

3. Reagents and Materials

Use ACS reagent-grade chemicals. Other grades may be used if it can be demonstrated that the reagent is of sufficiently high purity to permit its use without lessening accuracy of the determination.

a. *Carbon dioxide, argon, or nitrogen,* as recommended by the equipment manufacturer, purity 99.99%.

b. *Oxygen,* purity 99.99%.

c. *Aqueous acetic acid,* 70 to 85%, as recommended by the equipment manufacturer.

d. *Sodium chloride standard,* NaCl: Dissolve 0.1648 g NaCl and dilute to 100 mL with reagent water; 1 μL = 1 μg Cl⁻.

e. *Ammonium chloride standard,*

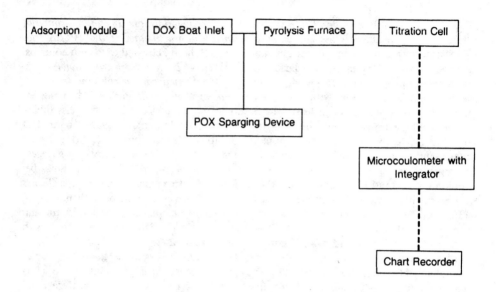

Figure 5320:1 DOX analysis system.

NH$_4$Cl: Dissolve 0.1509 g NH$_4$Cl and dilute to 100 mL with reagent water; 1 μL = 1 μg Cl$^-$.

f. Trichlorophenol stock solution: Dissolve 1.856 g trichlorophenol and dilute to 100 mL with methanol; 1 μL = 10 μg Cl$^-$.

g. Trichlorophenol standard solution: Make a 1:20 dilution of the trichlorophenol stock solution with methanol; 1 μL = 0.5 μg Cl$^-$.

h. Chloroform standard solution, CHCl$_3$: Dilute 100 mg CHCl$_3$ to 100 mL with methanol; 1 μL = 1 μg CHCl$_3$.

i. Blank standard: Use reagent water. Reagent water preferably is carbon-filtered, deionized water that has been heated and purged.

j. Nitrate wash solution, 0.08*N*: Dilute 8.2 g KNO$_3$ to 1000 mL with reagent water. Adjust to pH 2 with HNO$_3$. 1 L = 5000 mg NO$_3^-$.

k. Activated carbon, 100 to 200 mesh: Ideally use activated carbon having a very low apparent halide background that readily releases adsorbed inorganic halides on nitrate washing, and reliably adsorbs organic halides in the presence of a large excess or other organics.* See ¶ 5 below for preparation and evaluation of activated carbon. CAUTION: *Protect activated carbon from contact with halogenated organic vapors.*

l. Sodium sulfite, Na$_2$SO$_3$, crystals.

m. Nitric acid, HNO$_3$, conc.

n. Humic acid.†

4. Procedure

Use either the microcolumn (4*a*) or batch adsorption (4*b*) method. The microcolumn method utilizes small glass columns packed with activated carbon through which the sample is passed under positive pressure to adsorb the organic halogen compounds. The batch adsorption

---

* Westvaco or Calgon Filtrasorb 400 or equivalent.
† Aldrich Chemical Co. or equivalent.

method directly measures POX. A small quantity of activated carbon then is added to the NPDOX portion. After stirring, activated carbon is removed by filtration and analyzed.

a. *Microcolumn procedure:*

1) Apparatus setup—Adjust equipment in accordance with the manufacturer's instructions. Include several injections of NaCl solution directly into the titration cell [¶ 5c)] as a microcoulometer/titration cell check at the start of each day.

2) Sample pretreatment for DOX analysis—Adjust sample pH to 2 with HNO_3. If the samples contain undissolved solids, filter through a glass-fiber filter (other means of removing particulate matter may be used, if it can be demonstrated that they do not cause significant interferences). Also filter a blank and standard. Analyze these to determine the contribution of filtration to the organic halogen measurement. Vacuum filtration will cause some loss of volatile organic halogen. Analyze for POX before filtration and NPDOX after filtration, unless it is shown that POX losses during filtration are insignificant.

3) POX determination (optional)—Select sample volume by comparing expected POX value (if known) with the optimum instrument range. Using a gastight syringe, inject sample through the septum into the purge vessel and purge as recommended by the equipment manufacturer. Carefully control gas flow rate, sample temperature, and purging time.

4) Sample adsorption—Transfer a representative portion of sample to the cleaned sample reservoir with two activated carbon adsorption columns in series attached by the column housings to the reservoir outlet. Seal the reservoir. Adjust to produce a flow rate of about 3 mL/min. When the desired volume has been processed, stop the flow, detach the activated carbon housings and columns, and rinse the sample reservoir twice with reagent-grade water. Vary volume processed to produce optimum quantities of adsorbed DOX on the columns. Suggested volumes are as follows:

Volume Processed mL	Instrument Optimum Range $\mu g\ Cl^-$	Conc of DOX in Waters $\mu g/L$
100	0.5–50	5–500
50	12.5–50	250–1000
25	12.5–50	500–2000

If possible, avoid using volumes greater than 100 mL because the maximum adsorptive capacity of the activated carbon may be exceeded, leading to adsorbate breakthrough and loss of DOX. Larger sample volumes processed lead to an increased quantity of inorganic halide accumulated on the activated carbon and may result in a positive interference. Do not use a sample less than 25 mL to minimize volumetric errors. For samples exceeding 2000 μg DOX/L dilute before adsorption. Protect columns from the atmosphere until DOX is determined.

5) Inorganic halide removal—Attach columns through which sample has been processed in series to the nitrate wash reservoir and pass 2 to 5 mL NO_3^- solution through the columns at a rate of approximately 1 mL/min.

6) DOX determination—After concentrating sample on activated carbon and removing inorganic halogens by nitrate washing, pyrolyze contents of each microcolumn and determine organic halogen content. Remove top glass microcolumn from the column housing, taking care not to contaminate the sample with inorganic halides. Using a clean ejector rod, eject the activated carbon and noncombustible insulating material plugs into the sample boat. Prepare sample boat during the preceding 4 h by heating at 400 to 800°C for at least 4 min in an oxygen-rich atmosphere (i.e., in the pyrolysis furnace). Remove residual ash. Place ejector rod on the plug of the effluent end of the carbon microcolumn

and place the influent end of the carbon microcolumn in the quartz boat first. Seal sample inlet tube and let instrument stabilize. After NO_3^- wash avoid contact with inorganic halides such as the chloride from perspiration on the hands or contaminated bench surfaces. Wash hands frequently, especially after eating, and clean work area with deionized water often.

Pyrolyze the activated carbon and determine halide content. Repeat for each microcolumn. Check for excess breakthrough (¶ 5b) and repeat analysis as necessary.

7) Replicates—When DOX determination is used strictly as a screening tool, replicates are not necessary. Otherwise, repeat steps 4, 5 and 6 using a different dilution of the same sample. Use dilutions that differ so that the concentration ratios are either less than 0.7 or greater than 1.4.

8) Blanks—Analyze one method blank [¶ 5e2)] with each set of eight samples. Analyze no fewer than two blanks each day.

9) Preparation and analysis of calibration standard—Run several calibration standards daily in accordance with ¶ 5c3) for POX analysis or ¶ 5c5) for microcolumn-adsorption DOX analysis. Accompany by a suitable blank [¶ 5e3) or ¶ 5e4)]. Be certain that analytical conditions and procedures (e.g., purging temperature) are the same for the analysis of calibration standards as for the analysis of samples.

b. Batch adsorption procedure:

1) Apparatus setup—Adjust equipment in accordance with the manufacturer's instructions.

2) Sample pretreatment—Adjust sample pH to 2 with conc HNO_3.

3) POX determination—Select sample volume by comparing expected POX value (if known) with the optimum instrument range. Using a gas-tight syringe, inject sample through the septum into the purge vessel and purge as recommended by the equipment manufacturer. To compare POX values from different laboratories

standardized purging is essential. Adjust instrument temperature, purge rate, and purge time to just produce complete purging of bromoform using a bromoform standard. Take replicate samples from different sample bottles to minimize volatilization losses.

4) NPDOX determination—Prepare carbon suspension by adding high-quality activated carbon to high-purity, deionized, granular activated carbon (GAC)-treated water to produce a uniform suspension of 10 mg carbon/mL. To an erlenmeyer flask, transfer prepurged sample of optimum size from a purging flask standardized in the same manner as the instrument's purging vessel. Add 20 mg activated carbon (2 mL carbon suspension). Using a high-speed mixer (20 000 rpm), stir for 45 min in an organohalide vapor-free environment. Filter through a membrane filter under vacuum and collect filtrate. Remove flask containing filtrate. Wash carbon cake and filter with 10 mL NO_3^- wash solution. Add portions of wash solution serially to keep activated carbon and NO_3^- solution in contact for 15 min. Using clean instruments, transfer carbon cake and membrane filter to pyrolysis unit sample boat. Let instrument stabilize, pyrolyze, and determine halide content of the first serial filter.

Add 20 mg more activated carbon to filtrate in erlenmeyer flask. Repeat carbon mixing, filtering, and washing procedures. Pyrolyze and determine halide content of second serial filter. If the second value is greater than 10% of the total value (first plus second), perform the NPDOX determination on an additional sample portion.

5. Quality Control

a. Carbon quality: Prepare activated carbon by milling and sieving high-quality activated carbon. Use only 100- to 200-mesh carbon in the microcolumn method. During preparation, take care not to expose the activated carbon to organic vapors. Use of a clean room is helpful. Prepare only small quantities (a month's supply or less) at one time. Discard the activated carbon if its DOX background concentration has increased significantly from the time of preparation or if the background is greater than 1 μg apparent organic Cl$^-$/40 mg activated carbon. Uniformity of activated carbon is important; therefore, after sieving small portions, combine and mix thoroughly. Transfer representative portions to clean glass bottles with ground-glass stoppers or with rubber-backed TFE septa and open ring caps. Store bottles in a gas-purged, evacuated, sealed desiccator.

Test each newly prepared batch of activated carbon to insure adequate quality before use. Use only carbon meeting the guidelines outlined below.

1) Check carbon particle size by applying deionized water to two 40-mg activated carbon microcolumns. If flow rate is significantly less than 3 mL/min, resieve carbon to remove excess fines.

2) Analyze a pair of method blanks, ¶ 5e2). Reject carbon if the apparent organic halogen exceeds 1.2 μg/40 mg activated carbon.

If the activated carbon originated from a previously untested batch from a commercial supplier, test it for adsorption efficiency and inorganic halide rejection.

3) Adsorb replicate 100-mL portions of solutions containing 100, 500, and 1000 mg inorganic Cl$^-$/L deionized water. Wash with nitrate solution and analyze. The apparent organic halogen yield should not increase by more than 0.50 μg over the value determined in 2) above. A greater increase indicates significant interference at that concentration.

4) Prepare an adsorption test standard solution in deionized water to contain 10 mg organic carbon (as humic acids or equivalent)/L and an organic halide concentration of 100 μg organic chloride (from 2,4,6-trichlorophenol)/L. Prepare a blank solution containing only the 10 mg organic

carbon. Adsorb, nitrate wash, and analyze replicate 100-mL portions of these solutions. Directly inject 10 μg organic chloride (from 2,4,6-trichlorophenol) onto nitrate-washed 40-mg activated carbon microcolumns, in replicate. Analyze replicate method blanks. Recovery of the *aqueous* organic chloride should be $\geq$ 90% on the first microcolumn or filter and 5% or less on the second. Total recovery of organic chloride from water should be 95% or more (after subtraction of the organic carbon blank) of the amount applied.

b. Serial adsorption: Each aqueous standard and sample is serially adsorbed on activated carbon in both procedures given above. Of the net organic halide, 90% or more should be adsorbed on the first activated carbon portion and the remaining 10% or less on the second. If, upon separate analysis of the two serial activated carbon portions, the second shows more than 10% of the net (after subtracting the method blank), reanalyze sample. Inorganic halogen interference or organic breakthrough are the most common reasons for a high second activated carbon value. Sample dilution before adsorption may improve recovery on the first activated carbon in series, but the minimum detectable concentration will be affected.

c. Standards: The standards used in routine analysis, quality control testing, and isolating specific causes during corrective maintenance include:

1) Sodium chloride standard (¶ 3*d*)—Use to check functioning of the titration cell and microcoulometer by injecting directly into the acetic acid solution of the titration cell. By examining the height and shape of the peak produced on the chart recorder and from the integrated value, problems associated with the cell and coulometer may be isolated. Use this standard at startup each day and after cell cleaning throughout the day. At daily startup consecutive duplicates should be within 3% of the historical mean. Depending on sample

loading and number of analyses performed, it may be necessary to clean the titration cell several times per day. After cleaning, cell performance may be very unstable; therefore, inject a single NaCl standard before analyzing an instrument calibration standard [see ¶ 4) below]. Do *not* introduce NaCl standards into the pyrolysis furnace by application to the sample boat.

2) *Ammonium chloride standard* (¶ 3*e*)—Apply this standard to the sample boat to check for loss of halide in the pyrolysis furnace and entrance of the titration cell. When injection of a NaCl standard indicates proper titration cell and microcoulometer function but the recovery of the calibration standard is poor, suspect either poor conversion of organic chloride to hydrogen chloride or loss of hydrogen halide after conversion but before partitioning into the cell solution. To isolate the possible loss of hydrogen halides inject NH₄Cl standard directly onto the quartz sample boat. Recovery should be better than 95%, with a single peak of uniform shape produced. Use only a new quartz sample boat free of any residue; an encrusted boat dramatically reduces recovery. Use this standard for corrective maintenance problem isolation but not for routine analyses.

3) *Purgeable organic halide calibration standards*—For the POX analysis use aqueous chloroform solutions for instrument calibration. Also for POX analysis use an aqueous bromoform standard to insure acceptable purging conditions. Develop a standard curve over the dynamic range of the microcoulometer and check daily as in ¶ 5*c*5). Recovery of chloroform and bromoform should exceed 90% and 80%, respectively.

4) *Instrument calibration standard*— Direct injection of trichlorophenol working standard onto the nitrate-washed method blank in concentrations over the working range of the instrument determines linearity and calibration of the analyzer module. After checking for proper microcoulometer

function by injecting NaCl standard, pyrolyze duplicate instrument calibration standards and then duplicate method blanks. The net response to the calibration standards should be within 3% of the calibration curve value. If not, check for loss of halide in the pyrolysis furnace using the ammonium chloride standard [¶ 5*c*2)].

5) *Nonvolatile organic halide calibration standards*—Develop a standard curve by analyzing aqueous solutions of 2,4,6-trichlorophenol or another appropriate halogenated organic compound over the dynamic range of the microcoulometer. This dynamic range typically is from 0.5 to 50 μg chloride, but will vary between microcoulometers and titration cells. Because of the limited throughput of the DOX procedure, use single-instrument calibration standards at 50, 30, 15, 10, 5, 2.5, and 0.5 μg organic chloride to construct a standard curve after changes in an instrument's configuration, such as replacement of a titration cell or major instrument maintenance. Daily, analyze additional replicates of several nonvolatile organic halide calibration standards to insure reproducibility, linearity, and proper function of the instrumentation and procedures. Select standard concentrations in the range of samples to be analyzed that day. When sample filtration is used to remove particulate matter, also use this pretreatment with the calibration standards. If DOX recovery is less than 95%, analyze a set of instrument calibration standards [¶ 5*c*4)].

d. Standard addition recovery: During routine analyses, ideally make standard additions to every tenth sample. Where the compounds constituting the DOX are known, use standards of these compounds. Where the compounds constituting the DOX are wholly or partially unknown (e.g., halogenated humic acids), use standards reflecting the relative abundance of the halogens, the molecular size, and the volatility of the halogenated compounds presumed to be present. Recovery of 90% or more of the added amount indicates that the analyses are in control.

e. *Blanks:* High precision and accuracy of the background or blank value is important to the accurate measurement of DOX. Make blank measurements daily. Blanks that may be required are:

1) System blank—Analyze organic-free reagent water. The blank should have less than the minimum detectable concentration. Use this blank to insure that the equipment and procedures are not contributing to the DOX.

2) Method blank—Analyze activated carbon that has been nitrate-washed. Analyze duplicate method blanks daily before sample analysis and after each eight sample pyrolyses.

3) Standard blank—Analyze reagent water to determine the blank for standards.

4) Purgeable organic halogen blank—Analyze organic-free, pre-purged, reagent water to determine the POX blank.

6. Calculation

Calculate the net organic halide content as chloride (C_4) of each replicate of each sample and standard:

$$C_4 = \frac{C_1 - C_3 + C_2 - C_3}{V}$$

where:

C_1 = organic halide as Cl^- on the first activated carbon column or activated carbon cake, μg,

C_2 = organic halide as Cl^- on the second activated carbon column or activated carbon cake, μg,

C_3 = mean of method blanks on the same day and same instrument, μg X as Cl^-,

C_4 = uncorrected net organic halide as Cl^- of absorbed sample, μg organic halide as Cl^-/L, and

V = volume of sample absorbed, L.

If $C_2 \leq C_3$, then use:

$$C_4 = \frac{C_1 - C_3}{V}$$

If applicable, calculate net purgeable organic halide as Cl^- content (P_3):

$$P_3 = \frac{P_1 - P_3}{V}$$

where:

P_1 = sample purgeable organic halide as Cl^-, μg,

P_2 = blank purgeable organic halide as Cl^-, μg,

P_3 = uncorrected net purgeable organic halide as Cl^-, μg X as Cl^-/L, and

V = volume of sample or standard purged, L.

Report sample results and percent recovery of the corresponding calibration standards [¶ 5c3) or ¶ 5c5)]. Also report the calibration standard curve if it is significantly nonlinear.

7. Precision and Bias

Precision and bias depend on specific procedures, equipment, and analyst. Develop and routinely update precision and bias data for each procedure, each instrument configuration, and each analyst. Table 5230:I shows sample calculations of precision expressed as the standard deviation among replicates and bias in the recovery of 2,4,6-trichlorophenol.

8. Reference

1. STANBORO, W.D. & M.J. LENKEVICH. 1982. Slowly dechlorinated organic chloramines. *Science* 215:967.

9. Bibliography

KUHN, W. 1974. Thesis, Univ. Karlsruhe, West Germany.

KUHN, W., F. FUCHS & H. SONTHEIMER. 1977. Untersuchungen zur Bestimmung des organisch gebundenen Chlors mit Hilfe eines neuartigen Anreicherungsverfahrens. *Z. Wasser-Abwasser Forsch.* 10:6:162.

DRESSMAN, R.C., B.A. NAJAR & R. REDZIKOWSKI. 1979. The analysis of organohalides (OX) in water as a group parameter. Proc.

TABLE 5320:I. INTRALABORATORY, SINGLE-OPERATOR, DISSOLVED ORGANIC HALOGEN (MICROCOLUMN PROCEDURE)—PRECISION AND BIAS DATA

Characteristic of Analysis	Tap Water	Tap Water + 43.5 μg Organic Chloride	Ground Water (50:1)	Wastewater	Waste-water + 1000 μg Organic Chloride
Concentration determined, μg Cl⁻/L:					
Replicate 1	38.5	89.0	123.6	186.0	1178.0
Replicate 2	36.7	90.9	124.8	195.0	1183.0
Replicate 3	43.1	88.4	125.2	195.0	1185.5
Replicate 4	35.9	90.1	123.3	204.0	1196.5
Replicate 5	41.1	91.7	125.3	185.0	1183.0
Replicate 6	48.5	93.0	127.0	236.5	1204.0
Replicate 7	52.8	97.0	123.5	204.0	1138.0
Mean, μg Cl⁻/L	42.37	91.5	124.7	200.8	1181.1
Standard deviation:					
μg Cl⁻/L	±6.29	±3.0	±1.3	±17.47	±21.04
%	15	3	1	9	2
Value of blank + standard addition, μg Cl⁻/L	—	85.87	—	—	1200.8
Recovery, %	—	107	—	—	98
Error, %	—	7	—	—	2

7th Annual Water Quality Technology Conf., Philadelphia, Pa. American Water Works Assoc., Denver, Colo.

TAKAHASHI, Y., et al. 1980. Measurement of total organic halides (TOX) and purgeable organic halides (POX) in water using carbon adsorption and microcoulometric detection. Proc. Symp. on Chemistry and Chemical Analysis of Water and Waste Water Intended for Reuse, Houston, Tex. American Chemical Soc., Washington, D.C.

DRESSMAN, R. C. 1980. Total Organic Halide, Method 450.1—Interim. Drinking Water Research Div., Municipal Environmental Research Lab., U.S. Environmental Protection Agency, Cincinnati, Ohio.

JEKEL, M.R. & P.V. ROBERTS. 1980. Total organic halogen as a parameter for the characterization of reclaimed waters: measurement, occurence, formation, and removal. *Environ. Sci. Technol.* 14:970.

DRESSMAN, R.C. & A. STEVENS. 1983. Analysis of organohalides in water—An evaluation update. *J. Amer. Water Works Assoc.* 75:431.

* * *

5520   OIL AND GREASE*

5520 A.   Introduction

In the determination of oil and grease, an absolute quantity of a specific substance is not measured. Rather, groups of substances with similar physical characteristics are determined quantitatively on the basis of their common solubility in trichlorotrifluoroethane. "Oil and grease" is any material recovered as a substance soluble in trichlorotrifluoroethane. It includes

*Approved by Standard Methods Committee, 1985.

other material extracted by the solvent from an acidified sample (such as sulfur compounds, certain organic dyes, and chlorophyll) and not volatilized during the test. It is important that this limitation be understood clearly. Unlike some constituents that represent distinct chemical elements, ions, compounds, or groups of compounds, oils and greases are defined by the method used for their determination.

The methods presented here are suitable for biological lipids and mineral hydrocarbons. They also may be suitable for most industrial wastewaters or treated effluents containing these materials, although sample complexity may result in either low or high results because of lack of analytical specificity. The method is not applicable to measurement of low-boiling fractions that volatilize at temperatures below 70°C.

1. Significance

Certain constituents measured by the oil and grease analysis may influence wastewater treatment systems. If present in excessive amounts, they may interfere with aerobic and anaerobic biological processes and lead to decreased wastewater treatment efficiency. When discharged in wastewater or treated effluents, they may cause surface films and shoreline deposits leading to environmental degradation.

A knowledge of the quantity of oil and grease present is helpful in proper design and operation of wastewater treatment systems and also may call attention to certain treatment difficulties.

2. Selection of Method

For liquid samples, three methods are presented: the partition-gravimetric method (B), the partition-infrared method (C),

and the Soxhlet method (D). Method C is designed for samples that might contain volatile hydrocarbons that otherwise would be lost in the solvent-removal operations of the gravimetric procedure. Method D is the method of choice when relatively polar, heavy petroleum fractions are present, or when the levels of nonvolatile greases may challenge the solubility limit of the solvent. For low levels of oil and grease (< 10 mg/L), Method C is the method of choice because gravimetric methods do not provide the needed precision.

Method E is a modification of the Soxhlet method and is suitable for sludges and similar materials. Method F can be used in conjunction with Methods B, C, D, or E to obtain a hydrocarbon measurement in addition to, or instead of, the oil and grease measurement. This method separates hydrocarbons from the total oil and grease on the basis of polarity.

3. Sampling and Storage

Collect a representative sample in a wide-mouth glass bottle that has been rinsed with the solvent to remove any detergent film, and acidify in the sample bottle. Collect a separate sample for an oil and grease determination and do not subdivide in the laboratory. When information is required about average grease concentration over an extended period, examine individual portions collected at prescribed time intervals to eliminate losses of grease on sampling equipment during collection of a composite sample.

In sampling sludges, take every possible precaution to obtain a representative sample. When analysis cannot be made immediately, preserve samples with 1 mL conc HCl/80 g sample. Never preserve samples with $CHCl_3$ or sodium benzoate.

5520 B.   Partition-Gravimetric Method

1. General Discussion

a. Principle: Dissolved or emulsified oil and grease is extracted from water by intimate contact with trichlorotrifluoroethane. Some extractables, especially unsaturated fats and fatty acids, oxidize readily; hence, special precautions regarding temperature and solvent vapor displacement are included to minimize this effect.

b. Interference: Trichlorotrifluoroethane has the ability to dissolve not only oil and grease but also other organic substances. No known solvent will dissolve selectively only oil and grease. Solvent removal results in the loss of short-chain hydrocarbons and simple aromatics by volatilization. Significant portions of petroleum distillates from gasoline through No. 2 fuel oil are lost in this process. In addition, heavier residuals of petroleum may contain a significant portion of materials that are not extractable with the solvent.

2. Apparatus

a. Separatory funnel, 1-L, with TFE* stopcock.

b. Distilling flask, 125-mL.

c. Water bath.

d. Filter paper, 11-cm diam.†

3. Reagents

a. Hydrochloric acid, HCl, 1 + 1.

b. Trichlorotrifluoroethane‡ (1,1,2-trichloro-1,2,2-trifluoroethane), boiling point 47°C. The solvent should leave no measurable residue on evaporation; distill if necessary. Do not use any plastic tubing to transfer solvent between containers.

c. Sodium sulfate, Na_2SO_4, anhydrous crystal.

4. Procedure

Collect about 1 L of sample and mark sample level in bottle for later determination of sample volume. Acidify to pH 2 or lower; generally, 5 mL HCl is sufficient. Transfer to a separatory funnel. Carefully rinse sample bottle with 30 mL trichlorotrifluoroethane and add solvent washings to separatory funnel. Preferably shake vigorously for 2 min. However, if it is suspected that a stable emulsion will form, shake gently for 5 to 10 min. Let layers separate. Drain solvent layer through a funnel containing solvent-moistened filter paper into a clean, tared distilling flask. If a clear solvent layer cannot be obtained, add 1 g Na_2SO_4 to the filter paper cone and slowly drain emulsified solvent onto the crystals. Add more Na_2SO_4 if necessary. Extract twice more with 30 mL solvent each but first rinse sample container with each solvent portion. Combine extracts in tared distilling flask and wash filter paper with an additional 10 to 20 mL solvent. Distill solvent from distilling flask in a water bath at 70°C. Place flask on a water bath at 70°C for 15 min and draw air through it with an applied vacuum for the final 1 min. Cool in a desiccator for 30 min and weigh.

5. Calculation

If the organic solvent is free of residue, the gain in weight of the tared distilling flask is mainly due to oil and grease. Total gain in weight, *A*, of tared flask less calculated residue, *B*, from solvent blank is the amount of oil and grease in the sample:

$$\text{mg oil and grease/L} = \frac{(A - B) \times 1000}{\text{mL sample}}$$

---

*Teflon or equivalent.
†Whatman No. 40 or equivalent.
‡Freon or equivalent.

6. Precision and Bias

Methods B, C, and D were tested by a single laboratory on a sewage sample. By this method the oil and grease concentration was 12.6 mg/L. When 1-L portions of the sewage were dosed with 14.0 mg of a mixture of No. 2 fuel oil and Wesson oil, recovery of added oils was 93% with a standard deviation of 0.9 mg.

7. Bibliography

KIRSCHMAN, H.D. & R. POMEROY. 1949. Determination of oil in oil field waste waters. *Anal. Chem.* 21:793.

5520 C.   Partition-Infrared Method

1. General Discussion

a. Principle: Although the extraction procedure for this method is identical to that of Method B, infrared detection permits the measurement of many relatively volatile hydrocarbons. Thus, the lighter petroleum distillates, with the exception of gasoline, may be measured accurately. Adequate instrumentation allows for the measurement of as little as 0.2 mg oil and grease/L.

b. Interference: Some degree of selectivity is offered by this method to overcome some of the coextracted interferences discussed in Method B. Heavier residuals of petroleum may contain a significant portion of materials insoluble in trichlorotrifluoroethane.

c. Definitions: A "known oil" is defined as a sample of oil and/or grease that represents the only material of that type used or manufactured in the processes represented by a wastewater. An "unknown oil" is defined as one for which a representative sample of the oil or grease is not available for preparation of a standard.

2. Apparatus

a. Separatory funnel, 1-L, with TFE* stopcock.

b. Infrared spectrophotometer, double beam, recording.

c. Cells, near-infrared silica.

d. Filter paper, 11-cm diam.†

3. Reagents

a. Hydrochloric acid, HCl, 1 + 1.

b. Trichlorotrifluoroethane: See Section 5520B.3*b*.

c. Sodium sulfate, Na_2SO_4, anhydrous, crystal.

d. Reference oil: Prepare a mixture, by volume, of 37.5% iso-octane, 37.5% hexadecane, and 25% benzene. Store in sealed container to prevent evaporation.

4. Procedure

Refer to Method B for sample collection, acidification, and extraction. Collect combined extracts in a 100-mL volumetric flask and adjust final volume to 100 mL with solvent.

Prepare a stock solution of known oil by rapidly transferring about 1 mL (0.5 to 1.0 g) of the oil or grease to a tared 100-mL volumetric flask. Stopper flask and weigh to nearest milligram. Add solvent to dissolve and dilute to mark. If the oil identity is unknown (¶ 1*c*) use the reference oil (¶ 3*d*) as the standard. Using volumetric techniques, prepare a series of standards over the range of interest. Select a pair of

---

*Teflon or equivalent.

†Whatman No. 40 or equivalent.

matched near-infrared silica cells. A 1-cm-path-length cell is appropriate for a working range of about 4 to 40 mg. Scan standards and samples from 3200 cm^{-1} to 2700 cm^{-1} with solvent in the reference beam and record results on absorbance paper. Measure absorbances of samples and standards by constructing a straight base line over the scan range and measuring absorbance of the peak maximum at 2930 cm^{-1} and subtracting base-line absorbance at that point. If the absorbance exceeds 0.8 for a sample, select a shorter path length or dilute as required. Use scans of standards to prepare a calibration curve.

5. Calculation

$$\text{mg oil and grease/L} = \frac{A \times 1000}{\text{mL sample}}$$

where:

A = mg of oil or grease in extract as determined from calibration curve.

6. Precision and Bias

See 5520B.6. By this method the oil and grease concentration was 17.5 mg/L. When 1-L portions of the sewage were dosed with 14.0 mg of a mixture of No. 2 fuel oil and Wesson oil, the recovery of added oils was 99% with a standard deviation of 1.4 mg.

7. Bibliography

GRUENFELD, M. 1973. Extraction of dispersed oils from water for quantitative analysis by infrared spectrophotometry. *Environ. Sci. Technol.* 7:636.

5520 D.   Soxhlet Extraction Method

1. General Discussion

a. Principle: Soluble metallic soaps are hydrolyzed by acidification. Any oils and solid or viscous grease present are separated from the liquid samples by filtration. After extraction in a Soxhlet apparatus with trichlorotrifluoroethane, the residue remaining after solvent evaporation is weighed to determine the oil and grease content. Compounds volatilized at or below 103°C will be lost when the filter is dried.

b. Interference: The method is entirely empirical and duplicate results can be obtained only by strict adherence to all details. By definition, any material recovered is oil and grease and any filtrable trichlorotrifluoroethane-soluble substances, such as elemental sulfur and certain organic dyes, will be extracted as oil and grease. The rate and time of extraction in the Soxhlet apparatus must be exactly as directed because of varying solubilities of different greases. In addition, the length of time required for drying and cooling extracted material cannot be varied. There may be a gradual increase in weight, presumably due to the absorption of oxygen, and/or a gradual loss of weight due to volatilization.

2. Apparatus

a. Extraction apparatus, Soxhlet.

b. Vacuum pump or other source of vacuum.

c. Buchner funnel, 12-cm.

d. Electric heating mantle.

e. Extraction thimble, paper.

f. Filter paper, 11-cm diam.*

g. Muslin cloth disks, 11-cm diam.

---

*Whatman No. 40 or equivalent.

3. Reagents

a. Hydrochloric acid, HCl, 1 + 1.

b. Trichlorotrifluoroethane: See Section 5520B.3*b*.

c. Diatomaceous-silica filter aid suspension,† 10 g/L distilled water.

4. Procedure

Collect about 1 L of sample in a wide-mouth glass bottle and mark sample level in bottle for later determination of sample volume. Acidify to pH 2 or lower; generally, 5 mL HCl is sufficient. Prepare a filter consisting of a muslin cloth disk overlaid with filter paper. Wet paper and muslin and press down edges of paper. Using a vacuum, pass 100 mL filter aid suspension through prepared filter and wash with 1 L distilled water. Apply vacuum until no more water passes filter. Filter acidified sample. Apply vacuum until no more water passes through filter. Using forceps, transfer filter paper to a watch glass. Add material adhering to edges of muslin cloth disk. Wipe sides and bottom of collecting vessel and Buchner funnel with pieces of filter paper soaked in solvent, taking care to remove all films caused by grease and to collect all solid material. Add pieces of filter paper to filter paper on watch glass. Roll all filter paper containing sample and fit into a paper extraction thimble. Add any pieces of material remaining on watch glass. Wipe watch glass with a filter paper soaked in solvent and place in paper extraction thimble. Dry filled thimble in a

---

†Hyflo Super-Cel, Johns-Manville Corp., or equivalent.

hot-air oven at 103°C for 30 min. Fill thimble with glass wool or small glass beads. Weigh extraction flask. Extract oil and grease in a Soxhlet apparatus, using trichlorotrifluoroethane at a rate of 20 cycles/h for 4 h. Time from first cycle. Distill solvent from extraction flask in a water bath at 70°C. Place flask on a water bath at 70°C for 15 min and draw air through it using an applied vacuum for the final 1 min. Cool in a desiccator for 30 min and weigh.

5. Calculation

See Section 5520B.5.

6. Precision and Bias

See Section 5520B.6. By this method the oil and grease concentration was 14.8 mg/L. When 1-L portions of the sewage were dosed with 14.0 mg of a mixture of No. 2 fuel oil and Wesson oil, the recovery of added oils was 88% with a standard deviation of 1.1 mg.

7. Bibliography

HATFIELD, W.D. & G.E. SYMONS. 1945. The determination of grease in sewage. *Sewage Works J.* 17:16.

GILCREAS, F.W., W.W. SANDERSON & R.P. ELMER. 1953. Two new methods for the determination of grease in sewage. *Sewage Ind. Wastes* 25:1379.

ULLMANN, W.W. & W.W. SANDERSON. 1959. A further study of methods for the determination of grease in sewage. *Sewage Ind. Wastes* 31:8.

CHANIN, G., E.H. CHOW, R.B. ALEXANDER & J.F. POWERS. 1967. A safe solvent for oil and grease analyses. *J. Water Pollut. Control Fed.* 39:1892.

5520 E. Extraction Method for Sludge Samples

1. General Discussion

a. Principle: Drying acidified sludge by heating leads to low results. Magnesium

sulfate monohydrate is capable of combining with 75% of its own weight in water in forming $MgSO_4 \cdot 7H_2O$ and is used to dry sludge. After drying, the oil and grease can be extracted with trichlorotrifluoro-ethane.

b. Interference: See 5520D.1*b*.

2. Apparatus

a. Extraction apparatus, Soxhlet.

b. Vacuum pump or other source of vacuum.

c. Extraction thimble, paper.

d. Grease-free cotton: Extract nonabsorbent cotton with solvent.

3. Reagents

a. Hydrochloric acid, HCl, conc.

b. Magnesium sulfate monohydrate: Prepare $MgSO_4 \cdot H_2O$ by overnight drying of a thin layer in an oven at 150°C.

c. Trichlorotrifluoroethane: See Section 5520B.3*b.*

4. Procedure

In a 150-mL beaker weigh a sample of wet sludge, 20 ± 0.5 g, of which the dry-solids content is known. Acidify to pH 2.0 (generally, 0.3 mL conc HCl is sufficient). Add 25 g $MgSO_4 \cdot H_2O$. Stir to a smooth paste and spread on sides of beaker to facilitate subsequent removal. Let stand until

solidified, 15 to 30 min. Remove solids and grind in a porcelain mortar. Add the powder to a paper extraction thimble. Wipe beaker and mortar with small pieces of filter paper moistened with solvent and add to thimble. Fill thimble with glass wool or small glass beads. Extract in a Soxhlet apparatus, using trichlorotrifluoroethane, at a rate of 20 cycles/h for 4 h. If any turbidity or suspended matter is present in the extraction flask, remove by filtering through grease-free cotton into another weighed flask. Rinse flask and cotton with solvent. Distill solvent from extraction flask in water at 70°C. Place flask on a water bath at 70°C for 15 min and draw air through it using an applied vacuum for the final 1 min. Cool in a desiccator for 30 min and weigh.

5. Calculation

$$\text{Oil and grease as \% of dry solids}$$
$$= \frac{\text{gain in weight of flask, g} \times 100}{\text{weight of wet solids, g} \times \text{dry solids fraction}}$$

6. Precision

The examination of six replicate samples of sludge yielded a standard deviation of 4.6%.

5520 F. Hydrocarbons

1. Significance

In the absence of specially modified industrial products, oil and grease is composed primarily of fatty matter from animal and vegetable sources and hydrocarbons of petroleum origin. A knowledge of the percentage of each of these constituents in the total oil and grease minimizes the difficulty in determining the major source of the material and simplifies the correction of oil and grease problems in wastewater treatment plant operation and stream pollution abatement.

2. General Discussion

a. Principle: Silica gel has the ability to adsorb polar materials. If a solution of hydrocarbons and fatty materials in trichlorotrifluoroethane is mixed with silica gel, the fatty acids are selectively removed from solution. The materials not eliminated by silica gel adsorption are designated hydrocarbons by this test.

b. Interference: The more polar hydrocarbons, such as complex aromatic compounds and hydrocarbon derivatives of chlorine, sulfur, and nitrogen, may be adsorbed by the silica gel. Any compounds other than hydrocarbons and fatty matter recovered by the procedures for the determination of oil and grease also interfere.

3. Reagents

a. Trichlorotrifluoroethane: See Section 5520B.3*b*.

b. Silica gel, 100 to 200 mesh.* Dry at 110°C for 24 h and store in a tightly sealed container.

4. Procedure

Use the oil and grease extracted by Method B, C, D, or E for this test. When only hydrocarbons are of interest, introduce this procedure in any of the previous methods before final measurement. When hydrocarbons are to be determined after total oil and grease has been measured, redissolve, if necessary, the extracted oil and grease in trichlorotrifluoroethane. To 100 mL solvent containing less than 100 mg fatty material, add 3.0 g silica gel. Stopper container and stir on a magnetic stirrer for 5 min. For infrared measurement of

---

*Davidson Grade 923 or equivalent.

hydrocarbons no further treatment is required before measurement as described in Method C. For gravimetric determinations, filter solution through filter paper and wash silica gel and filter paper with 10 mL solvent and combine with filtrate before performing the solvent stripping steps outlined in Methods B, D, or E.

5. Calculation

Calculate hydrocarbon concentration, in milligrams per liter, as in oil and grease (Method B, C, D, or E).

6. Precision and Bias

The bias of this determination cannot be measured directly in wastewaters. The following data, obtained on synthetic samples, are indicative for natural animal, vegetable, and mineral products, but cannot be applied to the specialized industrial products previously discussed.

For hydrocarbon determinations on 10 synthetic solvent extracts containing known amounts of a wide variety of petroleum products, average recovery was 97.2%. Similar synthetic extracts of Wesson oil, olive oil, Crisco, and butter gave 0.0% recovery as hydrocarbons measured by infrared analysis.

5530 PHENOLS*

5530 A.   Introduction

Phenols, defined as hydroxy derivatives of benzene and its condensed nuclei, may occur in domestic and industrial wastewaters, natural waters, and potable water

---

*Approved by Standard Methods Committee, 1988.

supplies. Chlorination of such waters may produce odorous and objectionable-tasting chlorophenols. Phenol removal processes in water treatment include superchlorination, chlorine dioxide or chloramine treatment, ozonation, and activated carbon adsorption.

1. Selection of Method

The analytical procedures offered here use the 4-aminoantipyrine colorimetric method that determines phenol, ortho- and meta-substituted phenols, and, under proper pH conditions, those para-substituted phenols in which the substitution is a carboxyl, halogen, methoxyl, or sulfonic acid group. The 4-aminoantipyrine method does not determine those para-substituted phenols where the substitution is an alkyl, aryl, nitro, benzoyl, nitroso, or aldehyde group. A typical example of these latter groups is paracresol, which may be present in certain industrial wastewaters and in polluted surface waters.

The 4-aminoantipyrine method is given in two forms: Method C, for extreme sensitivity, is adaptable for use in water samples containing less than 1 mg phenol/L. It concentrates the color in a nonaqueous solution. Method D retains the color in the aqueous solution. Because the relative amounts of various phenolic compounds in a given sample are unpredictable, it is not possible to provide a universal standard containing a mixture of phenols. For this reason, phenol (C_6H_5OH) itself has been selected as a standard for colorimetric procedures and any color produced by the reaction of other phenolic compounds is reported as phenol. Because substitution generally reduces response, this value represents the minimum concentration of phenolic compounds. A gas-liquid chromatographic procedure given in the 17th Edition of *Standard Methods* may be applied to samples or concentrates to quantify individual phenolic compounds.

2. Interferences

Interferences such as phenol-decomposing bacteria, oxidizing and reducing substances, and alkaline pH values are dealt with by acidification. Some highly contaminated wastewaters may require specialized techniques for eliminating interferences and for quantitative recovery of phenolic compounds.

Eliminate major interferences as follows (see Section 5530B for reagents):

Oxidizing agents, such as chlorine and those detected by the liberation of iodine on acidification in the presence of potassium iodide (KI)—Remove immediately after sampling by adding excess ferrous sulfate ($FeSO_4$). If oxidizing agents are not removed, the phenolic compounds will be oxidized partially.

Sulfur compounds—Remove by acidifying to pH 4.0 with H_3PO_4 and aerating briefly by stirring. This eliminates the interference of hydrogen sulfide (H_2S) and sulfur dioxide (SO_2).

Oils and tars—Make an alkaline extraction by adjusting to pH 12 to 12.5 with NaOH pellets. Extract oil and tar from aqueous solution with 50 mL chloroform ($CHCl_3$). Discard oil- or tar-containing layer. Remove excess $CHCl_3$ in aqueous layer by warming on a water bath before proceeding with the distillation step.

3. Sampling

Sample in accordance with the instructions of Section 1060.

4. Preservation and Storage of Samples

Phenols in concentrations usually encountered in wastewaters are subject to biological and chemical oxidation. Preserve and store samples at 4°C or lower unless analyzed within 4 h after collection.

Acidify with 2 mL conc H_2SO_4/L. Samples may be stored for 4 weeks at 4°C.

Analyze preserved and stored samples within 28 d after collection.

5. Bibliography

ETTINGER, M.B., S. SCHOTT & C.C. RUCHHOFT. 1943. Preservation of phenol content in polluted river water samples previous to analysis. *J. Amer. Water Works Assoc.* 35:299.

CARTER, M.J. & M.T. HUSTON. 1978. Preservation of phenolic compounds in wastewaters. *Environ. Sci. Technol.* 12:309.

NEUFELD. R.D. & S.B. POLADINO. 1985. Comparison of 4-aminoantipyrine and gas-liquid chromatography techniques for analysis of phenolic compounds. *J. Water Pollut. Control Fed.* 57:1040.

5530 B.   Cleanup Procedure

1. Principle

Phenols are distilled from nonvolatile impurities. Because the volatilization of phenols is gradual, the distillate volume must ultimately equal that of the original sample.

2. Apparatus

a. Distillation apparatus, all-glass, consisting of a 1-L borosilicate glass distilling apparatus with Graham condenser.*

b. pH meter.

3. Reagents

Prepare all reagents with distilled water free of phenols and chlorine.

a. Phosphoric acid solution, H_3PO_4, 1 + 9: Dilute 10 mL 85% H_3PO_4 to 100 mL with water.

b. Methyl orange indicator solution.

c. Special reagents for turbid distillates:

1) *Sulfuric acid,* H_2SO_4, 1N.

2) *Sodium chloride,* NaCl.

3) *Chloroform,* $CHCl_3$, or *methylene chloride,* CH_2Cl_2.

4) *Sodium hydroxide,* NaOH, 2.5N: Dilute 41.7 mL 6N NaOH to 100 mL or dissolve 10 g NaOH pellets in 100 mL water.

4. Procedure

a. Measure 500 mL sample into a beaker, adjust pH to approximately 4.0 with H_3PO_4 solution using methyl orange indicator or a pH meter, and transfer to distillation apparatus. Use a 500-mL graduated cylinder as a receiver. Omit adding H_3PO_4 and adjust pH to 4.0 with 2.5N NaOH if sample was preserved as described in 5530A.4.

b. Distill 450 mL, stop distillation and, when boiling ceases, add 50 mL warm water to distilling flask. Continue distillation until a total of 500 mL has been collected.

c. One distillation should purify the sample adequately. Occasionally, however, the distillate is turbid. If so, acidify with H_3PO_4 solution and distill as described in ¶ 4*b*. If second distillate is still turbid, use extraction process described in ¶ 4*d* before distilling sample.

d. Treatment when second distillate is turbid: Extract a 500-mL portion of original sample as follows: Add 4 drops methyl orange indicator and make acidic to methyl orange with 1N H_2SO_4. Transfer to a separatory funnel and add 150 g NaCl. Shake with five successive portions of $CHCl_3$, using 40 mL in the first portion and 25 mL in each successive portion. Transfer $CHCl_3$ layer to a second separatory funnel and shake with three successive portions of 2.5N NaOH solution, using 4.0 mL in the first portion and 3.0 mL in each of the next two portions. Combine alkaline extracts, heat on a water bath until $CHCl_3$ has been removed, cool, and dilute to 500 mL with distilled water. Proceed with distillation as described in ¶s 4*a* and *b*.

NOTE: CH_2Cl_2 may be used instead of $CHCl_3$, especially if an emulsion forms when the $CHCl_3$ solution is extracted with NaOH.

---

*Corning No. 3360 or equivalent.

5530 C.   Chloroform Extraction Method

1. General Discussion

a. Principle: Steam-distillable phenols react with 4-aminoantipyrine at pH 7.9 ± 0.1 in the presence of potassium ferricyanide to form a colored antipyrine dye. This dye is extracted from aqueous solution with $CHCl_3$ and the absorbance is measured at 460 nm. This method covers the phenol concentration range from 1.0 $\mu g/L$ to over 250 $\mu g/L$ with a sensitivity of 1 $\mu g/L$.

b. Interference: All interferences are eliminated or reduced to a minimum if the sample is preserved, stored, and distilled in accordance with the foregoing instructions.

c. Minimum detectable quantity: The minimum detectable quantity for clean samples containing no interferences is 0.5 μg phenol when a 25-mL $CHCl_3$ extraction with a 5-cm cell or a 50-mL $CHCl_3$ extraction with a 10-cm cell is used in the photometric measurement. This quantity is equivalent to 1 μg phenol/L in 500 mL distillate.

2. Apparatus

a. Photometric equipment: A spectrophotometer for use at 460 nm equipped with absorption cells providing light paths of 1 to 10 cm, depending on the absorbances of the colored solutions and the individual characteristics of the photometer.

b. Filter funnels: Buchner type with fritted disk.*

c. Filter paper: Alternatively use an appropriate 11-cm filter paper for filtering $CHCl_3$ extracts instead of the Buchner-type funnels and anhydrous Na_2SO_4.

d. pH meter.

e. Separatory funnels, 1000-mL, Squibb form, with ground-glass stoppers and TFE stopcocks. At least eight are required.

---

*15-mL Corning No. 36060 or equivalent.

3. Reagents

Prepare all reagents with distilled water free of phenols and chlorine.

a. Stock phenol solution: Dissolve 1.00 g phenol in freshly boiled and cooled distilled water and dilute to 1000 mL. CAUTION— *Toxic; handle with extreme care.* Ordinarily this direct weighing yields a standard solution; if extreme accuracy is required, standardize as follows:

1) To 100 mL water in a 500-mL glass-stoppered conical flask, add 50.0 mL stock phenol solution and 10.0 mL bromate-bromide solution. Immediately add 5 mL conc HCl and swirl gently. If brown color of free bromine does not persist, add 10.0-mL portions of bromate-bromide solution until it does. Keep flask stoppered and let stand for 10 min; then add approximately 1 g KI. Usually four 10-mL portions of bromate-bromide solution are required if the stock phenol solution contains 1000 mg phenol/L.

2) Prepare a blank in exactly the same manner, using distilled water and 10.0 mL bromate-bromide solution. Titrate blank and sample with 0.025 M sodium thiosulfate, using starch solution indicator.

3) Calculate the concentration of phenol solution as follows:

$$\text{mg phenol/L} = 7.842 \, [(A \times B) - C]$$

where:

    A = mL thiosulfate for blank,
    B = mL bromate-bromide solution used for sample divided by 10, and
    C = mL thiosulfate used for sample.

b. Intermediate phenol solution: Dilute 10.0 mL stock phenol solution in freshly boiled and cooled distilled water to 1000 mL; 1 mL = 10.0 μg phenol. Prepare daily.

c. Standard phenol solution: Dilute 50.0 mL intermediate phenol solution to 500 mL with freshly boiled and cooled distilled water; 1 mL = 1.0 μg phenol. Prepare within 2 h of use.

d. Bromate-bromide solution: Dissolve 2.784 g anhydrous $KBrO_3$ in water, add 10 g KBr crystals, dissolve, and dilute to 1000 mL.

e. Hydrochloric acid, HCl, conc.

f. Standard sodium thiosulfate titrant, 0.025 *M:* See Section 4500-O.C.2*e*.

g. Starch solution: See Section 4500-O.C.2*d*.

h. Ammonium hydroxide, NH_4OH, 0.5*N:* Dilute 35 mL fresh, conc NH_4OH to 1 L with water.

i. Phosphate buffer solution: Dissolve 104.5 g K_2HPO_4 and 72.3 g KH_2PO_4 in water and dilute to 1 L. The pH should be 6.8.

j. 4-Aminoantipyrine solution: Dissolve 2.0 g 4-aminoantipyrine in water and dilute to 100 mL. Prepare daily.

k. Potassium ferricyanide solution: Dissolve 8.0 g $K_3Fe(CN)_6$ in water and dilute to 100 mL. Filter if necessary. Store in a brown glass bottle. Prepare fresh weekly.

l. Chloroform, $CHCl_3$.

m. Sodium sulfate, anhydrous Na_2SO_4, granular.

n. Potassium iodide, KI, crystals.

4. Procedure

Ordinarily, use Procedure *a;* however, Procedure *b* may be used for infrequent analyses.

a. Place 500 mL distillate, or a suitable portion containing not more than 50 μg phenol, diluted to 500 mL, in a 1-L beaker. Prepare a 500-mL distilled water blank and a series of 500-mL phenol standards containing 5, 10, 20, 30, 40, and 50 μg phenol.

Treat sample, blank, and standards as follows: Add 12.0 mL 0.5*N* NH_4OH and *immediately* adjust pH to 7.9 ± 0.1 with phosphate buffer. Under some circumstances, a higher pH may be required.† About 10 mL phosphate buffer are required. Transfer to a 1-L separatory funnel, add 3.0 mL aminoantipyrine solution, mix well, add 3.0 mL $K_3Fe(CN)_6$ solution, mix well, and let color develop for 15 min. The solution should be clear and light yellow.

Extract immediately with $CHCl_3$ using 25 mL for 1- to 5-cm cells and 50 mL for a 10-cm cell. Shake separatory funnel at least 10 times, let $CHCl_3$ settle, shake again 10 times, and let $CHCl_3$ settle again. Filter each $CHCl_3$ extract through filter paper or fritted glass funnels containing a 5-g layer of anhydrous Na_2SO_4. Collect dried extracts in clean cells for absorbance measurements; do not add more $CHCl_3$ or wash filter papers or funnels with $CHCl_3$.

Read absorbance of sample and standards against the blank at 460 nm. Plot absorbance against micrograms phenol concentration. Construct a separate calibration curve for each photometer and check each curve periodically to insure reproducibility.

b. For infrequent analyses prepare only one standard phenol solution. Prepare 500 mL standard phenol solution of a strength approximately equal to the phenolic content of that portion of original sample used for final analysis. Also prepare a 500-mL distilled water blank.

Continue as described in ¶ *a*, above, but measure absorbances of sample and standard phenol solution against the blank at 460 nm.

5. Calculation

a. For Procedure *a:*

$$\mu\text{g phenol/L} = \frac{A}{B} \times 1000$$

---

†For NPDES permit analyses, pH 10 ± 0.1 is required.

where:

$A = \mu g$ phenol in sample, from calibration curve, and

$B = mL$ original sample.

b. For Procedure *b,* calculate the phenol content of the original sample:

$$\mu g \text{ phenol/L} = \frac{C \times D \times 1000}{E \times B}$$

where:

$C = \mu g$ standard phenol solution,

$D =$ absorbance reading of sample,

$E =$ absorbance of standard phenol solution, and

$B = mL$ original sample.

6. Precision and Bias

Because the "phenol" value is based on C_6H_5OH, this method yields only an approximation and represents the minimum amount of phenols present. This is true because the phenolic reactivity to 4-aminoantipyrine varies with the types of phenols present.

In a study of 40 refinery wastewaters analyzed in duplicate at concentrations from 0.02 to 6.4 mg/L the average relative standard deviation was ± 12%. Data are not available for precision at lower concentrations.

7. Bibliography

SCOTT, R.D. 1931. Application of a bromine method in the determination of phenols and cresols. *Ind. Eng. Chem.*, Anal. Ed. 3:67.

EMERSON, E., H.H. BEACHAM & L.C. BEEGLE. 1943. The condensation of aminoantipyrine. II. A new color test for phenolic compounds. *J. Org. Chem.* 8:417.

ETTINGER, M.B. & R.C. KRONER. 1949. The determination of phenolic materials in industrial wastes. *Proc. 5th Ind. Waste Conf.*, Purdue Univ., p. 345.

ETTINGER, M.B., C.C. RUCHHOFT & R.J. LISHKA. 1951. Sensitive 4-aminoantipyrine method for phenolic compounds. *Anal. Chem.* 23:1783.

DANNIS, M. 1951. Determination of phenols by the aminoantipyrine method. *Sewage Ind. Wastes* 23:1516.

MOHLER, E.F., JR. & L.N. JACOB. 1957. Determination of phenolic-type compounds in water and industrial waste waters: Comparison of analytical methods. *Anal. Chem.* 29:1369.

BURTSCHELL, R.H., A.A. ROSEN, F.M. MIDDLETON & M.B. ETTINGER. 1959. Chlorine derivatives of phenol causing taste and odor. *J. Amer. Water Works Assoc.* 51:205.

GORDON, G.E. 1960. Colorimetric determination of phenolic materials in refinery waste waters. *Anal. Chem.* 32:1325.

OCHYNSKI, F.W. 1960. The absorptiometric determination of phenol. *Analyst* 85:278.

FAUST, S.D. & O.M. ALY. 1962. The determination of 2,4-dichlorophenol in water. *J. Amer. Water Works Assoc.* 54:235.

FAUST, S.D. & E.W. MIKULEWICZ. 1967. Factors influencing the condensation of 4-aminoantipyrine with derivatives of hydroxybenzene. II. Influence of hydronium ion concentration on absorptivity. *Water Res.* 1:509.

FAUST, S.D. & P.W. ANDERSON. 1968. Factors influencing the condensation of 4-aminoantipyrine with derivations of hydroxy benzene. III. A study of phenol content in surface waters. *Water Res.* 2:515.

SMITH, L.S. 1976. Evaluation of Instrument for the (Ultraviolet) Determination of Phenol in Water. EPA-600/4-76-048, U.S. Environmental Protection Agency, Cincinnati, Ohio.

5530 D.   Direct Photometric Method

1. General Discussion

a. Principle: Steam-distillable phenolic compounds react with 4-aminoantipyrine at pH 7.9 ± 0.1 in the presence of potassium ferricyanide to form a colored antipyrine dye. This dye is kept in aqueous solution and the absorbance is measured at 500 nm.

b. Interference: Interferences are eliminated or reduced to a minimum by using the distillate from the preliminary distillation procedure.

c. Minimum detectable quantity: This method has less sensitivity than Method C. The minimum detectable quantity is 10 μg phenol when a 5-cm cell and 100 mL distillate are used.

2. Apparatus

a. Photometric equipment: Spectrophotometer equipped with absorption cells providing light paths of 1 to 5 cm for use at 500 nm.

b. pH meter.

3. Reagents

See Section 5530C.3.

4. Procedure

Place 100 mL distillate, or a portion containing not more than 0.5 mg phenol diluted to 100 mL, in a 250-mL beaker. Prepare a 100-mL distilled water blank and a series of 100-mL phenol standards containing 0.1, 0.2, 0.3, 0.4, and 0.5 mg phenol.

Treat sample, blank, and standards as follows: Add 2.5 mL 0.5*N* NH$_4$OH solution and immediately adjust to pH 7.9 ± 0.1 with phosphate buffer. Add 1.0 mL 4-aminoantipyrine solution, mix well, add 1.0 mL K$_3$Fe(CN)$_6$ solution, and mix well.

After 15 min, transfer to cells and read absorbance of sample and standards against the blank at 500 nm.

5. Calculation

a. Use of calibration curve: Estimate sample phenol content from photometric readings by using a calibration curve constructed as directed in Section 5530C.4*a*.

$$\text{mg phenol/L} = \frac{A}{B} \times 1000$$

where:

A = mg phenol in sample, from calibration curve, and
B = mL original sample.

b. Use of single phenol standard:

$$\text{mg phenol/L} = \frac{C \times D \times 1000}{E \times B}$$

where:
C = mg standard phenol solution,
D = absorbance of sample, and
E = absorbance of standard phenol solution.

6. Precision and Bias

Precision and bias data are not available.

5540   SURFACTANTS*

5540 A.   Introduction

1. Occurrence and Significance

Surfactants enter waters and waste-waters mainly by discharge of aqueous wastes from household and industrial laundering and other cleansing operations. A surfactant combines in a single molecule a strongly hydrophobic group with a strongly hydrophilic one. Such molecules tend to congregate at the interfaces between the aqueous medium and the other phases of the system such as air, oily liquids, and particles, thus imparting properties such as foaming, emulsification, and particle suspension.

The surfactant hydrophobic group generally is a hydrocarbon radical (R) containing about 10 to 20 carbon atoms. The hydrophilic groups are of two types, those that ionize in water and those that do not. Ionic surfactants are subdivided into two categories, differentiated by the charge. An anionic surfactant ion is negatively charged, e.g., $(RSO_3)^- Na^+$, and a cationic one is positively charged, e.g., $(RMe_3N)^+ Cl^-$. Nonionizing (nonionic) surfactants commonly contain a polyoxyethylene hydrophilic group $(ROCH_2CH_2OCH_2CH_2......OCH_2CH_2OH,$ often abbreviated RE_n, where n is the average number of $-OCH_2CH_2-$ units in the hydrophilic group). Hybrids of these types exist also.

In the United States, ionic surfactants amount to about two thirds of the total surfactants used and nonionics to about one third. Cationic surfactants amount to less than one tenth of the ionics and are used generally for disinfecting, fabric softening, and various cosmetic purposes rather than for their detersive properties. At current detergent and water usage levels the surfactant content of raw domestic wastewater is in the range of about 1 to 20 mg/L. Most domestic wastewater surfactants are dissolved in equilibrium with proportional amounts adsorbed on particulates. Primary sludge concentrations range from 1 to 20 mg adsorbed anionic surfactant per gram dry weight.[1] In environmental waters the surfactant concentration generally is below 0.1 mg/L except in the vicinity of an outfall or other point source of entry.[2]

2. Analytical Precautions

Because of inherent properties of surfactants, special analytical precautions are necessary. Avoid foam formation because the surfactant concentration is higher in the foam phase than in the associated bulk aqueous phase and the latter may be significantly depleted. If foam is formed, let it subside by standing, or collapse it by other appropriate means, and remix the liquid phase before sampling. Adsorption of surfactant from aqueous solutions onto the walls of containers, when concentrations below about 1 mg/L are present, may seriously deplete the bulk aqueous phase. Minimize adsorption errors, if necessary, by rinsing container with sample, and for anionic surfactants by adding alkali phosphate (e.g., $0.03N$ KH_2PO_4).[3]

3. References

1. SWISHER, R.D. 1987. Surfactant Biodegradation, 2nd ed. Marcel Dekker, New York, N.Y.

---

*Approved by Standard Methods Committee, 1988.

2. ARTHUR D. LITTLE, INC. 1977. Human Safety and Environmental Aspects of Major Surfactants. Rep. No. PB-301193, National Technical Information Serv., Springfield, Va.

3. WEBER, W.J., JR., J.C. MORRIS & W. STUMM. 1962. Determination of alkylbenzenesulfonate by ultraviolet spectrophotometry. *Anal. Chem.* 34:1844.

5540 B.   Surfactant Separation by Sublation

1. General Discussion

a. Principle: The sublation process isolates the surfactant, regardless of type, from dilute aqueous solution, and yields a dried residue relatively free of nonsurfactant substances. It is accomplished by bubbling a stream of nitrogen up through a column containing the sample and an overlying layer of ethyl acetate. The surfactant is adsorbed at the water-gas interfaces of the bubbles and is carried into the ethyl acetate layer. The bubbles escape into the atmosphere leaving behind the surfactant dissolved in ethyl acetate. The solvent is separated, dehydrated, and evaporated, leaving the surfactant as a residue suitable for analysis. This procedure is the same as that used by the Organization for Economic Co-operation and Development (OECD),[1] following the development by Wickbold. [2,3]

b. Interferences: The sublation method is specific for surfactants, because any substance preferentially adsorbed at the water-gas interface is by definition a surfactant. Although nonsurfactant substances largely are rejected in this separation process, some amounts will be carried over mechanically into the ethyl acetate.

c. Limitations: The sublation process separates only dissolved surfactants. If particulate matter is present it holds back an equilibrium amount of adsorbed surfactant. As sublation removes the initially dissolved surfactant, the particulates tend to re-equi-librate and their adsorbed surfactants re-dissolve. Thus, continued sublation eventually should remove substantially all adsorbed surfactant. However, if the particulates adsorb the surfactant tightly, as sewage particulates usually do, complete removal may take a very long time. The procedure given herein calls for preliminary filtration and measures only dissolved surfactant. Determine adsorbed surfactant content by analyzing particulates removed by filtration; no standard method is available now.

d. Operating conditions: Make successive 5-min sublations from 1 L of sample containing 5 g $NaHCO_3$ and 100 g NaCl. Under the conditions specified, extensive transfer of surfactant occurs in the first sublation and is substantially complete in the second.[2-4]

e. Quantitation: Quantitate the surfactant residue by the procedures in 5540C or D. Direct weighing of the residue is not useful because the weight of surfactant isolated generally is too low, less than a milligram, and varied amounts of mechanically entrained nonsurfactants may be present. The procedure is applicable to water and wastewater samples.

2. Apparatus

a. Sublator: A glass column with dimensions as shown in Figure 5540:1. For the

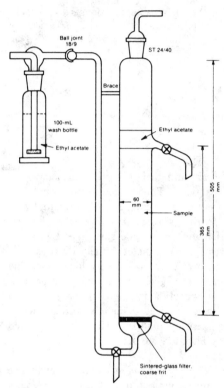

Figure 5540:1. Sublation apparatus.[1] See Section 5540B.2*a* and *b* and 4*c*. Bottom stopcock: TFE plug, 4-mm bore; side stopcocks: TFE plug, 2-mm bore.

sintered glass disk use a coarse-porosity frit (designation "c" - nominal maximum pore diam 40 to 60 μm as measured by ASTM E-128) of the same diameter as the column internal diameter. Volume between disk and upper stopcock should be approximately 1 L.

b. Gas washing bottle, as indicated in Figure 5540:1, working volume 100 mL or more.

c. Separatory funnel, working volume 250 mL, preferably with inert TFE stopcock.

d. Filtration equipment, suitable for 1-L samples, using medium-porosity qualitative-grade filter paper.

e. Gas flowmeter, for measuring flows up to 1 L/min.

3. Reagents

a. Nitrogen, standard commercial grade.

b. Ethyl acetate: CAUTION: *Ethyl acetate is flammable and its vapors can form explosive mixtures with air.*

c. Sodium bicarbonate, $NaHCO_3$.

d. Sodium chloride, NaCl.

e. Water, surfactant-free.

4. Procedure

a. Sample size: Select a sample to contain not more than 1 to 2 mg surfactant.[4] For most waters the sample volume will be about 1 L; for wastewater use a smaller volume.

b. Filtration: Filter sample through medium-porosity qualitative filter paper. Wash filter paper by discarding the first few hundred milliliters of filtrate.

c. Assembly: Refer to Figure 5540:1.

Connect nitrogen cylinder through flowmeter to inlet of gas washing bottle. Connect gas outlet at top of sublator to means for disposing ethyl acetate vapor such as by a gas scrubber or by venting to a hood or directly outdoors. In the absence of a flowmeter, ensure proper gas flow rate by measuring volume of gas leaving the sublator, with a water-displacement system.

d. Charging: Fill gas washing bottle about two-thirds full with ethyl acetate. Rinse sublation column with ethyl acetate and discard rinse. Place measured filtered sample in sublator and add 5 g $NaHCO_3$, 100 g NaCl, and sufficient water to bring the level up to or slightly above the upper stopcock (about 1 L total volume). If sample volume permits, add salts as a solution in 400 mL water or dissolve them in the sample and quantitatively transfer to the sublator. Add 100 mL ethyl acetate by running it carefully down the wall of the sublator to form a layer on top of the sample.

e. *Sublation:* Start the nitrogen flow, increasing the rate carefully to 1 L/min initially but do not exceed a rate at which the liquid phases begin vigorous intermixing at their interface. Avoid overly vigorous intermixing, which will lead to back-extraction of the surfactant into the aqueous phase and to dissolution of ethyl acetate. Continue sublation for 5 min at 1 L/min. If a lower flow rate is necessary to avoid phase intermixing, prolong sublation time proportionally. If the volume of the upper phase has decreased by more than about 20%, repeat the operation on a new sample but avoid excessive intermixing at the interface. Draw off entire ethyl acetate layer through upper stopcock into the separatory funnel; return any transferred water layer to the sublator. Filter ethyl acetate layer into a 250-mL beaker through a dry, medium-porosity, qualitative filter paper (prewashed with ethyl acetate to remove any adventitious surfactant) to remove any remaining aqueous phase.

Repeat process of preceding paragraph with a second 100-mL layer of ethyl acetate, using the same separatory funnel and filter, and finally rinse sublator wall with another 20 mL, all into the original beaker.

Evaporate ethyl acetate from the beaker on a steam bath in a hood, blowing a gentle stream of nitrogen or air over the liquid surface to speed evaporation and to minimize active boiling. Evaporate the first 100 mL during the second sublation to avoid overfilling the beaker. To avoid possible solute volatilization, discontinue heating after removing the ethyl acetate. The sublated surfactant remains in the beaker as a film of residue.

Draw off aqueous layer in the sublator and discard, using the stopcock just above the sintered disk to minimize disk fouling.

5. Precision and Bias

Estimates of the efficiency of surfactant transfer and recovery in the sublation process include the uncertainties of the analytical methods used in quantitating the surfactant. At present the analytical methods are semiquantitative for surfactant at levels below 1 mg/L in environmental samples.

With various known surfactants at 0.2 to 2 mg/L and appropriate analytical methods, over 90% of added surfactant was recovered in one 5-min sublation from 10% NaCl. Without NaCl, recovery of nonionics was over 90% but recovery of anionics and cationics was only 2 to 25%.[4]

Five laboratories studied the recovery of five anionic surfactant types from concentrations of 0.05, 0.2, 1.0, and 5.0 mg/L in aqueous solutions.[5] The amount in each solution was determined directly by methylene blue analysis and compared with the amount recovered in the sublation process, also analyzed by methylene blue. The overall average recovery was 95.9% with a standard deviation of ± 7.4 ($n = 100$). The extreme individual values for recovery were 65% and 115% and the other 98 values ranged from 75% to 109%. Recovery did not depend on surfactant concentration (average recoveries ranging from 94.7% at 5.0 mg/L to 96.8% at 1.0 mg/L) nor on the surfactant type (average recoveries ranging from 94.7% to 96.6%). Average recoveries at the five laboratories ranged from 90.0% to 98.0%.

Application of the sublation method in three laboratories to eight different samples of raw wastewater in duplicate gave the results shown in Table 5540:I. Methylene blue active substances (MBAS) recovery in double sublation averaged 87 ± 16% of that determined directly on the filtered wastewater; these results would have been influenced by any nonsurfactant MBAS that might have been present. Repeating

TABLE 5540:I. SURFACTANT RECOVERY BY SUBLATION

Variable	MBAS	CTAS
Sample volume, mL	200–300	500
Concentration without sublation, mg/L	2.2–4.7	—
Concentration found in sublate,* mg/L	1.8–4.4	0.3–0.6
Recovery in sublate, %	87 ± 16†	—
Amount in second sublate,‡ mg	0.02 ± 0.02†	0.08 ± 0.01†
Amount added, mg	0.05–0.10§	0.50–0.67‖
Recovery in sublation,# %	94 ± 17†	92 ± 6†

* Two 5-min sublations.
† Average ± SD ($n = 8$).
‡ Two more 5-min sublations.
§ Reference LAS.
‖ Linear alcohol ethoxylate $C_{12-18}E_{11}$.
Fifth and sixth 5-min sublations.

double sublation on the spent aqueous phase yielded another 0.02 mg MBAS and another 0.08 mg cobalt thiocyanate active substances (CTAS). Adding 0.05 to 0.10 mg of known linear alkylbenzene sulfonate (LAS) or 0.50 to 0.67 mg of known linear alcohol-based $C_{12-18}E_{11}$ to the same sublator contents and again running double sublation resulted in over 90% recovery of the amount added.

6. References

1. ORGANIZATION FOR ECONOMIC CO-OPERATION AND DEVELOPMENT ENVIRONMENTAL DIRECTORATE. 1976. Proposed Method for the Determination of the Biodegradability of Surfactants Used in Synthetic Detergents. Org. for Economic Co-Operation & Development, Paris.
2. WICKBOLD, R. 1971. Enrichment and separation of surfactants from surface waters through transport in the gas/water interface. *Tenside* 8:61.
3. WICKBOLD, R. 1972. Determination of non-ionic surfactants in river- and wastewaters. *Tenside* 9:173.
4. KUNKEL, E., G. PEITSCHER & K. ESPETER. 1977. New developments in trace- and microanalysis of surfactants. *Tenside* 14:199.
5. DIVO, C., S. GAFA, T. LA NOCE, A. PARIS, C. RUFFO & M. SANNA. 1980. Use of nitrogen blowing technique in microdetermination of anionic surfactants. *Riv. Ital. Sost. Grasse* 57:329.

5540 C.   Anionic Surfactants as MBAS

I. General Discussion

a. Definition and principle: Methylene blue active substances (MBAS) bring about the transfer of methylene blue, a cationic dye, from an aqueous solution into an immiscible organic liquid upon equilibration. This occurs through ion pair formation by the MBAS anion and the methylene blue cation. The intensity of the resulting blue color in the organic phase is a measure of MBAS. Anionic surfactants are among the most prominent of many substances, natural and synthetic, showing methylene blue activity. The MBAS method is useful for estimating the anionic surfactant content of waters and wastewaters, but the possible presence of other types of MBAS always must be kept in mind.

This method is relatively simple and precise. It comprises three successive extractions from acid aqueous medium containing excess methylene blue into chloroform (CHCl₃), followed by an aqueous backwash and measurement of the blue color in the CHCl₃ by spectrophotometry at 652 nm. The method is applicable at MBAS concentrations down to about 0.025 mg/L.

b. Anionic surfactant responses: Soaps do not respond in the MBAS method. Those used in or as detergents are alkali salts of C_{10-20} fatty acids $[RCO_2]^-Na^+$, and though anionic in nature they are so weakly ionized that an extractable ion pair is not formed under the conditions of the test. Nonsoap anionic surfactants commonly used in detergent formulations are strongly responsive. These include principally surfactants of the sulfonate type $[RSO_3]^-Na^+$, the sulfate ester type $[ROSO_3]^-Na^+$, and sulfated nonionics $[RE_nOSO_3]^-Na^+$. They are recovered almost completely by a single CHCl₃ extraction.

Linear alkylbenzene sulfonate (LAS) is the most widely used anionic surfactant and is used to standardize the MBAS method. LAS is not a single compound, but may comprise any or all of 26 isomers and homologs with structure $[R'C_6H_4SO_3]^-Na^+$, where R′ is a linear secondary alkyl group ranging from 10 to 14 carbon atoms in length. The manufacturing process defines the mixture, which may be modified further by the wastewate treatment process.

Sulfonate- and sulfate-type surfactants respond together in MBAS analysis, but they can be differentiated by other means. The sulfate type decomposes upon acid hydrolysis; the resulting decrease in MBAS corresponds to the original sulfate surfactant content while the MBAS remaining corresponds to the sulfonate surfactants. Alkylbenzene sulfonate can be identified

and quantified by infrared spectrometry after purification.[1] LAS can be distinguished from other alkylbenzene sulfonate surfactants by infrared methods.[2] LAS can be identified unequivocally and its detailed isomer-homolog composition determined by desulfonation-gas chromatography.[3]

c. Interferences: Positive interferences result from all other MBAS species present; if a direct determination of any individual MBAS species, such as LAS, is sought, all others interfere. Substances such as organic sulfonates, sulfates, carboxylates and phenols, and inorganic thiocyanates, cyanates, nitrates, and chlorides also may transfer more or less methylene blue into the chloroform phase. The poorer the extractability of their ion pairs, the more effective is the aqueous backwash step in removing these positive interferences; interference from chloride is eliminated almost entirely and from nitrate largely so by the backwash. Because of the varied extractability of nonsurfactant MBAS, deviations in CHCl₃ ratio and backwashing procedure may lead to significant differences in the total MBAS observed, although the recovery of sulfonate- and sulfate-type surfactants will be substantially complete in all cases.

Negative interferences can result from the presence of cationic surfactants and other cationic materials, such as amines, because they compete with the methylene blue in the formation of ion pairs. Particulate matter may give negative interference through adsorption of MBAS. Although some of the adsorbed MBAS may be desorbed and paired during the CHCl₃ extractions, recovery may be incomplete and variable.

Minimize interferences by nonsurfactant materials by sublation if necessary (Section 5540B). Other countermeasures are nonstandard. Remove interfering cationic surfactants and other cationic materials by using a cation-exchange resin under suitable conditions.[3] Handle adsorption of MBAS by particulates preferably by filtering and analyzing the insolubles. With or without filtration, adsorbed MBAS can be desorbed by acid hydrolysis; however, MBAS originating in any sulfate ester-type surfactant present is destroyed simultaneously.[1] Sulfides, often present in raw or primary treated wastewater, may react with methylene blue to form a colorless reduction product, making the analysis impossible. Eliminate this interference by prior oxidation with hydrogen peroxide.

d. *Molecular weight:* Test results will appear to differ if expressed in terms of weight rather than in molar quantities. Equimolar amounts of two anionic surfactants with different molecular weights should give substantially equal colors in the $CHCl_3$ layer, although the amounts by weight may differ significantly. If results are to be expressed by weight, as generally is desirable, the average molecular weight of the surfactant measured must be known or a calibration curve made with that particular compound must be used. Because such detailed information generally is lacking, report results in terms of a suitable standard calibration curve, for example "0.65 mg MBAS/L (calculated as LAS, mol wt 318)."

e. *Minimum detectable quantity:* About 10 µg MBAS (calculated as LAS).

f. *Application:* The MBAS method has been applied successfully to drinking water samples. In wastewater, industrial wastes, and sludge, numerous materials normally present can interfere seriously if direct determination of MBAS is attempted. Most nonsurfactant aqueous-phase interferences can be removed by sublation.

2. Apparatus

a. *Colorimetric equipment:* One of the following is required:

1) *Spectrophotometer,* for use at 652 nm, providing a light path of 1 cm or longer.

2) *Filter photometer,* providing a light path of 1 cm or longer and equipped with a red color filter exhibiting maximum transmittance near 652 nm.

b. *Separatory funnels:* 500-mL, preferably with inert TFE stopcocks and stoppers.

3. Reagents

a. *Stock LAS solution:* Weigh an amount of the reference material* equal to 1.00 g LAS on a 100% active basis. Dissolve in water and dilute to 1000 mL; 1.00 mL = 1.00 mg LAS. Store in a refrigerator to minimize biodegradation. If necessary, prepare weekly.

b. *Standard LAS solution:* Dilute 10.00 mL stock LAS solution to 1000 mL with water; 1.00 mL = 10.0 µg LAS. Prepare daily.

c. *Phenolphthalein indicator solution,* alcoholic.

d. *Sodium hydroxide,* NaOH, 1N.

e. *Sulfuric acid,* H_2SO_4, 1N and 6N.

f. *Chloroform,* $CHCl_3$: CAUTION: *Chloroform is toxic and a suspected carcinogen. Take appropriate precautions against inhalation and skin exposure.*

g. *Methylene blue reagent:* Dissolve 100 mg methylene blue† in 100 mL water. Transfer 30 mL to a 1000-mL flask. Add 500 mL water, 41 mL 6N H_2SO_4, and 50 g sodium phosphate, monobasic, monohydrate, $NaH_2PO_4 \cdot H_2O$. Shake until dissolved. Dilute to 1000 mL.

h. *Wash solution:* Add 41 mL 6 N H_2SO_4 to 500 mL water in a 1000-mL flask. Add 50 g $NaH_2PO_4 \cdot H_2O$ and shake until dissolved. Dilute to 1000 mL.

i. *Methanol,* CH_3OH. CAUTION: *Methanol vapors are flammable and toxic; take appropriate precautions.*

j. *Hydrogen peroxide,* H_2O_2, 30%.

k. *Glass wool:* Pre-extract with $CHCl_3$ to remove interferences.

l. *Water, distilled or deionized,* MBAS-

---

*A suitable reference material can be obtained from U.S. Environmental Protection Agency, Environmental Monitoring and Support Laboratory, Cincinnati, Ohio 45268.
†Eastman No. P573 or equivalent.

free. Use for making all reagents and dilutions.

4. Procedure

a. Preparation of calibration curve: Prepare a series of 10 separatory funnels with 0, 1.00, 3.00, 5.00, 7.00, 9.00, 11.00, 13.00, 15.00, and 20.00 mL standard LAS solution. Add sufficient water to make the total volume 100 mL in each separatory funnel. Treat each standard as described in ¶s 4*d* and *e* following, and plot a calibration curve of absorbance vs. micrograms LAS taken, specifying the molecular weight of the LAS used.

b. Sample size: For direct analysis of waters and wastewaters, select sample volume on the basis of expected MBAS concentration:

Expected MBAS Concentration *mg/L*	Sample Taken *mL*
0.025–0.080	400
0.08 –0.40	250
0.4 –2.0	100

If expected MBAS concentration is above 2 mg/L, dilute sample containing 40 to 200 µg MBAS to 100 mL with water.

For analysis of samples purified by sublation, dissolve sublate residue (Section 5540B.4*e*) in 10 to 20 mL methanol, quantitatively transfer the entire amount (or a suitable portion if more than 200 µg MBAS is expected) to 25 to 50 mL water, evaporate without boiling until methanol is gone, adding water as necessary to avoid going to dryness, and dilute to about 100 mL with water.

c. Peroxide treatment: If necessary to avoid decolorization of methylene blue by sulfides, add a few drops of 30% H_2O_2.

d. Ion pairing and extraction:

1) Add sample to a separatory funnel. Make alkaline by dropwise addition of 1*N* NaOH, using phenolphthalein indicator.

Discharge pink color by dropwise addition of 1*N* H_2SO_4.

2) Add 10 mL $CHCl_3$ and 25 mL methylene blue reagent. Rock funnel vigorously for 30 s and let phases separate. Alternatively, place a magnetic stirring bar in the separatory funnel; lay funnel on its side on a magnetic mixer and adjust speed of stirring to produce a rocking motion. Excessive agitation may cause emulsion formation. To break persistent emulsions add a small volume of isopropyl alcohol (< 10 mL); add same volume of isopropyl alcohol to all standards. Some samples require a longer period of phase separation than others. Before draining $CHCl_3$ layer, swirl gently, then let settle.

3) Draw off $CHCl_3$ layer into a second separatory funnel. Rinse delivery tube of first separatory funnel with a small amount of $CHCl_3$. Repeat extraction two additional times, using 10 mL $CHCl_3$ each time. If blue color in water phase becomes faint or disappears, discard and repeat, using a smaller sample.

4) Combine all $CHCl_3$ extracts in the second separatory funnel. Add 50 mL wash solution and shake vigorously for 30 s. Emulsions do not form at this stage. Let settle, swirl, and draw off $CHCl_3$ layer through a funnel containing a plug of glass wool into a 100-mL volumetric flask; filtrate must be clear. Extract wash solution twice with 10 mL $CHCl_3$ each and add to flask through the glass wool. Rinse glass wool and funnel with $CHCl_3$. Collect washings in volumetric flask, dilute to mark with $CHCl_3$, and mix well.

e. Measurement: Determine absorbance at 652 nm against a blank of $CHCl_3$.

5. Calculation

From the calibration curve (¶ 4*a*) read micrograms of apparent LAS (mol wt __) corresponding to the measured absorbance.

$$mg\ MBAS/L = \frac{\mu g\ apparent\ LAS}{mL\ original\ sample}$$

Report as "MBAS, calculated as LAS, mol wt __."

6. Precision and Bias

A synthetic sample containing 270 μg LAS/L in distilled water was analyzed in 110 laboratories with a relative standard deviation of 14.8% and a relative error of 10.6%.

A tap water sample to which was added 480 μg LAS/L was analyzed in 110 laboratories with a relative standard deviation of 9.9% and a relative error of 1.3%.

A river water sample with 2.94 mg LAS/L added was analyzed in 110 laboratories with a relative standard deviation of 9.1% and a relative error of 1.4%.[4]

7. References

1. AMERICAN PUBLIC HEALTH ASSOCIATION, AMERICAN WATER WORKS ASSOCIATION & WATER POLLUTION CONTROL FEDERATION. 1981. Carbon adsorption-infrared method. *In* Standard Methods for the Examination of Water and Wastewater, 15th ed. American Public Health Assoc., Washington, D.C.

2. OGDEN, C.P., H.L. WEBSTER & J. HALLIDAY. 1961. Determination of biologically soft and hard alkylbenzenesulfonates in detergents and sewage. *Analyst* 86:22.

3. OSBURN, Q.W. 1986. Analytical methodology for LAS in waters and wastes. *J. Amer. Oil Chem. Soc.* 63:257.

4. LISHKA, R.J. & J.H. PARKER. 1968. Water Surfactant No. 3, Study No. 32. U.S. Public Health Serv. Publ. No. 999-UIH-11, Cincinnati, Ohio.

8. Bibliography

BARR, T., J. OLIVER & W.V. STUBBINGS. 1948. The determination of surface-active agents in solution. *J. Soc. Chem. Ind.* (London) 67:45.

EPTON, S.R. 1948. New method for the rapid titrimetric analysis of sodium alkyl sulfates and related compounds. *Trans. Faraday Soc.* 44:226.

EVANS, H.C. 1950. Determination of anionic synthetic detergents in sewage. *J. Soc. Chem. Ind.* (London) 69:Suppl. 2, S76.

DEGENS, P.N., JR., H.C. EVANS, J.D. KOMMER & P.A. WINSOR. 1953. Determination of sulfate and sulfonate anion-active detergents in sewage. *J. Appl. Chem.* (London) 3:54.

AMERICAN WATER WORKS ASSOCIATION. 1954. Task group report. Characteristics and effects of synthetic detergents. *J. Amer. Water Works Assoc.* 46:751.

EDWARDS, G.P. & M.E. GINN. 1954. Determination of synthetic detergents in sewage. *Sewage Ind. Wastes* 26:945.

LONGWELL, J. & W.D. MANIECE. 1955. Determination of anionic detergents in sewage, sewage effluents, and river water. *Analyst* 80:167.

MOORE, W.A. & R.A. KOLBESON. 1956. Determination of anionic detergents in surface waters and sewage with methyl green. *Anal. Chem.* 28:161.

ROSEN, A.A., F.M. MIDDLETON & N. TAYLOR. 1956. Identification of synthetic detergents in foams and surface waters. *J. Amer. Water Works Assoc.* 48:1321.

SALLEE, E.M., et al. 1956. Determination of trace amounts of alkyl benzenesulfonates in water. *Anal. Chem.* 28:1822.

AMERICAN WATER WORKS ASSOCIATION. 1958. Task group report. Determination of synthetic detergent content of raw water supplies. *J. Amer. Water Works Assoc.* 50:1343.

McGUIRE, O.E., F. KENT, LAR. L. MILLER & G.J. PAPENMEIER. 1962. Field test for analysis of anionic detergents in well waters. *J. Amer. Water Works Assoc.* 54:665.

ABBOTT, D.C. 1962. The determination of traces of anionic surface-active materials in water. *Analyst* 87:286.

ABBOTT, D.C. 1963. A rapid test for anionic detergents in drinking water. *Analyst* 88:240.

REID, V.W., G.F. LONGMAN & E. HEINERTH. 1967. Determination of anionic-active detergents by two-phase titration. *Tenside* 4:292.

WANG, L.K., P.J. PANZARDI, W.W. SHUSTER & D. AULENBACH. 1975. Direct two-phase titration method for analyzing anionic nonsoap surfactants in fresh and saline waters. *J. Environ. Health* 38:159.

5540 D.   Nonionic Surfactants as CTAS

1. General Discussion

a. Definition and principle: Cobalt thiocyanate active substances (CTAS) are those that react with aqueous cobalt thiocyanate solution to give a cobalt-containing product extractable into an organic liquid in which it can be measured. Nonionic surfactants exhibit such activity, as may other natural and synthetic materials; thus, estimation of nonionic surfactants as CTAS is possible only if substantial freedom from interfering CTAS species can be assured.

The method requires sublation to remove nonsurfactant interferences and ion exchange to remove cationic and anionic surfactants, partition of CTAS into methylene chloride from excess aqueous cobalt thiocyanate by a single extraction, and measurement of CTAS in the methylene chloride by spectrophotometry at 620 nm. Lower limit of detectability is around 0.1 mg CTAS, calculated as $C_{12-18}E_{11}$. Beyond the sublation step the procedure is substantially identical to that of the Soap and Detergent Association (SDA).[1]

b. Nonionic surfactant responses: For pure individual molecular species the CTAS response is negligible up to about RE_5, where it increases sharply and continues to increase more gradually for longer polyether chains.[2,3] Fewer than about six oxygens in the molecule do not supply enough cumulative coordinate bond strength to hold the complex together. Commercial nonionic surfactants generally range from about RE_7 to RE_{15}; however, each such product, because of synthesis process constraints, is actually a mixture of many individual species ranging from perhaps RE_0 to RE_{2n} in a Poisson distribution averaging RE_n.

The hydrophobes used for nonionic surfactants in the U.S. household detergent industry are mainly linear primary and linear secondary alcohols with chain lengths ranging from about 12 to about 18 carbon

atoms. Nonionics used in industrial operations include some based on branched octyl- and nonylphenols. These products give strong CTAS responses that may differ from each other, on a weight basis, by as much as a factor of 2. Specifically, eight such products showed responses from 0.20 to 0.36 absorbance units/mg by the SDA procedure.[1]

As with anionic surfactants measured as MBAS, the nonionic surfactants found in water and wastewater might have CTAS responses at least as varied as their commercial precursors because the proportions of the individual molecular species will have been changed by biochemical and physicochemical removal at varied rates, and further because their original molecular structures may have been changed by biodegradation processes.

c. Reference nonionic surfactant: Until it is practical to determine the nature and molecular composition of an unknown mixed CTAS, and to calculate or determine the CTAS responses of its component species, exact quantitation of uncharacterized CTAS in a sample in terms of weight is not possible. Instead, express the analytical result in terms of some arbitrarily chosen reference nonionic surfactant, i.e., as the weight of the reference that gives the same amount of CTAS response. The reference is the nonionic surfactant $C_{12-18}E_{11}$, derived from a mixture of linear primary alcohols ranging from 12 to 18 carbon atoms in chain length by reaction with ethylene oxide in a molar ratio of 1:11. $C_{12-18}E_{11}$ is reasonably representative of nonionic surfactants in commercial use; its CTAS response is about 0.21 absorbance units/mg.

If the identity of the nonionic surfactant in the sample is known, use that same material in preparing the calibration curve.

d. Interferences: Both anionic and cationic surfactants may show positive CTAS response[1,4] but both are removed in the ion-exchange step. Sublation removes nonsurfactant interferences. Physical interferences occur if some of the CTAS is adsorbed on particulate matter. Avoid such interference by filtering out the particulates for the sublation step; this will measure only dissolved CTAS.

e. Minimum detectable quantity: About 0.1 mg CTAS, calculated as $C_{12-18}E_{11}$, which corresponds to 0.1 mg/L in a 1-L sample.

f. Application: The method is suitable for determining dissolved nonionic surfactants of the ethoxylate type in most aqueous systems.

2. Apparatus

a. Sublation apparatus: See Section 5540B.2.

b. Ion-exchange column, glass, about 1- × 30-cm. Slurry anion-exchange resin in methanol and pour into column to give a bed about 10 cm deep. Insert plug of glass wool and then add a 10-cm bed of cation-exchange resin on top in the same manner. One column may be used for treating up to six sublated samples before repacking.

c. Spectrophotometer and 2.0-cm stoppered cells, suitable for measuring absorbance at 620 nm.

d. Separatory funnels, 125-mL, preferably with TFE stopcock and stopper.

e. Extraction flasks, Soxhlet type, 150-mL.

3. Reagents

a. Sublation reagents: See Section 5540B.3.

b. Anion-exchange resin, polystyrene-quaternary ammonium-type,* 50- to 100-mesh, hydroxide form. To convert chloride form to hydroxide, elute with 20 bed volumes of $1N$ NaOH and wash with methanol until free alkali is displaced.

c. Cation-exchange resin, polystyrene-sulfonate type,† 50- to 100-mesh, hydrogen form.

d. Cobaltothiocyanate reagent: Dissolve 30 g $Co(NO_3)_2 \cdot 6H_2O$ and 200 g NH_4SCN in water and dilute to 1 L. This reagent is stable for at least 1 month at room temperature.

e. Reference nonionic surfactant, $C_{12-18}E_{11}$: Reaction product of C_{12-18} linear primary alcohol with ethylene oxide in 1:11 molar ratio.‡

f. Reference nonionic surfactant stock solution, methanolic, approximately 2 mg nonionic/mL methanol: Quantitatively transfer entire contents (approximately 1 g nonionic) from preweighed ampule into 500-mL volumetric flask, thoroughly rinse ampule with methanol, make up to volume with methanol, and reweigh dried ampule. Calculate concentration in milligrams per milliter as in ¶ 5a. Because of possible phase separation, use all material in the ampule.

g. Reference nonionic surfactant standard solution, methanolic, approximately 0.1 mg nonionic/mL methanol: Dilute 10.00 mL stock solution to 200 mL with methanol. Exact concentration is 1/20 that of the stock solution.

h. Sodium hydroxide, NaOH: $1N$.

i. Glass wool: Pre-extract with chloroform or methylene chloride.

j. Methanol, CH_3OH: CAUTION: *Methanol vapors are flammable and toxic; take appropriate precautions.*

k. Methylene chloride, CH_2Cl_2: CAUTION: *Methylene chloride vapors are toxic; take adequate precautions.*

l. Water: Use distilled or deionized, CTAS-free water for making reagents and dilutions.

4. Procedure

a. Purification by sublation: Proceed according to Section 5540B, using sample containing no more than 2 mg CTAS. (NOTE: For samples of known character

---

*Bio-Rad, AGl-X2, or equivalent.
†Bio-Rad AG 50W-X8, or equivalent.

‡This material can be obtained from U.S. Environmental Protection Agency, Environmental Monitoring and Support Laboratory, Cincinnati, Ohio 45268.

containing no interfering materials, omit this step.)

b. *Ion-exchange removal of anionic and cationic surfactants:* Dissolve sublation residue in 5 to 10 mL methanol and transfer quantitatively to ion-exchange column. Elute with methanol at 1 drop/s into a clean, dry 150-mL extraction flask until about 125 mL is collected. Evaporate methanol on a steam bath aided by a gentle stream of clean, dry nitrogen or air, taking care to avoid loss by entrainment; remove from heat as soon as the methanol is completely evaporated. (NOTE: With samples of known character containing no anionic or cationic materials, omit step b.)

c. *CTAS calibration curve:* Into a series of 150-mL extraction flasks containing 10 to 20 mL methanol place 0.00, 5.00, 10.00, 20.00, and 30.00 mL reference nonionic surfactant standard solution and evaporate just to dryness. Continue as in ¶s 4d and e, below, and plot a calibration curve of absorbance against milligrams of reference nonionic taken, specifying its identity (e.g., $C_{12-18}E_{11}$ and lot number).

d. *Cobalt complexing and extraction:* Charge a 125-mL separatory funnel with 5 mL cobaltothiocyanate reagent. With precautions against excessive and variable evaporation of the methylene chloride, dissolve residue from ion-exchange operation, ¶ 4b, by adding 10.00 mL methylene chloride and swirling for a few seconds. Immediately transfer by pouring into the separatory funnel. *Do not rinse flask.* (NOTE: Because of the volatility of methylene chloride, rigidly standardize these operations with respect to handling and elapsed time; alternatively, evaporate the methanol in 200-mL erlenmeyer flasks to be stoppered with glass or TFE stoppers during dissolution. Transfer as directed here is incomplete, but in this case it will not introduce error because the loss of nonionics is exactly compensated for by the diminished volume of the organic layer in the extraction.) Shake separatory funnel

vigorously for 60 s and let layers separate. Run lower layer into a 2.0-cm cell through a funnel containing a plug of pre-extracted glass wool and stopper. Be sure filtrate is absolutely clear. (NOTE: If desired, clarify by running the lower layer into a 12-mL centrifuge tube, stopper, spin at or above $1000 \times g$ for 3 min, and transfer to the cell by a Pasteur pipet; use same procedure for both calibration and samples.)

e. *Measurement:* Determine absorbance at 620 nm against a blank of methylene chloride. (NOTE: If haze develops in the cell, warm slightly with a hot air gun or heat lamp to clarify.)

5. Calculations

a. *Nonionic surfactant in reference nonionic stock solution* ¶ 3f:

mg nonionic/mL methanol
  = mg reference sample/500 mL

b. *Nonionic surfactant in sample:* From the calibration curve read milligrams of reference nonionic corresponding to the measured absorbance:

mg CTAS/L = mg apparent nonionic/L sample

Report as "CTAS, calculated as nonionic surfactant $C_{12-18}E_{11}$."

6. Precision and Bias

Twenty-four samples of 6.22% w/v solution of reference nonionic surfactant $C_{12-18}E_{11}$ were analyzed in three laboratories by CTAS alone, without sublation or ion exchange. The overall relative standard deviation was about 3%. Results of the three laboratories individually were:

Laboratory	% w/w ± SD
A	6.08 ± 0.14 ($n = 36$)
B	6.56 ± 0.17 ($n = 6$)
C	6.25 ± 0.14 ($n = 36$)
Overall	6.20 ± 0.19 ($n = 78$)

Samples of raw wastewater were freed of surfactants by four successive sublations, then 0.50 or 0.67 mg reference nonionic surfactant $C_{12-18}E_{11}$ was added and carried through the entire sequence of sublation, ion exchange, and CTAS extraction. Recoveries averaged 92% with overall standard deviation around 6%:

Laboratory	% Recovery ± SD
A	87 ± 4 ($n = 4$)
B	97 ± 1 ($n = 4$)
Overall	92 ± 6 ($n = 8$)

The above data relate to the bias and precision of the method when applied to a known nonionic surfactant. When the nature of the nonionic surfactant is unknown, there is greater uncertainty. The response of the reference $C_{12-18}E_{11}$ is about 0.21 absorbance units/mg, while that of the eight nonionic types mentioned under ¶ 1b ranged from 0.20 to 0.36, and environmental nonionics might differ still more. If the nonionic surfactant in the sample has a response of 0.42, the result calculated in terms of milligrams $C_{12-18}E_{11}$ would be double the actual milligrams of the unknown nonionic.

7. References

1. SOAP AND DETERGENT ASSOCIATION ANALYTICAL SUBCOMMITTEE. 1977. Analytical methods for nonionic surfactants in laboratory biodegradation and environmental studies. *Environ. Sci. Technol.* 11:1167.
2. CRABB, N.T. & H.E. PERSINGER. 1964. The determination of polyoxyethylene nonionic surfactants in water at the parts per million level. *J. Amer. Oil Chem. Soc.* 41:752.
3. CRABB, N.T. & H.E. PERSINGER. 1968. A determination of the apparent molar absorption coefficients of the cobalt thiocyanate complexes of nonylphenol ethylene oxide adducts. *J. Amer. Oil Chem. Soc.* 45:611.
4. GREFF, R.A., E.A. SETZKORN & W.D. LESLIE. 1965. A colorimetric method for the determination of parts per million of nonionic surfactants. *J. Amer Oil Chem. Soc.* 42:180.

8. Bibliography

TABAK, H.H. & R.L. BUNCH. 1981. Measurement of non-ionic surfactants in aqueous environments. Proc. 36th Ind. Waste Conf., p. 888. Purdue Univ., Lafayette, Ind.

* * *

5560   ORGANIC AND VOLATILE ACIDS*

5560 A.   Introduction

The measurement of organic acids, either by adsorption and elution from a chromatographic column or by distillation, can be used as a control test for anaerobic digestion. The chromatographic separation method is presented for organic acids (B), while a method using distillation (C) is presented for volatile acids.

Volatile fatty acids are classified as water-soluble fatty acids that can be distilled at atmospheric pressure. These vol-

---

*Approved by Standard Methods Committee, 1985.

atile acids can be removed from aqueous solution by distillation, despite their high boiling points, because of co-distillation with water. This group includes water-soluble fatty acids with up to six carbon atoms.

The distillation method is empirical and gives incomplete and somewhat variable recovery. Factors such as heating rate and proportion of sample recovered as distillate affect the result, requiring the determination of a recovery factor for each apparatus and set of operating conditions. However, it is suitable for routine control purposes. Removing sludge solids from the sample reduces the possibility of hydrolysis of complex materials to volatile acids.

5560 B.   Chromatographic Separation Method for Organic Acids

1. General Discussion

a. Principle: An acidified aqueous sample containing organic acids is adsorbed on a column of silicic acid and the acids are eluted with *n*-butanol in chloroform ($CHCl_3$). The eluate is collected and titrated with standard base. All short-chain (C_1 to C_6) organic acids are eluted by this solvent system and are reported collectively as total organic acids.

b. Interference: The $CHCl_3$-butanol solvent system is capable of eluting organic acids other than the volatile acids and also some synthetic detergents. Besides the so-called volatile acids, crotonic, adipic, pyruvic, phthalic, fumaric, lactic, succinic, malonic, gallic, aconitic, and oxalic acids; alkyl sulfates; and alkyl-aryl sulfonates are adsorbed by silicic acid and eluted.

c. Precautions: Basic alcohol solutions decrease in strength with time, particularly when exposed repeatedly to the atmosphere. These decreases usually are accompanied by the appearance of a white precipitate. The magnitude of such changes normally is not significant in process control if tests are made within a few days of standardization. To minimize this effect, store standard sodium hydroxide (NaOH) titrant in a tightly stoppered borosilicate glass bottle and protect from atmospheric carbon dioxide (CO_2) by attaching a tube of CO_2-absorbing material, as described in the inside front cover. For more precise analyses, standardize titrant or prepare before each analysis.

Although the procedure is adequate for routine analysis of most sludge samples, volatile-acids concentrations above 5000 mg/L may require an increased amount of organic solvent for quantitative recovery. Elute with a second portion of solvent and titrate to reveal possible incomplete recoveries.

2. Apparatus

a. Centrifuge or filtering assembly.

b. Crucibles, Gooch or medium-porosity fritted-glass, with filtering flask and vacuum source. Use crucibles of sufficient size (30 to 35 mL) to hold 12 g silicic acid.

c. Separatory funnel, 1000-mL.

3. Reagents

a. Silicic acid, specially prepared for chromatography, 50 to 200 mesh: Remove fines by slurrying in distilled water and decanting supernatant after settling for 15 min. Repeat several times. Dry washed acid in an oven at 103°C until *absolutely dry,* then store in a desiccator.

b. Chloroform-butanol reagent: Mix 300 mL reagent-grade $CHCl_3$, 100 mL *n*-butanol, and 80 mL 0.5*N* H₂SO₄ in a separatory funnel. Let water and organic layers separate. Drain off lower organic layer through a fluted filter paper into a dry bottle.

c. Thymol blue indicator solution: Dissolve 80 mg thymol blue in 100 mL absolute methanol.

d. Phenolphthalein indicator solution: Dissolve 80 mg phenolphthalein in 100 mL absolute methanol.

e. Sulfuric acid, H₂SO₄, conc.

f. Standard sodium hydroxide, NaOH, 0.02*N:* Dilute 20 mL 1.0*N* NaOH stock solution to 1 L with absolute methanol. Prepare stock in water and standardize in accordance with the methods outlined in Section 2310B.3*d*.

4. Procedure

a. Pretreatment of sample: Centrifuge or vacuum-filter enough sludge to obtain 10 to 15 mL clear sample in a small test tube or beaker. Add a few drops of thymol blue indicator solution, then conc H₂SO₄ dropwise, until definitely red to thymol blue (pH = 1.0 to 1.2).

b. Column chromatography: Place 12 g silicic acid in a Gooch or fritted-glass crucible and apply suction to pack column. Tamp column while applying suction to reduce channeling when the sample is applied. With a pipet, distribute 5.0 mL acidified sample as uniformly as possible over column surface. Apply suction momentarily to draw sample into silicic acid. Release vacuum as soon as last portion of sample has entered column. Quickly add 65 mL CHCl₃-butanol reagent and apply suction. Discontinue suction just before the last of reagent enters column. Use a new column for each sample.

c. Titration: Remove filter flask and purge eluted sample with N₂ gas or CO₂-free air immediately before titrating. (Ob-

tain CO₂-free air by passing air through a CO₂ absorbant.*)

Titrate sample with standard 0.02*N* NaOH to phenolphthalein end point, using a fine-tip buret and taking care to avoid aeration. The fine-tip buret aids in improving accuracy and precision of the titration. Use N₂ gas or CO₂-free air delivered through a small glass tube to purge and mix sample and to prevent contact with atmospheric CO₂ during titration.

d. Blank: Carry a distilled water blank through steps ¶s 4*a* through 4*c*.

5. Calculation

Total organic acids (mg as acetic acid/L)

$$= \frac{(a - b) \times N \times 60\,000}{\text{mL sample}}$$

where:

a = mL NaOH used for sample,
b = mL NaOH used for blank, and
N = normality of NaOH.

6. Precision

Average recoveries of about 95% are obtained for organic acid concentrations above 200 mg as acetic acid/L. Individual tests generally vary from the average by approximately 3%. A greater variation results when lower concentrations of organic acids are present. Titration precision expressed as the standard deviation is about ±0.1 mL (approximately ±24 mg as acetic acid/L).

7. Bibliography

MUELLER, H.F., A.M. BUSWELL & T.E. LARSON. 1956. Chromatographic determination of volatile acids. *Sewage Ind. Wastes* 28:255.

MUELLER, H.F., T.E. LARSON & M. FERRETTI. 1960. Chromatographic separation and identification of organic acids. *Anal. Chem.* 32:687.

WESTERHOLD, A.F. 1963. Organic acids in diges-

---

*Ascarite or equivalent.

ter liquor by chromatography. *J. Water Pollut. Control Fed.* 35:1431.

HATTINGH, W.H.J. & F.V. HAYWARD. 1964. An improved chromatographic method for the determination of total volatile fatty acid content in anaerobic digester liquors. *Int. J. Air Water Pollut.* 8:411.

POHLAND, F.G. & B.H. DICKSON, JR. 1964. Organic acids by column chromatography. *Water Works Wastes Eng.* 1:54.

5560 C.   Distillation Method

1. General Discussion

a. Principle: This technique recovers acids containing up to six carbon atoms. Fractional recovery of each acid increases with increasing molecular weight. Calculations and reporting are on the basis of acetic acid. The method often is applicable for control purposes. Because it is empirical, carry it out exactly as described. Because the still-heating rate, presence of sludge solids, and final distillate volume affect recovery, determine a recovery factor.

b. Interference: Hydrogen sulfide (H_2S) and CO_2 are liberated during distillation and will be titrated to give a positive error. Eliminate this error by discarding the first 15 mL of distillate and account for this in the recovery factor.

2. Apparatus

a. Centrifuge, with head to carry four 50-mL tubes or 250-mL bottles.

b. Distillation flask, 500-mL capacity.

c. Condenser, about 76 cm long.

d. Adapter tube.

e. pH meter or recording titrator: See Section 2310B.2a.

f. Distillation assembly: Use a conventional distilling apparatus. To minimize fluctuations in distillation rate, supply heat with a variable-wattage electrical heater.

3. Reagents

a. Sulfuric acid, H_2SO_4, 1 + 1.

b. Standard sodium hydroxide titrant, 0.1*N:* See Section 2310B.3c.

c. Phenolphthalein indicator solution.

d. Acetic acid stock solution, 2000 mg/L: Dilute 1.9 mL conc CH_3COOH to 1000 mL with deionized water. Standardize against 0.1*N* NaOH.

4. Procedure

a. Recovery factor: To determine the recovery factor, *f*, for a given apparatus, dilute an appropriate volume of acetic acid stock solution to 250 mL in a volumetric flask to approximate the expected sample concentration and distill as for a sample. Calculate the recovery factor

$$f = \frac{a}{b}$$

where:

a = volatile acid concentration recovered in distillate, mg/L, and

b = volatile acid concentration in standard solution used, mg/L.

b. Sample analysis: Çentrifuge 200 mL sample for 5 min. Pour off and combine supernatant liquors. Place 100 mL supernatant liquor in a 500-mL distillation flask. Add 100 mL distilled water, four to five clay chips or similar material to prevent bumping, and 5 mL H_2SO_4. Mix so that acid does not remain on bottom of flask. Connect flask to a condenser and adapter tube and distill at the rate of about 5 mL/min. Discard the first 15 mL and collect exactly 150 mL distillate in a 250-mL graduated cylinder. Titrate with $0.1N$ NaOH, using phenolphthalein indicator, a pH meter, or an automatic titrator. The end points of these three methods are, respectively, the first pink coloration that persists on standing a short time, pH 8.3, and the inflection point of the titration curve (see Section 2310). Titration at 95°C produces a stable end point.

5. Calculation

mg volatile acids as acetic acid/L

$$= \frac{\text{mL NaOH} \times N \times 60\,000}{\text{mL sample} \times f}$$

where:

N = normality of NaOH, and
f = recovery factor.

6. Bibliography

OLMSTEAD, W.H., W.M. WHITAKER & C.W. DUDEN. 1929-1930. Steam distillation of the lower volatile fatty acids from a saturated salt solution. *J. Biol. Chem.* 85:109.

OLMSTEAD, W.H., C.W. DUDEN, W.M. WHITAKER & R.F. PARKER. 1929-1930. A method for the rapid distillation of the lower volatile fatty acids from stools. *J. Biol. Chem.* 85:115.

BUSWELL, A.M. & S.L. NEAVE. 1930. Laboratory studies of sludge digestion. *Ill. State Water Surv. Bull.* 30:76.

HEUKELEKIAN, H. & A.J. KAPLOVSKY. 1949. Improved method of volatile-acid recovery from sewage sludges. *Sewage Works J.* 21:974.

KAPLOVSKY, A.J. 1951. Volatile-acid production during the digestion of seeded, unseeded, and limed fresh solids. *Sewage Ind. Wastes* 23:713.

*   *   *

PART 6000

DETERMINATION OF

INDIVIDUAL ORGANIC

CONSTITUENTS

6010 INTRODUCTION

6010 A.   General Discussion

The methods presented in Part 6000 are intended for the determination of individual organic compounds. Methods for determination of aggregate concentrations of groups of organic compounds are presented in Part 5000.

Most of the methods presented herein are highly sophisticated instrumental methods for determining very low concentrations of the organic constituents. Stringent quality control requirements are given with each method and require careful attention.

Many compounds are determinable by two or more of the methods presented in Part 6000. Table 6010:I shows the specific analytical methods applicable to each compound. Guidance on selection of method is provided in the introduction to each section. Sections 6040, 6210, 6232, 6630, and 6640 are included in this publication. For other methods, see 17th Edition, *Standard Methods.*

TABLE 6010:I. ANALYSIS METHODS FOR SPECIFIC ORGANIC COMPOUNDS*

Compound	Analysis Methods (section number)
Acenaphthene	6040B; 6410B; 6440B
Acenaphthylene	6410B; 6440B
Aldrin	6410B; 6630B,C
Anthracene	6040B; 6410B; 6440B
Benzene	6210B,C,D; 6220B,C; 6230D
Benzidine	6410B
Benzo(a)anthracene	6040B; 6410B; 6440B
Benzo(a)pyrene	6410B, 6440B
Benzo(b)fluoranthene	6410B, 6440B
Benzo(ghi)perylene	6410B, 6440B
Benzo(k)fluoranthene	6410B, 6440B
BHC(s)	6410B; 6630C
Bromobenzene	6040B; 6210C,D; 6220C; 6230C,D
Bromochloromethane	6210C,D; 6230C,D
Bromodichloromethane	6040B; 6210B,C,D; 6230B,C,D; 6232B
Bromoform	6040B; 6210B,C,D; 6230B,C,D; 6232B
Bromomethane	6210B,C,D; 6230B,C,D
Bromophenoxybenzene	6040B
Bromophenyl phenyl ether	6410B

*Compounds are listed under the names by which they are most commonly known and called in specific methods.

TABLE 6010:I, Cont.

Compound	Analysis Methods (section number)
Butyl benzyl phthalate	6410B
Butylbenzene(s)	6210C,D; 6220C; 6230C,D
Captan	6630B
Carbon tetrachloride	6210B,C,D; 6230B,C,D
Chlordane	6410B; 6630B,C
Chlorobenzene	6040B; 6210B,C,D; 6220B,C; 6230B,C,D
Chloroethane	6210B,C,D; 6230B,C,D
Chloroethoxy methane	6040B; 6410B
Chloroethyl ether	6040B; 6410B
Chloroethylvinyl ether	6210B; 6230B
Chloroform	6210B,C,D; 6230B,C,D; 6232B
Chloroisopropyl ether	6410B
Chloromethane	6210B,C,D; 6230B,C,D
Chloromethyl benzene	6040B
Chloromethylphenol	6410B; 6420B
Chloronaphthalene(s)	6040B; 6410B
Chlorophenol(s)	6401B; 6420B
Chlorophenoxy benzene	6040B
Chlorophenyl phenyl ether	6410B
Chlorotoluene	6210C,D; 6220C; 6230C,D
Chrysene	6040B; 6410B; 6440B
2,4-D (dichlorophenoxyacetic acid)	6640B
DDD	6410B; 6630B,C
DDE	6410B; 6630B,C
DDT	6410B; 6630B,C
Dibenzo(a,h) anthracene	6410B; 6440B
Dibromochloromethane	6040B; 6210B,C,D; 6230B,C,D; 6232B
Dibromochloropropane	6210C,D; 6230D; 6231B
Dibromoethane	6040B; 6210C,D; 6230C,D; 6231B
Dibromomethane	6210C,D; 6230C,D
Dibutyl phthalate	6410B
Dichloran	6630B
Dichlorobenzene(s)	6040B; 6210B,C,D; 6220B,C; 6230B,C,D; 6410B
Dichlorobenzidine	6410B
Dichlorodifluoromethane	6210C,D; 6230B,C,D
Dichloroethane	6210B,C,D; 6230B,C,D
Dichloroethene(s)	6210B,C,D; 6230B,C,D
Dichlorophenol(s)	6410B; 6420B
Dichloropropane(s)	6210B,C,D; 6230B,C,D
Dichloropropene	6040B; 6210B,C,D; 6230B,C,D
Dieldrin	6410B; 6630B,C
Diethyl phthalate	6040B; 6410B
Dimethyl phthalate	6410B
Dimethylphenol(s)	6410B; 6420B
Dinitrophenol(s)	6410B; 6420B
Dinitrotoluene(s)	6410B
Di-n-octyl phthalate	6410B

TABLE 6010:I, CONT.

Compound	Analysis Methods (section number)
Diphenyl hydrazine	6040B
Endosulfan	6410B; 6630B,C
Endosulfan sulfate	6410B; 6630C
Endrin	6410B; 6630B,C
Endrin aldehyde	6410B; 6630C
Ethenyl benzene (styrene)	6040B
Ethylbenzene	6040B; 6210B,C,D; 6220B,C; 6230D
Ethylhexyl phthalate	6410B
Fluoranthene	6040B; 6410B; 6440B
Fluorene	6040B; 6410B; 6440B
Geosmin	6040B
Heptachlor	6410B; 6630B,C
Heptachlor epoxide	6410B; 6630B,C
Hexachlorobenzene	6040B; 6410B
Hexachlorobutadiene	6040B; 6210C,D; 6220C; 6230D; 6410B
Hexachlorocyclopentadiene	6410B
Hexachloroethane	6040B; 6410B
Indeno(1,2,3-cd)pyrene	6410B; 6440B
Isobutylmethoxy pyrazine	6040B
Isophorone	6410B
Isopropylbenzene	6210C,D; 6220C; 6230D
Isopropyl methoxy pyrazine	6040B
Isopropyltoluene	6210D; 6220C; 6230D
Lindane (γ-BHC)	6630B
Malathion	6630B
Methane	6211
Methoxychlor	6630B
Methyldinitrophenol(s)	6410B; 6420B
Methylene chloride	6210B,C,D; 6230B,C,D
Methylisoborneol	6040B
Methyl parathion	6630B
Mirex	6630B
Naphthalene	6040B; 6210D; 6220C; 6230D; 6410B; 6440B
Nitrobenzene	6410B
Nitrophenol(s)	6410B; 6420B
Nitrosodi-n-propylamine	6410B
Nitrosodimethylamine	6410B
Nitrosodiphenylamine	6410B
Parathion	6630B
PCB-1016, 1221, 1232, 1242, 1248, 1254, 1260	6410B, 6630C
Pentachloronitrobenzene	6630B
Pentachlorophenol	6410B; 6420B
Phenanthrene	6040B; 6410B; 6440B
Phenol	6410B; 6420B
Phenylbenzamine	6040B
Propylbenzene	6040B; 6210C,D; 6220C; 6230D
Pyrene	6040B; 6410B; 6440B

TABLE 6010:I, CONT.

Compound	Analysis Methods (section number)
Silvex (trichlorophenoxy propionic acid)	6640B
Strobane	6630B
Styrene (ethenyl benzene)	6210C,D; 6220C; 6230D
2,4,5-T (trichlorophenoxy acetic acid)	6640B
Tetrachloroethane(s)	6040B; 6210B,C,D; 6230B,C,D
Tetrachloroethene	6040B; 6210B,C,D; 6220C; 6230B,C,D
Toluene	6210B,C,D; 6220B,C; 6230D
Toxaphene	6410B; 6630B,C
Trichloanisole	6040B
Trichlorobenzene(s)	6040B; 6210D; 6220C; 6230D; 6410B
Trichloroethane(s)	6040B; 6210B,C,D; 6230B,C,D
Trichloroethene	6040B; 6210B,C,D; 6220C; 6230B,C,D
Trichlorofluoromethane	6210B,C,D; 6230B,C,D
Trichlorophenol	6410B; 6420B
Trichloropropane	6210CD; 6230C,D
Trifluralin	6630B
Trimethylbenzene(s)	6210D; 6220C; 6230D
Vinyl chloride	6210B,C,D; 6230B,C,D
Xylene(s)	6040B; 6210C,D; 6220C; 6230D

6010 B.   Sample Collection and Preservation

1. Volatile Organic Compounds

Use 25- or 40-mL vial equipped with a screw cap with a hole in the center* and TFE-faced silicone septum.† Wash vials, caps, and septa with detergent, rinse with tap and distilled water, and dry at 105°C for 1 h before use in an area free of organic vapors. NOTE—Do not heat seals for extended periods of time (> 1 h) because the silicone layer slowly degrades at 105°C. When bottles are cool, seal with TFE seals. Alternatively purchase precleaned vials free from volatile organics.

Collect all samples in duplicate and prepare replicate field reagent blanks with each sample set. A sample set is all samples collected from the same general sampling site at approximately the same time. Prepare field reagent blanks in the laboratory by filling a minimum of two sample bottles with reagent water, sealing, and shipping to the sampling site along with empty sample bottles.

Fill sample bottle just to overflowing without passing air bubbles through sample or trapping air bubbles in sealed bottle. When sampling from a water tap, open tap and flush until water temperature has stabilized (usually about 10 min). Adjust flow rate to about 500 mL/min and collect duplicate samples from flowing stream. When sampling from an open body of water, fill a 1-L, wide-mouth bottle or breaker with a representative sample and carefully fill duplicate sample bottles from the container.

Preservation of samples is highly dependent on target constituents and sample matrix. Ongoing research indicates the following areas of concern: rapid biodegradation of aromatic compounds, even at

---

* Pierce 13075 or equivalent.
† Pierce 12722 or equivalent.

low temperatures;[1] dehydrohalogenation reactions such as conversion of pentachloroethane to tetrachloroethane;[2] reactions of alkylbenzenes in chlorinated samples, even after acidification; and possible interactions among preservatives and reductants when dechlorination is used to prevent artifact formation, especially in samples potentially containing many target compounds.

There is as yet no single preservative that can be recommended. Ideally, maintain a sample at 4°C and analyze it immediately. In practice, delays between sampling and analysis often necessitate preservation. The recommended preservation technique is summarized in Table 6010:II.

1) For samples and field blanks that contain volatile constituents but do not contain residual chlorine, add HCl (4 drops 6N HCl/40 mL) to prevent biodegradation and dehydrohalogenation. CAUTION: HCl may contain traces of organic solvents. Verify freedom from contamination before using a specific lot for preservation.

2) For samples and field blanks that contain residual chlorine, also add a reducing agent. Ascorbic acid (25 mg/40 mL) appears to be optimal, but demonstrate that this reductant is appropriate for the specific sample matrix. Sodium thiosulfate (3 mg/40 mL) or sodium sulfite (3 mg/40 mL) also may be appropriate reducing agents, but when either of these is added in the presence of HCl, SO_2 formation may in-

terfere with certain packed-column gas chromatographic or GC/MS techniques.

In all cases, run reagent blanks to insure absence of interferences. Add either ascorbic acid or HCl to the sample bottle immediately before shipping it to the sample site or immediately before filling sample bottle. When both preservatives are needed, add only one before filling the sample bottle, to prevent interactions between the acid and the reductant. Add the second preservative once the bottle is almost full. However, if there is evidence that interactions of acid and reducing agent will not create analytical or preservation problems, they may be added simultaneously.

Tightly seal sample bottles, TFE face down. After sampling and preservation invert several times to mix. Chill samples to 4°C immediately after collection and hold at that temperature in an atmosphere free of organic solvent vapors until analysis. Normally analyze all samples within 14 d of collection. Shorter or longer holding times may be appropriate, depending on constituents and sample matrix. Develop data to show that alternate holding times are appropriate.

2. Other Organic Compounds

See individual methods for sampling and preservation requirements.

3. References

1. BELLAR, T. & J. LICHTENBERG. 1978. Semi-automated headspace analysis of drinking waters and industrial waters for purgeable volatile organic compounds. In C. E. Van Hall, ed. Measurement of Organic Pollutants in Water and Wastewater. STP 686, American Soc. Testing & Materials. Philadelphia, Pa.

2. BELLAR, T. & J. LICHTENBERG. 1985. The Determination of Synthetic Organic Compounds in Water by Purge and Sequential Trapping Capillary Column Gas Chromatography. U.S. Environmental Protection Agency, Cincinnati, Ohio.

4. Bibliography

KEITH, L. H., ed. 1988. Principles of Environmental Testing. American Chemical Soc., Washington, D.C.

TABLE 6010:II. RECOMMENDED PRESERVATION FOR VOLATILES

Constituents	Chlorinated Matrix	Non-Chlorinated Matrix
Halocarbons	HCl + reducing agent	HCl
Aromatics	HCl + reducing agent	HCl
THMs	Reducing agent (HCl optional)*	None required
EDB/DBCP	None required	None required

* See 6232B.2.

6010 C. Analytical Methods

1. General Discussion

The methods presented in Part 6000 for identification and quantitation of trace organic constituents in water generally involve isolation and concentration of the organics from a sample by solvent or gas extraction (see Section 6040 and individual methods), separation of the components, and identification and quantitation of the compounds with a detector.

2. Gas Chromatographic Methods

Gas chromatographic (GC) methods are highly sophisticated microanalytical procedures. They should be used only by analysts experienced in the techniques required and competent to evaluate and interpret the data.

a. Gas chromatograph:

1) Principle—In gas chromatography a mobile phase (a carrier gas) and a stationary phase (column packing or capillary column coating) are used to separate individual compounds. The carrier gas is nitrogen, argon-methane, helium, or hydrogen. For packed columns, the stationary phase is a liquid that has been coated on an inert granular solid, called the column packing, that is held in borosilicate glass tubing. The column is installed in an oven with the inlet attached to a heated injector block and the outlet attached to a detector. Precise and constant temperature control of the injector block, oven, and detector is maintained. Stationary-phase material and concentration, column length and diameter, oven temperature, carrier-gas flow, and detector type are the controlled variables.

When the sample solution is introduced into the column, the organic compounds are vaporized and moved through the column by the carrier gas. They travel through the column at different rates, depending on differences in partition coefficients between the mobile and stationary phases.

2) Interferences—Some interferences in GC analyses occur as a result of sample, solvent, or carrier gas contamination, or because large amounts of a compound may be injected into the GC and linger in the detector. Methylene chloride, chloroform, and other halocarbon and hydrocarbon solvents are ubiquitous contaminants in environmental laboratories. Make strenuous efforts to isolate the analytical system from laboratory areas where these or other solvents are in use. An important sample contaminant is sulfur, which is encountered generally only in base/neutral extracts of water, although anaerobic groundwaters and certain wastewaters and sediment/sludge extracts may contain reduced sulfur compounds, elemental sulfur, or polymeric sulfur. Eliminate this interference by adding a small amount of mercury or copper filings to precipitate the sulfur as metallic sulfide. Sources of interference originating in the chromatograph, and countermeasures, are as follows:

• Septum bleed—This occurs when compounds used to make the septum on the injection port of the GC bleed from the heated septum. These high-molecular-weight silicon compounds are distinguished readily from compounds normally encountered in environmental samples. Nevertheless, minimize septum bleed by using septum sweep, in which clean carrier gas passes over the septum to flush out the "bleed" compounds.

• Column bleed—This term refers to loss of column coating or breakdown products when the column is heated. This interference is more prevalent in packed columns, but also occurs to a much lesser extent in capillary columns. It occurs when the column temperature is high or when water or oxygen are introduced into the system. Solvent injection can damage the stationary phase by displacing it. Certain organic compounds acting as powerful solvents, acids, or bases can degrade the column coating. Injection of large amounts of certain surface-active agents may destroy GC columns.

• Ghost peaks—These peaks occur when an injected sample contains either a large amount of a given compound, or a compound that adsorbs to the column coating or injector parts (e.g., septum). When a subsequent sample is injected, peaks can appear as a result of the previous injection. Eliminate ghost peaks by injecting a more dilute sample, by producing less reactive derivatives of a compound that may interact strongly with the column material, by selecting a column coating that precludes these interactions, or by injecting solvent blanks between samples.

b. Detectors: Various detectors are available for use with gas chromatographic systems. See individual methods for recommendations on appropriate detectors.

1) Electrolytic conductivity detector— The electrolytic conductivity detector is a sensitive and element-specific detector that has gained considerable attention because of its applicability to the gas chromatographic analysis of environmentally significant compounds. It is utilized in the analysis of purgeable halocarbons, pesticides, herbicides, pharmaceuticals, and nitrosamines. This detector is capable of operation in each of four specific modes: halogen (X), nitrogen (N), sulfur (S), and nitrosamine (NO). Only organic compounds containing these elements will be detected.

Compounds eluting from a gas chromatographic column enter a reactor tube heated to 800°C. They are mixed with a reaction gas, hydrogen for X, N, or NO modes, and air for the S mode. The hydrogen catalytically reduces the eluants while the air oxidizes them. The gaseous products are transferred to the detector through a conditioned ion exchange resin or scrubber. In the halogen mode, only HX is detected, while NH_3 or H_2S are elimi-

nated on the resin. In the nitrogen or nitrosamine mode, the NH_3 formed is ionized while HX and H_2S, if present, are eliminated with a KOH/quality wool scrubber. The sulfur mode produces SO_2 or SO_3, which is ionized while HX is removed with a silver wire scrubber. All other products either are not ionizable or are produced in such low yield that they are not detectable.

The electrolytic conductivity detector contains reference and analytical electrodes, a gas-liquid contactor, and a gas-liquid separator. The conductivity solvent enters the cell and flows by the reference electrode. It combines with the gaseous reaction products in the gas-liquid contactor. This heterogeneous mixture is separated into gas and liquid phases in the gas-liquid separator, with the liquid phase flowing past the analytical electrode. The electrometer monitors the difference in conductivity at the reference electrode (solvent) and the analytical electrode (solvent + carrier + reaction products).

2) Electron capture detector—The electron capture detector (ECD) usually is used for the analysis of compounds that have high electron affinities, such as chlorinated pesticides, drugs, and their metabolites. This detector is somewhat selective in its response, being highly sensitive toward molecules containing electronegative groups: halogens, peroxides, quinones, and nitro groups. It is insensitive toward functional groups, such as amines, alcohols, and hydrocarbons.

The detector is operated by passing the effluent from the gas chromatographic column over a radioactive beta particle emitter, usually nickel-63 or tritium adsorbed on platinum or titanium foil. An electron from the emitter ionizes the carrier gas, preferably nitrogen, and produces a burst of electrons. About 100 secondary electrons are produced for each initial beta particle. After further collisions, the energy of these electrons is reduced to the thermal level and they can be captured by electrophilic sample molecules.

The electron population in the ECD cell is collected periodically by applying a short voltage pulse to the cell electrodes and the resulting current is compared with a reference current. The pulse interval is adjusted automatically to keep the cell current constant, even when some of the electrons are being captured by the sample. The change in the pulse rate when a sample enters the ECD is then related to the sample concentration. The ECD offers linearity in the range of 10^4 and subpicogram detection limits for compounds with high electron affinities.

3) Flame ionization detector—The flame ionization detector (FID) is widely used because of its high sensitivity to organic carbon-containing compounds. The detector consists of a small hydrogen/air diffusion flame burning at the end of a jet. When organic compounds enter the flame from the column, electrically charged intermediates are formed. These are collected by applying a voltage across the flame. The resulting current is amplified by an electrometer and measured. The response of the detector is directly proportional to the total mass entering the detector per unit time and is independent of the concentration in the carrier gas.

The FID is perhaps the most widely used detector for gas chromatography because of several advantages: (*a*) it responds to virtually all organic carbon-containing compounds with high sensitivity (approximately 10^{-13} g/mL); (*b*) it does not respond to common carrier gas impurities such as water and carbon dioxide; (*c*) it has a large linear response range (approximately 10^7) and excellent baseline stability; (*d*) it is relatively insensitive to small column flow-rate changes during temperature programming; (*e*) it is highly reliable, rugged, and easy to use; and (*f*) it has low detector dead volume effects and fast response. Its limitations include: (*a*) it gives little or no response to noncombustible gases and all noble gases; and (*b*) it is a destructive de-tector that changes the physical and chemical properties of the sample irreversibly.

4) Photoionization detector—Photoionization occurs when a molecular species absorbs a photon of light energy and dissociates into a parent ion and an electron. The photoionization detector (PID) detects organic and some inorganic species in the effluent of a gas chromatograph with detection limits as low as the picogram range. The PID is equipped with a sealed ultraviolet light source that emits photons which pass through an optically transparent window (made of LiF, MgF_2, NaF, or sapphire) into an ionization chamber where photons are absorbed by the eluted species. Compounds having ionization potential less than the UV source energy are ionized. A positively biased high-voltage electrode accelerates the resulting ions to a collecting electrode and the resulting current is measured by an electrometer. This current is proportional to the concentration.

The PID has high sensitivity, low noise (approximately 10^{-14} A), and excellent linearity (10^7), is nondestructive, and can be used in series with a second detector for more selective detection. The PID can be operated as a universal detector or a selective detector by simply changing the photon energy of the ionization source. Tables of ionization potentials are used to select the appropriate UV source for a given measurement.

5) Mass spectrometer—The mass spectrometer (MS) has the ability to detect a wide variety of compounds, coupled with a capacity to deduce compound structures from fragmentation patterns. Among the different types of mass spectrometers, the quadrupole has become the most widely used in water and wastewater analysis.

The mass spectrometer detects compounds by ionizing molecules into charged species with a 70-eV beam. The ions are accelerated toward the quadrupole mass filter through a series of lenses held at 0 to 200 V. The differently sized, charged fragments are separated according to mass-to-charge ratio (related to molecular weight) by means of the quadrupole, which uses varying electric and radiofrequency (rf) fields. The quadrupole is connected to a computer, which varies these fields so that only fragments of one particular mass-to-charge ratio (± 0.5) can traverse the quadrupole at any one time. As the ions leave the quadrupole they are attracted to the electron multiplier through an electrical potential of several thousand volts. The charge fragments, in turn, are detected by the electron multiplier. Because the electric and the rf fields are cycled every few seconds, a fragmentation pattern is obtained. Each cycle is called a mass scan. Most chemicals have unique fragmentation patterns, called mass spectra. The computer contains, and can search, a library of known mass spectra to identify tentatively an unknown compound exhibiting a particular spectrum. Use authentic compounds for confirmation after tentative identifications are made.

Background mass interference can result from the ability of the mass spectrometer to detect any ions created in its ion volume (up to a specified mass). Any compounds continuously present in the source will be detected. Some mass ions always present are due to air components that leak into the system, such as oxygen (masses 16 and 32), nitrogen (masses 14 and 28), carbon dioxide (mass 44), argon (mass 40), and water (mass 18), or to helium carrier gas (masses 4 and 8), or to diffusion pump oil vapors.

3. High-Performance Liquid Chromatographic (HPLC) Methods

a. Principle: HPLC is an analytical technique in which a liquid mobile phase transports a sample through a column containing a liquid stationary phase. The interaction of the sample with the stationary phase selectively retains individual compounds and permits separation of sample components. Detection of the separated sample compounds is achieved mainly through the use of absorbance detectors for organic compounds and through conductivity and electrochemical detectors for metal and inorganic components.

b. Detectors:

1) Photodiode array detector (PDAD) —The PDAD measures the absorbance of a sample from an incident light source (UV-VIS). After passing through the sample cell, the light is directed through a holographic grating that separates the beam into its component wavelengths reflected on a linear array of photodiodes. This permits the complete absorbance spectrum to be obtained in 1 s or less and simultaneous multiwavelength analysis.

The PDAD is subject to the interference encountered with all absorbance detectors. Of special concern for HPLC is the masking of the absorbance region of the HPLC mobile phase and its additives. This may reduce the range and sensitivity of the detector to the sample components. Most interferences occur in monitoring the shorter wavelengths (200–230 nm). In this region, many organic compounds absorb light energy and can be sources of interference.

2) Post column reactor (PCR)—The PCR consists of in-line sample derivatizing/reacting equipment that permits chemical alteration of certain organic compounds. This equipment is used to enhance detection by attaching a chromophore to the compound(s) of interest. Sensitivity and selectivity of compounds that were initially undetectable are altered to make them detectable.

Interferences from this technique usually arise from the impurities in the reagents used in the reaction. When this technique is coupled with a selective detector such as fluorescence, these interferences are minimized. Generally, only compounds of the same class as the compounds of interest will cause interference.

3) Fluorescence detector—The fluorescence detector is an absorbance detector in which the sample is energized by a monochromatic light source. Compounds capable of absorbing the light energy do so and release it as fluorescence emission. Filters permit the detector to respond only to the fluorescent energy. The fluorescence detector is the most sensitive of the current HPLC detectors available and often is used in conjunction with a post column reactor.

Because of instrument sensitivity, minute quantities of contaminants can cause interferences to fluorescence detectors. Contamination can happen from glassware, mobile phase solvents, post-column reagents, etc. These sources will raise the background signal and thus narrow the range of the detector. Interference from individual compounds is minimal because of detector specificity (i.e., all interferences must fluoresce).

6040   CONSTITUENT CONCENTRATION BY GAS EXTRACTION*

6040 A.   Introduction

The ability to analyze ultratrace levels of organic pollutants in water has been limited, in part, by the concentration technique. With the development of closed-loop stripping analysis (CLSA) (Method B), organic compounds of intermediate volatility and molecular weight, i.e., from the heavier volatiles to the lighter polynuclear aromatic hydrocarbons, can be extracted from water and concentrated to allow quantitative and semiquantitative analysis (depending on the compound) at parts-per-trillion levels. This extract can be analyzed on a gas chromatograph (GC) connected to one of several detectors. A CLSA technique coupled with gas chromatographic/mass spectrometric (GC/MS) analysis for the determination of trace organic compounds is presented here. It is applicable to both treated and natural waters.

The purge and trap technique (Method C) is a valuable concentration method applicable to volatile organic compounds. The compounds are concentrated by bubbling of an inert gas through the sample followed by collection in, and desorption from, a sorbent trap. This extract may be analyzed by GC or GC/MS methods. The technique is applicable to both water and wastewater.

---

*Approved by Standard Methods Committee, 1988.

6040 B.   Closed-Loop Stripping, Gas Chromatographic/ Mass Spectrometric Analysis

1. General Discussion

a. *Principle:* This CLSA-GC/MS procedure is suitable for the analysis of a broad spectrum of organic compounds in water. It can be used for the identification and quantification of specific compounds, such as earthy-musty-smelling compounds (e.g., 2-methylisoborneol (MIB) and geosmin)[1-3] or U.S. Environmental Protection Agency (EPA) priority pollutants[4,5].

In closed-loop stripping, volatile organic compounds of intermediate molecular weight are stripped from water by a recirculating stream of air. The organics are removed from the gas phase by an activated carbon filter. They are extracted from the filter with carbon disulfide (CS_2). A portion of the extract is injected into a capillary-column GC/MS for identification of the organic compounds by retention time and spectrum matching; quantification is done by single-ion current integration.

b. *Interference:* Organic compounds that are stripped during this procedure may coelute with the compounds of interest. The uniqueness of the mass spectrum of each target compound makes it possible to confirm compound identity with a high probability when coeluting components are present. Problems may arise if several isomers of a compound are present that are not resolvable chromatographically.

c. *Detection limits:* Trace organics can be detected at low nanogram-per-liter levels. The CLSA-GC/MS detection limits are affected by many factors; especially important are the stripping efficiency and the condition of the GC/MS. Stripping efficiencies can be improved by using an elevated stripping temperature and/or the salting-out technique.

The instrumental detection limits for five earthy-musty-smelling compounds are shown in Table 6040:I. Detection limits for the salted CLSA method are less than half

those for the unsalted method for each compound. Using the elevated stripping temperature rather than the salting-out technique produces comparable recoveries[6] and similar detection limits. Detection limits for various organic compounds of interest, obtained with an elevated stripping temperature/salting-out technique, ranged from 0.1 to 100 ng/L (see Table 6040:II).[7]

2. Apparatus

Use clean glassware in sample collection and calibration standard preparation. Wash with soapy water, rinse with tap water, with demineralized water, and finally with reagent-grade acetone. Air-dry and bake at 180°C for 6 to 12 h. Do not bake sample bottle caps or volumetric ware. After drying and baking, store inverted or cover mouths with aluminum foil to prevent accumulation of dust or other contaminants.

a. *Sample bottles,* 1-L capacity or larger, glass, with TFE-lined screw caps.

b. *CLSA apparatus,* equipped with the following components (Figure 6040:1) or their equivalents[4].*

1) *Stripping bottle,* with mark at 1-L level and stainless-steel quick-connect stems (Figure 6040:2) or unpolished spherical glass joints sealed with TFE-covered silicone rubber O-rings and secured with metal clamps.†

2) *Gas heater,* with aluminum heating cylinder and soldering iron (25 W) controlled by a variable transformer (Figure 6040:3). Alternatively, use a temperature-controlled heater block to maintain temperature at the filter that is at least 10 to 20°C above temperature of thermostatic water bath.

---

*Model CLS 1, Tekmar, Cincinnati, Ohio; Brechbühler AG, 8952 Schlieren ZH, Switzerland, available from Chromapon, Whittier, Calif.; or equivalent.
†Rotulex Sovirel, Brechbühler AG or equivalent.

TABLE 6040:I. INSTRUMENTAL DETECTION LIMITS FOR EARTHY-MUSTY SMELLING COMPOUNDS BY CLSA-GC/MS

Compound	Detection Limit ng/L*	
	Unsalted Method[1]	Salting-Out Technique[3]
Geosmin	2	0.8
2-Methylisoborneol	2	0.8
2-Isopropyl-3-methoxy pyrazine	2	0.8
2-Isobutyl-3-methoxy pyrazine	2	0.8
2,3,6-Trichloranisole	5	0.8

*Stripping at 25°C.

TABLE 6040:II. INSTRUMENTAL DETECTION LIMITS FOR SELECTED ORGANIC COMPOUNDS BY CLSA-GC/MS[7]

Compound	Detection Limit ng/L*†	Compound	Detection Limit ng/L*†
1,1,1-Trichloroethane	2.0	1,2,3-Trichlorobenzene	2.0
Trichloroethene	100	bis(2-Chloro- ethoxy)methane	10
Dichlorobromomethane	5.0		
1,3-Dichloropropene	2.0	Methylisoborneol (MIB)	0.5
1,1,2-Trichloroethane	2.0	Geosmin	0.2
Chlorodibromomethane	1.0	Naphthalene	100
1,2-Dibromoethane	2.0	1,1,2,3,4,4-Hexachloro- 1,3-butadiene	2.0
Tetrachloroethene	100		
Chlorobenzene	10	1-Chloronaphthalene	0.5
Ethylbenzene	50	2-Chloronaphthalene	0.5
m,p-Xylene	100	Acenaphthene	0.5
Bromoform	1.0	Fluorene	2.0
Ethylbenzene	5.0	Diethylphthalate	100
o-Xylene	50	1-Chloro-4-phenoxybenzene	0.5
1,1,2,2-Tetrachloroethane	50	N-Phenylbenzamine	20
Bromobenzene	0.5	1,2-Diphenylhydrazine (as azobenzene)	1.0
Propylbenzene	0.5		
1-Chloro-3-methylbenzene	0.5	1-Bromo-4-phenoxybenzene	0.5
bis (2-Chloroethyl)ether	1.0	Hexachlorobenzene	1.0
o-Dichlorobenzene	0.1	Phenanthrene	10
m-Dichlorobenzene	10	Anthracene	50
p-Dichlorobenzene	10	Fluoranthene	20
Hexachloroethane	20	Pyrene	20
N-Nitrosodi-n-propylamine	5.0	Chrysene	50
1,3,5-Trichlorobenzene	0.1	Benzo(a)anthracene	50
1,2,4-Trichlorobenzene	10		

*Elevated stripping temperature and salting-out both utilized.
†Instrument detection limit based on a 2:1 signal: noise ratio (where a background interference existed, the target compound was required to be at least twice background).

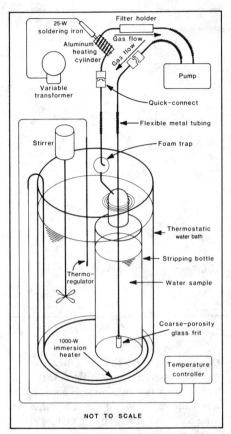

Figure 6040:1. Schematic of closed-loop stripping apparatus. Source: KRASNER, S.W., C.J. HWANG & M.J. McGUIRE. 1983. A standard method for quantification of earthy-musty odorants in water. *Water Sci. Technol.* 15(6/7):127.

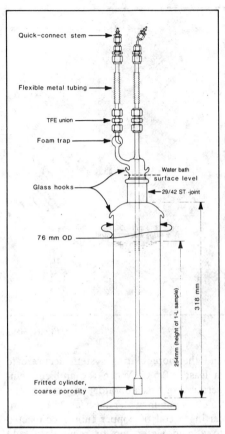

Figure 6040:2. One-liter "tall form" stripping bottle. Source: KRASNER, S.W., C.J. HWANG & M.J. McGUIRE. 1983. A standard method for quantification of earthy-musty odorants in water. *Water Sci. Technol.* 15(6/7):127.

3) *Filter holder,* stainless steel or glass.‡ If glass is used, also use an auxiliary heating device, e.g., an infrared light, to maintain proper filter temperature.

4) *Pump,* with stainless-steel bellows,§ providing air flow in the range of 1 to 1.5 L/min.

5) *Automatic timer* (optional), connected to pump.

6) *Circuit,* with stainless-steel parts: 1/8-in.-OD tubing, 4-in. × 1/4-in.-OD flexible tubing, tube fittings, and quick-connect bodies‖ or glass joints described in ¶ 1) above. Glass sample lines can be used except where circuit enters and exits pump. Use TFE ferrules in making connections to glass and flexible metal tubing.

7) *Thermostatic water bath,* with 222-mm-OD × 457-mm chromatography jar

---

‡Brechbühler AG or equivalent.
§Metal Bellows Model MB-21, Sharon, Mass., or equivalent.

‖Swagelok fittings or equivalent.

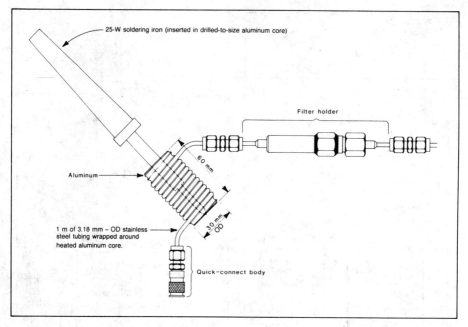

Figure 6040:3. Gas heater.

and thermoregulating system accurate to at least ±0.5°C. When the ambient temperature of the laboratory is greater than 25°C, maintain water bath at 25°C by inserting a coil of copper tubing connected to a cold water tap to recirculate cold water.

8) *Filters,* with 1.5 mg activated carbon # (Figure 6040:4). Use a set of filters matched in resistance for each group of samples and calibration standards. Determine filter resistance by measuring solvent flow rate through a solvent-wetted filter. Fill the longer glass tube above the charcoal with solvent and let solvent flow by gravity through filter disk. After several rinses with solvent to wet the filter, measure time necessary to empty the solvent (0.3-mL volume) from top of filter tube to surface of carbon. Rates for new, commercially prepared filters vary significantly, and decrease with use. Do not use filters

with flow rate less than 0.6 mL/min; for optimal recoveries, use filters with flow greater than 0.9 mL/min. Figure 6040:5 shows the reduction in air flow caused by using a "slow" filter. Figure 6040:6 shows the effect of filter resistance on recovery of earthy-musty odorants and one of the internal standards.

c. Stirrer (optional), with 5-cm-long TFE stirring bar.

d. Microsyringes, 5-, 10-, 25-, and 50-μL capacity.

e. Vials, 50-μL capacity (Figure 6040:4) with gastight stoppers or caps. Vials can be produced by a custom glass-blowing company: use a 1.6-mm-ID precision-bore capillary glass and grind to 5 mm OD, then heat-constrict to close off bore at approximately 29 mm from top. Mark vial at 20-μL level with glass scribe. Prepare gastight cap by purchasing 1-cm-OD TFE cylindrical bar stock, cutting it into 1-cm-long pieces, and drilling out a hole that is 5 mm ID × 7 mm deep. In practice, make the hole slightly smaller than the 5-mm OD of

_____
Brechbühler AG, Chromapon, Inc., or equivalent.

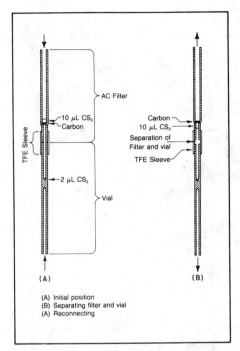

Figure 6040:4. Extraction of filter. Source: Krasner, S.W., C.J. Hwang & M.J.
McGuire. 1981. Development of
a closed-loop stripping technique
for the analysis of taste- and odor-
causing substances in drinking
water. *In* L.H. Keith, ed. Advances in the Identification and
Analysis of Organic Pollutants in
Water, Vol. 2. Ann Arbor Science
Publishers, Ann Arbor, Mich.

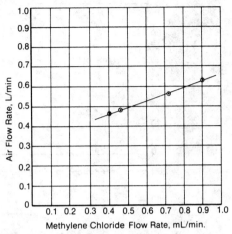

**Figure 6040:5. Flow rate through 1.5-mg carbon
filter.** Air flow rate with no filter
is 0.86 L/min.

the vial to get a gastight seal. Alternatively,
use a solid TFE tapered stopper. If cap or
stopper does not form gastight closure,
wrap vial with TFE tape. For permanent
storage or shipment of extract, transfer to
100-μL vial with TFE septum.**

f. TFE sleeve, 5-mm-ID TFE flexible
tubing approximately 19 mm long. If a 5-
mm-OD vial is not prepared as described
above, then connect filter and vial with a
piece of heat-shrink TFE tubing that is cus-
tom-shrunk to the dimensions of the filter
and vial.

_____

**Pierce Chemical Company #13100 or equivalent.

*g. Gas chromatograph (GC)/mass spec-
trometer (MS)/data system,* equipped with:

1) *Capillary injector,* Grob-designed
split-splitless injector or equivalent with
2.5-mm-ID glass insert or nonvaporizing,
septumless, cold on-column injector.

2) *Capillary column,* 30-m or 60-m ×
0.25-mm-ID DB-1 or DB-5 fused silica or
other capillary column capable of producing adequate and reproducible resolution.
Use a 0.32-mm-ID column for on-column
injection when a stainless-steel needle is
used. Use a 0.25-mm-ID column for on-
column work with a fused-silica needle.

3) *Microsyringes,* 5- and 10-μL capacity,
with 75-mm-long needles. Use 0.23-mm-
OD stainless-steel or 0.17-mm-OD fused-
silica needle for on-column injection.

4) *Mass spectrometer analyzer:* See Section 6210B.3 for suggested specifications.

5) *Data system,* with software capable of
performing reverse-library searches (optional).

3. Reagents

Use reagent-grade solvents or better and
obtain purest standards available.

a. Carbon disulfide, CS_2: Use only after
gas chromatographic verification of purity

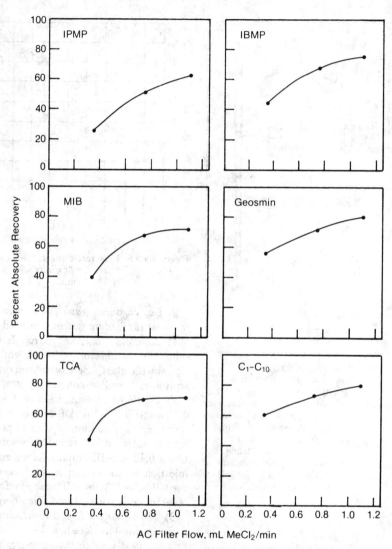

Figure 6040:6. Effect of filter resistance, measured as flow, on recovery of earthy-musty odorants and C₁-C₁₀ internal standard. Reprinted with permission from: HWANG, C.J., S.W. KRASNER, M.J. McGUIRE, M.S. MOYLAN & M.S. DALE. 1984. Determination of subnanogram per liter levels of earthy-musty odorants in water by the salted closed-loop stripping method. *Environ. Sci. Technol.* 18:535. Copyright 1984, American Chemical Society.

to ensure that the solvent does not contain components that coelute with the compounds of interest. CAUTION: *Use proper safety procedures; explosive, toxic, and occasionally allergenic.*

    b. Acetone.

    c. Methylene chloride.

    d. Carrier gas: Helium gas, ultrapurified grade, moisture- and oxygen-free.

    e. Internal standards:

    1) *1-Chlorooctane.*

    2) *1-Chlorodecane.*

3) *1-Chlorododecane.*

4) *1-Chlorohexane, 1-chlorohexadecane,* and *1-chlorooctadecane* can be added for broad-spectrum analysis.

f. Stock internal standard solutions: Dissolve 1 mL of each internal standard†† in acetone and dilute to 25 mL with acetone in a volumetric flask; 1 µL = 35 µg.

g. Combination internal standard solution: Combine 7.2 µL of each stock solution and dilute to 25 mL with acetone; 1 µL = 10 ng each.

h. Reference standards: Compounds of interest may be available commercially.‡‡

i. Stock reference solutions: Dissolve 20 mg of each target compound in acetone and dilute to 10 mL with acetone in a volumetric flask; 1 µL = 2 µg.

j. Combination reference standards solution: Combine 10 µL of each stock reference solution and dilute to 5 mL with acetone; 1 µL = 4 ng each.

k. Organic-free water: Prepare water by treating with activated carbon, mixed-bed deionization, and filtration through a membrane filter. Irradiate under ultraviolet light for 1 h (optional) and prestrip in the CLSA apparatus for 1 h, using a clean activated carbon filter or, alternatively, prestrip large quantities of water with nitrogen just before use. Store in a closed bottle tightly capped with TFE-lined screw cap, under nitrogen (optional), in a refrigerator and away from solvent contamination for not longer than 1 week.

l. Sodium sulfate, Na₂SO₄ (optional), granular, anhydrous. Bake at 625°C for 2 h before use; store at room temperature in desiccator.

---

†† 1-Chlorohexadecane and 1-chlorooctadecane solidify upon refrigeration. Warm before removing a portion.
‡‡ Geosmin and 2-methylisoborneol are available from Wako Chemicals, 12300 Ford Rd., Suite 130, Dallas, Texas 75234. NOTE: This synthetic geosmin includes nonodorous isomers that preclude its use in quantitative sensory analysis; however, its GC/MS characteristics (i.e., retention time and spectrum) are the same as those of natural geosmin.

4. Procedure

a. Sample collection and storage: Rinse sample bottle with sample, fill to overflowing, flush out air bubbles, and cap tightly. Collect duplicate samples and in the field keep in an insulated container stocked with ice. In the laboratory store at 4°C, but analyze as soon as possible, preferably within 3 d. For holding longer than 3 d, add 40 mg HgCl₂/L to inhibit biological activity. Adding a dechlorinating agent is optional, because disinfection byproducts may be affected. CAUTION: *HgCl₂ - containing samples must be disposed of as hazardous waste. See Section 1090 for precautions.*

b. Treatment of samples:

1) Stripping—Rinse stripping bottle with sample and fill to the 1-L mark, wetting the glass joint with sample. Fill stripping bottle slowly, with minimal aeration, to prevent loss of volatile compounds. Add 10 µL combination internal standard solution with the syringe needle tip immersed. Stopper tightly and attach springs. Place in thermostatic water bath at 25°C with glass joint below water level and connect bottle to the circuit. Operate gas heater at 45 to 50°C. Put an "auxiliary" carbon filter in the holder and prestrip for 10 s to flush air contaminants from system. Exchange auxiliary filter for a clean one and strip for 2 h. Auxiliary filter may be reused many times before cleaning. If stripping bottle has a smaller height-to diameter ratio than shown in Figure 6040:2, more than 2 h may be required for stripping. Optionally use an automatic timer to terminate each stripping run.

If sample contains a large amount of algae or turbidity or foaming agents, use only 900 mL sample and 9 µL combination internal standard solution. Because this additional headspace can result in different stripping efficiencies, comparably analyze a calibration standard.

Immediately after use clean stripping bottle by rinsing twice with demineralized water and once with organic-free water. For particularly adherent impurities, clean with acetone and methylene chloride and bake at 180°C for at least 2 h. Whenever sample carryover is observed, clean the circuit and pump as follows: Connect fittings to the quick-connect bodies on both ends of the circuit to open system. Turn on pump and flush with approximately 100 mL each organic-free water, acetone, and methanol. After the last rinse, dry with a heat gun until there is no residual methanol. If there is a noticeable drop in pump performance, clean valve assembly with distilled trichlorotrifluoroethane or replace.

2) Alternate stripping techniques—To improve stripping recovery, use either modification: a combination of a) and b) below can reduce stripping time. Optimize combination, depending on compounds to be analyzed.

a) Elevated stripping temperature—Increase temperature of thermostatic water bath to 45°C to increase recovery of many organic compounds.[5,6] Raise temperature of gas heater to at least 55°C (for a 45°C stripping temperature) to avoid condensation of water vapor on the activated carbon filter. Further increases in stripping temperature reduce recovery.[5]

b) Salting-out technique—Raising the ionic strength of the sample with Na_2SO_4 before stripping increases the stripping rate of many organic compounds.[3] Bring sample to room temperature before analysis by immersing it in a water bath at 25°C for approximately 15 min. Transfer 800 mL to the stripping bottle and add stirring bar. Using a glass funnel and with the stirring bar (at intermediate setting) in motion, add 72 g Na_2SO_4. Remove funnel and replace with a glass stopper. Continue stirring until Na_2SO_4 has dissolved (not more than 1 min). Remove stopper and stirring bar, then add remaining 100 mL of sample,§§

rinsing and wetting inside neck of bottle. Add 9 μL combination internal standard solution and strip at 25°C as described in standard stripping procedure above. Strip for 1 h and 30 min. Alternatively, combine salt and sample by pouring salt directly into 900 mL sample, stopper tightly, shake vigorously, let stand for several minutes, and add internal standards.

3) Extracting the filter—Remove activated carbon filter from holder. In a fume hood, extract with CS_2 as indicated in Figure 6040:4. Keep solvents well within the hood to avoid inhalation by analyst or contamination of stripping apparatus. Add 2 μL CS_2 to a clean vial and connect filter and vial with a TFE sleeve so as to leave no dead space between glass parts. Place 10 μL CS_2 above the carbon, taking care not to touch carbon with the needle. Warm vial with hands and alternately pull and push the CS_2 through the carbon 10 times by separating and reconnecting the filter and vial while still within the TFE sleeve. With filter and vial tightly butted, cool vial with ice or liquid nitrogen, taking care not to freeze CS_2. This cooling draws the CS_2 below the carbon. Tap the filter/vial assembly gently on a hard surface to complete transfer of CS_2 to bottom of vial.

Repeat filter extraction with a 10-μL and a 5-μL portion of CS_2 to yield approximately 20 μL of combined extract. Separate vial from filter and stopper. Label and store at −20°C until analysis.

Filter may be extracted while maintaining tight seal between filter and vial during the procedure. Using ice chips, cool closed volume in the vial; solvent accumulates on lower side of the filter disk. Push solvent back to upper side by warming the closed vial between two fingers. Repeat and then extract with more solvent as above.

Because methylene chloride is easier to obtain in higher purity than CS_2, and is less hazardous, it can be used as the extraction solvent. Changing solvent may reduce extraction efficiency for some compounds.[8]

Clean filter as soon as possible after use.

---

§§A total sample volume of 900 mL is preferred to minimize foaming-over due to salt addition.

Fill glass tube with CS_2 and let solvent flow through filter disk. Repeat three times with acetone and three times with methylene chloride. If solvent flow is slow (lower than 0.6 mL/min) because of salt deposits, pull $1N$ HNO_3 through filter, using a vacuum connection. After washing with acid, rinse with distilled water and acetone and continue with cleaning as above. After final rinse, remove residual solvent by connecting filter to a vacuum for approximately 5 min. Before reusing filter, repeat cleaning procedure. Clean auxiliary filter after 40 uses or 2 weeks, whichever comes first.

If the salting-out technique is used, carried over Na_2SO_4 ultimately will clog the filter. To avoid, routinely use a water rinse to remove deposited salts. For initial cleaning of filter only, after use, add solvents as follows: acetone, organic-free water, acetone, CS_2, acetone (three times), and methylene chloride (three times). Between samples repeat cleaning just before filter use beginning with CS_2 wash.

Rinse vials seven times with CS_2 and bake at 180°C overnight. Rinse several more times with CS_2 before using. Clean stoppers with methylene chloride, immersing at least overnight. Rinse TFE sleeve with methylene chloride and acetone and store in acetone until ready to use.

c. *Gas chromatography/mass spectrometry:*

1) "Hot-needle" injection technique—To reduce discrimination against higher-boiling compounds by distillation from the needle, use a hot-needle injection technique when the injector is a hot vaporizing type. (Do not use the following procedure for cold on-column injection.) Wet syringe needle and barrel with solvent and expel as much as possible. Pull syringe plunger back, leaving an air gap. Pull up approximately 1.5 µL sample and pull sample totally into syringe barrel. Close the split on the GC injector, wait 10 s, insert syringe needle into the injector, and let needle warm up for 1 to 2 s (analyst should op-

timize time). Rapidly push plunger to bottom of syringe barrel to inject sample. Remove syringe and rinse well with solvent. Open split valve approximately 30 s after the injection.

2) On-column injection technique—To more fully reduce discrimination against higher-boiling compounds, use an on-column injector. A cold on-column injector also can be used to avoid decomposition of thermally labile compounds, e.g., dimethyl polysulfides.[9] Determine thermally labile compounds quantitatively by using a cold on-column injector or an inactive, vaporizing injector.

With an on-column injector, increase sensitivity by injecting large sample volumes (up to 8 µL). To prevent problems from a heavy condensation of solvent with such large-volume injections, use a 2-m retention gap (an empty, deactivated piece of fused silica tubing connected to the head of the column with a zero-dead-volume connector).[10] To preclude backpressure from large-volume injections, inject slowly at about 1 µL/5 s. Keep initial column temperature at 10°C above boiling point of solvent for a full solvent effect and to produce sharp peaks (low peak widths).[10] Because the entire injection is deposited directly into the head of the column, the column can become active after as few as 50 to 80 injections. Check activity by injecting a polarity test mixture at least weekly. Breaking approximately 30 cm off the head of the column can restore inertness.

3) Operating conditions for GC/MS—After initial installation of the capillary column, condition it according to the manufacturer's instruction. Daily, make a conditioning run with a CS_2 injection before injecting any samples (optional). Typical instrument conditions are given in Table 6040:III.

d. *Calibration standard:* The method is semiquantitative for a large number of compounds, but has been shown to be

TABLE 6040:III. TYPICAL OPERATING
CONDITIONS FOR GC/MS ANALYSIS OF CLSA
EXTRACTS[6]

Variable	Description or Value
Column	30- or 60-m × 0.25-mm-ID DB-1 or DB-5 fused silica capillary column*
Column temperature program	35°C, 16 min; 35 to 260°C @ 4°C/min; 260°C, 18 min
Carrier gas	Helium
Carrier gas flow rate	1 mL/min
Sample size	About 1.5 μL (splitless injection)
Injector temperature	250°C
Transfer line temperature	250°C
Separator temperature	265°C
Ionizer temperature	280°C
Source pressure	About 7 × 10^{-5} Pa
Electron energy	70 eV
Mass range scanned	41 to 453 amu
Scan time	1 s

*J&W Scientific, Inc., or equivalent.

Reprinted from *Identification and Treatment of Tastes and Odors in Drinking Water*,[6] by permission. Copyright 1987, American Water Works Association.

quantitative for many of the compounds listed in this section. Prepare a 20-ng/L target-compound calibration standard by dosing 1 L organic-free water in the stripping bottle with 10 μL combination internal standard solution plus 5 μL combination reference standards solution. (Internal standards concentration is 100 ng/L each.) If the salting-out technique is used, add 72 g Na₂SO₄ to a total volume of 900 mL organic-free water before dosing with 9 μL combination internal standard solution plus 4.5 μL combination reference standards solution. Analyze as directed

above. Inject the calibration standard extract at least weekly, preferably daily, to determine GC/MS response factors and verify spectra.

Verify working linear range by analyzing standards and representative samples with added organics at different concentrations.

e. Blanks: Run a procedural blank daily to assess contamination from reagents, apparatus, and other sources. Run a blank immediately after analyzing any very high-level sample or after installing new parts in the system. Analyze organic-free water with internal standards under the same conditions as samples.

5. Calculations

a. Identification: Identify a compound by matching both retention time and spectra of sample and standard. If they are available, use both a reverse-search computer program with a target-compound library and a forward-search program with the National Institute of Standards and Technology (formerly National Bureau of Standards) library for tentative identification of other compounds present.

1) *Retention times*—Use each internal standard to calculate relative retention times for all the compounds in the same part of the chromatogram (Table 6040:IV). For compounds eluting on the solvent tail, use an early-eluting internal standard (e.g., 1-chlorohexane). Sample retention times should match predicted retention times within ± 15 s.

$$\text{Predicted } T_{z,x} = \frac{T_{z,s}}{T_{I,s}} \times T_{I,x}$$

where:

T = retention time,
z = target compound,
I = internal standard,
x = sample analysis, and
s = calibration standard analysis.

2) *Spectra*—Peaks of at least three characteristic ions should all maximize at the

TABLE 6040:IV. GC/MS DATA FOR THREE INTERNAL STANDARDS AND TWO EARTHY-MUSTY-SMELLING COMPOUNDS

Compound	Retention Time* min	Quantification Mass amu	Characteristic Ions (with relative intensities)
1-Chlorooctane	30.8	91	43 (100), 91 (86, 93 (27)
2-Methylisoborneol	36.4	95, 107†	95 (100), 107 (26), 135 (9)
1-Chlorodecane	39.8	91	43 (100), 91 (87), 93 (28)
Geosmin	45.1	112	112 (100), 111 (28), 125 (18)
1-Chlorododecane	47.2	85	43 (100), 91 (61), 93 (19), 85 (12)

*See Table 6040:III for GC conditions. Data accumulated using 30-m DB-5 capillary column.

†Quantify using two different masses and obtain an average value.

same retention time and have standard intensity ratios (spectra) within ±20% of those of the calibration-standard compounds. Characteristic ions and their typical relative intensities for three of the internal standards and two earthy-musty-smelling compounds are given in Table 6040:IV. Preferably, use reference spectra of 10 to 14 key masses. Determine reference spectra by analysis of standards; verify these frequently. The spectra of MIB are particularly dependent on instrument condition; both 107 and 95 amu have been reported as base peaks (Figure 6040:7). Figure 6040:8 shows the mass spectrum for geosmin.

b. *Quantitation:* Determine concentrations by comparison of peak areas of specific quantitation ions. A quantitation ion should be relatively intense in the mass spectrum, yet be free from interference problems caused by closely eluting compounds (see Table 6040:IV). Calculate a response factor for each compound from CLSA of a calibration standard as follows:

$$R_z = \frac{A_z \times C_I}{C_z \times A_I}$$

where:

R_z = response factor for target compound Z,
I = internal standard, 1-chlorodecane,
C = concentration, ng/L, and
A = peak area in consistent units.

Compound concentration in the sample (x) is:

$$C_{z,x}, \text{ng/L} = \frac{A_{z,x} \times C_{I,x}}{R_z \times A_{I,x}}$$

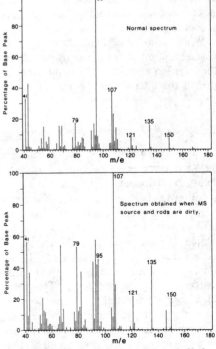

Figure 6040:7. **Mass spectra of 2-methylisoborneol under different instrumental conditions.**

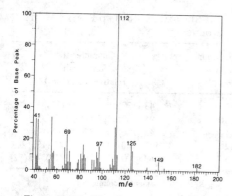

Figure 6040:8. Mass spectrum of geosmin.

Use the internal standard 1-chlorodecane for determining response factors. Use the other internal standards as a check on the system; calculated values should be to ±20%. Computerized reverse-search spectral matching and automatic quantitation are recommended to improve identification in complex matrices and to facilitate data processing.

Where calibration standards are unavailable, estimate concentrations by comparing the total ion current of the compounds to that of the internal standard 1-chlorodecane.

6. Quality Assurance/Quality Control

The CLSA method is semiquantitative for some compounds because of the variability of stripping efficiencies. However, quantitative data are obtainable for compounds that are reproducibly stripped (e.g., MIB and geosmin).[1-3, 6] Analyze a replicate sample at least once per 10 samples to check precision and reproducibility. If unusual or unexpected results are obtained, analyze a replicate to confirm. Typically, single-analyst determinations for a relatively simple matrix have a coefficient of variation less than or equal to 10%. Otherwise, precision is usually within 20%. For compounds that are poorly stripped, a higher coefficient of variation may be obtained.

Analyze a sample with a known addition at least once per 10 samples to check accuracy and recovery. If matrix problems exist, this will confirm the accuracy of results. Adjust these recoveries against the calibration standards results. Even when absolute recoveries are less than 50%, standard adjusted recoveries, which correct for stripping efficiencies, are usually between 80 and 120%.

7. Precision and Bias

Precision and bias data are given in Tables 6040:V and VI for the analysis of earthy-musty-smelling compounds. Table 6040:VII shows recovery and precision data for selected pollutants.

8. References

1. KRASNER, S.W., C.J. HWANG & M.J. McGUIRE. 1981. Development of a closed-loop stripping technique for the analysis of taste- and odor-causing substances in drinking water. *In* L.H. Keith, ed. Advances in the Identification and Analysis of Organic Pollutants in Water, Vol. 2. Ann Arbor Science Publishers, Ann Arbor, Mich.

2. KRASNER, S.W., C.J. HWANG & M.J. McGUIRE. 1983. A standard method for quantification of earthy-musty odorants in water. *Water Sci. Technol.* 15(6/7):127.

3. HWANG, C.J., S.W. KRASNER, M.J. McGUIRE, M.S. MOYLAN & M.S. DALE. 1984. Determination of subnanogram per liter levels of earthy-musty odorants in water by the salted closed-loop stripping method. *Environ. Sci Technol.* 18:535.

4. COLEMAN, W.E., J.W. MUNCH, R.W. SLATER, R.G. MELTON & F.C. KOPFLER. 1983. Optimization of purging efficiency and quantification of organic contaminants from water using a 1-L closed-loop-stripping apparatus and computerized capillary column GC/MS. *Environ. Sci. Technol.* 17:571.

5. THOMASON, M.M. & W. BERTSCH. 1983. Evaluation of sampling methods for the determination of trace organics in water. *J. Chromatogr.* 279:383.

6. MALLEVIALLE, J. & I.H. SUFFET, eds. 1987. Identification and Treatment of Tastes and Odors in Drinking Water. American Water

TABLE 6040:V. SINGLE-LABORATORY BIAS FOR SELECTED ORGANIC COMPOUNDS CAUSING TASTE AND ODOR

Stripping Technique Compound	Dose Level ng/L	Number of Samples*	Mean Recovery† %	Standard Deviation %
Unsalted method‡				
2-Isobutyl-3-methoxy pyrazine	4–20	23	89	21
2-Isobutyl-3-methoxy pyrazine	4–20	22	101	28
2-Methylisoborneol	4–120	30	101	21
2,3,6-Trichloroanisole	4–20	22	88	27
Geosmin	4–120	28	109	20
Salting-out method‡				
2-Isobutyl-3-methoxy pyrazine	4–20	44	120	24
2-Isobutyl-3-methoxy pyrazine	4–20	48	106	18
2-Methylisoborneol	4–20	48	106	15
2,3,6-Trichloroanisole	4–20	45	99	22
Geosmin	4–20	48	105	15

*Finished and natural surface waters.
†Standard-adjusted recovery.
‡Stripping at 25°C.

Reprinted with permission from *Environmental Science and Technology*, 18:535.[3] Copyright 1984. American Chemical Society.

Works Association & American Water Works Association Research Foundation, Denver, Colo.

7. Report of Analysis for Semivolatile Organics by Closed-Loop Stripping GC/MS. 1982. Environmental Research Lab., James M. Montgomery, Consulting Engineers, Inc., Pasadena, Calif.

8. GROB, K. & F. ZÜRCHER. 1976. Stripping of trace organic substances from water. Equipment and procedure. *J. Chromatogr.* 117:285.

9. WAJON, J.E., R. ALEXANDER & R.I. KAGI. 1985. Determination of trace levels of dimethyl polysulphides by capillary gas chromatography. *J. Chromatogr.* 319:187.

10. GROB, K. 1978. On-column injection onto capillary columns. Part 2: Study of sampling conditions; practical recommendations. *J.*

High Resolution Chromatogr. Chromatogr. Commun. 1:263.

9. Bibliography

BUDDE, W.L. & J.W. EICHELBERGER. 1979. Organic Analysis Using Gas Chromatography-Mass Spectrometry. Ann Arbor Science Publishers, Ann Arbor, Mich.

GROB, K. & K. GROB, JR. 1978. Splitless injection and the solvent effect. *J. High Resolution Chromatogr. Chromatogr. Commun.* 1:57.

GROB, K. & G. GROB. 1979. Practical gas chromatography—a systematic approach. *J. High Resolution Chromatogr. Chromatogr. Commun.* 2:109.

REINHARD, M., J.E. SCHREINER, T. EVERHART & J. GRAYDON. 1987. Specific analysis of trace organics in water using gas chromatography and mass spectroscopy. *J. Environ. Pathol., Toxicol. & Oncol.* 7:417.

TABLE 6040:VI. PRECISION DATA FOR SELECTED ORGANIC COMPOUNDS CAUSING TASTE AND ODOR*

Compound	Dose Level ng/L	Multiple Laboratories†			Single Laboratory‡		
		Mean ng/L	Standard Deviation ng/L	Coefficient of Variation %	Mean ng/L	Standard Deviation ng/L	Coefficient of Variation %
Sample A§							
2-Isopropyl-3-methoxy pyrazine	5.9	5.6	1.6	28	6.6	0.6	9
2-Isobutyl-3-methoxy pyrazine	3.0	3.0	0.7	24	3.2	0.3	11
2-Methylisoborneol	4.3	4.8	1.0	20	5.1	0.1	2
2,3,6-Trichloroanisole	8.7	7.3	3.1	43	9.3	2.0	22
Geosmin	2.9	3.3	0.9	27	3.6	0.5	14
Sample B§							
2-Isopropyl-3-methoxy pyrazine	25	22.3	8.0	36	27.5	2.8	10
2-Isobutyl-3-methoxy pyrazine	15	14.3	4.2	30	17.1	2.5	14
2-Methylisoborneol	20	18.3	6.2	34	22.6	2.0	9
2,3,6-Trichloroanisole	35	32.0	9.7	30	37.2	3.3	9
Geosmin	16	15.9	5.9	37	19.9	2.8	14

* Stripping at 25°C, unsalted method.
† Five analysts at three laboratories.
‡ Three analysts at one laboratory.
§ Organic-free water dosed with taste and odor compounds.

TABLE 6040:VII. RECOVERY AND PRECISION DATA FOR SELECTED PRIORITY POLLUTANTS*

Compound	Amount ng	Mean Recovered Amount† ng	Range	Recovery Efficiency %	RSD %
Thiophene	25.4	8.8	7.2 – 10.9	34.6	15.9
Dibromochloromethane	29.4	16.6	13.3 – 21.0	56.5	12.6
Styrene	21.8	17.4	15.9 – 19.6	79.8	6.9
Isopropylbenzene	24.2	25.9	23.8 – 28.7	107.0	7.7
2-Chlorotoluene	25.9	23.3	21.6 – 26.9	90.0	7.7
bis(2-Chloroethyl)ether	24.4	2.8	2.6 – 3.5	11.6	10.7
α-Methylstyrene	21.6	19.4	18.1 – 21.6	89.9	6.2
1,4-Dichlorobenzene	19.8	18.3	16.4 – 20.6	92.5	8.2
2-Ethyl-1,3-dimethylbenzene	24.1	22.3	20.8 – 24.7	92.4	5.8
4-Chloro-o-xylene	25.7	21.8	20.2 – 26.0	84.8	9.2
1,1-Dimethylindan	21.7	23.8	21.6 – 26.2	109.5	7.1
p-Methylphenol	26.6	ND‡			
Tetrahydronaphthalene	23.4	23.1	20.2 – 26.3	98.6	10.4
1,2,4-Trichlorobenzene	23.2	19.2	17.6 – 20.9	82.9	7.3
Hexachloro-1,3-butadiene	26.9	30.9	27.4 – 34.3	113.8	9.2
2-Methylbiphenyl	24.4	24.8	22.0 – 27.1	101.4	7.7
1,6-Dimethylnaphthalene	24.2	9.5	7.6 – 11.2	39.3	11.6
2-Isopropylnaphthalene	22.7	20.6	18.8 – 22.3	90.8	6.3
Pentachlorobenzene	26.1	12.4	10.7 – 14.3	47.7	11.3
Hexachlorobenzene	20.1	6.2	5.0 – 7.4	31.1	12.9
2,2',4,4',6,6'-Hexachlorobi- phenyl	27.1	28.2	26.1 – 32.3	104.3	7.1
2,2',4,5,5'-Pentachlorobi- phenyl	28.2	23.0	17.8 – 27.6	81.5	14.3

*Stripping at 40°C, unsalted method.
†Based on six purging analyses using single ion quantification.
‡ND = not detected.
Reprinted with permission from *Environmental Science and Technology*, 17:571.[4]
Copyright 1983. American Chemical Society.

6040 C.   Purge and Trap Technique

For applications of this technique to analyses for volatile organics, see Section 6210.

6210   VOLATILE ORGANICS

6210 A.   Introduction

1. Sources and Significance

Many organic compounds have been detected in ground and surface waters. While most groundwater contamination episodes are traceable to leaking underground fuel or solvent storage vessels, landfills, agriculture practices, and wastewater disposal, the most probable cause for contamination of some aquifers and surface waters has never been firmly established. Contamination may be due to past practices of on-site (leachfield) disposal of domestic and industrial wastes or to illegal discharges. Organohalides, particularly the trihalomethanes, are present in most chlorinated water systems, especially those using surface waters as a source of supply. Toxicological studies on animal models have shown that some of these organics have the potential for teratogenesis or carcinogenesis in human beings. To minimize these health risks, sensitive detection and accurate and reproducible quantitation of organics is of paramount importance.

2. Selection of Method

Three gas chromatographic/mass spectrometric (GC/MS) methods for purgeable organics are presented. While all three methods are similar in compound recovery, column materials, and chromatographic conditions, the methods are not interchangeable from a regulatory point of view.[1,2] See each method for list of specific compounds covered.

Method B is a packed-column GC/MS method useful for the determination of purgeable organics in municipal and industrial wastes. Method C, also a packed-column GC/MS method, is applicable to the determination of various volatile organic compounds in finished drinking water, raw source water, or drinking water in any stage of treatment. Method D is identical to Method C, except that a capillary column is used. Methods C and D are intended primarily for the detection of large numbers of contaminants at very low concentrations not detectable with the materials and conditions used in Method B. Quality assurance requirements and instrument and method performance criteria are more stringent for the methods applicable to drinking water.

All three methods are highly sophisticated microanalytical procedures that should be used only by analysts experienced in operation of purge and trap units and GC/MS systems and in evaluation and interpretation of mass spectra.

3. References

1. U.S. ENVIRONMENTAL PROTECTION AGENCY. 1987. National primary drinking water regulations—synthetic organic chemicals; monitoring for unregulated contaminants; final rule. 40 CFR Parts 141 & 142; *Federal Register* 52, No. 130.
2. U.S. ENVIRONMENTAL PROTECTION AGENCY. 1986. Guidelines establishing test procedures for the analysis of pollutants under the Clean Water Act. 40 CFR Part 136; *Federal Register* 51, No. 125.

6210 B.   Purge and Trap Packed-Column
Gas Chromatographic/Mass Spectrometric Method I*

This method[1] is applicable to the determination of purgeable organics† in municipal and industrial discharges. The method may be extended to screen samples for acrolein and acrylonitrile; however, another method[2] for these compounds is preferred.

1. General Discussion

a. *Principle:* Volatile organic compounds are transferred efficiently from the aqueous to the vapor phase by bubbling an inert gas through a water sample contained in a specially designed purging chamber at ambient temperature. The vapor is swept through a sorbent trap to collect the organics. After purging is completed, the trap is heated and backflushed with the same inert gas to desorb the compounds onto a gas chromatographic column. The gas chromatograph is temperature-programmed to separate the compounds. The detector is a mass spectrometer.[3,4] See Section 6010C for discussion of gas chromatographic and mass spectrometric principles.

b. *Interferences:* See Section 6010C. Impurities in the purge gas and organic compounds outgassing from the plumbing ahead of the trap account for most contamination problems. Demonstrate that the system is free from contamination under operational conditions by analyzing method blanks daily (see ¶ 7a). (NOTE: Use blanks for monitoring only; corrections for blank values are unacceptable.) Avoid using non-TFE plastic tubing, non-TFE thread sealants, or flow controllers with rubber components in the purge and trap system.

Samples can be contaminated by diffusion of volatile organics (particularly fluorocarbons and methylene chloride) through the septum seal during shipment and storage. Use a field reagent blank prepared from reagent water and carried through the sampling and handling procedure as a check on such contamination.

Contamination by carryover can occur whenever high-level and low-level concentration samples are analyzed sequentially. To reduce carryover, rinse purging device and sample syringe with reagent water between samples. Follow analysis of an unusually concentrated sample with an analysis of reagent water to check for cross-contamination. For samples containing large amounts of water-soluble materials, suspended solids, high boiling compounds, or high levels of the subject group of compounds, wash purging device with a detergent solution, rinse it with distilled water, and then dry it in an oven at 105°C between analyses. The trap and other parts of the system also are subject to contamination; therefore, frequently bake and purge the entire system. Loss of volatile constituents is also an important source of error.

c. *Detection limits:* The method detection limit (MDL) is the minimum concentration of a substance that can be measured and reported with 99% confidence that the value is above zero.[5] The MDL concentrations listed in Table 6210:I were obtained with reagent water.[6] The MDL actually obtained in a given analysis will vary, depending on instrument sensitivity and matrix effects.

---

* Approved by Standard Methods Committee, 1988. Accepted by U.S. Environmental Protection Agency as equivalent to EPA Method 624.

† Benzene, bromodichloromethane, bromoform, bromomethane, carbon tetrachloride, chlorobenzene, chloroethane, 2-chloroethylvinyl ether, chloroform, chloromethane, dibromochloromethane, 1,2-dichlorobenzene, 1,3-dichlorobenzene, 1,4-dichlorobenzene, 1,1-dichloroethane, 1,2-dichloroethane, 1,1-dichloroethene, *trans*-1,2-dichloroethene, 1,2-dichloropropane, *cis*-1,3-dichloropropene, *trans*-1,3-dichloropropene, ethylbenzene, methylene chloride, 1,1,2,2-tetrachloroethane, tetrachloroethene, toluene, 1,1,1-trichloroethane, 1,1,2-trichloroethane, trichloroethene, trichlorofluoromethane, and vinyl chloride.

TABLE 6210:I. CHROMATOGRAPHIC CONDITIONS AND METHOD DETECTION LIMITS (MDL)

Compound	Retention Time min	Method Detection Limit* μg/L
Chloromethane	2.3	nd
Bromomethane	3.1	nd
Vinyl chloride	3.8	nd
Chloroethane	4.6	nd
Methylene chloride	6.4	2.8
Trichlorofluoromethane	8.3	nd
1,1-Dichloroethene	9.0	2.8
1,1-Dichloroethane	10.1	4.7
trans-1,2-Dichloroethene	10.8	1.6
Chloroform	11.4	1.6
1,2-Dichloroethane	12.1	2.8
1,1,1-Trichloroethane	13.4	3.8
Carbon tetrachloride	13.7	2.8
Bromodichloromethane	14.3	2.2
1,2-Dichloropropane	15.7	6.0
cis-1,3-Dichloropropene	15.9	5.0
Trichloroethene	16.5	1.9
Benzene	17.0	4.4
Dibromochloromethane	17.1	3.1
1,1,2-Trichloroethane	17.2	5.0
trans-1,3-Dichloropropene	17.2	nd
2-Chloroethylvinyl ether	18.6	nd
Bromoform	19.8	4.7
1,1,2,2-Tetrachloroethane	22.1	6.9
Tetrachloroethene	22.2	4.1
Toluene	23.5	6.0
Chlorobenzene	24.6	6.0
Ethyl benzene	26.4	7.2
1,3-Dichlorobenzene	33.9	nd
1,2-Dichlorobenzene	35.0	nd
1,4-Dichlorobenzene	35.4	nd

Column conditions: Carbopack B (60/80 mesh) coated with 1% SP-1000 packed in a 1.8 m by 3 mm ID glass column with helium carrier gas at 30 mL/min flow rate. Column temperature held at 45°C for 3 min, then programmed at 8°C/min to 220°C and held for 15 min.

* nd = not determined.

d. *Safety:* The toxicity or carcinogenicity of each reagent has not been defined precisely. Benzene, carbon tetrachloride, chloroform, 1,4-dichlorobenzene, and vinyl chloride have been classified tentatively as known or suspected, human or mammalian carcinogens. Prepare primary standards of these compounds in a hood and wear a NIOSH/MESA-approved toxic gas respirator when handling high concentrations.

2. Sampling and Storage

See Section 6010B.1.

3. Apparatus

a. *Purge and trap system:* The purge and trap system consists of three separate pieces

of equipment: purging device, trap, and desorber. Several complete systems now are
available commercially.

1) *Purging device*, designed to accept 5-
mL samples with a water column at least
3 cm deep. Keep the gaseous head space
between the water column and the trap to
a total volume of less than 15 mL. Pass
the purge gas through the water column
as finely divided bubbles with a diameter
of less than 3 mm at the origin. Introduce
the purge gas no more than 5 mm from
the base of the water column. The purging
device illustrated in Figure 6210:1 meets
these design criteria.

2) *Trap*, at least 25 cm long and with an
inside diameter of at least 3 mm, packed
to contain the following minimum lengths
of adsorbents: 1.0 cm of methyl silicone-
coated packing, ¶ 4*b*2), 15 cm of 2,6-di-
phenylene oxide polymer, ¶ 4*b*1), and 8 cm

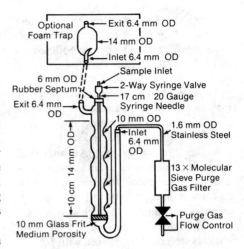

Figure 6210:1. Purging device.

of silica gel, ¶ 4*b*3). Figure 6210:2 illustrates the minimum specifications.

3) *Desorber*, capable of rapidly heating

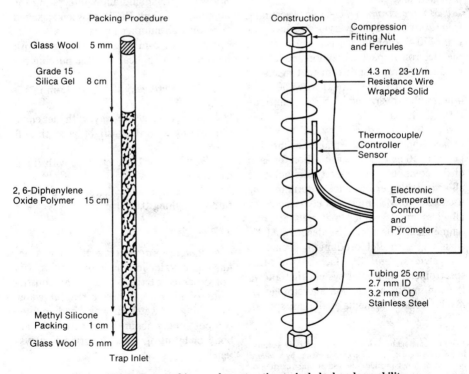

Figure 6210:2. Trap packings and construction to include desorb capability.

the trap to 180°C. Do not heat polymer section of trap above 180°C nor other sections above 200°C. The desorber illustrated in Figure 6210:2 meets these design criteria.

4) *Assembly*: The purge and trap system may be assembled as a separate unit or be coupled to a gas chromatograph as illustrated in Figures 6210:3 and 4.

b. Gas chromatograph:‡ An analytical system complete with a temperature-programmable gas chromatograph suitable for on-column injection and all required accessories including syringes, gases, and analytical column 1.8 m long $\times$ 3 mm ID stainless steel or glass, packed with 1% SP-1000 on Carbopack B (60/80 mesh) or equivalent. This column was used to develop the detection limit and precision and bias data presented herein. Guidelines for the use of alternate column packings are provided in ¶ 5a.

c. Mass spectrometer, capable of scanning from 20 to 260 amu every 7 s or less, utilizing 70-V (nominal) electron energy in the electron impact ionization mode, and producing a mass spectrum that meets all the criteria in Table 6210:II when 50 ng of 4-bromofluorobenzene (BFB) is injected through the GC inlet.

d. GC/MS interface: Any GC to MS interface that gives acceptable calibration points at 50 ng or less per injection for each of the compounds of interest and achieves all acceptable performance criteria may be used. GC to MS interfaces constructed of all glass or glass-lined materials are recommended. Glass can be deactivated by silanizing with dichlorodimethylsilane.

e. Data system: Interface to the mass spectrometer computer system that allows the continuous acquisition and storage on machine-readable media of all mass spectra

TABLE 6210:II. BFB KEY m/z ABUNDANCE CRITERIA

Mass	m/z Abundance Criteria
50	15 to 40% of mass 95
75	30 to 60% of mass 95
95	Base peak, 100% relative abundance
96	5 to 9% of mass 95
173	<2% of mass 174
174	>50% of mass 95
175	5 to 9% of mass 174
176	>95% but <101% of mass 174
177	5 to 9% of mass 176

obtained throughout the chromatographic program. Use computer software that allows searching any GC/MS data file for specific m/z (masses) and plotting such m/z abundances versus time or scan number. This type of plot is defined as an Extracted Ion Current Profile (EICP). Software also should allow integrating the abundance in any EICP between specified time or scan number limits.

f. Syringes, 5-mL glass hypodermic with luerlok tip, if applicable to the purging device.

g. Microsyringes, 25-μL, 0.15-mm ID needle.

h. Syringe valve, two-way, with luer ends.

i. Syringe, 5-mL, gastight with shutoff valve.

j. Bottle, 15-mL, screw-cap, with TFE cap liner.

k. Balance, analytical, capable of accurately weighing 0.0001 g.

4. Reagents

a. Reagent water: Reagent water is defined as a water in which an interferent is not observed at the MDL of the constituents of interest. Generate reagent water by passing tap water through a carbon filter bed containing about 0.5 kg activated carbon§ or by using a water purification system.‖

---

‡ Gas chromatographic methods are extremely sensitive to the materials used. Mention of trade names by *Standard Methods* does not preclude the use of other existing or as-yet-undeveloped products that give *demonstrably* equivalent results.

§ Filtrasorb-300, Calgon Corp., or equivalent.
‖ Millipore Super-Q or equivalent.

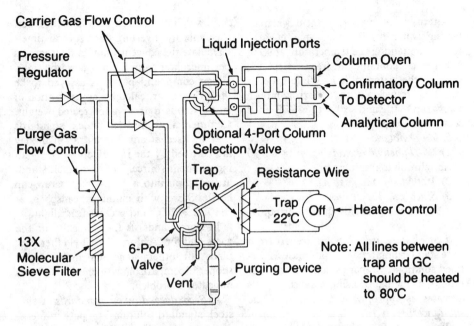

Figure 6210:3. Purge and trap system (purge mode).

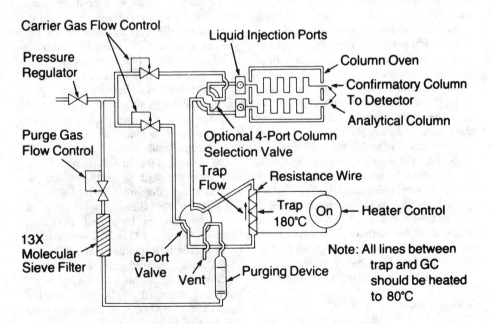

Figure 6210:4. Purge and trap system (desorb mode).

Alternatively, prepare reagent water by boiling water for 15 min. Subsequently, while maintaining the temperature at 90°C, bubble a contaminant-free inert gas through the water for 1 h. While water is still hot, transfer it to a narrow-mouth screw-cap bottle and seal with a TFE-lined septum and cap.

b. Trap materials:

1) *2,6-Diphenylene oxide polymer,* 60/80 mesh, chromatographic grade.#

2) *Methyl silicone packing.***

3) *Silica gel,* 35/60 mesh.††

c. Methanol, pesticide quality or equivalent.

d. Stock standard solutions: Prepare from pure standard materials or purchase as certified solutions. Prepare stock standard solutions in methanol using assayed liquids or gases as appropriate. CAUTION: *Toxic substances; see ¶ 1d.*

Place about 9.8 mL methanol in a 10-mL ground-glass-stoppered volumetric flask. Let stand, unstoppered, for about 10 min or until all alcohol-wetted surfaces have dried. Weigh flask to nearest 0.1 mg.

Add the assayed reference materials as follows: For liquids, using a 100-μL syringe or disposable capillary tip glass pipet, immediately add two or more drops of assayed reference material to flask, then reweigh. Be sure that the drops fall directly into the alcohol without contacting the flask neck. For gases, that is, any of the six halocarbons that boil below 30°C (bromomethane, chloroethane, chloromethane, dichlorodifluoromethane, trichlorofluoromethane, vinyl chloride), fill a 5-mL valved gastight syringe with the reference standard to the 5.0-mL mark. Lower needle to 5 mm above the methanol meniscus. Slowly introduce reference standard above the surface of the liquid (the heavy gas will rapidly dissolve into the methanol).

Tenax or equivalent.
** 3% OV-1 on Chromosorb W (60/80 mesh) or equivalent.
†† Davison grade 15 or equivalent.

Reweigh flask, dilute to volume, stopper, then mix by inverting flask several times. Calculate the concentration in micrograms per microliter from the net gain in weight. When compound purity is assayed to be 96% or greater, calculate concentration of stock standard from uncorrected weight. Commercially prepared stock standards may be used at any concentration if they are certified by the manufacturer or by an independent source. Transfer stock standard solution into a TFE-sealed screw-cap bottle. Store, with minimal headspace, at −10 to −20°C and protect from light.

Prepare standards fresh weekly for the gases and for 2-chloroethylvinyl ether. Replace all other standards monthly, or sooner if comparison with check standards indicates a problem.

e. Secondary dilution standards: Using stock standard solutions, prepare in methanol secondary dilution standards that contain the compounds of interest, either singly or mixed together. Prepare secondary dilution standards at concentrations such that the aqueous calibration standards will bracket the working range of the analytical system. Store secondary dilution standards with minimal headspace and check frequently for signs of degradation or evaporation, especially just before preparing calibration standards.

f. Surrogate standard known-addition solution: Select a minimum of three surrogate compounds from Table 6210:III. Prepare stock standard solutions for each surrogate standard in methanol as described above. Prepare a surrogate standard solution from these stock standards at a concentration of 15 μg/mL in water. Store solutions at 4°C in TFE-sealed glass containers with a minimum of headspace. Check solutions frequently for stability. Adding 10 μL of this solution to 5 mL sample or standard gives a concentration equivalent to 30 μg/L of each surrogate standard.

g. Calibration standards: Using a 25-μL

syringe, prepare at least three concentration levels for each compound by carefully adding 20.0 μL of one or more secondary dilution standards to 50, 250, or 500 mL reagent water. Prepare one standard at a concentration near, but above, the MDL and the others to correspond to the expected range of sample concentrations or to define the working range of the detector. Aqueous calibration standards can be stored up to 24 h, if held in sealed vials with zero headspace. Otherwise, discard after 1 h.

Prepare a known-addition solution containing each of the internal standards as directed in ¶s 4d and e above. Preferably prepare secondary dilution standard at a concentration of 15 μg/mL of each internal standard compound. Adding 10 μL of this standard to 5.0 mL sample or calibration standard gives a concentration equivalent to 30 μg/L.

h. BFB standard: Prepare a 25-μg/mL solution of BFB in methanol.

i. Quality control (QC) check sample: Obtain a check sample concentrate‡‡ con-

taining each compound at a concentration of 10 μg/mL in methanol. If such a sample is not obtainable from an external source, prepare using stock standards prepared independently from those used for calibration.

5. Procedure

a. Operating conditions: Table 6210:I summarizes recommended operating conditions for the gas chromatograph and gives estimated retention times and MDLs that can be achieved under these conditions. An example of the separations obtained with this column is shown in Figure 6210:5. Other packed columns or chromatographic conditions may be used if quality control requirements (¶ 7 below) are met.

b. GC/MS performance tests: At the beginning of each day on which analyses are to be performed, check GC/MS system to see that acceptable performance criteria are achieved for BFB.[7] The performance test must be passed before any samples, blanks, or standards are analyzed, unless the instrument has met DFTPP test[8] earlier.

These performance tests require the following instrumental parameters:

---

‡‡ For U.S. federal permit-related analyses, use samples obtainable from U.S. EPA Environmental Monitoring and Support Laboratory, Cincinnati, Ohio.

TABLE 6210:III. SUGGESTED SURROGATE AND INTERNAL STANDARDS

Compound	Retention Time* min	Primary m/z	Secondary Masses
Benzene-d$_6$	17.0	84	
4-Bromofluorobenzene	28.3	95	174, 176
1,2-Dichloroethane-d$_4$	12.1	102	
1,4-Difluorobenzene	19.6	114	63, 88
Ethylbenzene-d$_5$	26.4	111	
Ethylbenzene-d$_{10}$	26.4	98	
Fluorobenzene	18.4	96	70
Pentafluorobenzene	23.5	168	
Bromochloromethane	9.3	128	49, 130, 51
2-Bromo-1-chloropropane	19.2	77	79, 156
1,4-Dichlorobutane	25.8	55	90, 92

* For chromatographic conditions, see Table 6210:I.

Electron energy: 70 V (nominal)

Mass range: 20 to 260 amu

Scan time: To give at least 5 scans per peak but not to exceed 7 s per scan.

At the beginning of each day, inject 2 µL of BFB solution directly on the column. Alternatively, add 2 µL of BFB solution to 5.0 mL of reagent water or standard solution and analyze the solution according to ¶ d below. Obtain a background-corrected mass spectrum of BFB and confirm that all the key m/z criteria in Table 6210:II are achieved. If all criteria are not achieved, retune mass spectrometer and repeat test until all criteria are achieved.

c. Calibration: Calibrate system daily as follows:

1) System setup—Assemble the purge

and trap system. Condition trap overnight at 180°C by backflushing with an inert gas flow of at least 20 mL/min. Condition trap for 10 min once daily before use.

Connect purge and trap system to a gas chromatograph. Operate gas chromatograph using the specified temperature and flow rate conditions. Calibrate purge and trap gas chromatographic system using the internal standard technique, ¶ 2).

2) Internal standard calibration procedure—Select three or more internal standards that are similar in analytical behavior to the compounds of interest, chosen from the compounds listed in Table 6210:III, and demonstrate that the measurement of the internal standard is not affected by method or matrix interferences. Because of such limitations, no internal standard is

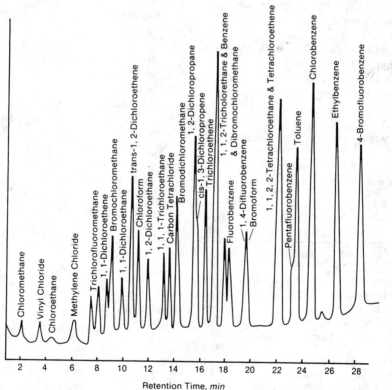

Figure 6210:5. Gas chromatogram of volatile organics. Column: 1% SP-1000 on Carbopack-B; program: 45°C for 3 min, 8°C/min to 220°C; detector: mass spectrometer.

applicable to all samples. The compounds recommended for use as surrogate known additions for quality control have been used successfully as internal standards because of their generally unique retention times. Prepare calibration standards at a minimum of three concentration levels for each compound as described in ¶ 4g. Prepare a known-addition solution containing each of the internal standards using the procedures described in ¶s 4d and e. Preferably prepare the secondary dilution standard at a concentration of 15 µg/mL of each internal standard compound. Adding 10 µL of this standard to 5.0 mL sample or calibration standard is equivalent to adding 30 µg/L. Analyze each calibration standard according to the procedure for samples, adding 10 µL of internal standard known-addition solution directly to the syringe. Tabulate peak height or area responses against concentration for each compound and internal standard, and calculate response factors (RF) for each compound as follows:

$$RF = \frac{(A_s)\,(C_{is})}{(A_{is})\,(C_s)}$$

where:

A_s = response for compound to be measured,
A_{is} = response for internal standard,
C_{is} = concentration of internal standard, and
C_s = concentration of compound to be measured.

Use average RF if RSD is less than 35%. Check calibration by procedure of ¶ 5b3) below, using calibration acceptance criteria found in Table 6210:IV.

3) Calibration check—Verify working calibration curve, calibration factor, or RF on each working day by analyzing a QC check sample [¶ 4i)] according to sample analysis procedure. For each compound, compare the response (Q) with the corresponding calibration acceptance criteria (Table 6210:IV). If the responses for all compounds of interest fall within the des-

ignated ranges, sample analysis may begin. NOTE: Because of the large number of compounds, there is a substantial probability that one or more will not meet the calibration acceptance criteria when all compounds are analyzed. If any individual Q falls outside the range, repeat test only for those compounds that failed to meet the calibration acceptance criteria. If the response does not fall within the range in this second test, prepare a new calibration curve, calibration factor, or RF for that compound.

d. *Sample analysis:* Adjust purge gas (nitrogen or helium) flow rate to 40 mL/min. Attach trap inlet to purging device and set purge and trap system to purge (Figure 6210:3). Open syringe valve on purging device sample introduction needle.

Let sample come to ambient temperature before introducing it into the syringe. Remove plunger from a 5-mL syringe and attach a closed syringe valve. Open sample bottle (or standard) and carefully pour sample into syringe barrel to just short of overflowing. Replace syringe plunger and compress sample. Open syringe valve and vent any residual air while adjusting sample volume to 5.0 mL. Because this process creates a headspace in the sample bottle and may destroy the validity of the sample if it is stored, fill and hold a second syringe at this time. Add 10.0 µL of the surrogate addition solution (¶ 7f), and 10.0 µL of the internal standard addition solution, ¶ c2), above through the valve bore, then close valve.

Attach syringe-syringe valve assembly to syringe valve on purging device. Open syringe valves and inject sample into purging chamber. Close both valves and purge sample for 11.0 ± 0.1 min at ambient temperature.

After purge time, attach trap to chromatograph, adjust purge and trap system to desorb mode (Figure 6210:4), and begin to temperature program the gas chromatograph. Introduce trapped materials to

TABLE 6210:IV. CALIBRATION AND QC ACCEPTANCE CRITERIA*

Compound	Range for Q $\mu g/L$	Limit for s $\mu g/L$	Range for $\overline{X}$ g/L	Range for P, P_s %
Benzene	12.8–27.2	6.9	15.2–26.0	37–151
Bromodichloromethane	13.1–26.9	6.4	10.1–28.0	35–155
Bromoform	14.2–25.8	5.4	11.4–31.1	45–169
Bromomethane	2.8–37.2	17.9	D–41.2	D–242
Carbon tetrachloride	14.6–25.4	5.2	17.2–23.5	70–140
Chlorobenzene	13.2–26.8	6.3	16.4–27.4	37–160
Chloroethane	7.6–32.4	11.4	8.4–40.4	14–230
2-Chloroethylvinyl ether	D–44.8	25.9	D–50.4	D–305
Chloroform	13.5–26.5	6.1	13.7–24.2	51–138
Chloromethane	D–40.8	19.8	D–45.9	D–273
Dibromochloromethane	13.5–26.5	6.1	13.8–26.6	53–149
1,2-Dichlorobenzene	12.6–27.4	7.1	11.8–34.7	18–190
1,3-Dichlorobenzene	14.6–25.4	5.5	17.0–28.8	59–156
1,4-Dichlorobenzene	12.6–27.4	7.1	11.8–34.7	18–190
1,1-Dichloroethane	14.5–25.5	5.1	14.2–28.5	59–155
1,2-Dichloroethane	13.6–26.4	6.0	14.3–27.4	49–155
1,1-Dichloroethene	10.1–29.9	9.1	3.7–42.3	D–234
trans-1,2-Dichloroethene	13.9–26.1	5.7	13.6–28.5	54–156
1,2-Dichloropropane	6.8–33.2	13.8	3.8–36.2	D–210
cis-1,3-Dichloropropene	4.8–35.2	15.8	1.0–39.0	D–227
trans-1,3-Dichloropropene	10.0–30.0	10.4	7.6–32.4	17–183
Ethyl benzene	11.8–28.2	7.5	17.4–26.7	37–162
Methylene chloride	12.1–27.9	7.4	D–41.0	D–221
1,1,2,2-Tetrachloroethane	12.1–27.9	7.4	13.5–27.2	46–157
Tetrachloroethene	14.7–25.3	5.0	17.0–26.6	64–148
Toluene	14.9–25.1	4.8	16.6–26.7	47–150
1,1,1-Trichloroethane	15.0–25.0	4.6	13.7–30.1	52–162
1,1,2-Trichloroethane	14.2–25.8	5.5	14.3–27.1	52–150
Trichloroethene	13.3–26.7	6.6	18.6–27.6	71–157
Trichlorofluoromethane	9.6–30.4	10.0	8.9–31.5	17–181
Vinyl chloride	0.8–39.2	20.0	D–43.5	D–251

* Q = concentration measured in QC check sample,
 s = standard deviation of four recovery measurements,
 $\overline{X}$ = average recovery of four recovery measurements,
P, P_s = percent recovery measured,
 D   = detected; result must be greater than zero.
Criteria calculated assuming a QC check sample concentration of 20 $\mu g/L$.

NOTE—These criteria are based directly on the method performance data in Table 6210:VI. Where necessary, the limits for recovery were broadened to assure applicability of the limits to concentrations below those used to develop Table 6210:VI.

GC column by rapidly heating trap to 180°C while backflushing trap with an inert gas at 20 to 60 mL/min for 4 min. If rapid heating of the trap cannot be achieved, use GC column as a secondary trap by cooling it to 30°C (subambient temperature, if poor peak geometry and random retention time problems persist) instead of initial program temperature.

While trap is being desorbed into gas

chromatograph, empty purging chamber using sample introduction syringe. Wash chamber with two 5-mL flushes of reagent water. Be sure all areas wetted during purging are also wetted during the rinse to maximize flushing.

After desorbing sample for 4 min, recondition trap by returning purge and trap system to purge mode. Wait 15 s, then close syringe valve on purging device to begin gas flow through trap. Maintain trap temperature at 180°C. After approximately 7 min, turn off trap heater and open syringe valve to stop gas flow through trap. The cool trap is ready for the next sample.

If response for any m/z exceeds the working range of the system, dilute sample from the portion in the second syringe and reanalyze with reagent water.

Obtain EICPs for the primary m/z (Table 6210:V) and at least two secondary masses for each compound of interest. Meet the following criteria to make a qualitative identification:

- The characteristic masses of each compound are a maximum in the same or within one scan of each other.
- The retention time is within 30 s of the retention time of the authentic compound.
- The relative peak heights of the three characteristic masses in the EICPs fall within 20% of the relative intensities of these masses in a reference mass spectrum. The reference mass spectrum can be obtained from a standard analyzed in the GC/MS system or from a reference library.

Structural isomers that have very similar mass spectra and less than 30 s difference in retention time can be identified explicitly only if the resolution between authentic isomers in a standard mix is acceptable. Acceptable resolution is achieved if the baseline to valley height between isomers is less than 25% of the sum of the two peak heights. Otherwise, structural isomers are identified as isomeric pairs.

6. Calculation

When a compound has been identified, base quantitation on the integrated abundance from the EICP of the primary characteristic m/z given in Table 6210:V. If the sample produces an interference for the primary m/z, use a secondary characteristic m/z to quantitate.

Calculate concentration in sample using the response factor (RF) and the following equation:

$$\text{Concentration, } \mu g/L = \frac{(A_s)(C_{is})}{(A_{is})(RF)}$$

where:

A_s = response for compound to be measured,
A_{is} = response for internal standard, and
C_{is} = concentration of internal standards.

Report results in micrograms per liter without correction for recovery. Report all quality control data with sample results.

7. Quality Control

a. Quality-control program: The analyst should be experienced in operation of a purge and trap system and a gas chromatographic/mass spectrometer and in interpretation of mass spectra. A minimum quality-control program consists of an initial demonstration of laboratory capability and an ongoing analysis of samples with known additions. Maintain records to document data quality. Compare ongoing data quality checks with established performance criteria to determine if results are acceptable. When results of known additions indicate atypical performance, analyze a quality control check standard to confirm that the operation is in control.

Make an initial, one-time, demonstration of acceptable bias and precision as described in ¶ *b* below.

Because advances are occurring in chromatography, certain options (¶ 5a) are permitted to improve separation or reduce

TABLE 6210:V. CHARACTERISTIC MASSES FOR PURGEABLE ORGANICS

Compound	Primary	Secondary
Chloromethane	50	52
Bromomethane	94	96
Vinyl chloride	62	64
Chloroethane	64	66
Methylene chloride	84	49, 51, 86
Trichlorofluoromethane	101	103
1,1-Dichloroethene	96	61, 98
1,1-Dichloroethane	63	65, 83, 85, 98, 100
trans-1,2-Dichloroethene	96	61, 98
Chloroform	83	85
1,2-Dichloroethane	98	62, 64, 100
1,1,1-Trichloroethane	97	99, 117, 119
Carbon tetrachloride	117	119, 121
Bromodichloromethane	127	83, 85, 129
1,2-Dichloropropane	112	63, 65, 114
trans-1,3-Dichloropropene	75	77
Trichloroethene	130	95, 97, 132
Benzene	78	
Dibromochloromethane	127	129, 208, 206
1,1,2-Trichloroethane	97	83, 85, 99, 132, 134
cis-1,3-Dichloropropene	75	77
2-Chloroethylvinyl ether	106	63, 65
Bromoform	173	171, 175, 250, 252, 254, 256
1,1,2,2-Tetrachloroethane	168	83, 85, 131, 133, 166
Tetrachloroethene	164	129, 131, 166
Toluene	92	91
Chlorobenzene	112	114
Ethyl benzene	106	91
1,3-Dichlorobenzene	146	148, 113
1,2-Dichlorobenzene	146	148, 113
1,4-Dichlorobenzene	146	148, 113

cost. For each modification, repeat the procedure in ¶ b below.

Each day, analyze a reagent water blank to demonstrate that interferences from the analytical system are under control.

On an ongoing basis, make known additions to, and analyze, a minimum of 10% of all samples to monitor and evaluate laboratory data quality according to ¶ c below.

Also demonstrate through the analyses of quality control check standards (¶ d below) that the measurement system is in control. The frequency of the check standard analyses should be 10% of all samples

analyzed but it may be reduced if known-addition recoveries meet all specified quality-control criteria.

Maintain performance records (¶ e below).

Also make known additions of surrogate standards to all samples to monitor continuing laboratory performance as described in ¶ f below.

b. Analyst proficiency check: To establish the ability to generate data with acceptable precision and bias, perform the following operations:

Prepare a QC check sample containing

20 μg/L of each compound by adding 200 μL of QC check sample concentrate (¶4i) to 100 mL reagent water. Analyze four 5-mL portions according to ¶ 5. Calculate average recovery ($\overline{X}$) in μg/L, and the standard deviation of the recovery (s) in μg/L, for each compound. Compare s and $\overline{X}$ with the corresponding acceptance criteria for precision and bias, respectively. If s and $\overline{X}$ for all compounds of interest meet the acceptance criteria (Table 6210:IV), system performance is acceptable and sample analysis may begin. If any individual s exceeds the precision limit or any individual X falls outside the range for bias, the system performance is unacceptable.

When results for one or more of the compounds fail at least one of the acceptance criteria, proceed as follows: Either

1) Locate and correct the source of the problem and repeat test for all compounds of interest beginning with analyses of four 5-mL portions, as above, or

2) Repeat test only for those compounds that failed to meet the criteria. Repeated failure, however, will confirm a general problem with the measurement system. If this occurs, locate and correct the source of the problem and retest for all compounds of interest beginning with the analytical step indicated.

c. *Analyses of samples with known additions:* On an ongoing basis, make known additions to at least 5% of the samples from each sample site being monitored. For laboratories analyzing one to 20 samples per month, analyze at least one such sample with a known addition per month.

Determine the concentration of the known addition as follows: If the concentration of a specific compound in the sample is being checked against a regulatory concentration limit, make an addition at that limit or one to five times higher than the background concentration determined below, whichever is larger. If the concentration of a specific compound is not being checked against a regulatory limit, add 20

μg/L or one to five times higher than the background concentration as determined below, whichever concentration is larger.

To determine background concentration (B), analyze one 5-mL sample portion. If necessary, prepare a new QC check sample concentrate (¶ 4i) appropriate for the background concentration in the sample. Add to a second 5-mL sample portion 10 μL of the QC check sample concentrate and analyze it to determine the concentration after addition (A) of each compound. Calculate each percent recovery (P) as 100($A-B$)%/T, where T is the true value of the addition.

Compare percent recovery (P) for each compound with the corresponding QC acceptance criteria (Table 6210:IV). These acceptance criteria include an allowance for error in measurement of both background and addition concentrations, assuming an addition:background ratio of 5:1. This error will be accounted for to the extent that the analyst's addition:background ratio approaches 5:1.[9] If the known addition was at a concentration lower than 20 μg/L, use either the tabulated QC acceptance criteria or optional QC acceptance criteria calculated for the specific addition concentration.

To calculate optional acceptance criteria use the equation in Table 6210:VI to calculate accuracy (X') and substitute the addition concentration (T) for C. Calculate overall precision (S') using the equation in Table 6210:VI, substituting X' for $\overline{X}$. Calculate the range for recovery at the addition concentration as (100 X'/T) $\pm$ 2.44 (100 S'/T)%.[9]§§

If any individual P falls outside the designated range for recovery, analysis for that constituent has failed the acceptance criteria. Analyze a check standard containing each compound that failed the criteria as described in ¶ d below.

d. *Quality-control check standard anal-*

---

§§ The value 2.44 is two times the value 1.22 derived in the reference.[9]

TABLE 6210:VI. METHOD BIAS AND PRECISION AS FUNCTIONS OF CONCENTRATION*

Compound	Bias, as Recovery, X' $\mu g/L$	Single-Analyst Precision, S_r $\mu g/L$	Overall Precision, S' $\mu g/L$
Benzene	$0.93C + 2.00$	$0.26\overline{X} - 1.74$	$0.25\overline{X} - 1.33$
Bromodichloromethane	$1.03C - 1.58$	$0.15\overline{X} + 0.59$	$0.20\overline{X} + 1.13$
Bromoform	$1.18C - 2.35$	$0.12\overline{X} + 0.34$	$0.17\overline{X} + 1.38$
Bromomethane†	$1.00C$	$0.43\overline{X}$	$0.58\overline{X}$
Carbon tetrachloride	$1.10C - 1.68$	$0.12\overline{X} + 0.25$	$0.11\overline{X} + 0.37$
Chlorobenzene	$0.98C + 2.28$	$0.16\overline{X} - 0.09$	$0.26\overline{X} - 1.92$
Chloroethane	$1.18C + 0.81$	$0.14\overline{X} + 2.78$	$0.29\overline{X} + 1.75$
2-Chloroethylvinyl ether†	$1.00C$	$0.62\overline{X}$	$0.84\overline{X}$
Chloroform	$0.93C + 0.33$	$0.16\overline{X} + 0.22$	$0.18\overline{X} + 0.16$
Chloromethane	$1.03C - 1.81$	$0.37\overline{X} + 2.14$	$0.58\overline{X} + 0.43$
Dibromochloromethane	$1.01C - 0.03$	$0.17\overline{X} - 0.18$	$0.17\overline{X} + 0.49$
1,2-Dichlorobenzene‡	$0.94C + 4.47$	$0.22\overline{X} - 1.45$	$0.30\overline{X} - 1.20$
1,3-Dichlorobenzene	$1.06C + 1.68$	$0.14\overline{X} - 0.48$	$0.18\overline{X} - 0.82$
1,4-Dichlorobenzene‡	$0.94C + 4.47$	$0.22\overline{X} - 1.45$	$0.30\overline{X} - 1.20$
1,1-Dichloroethane	$1.05C + 0.36$	$0.13\overline{X} - 0.05$	$0.16\overline{X} + 0.47$
1,2-Dichloroethane	$1.02C + 0.45$	$0.17\overline{X} - 0.32$	$0.21\overline{X} - 0.38$
1,1-Dichloroethene	$1.12C + 0.61$	$0.17\overline{X} + 1.06$	$0.43\overline{X} - 0.22$
trans-1,2-Dichloroethene	$1.05C + 0.03$	$0.14\overline{X} + 0.09$	$0.19\overline{X} + 0.17$
1,2-Dichloropropane†	$1.00C$	$0.33\overline{X}$	$0.45\overline{X}$
cis-1,3-Dichloropropene†	$1.00C$	$0.38\overline{X}$	$0.52\overline{X}$
trans-1,3-Dichloropropene†	$1.00C$	$0.25\overline{X}$	$0.34\overline{X}$
Ethyl benzene	$0.98C + 2.48$	$0.14\overline{X} + 1.00$	$0.26\overline{X} - 1.72$
Methylene chloride	$0.87C + 1.88$	$0.15\overline{X} + 1.07$	$0.32\overline{X} + 4.00$
1,1,2,2-Tetrachloroethane	$0.93C + 1.76$	$0.16\overline{X} + 0.69$	$0.20\overline{X} + 0.41$
Tetrachloroethene	$1.06C + 0.60$	$0.13\overline{X} - 0.18$	$0.16\overline{X} - 0.45$
Toluene	$0.98C + 2.03$	$0.15\overline{X} - 0.71$	$0.22\overline{X} - 1.71$
1,1,1-Trichloroethane	$1.06C + 0.73$	$0.12\overline{X} - 0.15$	$0.21\overline{X} - 0.39$
1,1,2-Trichloroethane	$0.95C + 1.71$	$0.14\overline{X} + 0.02$	$0.18\overline{X} + 0.00$
Trichloroethene	$1.04C + 2.27$	$0.13\overline{X} + 0.36$	$0.12\overline{X} + 0.59$
Trichlorofluoromethane	$0.99C + 0.39$	$0.33\overline{X} - 1.48$	$0.34\overline{X} - 0.39$
Vinyl chloride	$1.00C$	$0.48\overline{X}$	$0.65\overline{X}$

* X' = expected recovery for one or more measurements of a sample containing a concentration of C,
 S_r = expected single analyst standard deviation of measurements at an average concentration found of $\overline{X}$,
 S' = expected interlaboratory standard deviation of measurements at an average concentration found of $\overline{X}$,
 C = true value for the concentration,
 $\overline{X}$ = average recovery found for measurements of samples containing a concentration of C.
† Estimates based on the performance in a single laboratory.[11]
‡ Due to chromatographic resolution problems, performance statements for these isomers are based on the sums of their concentrations.

ysis: If analysis of any compound fails the acceptance criteria for recovery, prepare and analyze a QC check standard containing each compound that failed as follows:

Prepare the QC check standard by adding 10 µL of QC check sample concentrate (¶ 4i) to 5 mL reagent water. The QC check standard needs only to contain the compounds that failed criteria in the test in ¶ c above. Analyze the QC check standard to determine the concentration, A, of each compound. Calculate each percent recovery (P_s) as $100 (A/T)\%$, where T is the true value of the standard concentration. Compare percent recovery (P_s) for each compound that failed the test in ¶ c with the corresponding tabulated QC acceptance criteria. If the recovery of any compound falls outside the designated range, laboratory performance is out of control: identify and correct the problem immediately. The analytical result for that compound in the sample without a known addition is suspect.

e. Bias assessment and records: Assess method bias and maintain records. For example, after the analysis of five wastewater samples as in ¶ c above, calculate the average percent recovery $(\overline{P})$ and the standard deviation of the percent recovery (s_p). Express bias assessment as a percent recovery interval from $\overline{P} - 2s_p$ to $\overline{P} + 2s_p$. If $\overline{P} =$ 90% and $s_p = 10\%$, the recovery interval is expressed as 70–110%. Update bias assessment for each compound regularly, (e.g., after each five to ten new accuracy measurements).

f. Use of surrogate compounds: As a quality control check, make known additions to all samples of surrogate standard addition solutions as described in ¶ 5d, and calculate the percent recovery of each surrogate compound.

g. Additional quality-assurance practices: Other desirable practices depend on the needs of the laboratory and the nature of the samples. Analyze field duplicates to assess the precision of the environmental measurements. Whenever possible, analyze standard reference materials and participate in relevant performance evaluation studies.

8. Precision and Bias

This method was tested by 15 laboratories using reagent water, drinking water, surface water, and industrial wastewaters with additions at six concentrations over the range 5 to 600 µg/L.[10] Single-operator precision, overall precision, and method bias were found to be related directly to

the compound concentration and essentially independent of the sample matrix. Linear equations describing these relationships are presented in Table 6210:VI.

9. References

1. U.S. ENVIRONMENTAL PROTECTION AGENCY. 1984. Method 624—Purgeables. 40 CFR Part 136, 43373; *Federal Register* 49, No. 209.

2. U.S. ENVIRONMENTAL PROTECTION AGENCY. 1984. Method 603—Acrolein and acrylonitrile. 40 CFR Part 136, 43281; *Federal Register* 49, No. 209.

3. BELLAR, T.A. & J.J. LICHTENBERG. 1974. Determining volatile organics at microgram-per-litre levels by gas chromatography. *J. Amer. Water Works Assoc.* 66:739.

4. BELLAR, T.A. & J.J. LICHTENBERG. 1978. Semi-automated headspace analysis of drinking waters and industrial waters for purgeable volatile organic compounds. *In* C.E. Van Hall, ed. Measurement of Organic Pollutants in Water and Wastewater. STP 686, American Soc. Testing & Materials, Philadelphia, Pa.

5. U.S. ENVIRONMENTAL PROTECTION AGENCY. 1984. Definition and procedure for the determination of the method detection limit. 40 CFR Part 136, Appendix B. *Federal Register* 49, No. 209.

6. OLYNYK, P., W.L. BUDDE & J.W. EICHELBERGER. 1980. Method Detection Limit for Methods 624 and 625. Unpublished report.

7. BUDDE, W.L. & J.W. EICHELBERGER. 1980. Performance Tests for the Evaluation of Computerized Gas Chromatography/Mass Spectrometry Equipment and Laboratories. EPA-600/4-80-025, U.S. Environmental Protection Agency, Environmental Monitoring and Support Lab., Cincinnati, Ohio.

8. EICHELBERGER, J.W., L.E. HARRIS & W.L. BUDDE. 1975. Reference compound to calibrate ion abundance measurement in gas chromatography — mass spectrometry systems. *Anal. Chem.* 47:995.

9. PROVOST, L.P. & R.S. ELDER. 1983. Interpretation of percent recovery data. *Amer. Lab.* 15:58.

10. U.S. ENVIRONMENTAL PROTECTION AGENCY. 1984. EPA Method Study 29,

Method 624—Purgeables. EPA-600/2-84-054, National Technical Information Serv., PB84-209915, Springfield, Va.

11. SLATER, R. & T. PRESSLEY. 1984. Method Performance Data for Method 624 (memorandum). U.S. Environmental Protection Agency, Environmental Monitoring and Support Lab., Cincinnati, Ohio.

6210 C.   Purge and Trap Packed-Column Gas Chromatographic/Mass Spectrometric Method II*

This method[1] is applicable to the determination of purgeable organic compounds† in finished drinking water, raw source water, or drinking water in any treatment stage. The method varies only slightly from Section 6210B, which is intended for use with wastewater samples.

1. General Discussion

a. *Principle:* See Section 6210B.1a.

b. *Interferences:* See Section 6210B.1b. If possible, use this method with a purge and trap system devoted to analysis of low-level samples.

Take special precautions to analyze for methylene chloride. Isolate the analytical and sample storage area from all atmospheric sources of methylene chloride: otherwise random background levels will result. Construct all gas chromatography carrier gas lines and purge-gas plumbing from stainless steel or copper tubing because methylene chloride will permeate through TFE tubing. Wear clean laboratory clothing not previously exposed to methylene chloride.

c. *Detection limits:* Method detection limits (MDLs)[2] are compound-dependent and vary with purging efficiency and concentration. In a single laboratory using reagent water and known additions of 1.5 µg/L, observed MDLs were in the range of 0.1 to 0.5 µg/L. The applicable concentration range of this method is compound- and instrument-dependent, but is approximately 0.2 to 200 µg/L. Compounds that are inefficiently purged from water will not be detected when present at low concentrations, but they can be measured with acceptable bias and precision when present in sufficient amounts. Determination of some geometrical isomers (i.e., xylenes) may be hampered by coelution.

d. *Safety:* The toxicity or carcinogenicity of each reagent has not been defined precisely. Benzene, carbon tetrachloride, bis-1-chloroisopropyl ether, 1,4-dichlorobenzene, 1,2-dichloroethane, hexachlorobutadiene, 1,1,2,2-tetrachloroethane, 1,1,2-trichloroethane, chloroform, 1,2-dibromoethane, tetrachloroethene, trichloroethene, and vinyl chloride have been classified tentatively as known or suspected human or mammalian carcinogens. Handle pure standard materials and stock standard so-

---

* Approved by Standard Methods Committee 1988. Accepted by U.S. Environmental Protection Agency as equivalent to EPA Method 524.

† Benzene, bromobenzene, bromochloromethane, bromodichloromethane, bromoform, bromomethane, *sec*-butylbenzene, *tert*-butylbenzene, carbon tetrachloride, chlorobenzene, chloroethane, chloroform, chloromethane, 2-chlorotoluene, 4-chlorotoluene, dibromochloromethane, 1,2-dibromo-3-chloropropane, 1,2-dibromoethane, dibromomethane, 1,2-dichlorobenzene, 1,3-dichlorobenzene, 1,4-dichlorobenzene, dichlorodifluoromethane, 1,1-dichloroethane, 1,2-dichloroethane, 1,1-dichloroethene, *cis*-1,2-dichloroethene, *trans*-1,2-dichloroethene, 1,2-dichloropropane, 1,3-dichloropropane, 2,2-dichloropropane, 1,1-dichloropropene, ethylbenzene, hexachlorobutadiene, isopropylbenzene, methylene chloride, *n*-propylbenzene, styrene, 1,1,1,2-tetrachloroethane, 1,1,2,2-tetrachloroethane, tetrachloroethene, toluene, 1,1,1-trichloroethane, 1,1,2-trichloroethane, trichloroethene, trichlorofluoromethane, 1,2,3-trichloropropane, vinyl chloride, *o*-xylene, *m*-xylene, and *p*-xylene.

lutions of these compounds in a hood and wear a NIOSH/MESA- approved toxic gas respirator when handling high concentrations.

2. Sampling and Storage

See Section 6010B.1.

3. Apparatus

a. Purge and trap system: The purge and trap system consists of three separate pieces of equipment: purging device, trap, and desorber. Several complete systems now are available commercially.

1) *Purging device,* designed to accept 25-mL samples with a water column at least 5 cm deep. For other requirements, see Section 6210B.3a1).

Needle spargers may be used instead of the glass frit shown in Figure 6210:1; however, in either case, introduce purge gas at a point ≤ 5 mm from base of water column.

2) *Trap,* at least 25 cm long and with an inside diameter of at least 3 mm, packed with the following minimum lengths of adsorbents: 1.0 cm of methyl silicone-coated packing, Section 6210B.4b2), 7.7 cm of 2,6-diphenylene oxide polymer, Section 6210B.4b1), 7.7 cm of silica gel, Section 6210B.4b3), and 7.7 cm of coconut charcoal, ¶ 4b below). If analysis is not to be made for dichlorodifluoromethane, the charcoal can be eliminated and the polymer section lengthened to 15 cm. The minimum specifications for the trap are illustrated in Figure 6210:6.

The use of the methyl-silicone-coated packing is recommended, but not mandatory. The packing serves a dual purpose of protecting the diphenylene oxide polymer adsorbant from aerosols and of insuring that it is fully enclosed within the heated

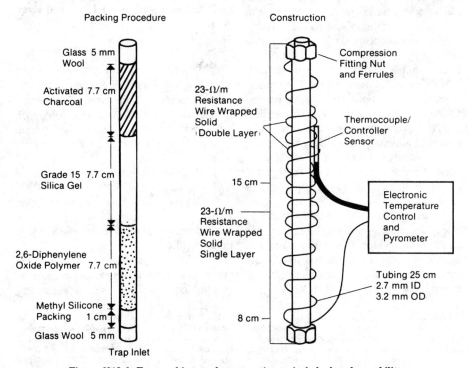

Packing Procedure

Glass 5 mm Wool
Activated 7.7 cm Charcoal
Grade 15 7.7 cm Silica Gel
2,6-Diphenylene Oxide Polymer 7.7 cm
Methyl Silicone Packing 1 cm
Glass Wool 5 mm
Trap Inlet

Construction

Compression Fitting Nut and Ferrules
23-Ω/m Resistance Wire Wrapped Solid (Double Layer)
Thermocouple/ Controller Sensor
15 cm
23-Ω/m Resistance Wire Wrapped Solid Single Layer
Electronic Temperature Control and Pyrometer
Tubing 25 cm 2.7 mm ID 3.2 mm OD
8 cm

Figure 6210:6. Trap packings and construction to include desorb capability.

zone of the trap, thus eliminating potential cold spots. Alternatively, silanized glass wool may be used as a spacer at the trap inlet.

Before initial use, condition trap overnight at 180°C by backflushing with an inert gas flow of at least 20 mL/min. Vent trap effluent to the room, not to the analytical column. Before daily use, condition trap for 10 min at 180°C with backflushing. The trap may be vented to the analytical column during daily conditioning; however, run the column through the temperature program before sample analysis.

3) *Desorber:* See Section 6210B.3*a*3). Trap failure is characterized by a pressure drop above 21 kPa across the trap during purging or by poor bromoform sensitivities.

b. Gas chromatograph:‡ See Section 6210B.3*b*.

During handling, packing, and programming, active sites can be exposed on the Carbopack-B packing, which can result in tailing peak geometry and poor resolution of many constituents. To protect the analytical column, pack the first 5 cm of column with 3% SP-1000 on Chromosorb-W (60/80 mesh) followed by the Carbopack-B packing. Condition the precolumn and Carbopack columns with carrier gas flow at 220°C overnight. Pneumatic shocks and rough treatment of packed columns will cause excessive fracturing of the Carbopack. If pressure above 415 kPa is required to obtain 40 mL/min carrier flow, repack column.

c. Mass spectrometer, capable of scanning from 35 to 450 amu every 7 s or less, utilizing 70-V (nominal) electron energy in the electron impact ionization mode, and producing a mass spectrum that meets all criteria in Table 6210:II when 50 ng or less

of 4-bromofluorobenzene is injected through the GC inlet. To ensure sufficient precision, the desired scan rate permits acquisition of at least five spectra while a sample component elutes from the gas chromatograph.

d. GC/MS interface: Use an all-glass enrichment device and an all-glass transfer line. Another enrichment device or transfer line can be substituted if the performance specifications described in ¶ 7 below can be achieved.

e. Data system: See Section 6210B.3*e*.

f. Syringes, 25-mL glass hypodermic with luerlok tip.

g. Syringe valves, two-way, with luer ends.

h. Microsyringes, 25-μL with a 5 cm × 0.15 mm ID, 22° bevel needle;§ also with 10- and 100-L capacity.

i. Syringes, 0.5-, 1.0-, and 5-mL, gastight with shutoff valve.

j. Bottles, 15-mL, with TFE-lined screw caps.

4. Reagents

a. Reagent water: See Section 6210B.4*a*.

b. Trap packing materials: See Section 6210B.4*b*. In addition, coconut charcoal, 6/20 mesh sieved to 26 mesh‖, is required.

c. Methanol, pesticide quality or equivalent.

d. Hydrochloric acid: HCl, 1 + 1.

e. Vinyl chloride, 99.9% pure.#

f. Standard stock solutions: See Section 6210B.4*d*.

g. Secondary dilution standards: See Section 6210B.4*e*.

h. Calibration standards: Use directions given in Section 6210B.4*g*, but prepare at least five concentration levels for each com-

---

‡ Gas chromatographic methods are extremely sensitive to the materials used. Mention of trade names by *Standard Methods* does not preclude the use of other existing or as-yet-undeveloped products that give *demonstrably* equivalent results.

§ Hamilton # 702N or equivalent.

‖ Barnebey Cheney, CA-580-26 lot M-2649, or equivalent.

Available from Ideal Gas Products, Inc., Edison, N.J. and from Matheson, East Rutherford, N.J. Certified mixtures of vinyl chloride in nitrogen at 1.0 and 10.0 ppm are available from several sources.

pound. More than one set of standards may be required.

i. Internal standard known-addition solution: Prepare a solution containing fluorobenzene and 1,2-dichlorobenzene-d$_4$ in methanol using the procedures described in Section 6210B.4*d* and *e*. Prepare the secondary dilution standard at a concentration of 25 μg/mL of each internal standard compound. Adding 10 μL of such a standard to 25.0 mL sample or calibration standard would yield a concentration equivalent to 10 μg/L.

j. BFB standard: Prepare a 25 μg/mL solution of bromofluorobenzene in methanol.

k. Laboratory control standard concentrate: Using standard stock solutions, prepare a solution containing each compound of interest at a concentration 500 times the MCL in methanol.

5. Procedure

a. Operating conditions: Table 6210:VII summarizes recommended operating conditions for the gas chromatograph. An example of the separation achieved is shown in Figure 6210:5.

b. GC/MS performance tests: Follow the procedure in Section 6210B.5*b* using 25 mL reagent water. Use a mass range of 35 to 300 amu, not 20 to 260 amu.

c. Calibration: Calibrate system daily after performance tests using the procedure of Section 6210B.5*c*.

The internal standard to be used is optional but aromatics usually are compared to 1,2-dichlorobenzene-d$_4$ and all other compounds are compared to the internal standard having the closest relative retention time.

To calibrate for vinyl chloride, use a certified gaseous mixture of vinyl chloride in nitrogen. Fill purging device with 25.0 mL reagent water or aqueous calibration standard. Start purging aqueous mixture. Inject a known volume (between 100 and 2000

TABLE 6210:VII. CHROMATOGRAPHIC CONDITIONS FOR VOLATILE ORGANIC COMPOUNDS ON PACKED COLUMNS

Compound	Retention Time *min*
Vinyl chloride	3.8
Dichlorodifluoromethane	3.8
Methylene chloride	6.4
Trichlorofluoromethane	8.3
1,1-Dichloroethene	9.0
Bromochloromethane	9.3
1,1-Dichloroethane	10.1
trans-1,2-Dichloroethene	10.8
Chloroform	11.4
Dibromomethane	12.1
1,2-Dichloroethane	12.1
2,2-Dichloropropane	12.7
1,1,1-Trichloroethane	13.4
Carbon tetrachloride	13.7
Bromodichloromethane	14.3
1,2-Dichloropropane	15.7
1,1-Dichloropropene	16.0
Trichloroethene	16.5
Benzene	17.0
Dibromochloromethane	17.1
1,2-Dibromoethane	17.9
1,3-Dichloropropane	18.4
Bromoform	19.8
1,1,2,2-Tetrachloroethane	22.1
Tetrachloroethene	22.2
Toluene	23.5
Chlorobenzene	24.6
1,2-Dibromo-3-chloropropane	25.8
Bromobenzene	26.7
Isopropylbenzene	28.5
m-Xylene	29.5
Styrene	29.7
n-Propylbenzene	30.7
o-Xylene	30.9
p-Xylene	30.9
t-Butylbenzene	31.5
2-Chlorotoluene	31.5
Hexachlorobutadiene	32.0
4-Chlorotoluene	32.5
sec-Butylbenzene	32.5
1,2-Dichlorobenzene	35.0
1,4-Dichlorobenzene	35.3

Column conditions: 2 m $\times$ 2 mm ID glass column packed with Carbopack B (60–80 mesh) coated with 1% SP-1000. Carrier gas: helium at flow of 30 mL/min. Column temperature held at 45°C for 3 min, then programmed at 8°C/min to 220°C and held until all compounds are eluted.

µL) of calibration gas (at room temperature) directly into purging device with a gastight syringe. Slowly inject gaseous sample through a septum seal at the top of purging device at 2000 µL/min. Do not inject standard through aqueous sample inlet needle. Inject gaseous standard before 5 min of the 11-min purge time have elapsed. Determine the aqueous equivalent concentration of vinyl chloride standard injected from the equation:

$$S = 0.51 \, (C)(V)$$

where:

S = aqueous equivalent concentration of vinyl chloride standard, µg/L,
C = concentration of gaseous standard, ppm (v/v), and
V = volume of standard injected, mL.

d. Sample analysis: Using two 25-mL syringes follow the procedure of Section 6210B.5*d*. Use purge chamber washes of 25 mL. Desorb compounds by backflushing the trap with an inert gas flow rate of 15 mL/min, not 20 to 60 mL/min.

Hold column temperature at 45°C for 3 min, then program at 8°C/min to 220°C and hold until all compounds elute.

When all sample components have been eluted, terminate mass spectrometer data acquisition and store data files. Use appropriate data output software to display full range mass spectra and appropriate extracted ion current profiles (EICPs). See Section 6210B.5*d*. If any ion abundance exceeds the system working range, dilute sample in second syringe with reagent water and analyze.

6. Calculation

When compound has been identified, base quantitation on integrated abundance from the EICP of the primary characteristic *m/z* given in Table 6210:VIII. If the sample produces an interference for the primary *m/z*, use a secondary characteristic *m/z* to quantitate.

Report results in micrograms per liter. Report all quality control data with sample results.

7. Quality Control

a. Quality control program: The analyst should be experienced in measuring purgeable organics at the low microgram-per-liter level. A minimum quality-control program consists of an initial demonstration of laboratory capability and an ongoing analysis of samples with known additions. Maintain records to document data quality. Compare ongoing data quality checks with established performance criteria to determine if results are acceptable. Analyze a quality control check standard to confirm that the operation is in control.

Make an initial demonstration of acceptable accuracy and precision as described in ¶ *b* below. If procedural modifications are made, repeat this initial demonstration.

Each day, analyze a reagent water blank to demonstrate that interferences from the analytical system are under control.

Demonstrate through the analyses of quality control check standards (¶ *c* below) that the measurement system is in control. Analyze check standards equivalent to 10% of all samples analyzed, with a minimum of two determinations per month.

Weekly, demonstrate the ability to analyze low-level samples as described in ¶ *d* below.

The laboratory reagent blank should represent a response of less than 0.1 µg/L.

b. Analyst proficiency check: Prepare a QC check sample concentrate containing each compound to be reported, at a concentration of 500 times the maximum contaminant level (MCL) or 5 µg/mL, whichever is smaller, in methanol. Prepare this check sample using stock standards prepared independently from those used for calibration. Analyze seven 25-mL check samples at 0.2 MCL or 2 µg/L. Produce

TABLE 6210:VIII. CHARACTERISTIC MASSES (m/z) FOR PURGEABLE ORGANICS

Compound	Primary Ion	Secondary Ions	Compound	Primary Ion	Secondary Ions
Benzene	78	—	1,2-Dichloropropane	63	112
Bromobenzene	156	77, 158	1,3-Dichloropropane	76	78
Bromochloromethane	128	49, 130	2,2-Dichloropropane	77	97
Bromodichloro-methane	83	85, 127	1,1-Dichloropropene	75	110, 77
			Ethylbenzene	91	106
Bromoform	173	175, 254	Hexachlorobutadiene	225	223, 227
Bromomethane	94	96	Isopropylbenzene	105	120
n-Butylbenzene	91	92, 134	p-Isopropyltoluene	119	134, 91
sec-Butylbenzene	105	134	Methylene chloride	84	86, 49
tert-Butylbenzene	119	91, 134	Naphthalene	128	—
Carbon tetrachloride	117	119	n-Propylbenzene	91	120
Chlorobenzene	112	77, 114	Styrene	104	78
Chloroethane	64	66	1,1,1-Tetrachloro-ethane	131	133, 119
Chloroform	83	85			
Chloromethane	50	52	1,1,2,2-Tetrachloro-ethane	83	131, 85
2-Chlorotoluene	91	126			
4-Chlorotoluene	91	126	Tetrachloroethene	166	168, 129
Dibromochloro-methane	129	127	Toluene	92	91
			1,1,1-Trichloroethane	97	99, 61
1,2-Dibromo-3-chloro-propane	75	155, 157	1,1,2-Trichloroethane	83	97, 85
			Trichloroethene	95	130, 132
1,2-Dibromoethane	107	109, 188	Trichlorofluoro-methane	101	103
Dibromomethane	93	95, 174			
1,2-Dichlorobenzene	146	111, 148	1,2,3-Trichloropropane	75	77
1,3-Dichlorobenzene	146	111, 148	Vinyl chloride	62	64
1,4-Dichlorobenzene	146	111, 148	m-Xylene	106	91
Dichlorodifluoro-methane	85	87	o-Xylene	106	91
			p-Xylene	106	91
1,1-Dichloroethane	63	65, 83			
1,2-Dichloroethane	62	98	Internal standards/surrogates:		
1,1-Dichloroethene	96	61, 63			
cis-1,2-Dichloroethene	96	61, 98	Fluorobenzene	96	70
trans-1,2-Dichloro-ethene	96	61, 98	1,2-Dichlorobenzene-d$_4$	150	115, 152
			p-Bromofluorobenzene	95	174, 176

each sample by injecting 10 μL check sample concentrate into 25 mL reagent water in a glass syringe through the syringe valve.

Calculate average recovery ($\overline{X}$), μg/L, and standard deviation of recovery (s), μg/L, for each compound. Calculate the MDL for each compound.[2] The calculated MDL should be less than the addition level. For each compound, ($\overline{X}$) should be between 90% and 110% of the true value. Additionally, s should be $\leq 35\%$ of $\overline{X}$. If s and $\overline{X}$ for all compounds meet the criteria, system performance is acceptable and sample analysis may begin. If any s exceeds the precision limit or if any $\overline{X}$ falls outside the range for recovery, system performance is unacceptable for that compound.

Because of the large number of compounds, a substantial probability exists that one or more will fail at least one of the acceptance criteria when all compounds are analyzed. When results for one or more of the compounds fail at least one of the acceptance criteria, repeat analysis of seven 25-mL check samples for failed compounds.

c. Quality-control check standard analysis: Regularly demonstrate that the measurement system is in control by analyzing a quality control sample for all compounds of interest at the MCL or 10 μg/L, whichever is smaller. Prepare a check standard by adding 50 μL of QC check sample concentrate to 25 mL reagent water in a glass syringe. Analyze and calculate recovery for each compound. Acceptable recovery is between 60% and 140% of the expected value. If recovery for any compound falls outside the designated range, the compound has failed the acceptance criteria and reanalysis is required.

d. Low-level analysis: Weekly demonstrate the ability to analyze low-level samples. Prepare a low-level check sample by adding 10 μL QC check sample concentrate to 25 mL reagent water. Analyze and calculate recovery, which should be between 60% and 140% of the expected

value. If a compound fails the test, reanalyze for that compound. Repeated failure confirms a general problem with the measurement system. If this occurs, locate and correct the problem and repeat the test for all compounds of interest.

e. Additional quality-assurance practices: Other desirable practices depend on the needs of the laboratory and the nature of the samples. Field duplicates may be analyzed to assess precision of environmental measurements. Whenever possible, analyze standard reference materials and participate in relevant performance evaluation studies.

8. Precision and Bias

This method was tested in a single laboratory using reagent water with additions at concentrations between 1 and 5 μg/L.[1] Single-operator precision and bias data are presented for some selected compounds in Table 6210:IX. Some method detection limits have been calculated from data collected in three laboratories.[1,3]

9. References

1. U.S. ENVIRONMENTAL PROTECTION AGENCY. 1985. Methods for the Determination of Organic Compounds in Finished Drinking Water and Raw Source Water (rev. Sept. 1986). Modified from A. Alford-Stevens, J.W. Eichelberger & W.L. Budde. 1983. Purgeable organic compounds in water by gas chromatography/mass spectrometry, Method 524. Environmental Monitoring and Support Lab., Cincinnati, Ohio.
2. GLASER, J.A., D.L. FOERST, G.D. MCKEE, S.A. QUAVE & W.L. BUDDE. 1981. Trace analyses for wastewaters. *Environ. Sci. Technol.* 15:1426.
3. SLATER, R.W. 1985. Method Detection Limits for Drinking Water Volatiles. Unpublished report, U.S. Environmental Protection Agency, Environmental Monitoring and Support Lab., Cincinnati, Ohio.

TABLE 6210:IX. SINGLE-LABORATORY BIAS AND PRECISION DATA FOR VOLATILE ORGANIC
COMPOUNDS IN REAGENT WATER (PACKED COLUMN)

Compound	Conc. Tested μg/L	Number of Samples	Average Conc. Measured μg/L	Standard Deviation μg/L	Rel. Std. Dev. %
Benzene	1.0	8	0.97	0.036	3.6
Bromobenzene	1.0	8	0.92	0.042	4.6
Bromodichloromethane	1.5	8	1.43	0.096	6.7
Bromoform	2.5	8	2.36	0.23	9.7
Carbon tetrachloride	1.0	8	0.88	0.098	11.1
Chlorobenzene	1.0	8	1.02	0.047	4.6
Chloroform	1.0	8	1.03	0.086	8.4
Dibromochloromethane	1.5	8	1.49	0.10	7.0
1,2-Dibromo-3-chloropropane	3.0	8	3.4	0.63	18.2
1,2-Dibromoethane	1.0	8	0.93	0.13	13.6
Dibromomethane	1.0	8	0.94	0.11	11.4
1,2-Dichlorobenzene	5.0	8	4.95	0.35	7.1
1,4-Dichlorobenzene	5.0	8	5.27	0.72	13.6
Dichlorodifluoromethane	1.0	8	0.96	0.11	11.9
1,1-Dichloroethane	1.0	8	1.05	0.060	5.9
1,2-Dichloroethane	1.0	8	0.97	0.077	7.9
1,1-Dichloroethene	1.0	8	1.09	0.066	6.1
trans-1,2-Dichloroethene	1.0	8	0.98	0.066	6.8
1,2-Dichloropropane	1.0	8	1.01	0.060	5.9
1,3-Dichloropropane	1.0	8	1.00	0.033	3.4
Methylene chloride	1.0	7	0.99	0.045	4.5
Styrene	1.0	8	1.06	0.066	6.2
1,1,2,2-Tetrachloroethane	1.0	8	1.11	0.14	12.8
Tetrachloroethene	1.0	8	0.93	0.10	10.9
Toluene	1.0	8	1.05	0.043	4.1
1,1,1-Trichloroethane	1.0	8	1.05	0.093	8.8
Trichloroethene	1.0	8	0.90	0.12	13.6
Trichlorofluoromethane	1.0	7	1.09	0.072	6.6
Vinyl chloride	1.0	8	0.98	0.11	10.8
o-Xylene	1.0	8	1.02	0.068	6.7
p-Xylene	1.0	8	1.11	0.047	4.2

6210 D.   Purge and Trap Capillary-Column Gas Chromatographic/Mass Spectrometric Method*

This procedure[1] is applicable to determining those compounds listed for Method 6210C and the following: *n*-butylbenzene, naphthalene, *p*-isopropyltoluene, 1,2,3-trichlorobenzene, 1,2,4-trichlorobenzene, 1,2,4-trimethylbenzene, and 1,3,5-trimethylbenzene. It differs primarily in the type of gas chromatographic column used, requiring either a wide-bore or a narrow-bore capillary column for analysis.

1. General Discussion

See Section 6210C.1 and Tables 6210:X and XI. Detection limits in this method were observed to be in the range of 0.02 to 0.2 µg/L for known additions of 0.1 to 0.5 µg/L.

2. Sampling and Storage

See Section 6010B.1.

3. Apparatus

Use the equipment specified in Section 6210C.3 with one of the columns described below. The capillary interface is required only with a narrow-bore column (Column 3).

a. Gas chromatographic column:

1) *Column 1:* 60-m-long × 0.75-mm-ID VOCOL† wide-bore capillary column with 1.5-µm film thickness.

2) *Column 2:* 30-m-long × 0.53-mm-ID DB-624‡ mega-bore capillary column with 3-µm film thickness.

3) *Column 3:* 30-m-long × 0.32-mm-ID

fused silica capillary column coated with Durabond DB-5‡ with 1-µm film thickness.

b. Mass spectrometer, capable of scanning from 35 to 300 amu every 2 s or less.

c. Capillary interface, to connect the purge and trap concentrator to the capillary column of the gas chromatograph. This interface condenses desorbed materials on an uncoated fused silica pre-column and when flash heated, transfers compounds to the analytical capillary column. In a stream of liquid nitrogen the fused silica is held at −150°C for cryofocusing. After desorption, the interface is heated to 250°C in 15 s or less.

4. Reagents

See Section 6210C.4.

5. Procedure

Retention times for wide-bore and narrow-bore columns are given in Tables 6210:X and XI, respectively. Follow the procedure specified in Section 6210C.5 with the following exceptions:

a. Desorption for wide-bore capillary column: Interface column through all-glass jet separator and desorb as specified in Section 6210C.5*d*. Hold column temperature at 10°C for 5 min, then program at 6°C/min to 160°C and hold until all compounds elute. See Figures 6210:7 and 8.

b. Desorption for narrow-bore capillary column: A jet separator usually is not required to interface column. Purge as specified in Section 6210B.5*d* for 11 min. Attach trap to cryogenically cooled interface at −150°C and adjust purge and trap system to desorb mode. Introduce trapped

---

* Approved by Standard Methods Committee 1988. Accepted by U.S. Environmental Protection Agency as equivalent to EPA Method 524.

† Supelco, Inc. or equivalent.

‡ J&W Scientific, Inc. or equivalent.

TABLE 6210:X. CHROMATOGRAPHIC CONDITIONS FOR VOLATILE ORGANIC COMPOUNDS ON
WIDE-BORE CAPILLARY COLUMNS

| | Retention Time min | |
Compound	Column 1*	Column 2†
Dichlorodifluoromethane	1.55	0.70
Chloromethane	1.63	0.73
Vinyl chloride	1.71	0.79
Bromomethane	2.01	0.96
Chloroethane	2.09	1.02
Trichlorofluoromethane	2.27	1.19
1,1-Dichloroethene	2.89	1.57
Methylene chloride	3.60	2.06
trans-1,2-Dichloroethene	3.98	2.36
1,1-Dichloroethane	4.85	2.93
2,2-Dichloropropane	6.01	3.80
cis-1,2-Dichloroethene	6.19	3.90
Chloroform	6.40	4.80
Bromochloromethane	6.74	4.38
1,1,1-Trichloroethane	7.27	4.84
Carbon tetrachloride	7.61	5.26
1,1-Dichloropropene	7.68	5.29
Benzene	8.23	5.67
1,2-Dichloroethane	8.40	5.83
Trichloroethene	9.59	7.27
1,2-Dichloropropane	10.09	7.66
Bromodichloromethane	10.59	8.49
Dibromomethane	10.65	7.93
Toluene	12.43	10.00
1,1,2-Trichloroethane	13.41	11.05
Tetrachloroethene	13.74	11.15
1,3-Dichloropropane	14.04	11.31
Dibromochloromethane	14.39	11.85
1,2-Dibromoethane	14.73	11.83
1-Chlorohexane	15.46	13.29
Chlorobenzene	15.76	13.01
1,1,1,2-Tetrachloroethane	15.94	13.33
Ethylbenzene	15.99	13.39
p-Xylene	16.12	13.69
m-Xylene	16.17	13.68
o-Xylene	17.11	14.52
Styrene	17.31	14.60
Bromoform	17.93	14.88
Isopropylbenzene	18.06	15.46
1,1,2,2-Tetrachloroethane	18.72	16.35
Bromobenzene	18.95	15.86
1,2,3-Trichloropropane	19.02	16.23
n-Propylbenzene	19.06	16.41
2-Chlorotoluene	19.34	16.42
1,3,5-Trimethylbenzene	19.47	16.90
4-Chlorotoluene	19.50	16.72

TABLE 6210:X, CONT.

Compound	Retention Time min	
	Column 1*	Column 2†
tert-Butylbenzene	20.28	17.57
1,2,4-Trimethylbenzene	20.34	17.70
sec-Butylbenzene	20.79	18.09
p-Isopropyltoluene	21.20	18.52
1,3-Dichlorobenzene	21.22	18.14
1,4-Dichlorobenzene	21.55	18.39
n-Butylbenzene	22.22	19.49
1,2-Dichlorobenzene	22.52	19.17
1,2-Dibromo-3-chloropropane	24.53	21.08
1,2,4-Trichlorobenzene	26.55	23.08
Hexachlorobutadiene	26.99	23.68
Naphthalene	27.17	23.52
1,2,3-Trichlorobenzene	27.78	24.18
Internal standards/surrogates:		
Fluorobenzene	8.81	6.45
p-Bromofluorobenzene	18.63	15.71
1,2-Dichlorobenzene-d₄	22.26	19.14

* Column 1 — 60 m × 0.75 mm ID VOCOL capillary column. Hold at 10°C for 5 min, then program to 160°C at 6°/min.
† Column 2 — 30 m × 0.53 mm ID DB-624 mega-bore capillary column. Hold at 10°C for 5 min, then program to 160°C at 6°/min.

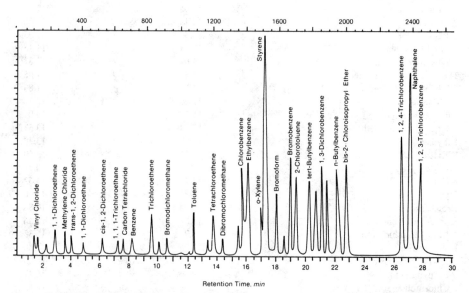

Figure 6210:7. Gas chromatogram of volatile organics (wide-bore capillary column). Column: 60 m × 0.75 mm ID VOCOL capillary; program: 10°C for 5 min, 6°C/min to 160°C.

TABLE 6210:XI. CHROMATOGRAPHIC CONDITIONS FOR VOLATILE ORGANIC COMPOUNDS ON NARROW-BORE CAPILLARY COLUMN

Compound	Retention Time min Column 3*
Dichlorodifluoromethane	0.88
Chloromethane	0.97
Vinyl chloride	1.04
Bromomethane	1.29
Chloroethane	1.45
Trichlorofluoromethane	1.77
1,1-Dichloroethene	2.33
Methylene chloride	2.66
trans-1,2-Dichloroethene	3.54
1,1-Dichloroethane	4.03
cis-1,2-Dichloroethene	5.07
2,2-Dichloropropane	5.31
Chloroform	5.55
Bromochloromethane	5.63
1,1,1-Trichloroethane	6.76
1,2-Dichloroethane	7.00
1,1-Dichloropropene	7.16
Carbon tetrachloride	7.41
Benzene	7.41
1,2-Dichloropropane	8.94
Trichloroethene	9.02
Dibromoethane	9.09
Bromodichloromethane	9.34
Toluene	11.51
1,1,2-Trichloroethane	11.99
1,3-Dichloropropane	12.48
Dibromochloromethane	12.80
Tetrachloroethene	13.20
1,2-Dibromoethane	13.60
Chlorobenzene	14.33
1,1,1,2-Tetrachloroethane	14.73
Ethylbenzene	14.73
p-Xylene	15.30
m-Xylene	15.30
Bromoform	15.70
o-Xylene	15.78
Styrene	15.78
1,1,2,2-Tetrachloroethane	15.78
1,2,3-Trichloropropane	16.26
Isopropylbenzene	16.42
Bromobenzene	16.42
2-Chlorotoluene	16.74
n-Propylbenzene	16.82
4-Chlorotoluene	16.82
1,3,5-Trimethylbenzene	16.99
tert-Butylbenzene	17.31

TABLE 6210:XI, CONT.

Compound	Retention Time min Column 3*
1,2,4-Trimethylbenzene	17.31
sec-Butylbenzene	17.47
1,3-Dichlorobenzene	17.47
p-Isopropyltoluene	17.63
1,4-Dichlorobenzene	17.63
1,2-Dichlorobenzene	17.79
n-Butylbenzene	17.95
1,2-Dibromo-3-chloropropane	18.03
1,2,4-Trichlorobenzene	18.84
Naphthalene	19.07
Hexachlorobutadiene	19.24
1,2,3-Trichlorobenzene	19.24
Internal standard:	
Fluorobenzene	8.81

* Column 3 — 30 m × 0.32 mm ID DB-5 capillary column. Hold at 10°C for 5 min, program at 6°C/min for 10 min, then program to 145°C at 15°C/min.

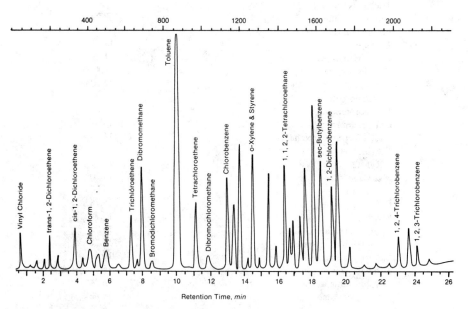

Figure 6210:8. Gas chromatogram of volatile organics (mega-bore capillary column). Column 2: 30 m long × 0.53 mm ID DB-624 mega-bore column; program: 10°C for 5 min, 6°C/min to 160°C.

materials to interface by rapidly heating trap to 180°C while backflushing trap with an inert gas at 4 mL/min for 5.0 ± 0.1 min while introducing sample into interface, empty purging device using sample syringe, rinse twice with 25 mL reagent water; leave syringe valve open to vent purge gas. After desorbing for 5 min, flash heat interface to 250°C to transfer sample to chromatographic column. Hold column temperature at 10°C for 5 min, program at 6°C/min to 70°C, then at 15°C/min to 145°C.

After desorbing sample for 5 min, recondition trap by returning system to purge mode. After about 15 min of heating at 180°C, cool for next sample. See Figure 6210:9.

6. Calculation

See Section 6210C.6.

7. Quality Control

See Section 6210C.7.

8. Precision and Bias

This method was tested in a single laboratory using a wide-bore capillary column and reagent water with additions at concentrations between 0.5 and 10 μg/L.[2] Single-operator precision and bias data are presented in Table 6210:XII.

The method was similarly tested using a cryofocused narrow-bore column with additions between 0.1 and 0.5 μg/L.[1] Bias and precision data are presented in Table 6210:XIII.

9. References

1. U.S. ENVIRONMENTAL PROTECTION AGENCY. 1985. Methods for the Determination of Organic Compounds in Finished Drinking Water

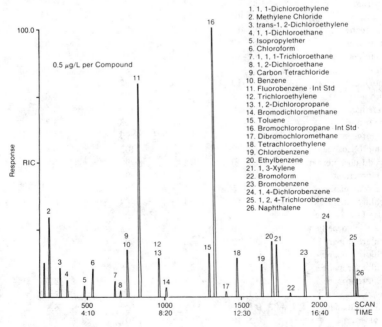

Figure 6210:9. Chromatogram of test mixture (narrow-bore capillary column).

and Raw Source Water (rev. Sept. 1986). Modified from A. Alford-Stevens, J.W. Eichelberger & W.L. Budde. 1983. Purgeable organic compounds in water by gas chromatography/mass spectrometry, Method 524. Environmental Monitoring and Support Lab., Cincinnati, Ohio.

2. SLATER, R.W. 1986. Method Detection Limits for Drinking Water Volatiles. Unpublished report, U.S. Environmental Protection Agency, Environmental Monitoring and Support Lab., Cincinnati, Ohio.

TABLE 6210:XII. SINGLE-LABORATORY BIAS AND PRECISION DATA FOR VOLATILE ORGANIC COMPOUNDS IN REAGENT WATER (WIDE-BORE CAPILLARY COLUMN)

Compound	Conc. Range $\mu g/L$	Number of Samples	Recovery* %	Standard Deviation of Recovery† %	Relative Std. Dev. %
Benzene	0.1–10	31	97	5.5	5.7
Bromobenzene	0.1–10	30	100	5.5	5.5
Bromochloromethane	0.5–10	24	90	5.7	6.4
Bromodichloromethane	0.1–10	30	95	5.7	6.1
Bromoform	0.5–10	18	101	6.4	6.3
Bromomethane	0.5–10	18	95	7.8	8.2
n-Butylbenzene	0.5–10	18	100	7.6	7.6
sec-Butylbenzene	0.5–10	16	100	7.6	7.6
tert-Butylbenzene	0.5–10	18	102	7.4	7.3
Carbon tetrachloride	0.5–10	24	84	7.4	8.8
Chlorobenzene	0.1–10	31	98	5.8	5.9
Chloroethane	0.5–10	24	89	8.0	9.0
Chloroform	0.5–10	24	90	5.5	6.1
Chloromethane	0.5–10	23	93	8.3	8.9
2-Chlorotoluene	0.1–10	31	90	5.6	6.2
4-Chlorotoluene	0.1–10	31	99	8.2	8.3
1,2-Dibromo-3-chloropropane	0.5–10	24	83	16.6	19.9
Dibromochloromethane	0.1–10	31	92	6.5	7.0
1,2-Dibromoethane	0.5–10	24	102	4.0	3.9
Dibromoethane	0.5–10	24	100	5.6	5.6
1,2-Dichlorobenzene	0.1–10	31	93	5.8	6.2
1,3-Dichlorobenzene	0.5–10	24	99	6.8	6.9
1,4-Dichlorobenzene	0.2–20	31	103	6.6	6.4
Dichlorodifluoromethane	0.5–10	18	90	6.9	7.7
1,1-Dichloroethane	0.5–10	24	96	5.1	5.3
1,2-Dichloroethane	0.1–10	31	95	5.1	5.4
1,1-Dichloroethene	0.1–10	34	94	6.3	6.7
cis-1,2-Dichloroethene	0.5–10	18	101	6.7	6.7
trans-1,2-Dichloroethene	0.1–10	30	93	5.2	5.6
1,2-Dichloropropane	0.1–10	30	97	5.9	6.1
1,3-Dichloropropane	0.1–10	31	96	5.7	6.0
2,2-Dichloropropane	0.5–10	12	86	14.6	16.9
1,1-Dichloropropene	0.5–10	18	98	8.7	8.9
Ethylbenzene	0.1–10	31	99	8.4	8.6
Hexachlorobutadiene	0.5–10	18	100	6.8	6.8
Isopropylbenzene	0.5–10	16	101	7.7	7.6
p-Isopropyltoluene	0.1–10	23	99	6.7	6.7

TABLE 6210:XII, CONT.

Compound	Conc. Range μg/L	Number of Samples	Recovery* %	Standard Deviation of Recovery† %	Relative Std. Dev. %
Methylene chloride	0.1–10	30	95	5.0	5.3
Naphthalene	0.1–100	31	104	8.6	8.2
n-Propylbenzene	0.1–10	31	100	5.8	5.8
Styrene	0.1–100	39	102	7.3	7.2
1,1,1,2-Tetrachloroethane	0.5–10	24	90	6.1	6.8
1,1,2,2-Tetrachloroethane	0.1–10	30	91	5.7	6.3
Tetrachloroethene	0.5–10	24	89	6.0	6.8
Toluene	0.5–10	18	102	8.1	8.0
1,2,3-Trichlorobenzene	0.5–10	18	109	9.4	8.6
1,2,4-Trichlorobenzene	0.5–10	18	108	9.0	8.3
1,1,1-Trichloroethane	0.5–10	18	98	7.9	8.1
1,1,2-Trichloroethane	0.5–10	18	104	7.6	7.3
Trichloroethene	0.5–10	24	90	6.5	7.3
Trichlorofluoromethane	0.5–10	24	89	7.2	8.1
1,2,3-Trichloropropane	0.5–10	16	108	15.6	14.4
1,2,4-Trimethylbenzene	0.5–10	18	99	8.0	8.1
1,3,5-Trimethylbenzene	0.5–10	23	92	6.8	7.4
Vinyl chloride	0.5–10	18	98	6.5	6.7
o-Xylene	0.1–31	18	103	7.4	7.2
m-Xylene	0.1–10	31	97	6.3	6.5
p-Xylene	0.5–10	18	104	8.0	7.7

* Recovery was calculated using internal standard of fluorobenzene.
† Standard deviation was calculated by pooling data from three concentration levels.

TABLE 6210:XIII. SINGLE-LABORATORY BIAS AND PRECISION DATA FOR VOLATILE ORGANIC
COMPOUNDS IN REAGENT WATER
(NARROW-BORE CAPILLARY COLUMN)

Compound	Conc. $\mu g/L$	Number of Samples	Recovery* %	Standard Deviation $\mu g/L$	Rel. Std. Dev. %
Benzene	0.1	7	99	6.2	6.3
Bromobenzene	0.5	7	97	7.4	7.6
Bromochloromethane	0.5	7	97	5.8	6.0
Bromodichloromethane	0.1	7	100	4.6	4.6
Bromoform	0.5	7	101	5.4	5.3
Bromomethane	0.5	7	99	7.1	7.2
n-Butylbenzene	0.5	7	94	6.0	6.4
sec-Butylbenzene	0.5	7	110	7.1	6.5
tert-Butylbenzene	0.5	7	110	2.5	2.3
Carbon tetrachloride	0.1	7	108	6.8	6.3
Chlorobenzene	0.1	7	91	5.8	6.4
Chloroethane	0.1	7	100	5.8	5.8
Chloroform	0.1	7	105	3.2	3.0
Chloromethane	0.5	7	101	4.7	4.7
2-Chlorotoluene	0.5	7	99	4.6	4.6
4-Chlorotoluene	0.5	7	96	7.0	7.3
1,2-Dibromo-3-chloropropane	0.5	7	92	10.0	10.9
Dibromochloromethane	0.1	7	99	5.6	5.7
1,2-Dibromoethane	0.5	7	97	5.6	5.8
Dibromoethane	0.5	7	93	5.6	6.0
1,2-Dichlorobenzene	0.1	7	97	3.5	3.6
1,3-Dichlorobenzene	0.1	7	101	6.0	5.9
1,4-Dichlorobenzene	0.1	7	106	6.5	6.1
Dichlorodifluoromethane	0.1	7	99	8.8	8.9
1,1-Dichloroethane	0.5	7	98	6.2	6.3
1,2-Dichloroethane	0.1	7	100	6.3	6.3
1,1-Dichloroethene	0.1	7	95	9.0	9.5
cis-1,2 Dichloroethene	0.1	7	100	3.7	3.7
trans-1,2-Dichloroethene	0.1	7	98	7.2	7.3
1,2-Dichloropropane	0.5	7	96	6.0	6.3
1,3-Dichloropropane	0.5	7	99	5.8	5.9
2,2-Dichloropropane	0.5	7	99	4.9	4.9
1,1-Dichloropropene	0.5	7	102	7.4	7.3
Ethylbenzene	0.5	7	99	5.2	5.3
Hexachlorobutadiene	0.5	7	100	6.7	6.7
Isopropylbenzene	0.5	7	102	6.4	6.3
p-Isopropyltoluene	0.5	7	113	13.0	11.5
Methylene chloride	0.5	7	97	13.0	13.4
Naphthalene	0.5	7	98	7.2	7.3
n-Propylbenzene	0.5	7	99	6.6	6.7
Styrene	0.5	7	96	19.0	19.8
1,1,1,2-Tetrachloroethane	0.5	7	100	4.7	4.7
1,1,2,2-Tetrachloroethane	0.5	7	100	12.0	12.0
Tetrachloroethene	0.1	7	96	5.0	5.2
Toluene	0.5	7	100	5.9	5.9

TABLE 6210:XIII, CONT.

Compound	Conc. $\mu g/L$	Number of Samples	Recovery* %	Standard Deviation $\mu g/L$	Rel. Std. Dev. %
1,2,3-Trichlorobenzene	0.5	7	102	8.9	8.7
1,2,4-Trichlorobenzene	0.5	7	91	16.0	17.6
1,1,1-Trichloroethane	0.5	7	100	4.0	4.0
1,1,2-Trichloroethane	0.5	7	102	4.9	4.8
Trichloroethene	0.1	7	104	2.0	1.9
Trichlorofluoromethane	0.1	7	97	4.6	4.7
1,2,3-Trichloropropane	0.5	7	96	6.5	6.8
1,2,4-Trimethylbenzene	0.5	7	96	6.5	6.8
1,3,5-Trimethylbenzene	0.5	7	101	4.2	4.2
Vinyl chloride	0.1	7	104	0.2	0.2
o-Xylene	0.5	7	106	7.5	7.1
m-Xylene	0.5	7	106	4.6	4.3
p-Xylene	0.5	7	97	6.1	6.3

* Recovery was calculated using internal standard of fluorobenzene.

6232 TRIHALOMETHANES

6232 A. Introduction

1. Sources and Significance

The trihalomethane (THM) compounds have been found in most chlorinated water supplies in the United States; typically they are produced in the treatment process as a result of chlorination. The formation of these compounds is a function of precursor concentration, contact time, chlorine dose, and pH. Toxicological studies suggest that chloroform is a potential human carcinogen. Consequently, total trihalomethanes are being regulated in potable waters.

2. Selection of Method

Several methods are available for measurement of the trihalomethanes. Some of these are specific for these compounds and others have a much broader spectrum. Method 6232B is a simple liquid-liquid extraction gas chromatographic (GC) method that is highly sensitive and very precise for these compounds. Method C refers to purge and trap gas chromatographic/mass spectrometric (GC/MS) methods that can detect not only THMs but also a wide variety of other compounds. All of these methods have approximately the same sensitivity for the trihalomethanes; method choice depends on availability of equipment, operator choice, and the list of desired target compounds. In addition, closed-loop stripping analysis can be used for several of these compounds (see Section 6040).

6232 B. Liquid-Liquid Extraction Gas Chromatographic Method*

This method[1-3] is applicable only to the determination of four trihalomethanes (THMs), i.e., chloroform, bromodichloromethane, dibromochloromethane, and bromoform in finished drinking water, drinking water during intermediate stages of treatment, and the raw source water. For other compounds or sample sources, collect precision and bias data on actual samples[4] and provide qualitative confirmation of results by gas chromatography/mass spectrometry (GC/MS) to demonstrate the usefulness of the method.

Make qualitative analyses using GC/MS[5] or the purge and trap method[6] to char-

---

* Approved by Standard Methods Committee, 1987. Accepted by U.S. Environmental Protection Agency as equivalent to EPA Method 501.2.

acterize each raw source water if peaks appear as interferences in the analysis.

1. General Discussion

a. Principle: Sample is extracted once with solvent and the extract is injected into a gas chromatograph equipped with a linearized electron capture detector for separation and analysis. Extraction and analysis time is 10 to 50 min per sample, depending on analytical conditions.

Confirmatory evidence is obtained by using dissimilar columns and temperature programming. When component concentrations are sufficiently high (> 50 $\mu g/L$), halogen-specific detectors may be used for improved specificity. Unequivocal confirmatory analyses at high levels (> 50 $\mu g/L$) can be made by using a mass spectrometer instead of the electron capture detector. At levels below 50 $\mu g/L$, only the purge and trap technique using GC/MS can provide unequivocal confirmation.[5,6]

Standards added to organic-free water and samples are extracted and analyzed identically to compensate for possible extraction losses.

The concentrations of the trihalomethanes are summed and reported as total trihalomethanes in micrograms per liter.

See Section 6010 for discussion of gas chromatographic principles.

b. Interferences: Impurities contained in the extracting solvent usually account for most analytical problems. Analyze solvent blanks before using a new bottle of solvent to extract samples. Make indirect daily checks on the extracting solvent by monitoring the sample blanks. Whenever an interference is noted in the sample blank, reanalyze the extracting solvent. Discard extraction solvent if a high level (> 10 $\mu g/L$) of interfering compounds is traced to it. Low-level interferences usually can be removed by distillation or column chromatography;[7] however, it usually is more economical to obtain a new solvent or se-

lect an approved alternative solvent. Interference-free solvent is defined as a solvent containing less than 0.4 $\mu g/L$ individual trihalomethane interference. Protect interference-free solvents by storing in a nonlaboratory area known to be free of organochlorine solvents. *Do not subtract blank values as a correction.*

Accidental sample contamination has been attributed to diffusion of volatile organics through the septum seal on a sample bottle during shipment and storage. Use the sample blank to monitor for this problem.

This liquid-liquid extraction technique efficiently extracts a wide boiling range of nonpolar organic compounds and also extracts the polar organic components of the sample with varying efficiencies. To analyze rapidly for trihalomethanes with sensitivities in the low microgram-per-liter range, use the semi-specific electron capture detector and chromatographic columns that have relatively poor resolving power. Because of these concessions, the probability of encountering chromatographic interferences is high. Trihalomethanes are primarily products of the chlorination process and seldom appear in raw source water. The absence of peaks with retention times similar to the trihalomethanes in raw source water analysis is evidence of an interference-free finished drinking water analysis. Because of these possible interferences, analyze a representative raw source water when analyzing finished drinking water. When potential interferences are noted in the raw source water, use the alternate chromatographic columns to reanalyze the sample set. If interferences still are noted, make confirmatory qualitative identifications as directed in ¶ *1a.* If the peaks are confirmed to be other than trihalomethanes and they add significantly to the total trihalomethane value in the finished drinking water, analyze sample set by the purge and trap method.

For further information on interferences in gas chromatographic methods, see Section 6010C.

c. Detection limits: The method is useful for trihalomethane concentrations from approximately 0.5 to 200 μg/L. Actual detection limits are highly dependent on the characteristics of the gas chromatographic system used.

2. Sampling and Storage

See Section 6010B.1.

Do not add any preservatives at the time of sample collection if maximum trihalomethane formation is to be measured. If chemical stabilization is not used at time of sampling, add the reducing agent just before extracting the sample.[8,9]

The raw source water sample history should resemble that of the finished drinking water. Take into account the average retention time of the finished drinking water within the water plant when sampling the raw source water.

For septum-seal screw-cap bottles, open bottle and fill to overflowing, place on a level surface, position TFE side of septum seal on convex sample meniscus, and screw cap on tightly. Invert sample and lightly tap cap on a solid surface. The absence of entrapped air indicates a successful seal. If bubbles are present, open bottle, add a few more drops of sample and reseal as above.

Store blanks and samples, collected at a given site (sample set), together in a protected area known to be free from contamination. A sample set is defined as all samples collected at a given site. At a water treatment plant, duplicate raw source water, duplicate finished water, and duplicate sample blanks comprise the sample set. When samples are collected and stored under these conditions, no measurable loss of trihalomethanes has been detected over extended periods of time.[8] If possible, analyze samples within 14 d of collection.

For samples collected soon after chlo-rination, quenching with reducing agent may not be sufficient to prevent formation of THMs completely because of hydrolysis of intermediates. In that case, acidification is necessary and consistent with the recommended preservation techniques.

3. Apparatus

a. Extraction vessel:

1) For sample that does not form an emulsion, use 14-mL (total volume) screw-cap vial† with a TFE-faced silicone septum.‡

2) For sample that forms emulsions (turbid source water), use 15-mL screw-cap centrifuge tube§ with a TFE cap liner.

Prepare extraction flasks according to directions for sample bottles, ¶ 2.

b. Microsyringes, 10-, 100-μL.

c. Microsyringe, 25-μL with 5.08-cm × 0.02-cm needle.‖

d. Syringes, 10-mL glass hypodermic with luerlok top (2 each).#

e. Syringe valve, two-way with luer ends (2 each).#

f. Pipet, 2.0-mL transfer.

g. Volumetric flasks, glass-stoppered, 10 and 100 mL.

h. Gas chromatograph, preferably temperature-programmable, with linearized electron capture detector. See ¶ *i*3), below.

*i. Chromatographic columns:***

1) 4-mm ID × 2 m long glass packed with 3% SP-1000 on Supelcoport (100/120 mesh) operated at 50°C with 60 mL/min flow. See Figure 6232:1 for a sample chromatogram and Table 6232:I for retention data.

2) 2-mm ID × 2 m long glass packed

† Pierce # 13310 or equivalent.
‡ Pierce # 12718 or equivalent.
§ Corning 8062-15 or equivalent.
‖ Hamilton 702N or equivalent.
Hamilton # 86570 or equivalent.
** Chromatographic methods are extremely sensitive to the materials used. Mention of trade names by *Standard Methods* does not preclude the use of other existing or as-yet-undeveloped products that give *demonstrably* equivalent results.

dichloromethane. See Figure 6232:2 for a sample chromatogram and Table 6232:I for retention data.

3) 2-mm ID × 3 m long glass packed with 6% OV-11/4% SP-2100 on Supelcoport (100/120 mesh); temperature program 45°C for 12 min, then program at 1°C/min to 70°C with a 25 mL/min flow. Hold until expected compounds have eluted. See Figure 6232:3 for a sample chromatogram and Table 6232:I for retention data.

j. Standard storage containers: 15-mL amber screw-cap septum bottles†† with TFE-faced silicone septa.‡‡

4. Reagents

a. Extraction solvent: See ¶ 1*b.* Recommended solvent is pentane.§§ Alternatively, use hexane, methylcyclohexane, or 2,2,4-trimethylpentane.

b. Methyl alcohol.

c. Activated carbon.∥∥

d. Reference standards.##

1) *Bromoform, 96%.*##

2) *Bromodichloromethane, 97%.****

3) *Dibromochloromethane.****†††

4) *Chloroform, 99%.****

e. THM-free water: Generate THM-free water, which is water free of interference

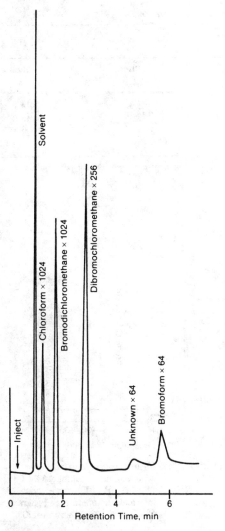

Figure 6232:1. Chromatogram of finished water extract. Column packing: 3% SP-1000; carrier gas: 5% CH₄ in argon; carrier flow: 60 mL/min; column temperature: 50°C; detector: electron capture.

with 10% squalane on Chromosorb WAW (80/100 mesh) operated at 67° C with 25 mL/min flow. This column is recommended as the primary analytical column. Trichloroethylene, a common raw source water contaminant, coelutes with bromo-

†† Pierce #19830 or equivalent.

‡‡ Pierce # 12716 or equivalent.

§§ Pentane has been selected as the best solvent for this analysis because it elutes, on all of the columns, well before any of the trihalomethanes. High altitudes or laboratory temperatures in excess of 24°C may make the use of this solvent impractical. Alternative solvents are acceptable; however, the analyst may experience baseline variations in the elution areas of the trihalomethanes due to coelution of these solvents. The degree of difficulty appears to depend on the design and condition of the electron capture detector. Such problems should be insignificant when concentrations of the coeluting trihalomethane exceed 5 μg/L.

∥∥ Filtrasorb 200, Calgon Corp., Pittsburgh, Pa., or equivalent.

As a precautionary measure, check all standards for purity by boiling point determination or GC/MS assays.

*** Aldrich Chemical Company or equivalent.

††† Columbia Organic Chemicals Company, Inc., Columbia, S.C., or equivalent.

TABLE 6232:I. RETENTION TIMES FOR TRIHALOMETHANES

	Retention Time *min*		
Trihalomethane	Column 1	Column 2	Column 3
Chloroform	1.0	1.3	4.9
Bromodichloromethane	1.5	2.5*	11.0
Dibromochloromethane	2.6	5.6	23.1
Bromoform	5.5	10.9	39.4

* On this column, trichloroethylene, a common raw source water contaminant, coelutes with bromodichloromethane.

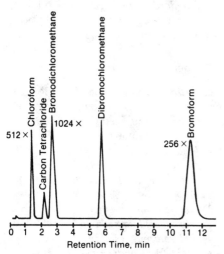

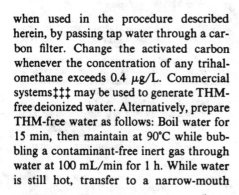

Figure 6232:2. Chromatogram of extract of standard. Column packing: 10% squalane; carrier flow: 25 mL/min; column temperature: 67°C.

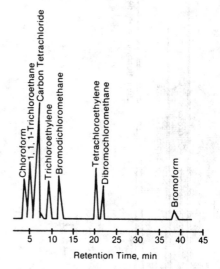

Figure 6232:3. Chromatogram of extract of standard. Column packing: 6% OV-11+4% SP-2100; carrier flow: 25 mL/min; temperature program: 45°C for 12 min, 1°/min to 70°C.

when used in the procedure described herein, by passing tap water through a carbon filter. Change the activated carbon whenever the concentration of any trihalomethane exceeds 0.4 μg/L. Commercial systems‡‡‡ may be used to generate THM-free deionized water. Alternatively, prepare THM-free water as follows: Boil water for 15 min, then maintain at 90°C while bubbling a contaminant-free inert gas through water at 100 mL/min for 1 h. While water is still hot, transfer to a narrow-mouth

‡‡‡ Millipore SuperQ Water System or equivalent.

screw-cap bottle with a TFE seal. Test THM-free water daily by analyzing for trihalomethanes.

f. Standard stock solutions: Place 9.8 mL methyl alcohol in a 10.0-mL ground-glass-stoppered volumetric flask. Let flask stand unstoppered about 10 min or until all alcohol-wetted surfaces dry. Weigh to nearest 0.1 mg. Using a 100-μL syringe, immediately add 2 to 3 drops of reference standard to flask, and reweigh. Be sure that reference standard falls directly into the alcohol without contacting flask neck. Dilute to volume, stopper, then mix by inverting flask several times. Transfer standard solution to a dated and labeled 15-mL screw-cap bottle with a TFE cap liner.

Calculate concentration in micrograms per microliter from the net gain in weight. Store solution at 4°C. Such standards are stable up to 4 weeks when stored under these conditions. If more time elapses, discard solutions.

CAUTION: *Trihalomethanes are toxic; prepare primary dilutions in a hood. Preferably also use a NIOSH/MESA-approved toxic gas respirator when handling high concentrations of such materials.*

g. Calibration standards: Either:

1) From standard stock solutions, prepare a multicomponent secondary dilution mixture in methyl alcohol so that a 20-μL injection into 100 mL THM-free water will generate a calibration standard that produces a response close ($\pm$ 25%) to that of the sample; or

2) Construct a calibration curve for each trihalomethane, using a minimum of three different concentrations. Two of the concentrations must bracket each sample.

In either case, prepare standards by injecting not more than 20 μL of alcoholic standards into 100 mL of THM-free water with a 25-μL microsyringe.§§§ Rapidly inject alcoholic standard into expanded area of filled volumetric flask, then remove needle immediately. Mix aqueous standards by inverting flask three times only. Discard contents in neck of flask. Fill sample syringe from standard solution in expanded area of flask as directed in ¶ 5. Never use pipets to dilute or transfer samples and aqueous standards. Aqueous standards, when stored with a headspace, are not stable; discard after 1 h. Store aqueous standards according to ¶s 2 and 5.

Extract and analyze aqueous calibration standards identically with samples.

Calibration procedures[8] that require delivery of less than 20 μL of methanolic standards to 10.0-mL volumes of water contained in the sample syringe are acceptable only if the methanolic standard is delivered by the solvent flush technique.[10]

h. Quality control check standard mixture: From standard stock solutions, prepare a secondary dilution mixture in methyl alcohol containing 10.0 ng of each compound/μL.|| || || Daily, inject 20.0 μL of this mixture into 100 mL of organic-free water and analyze (¶ 7a).

5. Procedure

Remove plungers from two 10-mL syringes and attach a closed syringe valve to each. Open sample bottle (or standard); if chemical reducing agent has not been added to the sample, add just before analysis at the ratio of 2.5 to 3 mg/40 mL or add 1 mg directly to sample in extraction flask. Carefully pour sample into one of the syringe barrels until it overflows. Replace plunger and compress sample. Open syringe valve and vent any residual air while adjusting sample volume to 10.0 mL. Close valve.

Fill second syringe in an identical manner from same sample bottle and reserve for replicate analysis (see ¶ 7 below).

Pipet 2.0 mL extraction solvent into a clean extraction flask, carefully inject contents of syringe into extraction flask, seal with a TFE-faced septum, and shake vigorously for 1 min. Let stand until phases separate (60 s). If phases do not separate

---

§§§ Hamilton 702N or equivalent. Variations in needle geometry will adversely affect the ability to deliver reproducible volumes of methanolic standards into water.

|| || || For U.S. federal permit-related analyses, use samples obtainable from U.S. EPA Environmental Monitoring and Support Laboratory, Cincinnati, Ohio.

on standing, centrifuge to facilitate separation.

Analyze sample by injecting 3.0 μL (solvent flush technique)[10] of the upper (organic) phase into the gas chromatograph.

6. Calculation

Locate each trihalomethane in the sample chromatogram by comparing retention time of suspect peak to average retention time and variance computed in ¶7g. The retention time of the suspect peak must fall within the limits established by those statistics for a single column identification.

Calculate concentration of each trihalomethane by comparing peak heights or peak areas of samples to those of standards as follows, using only two significant figures:

$$\text{Trihalomethane, μg/L} = \frac{S}{P} \times C$$

where:

S = sample peak height or area,
P = standard peak height or area that gives a detector response within ± 25% of sample response, and
C = concentration of standard giving response, P, μg/L.

Calculate total trihalomethane concentration as:

$$TTHM = CHCl_3 + CHBrCl_2 + CHBr_2Cl + CHBr_3$$

where:

$TTHM$ = total trihalomethane concentration, μg/L, and $CHCl_3$, $CHBrCl_2$, $CHBr_2Cl$, $CHBr_3$ = individual THM concentrations, μg/L.

Calculate limit of detection (LOD) for each trihalomethane not detected using the following criterion:

$$\text{LOD, μg/L} = \frac{A \times F \times (2 \text{ μg/L})}{(B \times F)}$$

where:

A = five times the noise level in millimeters at the exact retention time of the trihalomethane or the baseline displacement in millimeters from theoretical zero at exact retention time for the trihalomethane,
B = peak height in millimeters of 2-μg/L quality check standard, and
F = attenuation factor.

Report results obtained from lower limit of detection estimates along with data for samples.

7. Quality Control

a. *Quality check standards analysis*: Daily, before any samples are analyzed, extract and analyze a 2-μg/L quality check standard (¶ 4h). Calculate instrument status checks and lower limit of detection estimates on basis of response factor calculations at five times the noise level. The data also can be used to estimate concentration in samples. From this information, determine appropriate standard dilutions to be made.

b. *Interference monitoring*: Analyze sample blank and raw source water to monitor for potential interferences as described in ¶ 1b.

c. *Samples with known additions*: In a laboratory analyzing more than 10 samples daily, analyze a laboratory-generated known addition that closely duplicates the average finished drinking water in trihalomethane composition and concentration as each 10th sample (See ¶ 4g).

In a laboratory analyzing fewer than 10 samples daily, each time the analysis is made, analyze at least one laboratory-generated known-addition sample that closely duplicates the average finished drinking water in trihalomethane composition and concentration (See ¶ 4g).

d. *Duplicate analysis*: Randomly select and analyze in duplicate 10% of all samples. Maintain an up-to-date log on bias and precision data collected on known-addition samples and duplicate samples. If results are significantly different from those cited in ¶ 8 below, check entire analytical scheme to determine why the laboratory's precision and bias limits are excessive.

e. External quality-control samples: Quarterly, add an external reference trihalomethane quality control sample to organic-free water and analyze. The results from this sample should agree within 20% of the true value for each trihalomethane. If not, check each step in the standard generation procedure to solve the problem.

f. Electron capture system calibration: Be aware of the linear response characteristics of the electron capture system. Generate and recheck calibration curves quarterly for each trihalomethane over the concentration range encountered in samples to confirm linear response range of the system. Quantitative data can not be calculated from nonlinear responses. Whenever nonlinear responses occur, dilute sample and reanalyze.

g. Retention times: Maintain a record of retention times for each trihalomethane using data gathered from known-addition samples and standards. Daily calculate average retention time for each trihalomethane and the variance for the analyses. If individual trihalomethane retention time varies by more than 10% over an 8-h period or does not fall within 10% of an established norm, the system is "out of control." Seek and correct the source of retention data variation.

8. Precision and Bias

The single-laboratory precision and bias data in Table 6232:II were generated by adding known amounts of trihalomethanes to organic-free water as described in ¶ 4g. The mixtures were analyzed as true unknowns.

9. References

1. U.S. ENVIRONMENTAL PROTECTION AGENCY. 1980. Analysis of trihalomethanes in drinking water by liquid/liquid extraction. 40 CFR Part 141, Appendix C, Part II.

2. MIEURE, J.P. 1977. A rapid and sensitive method for determining volatile organohalides in water. *J. Amer. Water Works Assoc.* 69:60.

3. REDING, R., ET AL. 1978. THM's in drinking water: Analysis by LLE and comparison to purge and trap. *In* C. E. Van Hall, ed. Measurement of Organic Pollutants in Water and Wastewater. STP 686, American Soc. Testing & Materials, Philadelphia, Pa.

4. Handbook for Analytical Quality Control in Water and Waste Water Laboratories. 1972. Analytical Quality Control Lab., National Environmental Research Center, Cincinnati, Ohio.

5. BUDDE, W. L., & J. W. EICHELBERGER. 1979. Organic Analysis Using Gas Chromatography-Mass Spectrometry. Ann Arbor Science Publ., Ann Arbor, Mich.

6. U.S. ENVIRONMENTAL PROTECTION AGENCY. 1979. The Analysis of Trihalomethanes in Finished Water by the Purge and Trap Method. Environmental Monitoring & Support Lab., Environmental Research Center, Cincinnati, Ohio.

7. RICHARD, J. J. & G. A. JUNK. 1977. Liquid extraction for rapid determination of halomethanes in water. *J. Amer. Water Works Assoc.* 69:62.

8. BRASS, H. J., et al. 1977. *In* R. B. Pojasek, ed. National Organic Monitoring Survey: Sampling and Purgeable Organic Compounds, Drinking Water Quality Through Source Protection, p. 398. Ann Arbor Science Publ., Ann Arbor, Mich.

9. KOPFLER, F. C., et al. 1976. GC/MS determination of volatiles for the National Organics Reconnaissance Survey (NORS) of Drinking Water. *In* L. H. Keith, ed. Identification and Analysis of Organic Pollutants in Water. Ann Arbor Science Publ., Ann Arbor, Mich.

10. WHITE, L. D., et al. 1970. Convenient optimized method for the analysis of selected solvent vapors in industrial atmosphere. *Amer. Ind. Hyg. Assoc. J.* 31:225.

TABLE 6232:II. SINGLE-LABORATORY PRECISION AND BIAS

Compound	Dose Levels $\mu g/L$	Number of Samples	Mean $\mu g/L$	Precision (Relative Standard Deviation) %	Bias (Recovery) %
CHCl$_3$	9.1	5	10	11	110
CHCl$_3$	69	3	73	5.3	106
CHBrCl$_2$	1.2	5	1.3	9.8	108
CHBrCl$_2$	12	2	15	1.4	125
CHBr$_2$Cl	2.7	5	2.0	17	74
CHBr$_2$Cl	17	3	16	9.9	94
CHBr$_3$	2.9	5	2.2	10	76
CHBr$_3$	14	3	16	12	114

6232 C. Purge and Trap Gas Chromatographic/Mass Spectrometric Method

See Sections 6210B and C for packed-column methods and Section 6210D for capillary-column method.

*   *   *

6630   ORGANOCHLORINE PESTICIDES

6630 A.   Introduction

1. Sources and Significance

The organochlorine pesticides commonly occur in waters that have been affected by agricultural discharges. Some of the listed compounds are degradation products of other pesticides detected by this method. Several of the pesticides are bioaccumulative and relatively stable, as well as toxic or carcinogenic; thus they require close monitoring.

2. Selection of Method

Method 6630B consists of a gas chromatographic (GC) procedure following liquid-liquid extraction of water samples. It is a relatively sensitive method that can be used to detect numerous pesticides.

6630 B.   Liquid-Liquid Extraction
Gas Chromatographic Method I*

1. General Discussion

a. Application: This gas chromatographic procedure is suitable for quantitative determination of the following specific compounds: BHC, lindane, heptachlor, aldrin, heptachlor epoxide, dieldrin, endrin, captan, DDE, DDD, DDT, methoxychlor, endosulfan, dichloran, mirex, and pentachloronitrobenzene. Under favorable circumstances, strobane, toxaphene, chlordane (tech.), and others also may be determined when relatively high concentrations of these complex mixtures are present and the chromatographic fingerprint is recognizable in packed or capillary column analysis. Trifluralin and certain organophosphorus pesticides, such as parathion, methylparathion, and malathion, which respond to the electron-capture detector, also may be measured. However, the usefulness of the method for organophosphorus or other specific pesticides must be demonstrated before it is applied to sample analysis.

b. Principle: In this procedure the pesticides are extracted with a mixed solvent, diethyl ether/hexane or methylene chloride/hexane. The extract is concentrated by evaporation and, if necessary, is cleaned up by column adsorption-chromatography. The individual pesticides then are determined by gas chromatography. Although procedures detailed below refer primarily to packed columns, capillary column chromatography may be used provided that equivalent results can be demonstrated. See Section 6010C.2*a*1) for discussion of gas chromatographic principles and 6010C.2*b*2) for discussion of electron-capture detector.

*Approved by Standard Methods Committee, 1985.

As each component passes through the detector a quantitatively proportional change in electrical signal is measured on a strip-chart recorder. Each component is observed as a peak on the recorder chart. The retention time is indicative of the particular pesticide and peak height/peak area is proportional to its concentration.

Variables may be manipulated to obtain important confirmatory data. For example, the detector system may be selected on the basis of the specificity and sensitivity needed. The detector used in this method is an electron-capture detector that is very sensitive to chlorinated compounds. Additional confirmatory identification can be made from retention data on two or more columns where the stationary phases are of different polarities. A two-column procedure that has been found particularly useful is specified. If sufficient pesticide is available for detection and measurement, confirmation by a more definitive technique, such as mass spectrometry, is desirable.

c. Interference: See Sections 6010C.2*a*2) and 6010C.2*b*2). Some compounds other than chlorinated compounds respond to the electron-capture detector. Among these are oxygenated and unsaturated compounds. Sometimes plant or animal extractives obscure pesticide peaks. These interfering substances often can be removed by auxiliary cleanup techniques. A magnesia-silica gel column cleanup and separation procedure is used for this purpose. Such cleanup usually is not required for potable waters.

1) Polychlorinated biphenyls (PCBs)— Industrial plasticizers, hydraulic fluids, and old transformer fluids that contain PCBs are a potential source of interference in pesticide analysis. The presence of PCBs is suggested by a large number of partially

resolved or unresolved peaks that may occur throughout the entire chromatogram.
Particularly severe PCB interference will
require special separation procedures.

2) Phthalate esters—These compounds,
widely used as plasticizers, cause electron-
capture detector response and are a source
of interferences. Water leaches these esters
from plastics, such as polyethylene bottles
and plastic tubing. Phthalate esters can be
separated from many important pesticides
by the magnesia-silica gel column cleanup.
They do not cause response to halogen-
specific detectors such as microcoulometric
or electrolytic conductivity detectors.

d. *Detection limits:* The ultimate detection limit of a substance is affected by many
factors, for example, detector sensitivity,
extraction and cleanup efficiency, concentrations, and detector signal-to-noise level.
Lindane usually can be determined at 10
ng/L in a sample of relatively unpolluted
water; the DDT detection limit is somewhat higher, 20 to 25 ng/L. Increased sensitivity is likely to increase interference
with all pesticides.

e. *Sample preservation:* Some pesticides
are unstable. Transport under iced conditions, store at 4°C until extraction, and do
not hold more than 7 d. When possible,
extract upon receipt in the laboratory and
store extracts at 4°C until analyzed. Analyze extracts within 40 d.

2. Apparatus

Clean thoroughly all glassware used in
sample collection and pesticide residue
analyses. Clean glassware as soon as possible after use. Rinse with water or the
solvent that was last used in it, wash with
soapy water, rinse with tap water, distilled
water, redistilled acetone, and finally with
pesticide-quality hexane. As a precaution,
glassware may be rinsed with the extracting
solvent just before use. Heat heavily contaminated glassware in a muffle furnace at
400°C for 15 to 30 min. High-boiling-point

materials, such as PCBs, may require overnight heating at 500°C, but no borosilicate
glassware can exceed this temperature
without risk. Do not heat volumetric ware.
Clean volumetric glassware with special reagents.† Rinse with water and pesticide-
quality hexane. After drying, store glassware to prevent accumulation of dust or
other contaminants. Store inverted or cover
mouth with aluminum foil.

a. *Sample bottles:* 1-L capacity, glass,
with TFE-lined screw cap. Bottle may be
calibrated to minimize transfers and potential for contamination.

b. *Evaporative concentrator,* Kuderna-
Danish, 500-mL flask and 10-mL graduated lower tube fitted with a 3-ball Snyder
column, or equivalent.

c. *Separatory funnels,* 2-L capacity, with
TFE stopcock.

d. *Graduated cylinders,* 1-L capacity.

e. *Funnels,* 125-mL.

f. *Glass wool,* filter grade.

g. *Chromatographic column,* 20 mm in
diam and 400 mm long, with coarse fritted
disk at bottom.

h. *Microsyringes,* 10- and 25-μL capacity.

i. *Hot water bath.*

j. *Gas chromatograph,* equipped with:

1) *Glass-lined injection port.*

2) *Electron-capture detector.*

3) *Recorder:* Potentiometric strip chart,
25-cm, compatible with detector and associated electronics.

4) *Borosilicate glass column,* 1.8 m × 4-
mm ID or 2-mm ID.

Variations in available gas chromatographic instrumentation necessitate different operating procedures for each.
Therefore, refer to the manufacturer's operating manual as well as gas chromatography catalogs and other references (see
Bibliography). In general, use equipment
with the following features:

---

†No Chromix, Godax, 6 Varick Place, New York, N.Y.,
or equivalent.

• Carrier-gas line with a molecular sieve drying cartridge and a trap for removal of oxygen from the carrier gas. A special purifier‡ may be used. Use only dry carrier gas and insure that there are no gas leaks.

• Oven temperature stable to ±0.5°C or better at desired setting.

• Chromatographic columns—A well-prepared column is essential to an acceptable gas chromatographic analysis. Obtain column packings and pre-packed columns from commercial sources or prepare column packing in the laboratory.

It is inappropriate to give rigid specifications on size or composition to be used because some instruments perform better with certain columns than do others. Columns with 4-mm ID are used most commonly. The carrier-gas flow is approximately 60 mL/min. When 2-mm-ID columns are used, reduce carrier-gas flow to about 25 mL/min. Adequate separations have been obtained by using 5% OV-210 on 100/120 mesh dimethyl-dichlorosilane-treated diatomaceous earth§ in a 2-m column. The 1.5% OV-17 and 1.95% QF-1 column is recommended for confirmatory analysis. Two additional column options are included: 3% OV-1 and mixed-phase 6% QF-1 + 4% SE-30, each on dimethyl-dichlorosilane-treated diatomaceous earth, 100-120 mesh. OV-210, which is a refined form of QF-1, may be substituted for QF-1. A column is suitable when it effects adequate and reproducible resolution. Sample chromatograms are shown in Figures 6630:1 through 6630:4.

Alternately, use fused silica capillary ‖ columns, 30 m long with a 0.32-mm ID and 0.25-μm film thickness, or equivalent. See Figure 6630:5. To confirm identification use a column of different polarity.#

3. Reagents**

Use solvents, reagents, and other materials for pesticide analysis that are free from interferences under the condition of the analysis. Specific selection of reagents and distillation of solvents in an all-glass system may be required. "Pesticide quality" solvents usually do not require redistillation; however, always determine a blank before use.

a. Hexane.

b. Petroleum ether, boiling range 30 to 60°C.

c. Diethyl ether: CAUTION: *Explosive peroxides tend to form.* Test for presence of peroxides†† and, if present, reflux over granulated sodium-lead alloy for 8 h, distill in a glass apparatus, and add 2% methanol. Use immediately or, if stored, test for peroxides before use.

d. Ethyl acetate.

e. Methylene chloride.

f. Magnesia-silica gel,‡‡ PR grade, 60 to 100 mesh. Purchase activated at 676°C and store in the dark in glass container with glass stopper or foil-lined screw cap; do not accept in plastic container. Before use, activate each batch overnight at 130°C in foil-covered glass container.

g. Sodium sulfate, Na$_2$SO$_4$, anhydrous, granular: Do not accept in plastic container. If necessary, bake in a muffle furnace to eliminate interferences.

h. Silanized glass wool.

i. Column packing:

1) Solid support—Dimethyl dichlorosilane-treated diatomaceous earth,§§ 100 to 120 mesh.

---

‡Hydrox, Matheson Gas Products, P. O. Box E, Lyndhurst, N.J., or equivalent.
§Gas Chrom Q, Applied Science Labs., Inc., P. O. Box 440, State College, Pa., or equivalent.
‖ J & W Scientific, DB-5, DB-1701, or equivalent.
#J & W Scientific, DB-1, or equivalent.

**Gas chromatographic methods are extremely sensitive to the materials used. Mention of trade names by *Standard Methods* does not preclude the use of other existing or as-yet-undeveloped products that give *demonstrably* equal results.
††Use E. M. Quant™, MCB Manufacturing Chemists, Inc., 2909 Highland Ave., Cincinnati, Ohio, or equivalent.
‡‡Florisil™ or equivalent.
§§Gas-Chrom Q™, Supelcoport, or equivalent.

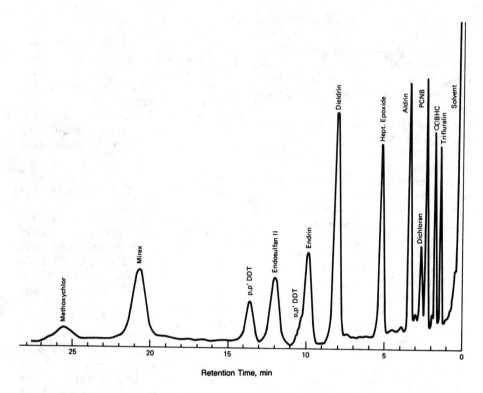

Figure 6630:1. Results of gas chromatographic procedure for organochlorine pesticides. Column packing: 1.5% OV-17 + 1.95% QF-1; carrier gas: argon/methane at 60 mL/min; column temperature: 200°C; detector: electron capture in pulse mode.

2) Liquid phases—OV-1, OV-210, 1.5% OV-17 (SP 2250) + 1.95% QF-1 (SP 2401), and 6% QF-1 + 4% SE-30, or equivalent.

j. Carrier gas: One of the following is required:

1) *Nitrogen gas,* purified grade, moisture- and oxygen-free.

2) *Argon-methane* (95 + 5%) for use in pulse mode.

k. Pesticide reference standards: Obtain purest standards available (95 to 98%) from gas chromatographic and chemical supply houses.

l. Stock pesticide solutions: Dissolve 100 mg of each pesticide in ethyl acetate and dilute to 100 mL in a volumetric flask; 1.00 mL = 1.00 mg.

m. Intermediate pesticide solutions: Dilute 1.0 mL stock solution to 100 mL with ethyl acetate; 1.0 mL = 10 μg.

n. Working standard solutions for gas chromatography: Prepare final concentration of standards in hexane solution as required by detector sensitivity and linearity.

4. Procedure

a. Preparation of chromatograph:

1) Packing the column—Use a column constructed of silanized borosilicate glass because other tubing materials may catalyze sample component decomposition. Before packing, rinse and dry column tubing with solvent, e.g., methylene chloride, then methanol. Pack column to a uniform den-

through detector by using the purge-gas line, or in dual-column ovens, by connecting an unpacked column to the detector. Adjust carrier-gas flow to about 50 mL/min and slowly (over a 1-h period) raise oven temperature to 230°C. After 24 to 48 h at this temperature the column is ready for pesticide conditioning.

Adjust oven temperature and carrier-gas flow rate to approximate operating levels. Make six consecutive 10-μL injections of a concentrated pesticide mixture through column at about 15-min intervals. Prepare this injection mixture from lindane, heptachlor, aldrin, heptachlor epoxide, dieldrin, endrin, and *p,p'*-DDT, each compound at a concentration of 200 ng/μL. After pesticide conditioning, connect column to detector and let equilibrate for at least 1 h, preferably overnight. Column is then ready for use.

3) Injection technique

a) Develop an injection technique with constant rhythm and timing. The "solvent flush" technique described below has been used successfully and is recommended to prevent sample blowback or distillation within the syringe needle. Flush syringe with solvent, then draw a small volume of clean solvent into syringe barrel (e.g., 1 μL in a 10-μL syringe). Remove needle from solvent and draw 1 μL of air into barrel. Draw 3 to 4 μL of sample extract into barrel. Remove needle from sample extract and draw approximately 1 μL air into barrel. Record volume of sample extract between air pockets. Rapidly insert needle through inlet septum, depress plunger, withdraw syringe. After each injection thoroughly clean syringe by rinsing several times with solvent.

b) Inject standard solutions of such concentration that the injection volume and peak height of the standard are approximately the same as those of the sample.

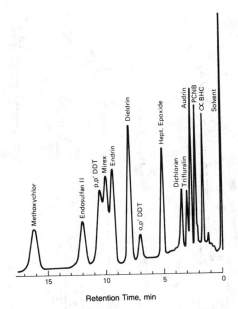

Figure 6630:2. Results of gas chromatographic procedure for organochlorine pesticides. Column packing: 5% OV-210; carrier gas: argon/methane at 70 mL/min; column temperature: 180°C; detector: electron capture.

sity not so compact as to cause unnecessary back pressure and not so loose as to create voids during use. Do not crush packing. Fill column through a funnel connected by flexible tubing to one end. Plug other end of column with about 1.3 cm silanized glass wool and fill with aid of *gentle* vibration or tapping but do not use an electric vibrator because it tends to fracture packing. Optionally, apply a vacuum to plugged end. Plug open end with silanized glass wool.

2) Conditioning—Proper thermal and pesticide conditioning are essential to eliminate column bleed and to provide acceptable gas chromatographic analysis. The following procedure provides excellent results: Connect packed column to the injection port. *Do not* connect column to detector; however, maintain gas flow

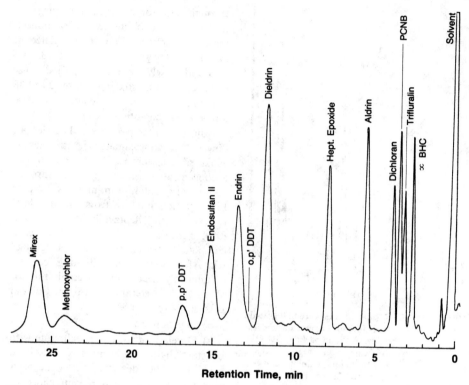

Figure 6630:3. Chromatogram of pesticide mixture. Column packing: 6% QF-1 + 4% SE-30; carrier gas; argon/methane at 60 mL/min; column temperature: 200°C; detector: electron capture.

b. Treatment of samples:

1) Sample collection—Fill sample bottle to neck. Collect samples in duplicate.

2) Extraction of samples—Shake sample well and accurately measure all the sample in a 1-L graduated cylinder in two measuring operations if necessary (or use a precalibrated sample bottle to avoid transfer operation). Pour sample into a 2-L separatory funnel. Rinse sample bottle and cylinder with 60 mL 15% diethyl ether or methylene chloride in hexane, pour this solvent into separatory funnel, and shake vigorously for 2 min. Let phases separate for at least 10 min.

Drain water phase from separatory funnel into sample bottle and carefully pour organic phase through a 2-cm-OD column

containing 8 to 10 cm of Na_2SO_4 into a Kuderna-Danish apparatus fitted with a 10-mL concentrator tube. Pour sample back into separatory funnel.

Rinse sample bottle with 60 mL mixed solvent, use solvent to repeat sample extraction, and pass organic phase through Na_2SO_4. Complete a third extraction with 60 mL of mixed solvent that was used to rinse sample bottle again, and pass organic phase through Na_2SO_4. Wash Na_2SO_4 with several portions of hexane and drain well. Fit Kuderna-Danish apparatus with a three-ball Snyder column and reduce volume to about 7 mL in a hot water bath (90 to 95°C). At this point all methylene chloride present in the initial extracting solvent has been distilled off. Cool, remove con-

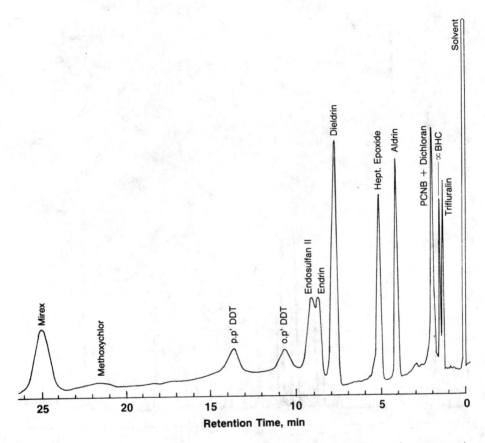

Figure 6630:4. Chromatogram of pesticide mixture. Column packing: 3% OV-1; carrier gas: argon/methane at 70 mL/min; column temperature: 180°C; detector: electron capture.

centrator tube from Kuderna-Danish apparatus, rinse ground-glass joint, and dilute to 10 mL with hexane. Make initial gas chromatographic analysis at this dilution.

3) *Gas chromatography*—Inject 3 to 4 μL of extract solution into a column. Always inject the same volume. Inspect resulting chromatogram for peaks corresponding to pesticides of concern and for presence of interferences.

a) If there are presumptive pesticide peaks and no significant interference, rechromatograph the extract solution on an alternate column.

b) Inject standards frequently to insure optimum operating conditions. If neces-

sary, concentrate or dilute (*do not use methylene chloride*) the extract so that peak size of pesticide is very close to that of corresponding peaks in standard. (See dilution factor, ¶ 5a).

c) If significant interference is present, separate interfering substances from pesticide materials by using the cleanup procedure described in the following paragraph.

4) *Magnesia-silica gel cleanup*—Adjust sample extract volume to 10 mL with hexane. Place a charge of activated magnesia-silica gel ‖ ‖ (weight determined by lauric-

‖ ‖ Florisil™ or equivalent.

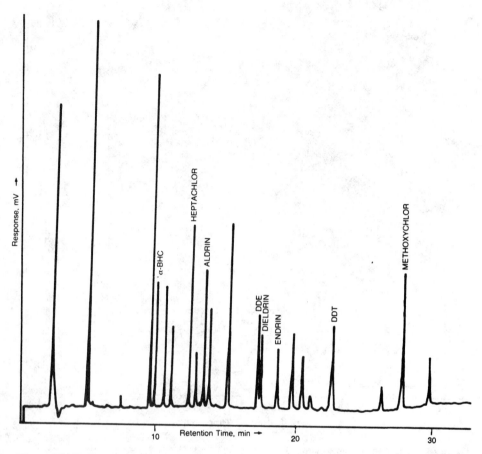

Figure 6630:5. Chromatogram of pesticide mixture. Column DB-5, 30 m long, multilevel program temperature, electron-capture detector.

acid value, see Appendix) in a chromatographic column. After settling gel by tapping column, add about 1.3 cm anhydrous granular Na$_2$SO$_4$ to the top. Pre-elute column, after cooling, with 50 to 60 mL petroleum ether. Discard eluate and just before exposing sulfate layer to air, quantitatively transfer sample extract into column by careful decantation and with subsequent petroleum ether washings (5 mL maximum). Adjust elution rate to about 5 mL/min and, separately, collect the eluates in 500-mL Kuderna-Danish flasks equipped with 10-mL receivers.

Make first elution with 200 mL 6% ethyl ether in petroleum ether, and the second with 200 mL 15% ethyl ether in petroleum ether. Make third elution with 200 mL 50% ethyl ether-petroleum ether and the fourth with 200 mL 100% ethyl ether. Follow with 50 to 100 mL petroleum ether to insure removal of all ethyl ether from the column. Alternatively, to separate PCBs elute initially with 0% ethyl ether in petroleum ether and proceed as above to yield four fractions.

Concentrate eluates in Kuderna-Danish evaporator in a hot water bath as in ¶ 4b2) preceding, dilute to appropriate volume, and analyze by gas chromatography.

Eluate composition—By use of an equivalent quantity of any batch of magnesia-silica gel as determined by its lauric acid value (see Appendix) the pesticides will be separated into the eluates indicated below:

6% Ethyl Ether Eluate

Aldrin	Heptachlor	Pentachloro-
BHC	Heptachlor	nitrobenzene
Chlordane	epoxide	Strobane
DDD	Lindane	Toxaphene
DDE	Methoxychlor	Trifluralin
DDT	Mirex	PCBs

15% Ethyl Ether Eluate	50% Ethyl Ether Eluate
Endosulfan I	Endosulfan II
Endrin	Captan
Dieldrin	
Dichloran	
Phthalate esters	

If present, certain thiophosphate pesticides will occur in each of the above fractions as well as in the 100% ether fraction. For additional information regarding eluate composition and the procedure for determining the lauric acid value, refer to the FDA Pesticide Analytical Manual (see Bibliography). For elution pattern test procedure see Appendix, Section 4.

5) Determination of extraction efficiency—Add known amounts of pesticides in ethyl acetate solution to 1 L water sample and carry through the same procedure as for samples. Dilute an equal amount of intermediate pesticide solution (¶ 3m above) to the same final volume. Call peak height from standard "a" and peak height from sample to which pesticide was added "b," whereupon the extraction efficiency equals b/a. Periodically determine extraction efficiency and a control blank to test the procedure. Also analyze one set of duplicates with each series of samples as a quality-control check.

5. Calculation

a. Dilution factor: If a portion of the extract solution was concentrated, the dilution factor, D, is a decimal; if it was diluted, the dilution factor exceeds 1.

b. Determine pesticide concentrations by direct comparison to a single standard when the injection volume and response are within 10% of those of the sample pesticide of interest (Table 6630:I). Calculate concentration of pesticide:

$$\mu g/L = \frac{A \times B \times C \times D}{E \times F \times G}$$

where:

A = ng standard pesticide,

B = peak height of sample, mm, or area count,

C = extract volume, μL,

D = dilution factor,

E = peak height of standard, mm, or area count,

F = volume of extract injected, μL, and

G = volume of sample extracted, mL.

Typical chromatograms of representative pesticide mixtures are shown in Figures 6630:1 through 6630:5.

Report results in micrograms per liter without correction for efficiency.

6. Precision and Bias

Ten laboratories in an interlaboratory study selected their own water samples and added four representative pesticides to replicate samples, at two concentrations in acetone. The added pesticides came from a single source. Samples were analyzed with and without magnesia-silica gel cleanup. Precision and recovery data are given in Table 6630:II.

7. Bibliography

MILL, P.A. 1968. Variation of Florisil activity: simple method for measuring absorbent capacity and its use in standardizing Florisil columns. J. Assoc. Off. Anal. Chem. 51:29.

TABLE 6630:I. RETENTION RATIOS OF VARIOUS ORGANOCHLORINE
PESTICIDES RELATIVE TO ALDRIN

Liquid phase*	1.5% OV-17 + 1.95% QF-1	5% OV-210	3% OV-1	6% QF-1 + 4% SE-30
Column Temperature	200°C	180°C	180°C	200°C
Argon/methane carrier flow	60 mL/min	70 mL/min	70 mL/min	60 mL/min
Pesticide	RR	RR	RR	RR
∝-BHC	0.54	0.64	0.35	0.49
PCNB	0.68	0.85	0.49	0.63
Lindane	0.69	0.81	0.44	0.60
Dichloran	0.77	1.29	0.49	0.70
Heptachlor	0.82	0.87	0.78	0.83
Aldrin	1.00	1.00	1.00	1.00
Heptachlor epoxide	1.54	1.93	1.28	1.43
Endosulfan I	1.95	2.48	1.62	1.79
p,p'-DDE	2.23	2.10	2.00	1.82
Dieldrin	2.40	3.00	1.93	2.12
Captan	2.59	4.09	1.22	1.94
Endrin	2.93	3.56	2.18	2.42
o,p'-DDT	3.16	2.70	2.69	2.39
p,p'-DDD	3.48	3.75	2.61	2.55
Endosulfan II	3.59	4.59	2.25	2.72
p,p'-DDT	4.18	4.07	3.50	3.12
Mirex	6.1	3.78	6.6	4.79
Methoxychlor	7.6	6.5	5.7	4.60
Aldrin (Min absolute)	3.5	2.6	4.0	5.6

* All columns glass, 180 cm × 4 mm ID, solid support Gas-Chrom Q (100/200 mesh).

FOOD AND DRUG ADMINISTRATION. 1968 (revised 1978). Pesticide Analytical Manual, 2nd ed. U.S. Dep. Health, Education & Welfare, Washington, D.C.

MONSANTO CHEMICAL COMPANY. 1970. Monsanto Methodology for Arochlors—Analysis of Environmental Materials for Biphenyls, Analytical Chemistry Method 71-35. St. Louis, Mo.

U.S. ENVIRONMENTAL PROTECTION AGENCY. 1971. Method for Organic Pesticides in Water and Wastewater. National Environmental Research Center, Cincinnati, Ohio.

STEERE, N.V., ed. 1971. Handbook of Laboratory Safety. Chemical Rubber Company, Cleveland, Ohio.

GOERLITZ, D.F. & E. BROWN. 1972. Methods for analysis of organic substances in water. *In* Techniques of Water Resources Investigations of the United States Geological Survey, Book 5, Chapter A3, p. 24. U.S. Dep. Interior, Geological Survey, Washington, D.C.

U.S. ENVIRONMENTAL PROTECTION AGENCY. 1978. Method for Organochlorine Pesticides in Industrial Effluents. National Environmental Research Center, Cincinnati, Ohio.

U.S. ENVIRONMENTAL PROTECTION AGENCY. 1978. Method for Polychlorinated Biphenyls in Industrial Effluents. National Environmental Research Center, Cincinnati, Ohio.

U.S. ENVIRONMENTAL PROTECTION AGENCY. 1979. Handbook for Analytical Quality Control in Water and Wastewater Laboratories. National Environmental Research Center, Analytical Quality Control Laboratory, Cincinnati, Ohio.

TABLE 6630:II. PRECISION AND BIAS DATA FOR SELECTED ORGANOCHLORINE PESTICIDES

Pesticide	Level Added ng/L	Pre-treatment	Mean Recovery ng/L	Recovery %	Precision* ng/L	
					S_T	S_o
Aldrin	15	No cleanup	10.42	69	4.86	2.59
	110		79.00	72	32.06	20.19
	25	Cleanup†	17.00	68	9.13	3.48‡
	100		64.54	65	27.16	8.02‡
Lindane	10	No cleanup	9.67	97	5.28	3.47
	100		72.91	73	26.23	11.49‡
	15	Cleanup†	14.04	94	8.73	5.20
	85		59.08	70	27.49	7.75‡
Dieldrin	20	No cleanup	21.54	108	18.16	17.92
	125		105.83	85	30.41	21.84
	25	Cleanup	17.52	70	10.44	5.10‡
	130		84.29	65	34.45	16.79‡
DDT	40	No cleanup	40.30	101	15.96	13.42
	200		154.87	77	38.80	24.02
	30	Cleanup†	35.54	118	22.62	22.50
	185		132.08	71	49.83	25.31

* S_T = overall precision and S_o = single-operator precision.
† Use of magnesia-silica gel column cleanup before analysis.
‡ $S_o < S_T/2$.

U.S. ENVIRONMENTAL PROTECTION AGENCY. 1980. Analysis of Pesticide Residues in Human and Environmental Samples. Environmental Toxicology Div., Health Effects Laboratory, Research Triangle Park, N.C.

Appendix—Standardization of Magnesia-Silica Gel* Column by Weight Adjustment Based on Adsorption of Lauric Acid

A rapid method for determining adsorptive capacity of magnesia-silica gel is based on adsorption of lauric acid from hexane solution. An excess of lauric acid is used and the amount not adsorbed is measured by alkali titration. The weight of lauric acid adsorbed is used to calculate, by simple proportion, equivalent quantities of gel for batches having different adsorptive capacities.

*Florisil™ or equivalent.

1. Reagents

a. Ethyl alcohol, USP or absolute, neutralized to phenolphthalein.

b. Hexane, distilled from all-glass apparatus.

c. Lauric acid solution: Transfer 10.000 g lauric acid to a 500-mL volumetric flask, dissolve in hexane, and dilute to 500 mL; 1.00 mL = 20 mg.

d. Phenolphthalein indicator: Dissolve 1 g in alcohol and dilute to 100 mL.

e. Sodium hydroxide, 0.05N: Dilute 25 mL 1N NaOH to 500 mL with distilled water. Standardize as follows: Weigh 100 to 200 mg lauric acid into 125-mL erlenmeyer flask; add 50 mL neutralized ethyl alcohol and 3 drops phenolphthalein indicator; titrate to permanent end point; and calculate milligrams lauric acid per milliliter NaOH (about 10 mg/mL).

2. Procedure

Transfer 2.000 g magnesia-silica gel to a 25-mL glass-stoppered erlenmeyer flask. Cover loosely with aluminum foil and heat overnight at 130°C. Stopper, cool to room temperature, add 20.0 mL lauric acid solution (400 mg), stopper, and shake occasionally during 15 min. Let adsorbent settle and pipet 10.0 mL supernatant into a 125-mL erlenmeyer flask. Avoid including any gel. Add 50 mL neutral alcohol and 3 drops phenolphthalein indicator solution; titrate with 0.05N NaOH to a permanent end point.

3. Calculation of Lauric Acid Value and Adjustment of Column Weight

Calculate amount of lauric acid adsorbed on gel as follows:

Lauric acid value = mg lauric acid/g gel = 200 − (mL required for titration × mg lauric acid/mL 0.05N NaOH).

To obtain an equivalent quantity of any batch of gel, divide 110 by lauric acid value for that batch and multiply by 20 g. Verify proper elution of pesticides by the procedure given below.

4. Test for Proper Elution Pattern and Recovery of Pesticides

Prepare a test mixture containing aldrin, heptachlor epoxide, *p,p'*-DDE, dieldrin, parathion, and malathion. Dieldrin and parathion should elute in the 15% eluate; all but a trace of malathion in the 50% eluate, and the others in the 6% eluate.

6640   CHLORINATED PHENOXY ACID HERBICIDES

6640 A.   Introduction

1. Sources and Significance

The chlorinated phenoxy herbicides occur in raw source waters and in corresponding finished drinking waters that have been subjected to industrial discharges or agricultural effluents affected by these herbicides. These compounds are used extensively for weed control and are very potent herbicides even at low concentrations. Esters and salts of 2,4-D and silvex have been used as aquatic herbicides in lakes, streams, and irrigation canals. Toxicological studies suggest that these compounds have detrimental effects on human health; therefore they should be closely monitored in water supplies.

2. Selection of Method

The gas chromatographic method presented here (6640B) utilizes derivatization and GC with electron-capture detector (ECD) to detect these compounds.

6640 B. Liquid-Liquid Extraction Gas Chromatographic Method*

1. General Discussion

a. Principle: Chlorinated phenoxy acid herbicides such as 2,4-D [2,4-dichlorophenoxyacetic acid], silvex [2-(2,4,5-trichlorophenoxy) propionic acid], 2,4,5-T [2,4,5-trichlorophenoxyacetic acid], and similar chemicals may be determined by a gas chromatographic procedure.

Because these compounds may occur in water in various forms (e.g., acid, salt, ester) a hydrolysis step is included to permit determination of the active part of the herbicide.

Chlorinated phenoxy acids and their esters are extracted from the acidified water sample with ethyl ether. The extracts are hydrolyzed and extraneous material is removed by a solvent wash. The acids are converted to methyl esters and are further cleaned up on a microadsorption column. The methyl esters are determined by gas chromatography.

b. Interference: See Section 6630B.1*c.* Organic acids, especially chlorinated acids, cause the most direct interference. Phenols, including chlorophenols, also may interfere. Alkaline hydrolysis and subsequent extraction eliminate many of the predominant chlorinated insecticides. Because the herbicides react readily with alkaline substances, loss may occur if there is alkaline contact at any time except in the controlled alkaline hydrolysis step. Acid-rinse glassware and glass wool and acidify sodium sulfate (Na$_2$SO$_4$) to avoid this possibility.

c. Detection limits: The practical lower limits for measurement of phenoxy acid herbicides depend primarily on sample size and instrumentation used. If the extract from a 1-L sample is concentrated to 2.00 mL and 5.0 μL of concentrate is injected

into the electron-capture gas chromatograph, reliable measurement of 50 ng 2,4-D/L, 10 ng silvex/L, and 10 ng 2,4,5-T/L is feasible. Concentrating extract to 0.50 mL permits detection of approximately 10 ng 2,4-D/L, 2 ng silvex/L, and 2 ng 2,4,5-T/L. The sensitivity of the electron-capture detector often is affected adversely by extraneous material in sample or reagents. Concentrating the extract progressively amplifies this complication. Thus, the practical lower limits of measurement are difficult to define.

2. Apparatus

Clean glassware with detergent in the usual manner, rinse in dilute HCl, and finally rinse in distilled water. To assure removal of organic matter, follow the procedure given in Section 6630B.2.

a. Sample bottles: 1-L capacity, glass, with TFE-lined screw caps. Bottles may be calibrated to minimize transfers and potential for contamination.

b. Evaporative concentrator, Kuderna-Danish, 250-mL flask and 5-mL volumetric receiver.†

c. Snyder columns, three-ball macro, one-ball micro.

d. Separatory funnels, 2-L and 60-mL sizes with TFE stopcocks and taper ground-glass stoppers.†

e. Pipets, Pasteur, disposable, 140 mm long and 5 mm ID, glass.

f. Microsyringes, 10-μL.

g. Sand bath, fluidized,‡ or water bath.

h. Erlenmeyer flask, 250-mL with ground-glass mouth to fit Snyder columns.

i. Gas chromatographic system: See Section 6630B.2*j.* Operating parameters that

---

*Approved by Standard Methods Committee, 1985.

†Kontes or equivalent.
‡TeCam or equivalent.

produce satisfactory chromatograms for herbicide analyses are: injector temperature, 215°C; oven temperature, 185°C; and carrier-gas flow, 70 mL/min in a 4-mm-ID column.

3. Reagents§

Check all reagents for purity by the gas chromatographic procedure. Save time and effort by selecting high-quality reagents that do not require further preparation. Some purification of reagents may be necessary as outlined below. If more rigorous treatment is indicated, obtain reagent from an alternate source.

a. Diethyl ether, reagent grade. See 6630B.3c.

b. Toluene, pesticide quality, distilled in glass, or equivalent.

c. Sodium sulfate, Na_2SO_4, anhydrous, granular. Store at 130°C.

d. Sodium sulfate solution: Dissolve 50 mg anhydrous Na_2SO_4 in distilled water and dilute to 1 L.

e. Sodium sulfate, acidified: Add 0.1 mL conc H_2SO_4 to 100 g Na_2SO_4 slurried with enough ethyl ether to just cover the solid. Remove diethyl ether by vacuum drying. Mix 1 g of resulting solid with 5 mL distilled water and confirm that mixture pH is below 4. Store at 130°C.

f. Sulfuric acid, H_2SO_4, conc.

g. Sulfuric acid, H_2SO_4, 1 + 3. Store in refrigerator.

h. Potassium hydroxide solution: Dissolve 37 g KOH pellets in distilled water and dilute to 100 mL.

i. Boron trifluoride-methanol, 14% boron trifluoride by weight.

j. Magnesia-silica gel,‖ PR grade, 60 to 100 mesh. Purchase activated at 676°C and store at 130°C.

k. Glass wool, filtering grade, acid-washed.

l. Herbicide standards, acids, and methyl esters, analytical reference grade or highest purity available.

m. Stock herbicide solutions: Dissolve 100 mg herbicide or methyl ester in 60 mL diethyl ether; dilute to 100 mL in a volumetric flask with hexane; 1.00 mL = 1.00 mg.

n. Intermediate herbicide solution: Dilute 1.0 mL stock solution to 100 mL in a volumetric flask with a mixture of equal volumes of diethyl ether and toluene; 1.00 mL = 10.0 μg.

o. Standard solution for chromatography: Prepare final concentration of methyl ester standards in toluene solution according to the detector sensitivity and linearity.

4. Procedure

a. Sample extraction: Accurately measure sample (850 to 1000 mL) in a 1-L graduated cylinder (or use a precalibrated sample bottle to avoid transfer operations). Acidify to pH 2 with conc H_2SO_4 and pour into a 2-L separatory funnel. Rinse sample bottle and cylinder with 150 mL ethyl ether, add ether to separatory funnel, and shake vigorously for 1 min. Let phases separate for at least 10 min. Occasionally, emulsions prevent adequate separation. If emulsion forms, drain off separated aqueous layer, invert separatory funnel, and shake rapidly. CAUTION: *Vent funnel frequently to prevent excessive pressure buildup.* Collect extract in a 250-mL ground-glass-stoppered erlenmeyer flask containing 2 mL KOH solution. Extract sample twice more, using 50 mL diethyl ether each time, and combine extracts in erlenmeyer flask.

b. Hydrolysis: Add 15 mL distilled water and a small boiling stone and fit flask with a three-ball Snyder column. Remove ether on a steam bath and continue heating for

---

§Chromatographic methods are extremely sensitive to the materials used. Mention of trade names by *Standard Methods* does not preclude the use of other existing or as-yet-undeveloped products that give *demonstrably* equal results.

‖Florisil™ or equivalent.

a total of 60 min. Transfer concentrate to a 60-mL separatory funnel. Extract twice, with 20 mL diethyl ether each time, and discard ether layers. The herbicides remain in the aqueous phase.

Acidify by adding 2 mL cold (4°C) 1 + 3 H_2SO_4. Extract once with 20 mL and twice with 10 mL diethyl ether each. Collect extracts in a 125-mL erlenmeyer flask containing about 0.5 g acidified anhydrous Na_2SO_4. Let extract remain in contact with Na_2SO_4 for at least 2 h.

c. *Esterification:* Fit a Kuderna-Danish apparatus with a 5-mL volumetric receiver. Transfer diethyl ether extract to Kuderna-Danish apparatus through a funnel plugged with glass wool. Use liberal washing of ether. Crush any hardened Na_2SO_4 with a glass rod. Before concentrating, add 0.5 mL toluene. Reduce volume to less than 1 mL on a sand or hot water bath heated to 60 to 70°C. Attach a Snyder micro-column to Kuderna-Danish receiver and concentrate to less than 0.5 mL.

Alternatively, if quantitative recovery is demonstrated, concentrate extract by placing concentrator ampule in a water bath at 70°C. Reduce volume to less than 1 mL using a gentle stream of clean, dry nitrogen (filtered through activated carbon). CAUTION: *Do not use new plastic tubing between the carbon trap and the sample as interferences may be introduced.* Rinse internal wall of ampule with hexane during concentration, never let extract go to dryness, and keep ampule solvent level below water level in the bath. Adjust final volume to 1 mL with hexane.

Cool and add 0.5 mL boron trifluoride-methanol reagent. Use the small one-ball Snyder column as an air-cooled condenser and hold contents of receiver at 50°C for 30 min in the sand bath. Cool and add enough Na_2SO_4 solution (¶ 3d above) so that the toluene-water interface is in the neck of the Kuderna-Danish volumetric receiver flask (about 4.5 mL). Stopper flask with a ground-glass stopper and shake vigorously for about 1 min. Let stand for 3 min for phase separation.

Pipet solvent layer from receiver to top of a small column prepared by plugging a disposable Pasteur pipet with glass wool and packing with 2.0 cm Na_2SO_4 over 1.5 cm magnesia-silica gel adsorbent. Collect eluate in a 2.5-mL graduated centrifuge tube. Complete transfer by repeatedly rinsing volumetric receiver with small quantities of toluene until a final eluate volume of 2.0 mL is obtained. Check calibration of centrifuge tubes to insure that graduations are correct.

d. *Gas chromatography:* Analyze a suitable portion, 5 to 10 μL, by gas chromatography, using at least two columns for identification and quantification. Inject standard herbicide methyl esters frequently to insure optimum operating conditions. Always inject the same volume. Adjust sample volume extract with toluene, if necessary, so that the sizes of the peaks obtained are close to those of the standards (see ¶ 5a below). For sample chromatograms, see Figures 6640:1 and 2.

e. *Determination of recovery efficiency:* Add known amounts of herbicides to 1-L water sample, carry through the same procedure as the samples, and determine recovery efficiency. Periodically determine recovery efficiency and a control blank to test the procedure. Analyze one set of duplicates with each series of samples as a quality-control check.

5. Calculation

a. *Dilution factor:* If a portion of the extract solution was concentrated, the dilution factor, *D,* is less than 1; if it was diluted, the dilution factor exceeds 1.

Compare peak height or area of a standard to peak height or area of sample to determine amount of herbicide injected (see Table 6640:I).

B = peak height or area of sample, mm or mm^2,

C = extract volume, μL,

D = dilution factor,

E = peak height or area of standard, mm or mm^2,

F = volume injected, μL, and

G = volume of sample extracted, mL.

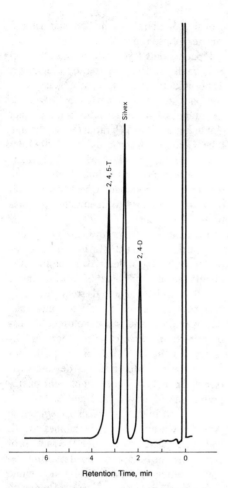

Figure 6640:1. Results of gas chromatographic procedure for chlorinated phenoxy acid herbicides. Column: 1.5% OV-17 + 1.95% QF-1; carrier gas: argon (5%)/methane at 70 mL/min; column temperature: 185°C; detector: electron capture.

Calculate concentration of herbicide:

$$\mu g/L = \frac{A \times B \times C \times D}{E \times F \times G}$$

where:

A = weight of herbicide standard injected, ng,

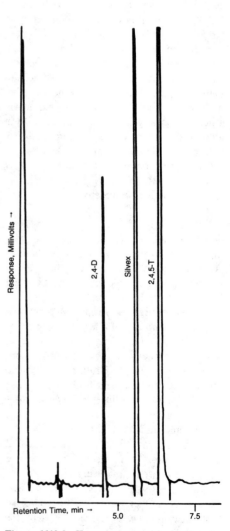

Figure 6640:2. Chromatogram of herbicide mixture. DB-5 column, 30 m long, electron-capture detector.

TABLE 6640:I. RETENTION TIMES FOR METHYL ESTERS OF SOME CHLORINATED PHENOXY ACID HERBICIDES RELATIVE TO 2,4-D METHYL ESTER

	Relative Retention Time for Given Liquid Phase*	
Herbicide	1.5% OV-17 + 1.95% QF-1	5% OV-210
2,4-D	1.00	1.00
Silvex	1.34	1.22
2,4,5-T	1.72	1.51
2,4-D (min absolute)	2.00	1.62

* All columns glass, 180 cm × 4 mm ID, solid support Gas Chrom Q (100/120 mesh); column temperature 185°C; argon/methane carrier flow, operated in pulse mode, 70 mL/min.

Report results as the methyl ester in micrograms per liter without correction for recovery efficiency.

6. Precision and Bias

Single-laboratory precision and recovery data are presented in Tables 6640:II and III. These data were obtained by analyzing surface water samples from six sources with three added herbicides.

7. Bibliography

METCALF, L.D. & A.A. SCHMITZ. 1961. The rapid preparation of fatty acid esters for gas chromatographic analysis. *Anal. Chem.* 33:363.

GOERLITZ, D.F. & W.L. LAMAR. 1967. Determination of phenoxy acid herbicides in water by electron-capture and microcoulometric gas chromatography. U.S. Geol. Surv. Water-Supply Paper 1817-C.

TABLE 6640:II. PRECISION OF PHENOXY ACID HERBICIDES FROM DOSED SURFACE WATER

Material	Concentration Range ng/L	Number of Samples	Recovery Average %	Single-Operator Precision S_o%
2,4-D	300–515	11	93	5.0
Silvex	70–290	12	94	6.5
2,4,5-T	90–290	12	100	8.0

TABLE 6640:III. RECOVERY OF PHENOXY ACID HERBICIDES FROM DOSED SURFACE WATER

Sample	Herbicide	Amount Added ng	Recovery %
1	2,4-D	308	94
	Silvex	70	87
	2,4,5-T	92	86
2	2,4-D	308	82
	Silvex	70	99
	2,4,5-T	92	110
3	2,4-D	308	90
	Silvex	70	81
	2,4,5-T	92	104
4	2,4-D	470	91
	Silvex	126	91
	2,4,5-T	140	86
5	2,4-D	470	97
	Silvex	126	86
	2,4,5-T	140	96
6	2,4-D	515	99
	Silvex	222	98
	2,4,5-T	221	104

PART 7000

EXAMINATION OF WATER

AND WASTEWATER FOR

RADIOACTIVITY

7010 INTRODUCTION*

7010 A. General Discussion

1. Occurrence and Monitoring

The radioactivity in water and waste-water originates from both natural sources and human activities. The latter include operations concerned with the nuclear fuel cycle, from mining to reprocessing; medical uses of radioisotopes; industrial uses of radioisotopes; worldwide fallout from atmospheric testing of nuclear devices; and enhancement of the concentration of naturally occurring radionuclides. Monitoring programs for water and wastewater should be designed to assess realistically the degree of environmental radioactive contamination. In some cases, for example, compliance monitoring for drinking water, the conditions are spelled out.[1] In others, it may be necessary to examine the individual situation[2] for consideration of the critical radionuclide(s), the critical pathway by which the critical radionuclide moves through the environment, and a critical population group that is exposed to the particular radionuclide(s) moving along this particular pathway. Use of the critical nuclide-pathway-population approach narrows the list of possible radionuclides to monitor. A list of the most hazardous radionuclides can be selected by examining the radioactivity concentration standards given by the International Committee on Radiation Protection (ICRP)[3], the Federal Radiation Council (FRC)[4], the National Committee on Radiation Protection and Measurement (NCRP)[2], the U.S. Environ-mental Protection Agency[1], and also agencies in other countries. Individual states within the United States may have their own radioactivity concentration standards if they are Nuclear Regulatory Commission (NRC) agreement states. With few exceptions, these numerical values for radioactivity concentrations in air and water are comparable if certain qualifying assumptions are applied.

Monitoring programs should provide adequate warning of unsafe environmental conditions so that proper precautions can be taken, and of course, to assure that conditions are safe when they are indeed safe. In either circumstance, it is necessary to establish base lines for the kinds and quantities of radionuclides present naturally and to measure additions to this natural background. In this way, measurements may be made to provide information for sound judgments regarding the hazardous or non-hazardous nature of increased concentrations.

2. Types of Measurement

Meaningful measurements require careful application of good scientific techniques. The types of measurements to be made are determined by the objectives of the testing. Gross alpha and gross beta measurements are relatively inexpensive, can be completed quickly, and are useful for screening to determine whether further analysis for specific radionuclides is merited. However, gross measurements give no information about the isotopic composition

---

*Approved by Standard Methods Committee, 1988.

of the sample, cannot be used to estimate radiation dose, and have poor sensitivity if the concentration of dissolved solids is high. Accurate gross beta and especially gross alpha measurements require careful preparation of standards to determine self-absorption and the ability to prepare samples in a similar manner.

Specific radionuclide measurements are required if dose estimates are to be made, results of gross analyses exceed a certain level, or long-term trends are being monitored. Specific analyses usually are more expensive and time-consuming than a gross analysis. Specific measurements identify radionuclides by the energy of emitted radiation, chemical techniques, half-life, or a combination of these characteristics. Gamma-emitting radionuclides can be measured rapidly and with a minimum of sample preparation by using gamma spectrometry. Measurements requiring chemical separations make it possible to increase the sensitivity by increasing the sample quantity measured.

Knowledge of the chemical and radio-chemical characteristics of the radionuclide being measured are critical for satisfactory results. Gross alpha and gross beta results will not provide accurate information about radionuclides having energies significantly different from the energy of the calibration standard. During concentration of water samples by evaporation, radionuclides present in elemental form (e.g., radioiodine, polonium) or as compounds (e.g., tritium, carbon-14) may be lost by volatilization. If the sample is ignited, the chance of volatilization loss is even greater. Groundwater generally contains nuclides of the uranium and thorium series. Use special care in sampling and analyzing such samples because members of these series often are not in secular equilibrium.

3. References

1. U.S. ENVIRONMENTAL PROTECTION AGENCY. 1986. Water Pollution Control; Radionuclides; Advance Notice of Proposed Rulemaking, 40 CFR, Part 141, 34836; *Federal Register* 51, No. 189.
2. NATIONAL COMMITTEE ON RADIATION PROTECTION AND MEASUREMENTS. 1959. Maximum Permissible Body Burdens and Maximum Permissible Concentrations of Radionuclides in Air and Water for Occupational Exposure. NBS Handbook No. 69, pp. 1, 17, 37, 38, & 93.
3. INTERNATIONAL COMMISSION ON RADIATION PROTECTION. 1979. Limits for Intakes of Radionuclides by Workers. ICRP Publ. 30, Pergamon Press, New York, N.Y.
4. FEDERAL RADIATION COUNCIL. 1961. Background Material for the Development of Radiation Protection Standards. Rep. No. 2 (Sept.), U.S. Government Printing Off., Washington, D.C.

4. Bibliography

CORYELL, C.D. & N. SUGARMAN, eds. 1951. Radiochemical Studies: The Fission Products. McGraw-Hill Book Co., New York, N.Y.

COMAR, C.I. 1955. Radioisotopes in Biology and Agriculture. McGraw-Hill Book Co., New York, N.Y.

FRIEDLANDER, G., J.W. KENNEDY & J.M. MILLER. 1964. Nuclear and Radiochemistry, 2nd ed. John Wiley & Sons, New York, N.Y.

LEDERER, C.M., J.M. HOLLANDER & I. PERLMANN. 1967. Table of Isotopes, 6th ed. John Wiley & Sons, New York, N.Y.

INTERNATIONAL ATOMIC ENERGY AGENCY. 1971. Disposal of Radioactive Wastes into Rivers, Lakes, and Estuaries. IAEA Safety Ser. No. 36, St. 1/PUB 283.

NATIONAL COUNCIL ON RADIATION PROTECTION AND MEASUREMENTS. 1976. Environmental Radiation Measurements. NCRP Rep. No. 50, Washington, D.C.

7010 B.   Sample Collection and Preservation

1. Collection

The principles of representative sampling of water and wastewater apply to sampling for radioactivity examinations (see Section 1060).

Because a radioactive element often is present in submicrogram quantities, a significant fraction may be lost by adsorption on the surface of containers used in the examination. Similarly, a radionuclide may be largely or wholly adsorbed on the surface of suspended particles.

Sample containers vary in size from 0.5 L to 18 L, depending on required analyses. Use containers of plastic (polyethylene or equivalent) or glass, except for tritium samples (use glass only). When radioactive industrial wastes or comparable materials are sampled, consider the possibility of deposition of radioactivity on surfaces of glassware, plastic containers, and equipment that may cause a loss of radioactivity and possible contamination of subsequent samples collected in inadequately cleansed containers.

2. Preservation

For general information on sample preservation see Section 1060. Add preservative at time of collection unless sample will be separated into suspended and dissolved fractions, but do not delay acid addition beyond 5 d. Use conc hydrochloric (HCl) or nitric (HNO$_3$) acid to obtain a pH < 2, except for radiocesium (use only conc HCl) and radioiodine and tritium (use no preservative). Hold acidified sample at least 16 h before analysis. For further details see references.[1-3]

Test preservatives and reagents for radioactive content.

3. Wastewater Samples

Wastewater often contains larger amounts of nonradioactive suspended and dissolved solids than does water and often most of the radioactivity is in the solid phase. Generally, the use of carriers in the analysis is ineffective without prior conversion of the solid phase to the soluble phase; even then high fixed solids may interfere with radioanalytical procedures. Table 7010:I shows the usual solubility characteristics of common radioelements in wastewater.

The radioelements may exhibit unusual chemical characteristics because of the presence of complexing agents or the method of waste production. For example, tritium may be combined in an organic compound when used in the manufacture of luminous articles; radioiodine from hospitals may occur as complex organic compounds, compared to elemental and iodide forms found in fission products from the processing of spent nuclear fuels; uranium and thorium daughter products often exist as inorganic complexes other than oxides after processing in uranium mills; the strontium 90 titanate waste from a radiois-

TABLE 7010:I. USUAL DISTRIBUTION OF COMMON RADIOELEMENTS BETWEEN THE SOLID AND LIQUID PHASES OF WASTEWATER

In Solution	In Suspension
HCO$_3$	Ce
Co	Cs
Cr	Mn
Cs	Nb
H	P
I	Pm
K	Pu
Ra	Ra
Rn	Sc
Ru	Th
Sb	U
Sr	Y
	Zn
	Zr

otope heat source would be quite insoluble compared to most other strontium wastes. Valuable information on the chemical composition of wastes, the behavior of radioelements, and the quantity of radioisotopes in use appears in the literature.[4,5]

4. References

1. U.S. GEOLOGICAL SURVEY. 1977. Methods for Determination of Radioactive Substances in Water and Fluvial Sediments. U.S. Government Printing Off., Washington, D.C.

2. HARLEY, J.H., ed. 1972. Environmental Measurements Procedures Manual. HASL-300, U.S. Dep. Energy, New York, N.Y.

3. U.S. ENVIRONMENTAL PROTECTION AGENCY. 1978. Manual for the Interim Certification of Laboratories Involved in Analyzing Public Drinking Water Supplies. EPA 600/8-78-008, Washington, D.C.

4. INTERNATIONAL ATOMIC ENERGY AGENCY. 1960. Disposal of Radioactive Wastes. International Atomic Energy Agency, Vienna, Austria.

5. NEMEROW, N.L. 1963. Industrial Waste Treatment Addison-Wesley, Reading, Mass.

7010 C. Counting Room

Design and construction of a counting room may vary widely. Provide a room free of dust and fumes that may affect electrical stability of instruments. Stabilize and reduce background radiation by making the walls, floor, and ceiling out of at least 5 cm of concrete but avoid using shales, granites, and sands containing sufficient natural activity to affect instrument background.

A modern chemical laboratory can be used to process routine environmental samples, but preferably segregate monitoring work from other laboratory operations.

Provide air-conditioning and humidity control depending on the number of instruments to be used and the prevailing climatic conditions. Generally, electronic instruments perform best when the temperature remains constant within 3°C and does not exceed 30°C. Keep the temperature inside the instrument chassis below the maximum specified by the manufacturer.

Humidity affects instrument performance even more than extremes of temperature because of moisture buildup on critical components. This causes leakage and arcing, and shortens the life of these components. A humidity between 30 and 80% usually is satisfactory.

Most counting instruments are supplied with constant-voltage regulators suitable for controlling minor fluctuations in line voltage. For unusual fluctuations use an auxiliary voltage regulator transformer. Use a manually reset voltage-sensitive device in series with a voltage regulator placed in the main power line to instruments to protect them in case of power failure or fluctuating line voltage.

Store samples containing appreciable activity at a distance so as not to affect instrument background counting rate.

Cover floors and desk tops with a material that can be cleaned easily or replaced as necessary.

7010 D. Counting Instruments

1. General Principles

Geiger-Mueller and proportional counters operate on the principle that the expenditure of energy by a radiation event causes ionization of counter gas and electron collection at the anode of the counting chamber. Through gas or electronic amplification, or both, the ion-collection event triggers an electronic scaler recorder.

The principle of scintillation counters is similar in that quanta of light produced by the interaction of a radiation event and the detection phosphor are seen by a photomultiplier tube. The tube converts the light pulse into an amplified electrical pulse that is recorded by an electronic scaler. Thallium-activated sodium iodide crystals and silver-activated zinc sulfide screens form useful scintillation detectors for counting gamma and alpha radioactivity, respectively. Semiconductor detectors are relatively new and are undergoing rapid changes. Alpha and gamma spectrometers using, respectively, silicon surface-barrier and lithium-drifted or intrinsic germanium detectors are available.

Characteristic of most counters is a background or instrument counting rate usually due to cosmic radiation, radioactive contaminants in instrument parts and counting room construction material, and the nearness of radioactive sources. The background is roughly proportional to the size or mass of the counting chamber or detector, but it can be reduced by metal shielding.

Instrument "noise," or the false recording of radiation events, may be caused by faulty circuitry, too sensitive a gain setting, high humidity, and variable line voltage or transients. Control these problems by using constant-voltage transformers with transient filters, properly adjusting gain setting as specified by the manufacturer, and air-conditioning the counting room.

2. Types of Counters

The internal proportional counter accepts counting pans within the counting chamber and at the beta operating voltage, records all alpha, all beta, and some gamma radiation emitted into the counting gas. Theoretically, half the radiation is emitted in the direction of the counting pan. Some of the beta radiation, but only 1 to 2% of the alpha radiation, is back-scattered into the counting gas by sample solids, the counting pan, or the walls of the counting chamber. For substantially weightless samples, considerably more than 60% of the beta radiation and about 50% of the alpha radiation are counted. However, take considerable care in sample preparation to prevent the sample or counting pan from distorting the electrical field of the counter and depressing the counting rate. Avoid nonconducting surfaces, airborne dusts, and vapor from moisture or solvents.

End-window Geiger-Mueller counting tubes are rugged and stable counting detectors. Samples usually are mounted 5 to 15 mm from the window. Under these conditions, most alpha and weak beta radiations are stopped completely by the air gap and mica window and are not counted. Counting efficiencies for mixed fission products frequently are less than 10% for substantially weightless samples having an area less than that of the window. Because most Geiger-Mueller tubes have diameters of about 2.5 cm, the pan size—and, as a consequence, the sample volume—is restricted. Under these conditions, detectability is low and uncertain, particularly for unknown sources of radiation. On the other hand, Geiger-Mueller tubes are excellent for counting samples of tracers or purified radionuclides. Prepare standard sample mounts that yield reproducible counting efficiencies for which counting is not affected by the electrical conductance of sample pans.

Thin-window (polyester plastic film* less than 250 µg/cm²) tubes approximately 5 cm in diameter provide counting efficiencies intermediate between those of conventional Geiger-Mueller tubes and internal counters. Counting alpha activity in these thin-window counters is satisfactory.

Thin-window counters with chamber diameter greater than 60 mm and sample mount diameter greater than 50 mm are preferable to Geiger-Mueller tubes. These counting chambers have good operational stability and less interference from non-conducting surfaces and moisture vapors than internal proportional counters.

3. Internal Proportional Counters

a. Uses: Internal proportional counters are suitable for determining alpha activity at the alpha operating plateau and alpha-plus-beta activity at the beta operating plateau. The alpha or beta activity, or both, can refer to a single or to several radionuclides.

Use instruments consisting of a counting chamber, a preamplifier, and a scaler with high-voltage power supply, timer, and register. Use the specified counting gas and accessories, make adjustments for sensitivity, and use in accordance with manufacturer's operating instructions.

b. Plateau (alpha or beta): Find the operating voltage where the counting rate is constant, i.e., varies less than 5% over a 150-V change in anode voltage:

1) With the instrument in operating order, place the alpha or beta standard (see Section 7010E.3) in the chamber, close, and flush with counter gas for 2 to 5 min.

2) Use the manufacturer's recommended operating voltage and count for a convenient time giving an acceptable coefficient of variation, preferably 2%. Repeat at voltages higher and lower than the suggested operating voltage in increments of 50 V. (CAUTION: *Instrument damage will result from prolonged continuous discharge at too high a voltage.*)

3) Plot relative counting rate (ordinate) against anode voltage (abscissa). A plateau at least 150 V long with a slope of 5% or less should result (see Figure 7010:1). Select an anode voltage near the center of this plateau as the operating voltage.

c. Counter stability: Check instrument stability at the operating voltage by counting the plateau source daily (see Section 7010E.3). If the source count is within two standard deviations of the previously determined mean count rate, proceed as in *d* following. If the source count is not so reproduced, repeat the test. If stability is not attained, service the instrument.

d. Background: Determine the background (with an empty counting pan in the counting chamber). Use a background counting time as long as the longest sample-counting time. Make control charts as an aid in stability testing.

e. Sample counting: Place dry sample on a counting pan in the counting chamber and ground pan to chamber piston. Flush with counter gas and count for a preset time, or preset count, to give the desired counting precision (see Section 7010G).

4. End-Window Counters

End-window counters may be used for beta-gamma and absorption examinations. Most alpha and soft beta radiations are stopped by the air gap and window. Use a sample pan with a diameter less than that of the window and, for maximum efficiency, place it as close to the window as possible. House detector inside a 5-cm-thick lead shield to improve counting sensitivity by decreasing background by about

---

*Mylar or equivalent.

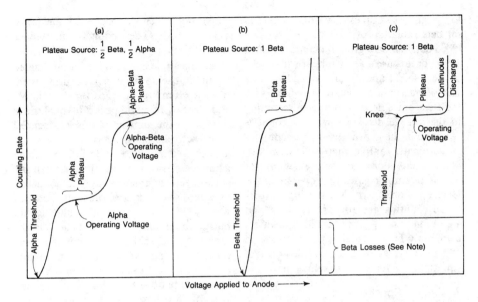

Figure 7010:1. Shape of counting rate—anode voltage curves. Key: (a) and (b) are for internal proportional counter with P-10 gas; (c) is for end-window Geiger-Mueller counter with Geiger gas. (Note: Beta losses are dependent on energy of radiation and thickness of window and air path.)

50%. Use associated equipment consisting of a scaler having a timer, a register, and a high-voltage power supply.

See ¶s 3a-e above for operation and calibration.

Coincidence correction: Geiger-Mueller counters commonly have resolving times of 100 to 400 μs; therefore, correct data on samples of high counting rate for loss in counts.

5. Thin-Window Proportional Counter

The thin-window proportional counter, without heavy shielding and/or anti-coincidence guard circuitry, has application for counting moderate to high levels and for counting residues that adhere poorly to the counting pan. The counters detect alpha and low-energy beta emitters. They are about one-half as sensitive as internal proportional counters because the geometry of counting is not as favorable and absorption losses (air path and window) are greater.

Because the sample is outside, this counter is less affected than the internal proportional counter by contamination from loose residues, losses due to residue moisture, and poor electrical conductance. See ¶s 3a-e above for operation and calibration.

6. Low-Background Beta Counter

The low-background counter is useful for measurements as low as 0.1 and as high as 50 pCi/sample. Higher activity levels, to about 1000 pCi, can be counted if other beta detectors are not available. The counters are designed primarily for beta emitters having a maximum beta energy above 0.3 MeV but are suitable also for determining alpha activity when operated in the proportional region.

The detector window thickness usually is less than 1.0 mg/cm^2 and attenuation of high-energy beta rays is relatively minor. Use sample pans with a diameter less than that of the window. Counting efficiencies for weightless samples vary from 30 to 55% for beta radiation of moderate energy.

To obtain a background counting rate of 1 cpm or less use an instrument with a lead or steel shield and an anticoincidence device of one or more guard detectors with the electronics needed to prevent counting in the sample detectors when a count is recorded in the guard. An instrument with an automatic sample changer is desirable. Some counters of this type use helium-isobutane or similar gases that operate in the Geiger region. Instruments using proportional counting gas also are available and are preferred. Geiger-Mueller counters commonly have resolving times of 100 to 400 μs. Correct data on samples of high counting rate for loss of counts.

7. Gamma Spectrometer

Gamma spectrum analysis may be made with a minimum of sample preparation. Unless a very complex spectrum with overlapping photopeaks is obtained, chemical separation followed by gamma analysis for quantitative measurements on each sample fraction is unnecessary. This method normally excludes nongamma-emitting radionuclides, and those having photon emission energies less than 0.01 MeV usually are measured with considerable uncertainty. Two types of gamma spectrometers are in use: the sodium iodide, thallium-activated [NaI(Tl)] crystal system using a scintillation phenomenon and germanium diodes, some with lithium activation [Ge(Li)]. For details on operation and calibration of gamma spectrum analyzer see manufacturer's instructions.

a. *Principle:* Gamma photons from a sample enter the sensitive volume of the detector and interact with detector atoms. The interactions are converted to an electrical voltage pulse proportional to the photon energy. Pulses are stored in sequence in finite energy-equivalent increments (such as 0.02 MeV/channel for NaI systems and 0.001 MeV/channel for Ge systems) over the entire spectrum range (such as 0.1 to 2 MeV) depending on instrument capabilities and operator choice.

After sample counting, the accumulated counts in each energy increment of an entire spectrum are analyzed for the number and energy of photopeaks (a qualitative test) or for the number of pulses associated with each photopeak, corrected for background count and interference from gamma emissions (a quantitative test). Because each gamma-emitting radionuclide usually has several photopeaks, one of which yields the greatest abundance of pulses, the number of radionuclides in the sample to be analyzed is limited by the probability that overlapping or interfering photopeaks will cause errors in a quantitative estimation. For NaI systems, analysis of four to eight components is practical. With more complex mixtures, use chemical separation followed by gamma spectrum analysis of each fraction, or use a Ge system.

1) In NaI crystal systems, the interaction of gamma photons with the detector gives rise to pulses of light that are proportional in intensity to the gamma photon energy. Light pulses enter a photomultiplier tube (PMT) and are converted to electrical voltage pulses proportional to the light (scintillation) intensity. Because of the components involved, the resolving time is about 10^{-9} s.

2) In Ge diode detector systems, the interaction of gamma photons with the detector ionizes detector atoms. A bias voltage applied to the detector allows collection of electrons proportional to the deposited photon energy with a resolving time of 10^{-9} to 10^{-13} s. Such a system has exceptionally high resolution.

b. *Components:* A gamma spectrometer consists of a detector, pulse-height analyzer system, data readout capability, and a shielded enclosure. Connect the detector to a preamplifier and a high-voltage power supply. Place detector and sample in a metal shield (10 to 20 cm steel or equivalent) to reduce external radiation background level. The pulse-height analyzer system consists of a linear amplifier, a biased linear amplifier, an analog-to-digital converter (ADC), memory storage, and a logic control mechanism. The logic control capability permits data storage in various modes and display or recall of data. The data readout system contains one or more of the following: an oscilloscope for visual display, a readout indicator, an electric typewriter or digital printer, a magnetic-tape recorder, a strip-chart recorder, an x-y recorder or plotter, and a computer terminal with associated capabilities. The oscilloscope is useful in aligning the instrument with standards such as ^{60}Co, ^{137}Cs, and ^{207}Bi. Computer capability is essential in data reduction and in complex spectrum stripping procedures.

A common scintillation (NaI) detector is a crystal 10 cm in diameter by 10 cm thick hermetically sealed in a container that is optically coupled to a photomultiplier tube.

A common high-resolution germanium detector consists of a diode of over 30 cm^3 sensitive volume encased in a 7.6-cm-diam vacuum-sealed cylinder with a dip-stick immersed in liquid nitrogen in a large cryostat, a preamplifier, and a detector bias voltage supply. The detector is cooled with liquid nitrogen to protect the diode and to reduce electronic noise generation. Both lithium-drifted and intrinsic germanium detectors are operated at the temperature of liquid nitrogen. The former detector must be maintained at the liquid nitrogen temperature at all times while the latter can be shipped or stored at ambient temperature. Use a linear amplifier that will maintain the pulse resolution provided by the detector.

A single-channel gamma spectrum analyzer is similar to a multichannel analyzer but is limited to the examination of a single energy range at a time. The instrument is best used for continuous monitoring of a waste having fixed radionuclide composition, making gross gamma measurements, or measuring a single gamma-emitting radionuclide. It is similar to the multichannel analyzer except that the design is comparatively inexpensive.

8. Alpha Spectrometer

Semiconductor particle detectors, that is, silicon surface-barrier detectors, are used for alpha spectrometry. Detector performance is affected primarily by resolution, active area, and depletion depth. Chemical separation of the sample followed by monomolecular electrodeposition on counting planchets is required. Count under a high vacuum. For details on operation and calibration of alpha spectrum analysis see manufacturer's instructions.

a. Principle: Alpha emissions from a sample enter a sensitive detector volume and interact with detector atoms. Ionization of the detector and collection of the electrons by use of a bias voltage applied to the detector allows the generation of an electrical voltage pulse proportional to the deposited alpha particle energy.

b. Components: An alpha spectrometer consists of a detector, a vacuum chamber for the detector and sample, a preamplifier, a detector bias voltage supply, a linear amplifier, a biased amplifier, a mechanical vacuum pump, a multichannel analyzer (with ADC and memory storage) or single-channel analyzer, and data readout capability similar to that discussed under gamma spectrometry.

9. Alpha Scintillation Counter

When an alpha particle bombards an impure crystal of zinc sulfide, a portion of the kinetic energy is transformed into visible light. The sulfide scintillates more efficiently when it contains silver impurities and when the duration of the light pulse is shortened by the presence of nickel ions.

The alpha scintillation counter consists

of a phosphor detector coupled to a photomultiplier, a high-voltage supply, an amplifier-discriminator, and a scaler. Generally, the photomultiplier tube has a window diameter greater than that of the sample unless the phosphor is coupled to a light-focusing optical system.

Place the silver-activated and nickel-quenched zinc sulfide phosphor near, or in contact with, the alpha-emitting sample and arrange it so that a photomultiplier tube observes the light pulses, which are amplified and recorded on the scaler.

Mount solid samples in a thin layer (less than 3 mg/cm^2) on a planchet. Place the phosphor between the sample and the photomultiplier tube. Enclose sample and detector in a light-tight chamber 3 to 5 mm from the phototube window. Under these conditions counting efficiency is from 35 to 40%.

Gaseous samples contained in a dome-shaped cell coated with zinc sulfide "paint" are observed more efficiently than solid samples.

10. Liquid Beta Scintillation Counter

When a sample containing radionuclides is mixed with an organic liquid scintillator, light is produced. The flashes of light are detected and amplified by one or more photomultiplier tubes.

Liquid scintillation counters are well suited for counting low-energy beta emitters such as tritium or carbon 14 because self-absorption losses are eliminated. Counting efficiencies approach 100% for high-energy betas, but for tritium the efficiency is much lower because the beta pulses, lowest in energy, are at the level of the "dark current" pulses from the photomultiplier tube and are discriminated against to reduce background. Most liquid scintillation instruments use two photomultipliers in coincidence to reduce background from "dark current." Most liquid scintillation counter systems incorporate at least a two-channel analyzer, which permits more than one beta emitter to be counted at the same time if the respective maximum beta energies differ by a factor of at least three.

Dissolve or suspend the sample in a liquid scintillation solution. Place sample in a transparent or translucent bottle to enable the light flashes to be transmitted to the phototube. Use a calibration standard containing the same radionuclide prepared in the same medium. Determine background by counting a bottle containing both solvent and scintillator. Measure background at least once daily.

11. Bibliography

NADER, J.S., G.R. HAGEE & L.R. SETTER. 1954. Evaluating the performance of the internal counter. *Nucleonics* 12(6):29.

CROUTHAMEL, C.E., ed. 1960. Applied Gamma-Ray Spectrometry. Pergamon Press, New York, N.Y., Vol. II.

TAYLOR, J.M. 1963. Semiconductor Particle Detectors. Butterworths, Washington, D.C.

GOULDING, F.S. 1964. A survey of the applications and limitations of various types of detectors in radiation energy measurement. *IEEE Trans. Nucl. Sci.* NS-11:177.

GOULDING, F.S. 1964. Semiconductor detectors—their properties and applications. *Nucleonics* 22(5):54.

HEATH, R.L. 1964. Scintillation Spectrometry, Gamma Ray Spectrum. IDO-16880, Technical Information Div., U.S. Atomic Energy Comm., Washington, D.C., Vols. 1 & 2.

SIEGBAHN, K., ed. 1965. Alpha, Beta, and Gamma Ray Spectroscopy. Vol. 1. North Holland Publishing Co., Amsterdam.

DEARNALEY, G. & D.C. NORTHROP. 1966. Semiductor Counters for Nuclear Radiations, 2nd ed. John Wiley & Sons, New York, N.Y.

DEARNALEY, G. 1966. Nuclear detection by solid state devices. *J. Sci. Instrum.* 43:869.

LOS ALAMOS SCIENTIFIC LABORATORY, RADIOCHEMISTRY GROUP J-11. 1967. Collected Radiochemical Procedures, 3rd ed. Rep. No. LA-1721, U.S. Atomic Energy Comm., Washington, D.C.

BOLOGNA, J.A. & S.B. HELMICH. 1969. An Atlas of Gamma Ray Spectra, LA 4312.

FRENCH, W.R., JR., R.L. LaSHURE & J.L. CURRAN. 1969. Lithium drifted germanium detectors. *Amer. J. Phys.* 37:11.

FRENCH, W.R., JR., W.M. WEHRBEIN & S.E. MOORE. 1969. Measurement of photoelectric, Compton, and pair-production cross sections in germanium. *Amer. J. Phys.* 37:391.

MCKENZIE, J.M. 1969. Index to the Literature of Semiconductor Detectors. U.S. Government Printing Off., Washington, D.C.

GOULDING, F.S. & Y. STONE. 1970. Semiconductor radiation detectors. *Science* 170:281.

HEATH, R.L. 1974. Gamma Ray Spectrum Catalogue, Ge(Li) and Si(Li) Spectrometry. ANCR-1000-2, National Technical Information Serv., Springfield, Va.

7010 E.   Laboratory Reagents and Apparatus

See Section 1070 for basic standards applying to laboratory reagents and apparatus. The following special instructions are pertinent:

1. Reagents and Distilled Water

Periodically check the background radioactivity of all solutions and reagents used. Discard those having a radioactivity level that significantly interferes with the test.

2. Apparatus

Before reuse, thoroughly decontaminate apparatus and glassware with detergents and complexing agents, followed, if necessary, by acid and distilled-water rinses. Segregate equipment and glassware for storage and reuse on samples of comparable activity, i.e., keep apparatus for background and low-level counting separate from that for higher levels by using distinctive markings and different storage cabinets or laboratories. Preferably use single-use counting pans, planchets, and auxiliary supplies. Glassware that is slightly radiocontaminated may be entirely satisfactory for use in chemical tests but is unsatisfactory for radioanalysis.

3. Radioactivity Sources

a. Solutions: Use standard solutions having calibrations traceable to sources of radioactivity certified by the National Institute of Standards and Technology (NIST), formerly National Bureau of Standards (NBS).

b. Plateau or check sources:

1) Alpha—Uranium oxide (U_3O_8) plated, not less than 45 mm in diameter, having an alpha activity of about 10 000 cpm, or plutonium or americium plated as a weightless alpha standard source.

2) Beta—Cover uranium oxide (U_3O_8), plated as described above, with 8 to 10 mg/cm^2 aluminum foil, or use cesium 137, strontium 90-yttrium 90 in equilibrium, or any other long-lived beta emitter.

7010 F.   Expression of Results

Preferably report results of radioactivity analyses in terms of picocuries per liter (pCi/L) at 20°C or, for samples of specific gravity significantly different from 1.00, picocuries per gram where 1 pCi = 10^{-12} Ci = 2.22 dpm. For samples normally containing 1000 to 1 000 000 pCi/unit volume or weight, use the nanocurie (nCi) unit (1 nCi = 10^{-9} Ci = 1000 pCi). For values higher than 1000 nCi, use the microcurie (μCi) unit (1 μCi = 10^{-6} Ci = 10^6 pCi).

Report results in such a way that they do not imply greater or lesser precision than can be obtained by the method used. See Section 1030.

"Gross alpha" implies unknown alpha

sources in which natural uranium, ^{239}Pu, or ^{241}Am has been used to determine self-absorption and efficiency factors.

"Gross beta" implies unknown sources of beta, including some gamma radiation, and calibration with ^{137}Cs or ^{90}Sr-^{90}Y in equilibrium.

7010 G. Statistics

Section 1030 discusses the statistics of analytical problems as applied to chemical constituents. These remarks also are generally applicable to radioactivity examinations.

1. Standard Deviation and Counting Error

The variability of any measurement is described by the standard deviation, which can be obtained from replicate determinations. There is an inherent variability in radioactivity measurements because disintegrations occur in a random manner described by the Poisson distribution. This distribution is characterized by the standard deviation of a large number of events, N, that equals its square root, or:

$$\sigma(N) = N^{1/2}$$

For ease in mathematical application, the normal (Gaussian) approximation to the Poisson distribution ordinarily is used. This approximation, which generally is valid at $N \geq 20$, is the particular normal distribution with a mean of N and standard deviation of $N^{1/2}$.

More often, the concern is not with the standard deviation of the number of counts but rather with the deviation in rate (number of counts per unit time):

$$R' = \frac{N}{t}$$

where:

t = time of observation.

The standard deviation in the counting rate, $\sigma(R')$, is calculated by usual methods for propagation of error:

$$\sigma(R') = \frac{N^{1/2}}{t} = \frac{(R' t)^{1/2}}{t} = \left(\frac{R'}{t}\right)^{1/2}$$

In practice, all counting instruments have a background counting rate, B, when no sample is present. With a sample, the counting rate increases to R_O. The counting rate R due to the sample is:

$$R = R_o - B$$

By propagation-of-error methods, calculate the standard deviation of R as follows:

$$\sigma(R) = \left(\frac{R_o}{t_1} + \frac{B}{t_2}\right)^{1/2}$$

where:

t_1, t_2 = times at which the gross sample and background counting rates were measured, respectively.

Counting times depend on the limit of detection required (see ¶ 2 below). It is desirable to divide the counting time into equal periods to check constancy of the observed counting rate. For low-level counting, use $t_1 = t_2$. The error thus calculated includes only the error caused by inherent variability of the radioactive disintegration process. Report it as the "counting error."

Use a confidence level of 95%, or 1.96 standard deviations, as the counting error.

2. Limit of Detection

Different conventions with differing terminology and mathematics have been used to estimate the lower limit of detection (LLD) or the minimum detectable activity (MDA).[1-3] To eliminate confusion and the production of noncomparable data, it is proposed that the Environmental Measurements Laboratory procedure[1] be used exclusively. The basis of this procedure is hypothesis testing. LLD is defined as the smallest quantity of sample radioactivity that will yield a net count for which there is a predetermined level of confidence that radioactivity is present. Two errors may occur: Type I, in which a false conclusion is reached that radioactivity is present, and Type II, with a false conclusion that radioactivity is absent.

The LLD may be approximated as

$$LLD \cong (K_\alpha + K_\beta) S_O$$

where:

K_α = value for the upper percentile of the standardized normal variate corresponding to the preselected risk of concluding falsely that activity is present (α),

K_β = the corresponding value for the predetermined degree of confidence for detecting presence of activity ($1 - \beta$), and

S_O = estimated standard error of the net sample counting rate.

For sample and background counting rates that are similar (as is expected at or near the LLD) and for α and β equal to 0.05, the smallest amount of radioactivity that has a 95% probability of being detected is,

$$LLD_{95} = 4.66 \, S_b$$

where:

S_b = standard deviation of the instrument background counting rate.

The LLD thus calculated is in units of counts per minute; to convert to concentration use the appropriate factors of sample volume, counting efficiency, etc. Note that the approximation $LLD = 4.66 \, S_b$ can be used only for determinations where S_b is known so that $S_O = \sqrt{2} \, S_b$ and there are no counting interferences. Examples of appropriate determinations are tritium, gross alpha or beta, or any single nuclide determination.

Where tracers are added to determine yield or more than one radionuclide is counted in a sample, use the general form of the equation above, for which the 95% confidence level would be $LLD \simeq 3.29 \, S_O$.

3. References

1. HARLEY, J.H., ed. 1972. Environmental Measurements Procedures Manual. HASL-300, U.S. Dep. Energy, New York, N.Y.

2. NATIONAL COUNCIL ON RADIATION PROTECTION AND MEASUREMENTS. 1978. A Handbook of Radioactivity Measurement Procedures. NCRP Rep. No. 58, Washington, D.C.

3. AMERICAN NATIONAL STANDARDS INSTITUTE. 1974. American National Standard Specifications and Performance of On-Site Instrumentation for Continuously Monitoring Radioactivity in Effluents. ANSI N13 10-1974, Inst. Electrical Electronics Engineers, Inc., New York, N.Y.

4. Bibliography

JARRETT. A.A. 1946. Statistical Methods Used in the Measurement of Radioactivity (Some Useful Graphs). Document No. AECU-262 (June 17). U.S. Atomic Energy Comm., Washington, D.C.

7020   QUALITY ASSURANCE*

7020 A.   Basic Quality Assurance Program

1. Program Elements

The continuous application of quality assurance principles to radiological measurements results in consistent data, but does not guarantee accuracy. Accurate data are both precise and unbiased. To obtain them requires day-to-day control over instrumentation, chemical processing, and associated factors. Use of three allied but independent procedures is most useful: (a) "blind" replicate analysis of real samples to evaluate within laboratory precision or reproducibility; (b) cross-check analysis of natural samples among several laboratories to determine agreement with other laboratories; and (c) analysis of standard samples to determine accuracy, i.e., the agreement of results with a known value. Process real samples as part of the normal laboratory workload but submit replicates to analysis without the knowledge of the analyst. Obtain natural samples for interlaboratory checking by collecting larger-than-normal samples and subdividing them for distribution. Standard samples may be natural samples or carefully prepared simulated environmental samples to which have been added known or accurately determined concentrations of appropriate radionuclides.

To conduct cross-check and standard analysis evaluations most effectively, use an independent referee laboratory. Standard samples may be used within a single laboratory, but exercise extreme care to prepare the samples by an accurate means divorced from the analytical method being studied. Statistically analyze all quality-assurance data to permit making firm conclusions about validity. Use control charts to simplify measuring the amounts by which the mean value of several individual determinations is biased from the true value. If a mean value fails to fall within the limits established by the mean chart, the analytical results are not from the expected normal distribution.

The overriding factor in a successful quality-control program is proper selection of criteria for acceptable and attainable accuracy. Through experimentation and experience, select criteria that reflect both the capabilities of the laboratory and the requirements of the users of the laboratory output. Secondly, select a sufficient number of samples to test properly whether the analytical data meet the established criteria.

2. Standard Sample Sources

At present standard samples of environmental materials and standardized radioisotope solutions are available from the International Atomic Energy Agency (IAEA),[†] the U.S. National Institute of Standards and Technology,[‡] and the U.S. Environmental Protection Agency.[§] Participation is possible in intercomparison programs sponsored by IAEA, EPA, or the World Health Organization.[||]

---

*Approved by Standard Methods Committee, 1988.

[†]International Atomic Energy Agency, Div. of Research and Laboratories, Kaerntner Ring, 1010 Vienna, Austria.
[‡]National Institute of Standards and Technology (formerly National Bureau of Standards), Center for Radiation Research, Radiochemistry Section, Washington, D.C. 20234.
[§]Environmental Monitoring Systems Laboratory, Nuclear Radiation Division, Radioanalysis Branch, P.O. Box 93478, Las Vegas, Nev. 89193-3478.
[||]World Health Organization, Geneva, Switzerland.

3. Bibliography

INHORN, S.L., ed. 1978. Quality Assurance Practices for Health Laboratories American Public Health Assoc., Washington, D.C.

WATSON, J.E. 1980. Upgrading Environmental Radiation Data. Health Physics Soc. Rep. HPSR-1, EPA 520/1-80-012.

7020 B.   Quality Assurance for Wastewater Samples

Generally it is not feasible to perform collaborative (interlaboratory) analyses of wastewater samples because of the variable composition of elements and solids from one facility to the next. The methods included herein have been evaluated by use of homogeneous samples and are useful for nonhomogeneous samples after sample preparation (wet or dry oxidation and/or fusion and solution) resulting in homogeneity. A potential problem or characteristic of reference samples used for collaborative testing is that they may be deficient in radioelements exhibiting interferences because of decay during shipment of short-half-life radionuclides. Generally, however, analytical steps have been incorporated into the methods to eliminate these interferences, even though they may not be necessary for the reference samples under study.

7110   GROSS ALPHA AND GROSS BETA RADIOACTIVITY (TOTAL, SUSPENDED, AND DISSOLVED)*

7110 A.   Introduction

1. Occurrence

a. Natural radioactivity: Uranium, thorium, and radium are naturally occurring radioactive elements that have a long series of radioactive daughters that emit alpha or beta and gamma radiations until a stable end-element is produced. These naturally occurring elements, through their radioactive daughter gases, radon and thoron, cause an appreciable airborne particulate activity and contribute to the radioactivity of rain and groundwaters. Additional naturally radioactive elements include potassium 40, rubidium 87, samarium 147, lutetium 176, and rhenium 187.

b. Artificial radioactivity: With the development and operation of nuclear reactors and other atom-smashing machines, large quantities of radioactive elements are being produced. These include almost all the elements in the periodic table.

2. Significance

The Environmental Protection Agency has established maximum contaminant levels for radium 226, radium 228, and gross alpha as follows: combined radium 226 and 228, 5 pCi/L; gross alpha (including rad-

---

*Approved by Standard Methods Committee, 1985.

ium 226 but excluding radon and uranium), 15 pCi/L. For beta particles and photon radioactivity from artificial radionuclides in community water systems, the maximum contaminant levels are intended to produce an annual dose equivalent to the total body or any internal organ of less than 4 millirem/year. Specifically, if the average annual concentration of gross beta activity is less than 50 pCi/L and if the average annual concentrations of tritium and strontium 90 are less than 20 000 pCi/L and 8 pCi/L, respectively, no further analyses are required. If the gross beta activity exceeds 50 pCi/L, the major radioactive contaminants must be identified and organ and whole body doses calculated; the combined doses shall not exceed 4 millirem/year.

With the simpler techniques for routine measurement of gross beta activity, the presence of contamination may be determined in a matter of hours, whereas days may be required to make the radiochemical analyses necessary to identify radionuclides present.

Regular measurements of gross alpha and gross beta activity in water may be invaluable for early detection of radioactive contamination and indicate the need for supplemental data on concentrations of more hazardous radionuclides.

3. Bibliography

U.S ENVIRONMENTAL PROTECTION AGENCY. 1976. Drinking Water Regulations. Radionuclides. *Fed. Reg.* 41:28402.

7110 B.   Counting Method

1. General Discussion

a. Selection of counting instrument: The thin-window, heavily shielded, gas-flow, anticoincidence-circuitry proportional counter is the recommended instrument for counting gross alpha and beta radioactivity because of its superior operating characteristics. These include a very low background and a high sensitivity to detect and count an alpha and beta radiation range that is reasonable but not so wide as that of internal proportional counters. Calibrate the instrument by adding standard nuclide portions to media comparable to the samples and preparing, mounting, and counting the standards exactly as the samples.

An internal proportional or Geiger counter also may be used; however, the internal proportional counter has a higher background for beta counting than the thin-window counter and alpha activity cannot be determined separately with a Geiger counter. Alpha activity can be measured with either a thin-window or internal proportional counter; counting efficiency is higher for the internal counter.

b. Calibration standard: When gross beta activity is assayed in samples containing mixtures of naturally radioactive elements and fission products, the choice of a calibration standard may influence the beta results significantly because self-absorption factors and counting chamber characteristics are beta-energy-dependent.

A standard solution of cesium 137, certified by the National Institute of Standards and Technology (NIST, formerly National Bureau of Standards, NBS) or traceable to a certified source, is recommended for calibration of counter efficiency and self-absorption for gross beta determinations. The half-life of cesium 137 is about 30 years. The daughter products after beta decay of cesium 137 are stable barium 137 and metastable barium 137, which in turn disintegrates by gamma emission. For this reason, the standardization of cesium 137 solutions may be stated in terms of the gamma emission rate per milliliter or per gram. To convert gamma rate to equivalent beta disintegration rate, multiply the calibrated gamma emission rate by 1.29.

Strontium 90 in equilibrium with its daughter yttrium 90 also is a suitable gross beta standard; its use is recommended by EPA.[1]

Note that gross beta results are meaningless unless the calibration standard also is reported.

c. Radiation lost by self-absorption: The radiation from alpha emitters having an energy of 8 MeV and from beta emitters having an energy of 60 KeV will not escape from the sample if the emitters are covered by a sample thickness of 5.5 mg/cm^2. The radiation from a weak alpha emitter will be stopped if covered by only 4 mg/cm^2 of sample solids. Consequently, for low-level counting it is imperative to evaporate all moisture and preferable to destroy organic matter before depositing a thin film of sample solids from which radiation may enter the counter. In counting water samples for gross beta radioactivity, a solids thickness of 10 mg/cm^2 or less on the bottom area of the counting pan is recommended. For the most accurate results, determine the self-absorption factor as outlined below.

d. Calibration of overall counter efficiency: Correct observed counting rate for geometry, back-scatter, and self-absorption (sample absorption).

Although it is useful to know the variation in these individual factors, determine overall efficiency by preparing standard sample sources and unknowns.

1) For measuring mixed fission products or beta radioactivity of unknown composition, use a standard solution of cesium 137 or strontium 90 in equilibrium with its daughter yttrium 90.

Prepare a standard (known disintegration rate) in an aqueous solution of sample solids similar in composition to that present in samples. Dispense increments of solution in tared pans and evaporate. Make a series of samples having a solids thickness of 1 to 10 mg/cm^2 of bottom area in the counting pan. Evaporate carefully to obtain uniform solids deposition. Dry (103 to 105°C), weigh, and count. Calculate the ratio of counts per minute to disintegrations per minute (efficiency) for different weights of sample solids. Plot efficiency as a function of sample thickness and use the resulting calibration curve to convert counts per minute (cpm) to disintegrations per minute (dpm).

2) If other radionuclides are to be tested, repeat the above procedure, using certified solutions of each radionuclide. Avoid unequal distribution of sample solids, particularly in the 0- to 3-mg/cm^2 range, in both calibration and sample preparation.

3) For alpha calibration, proceed as above, using a standard solution of natural uranium salt (not depleted uranium), plutonium 239, or americium 241. Recount alpha standard at the beta operating voltage and determine alpha amplification factor (¶5*b* below). Report calibration standard used with results.

2. Apparatus

a. Counting pans, of metal resistant to corrosion from sample solids or reagents, about 50 mm diam, 6 to 10 mm in height, and thick enough to be serviceable for one-time use. Stainless steel planchets are recommended for acidified samples.

b. Thin end-window proportional counter, capable of accommodating a counting pan.

c. Alternate counters: Other beta counters are internal proportional and Geiger counters.

d. Membrane filter, * 0.45-μm pore diam.

e. Gooch crucibles.

f. Counting gas, as recommended by the instrument manufacturer.

---

*Type HA, Millipore Filter Corp., Bedford, Mass., or equivalent.

3. Reagents

a. Methyl orange indicator solution.

b. Nitric acid, HNO_3, *1N.*

c. Clear acrylic solution: Dissolve 50 mg clear acrylic† in 100 mL acetone.

d. Ethyl alcohol, 95%.

e. Conducting fluid:‡ Prepare according to manufacturer's directions (for internal counters).

f. Standard certified cesium 137 or strontium 90-yttrium 90 solution.§

g. Standard certified americium 241,§ *plutonium 239,*§ *or natural uranium solution.*§ For natural uranium, use material in secular equilibrium.

h. Reagents for wet-combustion procedure:

1) *Nitric acid,* HNO_3, *6N.*

2) *Hydrogen peroxide solution:* Dilute 30% H_2O_2 with an equal volume of water.

4. Procedure

a. Total sample activity:

1) For each 20 cm² of counting pan area, take a volume of sample containing not more than 200 mg residue for beta examination and not more than 100 mg residue for alpha examination. The specific conductance test helps to select the appropriate sample volume.

2) Evaporate by either of the following techniques:

a) Add sample directly to a tared counting pan in small increments, with evaporation at just below boiling temperature. This procedure is not recommended for large samples.

b) Place sample in a borosilicate glass beaker or evaporating dish, add a few drops of methyl orange indicator solution, add 1N HNO_3 dropwise to pH 4 to 6, and evaporate on a hot plate or steam bath to near dryness. Avoid baking solids on evaporation vessel. Transfer to a tared counting pan with the aid of a rubber policeman and distilled water from a wash bottle. Using a rubber policeman, thoroughly wet walls of evaporating vessel with a few drops of acid and transfer washings to counting pan. (Excess alkalinity or mineral acidity is corrosive to aluminum counting pans.)

3) Complete drying in an oven at 103 to 105°C, cool in a desiccator, weigh, and keep dry until counted.

4) Treat sample residues having particles that tend to be airborne with a few drops of clear acrylic solution, then air- and oven-dry and weigh.

5) With a thin end-window counter count alpha and/or beta activity.

6) Store sample in a desiccator and count for decay if necessary. Avoid heat treatment because it will increase the escape rate of gaseous daughter products.

b. Activity of dissolved matter: Proceed as in ¶ 4a1) above, using a sample filtered through a 0.45-µm membrane filter.

c. Activity of suspended matter:

1) For each 10 cm² of membrane filter area, take a volume of sample not to exceed 50 mg suspended matter for alpha assay and not to exceed 100 mg for beta assay.

2) Filter sample through membrane filter with suction; then wash sides of filter funnel with a few milliliters of distilled water.

3) Transfer filter to a tared counting pan and oven-dry.

4) If sample is to be counted in an internal counter, saturate membrane with alcohol and ignite. (When beta or alpha activity is counted with another type of counter, ignition is not necessary provided that the sample is dry and flat.) When burning has stopped, direct flame of a Meker burner down on the partially ignited sample to fix sample to pan.

5) Cool, weigh, and count alpha and beta activities.

6) If sample particles tend to be airborne,

---

† Lucite or equivalent.
‡ Anstac 2M, Chemical Development Corporation, Danvers, Mass., or equivalent.
§ Pesticide and Radiation Quality Assurance Branch, Environmental Monitoring Systems Laboratory, P. O. Box 15027, Las Vegas, Nev. 89114.

treat sample with a few drops of clear acrylic solution, air-dry, and count.

7) Alternatively, prepare membrane filters for counting in internal counters by wetting filters with conducting fluid, drying, weighing, and counting. (Include weight of membrane filter in the tare.)

d. *Activity of suspended matter (alternate):* If it is impossible to filter sewage, highly polluted waters, or industrial wastes through membrane filters in a reasonable time, proceed as follows:

1) Determine total and dissolved activity by the procedures given in ¶s 4a and 4b and estimate suspended activity by difference.

2) Filter sample through an ashless mat or filter paper of stated porosity. Dry, ignite, and weigh suspended fixed residue. Transfer and fix a thin uniform layer of sample residue to a tared counting pan with a few drops of clear acrylic solution. Dry, weigh, and count in a thin end-window counter for alpha and beta activity.

e. *Activity of nonfatty semisolid samples:* Use the following procedure for samples of sludge, vegetation, soil, etc.:

1) Determine total and fixed solids of representative samples according to Section 2540.

2) Reduce fixed solids of a granular nature to a fine powder with pestle and mortar.

3) Transfer a maximum of 100 mg fixed solids for alpha assay and 200 mg fixed solids for beta assay for each 20 cm² of counting pan area (see NOTE below).

4) Distribute solids to uniform thickness in a tared counting pan by (a) spreading a thick aqueous cream of solids that is weighed after oven-drying, or (b) dispensing dry solids of known weight and spreading with acetone and a few drops of clear acrylic solution.

5) Oven-dry at 103 to 105°C, weigh, and count.

NOTE: The fixed residue of vegetation and similar samples usually is corrosive to aluminum counting pans. To avoid difficulty, use stainless steel pans or treat a weighed amount of fixed residue with HCl or HNO_3 in the presence of methyl orange indicator to pH 4 to 6, transfer to an aluminum counting pan, dry at 103 to 105°C, reweigh, and count.

f. *Alternate wet-combustion procedure for biological samples:* Some samples, such as fatty animal tissues, are difficult to process according to ¶ 4e above. An alternate procedure consists of acid digestion. Because a highly acid and oxidizing state is created, volatile radionuclides may be lost under these conditions.

1) To a 2- to 10-g sample in a tared silica dish or equivalent, add 20 to 50 mL 6N HNO_3 and 1 mL 15% H_2O_2 and digest at room temperature for a few hours or overnight. Heat gently and, when frothing subsides, heat more vigorously but without spattering, until nearly dry. Add two more 6N HNO_3 portions of 10 to 20 mL each, heat to near boiling, and continue gentle treatment until dry.

2) Ignite in a muffle furnace for 30 min at 600°C, cool in a desiccator, and weigh.

3) Continue the test as described in ¶s 4e3)-5) above.

5. Calculation and Reporting

a. *Alpha activity:* Calculate alpha activity, in picocuries per liter, by the equation

$$\text{Alpha} = \frac{\text{net cpm} \times 1000}{2.22\, e\, v}$$

where:
  e = calibrated overall counter efficiency (see ¶1d, above), and
  v = volume of sample counted, mL.

Express the counting error in picocuries per sample size by dividing picocuries per sample by sample size expressed in appropriate units. Similarly, calculate and report alpha activity in picocuries or nanocuries per kilogram of moist biological material or per kilogram of moist and per kilogram of dry silt.

b. *Beta activity:* Calculate and report gross beta activity and counting error in picocuries or nanocuries per liter of fluid, per kilogram of moist (live weight) biological material, or per kilogram of moist and per kilogram of dry silt, according to ¶s *a*, above, and *c*, below.

To calculate picocuries of beta activity per liter, determine the value of *e* in the above equation as described in ¶1*d*, above.

When counting beta activity in the presence of alpha activity by gas-flow proportional counting systems (at the beta plateau) alpha particles also are counted. Because alpha particles are more readily absorbed by increased sample thickness than beta particles, alpha/beta count ratios vary. Therefore, prepare a calibration curve by counting standards (americium 241 or plutonium 239) with increasing solids thickness, first on the alpha plateau, then on the beta plateau. Plot the ratios of the two counts against mg/cm^2 thickness, determine the alpha amplification factor (M), and correct the amplified alpha count on the beta plateau for the sample.

$$M = \frac{\text{net cpm on beta plateau}}{\text{net cpm on alpha plateau}}$$

If significant alpha activity is indicated by the sample alpha plateau count, determine beta activity by counting the sample at the beta plateau and calculating:

$$\text{Beta, pCi/L} = \frac{B - AM}{2.22 \times D \times V}$$

where:

B = net beta counts at the beta plateau,
A = net alpha counts at the alpha plateau,
M = alpha amplification factor (from ratio plot),
2.22 = cpm/pCi,
D = beta counting efficiency, and
V = sample volume, liters.

Some gas-flow proportional counters have electronic discrimination to eliminate alpha counts at the beta operating voltage. For these instruments the alpha amplification factor will be less than 1.

Where greater precision is desired, for example, when the count of alpha activity at the beta plateau is a substantial fraction of the net counts per minute of gross beta activity, the beta counting error equals $(E_a^2 + E_b^2)^{1/2}$, where E_a is the alpha counting error and E_b the gross beta counting error.

c. *Counting error:* Determine the counting error, E (in picocuries per sample), at the 95% confidence level from:

$$E = \frac{1.96 \ \sigma(R)}{2.22 e}$$

where $\sigma(R)$ is calculated as shown in Section 7010G, using $t_1 = t_2$ (in minutes); and e, the counter efficiency, is defined and calculated as in ¶1*d*.

d. *Miscellaneous information to be reported:* In reporting radioactivity data, identify adequately the sample, sampling station, date of collection, volume of sample, type of test, type of activity, type of counting equipment, standard calibration solutions used (particularly when counting standards other than those recommended in ¶1*d* are used), time of counting (particularly if short-lived isotopes are involved), weight of sample solids, and kind and amount of radioactivity. So far as possible, tabulate the data for ease of interpretation and incorporate repetitious items in the table heading or in footnotes. Unless especially inconvenient, do not change quantity units within a given table. For low-level assays, optimally report the counting error to assist in the interpretation of results.

6. Precision and Bias

In a collaborative study of two sets of paired water samples containing known additions of radionuclides, 15 laboratories determined the gross alpha activity and 16 analyzed gross beta activity. The samples contained simulated water minerals of approximately 350 mg fixed solids/L. The alpha results of one laboratory were rejected as outliers.

The average recoveries of added gross alpha activity were 86, 87, 84, and 82%. The precision (random error) at the 95% confidence level was 20 and 24% for the two sets of paired samples. The method was biased low, but not seriously.

The average recoveries of added gross beta activity were 99, 100, 100, and 100%. The precision (random error) at the 95% confidence level was 12 and 18% for the two sets of paired samples. The method showed no bias.

7. Reference

1. U.S. ENVIRONMENTAL PROTECTION AGENCY. 1980. Prescribed Procedures of Measurement of Radioactivity in Drinking Water. EPA-600/4-80-032.

8. Bibliography

BURTT, B.P. 1949. Absolute beta counting. *Nucleonics* 5:8, 28.

GOLDIN, A.S., J.S. NADER & L.R. SETTER. 1953. The detectability of low-level radioactivity in water. *J. Amer. Water Works Assoc.* 45:73.

SETTER, L.R., A.S. GOLDIN & J.S. NADER. 1954. Radioactivity assay of water and industrial wastes with internal proportional counter. *Anal. Chem.* 26:1304.

SETTER, L.R. 1964. Reliability of measurements of gross beta radioactivity in water. *J. Amer. Water Works Assoc.* 56:228.

THATCHER, L.L., V.J. JANZER & K.W. EDWARDS. 1977. Techniques of water resources investigations of the US Geological Survey. Chap. A5 *in* Methods for Determination of Radioactive Substances in Water and Fluvial Sediments. Stock No. 024-001-02928-6, U.S. Government Printing Off., Washington, D.C.

JOHNS, F.B., ET AL. 1979. Radiochemical Analytical Procedures for Analysis of Environmental Samples. EMLS-LV-0539-17, Environmental Monitoring Systems Lab., Off. Research & Development, U.S. Environmental Protection Agency, Las Vegas, Nev.

*   *   *

INDEX

Page numbers followed by "i" and "t" denote references to illustrations and tables, respectively.

A

ABBREVIATIONS

The following symbols and abbreviations are used throughout this book:

Abbreviation	Referent
AA	atomic absorption
A or amp	ampere(s)
AC	alternating current
ACS	American Chemical Society
amu	atomic mass units
APHA	American Public Health Association
ASTM	American Society for Testing and Materials
AWWA	American Water Works Association
BOD	biochemical oxygen demand
°C	degree(s) Celsius
c	count(s)
Ci	curie(s)
cm, cm^2, cm^3	centimeter(s), square centimeter(s), cubic centimeter(s)
COD	chemical oxygen demand
conc	concentrated
cpm	counts per minute
cps	counts per second
d	day
DC	direct current
diam	diameter
DO	dissolved oxygen
DOX	Dissolved Organic Halogen
dpm	disintegrations per minute
g	gram(s)
g	gravity, unit acceleration of
GC	gas chromatograph
GC/MS	gas chromatograph/mass spectrometer
h	hour
IC	ion chromatograph
ICP	inductively coupled plasma
ID	inside diameter

Abbreviation	Referent
IU	international unit(s)
KeV	kiloelectron volt(s)
kg	kilogram(s)
kPa	kilopascal
L	liter(s)
M	mole or molar
m, m^2, m^3	meter(s), square meter(s), cubic meter(s)
MCL	maximum contaminant level
me	milliequivalent(s)
meV	megaelectron volt(s)
mg	milligram(s)
min	minute(s)
mL	milliliter(s)
mm, mm^2, mm^3	millimeter(s), square millimeter(s), cubic millimeter(s)
mol wt	molecular weight
MPN	most probable number
MS	mass spectrometer
mV	millivolt(s)
μA	microampere(s)
μCi	microcurie(s)
μg	microgram(s)
μL	microliter(s)
μm	micrometer(s)
N	normal
NBS	see NIST
nCi	nanocurie(s)
ng	nanogram(s)
NIST	National Institute of Standards and Technology (formerly National Bureau of Standards)
No.	number
NTU	nephelometric turbidity unit(s)
OD	outside diameter